CW01064280

Ananthanarayan and Paniker's
Textbook of
Microbiology

TENTH EDITION

DEY APRAJITA

Ananthanarayan and Paniker's
Textbook of
Microbiology

TENTH EDITION

Editor

Reba Kanungo

Dean-Research
and
Professor and Head
Department of Microbiology
Pondicherry Institute of Medical Sciences (PIMS)
Puducherry

Universities Press

ANANTHANARAYAN AND PANIKER'S TEXTBOOK OF MICROBIOLOGY, TENTH EDITION

UNIVERSITIES PRESS (INDIA) PRIVATE LIMITED

Registered Office
3-6-747/1/A & 3-6-754/1, Himayatnagar, Hyderabad 500 029, Telangana, India
info@universitiespress.com, www.universitiespress.com

Distributed by
Orient Blackswan Private Limited

Registered Office
3-6-752 Himayatnagar, Hyderabad 500 029, Telangana, India

Other Offices
Bengaluru, Bhopal, Chennai, Guwahati, Hyderabad, Jaipur, Kolkata,
Lucknow, Mumbai, New Delhi, Noida, Patna, Visakhapatnam

© Universities Press (India) Private Limited 2013, 2017
First published 1978: Reprinted 1979, 1980; Second edition 1981: Reprinted 1982, 1983, 1984, 1985
Third edition 1986: Reprinted 1987, 1988, 1989; Fourth edition 1990: Reprinted 1991, 1992 (twice), 1994, 1995 (twice)
Fifth edition 1996: Reprinted 1996, 1997 (thrice); Reissued with revision 1998: Reprinted 1999
Sixth edition 2000: Reprinted 2001 (twice), 2002 (twice), 2003 (twice), 2004 (thrice)
Seventh edition 2005: Reprinted 2005 (five times), 2006 (twice), 2007, 2008 (twice)
First Universities Press Impression 2008: Reprinted 2009; Eighth edition 2009: Reprinted 2009, 2010, 2011, 2012
Ninth edition 2013: Reprinted 2013 (twice), 2014, 2015, 2016
Tenth edition 2017: Reprinted 2017, 2018 (twice), 2019

ISBN 978 93 86235 25 1

All rights reserved. No part of the material may be reproduced or utilised in any form, or by any means, electronic or mechanical, including photocopying, recording, or by any information storage and retrieval system, without written permission from the publisher.

Cover and book design:
© Universities Press (India) Private Limited 2013, 2017

Cover image source: Public Health Image Library/ID# 18140/ Frank DeLeo,
National Institute of Allergy and Infectious Diseases (NIAID)

Typeset in Life 10.5/13.3 *by*
OSDATA, Hyderabad 500 029

Printed in India by
Rasi Graphics Private Limited
Chennai 600 014

Published by
Universities Press (India) Private Limited
3-6-747/1/A & 3-6-754/1, Himayatnagar, Hyderabad 500 029, Telangana, India

501558

Care has been taken to confirm the accuracy of information presented in this book. The editors and the publisher, however, cannot accept any responsibility for errors or omissions or for consequences from application of the information in this book and make no warranty, express or implied, with respect to its contents.

Contents

Part I General Microbiology

Part II Immunology

Part III   Bacteriology

Part IV   Virology

Part V Medical Mycology

Part VI Applied Microbiology

Part VII Clinical Microbiology

Preface to the Tenth Edition

The tenth edition of *Ananthanarayan and Paniker's Textbook of Microbiology* upholds the vision of the pioneering authors Dr R Ananthanarayan and Dr CK Jayaram Paniker. Previous editions brought in changes in the contents by including clinical cases relevant to individual organisms, and microbiology pertinent to infectious diseases. However, with the deluge of new information, compounded with the challenges in contending with infectious diseases and the rapid evolution of microorganisms, there is a constant need to revise existing knowledge. As microbiology moves from a laboratory-based subject to the domain of infectious diseases, students need to reorient themselves from the concept of microbiology as a non-clinical speciality to that of a clinically relevant subject, with applications ranging from basic concepts in infectious diseases to healthcare-associated and community-acquired infections, disease detection and prevention, outbreaks and epidemic management, and other public health challenges.

The Medical Council of India has emphasised the need for integrated teaching, underscoring the requirement for applied microbiology. Keeping this in mind, the chapters have been thoroughly reviewed, while retaining their basic themes and concepts. Some of the significant updates are listed below.

- New concepts in sterilisation and disinfection, including plasma sterilisation and practices in healthcare settings
- New and automated methods for identification of bacteria
- Updated molecular techniques as applied to microbiology
- Simple diagrammatic presentations of current immunological techniques for antigen and antibody detection, and their applications
- Clinical implications of bacterial organisms, current methods of detection, and suggested antibiotic treatment
- Salient features of the Revised National Tuberculosis Program (RNTCP)
- Strategies for diagnosis of MDR and XDR tuberculosis, and the STOP TB strategy of WHO
- New and emerging viral infections such as SARS, MERS-CoV, influenza epidemics, the Zika virus outbreak, and the Ebola outbreak
- NACO guidelines for HIV testing strategies for different categories of the population, and HIV exposure and source codes
- Latest vaccines for immunisation against childhood infections in India, including Rotavirus, *Haemophilus influenzae* and pneumococci
- Healthcare-associated infections leading to CAUTI, VAP, HCA-BSI and SSI, and strategies for prevention with pictorial representations
- Biomedical waste management rules (2016)
- Recent advances in diagnostic microbiology and the work flow in a clinical microbiology laboratory
- Quality control and accreditation of diagnostic tests performed by laboratories
- Easy-to-understand line diagrams
- Flowcharts to make the conceptualisation of processes easy to comprehend by the undergraduate student
- Relevant points boxed as highlights
- Recaps updated and retained for quick review by the students

Universities Press and its editorial team deserve special appreciation for the meticulous and methodical editing process right from the time I took up the assignment. Constant communication and interaction helped to fine-tune the rough edges of the book. My heartfelt thanks to Dr Sudha Ganesan for her timely feedback, and to Mr Madhu Reddy and Ms Aathira Varma for their valuable inputs. It is hoped that the changes made in this revised edition will be helpful to the students of microbiology, and to those pursuing infectious diseases.

We welcome suggestions for further improvement of the book in subsequent editions.

Reba Kanungo

Preface to the First Edition

Many of the health problems in developing countries like India are different from those of developed countries. Bacterial diseases still play a considerable role in our country. Topics such as cholera and enteric diseases are important to us though only of less or academic interest to the developed countries. The increasing importance of the newer knowledge in immunology to health and disease is not adequately stressed in most of the extant textbooks. Virus diseases which are responsible for nearly 60 per cent of human illness require wider coverage. The general approach to the teaching of microbiology in our country has also been rather static. All these factors called for a textbook of microbiology more suited to countries like India.

We therefore undertook this endeavour based on our experience of teaching undergraduates and postgraduates for over two decades. We omitted the discipline of parasitology from our book since we already have an excellent textbook on the subject published in India.

This book has taken us over three years to write and over a year in publication. Naturally we would be out of date to a certain and inevitable extent. We do not claim any perfection. On the contrary, we have requested medical students and teachers all over the country to write to us about any shortcomings and give us suggestions as to how to improve the book. We shall spare no pains in seeing that their valuable suggestions are given effect to in our second edition.

R Ananthanarayan
CK Jayaram Paniker

Acknowledgements

For kind permission to use photographs, the publishers are indebted to the following institutions and individuals:

Lister Metropolis Laboratory and Research Centre Pvt. Ltd., Chennai, for figures 32.2, 38.3, 43.1a, 43.1b, 47.6, 64.8a; **Sudha Gangal and Shubhangi Sontakke**, for figures 10.1a, 10.1b, 10.2, 11.1, 11.2b, 11.3, 11.6, 12.10b, 13.1, 13.4, 14.6, 14.8, from *Textbook of Basic and Clinical Immunology* (2013) published by Universities Press India Pvt Ltd.; Department of Microbiology, **Nizam's Institute of Medical Sciences**, Hyderabad, for figures 5.3a, 5.3b, 5.3c, 21.4, 23.1, 26.4, 28.1, 61.4, 64.10; **Dr Ratna Rao**, Senior Consultant Microbiologist, Apollo Hospitals, Jubilee Hills, Hyderabad for figures 2.3a, 2.3b, 2.3c, 2.3d, 21.1, 38.1, 64.9b; **Dr Swarajya Lakshmi**, Assistant Professor, Department of Microbiology, MNR Medical College, Andhra Pradesh for figure 64.9a; **National Institute of Virology**, Pune, for figures 56.1, 56.3; **Dr Pallab Ray**, Additional Professor, Department of Medical Microbiology, PGIMER, Chandigarh, for figures 6.7, 27.3; **Dr Asha Mary Abraham**, Professor, Department of Clinical Virology, Christian Medical College, Vellore, for figures 47.7, 52.2a, 52.2b; **Dr G Sasikala**, Professor of Microbiology, STD Regional Laboratory, Osmania General Hospital, Hyderabad, for figures 27.6, 27.2, 32.3, 33.1, 38.2, 44.1, 58.1; **Dr Subha Parameswaran**, Professor and Head, Department of Microbiology, K J Somaiya Medical College, Mumbai, for figures 36.1, 41.2, 51.3, 51.4, 64.8b; **Dr Uma Tendolkar**, Department of Microbiology, Lokmanya Tilak Municipal Medical College, Mumbai, for figure 51.5; **Belnap, D M, McDermott, B M, Jr, Filman, D J, Cheng, N, Trus, B L, Zuccola, H J, Racaniello, V R, Hogle, J M**, and **Steven**, A C (2000), for figure 53.1; **World Health Organization**, Global Programme for Vaccines and Immunization EPI, for figure 53.2; **Centers for Disease Control and Prevention Archives** for figure 34.2; **FA Murphy**, University of Texas Medical Branch, Galveston, Texas, for figures 59.2, 59.3; **Prof. L. Dar**, *Department of Microbiology, AIIMS*, New Delhi for figure 57.3; **Prof. MC Sharma**, *Department of Microbiology, AIIMS*, New Delhi for figure 43.1(a).

www.wikimedia.org for figures 1.1, 1.2, 1.3, 1.4, 48.1 and 57.3; *www.purifiers.co.za* for figure 3.4a; *www.pharmlabs.unc.edu* for figure 3.4b; *www.healthessentials4you.com* for figure 3.4c; *www.tjclarkinc.com* for figure 25.1; *www.webak.upce.cz* for figure 31.1; *www.home.kku.ac.th* for figure 33.2; *www.michigan.gov* for figure 38.4; *www.leprosyhistory.org* for figure 40.1; *www.bilkent.edu.tr* for figure 40.2b; *www.granuloma.homestead.com* for figure 40.2a; *www.farm1.static.flickr.com* for figure 52.2; *www.umanitoba.ca* for figure 47.3; *www.biochem.wisc.edu* for figure 49.2; *www.zunsanwong.blogspot.com* for figure 59.4; *www.med.ncku.edu.tw* for figure 63.2

Every effort has been made to contact holders of copyright to obtain permission to reproduce copyright material. However, if any have been inadvertently overlooked, or have credited the wrong source, the publishers, on information, will be pleased to rectify the error at the first opportunity. Images for which such permission was awaited at the time of publication will be replaced in subsequent editions if such permission is not granted.

Special Acknowledgements

For their most helpful suggestions in the formulation of this edition, the publishers are grateful to **Dr Anuradha Makkar,** Professor and Head, Department of Microbiology, Army College of Medical Sciences, New Delhi; **Dr Prerna Bhalla,** Professor, Department of Microbiology, Hindu Rao Medical College, New Delhi (former Head, Maulana Azad Medical College, New Delhi); **Dr A K Praharaj,** Professor and Head, Department of Microbiology, AIIMS, Bhubaneswar, Odisha; **Dr Rajni Gaind,** Professor and Head, Department of Microbiology, VMMC, New Delhi; **Dr Sai Leela Kondapaneni,** Professor and Head, Department of Microbiology, KIMS, Hyderabad.

For valuable feedback and help in developing the MCQs for the tenth edition, we are profoundly thankful to **Dr Sarada Devi K.L,** Professor and Head, Department of Microbiology, GMC, Thiruvananthapuram, and her team members **Dr Beena Philomina,** Professor and Head, GMC Kozhikode; **Dr Anitha PM,** Additional Professor, GMC Kozhikode and **Dr Shabina MB,** Associate Professor, GMC Kozhikode.

Our special thanks are also due to **Dr G Jyothi Lakshmi,** Professor, Department of Microbiology, Osmania Medical College, Hyderabad; **Lieutenant Colonel Dr Nandita Hazra,** Sr Adv (Pathology and Microbiology) and Head, Department of Laboratory Medicine, Command Hospital (Central Command), Lucknow; **Dr Thyagarajan Ravinder,** Professor and Head, Department of Microbiology, Kilpauk Medical College, Chennai; **Dr S Manick Dass,** Professor and Head, Department of Microbiology, Apollo Medical College, Hyderabad; **Dr G Jayalakshmi,** Director and Professor, Department of Microbiology, Madras Medical College, Chennai; **Dr Mary Mathews,** Retired Professor and Head, Department of Microbiology, Christian Medical College, Vellore.

DEY   APRAJITA

Part I General Microbiology

1 Introduction and Bacterial Taxonomy

HISTORY

Medical microbiology is the study of microbes that infect humans, the diseases they cause, and their diagnosis, prevention and treatment. It also deals with the response of the human host to microbial and other antigens.

As microbes are invisible to the unaided eye, definitive knowledge about them had to await the development of the microscope. The credit for having first observed and reported bacteria belongs to **Antony van Leeuwenhoek**, a draper in Delft, Holland, whose hobby was grinding lenses and observing diverse materials through them (Fig. 1.1).

In fact, even before the microbial cause of infections had been established, **Ignaz Semmelweis** in Vienna (1846) had independently concluded that puerperal sepsis was contagious. Semmelweis also identified its mode of transmission by doctors and medical students attending on women in labour in the hospital and had prevented it by the simple measure of washing his hands in an antiseptic solution, for which service to medicine and humanity, he was persecuted by medical orthodoxy and driven insane.

The development of microbiology as a scientific discipline dates from **Louis Pasteur** (1822–95) (Fig. 1.2). He introduced techniques of sterilisation and developed the steam steriliser, hot-air oven and autoclave. He also established the differing growth needs of different bacteria and contributed to the knowledge of anthrax, chicken cholera and hydrophobia. An accidental observation that chicken cholera bacillus cultures left on the bench for several weeks lost their pathogenic property but retained their ability to protect the birds against subsequent infection by them, led to the discovery of the process of attenuation and the development of live vaccines. He attenuated cultures of the anthrax bacillus by incubation at high temperature (42–43°C) and proved that inoculation of such cultures in animals induced specific protection against anthrax. It was Pasteur who coined the term **vaccine** for such prophylactic preparations to commemorate the first of such preparations, namely cowpox, employed by **Edward Jenner** for protection against smallpox. The greatest impact on medicine was made by Pasteur's development of a vaccine for hydrophobia.

Fig. 1.1 Antony van Leeuwenhoek

Fig. 1.2 Louis Pasteur

An immediate application of Pasteur's work was the introduction of antiseptic techniques in surgery by **Joseph Lister** (1867), effecting a pronounced drop in mortality and morbidity due to surgical sepsis. Lister's antiseptic surgery involving the use of carbolic acid was a milestone in the evolution of surgical practice, from the era of 'laudable pus' to modern aseptic techniques.

While Pasteur in France laid the foundations of microbiology, **Robert Koch** (1843–1910) in Germany perfected bacteriological techniques during his studies on the culture and life cycle of the anthrax bacillus (1876). He introduced staining techniques and methods of obtaining bacteria in pure culture using solid media (Fig. 1.3). He discovered the bacillus of tuberculosis (1882) and the cholera vibrio (1883).

Roux and **Yersin** (1888) identified a new mechanism of pathogenesis when they discovered the diphtheria toxin. Similar toxins were identified in tetanus and some other bacteria. The toxins were found to be

Fig. 1.3   Robert Koch

Fig. 1.4   Paul Ehrlich

specifically neutralised by their antitoxins. **Paul Ehrlich** who studied toxins and antitoxins in quantitative terms laid the foundations of biological standardisation (Fig. 1.4). **Ernst Ruska** (1934) developed the electron microscope, enabling visualisation of the microbes we now call viruses. The development of tissue culture techniques has permitted the cultivation of viruses.

The causative agents of various infectious diseases were being reported by different investigators in such profusion that it became necessary to introduce criteria for proving the claims that a microorganism isolated from a disease was indeed causally related to it. These criteria were enunciated by Koch and are known as **Koch's postulates**. According to these, a microorganism can be accepted as the causative agent of an infectious disease only if the following conditions are satisfied:

- The bacterium should be constantly associated with the lesions of the disease.
- It should be possible to isolate the bacterium in pure culture from the lesions.
- Inoculation of such pure culture into suitable laboratory animals should reproduce lesions of the disease.
- It should be possible to re-isolate the bacterium in pure culture from the lesions produced in experimental animals.

An additional criterion introduced subsequently requires that specific antibodies to the bacterium should be demonstrable in the serum of patients suffering from the disease. Though it may not always be possible to satisfy all the postulates in every case, they have proved extremely useful in sifting doubtful claims made regarding the causative agents of infectious diseases.

The study of **immunity** had to await advances in protein chemistry. The pioneering work of **Karl Landsteiner** laid the foundations of immunochemistry. In 1955, **Niels Jerne** proposed the natural selection theory of antibody synthesis which attempted to explain the chemical specificity and biological basis of antibody synthesis, signifying a return to the original views of antibody formation proposed by Ehrlich (1898). **Frank Burnet** (1957) modified this into the clonal selection theory, a concept which, with minor alterations, holds sway even now. The last few decades have witnessed an explosion of conceptual and technical advances in immunology. Immunological processes in health and disease are now better understood following the identification of the two components of immunity—humoral or antibody-mediated processes and cellular or cell-mediated processes—which develop and manifest in separate pathways.

Alexander Fleming (1929) made the accidental discovery that the fungus *Penicillium* produces a substance that destroys staphylococci. Work on this at Oxford by Florey, Chain and their team during the Second World War led to the isolation of the active substance penicillin and its subsequent mass production. This was the beginning of the antibiotic era. Other similar antibiotics were discovered in rapid succession. With the sudden availability of a wide range of antibiotics with potent antibacterial activity, it was hoped that bacterial infections would be controlled within a short period. But soon the development of drug resistance in bacteria presented serious difficulties.

With the development of a wide variety of antibiotics active against the whole spectrum of pathogenic bacteria, and of effective vaccines against most viral diseases, expectations were raised about the eventual elimination of all infectious diseases. The global eradication of smallpox inspired visions of similar campaigns against other major pestilences. However, when new infectious diseases began to appear, caused by hitherto unknown microorganisms, or by known microbes producing novel manifestations, it was realised that controlling microbes was a far more difficult task than was imagined. The climax came in 1981 when AIDS was identified in the USA and began its pandemic spread. Unceasing vigil is essential to protect humans from microbes.

Apart from obvious benefits such as specific methods of diagnosis, prevention and control of infectious diseases, medical microbiology has contributed to scientific knowledge and human welfare in many other ways. Microorganisms constitute the smallest forms of living beings and, therefore, have been employed as models of studies on genetics and biochemistry. As nature's laws are universal in application, information derived from the investigation of microbes holds true, in the main, for humans as well.

Studies on microorganisms have contributed, more than anything else, to the unravelling of the genetic code and other mysteries of biology at the molecular level. Bacteria and their plasmids, yeasts and viruses are routinely employed as vectors in recombinant DNA technology. They have made available precious information and powerful techniques for genetic manipulation and molecular engineering. They need to be used wisely and well for the benefit of all living beings.

The number of **Nobel laureates** in Medicine and Physiology awarded the prize for their work in microbiology, listed in Table 1.1, is evidence of the positive contribution made to human health by the science of microbiology.

CLASSIFICATION, NOMENCLATURE AND TAXONOMY

All organisms are classified primarily to enable easy identification, all classification systems aim to group organisms with similar properties and to separate those that are different. The basic taxonomic unit in bacteria is the species; two species differ from one another in several features determined by genes.

The method most widely adopted is presented in successive editions of **Bergey's Manual of Determinative Bacteriology.**

Bacterial taxonomy or systematics comprises three components:

- Classification, or the orderly arrangement of units. A group of units is called a **taxon** (pl **taxa**), irrespective of its hierarchic level.
- Identification of an unknown with a defined and named unit.
- Nomenclature, or the naming of units.

Bacterial classification

A kingdom is divided successively into division, class, order, family, tribe, genus and species. An important difference between the classification of bacteria and that of other organisms is that in the former, the properties of a population are studied, and not of an individual.

- A population derived by binary fission from a single cell is called a **clone**.
- A single bacterial colony represents a clone. Though all the cells in a clone are expected to be identical in all respects, a few of them may show differences due to mutation.
- A population of bacteria derived from a particular source, such as a patient, is called a **strain**.

The general absence of sexual reproduction in bacteria serves to keep their character constant. But bacteria possess several features that contribute to some degree of heterogeneity in their populations. Their short generation time and high rate of mutation

Table 1.1   *Nobel laureates in Physiology and Medicine*

Year	Nobel Laureate	Work
1901	Emil A von Behring	Serum therapy
1902	Ronald Ross	Malaria
1905	Robert Koch	Tuberculosis
1907	C L A Laveran	Role of Protozoa in causing diseases
1908	P Ehrlich and E Metchnikof	Immunity
1913	Charles Robert Richet	Anaphylaxis
1919	Jules Bordet	Immunity
1926	Johannes Fibiger	*Spiroptera carcinoma*
1928	Charles Nicolle	Typhus
1930	Karl Landsteiner	Discovery of human blood groups
1939	Gerhard Domagk	Prontosil
1945	A Fleming, E Boris Chain and Howard Walter Florey	Penicillin
1951	Max Theiler	Yellow fever
1952	Selman A Waksman	Streptomycin
1954	Franklin Enders, T H Weller and F C Robbins	Poliomyelitis growth in tissue
1958	George Beadle & E L Tatum and J Lederberg	Gene action and genetic recombination
1960	F M Burnet and P B Medawar	Acquired immunological tolerance
1965	François Jacob, André Lwoff and Jacques Monod	Genetic control of enzymes
1966	Peyton Rous	Tumour-inducing viruses
1969	M Delbrück, A D Hershey and S E Luria	Replication mechanism and the genetic structure of viruses
1972	Gerald M Edelman and Rodney R Porter	Chemical structure of antibodies
1975	D Baltimore, R Dulbecco and H Martin Temin	Interaction between tumour viruses and the genetic material of the cell
1976	Baruch S Blumberg and D Carleton Gajdusek	New mechanisms of infectious disease dissemination
1978	Werner Arber, Daniel Nathans and Hamilton O Smith	Restriction enzymes
1980	Baruj Benacerraf, Jean Dausset and George D Snell	Immunological regulation by cell surface
1984	Niels K Jerne, Georges J F Köhler and César Milstein	Control of immune system and monoclonal antibodies
1987	Susumu Tonegawa	Generation of antibody diversity
1989	J Michael Bishop and Harold E Varmus	Origin of retroviral oncogenes
1996	Peter C Doherty and Rolf M Zinkernagel	Specificity in cell mediated immune defence
1997	Stanley B Prusiner	Prions
2005	Barry J Marshall and J Robin Warren	*Helicobacter pylori*
2008	Harald Hausen and Françoise Barré-S and L Montagnier	Human papilloma viruses, human immuno-deficiency virus
2011	Bruce A Beutler, Jules A Hoffmann, Ralph M Steinman	Activation of innate immunity, and the dendritic cell and its role in adaptive immunity
2012	Sir John B Gurdon, Shinya Yamanaka	Mature cells can be reprogrammed to become pluripotent
2015	William C Campbell and Satoshi Ōmura	Discoveries concerning a novel therapy against infections caused by roundworm parasites
	Youyou Tu	Discoveries concerning a novel therapy against Malaria

lead to the presence, in any population, of cells with altered characters. Methods of genetic exchange such as transformation, transduction and conjugation cause differences in character. Prophage and plasmid DNA can induce new properties.

Phylogenetic classification: The hierarchical classification represents a branching tree-like arrangement, one characteristic being employed for division at each branch or level. This system is called phylogenetic because it implies an evolutionary arrangement of species. Here some characteristics are arbitrarily given special weightage. Depending on the characteristic so chosen, the classification would give different patterns. While classification based on a weighted characteristic is a convenient method, it has the serious drawback that the characters used may not be valid. Fermentation of lactose, in the example cited, is not an essential and permanent characteristic. It may be acquired or lost, upsetting the system of arrangement.

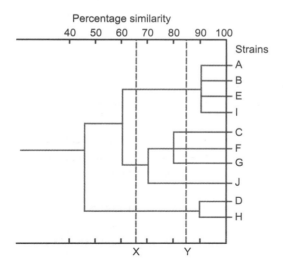

Fig. 1.5 Adansonian classification

Adansonian classification: This avoids the use of weighted characteristics (Fig. 1.5). It takes into account all the characteristics expressed at the time of study. The availability of computers has extended the scope by permitting comparison of very large numbers of properties of several organisms at the same time. This is known as **numerical taxonomy.**

Molecular or genetic classification: This is based on the degree of genetic relatedness of different organisms. Since all properties are ultimately based on the genes present, this classification is said to be the most natural or fundamental method. DNA relatedness can be tested by studying the nucleotide sequences of DNA and by DNA hybridisation or recombination methods. The nucleotide base composition and base ratio (adenine–thymine: guanine–cytosine ratio) varies widely among different groups of microorganisms, though it is constant for members of the same species. Molecular classification has been employed more with viruses than with bacteria.

Intraspecies classification: For diagnostic or epidemiological purposes, it is often necessary to subclassify bacterial species. This may be based on biochemical properties (biotypes), antigenic features (serotypes), bacteriophage susceptibility (phage types) or production of bacteriocins (colicin types). A species may be

divided first into groups and then into types, as for example, in streptococci.

Much greater discrimination in intraspecies typing has been achieved by the application of newer techniques from immunology, biochemistry and genetics. Investigations of epidemiology and pathogenesis using these techniques have been collectively referred to as **molecular epidemiology**. The methods used are of two types: phenotypic (study of expressed characteristics) and genotypic (direct analysis of genes, chromosomal and extrachromosomal DNA). Molecular phenotypic methods include electrophoretic typing of bacterial proteins and immunoblotting. Genotypic methods include plasmid profile analysis, restriction endonuclease analysis of chromosomal DNA with Southern blotting, PCR and nucleotide sequence analysis.

Nomenclature

The need for applying generally accepted names for bacterial species is self-evident. The scientific name usually consists of two words, the first being the name of the genus and the second the specific epithet (for example, *Bacillus subtilis*). The generic name is usually a Latin noun. The specific epithet is an adjective or noun and indicates some property of the species (for example, *albus*, meaning white), the animal in which it is found (for example, *suis*, means pig), the disease it causes (*tetani*, of tetanus), the person who discovered it (*welchii*, after Welch) or the place of its isolation (*london*). The generic name always begins with a capital letter and the specific epithet with a small letter, even if it refers to a person or place (for example, *Salmonella london*).

Type cultures

As a point of reference, type cultures of bacteria are maintained in international reference laboratories. The type cultures contain representatives of all established species. The original cultures of any new species described are deposited in type collections. They are made available by the reference laboratories to other workers for study and comparison.

RECAP

- Over the centuries, the experiments and work of a number of individuals from many different countries have provided a scientific basis to the study of diseases.
- Louis Pasteur (1822–1895) discovered methods of sterilisation and developed methods for culture of microbes, showed that microorganisms cause disease and established the principles of immunisation.
- Joseph Lister (1827–1912) introduced 'antisepsis', wherein he sprayed the patient and operating field with carbolic acid.
- Robert Koch (1843–1910) defined the criteria used to attribute a disease to an organism (Koch's postulates):
  - The organism must be found in all cases of the disease; the distribution in the body should correspond to that of lesions observed.
  - The organism should be cultured outside the body in pure culture for several generations.
  - The organism should reproduce the disease in other susceptible animals.
  - The organism should be isolated in pure culture from the lesion in animals.
    (an additional postulate, not formulated by Koch, is added—specific antibody to the organism should develop during the course of the disease).
- Ruska (1934) developed the electron microscope enabling visualisation of the microbes we now call viruses. The development of tissue culture techniques has permitted the cultivation of viruses.
- Roux and Yersin (1888) demonstrated that the harmful effects of diphtheria are caused by the exotoxin produced by *Corynebacterium diphtheriae* during its growth.
- Paul Ehrlich (1854–1915) was a pioneer in the study of antitoxin and toxin neutralisation.
- Sir Alexander Fleming (1885–1955) discovered that the fungus *Penicillium* produces a substance, penicillin, that destroys staphylococci; this discovery led to the formulation of other antimicrobials.
- Classification is the arrangement of organisms into related groups or taxa; taxonomy is the science of classification.
- Since all organisms are classified primarily to enable easy identification, all classification systems aim to group organisms with similar properties and to separate those that are different. However, the best classification schemes are those that are based on evolutionary relatedness.
- The basic taxonomic unit in bacteria is the species; two species differ from one another in several features determined by genes.

SHORT NOTES

1. Robert Koch
2. Louis Pasteur
3. Paul Ehrlich
4. Joseph Lister
5. Koch's postulates
6. Bacterial classification

MORPHOLOGY OF BACTERIA

INTRODUCTION

Microorganisms are a heterogeneous group of several distinct classes of living beings. The original classifi-cation under the Plant and Animal kingdoms proved unsatisfactory; they were then classified under a third kingdom, **Protista**. Based on differences in cellular organisation and biochemistry, this kingdom has been divided into two groups: **prokaryotes** and **eukaryotes** (Table 2.1). Bacteria and blue-green algae are prokaryotes, while fungi, other algae, slime moulds and protozoa are eukaryotes (Fig. 2.1).

Bacteria are prokaryotic microorganisms that do not contain chlorophyll. They are unicellular and do not show true branching, except in the so-called 'higher bacteria' (actinomycetales).

MORPHOLOGY OF BACTERIA

SIZE OF BACTERIA

The unit of measurement used in bacteriology is the micron (micrometre, μm).

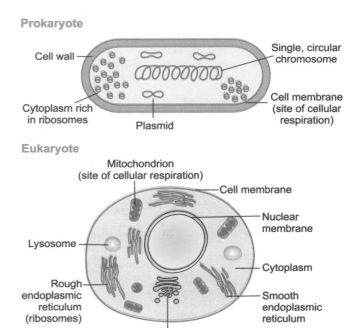

Fig. 2.1 Prokaryote and eukaryote cells

Table 2.1 *Some differences between prokaryotic and eukaryotic cells*

Character	Prokaryotes	Eukaryotes
Nucleus		
Nuclear membrane	Absent	Present
Nucleolus	Absent	Present
Deoxyribonucleoprotein	Absent	Present
Chromosome	One (circular)	More than one (linear)
Mitotic division	Absent	Present
Cytoplasm		
Cytoplasmic streaming	Absent	Present
Pinocytosis	Absent	Present
Mitochondria	Absent	Present
Lysosomes	Absent	Present
Golgi apparatus	Absent	Present
Endoplasmic reticulum	Absent	Present
Chemical composition		
Sterols	Absent	Present
Muramic acid	Present	Absent

1 micron (μ) or micrometre (μm) = one thousandth of a millimetre

1 millimicron (mμ) or nanometre (nm) = one thousandth of a micron or one millionth of a millimetre

1 Angstrom unit (Å) = one tenth of a nanometre

The limit of resolution with the unaided eye is about 200 microns. Bacteria, being much smaller, can be visualised only under magnification. Bacteria of medical importance generally measure 0.2–1.5 μm in diameter and about 3–5 μm in length.

MICROSCOPY

The morphological study of bacteria requires the use of microscopes. Microscopy has come a long way since Leeuwenhoek first observed bacteria over three hundred years ago using hand-ground lenses. The following **types** of microscopes are in use today:

Optical or light microscope: Bacteria may be examined under the compound microscope, either in the living state or after fixation and staining. Examination of wet films or 'hanging drops' indicates the shape, arrangement, motility and approximate size of the cells. But due to lack of contrast, details cannot be appreciated (Fig. 2.2a).

Phase contrast microscopy: This improves the contrast and makes evident the structures within cells that differ in thickness or refractive index. Also, the differences in refractive index between bacterial cells and the surrounding medium make them clearly visible. Retardation, by a fraction of a wavelength, of the rays of light that pass through the object, compared to the rays passing through the surrounding medium, produces 'phase' differences between the two types of rays. In the phase contrast microscope, 'phase' differences are converted into differences in intensity of light, producing light and dark contrast in the image.

Fluorescent microscope: This uses light of a high intensity source which excites a fluorescent agent, which in turn emits a low energy light of a longer wave-

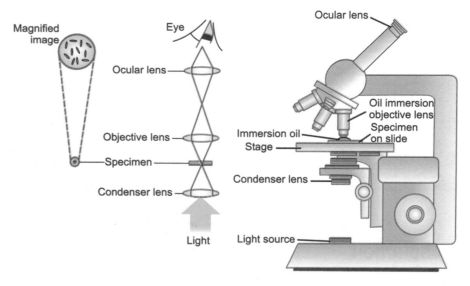

Fig. 2.2 (a) Principle of bright-field (light) microscopy

length that produces the image. The fluorescent light can be separated from the surrounding radiation using filters designed for that specific wavelength, allowing the viewer to see only that which shows fluorescence. Microorganisms in a specimen can be stained with a fluorescent dye. On exposure to excitation light, organisms are visually detected by the emission of

fluorescent light by the dye with which they have been stained (Fig. 2.2b). This can be of two types: **fluorochroming** and **immunofluorescence**. Fluorochroming involves the non-specific staining of any bacterial cell with a fluorescent dye. Immunofluorescence uses antibodies labelled with fluorescent dye (a conjugate) to specifically stain a particular bacterial species (Fig. 2.2c).

Dark field/Dark ground microscope: Another method of improving the contrast is the dark field (dark ground) microscope in which reflected light is used instead of the transmitted light used in the ordinary microscope. The essential part of the dark field microscope is the dark field condenser with a central circular stop, which illuminates the object with a cone of light, without letting any ray of light fall directly on the objective lens. Light rays falling on the object are reflected or scattered on to the objective lens, with the result that the object appears self-luminous against a dark background. The contrast gives an illusion of increased resolution, so that very slender organisms such as spirochetes, not visible under ordinary illumination, can be clearly seen under the dark field microscope (Fig. 2.2d).

The **resolving power** of the light microscope is limited by the wavelength of light. In order to be seen and delineated (resolved), an object has to have a size of approximately half the wavelength of the light used. With visible light, using the best optical systems, the limit of resolution is about 300 nm. If light of shorter wavelength is employed, as in the

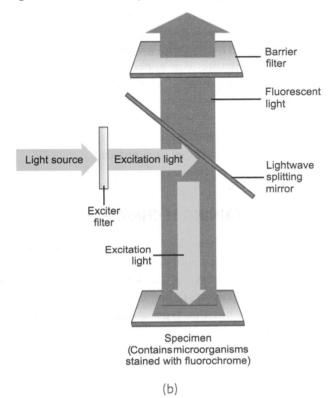

(b)

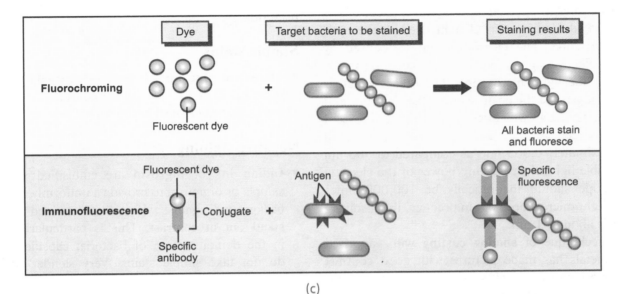

(c)

Fig. 2.2   (b) Principle of fluorescent microscopy; (c) Principles of fluorochroming and immunofluoresence

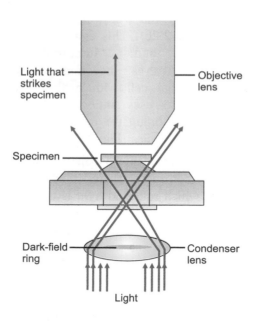

Fig. 2.2 (d) Dark field microscopy

ultraviolet microscope, the resolving power can be proportionately extended.

Two specialised types of microscopes are the **interference microscope** which not only reveals cell organelles but also enables quantitative measurement of the chemical constituents of cells such as lipids, proteins and nucleic acids, and the **polarisation microscope** which enables the study of intracellular structures using differences in birefringence.

Electron microscope: Here, a beam of electrons is used instead of the beam of light used in the optical microscope. The electron beam is focused by circular electromagnets, which are analogous to the lenses in the light microscope. The object which is held in the path of the beam scatters the electrons and produces an image which is focused on a fluorescent viewing screen. As the wavelength of electrons used is approximately 0.005 nm, as compared to 500 nm with visible light, the resolving power of the electron microscope should theoretically be 100,000 times that of light microscopes but in practice, the resolving power is about 0.1 nm.

The technique of **shadow-casting** with vaporised heavy metals has made pictures with good contrast and three-dimensional effect possible. Another valuable technique in studying fine structure is **negative staining** with phosphotungstic acid.

Gas molecules scatter electrons, and it is therefore necessary to examine the object in a vacuum. Hence, only dead and dried objects can be examined in the electron microscope. This may lead to considerable distortion in cell morphology. A method introduced to overcome this disadvantage is **freeze-etching**, involving the deep-freezing of specimens in a liquid gas and the subsequent formation of carbon-platinum replicas of the material. Since such frozen cells may remain viable, it is claimed that freeze-etching enables the study of the cellular ultrastructure as it appears in the living state. The recent development of very high voltage electron microscopes may eventually render the examination of live objects possible. The scanning electron microscope is a useful innovation that permits the study of cell surfaces with greater contrast and higher resolution than with the shadow-casting technique.

STAINING TECHNIQUES

Live bacteria do not show much structural detail under the light microscope due to lack of contrast. Hence it is customary to use staining techniques to produce colour contrast. Bacteria may be stained in the living state, but this type of staining is employed only for special purposes. Routine methods of staining of bacteria involve drying and fixing smears—procedures that kill them. Bacteria have an affinity to basic dyes due to the acidic nature of their protoplasm. The following are staining techniques commonly used in bacteriology.

Simple stains

● **Methylene blue** or **basic fuchsin** are used for simple staining. They provide colour contrast, but impart the same colour to all bacteria.

Negative staining

● **Indian ink** or **nigrosin** are emulsified with the sample or organism to provide a uniformly coloured background against which the unstained bacteria stand out in contrast. This is particularly useful in the demonstration of bacterial capsules which do not take simple stains. Very slender bacteria such as spirochetes that are not demonstrable by simple staining methods can be viewed by negative staining.

Impregnation methods

- **Silver impregnation** cells and structures too thin to be seen under the ordinary microscope may be rendered visible if they are thickened by impregnation of silver on the surface. Such methods are used for the demonstration of spirochetes and bacterial flagella.

Differential stains

- These stains impart different colours to different bacteria or bacterial structures. The two most widely used differential stains are the **Gram stain** and the **acid fast stain**.

Gram stain

The **Gram stain** was originally devised by the histologist Christian Gram (1884) as a method of staining bacteria in tissues.

Principle: The exact mechanism of the Gram reaction is not understood. Various theories that have been suggested are as follows:

- Gram-positive cells have a more acidic protoplasm, which may account for their retaining the basic primary dye more strongly than Gram-negative bacteria.
- The peptidoglycan of Gram-positive bacteria is thick and thus able to retain the dye-iodine complex.
- The high lipid content of Gram-negative bacteria makes them permeable to secondary dye after decolourisation with organic solvents like acetone.

Decolourisation is not an all-or-none phenomenon. Even Gram-positive cells may be decolourised by prolonged treatment with the organic solvent. Conversely, inadequate decolourisation may cause all cells to appear Gram positive. Gram-positive bacteria become Gram negative when the cell wall is damaged.

Procedure:

1. Primary staining with a pararosaniline dye such as crystal violet, methyl violet or gentian violet
2. Application of a dilute solution of iodine
3. Decolourisation with an organic solvent such as ethanol, acetone or aniline
4. Counterstaining with a dye of contrasting colour, such as carbol fuchsin, safranine or neutral red

The Gram stain differentiates bacteria into two broad groups. Gram-positive bacteria are those that resist decolourisation and retain the primary stain, appearing violet. Gram-negative bacteria are decolourised by organic solvents and, therefore, take the counterstain, appearing red (Figs 2.3a and 2.3b).

Application: Gram staining is an essential procedure used in the identification of bacteria and is frequently the only method required for studying their morphology. Gram reactivity is of considerable importance as Gram-positive and -negative bacteria differ not merely in staining characteristics and in structure but also in several other properties such as growth requirements, susceptibility to antibiotics and pathogenicity.

Acid fast stain

This was discovered by Ehrlich, who found that after staining with aniline dyes, tubercle bacilli resist decolourisation with acids. The method, as modified by Ziehl and Neelsen, is in common use today (Figs 2.3c and 2.3d).

Principle: Acid fastness has been ascribed to the high content and variety of lipids, fatty acids and higher alcohols found in tubercle bacilli.

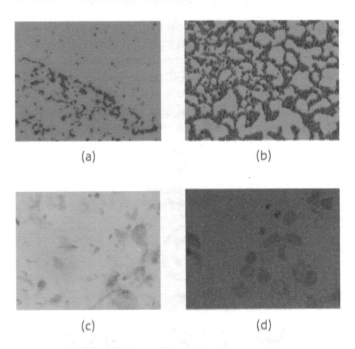

(a)   (b)

(c)   (d)

Fig. 2.3 Colour images of bacteria stained using different stains; (a) Gram-positive cocci; (b) Gram-negative bacilli; (c) Ziehl–Neelsen acid fast *M.tuberculosis;* (d) Acid fast *M.leprae*

- A lipid peculiar to acid fast bacilli, a high molecular weight hydroxy acid wax containing carboxyl groups (mycolic acid), is acid fast in the free state.
- Acid fastness is not a property of lipids alone but depends also on the integrity of the cell wall.

Procedure:

1. The smear is stained by a strong solution of carbol fuchsin with the application of heat.
2. It is then decolourised with 20% sulphuric acid and counterstained with a contrasting dye such as methylene blue.
3. The acid fast bacteria retain the fuchsin (red) colour, while the others take the counterstain.

Mycobacterium leprae resists decolourisation with 5% sulphuric acid.

Albert's stain

Principle: On staining with Albert's stain the granules of *Corynebacterium diphtheriae* take up a bluish purple colour and hence they are called metachromatic granules.

Procedure:

1. The smear is stained with Albert I stain, drained and washed.
2. Albert II is poured to cover the smear and drained.

Application: *Corynebacterium diphtheria* are slender bacilli with an arrangement resembling the letters V or L. They have metachromatic granules at the poles of bacilli which are also called **polar bodies**, volutin or **Babes–Ernst granules.**

The **Albert's, Neisser's,** and **Ponder's** stains demonstrate these granules.

SHAPE OF BACTERIA

Depending on their shape, bacteria are classified into several types (Fig. 2.4):

- **Cocci** (from *kokkos* meaning berry) are spherical or oval cells.
- **Bacilli** (from *baculus* meaning rod) are rod-shaped cells.
- **Vibrios** are comma-shaped, curved rods and derive their name from their characteristic vibratory motility.
- **Spirilla** are rigid spiral forms.
- **Spirochetes** (from *speira* meaning coil and *chaite* meaning hair) are flexuous spiral forms (Fig. 2.5).
- **Actinomycetes** are branching filamentous bacteria, so called because of a fancied resemblance to the radiating rays of the sun when seen in tissue lesions (from *actis* meaning ray and *mykes* meaning fungus).
- **Mycoplasmas** are bacteria that are cell wall deficient and hence do not possess stable morphology. They occur as round or oval bodies and as interlacing filaments. When cell wall synthesis becomes defective, either spontaneously or as a result of drugs like penicillin, bacteria lose their distinctive shape. Such cells are called protoplasts, spheroplasts or L forms. Bacteria sometimes show characteristic cellular arrangement or grouping. Thus, cocci may be arranged in pairs (diplococci), chains (streptococci), groups of four (tetrads) or eight (sarcina), or as grape-like clusters (staphylococci).

Some bacilli too may be arranged in chains (streptobacilli). Others are arranged at angles to each other,

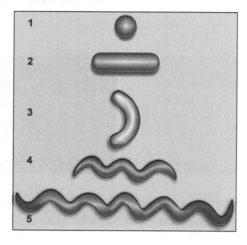

Fig. 2.4 Shapes of bacteria: 1. coccus; 2. bacillus; 3. vibrio; 4. spirillum; 5. spirochete

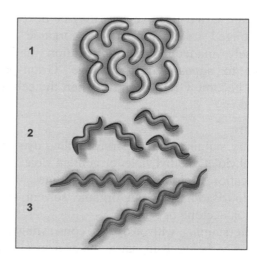

Fig. 2.5 Arrangement of curved bacteria: 1. vibrio; 2. spirilla; 3. spirochetes

presenting a cuneiform or Chinese letter pattern (corynebacteria). The type of cellular arrangement is determined by the plane through which binary fission takes place and by the tendency of the daughter cells to remain attached even after division.

BACTERIAL ANATOMY

The structure of an idealised bacterial cell shows:
- The **outer layer** or **cell envelope** consists of two components:
  - A **rigid cell wall**
  - A **cytoplasmic** or **plasma membrane** (beneath the cell wall)
- Components of the **cell interior**
  The cell envelope encloses the protoplasm, comprising the cytoplasm, cytoplasmic inclusions such as ribosomes and mesosomes, granules, vacuoles and the nuclear body.
- **Additional structures**
  The cell may be enclosed in a viscid layer, which may be a loose slime layer, or organised as a capsule. Some bacteria carry filamentous appendages protruding from the cell surface—the flagella which are organs of locomotion and the fimbriae which appear to be organs for adhesion (Fig. 2.6).

Cell wall

The cell wall accounts for the shape of the bacterial cell and confers on it rigidity and ductility. The cell wall cannot be seen by direct light microscopy and does not stain with simple stains.

Demonstration:
- It may be demonstrated by plasmolysis. When placed in a hypertonic solution, the cytoplasm loses water by osmosis and shrinks, while the cell wall retains its original shape and size (bacterial ghost).
- The cell wall may also be demonstrated by:
  - microdissection,
  - reaction with specific antibodies,
  - mechanical rupture of the cell,
  - differential staining procedures,
  - electron microscopy.

Structure: Bacterial cell walls are about 10–25 nm thick and account for about 20–30 per cent of the dry weight of the cell. Chemically the cell wall is composed of mucopeptide (**peptidoglycan** or **murein**) scaffolding

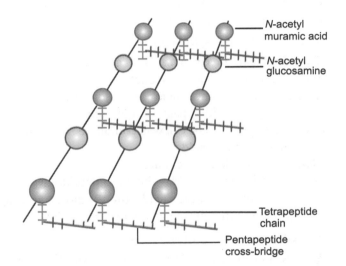

Fig. 2.7 Chemical structure of bacterial cell wall

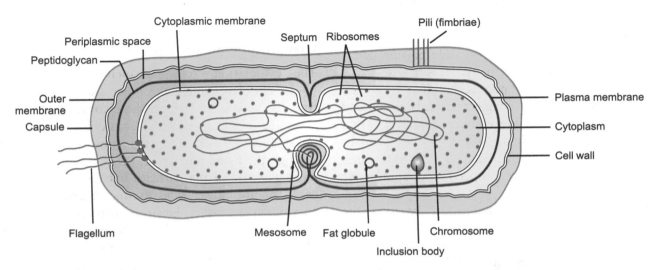

Fig. 2.6 Diagram of an idealised bacterial cell

Table 2.2   *Comparison of cell walls of Gram-positive and Gram-negative bacteria*

	Gram-positive	Gram-negative
Thickness (peptidoglycan)	Thicker	Thinner
Variety of amino acids	Few	Several
Aromatic and sulphur containing amino acids	Absent	Present
LPS and outer membrane	Absent	Present
Teichoic acid	Present	Absent

formed by *N*-acetyl glucosamine and *N*-acetyl muramic acid molecules alternating in chains, which are cross-linked by peptide chains (Fig. 2.7). The interstices of this scaffolding contain other chemicals, varying in the different species.

In general, the walls of Gram-positive bacteria have a simpler chemical nature than those of Gram-negative bacteria (Table 2.2). The cell wall carries bacterial antigens that are important in virulence and immunity.

Cell wall of Gram-positive bacteria:

- **Peptidoglycan layer:** This is thicker (15–80 nm) than that of Gram-negative bacteria (2–3 nm)
- **Teichoic acid:** Teichoic acid is a major surface antigen of Gram-positive bacteria containing ribitol or glycerol polymers. The cell wall contains a significant amount of teichoic acid.

  Two types of teichoic acid are present:
  - Cell wall teichoic acid – linked to peptidoglycan
  - Membrane teichoic acid (lipoteichoic acid) – linked to membrane glycolipid (Fig. 2.8a).

Cell wall of Gram-negative bacteria:

- **Lipopolysaccharides (LPS)** present on the cell walls of Gram-negative bacteria account for their **endotoxic activity** and O antigen specificity. They were formerly known as the Boivin antigen. The **LPS** consists of three regions:
  - Region I is the O polysaccharide portion determining O antigen specificity.
  - Region II is the core polysaccharide.
  - Region III is the glycolipid portion (**lipid A**) and is responsible for the **endotoxic** activities, that is, pyrogenicity, lethal effect, tissue necrosis, anticomplementary activity, B cell mitogenicity, immunoadjuvant property and antitumour activity.
- **Outer membrane:** The outermost layer of the Gram-negative bacterial cell wall is called the outer membrane, which contains various proteins known as outer membrane proteins (OMP). Among these are porins which form transmembrane pores that

serve as diffusion channels for small molecules. They also serve as specific receptors for some bacteriophages.

- **Lipoprotein:** Attaches the protein of peptidoglycan to lipid of outer membrane.
- **Peptidoglycan:** Is thin (2–3 nm) and is bound by the lipoprotein and plasma membrane (Fig. 2.8b).

Inhibition of cell wall synthesis: **Lysozyme**, an enzyme normally present in many tissue fluids, lyses susceptible bacteria by splitting the cell wall mucopeptide links.

Protoplasts and spheroplasts:

Protoplasts: When lysozyme acts on a Gram-positive bacterium in a hypertonic solution, a protoplast is formed, consisting of the cytoplasmic membrane and its contents.

Spheroplast: When lysozyme acts on Gram-negative bacteria, the result is a spheroplast which differs from the protoplast in that some cell wall material is retained. Protoplasts and spheroplasts are spherical, regardless of the original shape of the bacterium.

Cell wall–deficient forms of bacteria may have a role in the persistence of certain chronic infections such as pyelonephritis.

Cytoplasmic membrane

The cytoplasmic (plasma) membrane is a thin (5–10 nm) layer lining the inner surface of the cell wall and separating it from the cytoplasm. It acts as a semipermeable membrane controlling the flow of metabolites to and from the protoplasm. Passage through the membrane is not solely a function of the molecular size of the particles but depends, in many cases, on the presence in the membrane of specific enzymes (permeases). Electron microscopy shows the presence of three layers constituting a **unit membrane** structure. Chemically, the membrane consists of lipoproteins with small amounts of carbohydrates. Sterols are absent, except in mycoplasma.

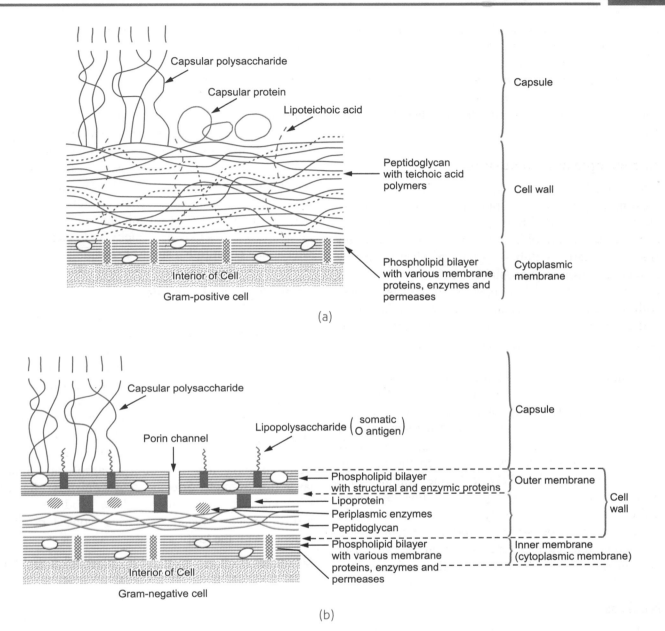

Fig. 2.8   (a) Gram-positive and (b) Gram-negative cell wall

Cytoplasm

The bacterial cytoplasm is a colloidal system of a variety of organic and inorganic solutes in a viscous watery solution. It differs from eukaryotic cytoplasm in not exhibiting internal mobility (**protoplasmic streaming**) and in the absence of endoplasmic reticulum or mitochondria. The cytoplasm stains uniformly with basic dyes in young cultures but becomes increasingly granular with age. The cytoplasm contains ribosomes, mesosomes, inclusions and vacuoles.

Ribosomes

These are centres of protein synthesis. They are slightly smaller than the ribosomes of eukaryotic cells (sedimentation constant 70 S) and are seen integrated in linear strands of mRNA to form polysomes.

Mesosomes (chondroids)

These are vesicular, convoluted or multilaminated structures formed as invaginations of the plasma membrane into the cytoplasm. They are more prominent in Gram-positive bacteria. They are the principal sites of respiratory enzymes in bacteria and are analogous to the mitochondria of eukaryotes. Mesosomes are often seen in relation to the nuclear body and the site of synthesis of cross-wall septa, suggesting that they coordinate nuclear and cytoplasmic division during binary fission.

Intracytoplasmic inclusions

These may be of various types, the chief of which are volutin, polysaccharide, lipid and crystal. They are characteristic for different species and depend on the age and condition of the culture. **Volutin granules (metachromatic or Babes–Ernst granules)** are highly refractive, strongly basophilic bodies consisting of polymetaphosphate. They appear reddish when stained with polychrome methylene blue or toluidine blue (**metachromasia**). Special staining techniques such as Albert's or Neisser's demonstrate the granules more clearly.

Volutin granules are characteristically present in diphtheria bacilli. Their function is uncertain. They have been considered to represent a reserve of energy and phosphate for cell metabolism but they are most frequent in cells grown under conditions of nutritional deficiency and tend to disappear when the deficient nutrients are supplied. Polysaccharide granules may be demonstrated by staining with iodine, and lipid inclusions with fat soluble dyes such as Sudan black. They appear to be storage products. Vacuoles are fluid-containing cavities separated from the cytoplasm by a membrane. Their function and significance are uncertain.

Nucleus

Bacterial nuclei can be demonstrated by acid or ribonuclease hydrolysis and subsequent staining for nuclear material. They may be seen by electron microscopy. They appear as oval or elongated bodies, generally one per cell. Some cells may possess two or more nuclear bodies due to asynchrony between nuclear and cytoplasmic division.

Bacterial nuclei have no nuclear membrane or nucleolus. The nuclear deoxyribonucleic acid (DNA) is not associated with basic protein. The genome consists of a single molecule of double-stranded DNA arranged in the form of a circle, which may open under certain conditions to form a long chain, about 1 mm in length. The bacterial chromosome is haploid and replicates by simple fission instead of by mitosis as in other cells. The differences between the nuclei of bacteria and that of other organisms form the main basis for classifying them as prokaryotes and eukaryotes (Table 2.1).

Bacteria may possess extranuclear genetic elements consisting of DNA. These cytoplasmic carriers of genetic information are termed **plasmids** or **episomes**. Besides being transmitted to daughter cells during binary fission, they may be transferred from one bacterium to another either through conjugation or the agency of bacteriophages. They are not essential for the life of the cell they inhabit but may confer on it certain properties like toxigenicity and drug resistance which may constitute a survival advantage.

Slime layer and capsule

Many bacteria secrete a viscid material around the cell surface. When this is organised into a sharply defined structure, as in *S.pneumoniae*, it is known as the **capsule**. When it is a loose undemarcated secretion, as in leuconostoc, it is called the **slime layer**. Capsules too thin to be seen under the light microscope are called **microcapsules**. The slime is generally, but not invariably, polysaccharide (for example, *S.pneumoniae*) or polypeptide (for example, anthrax bacillus) in nature. Some bacteria may have both a capsule and a slime layer (for example, *Streptococcus salivarius*). Bacteria secreting large amounts of slime produce mucoid growth on agar, which is of a stringy consistency when touched with the loop.

Demonstration of capsule: Slime has little affinity for basic dyes and is not visible in Gram-stained smears. **Special capsule staining** techniques are available, usually employing copper salts as mordants. Capsules may be readily demonstrated by **negative staining in wet films with India ink,** when they are seen as clear halos around the bacteria, against a black background (Fig. 2.9).

Capsular material is antigenic and may be demonstrated by **serological methods**. When a suspension of a capsulated bacterium is mixed with its specific anticapsular serum and examined under the microscope, the capsule becomes very prominent and appears 'swollen' due to an increase in its refractivity. This **capsule swelling or Quellung reaction**, described by Neufeld (1902), was widely employed for the typing of *S.pneumoniae* in the pre-sulphonamide days when lobar pneumonia used to be treated with specific

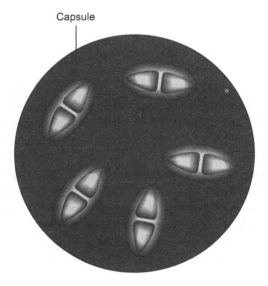

Fig. 2.9 *S.pneumoniae* capsule seen by India ink staining

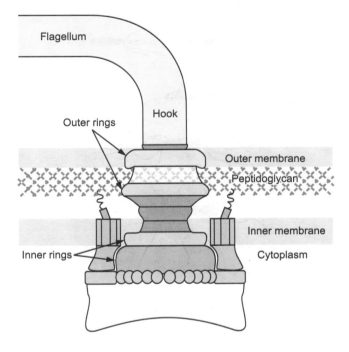

Fig. 2.10   General structure of the flagellum of a Gram-negative bacterium.

anticapsular sera. Capsules protect bacteria from deleterious agents such as lytic enzymes found in nature. They also contribute to the virulence of pathogenic bacteria by inhibiting phagocytosis. Loss of the capsule by mutation may render the bacterium avirulent. Repeated subcultures in vitro lead to loss of the capsule and also of virulence.

Flagella

Motile bacteria, except spirochetes, possess one or more unbranched, long, sinuous filaments called flagella, which are the organs of locomotion. Each flagellum consists of three distinct parts, the filament, the hook and the basal body. The filament is external to the cell and connected to the hook at the cell surface.

Structure: The hook–basal body portion is embedded in the cell envelope. The hook and basal body are antigenically different. Mechanical detachment of the filament does not impair the viability of the cell. The flagella are 3–20 µm long and are of uniform diameter (0.01–0.013 µm) and terminate in a square tip. The wavelength and thickness of the filament are characteristic of each species but some bacteria exhibit biplicity, that is, they have flagella of two different wavelengths. Flagella are made up of a protein (**flagellin**) similar to keratin or myosin. Though flagella of different genera of bacteria have the same chemical composition, they are antigenically different. Flagellar antigens induce specific antibodies in high titres. Flagellar antibod-

ies are not protective but are useful in serodiagnosis (Fig. 2.10).

The presence or absence of flagella and their number and arrangement are characteristic of different genera of bacteria. Flagella may be arranged all round the cell (**peritrichous**) as in typhoid bacilli, or situated at one or both ends of the cell (**polar**). Polar flagella may be single (**monotrichous**) as in cholera vibrios, in tufts (lophotrichous) as in spirilla or with flagella at both poles (**amphitrichous**) (Fig. 2.11).

Demonstration: Flagella are less than 0.02 µm in thickness and hence beyond the limit of resolution of the light microscope. They may, in some instances, be seen under **dark ground illumination**. They can be visualised by **special staining techniques** in which their thickness is increased by mordanting, or. by **electron microscopy**.

Motility: Due to the difficulty of demonstrating flagella directly, their presence is usually inferred from the motility of bacteria. Motility can be observed by noting the spreading type of growth on a semisolid agar medium. Under the microscope, active motility has to be differentiated from the passive movements of the cells, either due to air currents or due to Brownian movement. Bacterial motility may range from the slow

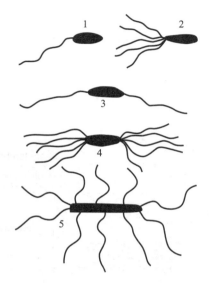

Fig. 2.11   Types of flagellar arrangement: 1. monotrichous; 2. lophotrichous; 3. amphitrichous; 4. amphilophotrichous; 5. peritrichous flagella

'stately' motion of peritrichate bacteria (for example, *Bacillus*) to the darting movement of polar flagellated vibrios. The cholera vibrio may move as quickly as 200 μm per second.

Fimbriae

Some Gram-negative bacilli carry very fine, hair-like surface appendages called fimbriae or pili. They are shorter and thinner than flagella (about 0.5 μm long and less than 10 nm thick) and project from the cell surface as straight filaments. At least eight morphological types of pili are known, classifiable as either **common** or **sex pili** on the basis of their function. Pili comprise self-aggregating monomers of pilin. They originate in the cell membrane. Fimbriae can be seen only under the electron microscope. They are unrelated to motility and are found on motile as well as non-motile cells. They are best developed in freshly isolated strains and in liquid cultures. They tend to disappear following subculture on solid media.

Fimbriae function as organs of adhesion, helping the cells to adhere firmly to particles of various kinds. This property may serve to anchor the bacteria in nutritionally favourable microenvironments. Fimbriated bacteria form surface pellicles in liquid media. Many fimbriated cells (for example, *Escherichia, Klebsiella*) agglutinate red blood cells of guinea pigs, fowl, horses and pigs strongly, human and sheep cells weakly, and ox cells scarcely.

Hemagglutination provides a simple method of detecting the presence of such fimbriae. The hemagglutination is specifically inhibited by D-mannose (mannose sensitive).

Fimbriae are antigenic. As members of different genera may possess the same fimbrial antigen, it is necessary to ensure that the bacterial antigens employed for serological tests and preparation of antisera are devoid of fimbriae.

A special type of fimbria are the sex pili. These are longer and fewer in number than other fimbriae. They are found on 'male' bacteria and help in the attachment of those cells to 'female' bacteria, forming hollow conjugation tubes through which, it is assumed, genetic material is transferred from the donor to the recipient cell. Pili are classified into different types (for example, F, I) based on susceptibility to specific bacteriophages.

Spore

Some bacteria, particularly members of the genera *Bacillus* and *Clostridium* have the ability to form highly resistant resting stages called spores. Each bacterium forms one spore, which on germination forms a single vegetative cell. Sporulation in bacteria, therefore, is not a method of reproduction. As bacterial spores are formed inside the parent cell, they are called endospores.

While the exact stimulus for sporulation is not known, it occurs after a period of vegetative growth and is presumed to be related to the depletion of exogenous nutrients. Sporulation is initiated by the appearance of a clear area, usually near one end of the cell, which gradually becomes more opaque to form the '**forespore**'. The fully developed spore has at its core the nuclear body, surrounded by the spore wall, a delicate membrane from which the cell wall of the future vegetative bacterium will develop. Outside this is the thick spore cortex, which in turn is enclosed by a multilayered tough spore coat. Some spores have an additional outer covering called **exosporium,** which may have distinctive ridges and grooves (Fig. 2.12). New antigens appear on sporulation.

Young spores are seen attached to the parent cell. The shape and position of the spore and its size relative to the parent cell are species characteristics. Spores may be **central** (equatorial), **terminal** or **subterminal**. They may be oval or spherical. They may or may not distend the bacillary body (Fig. 2.13).

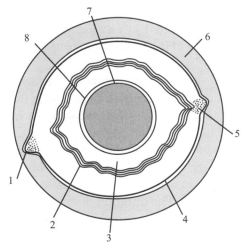

Fig. 2.12 Diagrammatic representation of a bacterial spore: 1. germinal groove; 2. outer cortical layer; 3. cortex; 4. internal spore coat; 5. subcoat material; 6. outer spore coat; 7. cytoplasmic membrane; 8. cell wall primordium.

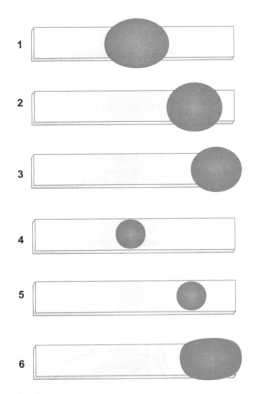

Fig. 2.13 Types of bacterial spores: 1. central, bulging; 2. subterminal, bulging; 3. terminal, spherical; 4. central, not bulging; 5. subterminal, not bulging; 6. terminal, oval

Resistance: Bacterial spores constitute some of the most resistant forms of life. They may remain viable for centuries. They are extremely resistant to desiccation and relatively so to chemicals and heat. Though

some spores may resist boiling for prolonged periods, spores of all medically important species are destroyed by autoclaving at 120°C for 15 minutes. Methods of sterilisation and disinfection should ensure that spores are also destroyed. Sporulation helps bacteria survive for long periods under unfavourable conditions.

When transferred to conditions conducive for growth, spores germinate. The spore loses its refractility and swells. The spore wall is shed and the germ cell appears by rupturing the spore coat and elongates to form the vegetative bacterium.

Demonstration: Spores may be seen in unstained preparations as refractile bodies. The forespore stains intensely, but once the spore envelope is laid down, the spore does not stain readily. Spores appear as unstained areas in Gram-stained preparations, but being more acid fast than the vegetative cells, they can be stained by a **modification of the Ziehl–Neelsen technique**.

Pleomorphism and involution forms

Some species of bacteria exhibit great variation in the shape and size of individual cells. This is known as pleomorphism. Certain species (for example, plague bacillus, gonococcus) show swollen and aberrant forms in ageing cultures, especially in the presence of high salt concentration. These are known as involution forms. Many of the cells may be non-viable. Pleomorphism and involution forms are often caused by defective cell wall synthesis. Involution forms may also develop due to the activity of autolytic enzymes.

L forms

Kleineberger-Nobel, studying cultures of *Streptobacillus moniliformis*, observed swollen cells and other aberrant morphological forms and named them L forms, after Lister Institute, London, where the observation was made. L forms are seen in several species of bacteria, developing either spontaneously or in the presence of penicillin or other agents that interfere with cell wall synthesis. L forms may be unstable in that the morphological abnormality is maintained only in the presence of penicillin or other inducing agents, or stable, when the aberrant form becomes the permanent feature of the strain and is retained in serial subcultures. L forms resemble mycoplasma in several ways, including morphology, type of growth on agar and filterability. It is possible that mycoplasmas represent stable L forms of as yet unidentified parent bacteria.

PHYSIOLOGY OF BACTERIA

GROWTH AND MULTIPLICATION OF BACTERIA

Cell division

Multiplication: Bacteria divide by binary fission. When a bacterial cell reaches a certain size, it divides to form two daughter cells. Nuclear division precedes cell division and, therefore, in a growing population, many cells carrying two nuclear bodies can be seen. The cell divides by a constrictive or pinching process, or by the ingrowth of a transverse septum across the cell. In some species, the daughter cells may remain partially attached after division.

Generation time: The interval of time between two cell divisions, or the time required for a bacterium to give rise to two daughter cells under optimum conditions, is known as the generation time or population doubling time. In coliform bacilli and many other medically important bacteria, the generation time is about 20 minutes. Some bacteria are slow-growing; the generation time in tubercle bacilli is about 20 hours and in lepra bacilli as long as about 20 days. As bacteria reproduce so rapidly and by geometric progression, a single bacterial cell can theoretically give rise to 10^{21} progeny in 24 hours, with a mass of approximately 4000 tonnes!

Growth

In actual practice, when bacteria are grown in a vessel of liquid medium **(batch culture),** multiplication is arrested after a few cell divisions due to depletion of nutrients or accumulation of toxic products. By the use of special devices for replenishing nutrients and removing bacterial cells **(chemostat or turbidistat)**, it is possible to maintain **continuous culture** of bacteria for industrial or research purposes. When pathogenic bacteria multiply in host tissues, the situation may be intermediate between a batch culture and a continuous culture; the source of nutrients may be inexhaustible but the parasite has to contend with the defence mechanisms of the body. Bacteria growing on solid media form colonies. Each colony represents a clone of cells derived from a single parent cell. In liquid media, growth is diffuse.

Bacterial growth curve

When a bacterium is seeded into a suitable liquid medium and incubated, its growth follows a definite course. If bacterial counts are made at intervals after inoculation and plotted in relation to time, a growth curve is obtained (Fig. 2.14). The curve shows the following phases:

1. **Lag phase:** Immediately following the seeding of a culture medium, there is no appreciable increase in number, though there may be an increase in the size of the cells. This initial period is the time required for adaptation to the new environment, during which the necessary enzymes and metabolic intermediates are built up in adequate quantities for multiplication to proceed. The duration of the lag phase varies with the species, size of the inoculum, nature of the culture medium and environmental factors such as temperature.

2. **Log (logarithmic) or exponential phase:** Following the lag phase, the cells start dividing and their numbers increase exponentially or by geometric progression with time. If the logarithm of the viable count is plotted against time, a straight line will be obtained.

3. **Stationary phase:** After a varying period of exponential growth, cell division stops due to depletion of nutrients and accumulation of toxic products. The number of progeny cells formed is just enough to replace the number of cells that die. The viable count remains stationary as an equilibrium exists between the dying and the newly formed cells.

4. **Phase of decline:** This is the phase when the population decreases due to cell death. Besides nutritional exhaustion and toxic accumulation, cell death may also be caused by autolytic enzymes.

When the total count is plotted, it parallels the viable count up to the stationary phase but it continues

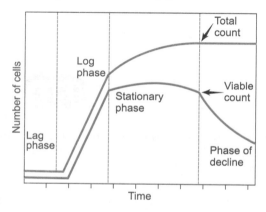

Fig. 2.14 Bacterial growth curve. The viable count shows the lag, log, stationary and decline phases. In the total count, the phase of decline is not evident.

steadily without any phase of decline. With autolytic bacteria, even the total count shows a phase of decline.

The various stages of the growth curve are associated with **morphological** and **physiological** alterations of the cells.

Lag phase maximum cell size is obtained towards the end of the lag phase.

Log phase, cells are smaller and stain uniformly.

Stationary phase, cells are frequently Gram variable and show irregular staining due to the presence of intracellular storage granules. Sporulation occurs at this stage. Also, many bacteria produce secondary metabolic products such as exotoxins and antibiotics.

Phase of decline involution forms are common.

Bacterial counts

Bacterial growth may be considered at two levels: increase in the size of the individual cell and increase in the number of cells. The former is ordinarily limited and when the critical size is reached, the cell divides, except when cell division is inhibited by substances like penicillin or acriflavine or by growth in magnesium deficient media. Growth in numbers can be studied by bacterial counts. Two types of bacterial counts can be made: total and viable.

● The **total count** gives the total number of cells in the sample, irrespective of whether they are living or not. It can be obtained by:
   – direct counting under the microscope using counting chambers,
   – counting in an electronic device as in the Coulter counter,
   – direct counting using stained smears prepared by spreading a known volume of the culture over a measured area of a slide,
   – comparing relative numbers in smears of the culture mixed with known numbers of other cells,
   – by opacity measurements using an absorptiometer or nephalometer,
   – by separating the cells by centrifugation or filtration and measuring their wet or dry weight, and
   – by chemical assay of cell components such as nitrogen.

● The **viable count** measures the number of living cells, that is, cells capable of multiplication. Viable counts are obtained by **dilution or plating methods**. In the dilution method, the suspension is diluted to a point beyond which unit quantities do not yield growth when inoculated into suitable liquid media (extinction). Several tubes are inoculated with varying dilutions and the viable count calculated statistically from the number of tubes showing growth. This method does not give accurate values but is used widely in water bacteriology for estimation of the 'presumptive coliform count' in drinking water. In the plating method, appropriate dilutions are inoculated on solid media, either on the surface of plates or as pour plates. The number of colonies that develop after incubation gives an estimate of the viable count. The method commonly employed is that described by **Miles and Misra** (1938) in which serial dilutions are dropped on the surface of dried plates and colony counts obtained.

BACTERIAL NUTRITION

The bacterial cell has the same general chemical pattern as the cells of other organisms. The principal constituent of bacterial cells is water, which represents about 80 per cent of the total weight. Proteins, polysaccharides, lipids, nucleic acids, mucopeptides and low molecular weight compounds make up the rest. Bacterial metabolism is closely similar to that of other organisms, exemplifying the 'unity of biochemistry'. There are, however, some differences which are exploited in selective toxicity and chemotherapy.

Factors that affect growth

For growth and multiplication of bacteria, the minimum nutritional requirements are **water, a source of carbon, a source of nitrogen and some inorganic salts.** Water is the vehicle for the entry of all nutrients into the cell and for the elimination of all waste products. It participates in metabolic reactions and also forms an integral part of the protoplasm.

● Bacteria can be classified nutritionally, based on their **energy requirements** and on their ability to synthesise essential metabolites. Bacteria which derive their energy from sunlight are called **phototrophs** and those that obtain energy from chemical reactions are called **chemotrophs.** Bacteria that can synthesise all their organic compounds are called **autotrophs.** Those that are unable to synthesise their own metabolites and depend on preformed organic compounds are called **heterotrophs.** Autotrophs are able to utilise atmospheric carbon dioxide and nitrogen. They are capable of independent existence in water and soil and are of no medical importance, though they are of vital concern in agriculture and the maintenance of soil fertility. Heterotrophic bacteria are unable to grow with carbon dioxide as the sole source of carbon. The nutritional requirements of heterotrophs vary widely. Some may require only a single organic substance such as glucose, while others may need a large number of different compounds such as amino acids, nucleotides, lipids, carbohydrates and co-enzymes.

- Bacteria require a supply of **inorganic salts**, particularly the anions phosphate and sulphate, and the cations sodium, potassium, magnesium, iron, manganese and calcium. These are normally present in the natural environment where bacteria live but will have to be supplied in culture media. Some ions such as cobalt may be needed in trace amounts.

- Some bacteria require certain **organic compounds** in minute quantities. These are known as growth factors or bacterial vitamins. **Growth factors** are called **essential** when growth does not occur in their absence, and **accessory** when they enhance growth, without being absolutely necessary for it. In many cases, bacterial vitamins are identical to the vitamins necessary for mammalian nutrition, particularly those belonging to the B group: thiamine, riboflavin, nicotinic acid, pyridoxine, folic acid and vitamin B12.

If a microorganism requiring an essential growth factor is inoculated into a medium containing an excess of all other nutrients, its growth will be proportional to the amount of the limiting substance added. Within a certain range, the concentration of the growth factor will bear a linear relationship to the growth of the organism. This is the principle of microbiological assays, which provide a very sensitive and specific method for the estimation of many amino acids and vitamins, as in the determination of vitamin B12 using *Lactobacillus leichmannii*.

- **Oxygen requirement and metabolism**: Depending on the influence of oxygen on growth and viability, bacteria are divided into aerobes and anaerobes. **Aerobic bacteria** require oxygen for growth. They may be obligate aerobes like the cholera vibrio, which will grow only in the presence of oxygen, or facultative anaerobes which are ordinarily aerobic but can also grow in the absence of oxygen, though less abundantly. Most bacteria of medical importance are facultative anaerobes. **Anaerobic bacteria**, such as clostridia, grow in the absence of oxygen and the **obligate anaerobes** may even die on exposure to oxygen. **Microaerophilic** bacteria are those that grow best in the presence of **low oxygen tension**.

The reason for the apparent toxicity of oxygen for anaerobic bacteria is not well understood. It has been suggested that in the presence of oxygen, hydrogen peroxide and other toxic peroxides accumulate. The enzyme catalase which splits hydrogen peroxide is present in most aerobic bacteria but is absent in anaerobes. Another reason is that obligate anaerobes possess essential enzymes that are active only in the reduced state.

The influence of free oxygen is related to the metabolic character of the bacterium. Aerobic bacteria obtain their energy and intermediates only through oxidation, involving oxygen as the ultimate hydrogen acceptor, while the anaerobes use hydrogen acceptors other than oxygen. Facultative anaerobes may act in both ways. In the case of aerobes, where the ultimate electron acceptor is atmospheric oxygen (aerobic respiration), the carbon and energy source may be completely oxidised to carbon dioxide and water. Energy is provided by the production of energy-rich phosphate bonds and the conversion of adenosine diphosphate (ADP) to adenosine triphosphate (ATP). This process is known as **oxidative phosphorylation**. Anaerobic bacteria use as electron acceptors compounds such as nitrates or sulphates instead of oxygen (anaerobic respiration).

A more common process in anaerobic metabolism may be a series of oxidoreductions in which the carbon and energy source acts as both the electron donor and the electron acceptor. This process is known as **fermentation** and leads to the formation of several organic end products such as acids and alcohols, as well as of gas (carbon dioxide and hydrogen). During the process of fermentation, energy-rich phosphate bonds are produced by the introduction of organic phosphate into intermediate metabolites. This process is known as **substrate-level phosphorylation**. The energy-rich phosphate groups so formed are used for conversion of ADP to ATP.

In determining the growth of aerobic and anaerobic bacteria, what is more important than the presence or absence of oxygen is the state of oxidation of the environment. The oxidising or reducing condition of a system is indicated by the net readiness of all the components in that system to take up or part with electrons. This is known as the **oxidation–reduction (redox) potential** of the system. The redox potential of a medium is best estimated by measuring the electrical potential difference set up between the medium and an unattackable electrode immersed in it. This electrode potential (Eh) is measured in millivolts. The more oxidised the system, the higher the potential. A simpler, though less accurate, method of measuring the redox potential is using oxidation–reduction indicators such as methylene blue, and noting the change in colour.

- **Carbon dioxide**: All bacteria require small amounts of carbon dioxide for growth. This requirement is usually met by the carbon dioxide present in the atmosphere, or produced endogenously by cellular metabolism. Some bacteria like *Brucella abortus* require much higher levels of carbon dioxide (5–10 per cent) for growth, especially on fresh isolation (capnophilic).

- **Temperature**: Bacteria vary in their requirement of temperature for growth. For each species, there is a 'temperature range', and growth does not occur above the maximum or below the minimum of this range. The temperature at which growth occurs best is known as the **'optimum temperature'**, which in the case of most **pathogenic bacteria** is 37°C. Bacteria which grow best at temperatures of 25–40°C are called **mesophilic**. All parasites of warm-blooded animals are mesophilic. Within the group of mesophilic bacteria, some like *Pseudomonas aeruginosa* have a wider range (5–43°C), while others like the gonococcus have a restricted range (30–39°C).

  Psychrophilic bacteria are those that grow best at temperatures below 20°C, some of them even growing at temperatures as low as −7°C. They are soil and water saprophytes and, though not of direct medical importance, may cause spoilage of refrigerated food. Another group of non-pathogenic bacteria, the **thermophiles**, grow best at high temperatures, 55–80°C. They may cause spoilage of underprocessed canned food. Some thermophiles (like *Bacillus stearothermophilus*) form spores that are exceptionally thermoresistant. Extremely thermophilic bacteria have been identified which can grow at temperatures as high as 250°C.

  Bacteria also differ in the effect of temperature on viability. Heat is an important method for the destruction of microorganisms (sterilisation), moist heat causing coagulation and denaturation of proteins and dry heat causing oxidation and charring. Moist heat is more lethal than dry heat. The lowest temperature that kills a bacterium under standard conditions in a given time is known as the **thermal death point**. Under moist conditions most vegetative, mesophilic bacteria have a thermal death point between 50 and 65°C and most spores between 100 and 120°C.

  At low temperatures some species die rapidly but most survive well. Storage in the refrigerator (3–5°C) or the deep freeze cabinet (−30 to −70°C) preserves cultures. Rapid freezing as with solid carbon dioxide or the use of a stabiliser such as glycerol, minimises the death of cells on freezing.

- **Moisture and drying**: Water is an essential ingredient of bacterial protoplasm and hence drying is lethal to cells. However, the effect of drying varies in different species. Some delicate bacteria like *Treponema pallidum* are highly sensitive, while others like staphylococci withstand drying for months. Spores are particularly resistant to desiccation and may survive in the dry state for several decades. Drying in vacuum in the cold (freeze drying or lyophilisation) is a method for the preservation of bacteria, viruses and many labile biological materials.

- **Hydrogen ion concentration**: Bacteria are sensitive to variations in pH. Each species has a pH range, above or below which it cannot survive, and an optimum pH at which it grows best. The majority of pathogenic bacteria grow best at neutral or slightly alkaline reactions (pH 7.2–7.6). Some acidophilic bacteria such as lactobacilli grow under acidic conditions. Others, such as the cholera vibrio, are very sensitive to acid, but tolerate high degrees of alkalinity. Strong solutions of acid or alkali (5% hydrochloric acid or sodium hydroxide) readily kill most bacteria, though mycobacteria are exceptionally resistant to them.

- **Light**: Bacteria (except the phototrophic species) grow well in the dark. They are sensitive to ultraviolet light and other radiation. Cultures die if exposed to sunlight. Exposure to light may influence pigment production. Photochromogenic mycobacteria form a pigment only on exposure to light and not when incubated in the dark.

- **Osmotic effect**: Bacteria are more tolerant to osmotic variation than most other cells due to the mechanical strength of their cell walls. Sudden exposure to hypertonic solutions may cause osmotic withdrawal of water and shrinkage of protoplasm—plasmolysis.

This occurs more readily in Gram-negative than in Gram-positive bacteria. Sudden transfer from a concentrated solution to distilled water may cause plasmoptysis (excessive osmotic imbibition leading to swelling and rupture of the cell).

- **Mechanical and sonic stress**: Though bacteria have tough cell walls, they may be ruptured by mechanical stress such as grinding or vigorous shaking with glass beads. They may also be disintegrated by exposure to ultrasonic vibration.

BACTERIOCINS

Gratia (1925) observed the production of a highly specific antibiotic substance by one strain of *E.coli* which was active against another strain of the same species. The name colicin was given to such substances produced by *E.coli* and other members of the family Enterobactericeae. With the recognition that colicin-like substances are produced by several other bacteria as well, the generic name **bacteriocin** was proposed for the group of highly specific antibiotic-like substances produced by certain strains of bacteria which are active against other strains of the same or different species. Bacteriocins are given specific names based on the bacterial species of origin, for example **colicins** from *E.coli*, **pyocins** from *Ps.pyocyanea* (*aeruginosa*), **megacins** from *B.megaterium* and **diphthericins** from *C.diphtheriae*.

Bacteriocins are proteins but some may have associated lipopolysaccharides derived from the cell walls of bacteria producing them. Bacteriocins and phages resemble each other in a number of respects. Both adsorb on the surface of susceptible bacterial cells on specific receptor sites, some of which may be the same for phages and bacteriocins. Under the electron microscope, some bacteriocins, especially pyocins, appear like the tail structures of phages. They may be considered products of defective phage genomes, able to code only for parts of phage particles.

The **synthesis** of bacteriocins is determined by the presence in bacteria of colicinogenic factors (**Col factors**). Col factors are episomes and can be transmitted from cell to cell by conjugation or transduction. Certain physical and chemical agents (UV rays, nitrogen mustard) induce colicin production by the cells harbouring Col factors.

A cell producing a bacteriocin is immune to it but may be sensitive to other bacteriocins. Bacteriocins have very specific activity on bacteria, being capable of killing some but not all strains of a species. The specificity is made use of in typing certain species such as *S.sonnei*, *Proteus* sp, *Ps.aeruginosa*. Bacteriocins kill susceptible cells without lysing them.

While phage typing schemes are generally based on the sensitivity of the test strains to the lytic action of phages, **bacteriocin typing schemes** depend on the ability of bacteriocins produced by the test strain to kill standard indicator strains of bacteria. The usual method of bacteriocin typing employs the plate diffusion technique. The test bacterium is inoculated as a broad streak on the centre of a culture medium, the bacterial growth is scraped off and the remaining cells killed by exposure to chloroform vapour. Standard indicator strains of bacteria are then streaked at right angles to the original inoculum. After incubation, the pattern of inhibition of the indicator strains represents the bacteriocin type of the test bacterium.

RECAP

- The kingdom protista has been divided into two groups: prokaryotes and eukaryotes.
- Bacteria and blue-green algae are prokaryotes, fungi, other algae and protozoa are eukaryotes.
- Bacteria possess a single circular chromosome (eukaryotes have multiple linear chromosomes) and have muramic acid (eukaryotes do not).
- The morphological study of bacteria requires the use of microscopes. The microscopes currently in use are:
  - Optical or light microscope (bright field microscope)
  - Phase contrast microscope

- ❖ Fluorescent microscope
- ❖ Dark field/ground microscope
- ❖ Electron microscope
- Staining techniques used for study of bacteria are:
  - ❖ Simple stains (methylene blue, basic fuchsin), where all bacteria are stained the same colour
  - ❖ Negative stains
  - ❖ Impregnation methods
  - ❖ Differential stains, where stains impart different colours to different bacteria or bacterial structures (Gram stain, acid fast stain)
- Depending on their shape, bacteria are classified into cocci (spherical or oval), bacilli (rod-shaped), vibrios (comma-shaped curved rods), spirilla (rigid spiral forms), spirochetes (flexuous spiral forms) and actinomycetes (branching filamentous bacteria).
- A bacterial cell has a rigid cell wall, a phospholipid cytoplasmic) membrane, flagella, fimbriae and pili. Gram-positive cell wall is 90% peptidoglycan and Gram-negative cell wall is composed of lipopolysaccharide which also contains lipid A, a toxic substance that imparts the pathogenic virulence associated with some Gram-negative bacteria.
- Bacteria divide by binary fission. The time interval between two cell divisions is the generation or population doubling time. This may vary from 20 minutes (coliform bacilli) to 20 hours (tubercle bacilli) to 20 days (lepra bacilli).
- The bacterial growth curve consists of a lag phase (no appreciable increase in number), a log phase (an exponential increase in bacterial number), a stationary phase (no increase or decrease in number) and a decline phase (decrease in the bacterial population due to cell death).
- Bacteria vary in their requirements of temperature for growth. Mesophilic bacteria grow best at temperatures of 25–40°C, psychrophilic bacteria at temperatures below 20°C and thermophilic bacteria at high temperatures, 55–80°C.
- Bacteriocins are a group of highly specific antibiotic-like substances produced by certain strains of bacteria active against other strains of the same or different species. Bacteriocins are given specific names based on the bacterial species of origin, for example colicins from *E.coli,* pyocins from *Ps.pyocyanea* (*aeruginosa*), megacins from *B.megaterium* and diphthericins from *C.diphtheriae.*

SHORT ANSWERS

1. Principles of Gram staining
2. Draw a labelled diagram of the structure of a bacterial cell.
3. L forms of bacteria
4. Bacterial cell wall (Gram-positive, Gram-negative)

SHORT NOTES

1. Structure of flagella
2. Arrangment of flagella with diagram
3. a) Spores
   b) Arrangement of spores
4. Bacterial growth curve
5. Bacterocins
7. Capsule

3 Sterilisation and Disinfection

INTRODUCTION

Microorganisms are ubiquitous. They are found in the surroundings, on inanimate objects and on the surface of the human body. Since they cause contamination, infection and decay, it becomes necessary to remove or destroy them. This is the object of sterilisation. Methods to remove or kill microorganisms are known as **sterilisation**. The methods of sterilisation used depend on the purpose for which it is carried out, the material to be sterilised and the nature of the microorganisms to be removed or destroyed.

Sterilisation is defined as the process by which an article, surface or medium is freed of all living microorganisms either in the vegetative or spore state.

Disinfection is the destruction of all pathogenic organisms. **Asepsis** is the state of complete absence of viable pathogenic microorganisms in any environment.

Antiseptics are agents that can be safely applied on the skin or mucous membrane to prevent infection by inhibiting the growth of bacteria.

Bactericidal agents (or **germicides**) are substances that can kill bacteria.

Bacteriostatic agents prevent the multiplication of bacteria which may, however, remain alive. A chemical which is bactericidal at a particular concentration may become bacteriostatic at a higher dilution.

Decontamination is the process of rendering an article or area free of contaminants, including microbial, chemical, radioactive and other hazardous materials from an area, object or body surface.

STERILISING AGENTS

Methods used for sterilising an object are:

1. **Physical agents**
   - Dry heat: By flaming, incineration or using hot air
   - Moist heat: By boiling, steam at atmospheric pressure, steam above atmospheric pressure
   - Filtration: Using candles, asbestos pads, membranes
   - Radiation

2. **Chemical agents**
   - Alcohols: ethyl, isopropyl, trichlorobutanol
   - Aldehydes: formaldehyde, glutaraldehyde
   - Orthophthalaldehyde
   - Peracetic acid,
   - Hydrogen peroxide
   - Hypochlorous acid
   - Dyes
   - Halogens
   - Phenols
   - Surface-active agents
   - Metallic salts

- Gases: ethylene oxide, formaldehyde, beta propiolactone

Some of the agents mentioned above are also used as disinfectants.

PHYSICAL AGENTS

Heat

Applying heat to an object is the most reliable method of sterilisation. Materials that may be damaged by heat can be sterilised by exposing them to low heat for longer periods or by repeated cycles.

The **factors influencing sterilisation** by heat are:
- Nature of heat—dry or moist
- Temperature and time
- Number of microorganisms present
- Characteristics of the organisms, such as species, strain, presence of spores
- Type of material from which the organisms must be eradicated

Mechanism of action: The killing effect of **dry heat** is due to protein denaturation, damage by oxidising molecules, destroying cell constituents and the toxic effect of elevated levels of electrolytes. The lethal effect of **moist heat** is due to the denaturation and coagulation of proteins. The advantage of steam lies in the latent heat liberated when it condenses on a cooler surface, raising the temperature of that surface. In the case of spores, steam condenses on them, increasing their water content resulting in the ultimate hydrolysis and breakdown of the bacterial protein. In a completely moisture-free atmosphere (as in dry heat), bacteria, like many proteins, are more resistant to heat. They are killed when oxidation of the cell constituents occurs, and this requires much higher temperatures than that needed for coagulation of proteins (by moist heat).

The time required for sterilisation is inversely proportional to the temperature of exposure and can be expressed as **thermal death time**. This is the minimum time required to kill a suspension of organisms at a predetermined temperature in a specified environment. The sterilisation time is related to the number of organisms in the suspension, presence or absence of spores, and the strain and characteristics of the organism. It does not include the time taken to reach the specified temperature. The nature of the material in which the organisms are present affects the rate of killing. The presence of organic substances, proteins, nucleic acids, starch, gelatin, sugar, fats and oils increases the thermal death time. The presence of disinfectants and high acid or alkaline pH hastens bacterial killing.

Dry heat

- **Flaming:** An inoculating loop or wire, the tip of forceps and searing spatulas can be sterilised by holding them over a Bunsen flame till they become red hot. Inoculation loops carrying infective material may be dipped in a disinfectant before flaming to prevent spattering.
- **Incineration:** This is an excellent method for terminal sterilisation for destroying biomedical waste. Plastics such as PVC and polythene can be dealt with similarly, but polystyrene materials emit clouds of dense toxic smoke which pollute the environment.

> In order to check the proliferation of poorly designed bio-medical waste incinerators, guidelines on 'Design and Construction of Bio-medical Waste Incinerator' recommend various design features of an incinerator as well as the air pollution control device.

- **Hot-air oven:** This is the most widely used method of sterilisation by dry heat. Sterilisation is achieved by conduction. The heat is absorbed by the surface of the item to be sterilised, which then penetrates to the centre, until the entire item reaches the desired temperature. A holding period of 160°C for two hours is necessary to sterilise glassware, forceps, scissors, scalpels, all-glass syringes, swabs and some pharmaceutical products such as liquid paraffin, dusting powder, fats and grease. The oven is usually heated by electricity. A fan is fitted inside to ensure even distribution of air and elimination of air pockets (Fig. 3.1). The chamber should not be overloaded. Free circulation of air in between the objects should be ensured. Glassware should be perfectly dry before being placed in the oven. Test tubes

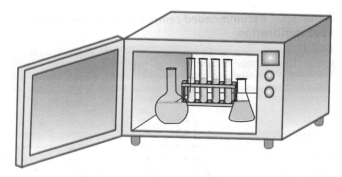

Fig. 3.1 Hot-air oven

and flasks should be wrapped in craft paper. Rubber materials, except silicon rubber, will not withstand the temperature. At 180°C, cotton plugs may get charred. Sharp instruments, such as those used in ophthalmic surgery, should ideally be sterilised for two hours at 150°C. The British Pharmacopoeia recommends a holding time of one hour at 150°C for oils, glycerol and dusting powder. The oven must be allowed to cool slowly for about two hours before the door is opened, since the glassware may crack due to sudden or uneven cooling. Table 3.1 lists the recommended temperature and duration for heat sterilisation.

Sterilisation control:
- **Physical:** Temperature monitoring by thermocouples
- **Chemical:** A **Browne's tube** (green spot) is used. A green colour is produced after 60 minutes at 160°C or 115 minutes at 150°C, suggesting complete sterilisation.
- **Biological:** Heat-resistant spores of a non-toxigenic strain of *Clostridium tetani* or *Bacillus subtilis* subsp. *niger* are used to indicate efficiency of dry heat sterilisation.

Moist heat

Temperatures below 100°C
- **Pasteurisation of milk:** The milk is heated at either 63°C for 30 minutes (the **holder** method) or 72°C for 15–20 seconds (the **flash process**), followed by cooling quickly to 13°C or lower. By these processes, all non-sporing pathogens such as mycobacteria, brucellae and salmonellae are destroyed. *Coxiella burnetii* is relatively heat-resistant and may survive the holder method.
- **Inspissation:** Media such as Lowenstein–Jensen and Loeffler's serum are rendered sterile by heating at 80–85°C for half an hour on three successive days in an **inspissator** (Fig. 3.2).

Table 3.1 *Recommended temperature and duration for heat sterilisation*

Method	Temperature (°C)	Holding time (in minutes)
Autoclave	121	15
	126	10
	134	3
Hot-air oven*	160	120
	170	60
	180	30

British Pharmacopeia 1988, European Pharmacopeia 1990

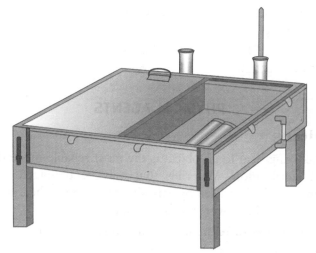

Fig. 3.2   Inspissator

Bacterial vaccines are heat-inactivated in special vaccine baths at 60°C for one hour. Serum or body fluids containing coagulable proteins can be sterilised by heating for one hour at 56°C in a water bath on several successive days.

- All non-sporing bacteria are killed at 60°C in 30 minutes.
- *Streptococcus faecalis* and *Staphylococcus aureus* are killed at 60°C for 60 minutes.
- Yeasts, moulds and vegetative bacteria are killed at 80°C in 5–10 minutes.
- Spores of *Clostridium botulinum* require 120°C for 4 minutes or 100°C for 330 minutes.
- Most viruses are killed rapidly at 60°C except for polio and Hepatitis B viruses which may survive at this temperature for 30 minutes and 10 hours respectively.

Temperature at 100°C
- **Boiling:** Vegetative bacteria are killed almost immediately at 90–100°C, but bacterial spores can withstand long periods of boiling. In cases where boiling is considered adequate, the material should be immersed in the water and boiled for 10–30 minutes. The lid of the steriliser should not be opened during this period. Boiling is not recommended for sterilisation of instruments used for surgical procedures. Hard water should not be used for boiling. Addition of 2% sodium bicarbonate to the water may render it soft and make it suitable for sterilisation.
- **Steam at atmospheric pressure (100°C):** An atmosphere of free steam is used to sterilise culture media which may decompose if subjected to higher temperatures. A **Koch** or **Arnold steamer** is usually used.

Tyndallisation or intermittent sterilisation: This method is used for media containing sugars or gelatin. An exposure to 100°C for 20 minutes on three successive days is used. The principle is that the first exposure kills all vegetative bacteria, and the spores, since they are in a favourable medium, will germinate and be killed on subsequent exposure to **100°C for 20 minutes**. However, this method may fail to kill spores of certain anaerobes and thermophiles.

Steam under pressure: The equipment used is an autoclave. The principle of the **autoclave** or steam steriliser is that when water boils, its vapour pressure equals that of the surrounding atmosphere. Hence, when pressure inside a closed vessel increases, the temperature at which water boils also increases, generating steam. When steam comes into contact with a cooler surface, it condenses and transmits its latent heat to that surface (1600 ml steam at 100°C and at atmospheric pressure condenses into 1 ml of water at 100°C and releases 518 calories of heat). The large reduction in volume sucks in more steam and the process continues till the temperature of that surface equalises with that of steam. Condensed water ensures moist heat for killing the microbes present on the material.

Sterilisation by steam under pressure is carried out at temperatures between 108°C and 147°C. Materials such as linen, instruments, laboratory ware, media and pharmaceutical products can be sterilised in an autoclave. Aqueous solutions are sterilised between 108°C and 126°C. Heat is conducted through the walls of the sealed containers until the temperature of the fluid inside is the same as that of the steam outside.

Autoclaves (**steam sterilisers**) used in a healthcare setup:
- Laboratory autoclaves
- Hospital dressing sterilisers
- Instrument sterilisers
- Rapid cooling sterilisers

Two types of autoclaves are available: **gravity displacement** type and **high vacuum sterilisers**.

The laboratory autoclave consists of a vertical or horizontal cylinder of gunmetal or stainless steel, in a supporting sheet iron case. The lid is fastened by screw clamps and made airtight. An exit tap for air and steam, and a pressure gauge are attached to the autoclave. A safety valve that can be set to blow off, if pressure rises beyond the desired level, is also attached to the autoclave. Heating is by electricity (Fig. 3.3).

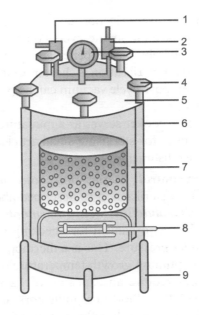

Fig. 3.3 A simple autoclave; 1. release valve; 2. safety valve; 3. pressure gauge; 4. tightening screws; 5. cover; 6. body; 7. bin containing material; 8. heating element; 9. stand

Mechanism: Sufficient water is added to the cylinder, and the material to be sterilised is placed on the tray. The lid is screwed tight with the discharge tap open, and the autoclave is heated. The steam–air mixture is allowed to escape freely till all the air has been displaced. This can be tested by leading the escaping steam into a pail of water through rubber tubing. When no more air bubbles come out in the pail, the discharge tap is closed. The steam pressure rises inside and, when it reaches the desired set level, the safety valve opens and the excess steam escapes. From this point, the **holding period** is calculated (Table 3.1). When the holding period is over, the heater is turned off and the autoclave is allowed to cool till the pressure reaches atmospheric pressure. The discharge tap is opened slowly and air is let into the autoclave. If the tap is opened when the internal pressure is high, liquid media boils violently, spills from the container and may explode. If opened after the pressure inside has fallen below atmospheric pressure, an excessive amount of water will evaporate and be lost from the media.

The **defects** in this type of autoclave are:
- The method of **air discharge is inefficient**, and it is difficult to decide when the discharge is complete.
- Materials remain **moist** after removal from the autoclave.

Vacuum sterilisers do not have this disadvantage. They usually have automatic cycle control. The air is drawn out, whereby steam penetrates faster and the time required for sterilisation is shorter. Once the sterilisation is over, post-cycle vacuum can be programmed for quick drying.

The pressure cooker serves as a miniature autoclave and may be used for sterilising small articles in clinics and small establishments.

Sterilisation control: Sterilisation control is similar to that of dry heat sterilisation as described above except for the use of *Geobacillus stearothermophilus*, which is used as the test organism for checking sterilisation by steam under pressure. This is a thermophilic organism with an optimum growth temperature of 55–60°C and its spores require an exposure of 12 minutes at 121°C to be killed. Biological indicators are the only process indicators that directly monitor the lethality of a given sterilisation process. Rapid readout biological indicators, which provide results within one to three hours, are available for shorter turnaround time for reading the results.

Filtration

Filtration helps remove bacteria from heat labile liquids such as sera and solutions of sugars or antibiotics. As viruses can pass through ordinary filters, filtration only renders the material bacteria-free.

Bacterial toxins can be obtained by passing cultures through filters. Asbestos filters are no longer used due to their carcinogenic property (Fig. 3.4a).

Types of filters
- **Candle filters** are manufactured in different grades of porosity and have been used widely for the purification of water for industrial and drinking purposes. They are of two types: **unglazed ceramic** filters (for example, Chamberland and Doulton) and **diatomaceous earth** filters (for example, Berkefeld and Mandler).
- **Sintered glass filters** are prepared by heat-fusing finely powdered glass particles of graded sizes. They have low absorptive property and can be cleaned easily, but are brittle and expensive (Fig. 3.4b).
- **Membrane filters** made of cellulose esters or other polymers have largely replaced other types of filters. They are routinely used in water purification and analysis, sterilisation and sterility testing, and for the preparation of solutions for parenteral use. They come in a wide range of average pore diameters

(a)   (b)

(c)

Fig. 3.4 (a) Asbestos filter; (b) Sintered glass filter; (c) Membrane filter

(APD), the 0.22 mm size being the most widely used for sterilisation (Fig. 3.4c).

Cold sterilisation is a process in which sterilisation is carried out at low temperatures with the help of chemicals, radiation, membranes (filters) and all other means excluding high temperature.

Radiation

Two types of radiation are used for sterilisation: non-ionising and ionising. Infrared and ultraviolet rays are of the non-ionising, low-energy type, while gamma rays and high-energy electrons are the ionising, high-energy type.
- **Non-ionising radiation:** Here, electromagnetic rays with wavelengths longer than those of visible light are used. These are, to a large extent, absorbed as heat. Infrared radiation is used for rapid mass-sterilisation of prepacked items such as syringes and catheters. Ultraviolet radiation is used for disinfecting enclosed areas such as biosafety cabinets in laboratories, entryways, operation theatres and laboratories.
- **Ionising radiation:** X-rays, gamma rays and cosmic rays are highly lethal to DNA and other vital con-

stituents. They have very high penetrative power. Since there is no appreciable increase in temperature in this method, it is referred to as cold sterilisation. Commercial plants use gamma radiation for sterilising items like plastics, syringes, swabs, catheters, animal feeds, cardboard, oils, greases, fabric and metal foils.

CHEMICAL AGENTS

Several chemical agents are used as antiseptics and disinfectants.

An **ideal antiseptic or disinfectant** should:
- Have a wide spectrum of activity and be effective against all microorganisms
- Be active in the presence of organic matter
- Be effective in acid as well as alkaline media
- Have speedy action
- Have high penetrating power
- Be stable

Factors that affect the potency of a disinfectant:
- Concentration of the substance
- Contact period
- pH of the medium
- Temperature
- Nature of the organisms
- Presence of extraneous material

Mode of action of chemical agents
- By protein coagulation
- By disruption of the cell membrane resulting in exposure, damage or loss of contents
- By removal of free sulphydryl groups essential for the functioning of the enzymes
- By substrate competition of enzymes necessary for the metabolism of the cell

---

Alcohols

Ethyl alcohol (ethanol) and **isopropyl alcohol** are the most frequently used. They are used mainly as skin antiseptics at a concentration of 60–90% in water. They act by denaturing bacterial proteins. They have no action on spores. Protein slows its action whereas 1% mineral acid or alkali enhances it. Isopropyl alcohol is preferred as it is a better fat solvent, is more bactericidal and less volatile. It is used for the disinfection of clinical thermometers.

Methyl alcohol is effective against fungal spores and is used for cleaning cabinets and incubators. The insides of the chambers are wiped with liberal amounts of methanol. A pad moistened with methanol and a dish of water (to ensure high humidity) are kept inside the chamber which is left at working temperature for several hours. Methyl alcohol vapour is toxic and inflammable.

Aldehydes

Formaldehyde is active against the amino group in the protein molecule. In aqueous solutions, it is markedly bactericidal, sporicidal and virucidal.

It is used to preserve anatomical specimens, and for destroying anthrax spores in hair and wool; 10% formalin containing 0.5% sodium tetraborate is used to sterilise clean metal instruments.

Formaldehyde gas is used for sterilising instruments, heat-sensitive catheters and for fumigating wards, isolation rooms and laboratories. Under properly controlled conditions, clothing, bedding, furniture and books can be satisfactorily disinfected.

The gas is an irritant and toxic when inhaled. This can be nullified by exposing the environment to ammonia vapour after disinfection has been completed.

Glutaraldehyde has an action similar to that of formaldehyde. It is especially effective against the tubercle bacilli, fungi and viruses. It has no deleterious effect on the cement or lenses of instruments. Hence, it is used to sterilise cystoscopes, bronchoscopes, rubber anaesthetic tubes, plastic endotracheal tubes and polythene tubing. It can also be used for metal instruments.

Orthophthalaldehyde has bactericidal activity. It is used to cleanse endoscopes between patients as it is quick, effective and safe.

Peracetic acid has a good sterilisation effect on bacteria, particularly common antibiotic-resistant bacteria such as methicillin-resistant *Staphylococcus aureus*, vancomycin-resistant *Enterococcus* and *Clostridium difficile*.

Hypochlorous acid is generated from the reverse reaction of sodium hypochlorite and hydrogen peroxide. It has bactericidal activity against common pathogenic organisms. It is active against biofilms and microorganisms within the biofilms.

Dyes

Two groups of dyes, aniline and acridine, are used extensively as skin and wound antiseptics. Both are bacteriostatic in high dilution but have low bactericidal activity. They are more active against Gram-positive than Gram-negative bacteria.

The **aniline dyes** include brilliant green, malachite green and crystal violet. They do not act against tubercle bacilli. Hence, malachite green is used in the Lowenstein–Jensen medium as a selective agent. They are non-irritant and non-toxic to the tissues. They are inhibited by organic material. Lethal effects on bacteria are believed to be due to their reaction with the acid groups in the cell.

Acridine dyes are not as selective as the aniline dyes. They are minimally affected by the presence of organic matter. Important dyes in this group are proflavine, acriflavine, euflavine and aminacrine. They impair the DNA complexes of the organisms and prevent replication.

Halogens

Iodine in an aqueous and alcoholic solution has been widely used as a skin disinfectant. It is bactericidal, with moderate action against spores. It is active against the tubercle bacteria and viruses. Compounds of iodine with non-ionic wetting or surface-active agents known as iodophores have better action than aqueous or alcoholic solutions of iodine.

Chlorine and its compound hypochlorite have been used as disinfectants over time. They are markedly bactericidal and virucidal. Town water supplies, swimming pools, food and dairy industries use chlorine for disinfection. The organic chloramines are used as antiseptics for dressing wounds.

> **Disadvantages of chlorine**
> Certain types of microorganisms have shown resistance to low doses of chlorine.

Phenols

These compounds are obtained by distillation of coal tar between temperatures of 170°C and 270°C. Bactericidal effect of phenols is due to their capacity to cause cell membrane damage, inactivation of membrane-bound oxidases and dehydrogenases leading to lysis and death of the microorganism. Low concentrations of phenol precipitate proteins.

Phenol (carbolic acid) is widely used as disinfectants in hospitals. Commonly used compounds are **lysol** and **cresol** which are active against a wide range of organisms. They are not readily inactivated by the presence of organic matter; hence, they are good general disinfectants. Various proprietary preparations or formulations of phenol are in wide use. The related chlorophenols and chloroxyphenols, though less toxic and irritant, are less active (inactive against *Pseudomonas*), and readily inactivated by organic matter. Chlorhexidine (Hibitane) is a relatively non-toxic skin antiseptic and wound dressing. They are active against most Gram-positive organisms and fairly effective against Gram-negative bacteria. Hexachlorophene, on the other hand, is potentially toxic and should be used with care.

Gases

Ethylene oxide: This is a colourless liquid with a boiling point of 10.7°C, and highly penetrating at normal temperature and pressure. It has a sweet, ethereal smell and is highly inflammable. It is highly explosive at concentrations greater than 3%. Combination with 10% carbon dioxide or nitrogen makes it less explosive.

It acts by alkylating the amino, carboxyl, hydroxyl and sulphydryl groups in protein molecules within the microbes and spores. It also reacts with DNA and RNA (rendering them virucidal). It is potentially toxic to human beings, causing mutagenicity and carcinogenicity.

It diffuses through many types of porous materials and readily penetrates some plastics. It is especially used for sterilising heat-sensitive equipment like heart–lung machines, respirators, suture materials, dental equipment, books and clothing. It has a wide application within and outside the hospital. It is unsuitable for fumigating rooms because of its explosive property. It is an irritant, and personnel working with it have to take strict precautions.

Formaldehyde gas: This is employed for fumigation of operation theatres and other rooms. Formaldehyde gas is generated by adding 150 g of $KMnO_4$ to 280 ml formalin for every 1000 cu. ft (28.3 cu. m) of room volume. The sealed room is left unopened for 48 hours after fumigation. The gas is neutralised with ammonia (300 ml for every litre of formaldehyde used). Fumigation of operation theatres is no longer preferred.

Betapropiolactone (BPL): This is a condensation product of ketane and formaldehyde. It is no longer used for fumigation as it is carcinogenic.

Hydrogen peroxide fogging: Bactericidal action is by oxidising the cell wall of the organism. This has replaced fumigation. It has the advantage of short cycle time and is non-toxic.

Surface-active agents

Surface-active agents are substances that alter the energy relationship at interfaces, producing a reduction in surface tension (Table 3.2). They are widely used as wetting agents, detergents and emulsifiers.

Mechanism: These act on the phosphate groups of the cell membrane and also enter the cell. The membrane loses its semi-permeability and the cell proteins are denatured. They act on bacteria, but have no action on spores, tubercle bacilli and most viruses.

The common compounds are acetyl trimethyl ammonium bromide (Cetavlon or Cetrimide) and benzalkonium chloride. These are most active at alkaline pH. Acid inactivates them. Organic matter reduces their action and anionic surface-active agents, like ordinary soaps, render them inactive. The anionic compounds, for example, common soap, have moderate action. Soaps prepared from saturated fatty acids (such as coconut oil) are more effective against Gram-negative bacilli while those prepared from unsaturated fatty acids (oleic acid) have greater action against Gram-positive and the *Neisseria* group of organisms.

Metallic salts

Though all salts have a certain amount of germicidal action, salts of heavy metals have greater action. Silver, copper and mercury salts are used as disinfectants. They are protein coagulants and have the capacity to combine with free sulphydryl groups of cell enzymes. Thiomersal, phenyl mercury nitrate and mercurochrome are less toxic and are used as mild antiseptics and have marked bacteriostatic but weak bactericidal and limited fungicidal action. Copper salts are used as fungicides.

The commonly used methods of sterilisation and antisepsis/disinfection are given in Tables 3.3 and 3.4.

TESTING OF DISINFECTANTS

There is no single reliable test available to determine the efficiency of a disinfectant, as several parameters influence its activity. Traditionally, phenol is taken as the standard, as the action of the test agent is compared to it.

Rideal–Walker test: This test is now of historical importance. It is the ratio of the dilution of any disinfectant that kills a microorganism to the dilution of phenol which kills the microorganism in the same time under identical conditions. It is expressed as **phenol coefficient** (phenol = 1) of the disinfectant. It does not take into account the presence of organic matter. Modifications have been made in the **Chick–Martin test**. The disinfectant acts in the presence of organic matter (dried yeast or feces). Various other modifications have been introduced, but no test is entirely satisfactory.

For practical purposes, the **Kelsey–Sykes** or **in-use** test is performed for disinfectants. Here, working solutions of the disinfectants used in the hospital are sampled at different times during their use. Table 3.5 lists the concentrations used for disinfectants in clinical practice.

STERILISATION AND DISINFECTION IN A HEALTHCARE SETTING

Sterilisation and disinfection form key components of ensuring patient safety in a healthcare setup. Spaulding's classification has been used to classify the devices used on the patient. It determines the type of method selected for disinfection or sterilisation.

Spaulding's classification

Critical items

Critical items are those which enter sterile tissue or the vascular system and pose a high risk of infection if the article is contaminated. This category includes surgical instruments, cardiac catheters, implants, etc. They must be sterilised by autoclaving if heat-stable or with ethylene oxide or hydrogen peroxide gas plasma if heat-sensitive.

Semi-critical items

Articles which come in contact with mucous membranes or non-intact skin are called semi-critical items. They require high-level disinfection. Glutaraldehyde is the most commonly used high-level disinfectant. Endoscopes and bronchoscopes undergo high-level disinfection prior to and between patients. Some

Table 3.2 *Classification of surface-active agents*

S.No	Category	Agents
1	Anionic	Sulphide, fluoride, bromide, iodide
2	Cationic	Sodium, iron, lead
3	Non-ionic	Polyoxyethylene (e.g., Tween, triton)
4	Amphoteric	Tego compounds

Table 3.3   *Commonly used methods of sterilisation*

S.No	Method	Types/Equipment	Agents for which used
1	Dry heat	Flaming	Inoculating loop/wire, tip of forceps, searing spatulas
2		Hot-air oven	Glassware, all glass syringes, sharp instruments, liquid paraffin, dusting powder, fats and grease
3	Moist heat	Below 100°C: • Pasteurisation • Inspissation • Vaccine baths	Milk Lowenstein–Jensen medium, Loeffler's serum slope Vaccines and sera
4		100°C: • Boiling • Tyndallisation or intermittent sterilisation at 100°C intermittently for three consecutive days	Material used for domestic appliances, baby bottle, teats and caps Media containing sugars or gelatin
5		Steam at atmospheric pressure: Steam sterilisers (Koch or Arnold steamer)	Culture media which are sensitive to higher temperature
6		Steam under pressure: Autoclave • Gravity displacement type • High vacuum type	Hospital linen, instruments, laboratory ware, media and pharmaceutical products
7	Filtration	Sintered glass filters Asbestos filters (Seitz – Not recommended due to carcinogenic property) Candle filters Membrane filters	Water purification and analysis, sterilisation and sterility testing of liquids Solutions for parenteral use
8	Cold sterilisation	Radiation: Ionising: • X-rays • Gamma rays • Cosmic rays	Plastics, syringes, swabs, catheters, oils, grease Industrial use: animal feeds, fabric and metal foils
		Non-ionising: Infrared Ultraviolet	Mass pre-packed: plastic syringes, catheters Laboratory cabinets, closed chambers
9	Liquid chemical sterilising agents	Glutaraldehyde Orthophthalaldehyde Peracetic acid Hydrogen peroxide Hypochlorous acid	Cystoscopes, endoscopes, tubings and metal instruments

Table 3.4   *Methods of antisepsis/disinfection (by chemical agents)*

Agents		Use
Alcohols	Ethyl alcohol (ethanol) Isopropyl alcohol	Skin antiseptics
	Methyl alcohol	Cleaning cabinets and incubators
Aldehydes	Glutaraldehyde	Sterilising instruments, heat-sensitive catheters, cystoscopes, bronchoscopes, rubber anaesthetic tubes, plastic endotracheal tubes and polythene tubing.
	Formaldehyde (Gas)	Fumigating OTs, wards, isolation rooms and laboratories (not preferred now). Under properly controlled conditions, clothing, bedding, etc.

Table 3.4 *(Continued)...* *Methods of antisepsis/disinfection (by chemical agents)*

Agents		Use
Dyes	Aniline dyes	Used on skin and in some culture media (Lowenstein–Jensen medium)
	• Brilliant green	
	• Malachite green	
	• Crystal violet	
	• Acridine dyes	
	• Acriflavine	
	• Proflavine	Used as antiseptics on skin
Halogens	Iodine	Skin disinfectant
	Chlorine	Water supply, swimming pools
	Hypochlorites	Disinfectant widely used in the hospitals at different concentrations
	Chlorhexidine (Hibitane)	Skin antiseptic, wound dressing
	Hexachlorophene	
Phenols	Lysol and cresol	Work benches, floors and walls
Gas	Ethylene oxide	Heart–lung machines, respirators, suture materials, dental, equipment, clothing
	Hydrogen peroxide	Used for fogging
	Betapropiolactone	No longer used

Table 3.5 *Commonly used concentration of disinfectants*

S.No.	Name of the disinfectant	Concentration
1	Glutaraldehyde	2%
2	Phenol	5%
3	Sodium hypochlorite	0.5–5%*
4	Chlorhexidine	1–4%*
5	Poviodine iodine	10%
6	Alcohol	70–80%
* Concentration will vary with the clinical situation		

High-level disinfectant: This is a chemical that kills all microbial pathogens except large numbers of spores. It may have some activity against a smaller number of spores if the contact time is increased. For example, glutaraldehyde and hydrogen peroxide.

Intermediate-level disinfectant: A chemical that kills all microbial pathogens including mycobacteria and non-enveloped viruses except spores. For example, alcohol, phenolic compounds and iodophores.

Low-level disinfectant: A chemical that kills only vegetative bacteria, fungi and lipid-enveloped viruses. For example, quaternary ammonium compound. Table 3.4.

semi-critical items like thermometers and blood pressure cuffs for neonates require only intermediate-level disinfection. This is done by disinfecting with alcohol as the articles may not be compatible with glutaraldehyde.

Non-critical items

These items come in contact with intact skin but not mucous membranes. Examples are bedpans, blood pressure cuffs, bed rails, bedside tables, etc. They can be cleaned or treated with low-level disinfectants as they carry no risk of transmitting microorganisms to the patients directly.

New methods of sterilisation of heat-sensitive articles

Plasma sterilisation: Plasma is known as the fourth state of matter and consists of ions, electrons or neutral particles. A radio frequency energy is applied to create an electromagnetic field. Into this, hydrogen peroxide vapours are introduced which generates a state of plasma containing free radicals of hydrogen and oxygen. This state renders the articles sterile by denaturing all microorganisms. Arthroscopes, urethroscopes, etc., are sterilised by **plasma sterilisation.**

RECAP

- Sterilisation is the process by which an article, surface or medium is freed of all living microorganisms, either in the vegetative or spore state.
- Disinfection is the destruction or removal of all pathogenic organisms, or organisms capable of giving rise to infection.
- The factors that determine the type of sterilising or disinfecting process to be used include time, temperature, stage of growth of the organism, nature of the medium in which the organism is present and number of organisms present.
- Physical methods of sterilisation use heat (dry heat, moist heat), filtration, and radiation.
- Chemical methods include alcohol, aldehyde, dyes, halogens, phenol, surface-active agents and gases.
- Spaulding's classification categorises devices used on the patient.

ESSAYS

1. Define sterilisation. Describe the principle and functioning of an autoclave.
2. Enumerate the methods of sterilisation by dry heat. Discuss the functioning of a hot-air oven.
3. Enumerate the disinfection techniques used in hospitals. Mention their mechanism of action and uses.

SHORT ANSWERS

1. Pasteurisation
2. Tyndallisation
3. Use of antiseptics
4. Uses of gamma radiation for sterilisation
5. Methods of testing disinfectants
6. Sterilisation control
7. Methods of monitoring autoclaves
8. Plasma sterilisation
9. Cold sterilisation

SHORT NOTES

1. Inspissator
2. Spaulding's classification
3. Gaseous sterilisation
4. Filtration for sterilisation
5. High-level disinfection (definition)

4 Culture Media

INTRODUCTION

To identify clinically important bacteria, they need to be isolated from the samples submitted to the laboratory. This is done by inoculating the samples on growth media required for the bacteria to replicate and form colonies on solid media or suspensions in liquid media.

This forms the starting point in the identification and antibiotic susceptibility testing of the organism. Classification of culture media is given in Table 4.1.

TYPES OF CULTURE MEDIA

Liquid media

Liquids are used to obtain bacterial growth from blood or water when large volumes have to be tested, and for preparing bulk cultures of antigens or vaccines. Bacteria grow diffusely in liquids. They produce discrete, visible growth on solid media. If inoculated in suitable dilutions, bacteria form **colonies**, which are clones of cells originating from a single bacterial cell. Fluid enrichment media are first incubated at 37°C and then sub-cultured on a solid medium to get individual isolated colonies.

Solid media

On solid media, bacteria have distinct colony morphology and exhibit many characteristic features such as pigmentation or hemolysis, making identification easy.

Agar (or agar-agar) is used to prepare solid media. Agar is obtained from a type of seaweed. It has virtually no nutritive value and is not affected by the growth

Table 4.1 *Classification of culture media*

S.No.	Type of culture media	Examples
1	Liquid	Brain–heart infusion broth, peptone water, nutrient broth
2	Solid	Nutrient agar, blood agar, chocolate agar
3	Simple	Non-nutrient agar, nutrient agar
4	Complex	Thiosulphate citrate bile salt sucrose agar (TCBS)
5	Synthetic or defined	Hank's balanced salt solution (used for virus transport)
Based on their functional requirement, media can be further classified as:		
1	Enriched	Todd–Hewitt broth (for fastidious, nutritionally demanding organisms)
2	Enrichment	Selenite F medium (for fecal samples to suppress gut commensals)
3	Selective	Salmonella Shigella agar (isolates Salmonella and Shigella in fecal samples)
4	Indicator	MacConkey agar (lactose fermenter from non-lactose fermenters)
5	Differential	Mannitol salt agar (*Staphylococcus aureus* from *Staphylococcus epidermidis*)
6	Transport	Stuart's transport medium (for transporting swabs to isolate pathogens from throat swabs and genital tract swabs)

of bacteria. It melts at 98°C and usually sets at 42°C depending on the agar concentration. Approximately 2% agar is used for solid media. Another ingredient of common media is **peptone**. It is a complex mixture of partially digested proteins. Its constituents are proteoses, polypeptides and amino acids, a variety of inorganic salts including phosphates, potassium and magnesium and certain accessory growth factors such as riboflavin.

Blood, serum and **yeast extract** are other common ingredients of media.

Simple media (basal media)

An example is **nutrient broth**. It consists of peptone, meat extract, sodium chloride and water. Nutrient agar, made by adding 2% agar to nutrient broth, is the simplest and most common medium in routine diagnostic laboratories.

Complex media

These have added ingredients for special purposes or for bringing out certain characteristics or for providing special nutrients required for the growth of the bacterium under study.

Synthetic or defined media

These media are prepared from pure chemical substances and the exact composition of the medium is fully documented. These are used for various special studies such as metabolic requirements.

Enriched media

To cultivate bacteria with exacting nutritional requirements, substances such as blood, serum or egg are added to a basal medium. Examples are blood agar, chocolate agar and media containing egg.

Brain–heart infusion broth (BHIB)

This is a highly nutritious, buffered fluid culture medium prepared by non-enzymic infusion from calf brain and cow heart, often with peptone and dextrose added. It is suitable for the cultivation of fastidious organisms.

Blood agar

This is a solid culture medium consisting of agar, peptones and blood. The blood is usually from sheep, but horse, cow and pig blood may be used.

Blood agar supports the growth of most aerobic and anaerobic bacteria (vitamin K, cysteine and hemin supplementation enhances growth of anaerobic bacteria) and fungi. Blood agar can indicate the degree of hemolysis caused by hemolysin. Based on this, it is used to differentiate among Gram-positive cocci. Hence, it is also known as a differential medium.

- **Beta hemolysis** refers to complete lysis of the red blood cells and hemoglobin; this results in complete clearing of the blood agar medium surrounding the colonies, e.g., Group A Streptococci (Fig. 4.1).
- **Alpha hemolysis** refers to the partial lysis of red blood cells and hemoglobin; this results in a greenish discolouration of the blood agar around the colonies (Fig. 4.2), e.g., Viridans Streptococci.
- No hemolysis results in no change of the blood agar medium, e.g., Enterococci.

Chocolate agar

This is made by heating a mixture of sheep blood and nutrient agar, hemoglobin and the related substance hemin (also called **X factor**) and nicotinamide adenine dinucleotide (NAD, also called **V factor**). These are released during the process of heating. The medium is called 'chocolate' agar because of its colour. Chocolate agar is used to grow fastidious organisms, including *H.influenzae, N.meningitidis* and *N.gonorrhoeae* and *Pneumococcus*.

Enrichment media

These media are used to suppress commensal bacteria while allowing the pathogen to remain viable and grow. It is employed for specimens with mixed flora, e.g., fecal sample to isolate diarrheagenic bacteria. Substances that have a stimulating effect on the bacteria to be grown or an inhibitory effect on those to be suppressed are incorporated in the medium. Examples of enrichment media are tetrathionate broth where the tetrathionate inhibits coliforms while allowing typhoid-paratyphoid bacilli to grow, and Selenite F broth for the bacteria which cause dysentery.

Selective media

As in the above case, if the inhibiting substance is added to a solid medium, it enables a greater number of the required bacterium to form colonies than the other bacteria; for example, **Desoxycholate Citrate Agar (DCA)** for fecal samples and **Thiosulphate Citrate Bile Sucrose agar (TCBS)** for *Vibrio* species

Fig. 4.1   Blood agar: *S.pyogenes* showing beta hemolysis

Fig. 4.2   Blood agar with alpha hemolytic viridans streptococci

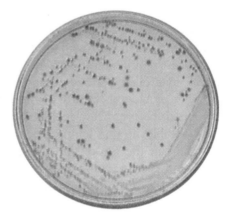

Fig. 4.3   TCBS agar with green colonies of *V.parahaemolyticus*

Fig. 4.4   Potassium Tellurite Agar (PTA) showing black colonies of *C.diphtheriae*

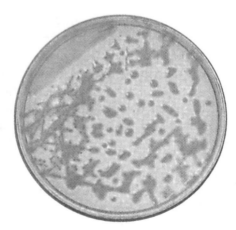

Fig. 4.5   MacConkey agar with large, mucoid colonies of *K.pneumoniae*

Fig. 4.6   MacConkey agar with flat, smooth, pink colonies of *Escherichia coli*

in cholera (Fig. 4.3). The alkaline pH of the medium isolates *Vibrio*. Organisms that ferment sucrose appear yellow, while those that do not, appear green, thus acting as an indicator medium too.

Thayer–Martin medium

The Thayer–Martin medium containing antimicrobials (vancomycin 3.0 mg, colistin 7.5 mg and nystatin 12.5 units per ml of agar) in chocolate agar is used to isolate *N.gonorrhoeae* from clinical specimens. The antimicrobials suppress the growth of other commensal organisms which may inhibit the growth of *N.gonorrhoeae*. Thayer–Martin plates are incubated in an atmosphere containing 3–10% CO_2.

Lowenstein–Jensen medium

This medium is used for primary isolation of *Mycobacterium* species. It consists of mineral salts, asparagine, glycerol, malachite green and hen's eggs. The medium is sterilised by inspissation (the application of a temperature of 75°C for three consecutive days). The malachite green prevents the growth of most other microorganisms. This medium is used since it will support the growth of a very small inoculum.

Indicator media

These media contain an indicator that changes colour when a bacterium grows in them, e.g., **sulphite** in Wilson–Blair medium. *S.typhi* reduces sulphite to sulphide to give a black metallic sheen on the colony. **Potassium tellurite** in McLeod's medium (Potassium Tellurite Agar) is reduced to metallic tellurium by *Corynebacterium diphtheriae* to produce black colonies (Fig. 4.4).

Differential media

The MacConkey medium which consists of peptone, lactose, agar, neutral red and taurocholate shows lactose fermenters as pink colonies, while non-lactose fermenters are colourless or pale. This may also be termed indicator medium. Many facultative anaerobes in the intestine are lactose fermenters and are pink in colour (*E.coli*). Several well-known pathogens do not ferment lactose and are colourless (*Shigella* and *Salmonella* species). (Figs 4.5 and 4.6). There are many special media for demonstrating particular characteristics, like Nagler's medium which enables us to view lecithinase activity.

Transport media

Special media are devised for transporting specimens suspected to have fastidious organisms. These are termed transport media, e.g., Stuart's medium—a non-nutrient, soft agar gel containing a reducing agent to prevent oxidation, and charcoal to neutralise certain bacterial inhibitors—is used to transport specimen for isolation of gonococci, and buffered glycerol saline for enteric bacilli.

Anaerobic media

Anaerobic media includes Robertson's cooked meat medium and thioglycollate medium.

These media are used to grow anaerobic organisms in the presence of reducing substances or absence of oxygen.

Thioglycollate medium

This medium supports the growth of all organisms with varied oxygen requirements: anaerobes, aerobes, and facultative anaerobes. An oxygen indicator turns the medium pink or blue at the top of the tube. This medium is boiled before use to eliminate oxygen, which is less soluble at hot temperatures. Obligate aerobes grow only at the top of the tube of medium, microaerophiles in the middle, while anaerobes grow only at the bottom. The medium contains yeast extract; casitone, sodium chloride, *l*-cystine; thioglycollic acid; agar, methylene blue and deionised water at a final pH of 7.2.

Media for fungus culture

Sabouraud dextrose agar

This culture medium permits the growth of yeasts and most filamentous fungi. It has a high concentration of either glucose or maltose and also contains mycological peptone. The medium has a low pH (about 5.0), which inhibits the growth of most bacteria. Antibacterial agents (chloramphenicol 40 mg or gentamicin 50 mg per litre of medium) can also be added to augment the antibacterial effect.

Incubation of culture media

Culture plates are incubated for a minimum of 48 hours at 37°C for bacteria and 22°C and 30°C for fungi. If a microaerophilic bacterium is suspected, then that growth condition should also be included. Both bacteria and fungi grow better in 5% carbon dioxide than in air alone. Anaerobic plates should be incubated in an anaerobic cabinet for 7 or 14 days.

Media for special use

- Media for antibiotic susceptibility testing is cation-adjusted Mueller–Hinton agar (**CAMHA**).

- Media incorporated with enzymes (e.g., Betalactamase detection) to detect antibiotic resistance.
- **Screen agars** to select out MRSA and vancomycin resistance in staphylococci.
- **CHROM agar** to speciate candida depending on the colour produced by the species.

RECAP

- A culture medium is a mixture of chemicals that can support the growth of microorganisms. It should contain a source of carbon and energy.
- Culture media can be categorised as solid and liquid. Solid media are generally produced in the form of a gel by the addition of agar, but sometimes heated serum or egg.
- They can be enriched, enrichment, selective, indicator, differential, sugar, transport or anaerobic.
- Enriched media are used for bacteria which have exacting nutritional needs, for example, brain–heart infusion broth, blood agar, chocolate agar and others.
- Enrichment media are liquid media to which substances that have a stimulating effect on the bacteria to be grown or an inhibitory effect on those to be suppressed are incorporated in the medium, for example, tetrathionate broth and selenite F broth.
- Selective media are solid media to which an inhibiting substance is added, for example, Thayer–Martin medium, desoxycholate citrate medium and others.
- An indicator medium changes colour when a bacterium grows in them, for example, Wilson–Blair medium.
- A differential medium helps to differentiate characteristics of bacteria, for example, MacConkey medium.
- A transport media is used for transport of samples containing delicate organisms.

SHORT NOTES

1. Classify media. Mention their uses in the laboratory.
2. List the properties of indicator media and mention their specific use.

5 Culture Methods

INTRODUCTION

Microorganisms exist as mixed population in clinical material or as resident flora. There is a need to cultivate them in pure form for several reasons as shown below.

Reasons to cultivate microorganisms in pure form
- To demonstrate their properties so as to identify them for their clinical significance
- To determine their sensitivity to antibiotics
- To study their physiological virulence and genetic properties
- To obtain sufficient growth for preparation of antigens and vaccines
- To type isolates for epidemiological purposes
- To archive them for research purposes

The methods employed to isolate the organisms in the laboratory are streak, lawn, stroke, stab and pour plate on solid media. They can be grown in liquid cultures. These can be done both for aerobic and anaerobic bacteria. Anaerobic bacteria require an environment devoid of oxygen for growth.

INOCULATION METHODS ON SOLID MEDIA

1. Loops or straight wires made of platinum or nichrome (24 SWG) are used to transfer material on to culture plates or tubes. The loops are sterilised by heating over a flame to red hot and cooling prior to picking the material. One loopful of the specimen is transferred onto the surface of a well-dried plate. The inoculum is then distributed thinly over the plate by streaking it with the loop in a series of parallel lines, in different segments of the plate.

   Well-separated colonies are obtained over the final series of streaks (Fig. 5.1).

2. The **lawn** or **carpet culture** provides uniform surface growth of the bacterium and is useful for antibiotic sensitivity testing (disc method) or bacteriophage typing. It may also be employed when a large amount of growth is required for preparation of bacterial antigens and vaccines. Lawn cultures are

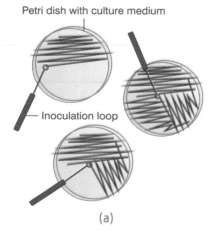

Petri dish with culture medium

Inoculation loop

(a)

(b)

Fig. 5.1 Streak cultures

prepared by flooding the surface of the plate with a liquid culture.

3. **Stab cultures** are prepared by puncturing a suitable medium with a long, straight, charged wire. Stab cultures are employed mainly for demonstration of oxygen requirements of the bacterium under study.

    Bacteria requiring oxygen grow on the surface while those which do not, grow at the bottom of the stab. They are also used in the maintenance of stock cultures and demonstrating other properties like gelatin liquefaction on appropriate media.

4. **Pour plate culture method:** The pour plate method gives an estimate of the viable bacterial count in a suspension. It is done for quantitative urine cultures. Appropriate dilutions of the inoculum (of 1 ml) are added to the molten (40–45°C) agar, mixed well, poured into sterile petri dishes and allowed to set. After incubation, colonies are seen to be distributed throughout the depth of the medium. These can be counted using colony counters to give the exact colony count in 1 ml of urine or any other fluid.

5. **Liquid cultures** in tubes, bottles or flasks may be inoculated by touching with a charged loop, pipettes or syringes. Large inocula can be inoculated into liquid culture media. This is ideal for blood culture and sterility tests where larger quantity of inoculum is required to isolate the organism. Liquid cultures are preferable for inocula containing antibiotics and other inhibitory substances, as these are diluted out in the medium. Yield can be enhanced by agitation, aeration, addition of nutrients and removal of toxic metabolites (continuous culture methods). The major disadvantage of liquid culture is that it does not differentiate in mixed inocula.

Culture plates and tubes with liquid culture are incubated at 37°C in a **bacteriological incubator** overnight or longer before reading the plates/tubes to look for growth in the form of colonies (on solid media) or for turbidity.

ANAEROBIC CULTURE METHODS

Anaerobic bacteria differ in their requirements of and sensitivity to oxygen. Growth conditions may be different for strict anaerobes (*C.tetani*) and aerotolerant bacteria (*C.histolyticum*).

Some of the commonly used methods of anaerobiosis are:

1. McIntosh and Filde's anaerobic jar

This is the most reliable and widely used anaerobic method (Fig. 5.2). It consists of a stout glass or metal jar with a metal lid that can be clamped airtight with a screw. The lid has two tubes with taps, one acting as the gas inlet and the other as the outlet. The lid also has two terminals which can be connected to an electrical supply. Leading from the terminals and suspended by stout wires on the underside of the lid is a small grooved porcelain spool around which is wrapped a layer of palladinised asbestos. Inoculated culture plates are placed in the jar, and the lid is clamped tight. The outlet tube is connected to a **vacuum pump and the air from within the jar is evacuated.** The outlet tap is then closed and the inlet tube connected to a hydrogen supply. After the jar is filled with hydrogen, the palladinised asbestos is heated by electric terminals. This **catalyses** the combination of hydrogen and residual oxygen in the jar. This ensures complete anaerobiosis but carries a risk of explosion, due to hydrogen and gas. However, this risk can be eliminated by modification of the catalyst. **Alumina pellets coated with palladium,** kept dry in a sachet within the jar, act as a catalyst at room temperature. An **indicator** is used for verifying the anaerobic condition in the jars. Reduced methylene blue is generally used for this purpose. It remains colourless anaerobically but turns blue on exposure to oxygen. Anoxomat is an automated microprocessor-controlled system for the cultivation of anaerobic, microaerophilic, and capnophilic bacteria.

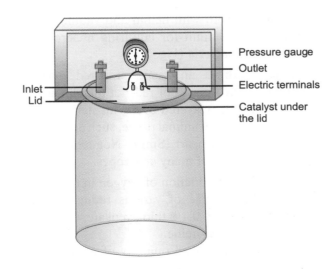

Fig. 5.2   McIntosh and Filde's anaerobic jar

2. Gaspak

This is now the method of choice for anaerobiosis. The Gaspak is commercially available as a disposable envelope, containing chemicals which generate hydrogen and carbon dioxide on addition of water. After the inoculated plates are kept in the jar, the Gaspak envelope, with water added, is placed inside and the lid screwed tight. Hydrogen and carbon dioxide are liberated in the presence of a cold catalyst in the envelope. This permits the combination of hydrogen and oxygen to produce an anaerobic environment. The Gaspak is simple and effective, eliminating the need for creating a vacuum and adding hydrogen.

3. Pre-reduced anaerobic system (PRAS)

Pre-reduced media are commercially available for fastidious anaerobes.

4. Anaerobic chamber ('glove box')

The anaerobic chamber is an airtight, glass-fronted cabinet filled with inert gas, with an entry lock for the introduction and removal of materials, and gloves for the hands.

5. Other methods of anaerobiosis

Robertson's cooked meat medium is probably the most widely used fluid medium for the culture of anaerobes. It consists of fat-free minced cooked meat in broth. It permits the growth of even strict anaerobes and indicates their saccharolytic or proteolytic activities, by the meat being turned red or black, respectively.

Thioglycollate broth with hemin and vitamin K is an enriched liquid medium for culturing anaerobic and microaerophilic bacteria (Fig. 5.3).

Anaerobic broth is an easily prepared anaerobic medium into which pieces of red-hot metallic iron are introduced. It is then layered over with sterile vaseline. Broth containing fresh animal tissue, such as rabbit kidney, spleen, testes or heart (Smith–Noguchi medium), supports the growth of many anaerobes.

Reducing agents: Reduction of oxygen in the medium is achieved by the use of various reducing agents, including 1% glucose, 0.1% thioglycollate, 0.1% ascorbic acid and 0.05% cysteine.

The addition of a small quantity of **agar** enhances the anaerobic capacity of the medium by slowing the diffusion of oxygen in it.

Fig. 5.3 Growth in thioglycollate broth: (a) uniform turbidity; (b) surface growth; (c) granular turbidity

METHODS OF ISOLATING PURE CULTURES

- **Surface plating** is the method routinely employed in clinical bacteriology and enables isolation of distinct colonies.
- **Enrichment, selective** and **indicator media** are widely used for the isolation of pathogens from specimens, with varied flora, e.g., feces.
- Pure cultures may be obtained by **pretreatment** of specimens with appropriate bactericidal substances which destroy the commensal bacteria. Tubercle bacilli are isolated from sputum and other clinical specimens, by treating the material with alkali, acid or other substances to which most commensals are susceptible but the tubercle bacilli are resistant.
- Separation of bacteria with different temperature optima can be effected by **incubation at different temperatures.** Only thermophilic bacteria grow at 60°C. A mixture containing *N.meningitidis* and *N.catarrhalis* can be purified by incubation at 22°C when only the latter grows.
- By **heating** a mixture containing vegetative and spore-forming bacteria at 80°C, the former can be eliminated. This method is useful for the isolation of tetanus bacilli from dust and similar sources.
- Separation of motile from non-motile bacteria can be effected using **Craigie's tube.** This consists of a tube of semisolid agar, with a narrow tube open at both ends placed in the centre of the medium, one end projecting above the level of the medium.

The mixture is inoculated into the central tube. On incubation, the motile bacteria alone traverse the agar and are recovered from the surface of the medium outside the central tube. A U-tube also serves the same purpose. Material is inoculated on one end and the subculture taken from the other. This method is used to obtain phase variants in motile bacteria.

Pathogenic bacteria may be isolated from mixtures by **inoculation** into susceptible animals. Anthrax bacilli can be distinguished from other aerobic sporulating bacilli by inoculating the bacteria into mice or guinea pigs. They produce fatal septicemia and can be cultured pure from heart blood. Bacteria of differing sizes may be separated by **selective filters** (used to separate viruses from bacteria).

RECAP

- Culture methods are used in the laboratory to isolate bacteria in pure culture and demonstrate their properties.
- The methods of inoculation include streak, lawn, stroke, stab, pour plate and liquid cultures.
- Aerobic bacteria require oxygen for growth and may be obligate aerobes or facultative.
- Anaerobic bacteria grow in the absence of oxygen; obligate anaerobes may even die on exposure to oxygen.
- Microaerophilic bacteria are those that grow best in the presence of low oxygen tension.
- Anaerobic culture methods include exclusion or displacement of oxygen with other gases, production of vacuum, absorption of oxygen by chemical, biological means and reduction of oxygen.
- The most reliable and widely used anaerobic method is the McIntosh–Fildes anaerobic jar.
- Gaspak is a commercially available method for creating anaerobic atmosphere.
- The culture media used for anaerobic culture include thioglycollate broth, Robertson's cooked meat medium and Smith-Noguchi medium.
- For fastidious anaerobes, pre-reduced media and anaerobic chamber are used.
- Pure culture of bacteria from mixtures is obtained by surface plating; enrichment, selective and indicator media; pretreatment with appropriate bactericidal substances; separation of bacteria by incubation at different temperatures; and separation of motile and non-motile bacteria by using Craigie's tube.
- Pathogenic bacteria may be purified from mixtures by inoculation into appropriate animals.
- Bacteria of different sizes can be separated by use of selective filters.

SHORT ANSWERS

1. Robertson's cooked meat medium
2. Gaspak system

SHORT NOTES

1. Anaerobic culture methods
2. McIntosh–Fildes anaerobic jar
3. Methods of isolating pure cultures of bacteria
4. Craigie's tube

6 | Identification of Bacteria

Morphology
Staining reactions
Cultural characteristics
Biochemical tests
Composite media for biochemicals
Immunological methods
Pathogenicity
Automated systems
Applications
Nucleic acid-based platforms
MALDI-TOF

INTRODUCTION

Once a bacterium is obtained in pure culture, it must be identified. The following methods based on bacterial characteristics are studied for identification.

A systematic stepwise procedure is adopted in a clinical microbiology laboratory for the identification and susceptibility testing of bacteria.

Morphology

The morphology of the bacterium depends on a number of factors such as the strain studied, nature of the culture medium, temperature and time of incubation, age of the culture and the number of subcultures it has undergone. This is studied best by microscopy after staining the bacteria.

Microscopy

The **characteristics** noted are shape, size, arrangement, motility, flagella, spores and capsules. All these cannot be made out in a single medium and may require use of multiple media.

- **Shape:** The organism may be spherical, filamentous, rod-shaped, comma-shaped or a spiral. The axis of the organism may be straight or curved.
- **Size:** The length and breadth may vary. The sides of the organism may be parallel, convex, concave or irregular. The ends may be cut straight, rounded or

tapering. Considerable variation in shape and size leading to club, navicular and swollen or shadow or giant forms may be seen.

- **Arrangement:** They may be arranged singly, in pairs, in tetrads or in packets of eight, or in chains, short or long, in the case of cocci; bacilli may be arranged at random, in short or long chains, in Chinese letter patterns, as palisades or in bundles; vibrios may be single or in S or spiral forms (Fig. 6.1).
- **Motility:** They may be non-motile, sluggishly motile, actively motile or may exhibit darting motility. This is seen best by **hanging drop method** in unstained preparations.
- **Flagella:** They may be without flagella, that is, atrichate, or monotrichate, lophotrichate, amphitrichate or peritrichate. They cannot be visualised by light microscope unless stained by special methods.
- **Spores:** These, when present, may be oval, spherical or ellipsoidal and may be of the same width or wider

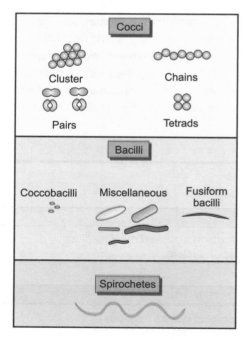

Fig. 6.1 Examples of common bacterial cellular morphologies

than that of the bacillary body. The spores may be equatorial, subterminal or terminal.

- **Capsules:** Capsules may or may not be present. It can be demonstrated by negative staining, dark ground illumination, phase contrast or electron microscopy.

Staining reactions

The age of the culture is important. In older cultures, staining characteristics either vary or are not brought out well. Simple stains bring out the morphology best. Differential and special stains are necessary to study characteristics like flagella, capsules, spores and metachromatic granules. The **Gram stain** divides bacteria into the Gram-positive and the Gram-negative; the **Ziehl–Neelsen stain** into acid fast and non–acid fast. The **fluorescent antibody technique** enables identification by surface antigens.

The study of morphology and staining characteristics helps in the preliminary identification of the isolate (Figs 6.2 to 6.4).

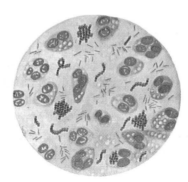

Fig. 6.2   Gram stain of a pus smear. Plate shows Gram-positive, violet-coloured cocci in clusters (staphylococci), chains (streptococci) and pink rods (Gram-negative bacilli). Pus cells show up stained pink.

Fig. 6.3   Gonococci in urethral discharge. Gram stain showing Gram-negative diplococci.

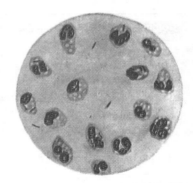

Fig. 6.4   Acid fast stain (Ziehl–Neelsen stain) of sputum. *M.tuberculosis* are seen as red rods.

Cultural characteristics

These provide additional information for the identification of the bacterium. The characteristics revealed in different types of media are noted.

1. Solid media

While studying colonies on **solid media**, the following features are noted:
- **Shape**—circular, irregular or rhizoid
- **Size** in millimetres
- **Elevation**—effuse, elevated, convex, concave, umbonate or umbilicate
- **Margins**—bevelled or otherwise
- **Surface**—smooth, wavy, rough, granular, papillate or glistening
- **Edges**—entire, undulate, crenated, fimbriate or curled (Fig. 6.5)
- **Colour**—white, buff, pink, etc.
- **Structure**—opaque, translucent or transparent
- **Consistency**—membranous, friable, butyrous or viscid
- **Emulsifiability**

2. Liquid media

In a **liquid culture**, the degree of growth, presence of turbidity and its nature, presence of deposit and its character, nature of surface growth such as pellicle and its quality and ease of disintegration, and odour are noted.

Biochemical tests

The tests based on fermentation of sugars and other biochemical properties are widely used for the identification of bacteria.

The important and commonly used tests are described below:

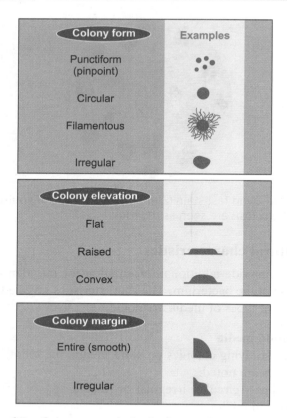

Fig. 6.5 Colony morphologic features and descriptive terms for commonly encountered bacterial colonies

Sugar fermentation

This is tested in media containing a single carbohydrate(sugar) and is used in diagnostic bacteriology. The term 'sugar' in microbiology denotes any fermentable substance. They may be:

- Monosaccharides: a) pentoses, for example, arabinose, xylose; b) hexoses, for example, dextrose, mannose
- Disaccharides, for example, saccharose, lactose
- Polysaccharides, for example, starch, inulin
- Trisaccharides, for example, raffinose
- Alcohols, for example, glycerol, sorbitol
- Glucosides, for example, salicin, esculin
- Non-carbohydrate substances, for example, inositol

The usual sugar media consist of 1% of the sugar in peptone water along with an appropriate indicator. A small tube (Durham's tube) is kept inverted in the sugar tube to detect gas production. Acid production is shown by change in the colour of the medium to pink or red, and the gas produced collects in Durham's tube.

For organisms which are exacting in their growth requirements (for example, *N.gonorrhoeae*), **Hiss' serum sugars** are used. They contain 3% serum.

Litmus milk

There may be no change in the medium, or acid or alkali may be produced. Clotting of milk, peptonisation or saponification may occur. The clot may be disrupted by the gas produced **(stormy fermentation)**.

Indole production

This is tested in a peptone water culture after 48 or 96 hours of incubation at 37°C. This test demonstrates the production of indole from tryptophane. 0.5 ml **Kovac's reagent** is added and shaken gently. Red colour indicates a positive reaction.

This is prepared in small quantities and stored in the refrigerator.

Methyl red test (MR)

This test is used to detect the production of acid during the fermentation of glucose and the maintenance of pH below 4.5 in an old culture. Five drops of 0.04% solution of methyl red are added to the culture in glucose phosphate medium which had been incubated at 30°C for five days, mixed well and read at once. The presence of the colour red means positive while yellow signifies a negative test.

Voges–Proskauer test (VP)

This test depends on the production of acetyl methyl carbinol from pyruvic acid as an intermediate stage in its conversion to 2:3 butylene glycol. In the presence of alkali and atmospheric oxygen, the small amount of acetyl methyl carbinol present in the medium is oxidised to diacetyl which reacts with the peptone of the broth to give a red colour.

The test is performed by adding 0.6 ml of a 5% solution of α-naphthol in ethanol and 0.2 ml of 40% KOH to 1 ml of a glucose phosphate medium culture of the organism incubated at 30°C for five days or 37°C for 48 hours. In a positive reaction, a pink colour appears in 2–5 minutes, deepening to magenta or crimson in half an hour. In a negative reaction, it remains colourless for half an hour. Traces of pink colouration should be ignored.

Citrate utilisation

Koser's citrate medium uses citrate as the sole source of carbon. The ability to use this substance is indicated by the production of turbidity in the medium.

Indole, MR, VP and citrate tests are very useful in the identification and classification of enteric Gram-negative bacteria. These tests are commonly referred to by the term '**IMViC**' tests.

Nitrate reduction

This is tested after growing the bacterium for five days at 37°C in a broth containing 1% KNO_3. The test reagent consists of a mixture of equal volumes of solutions of sulphanilic acid and α-naphthylamine in 5N acetic acid mixed just before use. 0.1 ml of the test reagent is added to the culture. A red colour developing within a few minutes signifies a positive reaction, while absence of colour indicates a negative reaction. This is a test for the presence of the enzyme nitrate reductase which reduces nitrate to nitrite.

Urease test

This test is done in **Christensen's urease medium**. The slope is heavily inoculated and incubated at 37°C. It must be examined after four hours and after overnight incubation. The test should not be considered negative till after four days of incubation. Urease-positive cultures produce a purple-pink colour. Urease-producing bacteria reduce urea to ammonia which is responsible for the colour.

Hydrogen sulphide production

Some organisms decompose sulphur-containing amino acids producing H_2S among the products. When cultured in media containing **lead acetate**, they turn them black or brown. Instead of lead acetate, **ferric ammonium citrate** or **ferrous acetate** can be used. The organisms can be grown in culture tubes. Between the cotton plug and the tube, a filter paper strip, soaked in 10% lead acetate solution and dried, is inserted. Browning of the paper indicates H_2S production.

Methylene blue reduction

One drop of 1% **aqueous methylene blue** is added to the broth culture and incubated at 37°C. Complete decolourisation is strongly positive, while green is weakly positive.

Catalase production

A loopful of H_2O_2 is placed on colonies on **nutrient agar**. Prompt effervescence indicates catalase production. Culture media containing blood are unsuitable for the test as blood contains catalase.

Oxidase reaction

This reaction is due to cytochrome oxidase which catalyses oxidation of reduced cytochrome by oxygen. A 1.0–1.5% solution of tetramethyl p-phenylene diamine hydrochloride is poured over the colonies. Oxidase-positive colonies become maroon, purple and black in 30 seconds to 1 minute. The test can also be done by **Kovac's method**. A strip of filter paper soaked in the oxidase reagent is placed in a petri dish and the colony to be tested is smeared on the paper in a line about 5 mm long. In a reaction, the smeared area turns dark in 10 seconds. The solution should be freshly prepared.

Egg yolk reaction

Organisms producing lecithinase (for example, *C.perfringens*), when grown on a solid egg yolk medium, form colonies surrounded by a zone of clearing.

Growth in the presence of KCN

Buffered liquid medium containing potassium cyanide (KCN) in a final concentration of about 1/13,000 is used to identify some KCN-tolerant enteric bacilli.

Composite media for biochemicals

These are being used increasingly for the identification of isolates. These are convenient and economical, as a single composite medium indicates different properties of the bacterium which otherwise would have required the use of many separate media. A popular composite medium is the **Triple Sugar Iron (TSI) medium** which indicates whether a bacterium ferments glucose only, or lactose and sucrose also, with or without gas formation, besides indicating H_2S production as well. The medium is distributed in tubes, with a butt and slant. For example, after inoculation, if the slant and the butt become yellow, all the sugars—glucose, lactose and sucrose—are fermented. Bubbles in the butt indicate gas production and blackening of the medium shows formation of H_2S. The TSI medium facilitates preliminary identification of Gram-negative bacilli. **Bile esculin medium** is used to differentiate between *Enterococcus* (group D) from other streptococci (for example *S.mitis*, which is not group D). This medium helps to look for growth in the presence of 40% bile and the ability to hydrolyse esculin to esculetin and glucose. Esculetin combines with ferric ions to produce a black complex (phenolic iron complex).

Other tests

Tests such as fermentation of organic acids, oxidation of gluconate, amino acid decarboxylation, and hydrolysis of sodium hippurate are sometimes employed. The resistance of the organism to heat and disinfectants is tested, both for vegetative and spore forms. The resistance of *E.faecalis* to heat at 60°C for half an hour and of clostridial spores to boiling for various periods are examples. Resistance to antibiotic and chemotherapeutic agents and bacteriocins would also help in differentiation and identification.

Immunological methods

These are based on the antigenic structure of bacteria. We can identify the serotypes or serovars by using specific antisera. Methods are based on agglutination or other suitable serological reactions. Immunofluorescence test is useful in some cases.

Pathogenicity

Pathogenicity tests by inoculation of the test organism into laboratory animals like the guinea pig, rabbit, rat and mouse by intradermal, subcutaneous, intramuscular, intraperitoneal, intracerebral or intravenous routes, or by oral or nasal spray were common procedures for the identification of isolates in the past. They are rarely used now because simpler in vitro tests are available and also because of ethical considerations.

Automated systems

With the advances in technology and increasing use of computers in microbiology, the use of automation is slowly replacing the conventional methods of identification. The automated systems have the advantage of a rapid turnaround time and uniformity in the methods. But since it is based on a database, there is a need to upgrade the database as more information gets generated.

Applications

There are different uses in bacteriology:

- **Detection of bacterial growth**: These are continuous monitoring systems and used mainly for detecting bacteria in blood cultures. They detect the presence of bacteria based on the production of CO_2 as an end product of the metabolism of bacteria which is detected by sensors which get transmitted to the computers and analysed by software. Examples of available commercial systems are BacT Alert, BACTEC, etc.
- **Identification systems:** These methods are based on the biochemical characteristics or metabolic properties of bacteria. The pattern is analysed based on the database in the computer software. They also additionally have methods for performing antimicrobial susceptibility tests. The common commercial systems available at present are VITEK, Phoenix, etc.

Nucleic acid-based platforms

These systems identify bacteria by recognising specific DNA sequences. This is done by direct detection of the target gene by microarrays or real-time polymerase chain reaction (PCR) or sequencing-based methods (principle and details in Part IV).

MALDI-TOF

This is matrix-assisted laser desorption/ionisation-time of flight (MALDI-TOF) mass spectrometry method in which the identification is based on the unique protein composition of bacterial cell.

Conventional method of identification of bacteria in a clinical microbiology laboratory follows a simple algorithm to identify common pathogens causing infections.

Example:

Microscopy – To detect the morphology
Bacilli (Gram-negative)   Cocci (Gram-positive)

Motility (Hanging drop)
Carbohydrate fermentation (TSI or sugars, etc.)
Enzyme production (indole, oxidase, urease, etc.)
Ability to grow in single substrate medium (citrate)
Deamination of amino acids (lysine, arginine, etc.)

- Coagulase (Staphylococci)
- Sensitive to Bacitracin (Streptococci)
- Sensitive to Optochin (Pneumococci)
- Growth in bile esculin (Enterococci)

Serotyping/Serogrouping for confirmation ⟶ Antibiotic susceptibility on appropriate media
(Salmonella, Shigella, Streptococci, etc.)   (Mueller–Hinton agar (MHA), or MH blood agar for fastidious organisms.)

RECAP

- The approaches to the identification of bacteria include morphology of bacterial colony on culture and detection of bacterial products released during metabolism.
- Techniques for direct microscopic examination of specimens include wet mounts (wet films) and stained preparations (Gram).
- Culture techniques where bacteria are isolated in pure culture are generally necessary because bacteria may be present in numbers too small to be seen by direct microscopy. Moreover, if bacteria are isolated, they can be precisely identified and antibacterial susceptibility tests can be run.
- Automated systems are replacing conventional methods for identification of bacteria. They identify the bacteria by computer-based software.
- Molecular methods for detection by microarray or real-time PCR or sequencing can be used.
- MALDI-TOF is the identification system based on the unique protein composition of bacterial cell.

SHORT NOTES

1. IMViC tests
2. TSI test
3. Indole test
4. Nitrate test
5. Oxidase test
6. Catalase test
7. Urease test
8. Citrate test

7 Bacterial Genetics

INTRODUCTION

Bacteria, like other organisms, obey the laws of genetics. It was only since the 1940s that the principles of genetics were applied to bacteria and their viruses, and, ultimately, led to the birth of a new branch of science—**molecular biology**.

BASIC PRINCIPLES OF MOLECULAR BIOLOGY

'Central dogma' of molecular biology

Deoxyribonucleic acid (DNA) carries genetic information, which is transcribed onto ribonucleic acid (RNA) and then translated as the particular polypeptide (DNA $\rightarrow$ RNA $\rightarrow$ polypeptide). As the nature and functions of a cell are basically determined by the specific polypeptides that constitute its proteins and enzymes, it is evident that the essential material of heredity is DNA, which is the storehouse of all information for protein synthesis. (An exception exists in the case of some viruses in which the genetic material is RNA instead of DNA, discussed in the Virology section.)

Structure of DNA

The DNA molecule is composed of two chains of nucleotides wound together in the form of a '**double helix**'. Each chain has a backbone of deoxyribose and phosphate residues arranged alternately. Attached to each deoxyribose is one of four nitrogenous bases: the **purines, adenine** (A) and **guanine** (G), and the **pyrimidines, thymine** (T) and **cytosine** (C). The double-stranded nature of the molecule is stabilised by hydrogen bonding between the bases on the opposite strands in such a way that adenine is always linked to thymine, and guanine to cytosine (Fig. 7.1).

Adenine and thymine thus form a complementary base pair, and guanine and cytosine form another. A molecule of DNA will, therefore, contain as many units of adenine as thymine, and of guanine as cytosine; but the ratio of each pair of bases $(A + T)/(G + C)$, though constant for each species, varies widely from one bacterial species to another. The DNA molecule replicates by first unwinding at one end to form a fork, each strand of the fork acting as a template for the

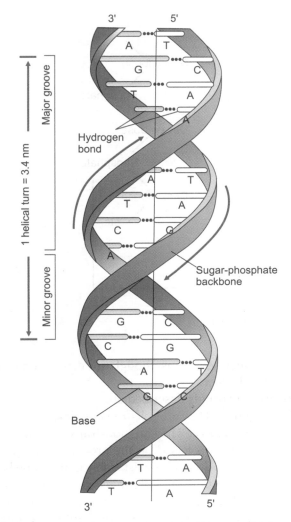

Fig. 7.1 A schematic drawing of the Watson–Crick structure of DNA, showing helical sugar-phosphate backbone of the two strands held together by hydrogen bonding between the bases.

synthesis of a complementary strand, with which it then forms a double helix (Fig. 7.2).

Structure of RNA

RNA is structurally similar to DNA, except for two major differences. It contains the **sugar ribose** (instead of deoxyribose which is present in DNA) and the **base uracil** (instead of thymine which is present in DNA).

Types of RNA
Three distinct types of RNA can be distinguished on the basis of structure and function:
- **Messenger RNA (mRNA)**
- **Ribosomal RNA (rRNA)**
- **Transfer RNA (tRNA)**

DNA acts as the template for the synthesis of mRNA and, therefore, the bases in the two will be complementary to each other. Adenine, guanine, cytosine and uracil in mRNA will be complementary to thymine, cytosine, guanine and adenine, respectively, in DNA.

TERMS RELATED TO GENETICS

Codon

Genetic information is stored in the DNA as code, the unit of the code consisting of a **sequence of three bases**. Each triplet (codon) transcribed on mRNA specifies for a single amino acid. More than one codon may exist for the same amino acid. Thus, the triplet AGA codes for arginine but the triplets AGG, CGU, CGC, CGA and CGG also code for the same amino acid. The code is **non-overlapping**, each triplet being a distinct entity, and no base in one codon is employed as part of the message of an adjacent codon. Three codons (UAA, UAG and UGA) do not code for any amino acid and are called '**nonsense codons**'. They act as punctuation marks **(stop codons)** terminating the message for the synthesis of a polypeptide.

Gene

A segment of DNA carrying codons specifying for a particular polypeptide is called a gene. A DNA molecule consists of a large number of genes, each of which contains hundreds of thousands of nucleotides. The bacterial chromosome consists of a double-stranded molecule of DNA arranged in a circular form. When straightened, it is about 1000 µm in length. The length of DNA is usually expressed as **kilobases (1 kb = 1000 base pairs)**. Bacterial DNA is about 4000 kb and the human genome about 3 million kb long.

Exons and introns

The stretches of coded genes are called **exons**. In other forms of life, stretches of DNA occur between the coding sequences which do not have any function as codons and are called **introns**. During transcription, the genome is copied in its entirety, both introns and exons. The introns are then excised from the RNA copy before being translated by the ribosomes into proteins.

Extrachromosomal genetic elements

In addition to chromosomal DNA, most bacteria possess extrachromosomal genetic elements.

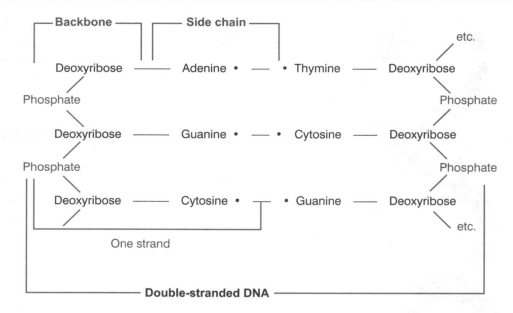

Fig. 7.2   A segment of double-stranded DNA illustrating its chemical structure

Functions: These are not essential for the normal life and functioning of the host bacterium, but may confer on it properties such as drug resistance and toxigenicity, leading to survival advantage under appropriate conditions.

Plasmids

These are circular DNA molecules present in the cytoplasm of bacteria, capable of autonomous replication (**independent replicons**). By their ability to transfer genes from one cell to another, plasmids have become **important vectors in genetic engineering** (Fig. 7.3). Plasmids may also be seen in yeasts, which are eukaryotes. Plasmid DNA may sometimes be integrated with chromosomal DNA. The name **episome** was employed

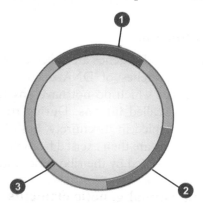

Fig. 7.3   Plasmid: 1. ampicillin resistance sequence; 2. origin of replication site; 3. multiple cloning site

for such integrated forms, though this distinction is not usually made now.

Types of plasmids described are
- **Conjugative:** They are self-transmissible.
- **Non-conjugative:** They are non-transmissible.

Classification is based on the property that closely related plasmids do not co-exist stably in the same bacterial cell, while unrelated plasmids can. This is called **incompatibility typing.** On this basis, plasmids have been classified into different **incompatibility groups.**

Phenotype and genotype

Phenotype

The **phenotype** (*phaeno* meaning display) is the **physical expression of the genotype in a given environment, limited in range by the genotype, temporary and not heritable.** It follows, therefore, that a cell may exhibit different phenotypic appearances in different situations; for example, the typhoid bacillus is normally flagellated but when grown in phenol agar, the flagella are not synthesised. This is only a phenotypic variation determined by the environment and is reversed when subcultured from phenol agar into broth.

Genotype

The sum total of the genes that make up the genetic apparatus of a cell (genome) establishes its genotype, which is the hereditary constitution of the cell that is transmitted to its progeny. The genotype includes the complete genetic potential of the cell, all of which may or may not be expressed in a given environmental situation.

Genetic variations

Genotypic variations occur due to alterations in the genome and are stable and heritable. They may occur by mutation or by one of the mechanisms of genetic transfer or exchange, such as transformation, transduction, lysogenic conversion and conjugation.

Mutation

Mutation is a random, undirected, heritable variation caused by an alteration in the nucleotide sequence at some point of the DNA of the cell. It may be due to addition, deletion or substitution of one or more bases (**point mutation**), or can be **frame shift mutations** which occur due to deletion or insertion of a number of nucleotides (Table 7.1). **Multiple mutations** cause extensive chromosomal rearrangement (Figs 7.4a and 7.4b). Mutation can occur in two directions, from wild type to mutant, called a **forward** mutation, and from a mutant to a wild type called **reverse mutation** (from the aberrant state of a gene back to its normal or wild type).

- **Spontaneous mutations:** Each gene undergoes mutation with a fixed frequency. Mutation rates of

Table 7.1 *Types of mutations in bacteria*

S.No	Type	Description
1	Missense mutation	Mutation where the triplet code is altered so as to specify an amino acid different from that normally located at a particular position in the protein.
2	Nonsense mutation	Deletion of a nucleotide within a gene may cause premature polypeptide chain termination by generating a nonsense codon.
3	Transversion	Substitution of a purine for a pyramidine and vice versa in base pairing.
4	Suppressor mutation	Reversal of a mutant phenotype by another mutation at a position on the DNA distinct from that of the original mutation.
5	Lethal mutation	Some mutations involve vital functions, and such mutants are non-viable. A type of lethal mutation which is of great interest is 'conditional mutation'.
6	Conditional lethal mutant	Ability to be able to live under certain conditions (permissive conditions). The commonest type of conditional mutant is the temperature-sensitive (ts) mutant, which can live at the permissive temperature (say, 35°C), but not at the restrictive temperature (say, 39°C).

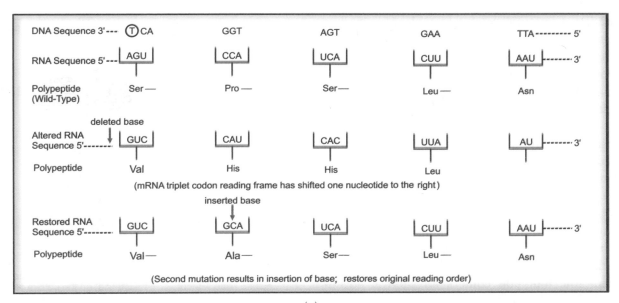

(a)

Fig. 7.4 (a) Frame shift mutation

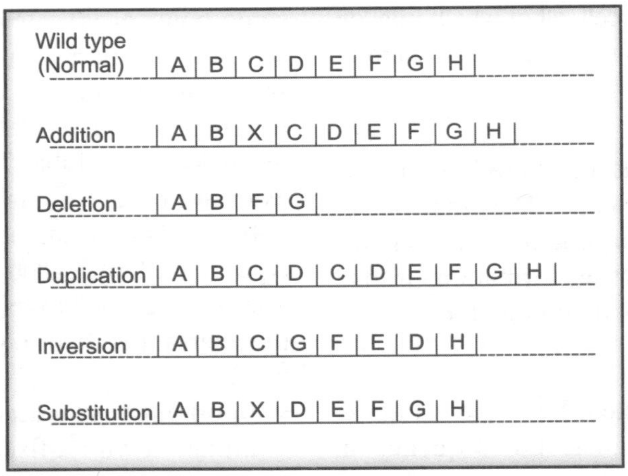

```
Wild type
(Normal)    | A | B | C | D | E | F | G | H |

Addition    | A | B | X | C | D | E | F | G | H |

Deletion    | A | B | F | G |

Duplication | A | B | C | D | C | D | E | F | G | H |

Inversion   | A | B | C | G | F | E | D | H |

Substitution| A | B | X | D | E | F | G | H |
```

(b)

Fig. 7.4 (b) Examples of types of mutations

individual genes in bacteria range from 10^{-4} to 10^{-10} per bacterium per division. The molecular mechanism of mutation is that during DNA replication, some 'error' creeps in while the progeny strands are copied. For instance, instead of thymine bonding with adenine, it may, due to tautomerism, sometimes bond with guanine.

- **Induced mutation:** Though mutation occurs spontaneously, its frequency can be increased by several agents (**mutagens**) such as UV rays, alkylating agents, acridine dyes, 5-bromouracil and 2-aminopurine.

Mutation is a natural event, taking place all the time at its particular frequency in all the dividing forms of life. Most mutants, however, go unrecognised as the mutation may be lethal or may affect some minor function that may not be expressed. Mutation is best appreciated when it involves a function that can be readily observed. For example, an **E.coli** mutant that loses its ability to ferment lactose can be readily detected on MacConkey agar but is unrecognisable on nutrient agar. Mutation is of vital importance when it confers a **survival advantage**. If a streptomycin-resistant mutant of the tubercle bacillus develops in a patient under treatment with the drug, it multiplies selectively and ultimately replaces the original drug-sensitive population of bacteria. But in a patient who is not on treatment, the mutation confers no survival advantage and, therefore, preferential multiplication of the mutant does not occur. Such changes in the character of bacterial populations, observed in the presence of a selective environment, were formerly considered to be 'adaptations'.

The '**replica plating**' technique is used in the isolation of new resistant mutants in pure culture without prior exposure to the agent responsible for mutation (Fig. 7.5). It is no longer used in clinical laboratories.

Mutation may affect any gene and, hence, may modify any characteristic of the bacterium. Mutants may vary in properties such as nutritional requirements, biochemical reaction, antigenic structure, morphological features, colony form, drug susceptibility, virulence

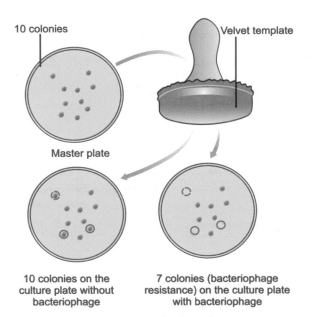

Fig. 7.5   Replica plating method to demonstrate mutation in a population of bacteria.

and host range. The practical importance of bacterial mutation lies mainly in the field of drug resistance and the development of live vaccines.

TRANSMISSION OF GENETIC MATERIAL (GENE TRANSFER)

Transformation

Transformation is the **transfer of genetic information through the agency of free DNA** (Fig. 7.6a). It was the first example of genetic exchange in bacteria to be discovered. Griffith in 1928 found that mice died when injected with a mixture of live non-capsulated (R) *S.pneumoniae* and heat-killed capsulated (S) *S.pneumoniae*, neither of which separately proved fatal. If, in the experiment, the live (R) *S.pneumoniae* were derived from capsular type II and the killed (S) strain from type I, from blood cultures of the mice that had died, live type I capsulated *S.pneumoniae* could be isolated. This showed that some factor in the heat-killed type I *S.pneumoniae* had transferred the information for capsule synthesis to the live rough strain. Such transformation was subsequently demonstrated in vitro also. The nature of the transforming principle was identified as DNA by Avery, MacLeod and McCarty in 1944.

Transduction

The transfer of a portion of the DNA from one bacterium to another by a bacteriophage is known as transduction (Fig. 7.6b). Bacteriophages are viruses that parasitise bacteria and consist of a nucleic acid core and a protein coat. During the assembly of bacteriophage progeny inside infected bacteria, 'packaging errors' may occur occasionally. A phage particle may have at its core, besides its own nucleic acid, a segment of the host DNA. When this particle infects another bacterium, DNA transfer is effected and the recipient cell acquires new characteristics coded by the donor DNA.

Types: Transduction may be

- **Generalised**, when it involves any segment of the donor DNA at random
- **Restricted**, when a specific bacteriophage transduces only a particular genetic trait. Restricted transduction has been studied intensively in the 'lambda' phage of *E.coli*. The prophage lambda is inserted in the bacterial chromosome only between

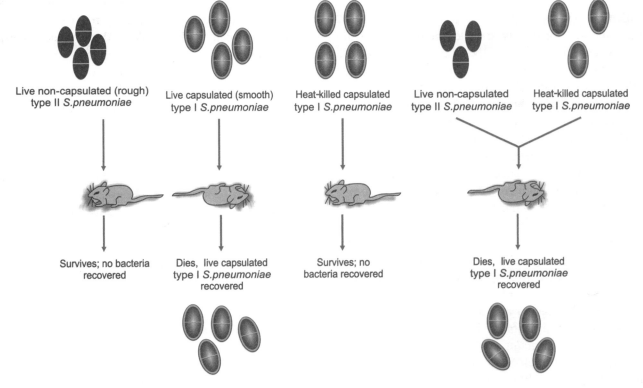

Live non-capsulated (rough) type II *S.pneumoniae*

Live capsulated (smooth) type I *S.pneumoniae*

Heat-killed capsulated type I *S.pneumoniae*

Live non-capsulated type II *S.pneumoniae*

Heat-killed capsulated type I *S.pneumoniae*

Survives; no bacteria recovered

Dies, live capsulated type I *S.pneumoniae* recovered

Survives; no bacteria recovered

Dies, live capsulated type I *S.pneumoniae* recovered

Fig. 7.6 (a) Transformation experiment of Griffith

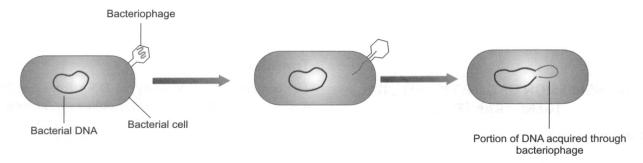

Fig. 7.6   (b) Transduction

the genes determining galactose utilisation (*gal*) and biotin synthesis (*bio*) and, therefore, it transduces only either of these.

Transduction is not confined to the transfer of chromosomal DNA. Episome and plasmid genes may also be transduced.

Life cycle of bacteriophages

Bacteriophages exhibit two types of life cycles.

Lytic

In the virulent or lytic cycle, large numbers of progeny phages are built up inside the host bacterium, which ruptures to release them.

Lysogenic

In the temperate or non-lytic cycle, the host bacterium is unharmed. The phage DNA becomes integrated with the bacterial chromosome as the prophage, which multiplies synchronously with the host DNA and is transferred to the daughter cells. This process by which the prophage DNA confers genetic information to a bacterium is called lysogenic or phage conversion and bacteria harbouring prophages are called lysogenic bacteria. In lysogenic bacteria, the prophage behaves like an additional segment of the bacterial chromosome, coding for new characteristics. In transduction, the phage acts only as a vehicle carrying bacterial genes from one cell to another, but, in lysogenic conversion, the phage DNA itself is the new genetic element. Lysogenic conversion influences susceptibility to bacteriophages (immunity to superinfection with the same or related phages) and antigenic characteristics. Of great medical importance is the lysogenic conversion in *Corynebactericum diphtheriae*, which acquire toxigenicity (and therefore virulence) by lysogenisation with the phage beta. Elimination of the phage from a toxigenic strain renders it non-toxigenic.

Conjugation

Conjugation is a process whereby a 'male' or 'donor' bacterium 'mates' or makes physical contact with a 'female' or 'recipient' bacterium and transfers genetic elements into it. Plasmids are the extrachromosomal elements frequently transferred by conjugation. Bacterial conjugation was first described by Lederberg and Tatum (1946) in a strain of *E.coli* called K_{12} and has been most extensively studied in this strain.

Conjugation takes place between a male cell and a female cell (Fig. 7.6c). The maleness or donor status of a cell is determined by the presence of a plasmid that codes for a specialised fimbria (**sex pilus**) which projects from the surface of the cell. The plasmid DNA replicates and a copy of it passes from the donor to the recipient cell, probably along the sex pilus (**conjugation tube**). As a result, the recipient attains donor status and can, in turn, conjugate with other female cells. The maleness in bacteria is thus a transmissible or 'infectious' characteristic. Along with plasmid DNA, portions of the host DNA also are sometimes transferred to the recipient. The donor DNA then combines with the DNA of the recipient, effecting genetic recombination. It was in *E.coli* K_{12} that the role of plasmids in conjugation was first recognised. The plasmid responsible was termed the **'sex factor'** or **'fertility (F) factor'**. When other similar plasmids were discovered, the term **'transfer factor'** came to be used for all such plasmids which conferred on their host cells the ability to act as donors in conjugation.

The F factor

The F factor is a transfer factor that contains the genetic information necessary for the synthesis of the sex pilus and for self-transfer, but is devoid of other identifiable genetic markers such as drug resistance. Cells carrying the F factor (**F⁺ cells**) have no distinguishing features other than their ability to mate with F⁻ cells and render them F⁺. The F factor is actually an episome and has

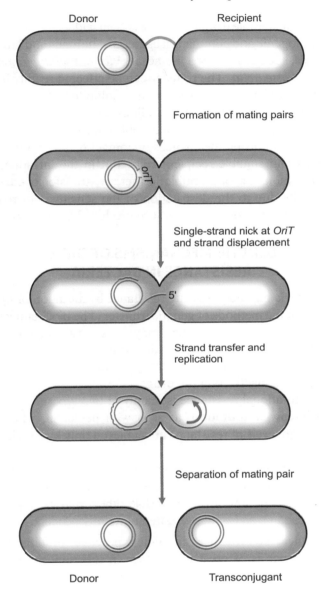

Donor   Recipient

Formation of mating pairs

Single-strand nick at *OriT* and strand displacement

Strand transfer and replication

Separation of mating pair

Donor   Transconjugant

Fig. 7.6 (c) Mechanism of DNA transfer during conjugation

the ability to exist in some cells in the '**integrated state**' or inserted into the host chromosome. Such cells can transfer chromosomal genes to recipient cells with high frequency and are known as **Hfr cells**. Following conjugation with an Hfr cell, an F⁻ only rarely becomes F⁺, though it receives chromosomal genes from the donor.

This conversion of an F⁺ cell into the Hfr state is reversible. When the F factor reverts from the integrated state to the free state, it may sometimes carry with it some chromosomal genes from near its site of attachment. Such an F factor incorporating some chromosomal genes is called an **F prime (F') factor**. When an F' cell mates with a recipient, it transfers, along with the F factor, the host genes incorporated with it. This process of transfer of host genes through the F' factor resembles transduction and has, therefore, been called **sexduction** (Fig. 7.7).

Colicinogenic (Col) factor

Several strains of coliform bacteria produce **colicins**—antibiotic-like substances that are specifically and selectively lethal to other enterobacteria. As similar substances are produced by bacteria other than coliforms (pyocin by *Pseudomonas pyocyanea*, diphthericin by *Corynebacterium diphtheriae*), the name **bacteriocin** has been given to this group of substances. The specificity of action of bacteriocins enables intraspecies classification of certain bacteria (for example, *Shigella sonnei*, *P.aeruginosa*).

Colicin production is determined by a plasmid called the **Col factor**, which resembles the F factor in promoting conjugation, leading to self-transfer and, at times, transfer of chromosomal segments.

Resistance transfer factor (RTF)

This plasmid is of great medical importance as it leads to the spread of multiple drug resistance among bacteria.

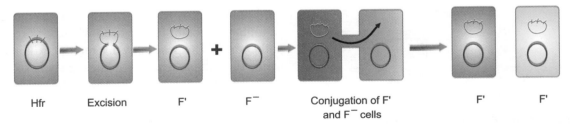

Hfr   Excision   F'   F⁻   Conjugation of F'   F'   F'
                                                and F⁻ cells

Fig. 7.7 Sexduction. The integrated F factor of an Hfr cell may revert to the cytoplasmic state. During excision, some host genes may be incorporated in the F' factor (F). When an F' cell mates with an F⁻ cell, the host gene is transferred to the recipient.

This extrachromosomal mechanism of drug resistance was first reported by Japanese workers (1959) investigating the sudden increase in infections caused by *Shigella* strains resistant simultaneously to sulphonamides, streptomycin, chloramphenicol and tetracycline. They observed that patients excreting such *Shigella* strains also shed in their feces *E.coli* strains resistant to the same drugs. Transfer of multiple drug resistance was demonstrated between *E.coli* and *Shigella* strains both in vitro and in vivo. The resistance is plasmid-mediated and is transferred by conjugation. This mechanism of drug resistance is known as **transferable, episomal** or **infectious drug resistance.**

Components: This plasmid consists of two components: the transfer factor called the **resistance transfer factor (RTF)** which is responsible for conjugational transfer, and a **resistance determinant (r)** for each of the several drugs. The whole plasmid (RTF + r determinants) is known as the **R factor.** An R factor can have several r determinants, and resistance to as many as eight or more drugs can be transferred simultaneously (Fig. 7.8). Sometimes, the RTF may dissociate from the r determinants, the two components existing as separate plasmids. In such cases, though the host cell remains drug-resistant, the resistance is not transferable. The RTF can have determinants attached to it,

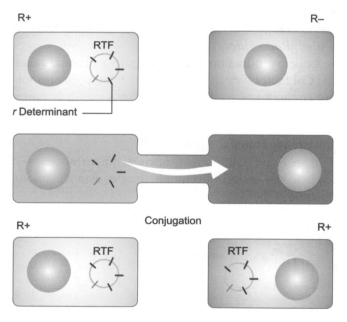

Fig. 7.8 Transferable drug resistance. The R+ cell carries the R factor, consisting of the RTF and r determinants. Its transfer to a sensitive R− bacterium converts the recipients into a resistant R+ cell.

other than those for drug resistance. Enterotoxin and hemolysin production in some enteropathogenic *E.coli* are transmitted by this transfer factor.

Transferable drug resistance is seen widely in various pathogenic and commensal bacteria of humans and animals, such as Enterobacteriaceae, *Vibrio, Pseudomonas* and *Pasteurella*. The transfer can be effected readily in vitro but in the normal gut, it is inhibited by several factors such as anaerobic conditions, bile salts, alkaline pH and the abundance of anaerobic Gram-positive bacteria minimising the chances of contact between donor cells and suitable recipient cells. But in the intestines of persons on oral antibiotic therapy, transfer occurs readily due to the destruction of the sensitive normal flora and the selection pressure produced by the drug.

GENETIC MECHANISMS OF DRUG RESISTANCE IN BACTERIA

Bacteria may acquire drug resistance by mutation or by one of the methods of genetic transfer. The biochemical mechanisms of resistance may be several, including decreased permeability to the drug, development of alternative metabolic pathways and production of enzymes inactivating the drugs.

Mutational resistance is mainly of two types:
- **Stepwise mutation**, as seen with penicillin, where high levels of resistance are achieved only by a series of small-step mutations
- **'One-step' mutation**, as seen with streptomycin, where the mutants differ widely in the degree of resistance, some exhibiting low resistance, while others may be highly resistant, and some even streptomycin-dependent

Clinical significance: In clinical practice, mutational resistance is of great importance in tuberculosis. If a patient is treated with streptomycin alone, initially the bacilli die in large numbers but soon resistant mutants appear and multiply unchecked. If two or more anti-tuberculous drugs are used for combined treatment, re-population by resistant mutants does not occur, as a mutant resistant to one drug will be destroyed by the other drug. The possibility of a mutant exhibiting resistance to multiple drugs simultaneously is so remote as to be virtually non-existent. This is the rationale behind combined treatment in tuberculosis. However, in spite of this knowledge, inadequate or inappropriate treatment over the years has caused extensive resistance in tubercle bacilli, leading to a pandemic of multidrug-resistant tuberculosis (MDR-TB) across the world.

Resistance transfer by transformation can be demonstrated experimentally but its significance in nature is not known. Acquisition of resistance by transduction is common in staphylococci. The penicillinase plasmids, which are transmitted by transduction, may also carry determinants for resistance to mercuric chloride and erythromycin.

Plasmid-mediated transferable drug resistance, mediated by the R factor, is the most important method of drug resistance. Acquisition of an R factor simultaneously confers resistance to several drugs and, therefore, treatment with a combination of drugs is not useful. The resistance is due to the production of **degrading enzymes**, and the level of resistance is usually high. Resistance may be transferred between bacteria of different taxonomic groups. While resistant mutants usually have a lower growth rate and reduced virulence as compared to the wild strains, bacteria carrying R factors are apparently normal in other respects. R factors in some cases may even lead to enhanced virulence. Multiple drug resistance was initially seen in bacteria causing diarrhea and other mild infections that did not call for antibiotic treatment as a routine. But, subsequently, it spread to virtually all pathogenic bacteria affecting humans and animals, making antibiotic therapy of infections ineffective.

Transferable drug resistance is now universal in distribution and involves all antibiotics in common use (Table 7.2). Its incidence is directly proportional to the frequency of use of antibiotics in the area. Bacteria carrying R factors can be transmitted from animals to humans. Hence, the indiscriminate use of antibiotics in veterinary practice or in animal feeds can also lead to an increase in multiple drug resistance in the community. The addition of antibiotics in animal feeds has for this reason been prohibited by legislation in some countries. Widespread resistance has considerably diminished the clinical efficacy of most antibiotics.

In the laboratory, R factors may sometimes be eliminated by treating bacteria with acridine dyes or ethidium bromide. But, in the community, the only way to prevent widespread dissemination of multiple resistance is to restrict the use of antibiotics to the essential minimum.

Transposable genetic elements

Certain structurally and genetically discrete segments of DNA have been identified that have the ability to move around in a 'cut-and-paste' manner between chromosomal and extrachromosomal DNA molecules within cells. These DNA molecules are called **transposons ('jumping genes')** and this mode of genetic transfer, **transposition**. The earliest of such mobile genes was discovered by Barbara McClintock in plants during work in the 1940s and 50s, for which she was awarded the Nobel Prize for Medicine in 1983. A transposon is a segment of DNA with one or more genes in the centre, and the two ends carrying **'inverted repeat' sequences** of nucleotides—nucleotide sequences complementary to each other but in the reverse order. Because of this feature, each strand of the transposon can form a single-stranded loop carrying the gene, and a double-stranded stem formed by hydrogen bonding between the terminal inverted repeat sequences (Fig. 7.9). Small transposons (1–2 kb) are known as **'insertion sequences'** or **IS**. Transposons attach at certain regions of chromosomal, plasmid or phage DNA. Insertion of a transposon leads to the acquisition of new characteristics by the recipient DNA molecule. Unlike plasmids, transposons are not self-replicating and depend on chromosomal or plasmid DNA for replication. A **composite transposon** is similar in function to simple **transposons** and insertion sequence (IS) elements in that it has protein coding DNA segments flanked by inverted, repeated sequences that can be recognised by transposase enzymes.

Table 7.2 *Comparison of mutational and transferable drug resistance*

S.No.	Mutational drug resistance	Transferable resistance
1	Bacteria are resistant to one drug at a time.	Bacteria are resistant to multiple drugs.
2	Low-degree resistance is seen.	High-degree resistance is seen.
3	It can be overcome by high drug dose.	High doses are ineffective.
4	Drug combinations can prevent development of resistance.	Drug combinations cannot prevent development of resistance.
5	Resistance does not spread.	Resistance spreads to same or different species.
6	Mutants may be defective.	Mutants are not defective.
7	Virulence may be low.	Virulence is not decreased.

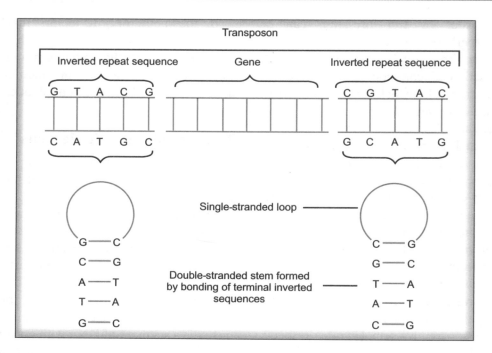

Fig. 7.9   Structure of transposon

By transposition, a segment of the DNA can be transferred from a molecule to another molecule that has no genetic homology with either the transposable element or with the donor DNA. In this, it differs from recombination. As sizeable chunks of DNA are added by transposition, the recipient molecule becomes heavier.

Characteristics transferred by transposons may sometimes confer survival advantages under appropriate environmental conditions. It has been suggested that the resistance-determinant segments of the R factors may have evolved as collections of transposons, each carrying a gene that confers resistance to one or several antibiotics.

Transposition is a mechanism for amplifying genetic transfer in nature and has been identified in microorganisms, plants and animals. Transposons appear to accomplish in nature, gene manipulations similar to the laboratory manipulations that have been called 'genetic engineering'.

MOLECULAR GENETICS

Discoveries in microbial genetics have provided the basis for the discipline of molecular genetics, which is concerned with the analysis and manipulation of DNA using biochemical and microbiological techniques.

Some techniques and applications of molecular genetics are discussed below.

Genetic engineering

The most important application of molecular genetics in biotechnology is genetic engineering or **recombinant DNA (rDNA) technology**. It is a process by which the DNA of a microorganism can be manipulated. The more common use involves **cloning**. The steps involved are isolation of the genes coding for any desired protein from microorganisms or from cells of higher forms of life including human beings, and their introduction into suitable microorganisms, in which the genes would be functional, directing the production of the specific protein. Such cloning of genes in microorganisms enables the preparation of the desired protein in pure form, in large quantities and at a reasonable cost.

The DNA can be cleaved by specific enzymes called **restriction endonucleases** (described below) and the fragments containing the desired genes isolated. This is incorporated into suitable vectors or carriers, such as plasmids or temperate bacteriophages, for insertion into microorganisms. The microorganism commonly employed is *E.coli* K_{12}, though many other bacteria and yeasts have also been used. These bacteria multiply and give a large amount of the desired gene product.

Applications: Genetic engineering has become an established branch of biotechnology with great scope for commercial exploitation. Cloned human insulin, interferons, somatostatin, growth hormones and many other biologicals have already been marketed. Safer vaccines can be produced by cloning the protective antigens of pathogens, as has already been done, as in the case of foot and mouth disease, and hepatitis B and rabies viruses.

Restriction endonucleases (restriction enzymes)

These are microbial enzymes which cleave double-stranded DNA at specific oligonucleotide sequences. Many such enzymes which act at different nucleotide sequences (for example, *Eco* RI, *Hind* III, *Taq* I) have been recognised. Restriction enzymes split DNA strands into fragments of varying lengths which can be separated by gel electrophoresis.

Detection methods

DNA probes

The specificity of the interaction in base pairing during DNA or RNA synthesis enables the production of specific DNA probes. These are radioactive, biotinylated or otherwise, labelled copies of cloned single-stranded DNA fragments, usually 20–25 nucleotides long and containing unique nucleotide sequences which can be used for the detection of homologous DNA by hybridisation. DNA probes are being used increasingly in the diagnosis of infectious diseases. Probes containing sequences unique to the microbe (strain, species or group) to be detected can be added to microbial cultures, body fluids, tissues or other materials suspected to contain the microbe or its DNA. The DNA probe hybridises with the complementary specific sequences on the microbe's DNA. The advantages of DNA probes for diagnosis are their high degree of specificity, ability to detect minute quantities of complementary DNA even in the presence of other microbes, and the capacity to recognise microbes that are either difficult or impossible to culture. DNA probes for the detection of many pathogens are now commercially available.

Blotting techniques

These are the techniques used for detection of DNA, RNA or proteins of interest.

Southern blotting

The technique for **identifying DNA fragments by DNA–DNA hybridisation** is called Southern blotting, after E. M. Southern who devised it. DNA fragments obtained by restriction enzyme digestion and separation on gel can be transferred from the gel by blotting to nitrocellulose or nylon membranes that bind the DNA. The DNA bound to the membrane is denatured (converted to the single-stranded form) and treated with radioactive single-stranded DNA probes. These hybridise with homologous DNA to form radioactive double-stranded segments, which can be detected on x-ray film (Fig. 7.10).

Northern blotting

An analogous procedure for the analysis of RNA has been called Northern blotting (as opposed to Southern blotting!). Here, the **RNA mixture is separated by gel electrophoresis, blotted and identified** using labelled DNA or RNA probes.

Western blotting

A similar technique for the identification of proteins (antigens) is called **immunoblotting** (or, in conformity with other blotting techniques, Western blotting). Here, the **protein antigen mixture is separated by SDS–PAGE** (sodium dodecylsulphate–polyacrylamide gel electrophoresis), **blotted on to nitrocellulose strips and identified** by radiolabelled or enzyme-labelled antibodies as probes. The western blot test is used as the confirmatory test for the diagnosis of HIV antibody in sera.

Molecular epidemiology

One offshoot of molecular genetics is molecular epidemiology. Here, molecular methods such as plasmid profile analysis, genomic fingerprinting and PCR are used for the identification and matching of microbial isolates for epidemiological purposes (discussed in Chapter 69).

DNA AMPLIFICATION TECHNIQUES

Polymerase chain reaction (PCR)

This is a rapid automated method for the amplification of specific DNA sequences (or genes), invented by Kary B. Mullis in 1983, for which he won the Nobel Prize in Chemistry in 1993. PCR consists of several cycles of sequential DNA replication where the products of the first cycle become the template for the next cycle. It makes available abundant quantities of specific DNA sequences starting from sources containing minimal quantities of the same (Fig. 7.11).

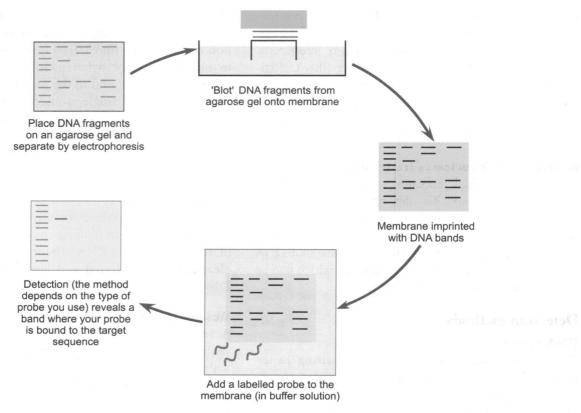

Place DNA fragments
on an agarose gel and
separate by electrophoresis

'Blot' DNA fragments from
agarose gel onto membrane

Membrane imprinted
with DNA bands

Detection (the method
depends on the type of
probe you use) reveals a
band where your probe
is bound to the target
sequence

Add a labelled probe to the
membrane (in buffer solution)

Fig. 7.10 Southern blotting

Applications: With its enormous capacity to amplify DNA, PCR is a versatile tool useful in diverse areas such as diagnosis of infectious, genetic or neoplastic diseases, in forensic investigations, in archaeo-biological studies of ancient specimens and in the examination of phylogenetic relationships in evolution.

Based on the principle of PCR, other target amplification systems have been developed.

Reverse transcriptase PCR (RT-PCR)

The conventional PCR technique can only amplify the dsDNA sequences. Therefore, the RNA viruses cannot be amplified by this method directly. In this modification with a help of reverse transcriptase (RT) enzyme, a complementary copy of DNA is made from the RNA and this cDNA is then used a template for PCR.

qPCR

qPCR or Quantitative PCR or Real-time PCR (earlier also called RT-PCR and could be confused with Reverse transcriptase RT-PCR). In this method, the advantage over the conventional method is that it quantifies the PCR by monitoring the amplification process while the PCR is ongoing. Hence, it is called real time. This gives the estimate of the pathogen DNA load in the test specimen.

The detection is done using:
- **Non-specific fluorescent dyes** like SYBR green that intercalate with dsDNA as it gets synthesised, the fluorescence being proportional to the DNA synthesised.
- **Specific set of DNA probes** which are labelled with fluorescent reporters that get detected only after the probe hybridises with the complementary DNA sequence.

Nested PCR

In conventional PCR, sometimes, the primers bind to non-specific regions. In order to take care of this non-specificity, a second set of primers are used in the successive cycles to amplify a secondary target within the first target.

Multiplex PCR

Primers specific to more than one pathogen are used simultaneously in the same reaction to give multiple PCR products.

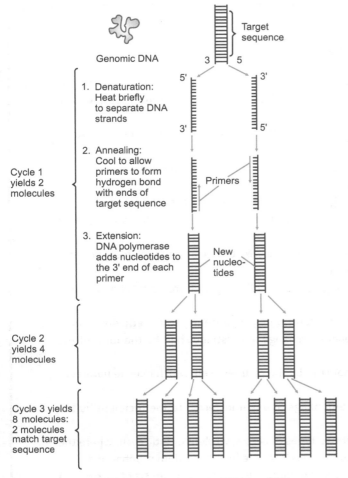

Genomic DNA

Target sequence

Cycle 1 yields 2 molecules

1. Denaturation: Heat briefly to separate DNA strands

2. Annealing: Cool to allow primers to form hydrogen bond with ends of target sequence

Primers

3. Extension: DNA polymerase adds nucleotides to the 3' end of each primer

New nucleo-tides

Cycle 2 yields 4 molecules

Cycle 3 yields 8 molecules: 2 molecules match target sequence

Fig. 7.11   Amplification of genomic DNA by PCR

NON-AMPLIFICATION TESTS

Loop-mediated isothermal assay (LAMP)

This is a simple method done at constant temperature. There is no need to carry out the reaction in a series of different temperatures and, therefore, does not require a thermocycler.

This has potential for use as a screening test in the field or point of care test. In a common format, four sets of primers are used to bind to six regions on the target DNA. The primers have a specific nature called 'loop primers' which help in yield of higher amount of DNA. The polymerase enzyme used is also special as it has a 'high strand displacement' activity.

DNA microarray

It is a method in molecular biology in which many DNA spots are coated on a solid surface, e.g., silicon or glass chip. These spots are specific DNA sequences which serve as probes. These probes hybridise with cDNA in the test sample, where the DNA in the sample does not have to be amplified. This method can detect a large number of nucleic acid sequences in the target simultaneously.

SEQUENCING-BASED ASSAYS

Genetic mapping

As a result of the remarkable advances in molecular genetics, it has been possible to delineate the complete genomic sequence of bacteriophages and other viruses, bacteria and their plasmids, and even of some eukaryotes including mammals. Quite apart from the useful information it has provided in microbiology, its success emboldened the international scientific community to embark on the Human Genome Project, the most expensive and ambitious scientific project thus far undertaken in biology. The results of this mammoth study became available at the beginning of the twenty-first century and have opened vistas in human biology and medicine, as well as controversies and dilemmas that transcend medicine. The techniques of next-generation sequencing have enabled the study of the whole genome or pangenome of bacteria for use in diagnosis and research (discussed in Chapter 72).

NEXT – GENERATION SEQUENCING

It is a DNA sequencing technology which has the advantage of high turnover and high speed as compared to conventional Sanger's sequencing. Here, many DNA fragments can be sequenced in parallel followed by bioinformatics analysis. It is presently used for research purposes but has a potential for rapid infectious disease diagnosis. The cost of equipment and infrastructure like computer capacity and storage, expertise in analysis of a big data, etc., are limitations for its wider use at present.

RECAP

- The 'central dogma' of molecular biology is that deoxyribonucleic acid (DNA) carries genetic information, which is transcribed onto ribonucleic acid (RNA) and then translated as the particular polypeptide (DNA → RNA → polypeptide).
- Plasmids are circular DNA molecules present in the cytoplasm of bacteria, capable of autonomous replication (independent replicons).
- The total genetic constitution of an organism is its genotype. The genotype of a cell is determined by the genetic information contained in its entire DNA content or genome.
- The characteristics displayed by an organism in any given environment comprise its phenotype.
- Mutation is a random, undirected, heritable variation caused by an alteration in the nucleotide sequence at some point of the DNA of the cell.
- Each gene undergoes spontaneous mutation with a fixed frequency. Mutation rates of individual genes in bacteria range from 10^{-4} to 10^{-10} per bacterium per division.
- Several agents (mutagens) such as UV rays, alkylating agents, acridine dyes, 5-bromouracil and 2-aminopurine can induce mutations.
- Transfer of DNA among prokaryotes is ubiquitous and contributes significantly to genetic diversity in bacteria. The three major forms of prokaryotic genetic exchange are distinguished by the form of the donor DNA:
  - In transformation, there is direct uptake of donor DNA by the recipient cell, which may be natural or forced.
  - In transduction, donor DNA is carried in a bacteriophage and is transferred to the recipient by the mechanism used for phage infection.
  - In lysogenic conversion, bacteriophages exhibit two types of cycles, virulent or lytic cycle where the host bacterium is lysed and the temperate or nonlytic cycle where host bacterium is unharmed.
  - In conjugation, the donor cell contributes energy and building blocks to the synthesis of a new DNA strand, which is physically transferred into the recipient cell, usually by a tube called a sex pilus.
- Transferable drug resistance mediated by the R factor is the most important method of drug resistance.
- Certain structurally and genetically discrete segments of DNA have the ability to move around in a 'cut-and-paste' manner between chromosomal and extrachromosomal DNA molecules within cells. These DNA molecules are called transposons ('jumping genes') and this mode of genetic transfer, transposition.
- Genetic engineering or recombinant DNA (rDNA) technology consists of isolation of the genes coding for any desired protein from microorganisms or from cells of higher forms of life including human beings, and their introduction into suitable microorganisms, in which the genes would be functional, directing the production of the specific protein.
- The methods of genetic engineering have been used for the molecular diagnosis of infectious diseases and understanding the biology of the infectious agent.
- PCR and its modifications are based on amplification of the small amount of DNA sequences in a test sample to numbers that can be detected.
- Next-generation sequencing is a technology where many DNA fragments can be sequenced in parallel followed by bioinformatics analysis.

ESSAY

1. Enumerate the methods of transfer of genetic materials in bacteria. Explain the mechanism of any one.

SHORT ANSWERS

1. Principle of polymerase chain reaction
2. Differences between resistance acquired by mutation and transferable drug resistance

SHORT NOTES

1. Transformation
2. Transduction
3. Conjugation
4. Plasmids
5. Transferable drug resistance
6. Mutations in bacteria
7. Transposons
8. Phenotypes and genotypes

8 Infection

INTRODUCTION

Infection and immunity involve interaction between the animal body (host) and the infecting microorganism. Based on their relationship to their hosts, microorganisms can be classified as saprophytes (from Greek *sapros* decayed; and *phyton* plant) and parasites.

Saprophytes are free-living microbes that subsist on dead or decaying organic matter. They are found in soil and water and play an important role in the degradation of organic materials in nature. They are generally incapable of multiplying on living tissues and therefore are of little relevance in infectious disease. Exceptionally, however, some saprophytes like *B.subtilis* may infect devitalised hosts whose natural resistance is greatly reduced (opportunistic infection).

Parasites are microbes that can establish themselves and multiply in hosts. Parasitic microbes may be either pathogens (from Greek *pathos* suffering, and *gen* produce, that is, disease-producing) or *commensals* (from Latin *com* with; and *mensa* table, that is living together).

Pathogens are microorganisms that are capable of producing disease in the host. **Commensal** microbes live in complete harmony with the host without causing any damage to it. The normal bacterial flora of the body consist largely of commensals. Many commensals behave as facultative pathogens in that they can produce disease when the host resistance is lowered.

It is necessary to distinguish between the terms 'infection' and 'infectious disease'. The lodgement and multiplication of a parasite in or on the tissues of a host constitutes **infection**. It does not invariably result in disease. In fact, disease is but a rare consequence of infection, which is a common natural event.

CLASSIFICATION OF INFECTIONS

Infections may be classified in various ways.

- Initial infection with a parasite in a host is termed **primary infection**.
- Subsequent infections by the same parasite in the host are termed **re-infections**.
- When a new parasite sets up an infection in a host whose resistance is lowered by a pre-existing infectious disease, this is termed **secondary infection**.
- **Focal infection** (more appropriately **focal sepsis**) indicates a condition where, due to infection or sepsis at localised sites such as the appendix or tonsils, generalised effects are produced.
- When in a patient already suffering from a disease a new infection is set up from another host or another external source, it is termed **cross-infection**.
- Cross-infections occurring in hospitals are called **nosocomial infections** (from Greek *nosocomion* or hospital).
- The term **iatrogenic infection** refers to physician-induced infections resulting from investigative, therapeutic or other procedures.
- Depending on whether the source of infection is within or outside the host's own body, infections are classified as **endogenous** or **exogenous**, respectively.

Based on the clinical effects of infections, they may be classified into different varieties.

- **Inapparent infection** is one where the clinical effects are not apparent. The term **subclinical infection** is often used as a synonym.
- **Atypical infection** is one in which the typical or characteristic clinical manifestations of the particular infectious disease are not present.

- **Latent infection** is one in which some parasites, following infection, may remain in the tissues in a latent or hidden form, proliferating and producing clinical disease when the host resistance is lowered.

SOURCES OF INFECTION

Humans: The commonest source of infection in humans are humans themselves. The parasite may originate from a patient or a carrier. A **carrier** is a person who harbours the pathogenic microorganism without suffering any ill effect because of it. Several types of carriers have been identified. A **healthy carrier** is one who harbours the pathogen but has never suffered from the disease caused by the pathogen, while a **convalescent carrier** is one who has recovered from the disease and continues to harbour the pathogen in his body. Depending on the duration of carriage, carriers are classified as temporary and chronic. The **temporary carrier** state lasts less than six months, while **chronic carrier** stage may last for several years and sometimes even for the rest of one's life. The term **contact carrier** is applied to a person who acquires the pathogen from a patient, while the term **paradoxical carrier** refers to a carrier who acquires the pathogen from another carrier.

Animals: Many pathogens are able to infect both human beings and animals (Fig. 8.1). Animals may, therefore, act as sources of human infection. In some instances, the infection in animals may be asymptomatic. Such animals serve to maintain the parasite in nature and act as the reservoir of human infections. They are, therefore, called **reservoir hosts**. Infectious diseases transmitted from animals to human beings are called **zoonoses**. Zoonotic diseases may be bacterial (plague from rats), viral (rabies from dogs), protozoal (toxoplasmosis from cats), helminthic (hydatid disease from dogs) or fungal (zoophilic dermatophytes from cats and dogs).

Insects: Blood sucking insects may transmit pathogens to human beings. The diseases so caused are called **arthropod-borne diseases**. Insects such as mosquitoes, ticks, mites, flies, fleas and lice that transmit infections are called **vectors**. Transmission may be mechanical (for example, transmission of dysentery or typhoid bacilli by the domestic fly). Such vectors are called **mechanical vectors**. In other instances, the pathogen multiplies in the body of the vector, often undergoing part of its developmental cycle in it. Such vectors are termed **biological vectors** (for example, Aedes aegypti mosquito in yellow fever, Anopheles mosquito in malaria). Biological vectors transmit infection only after the pathogen has multiplied in them sufficiently or has undergone a developmental cycle. The interval between the time of entry of the pathogen into the vector and the vector becoming infective is called the **extrinsic incubation period**.

Besides acting as vectors, some insects may also act as reservoir hosts (for example, ticks in relapsing fever and spotted fever). Infection is maintained in such insects by transovarial or transstadial passage.

Soil and water: Some pathogens can survive in the soil for very long periods. Spores of tetanus bacilli may remain viable in the soil for several decades and serve as the source of infection. Fungi (*Histoplasma capsulatum, Nocardia asteroides*) and parasites such

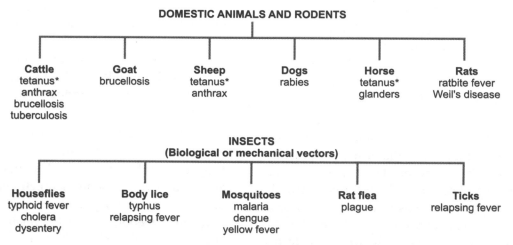

Fig. 8.1   Possible sources of infection (*Tetanus bacilli occur in the feces of these animals)

as roundworm and hookworm survive in the soil and cause human infection.

Water may act as the source of infection either due to contamination with pathogenic microorganisms (cholera vibrio, infective hepatitis virus) or due to the presence of aquatic vectors (cyclops in guineaworm infection).

Food: Contaminated food may act as a source of infection. The presence of pathogens in food may be due to external contamination (food poisoning by staphylococcus) or pre-existent infection in meat or other animal products (salmonellosis).

METHODS OF TRANSMISSION OF INFECTION

Contact: Infection may be acquired by contact, which may be direct or indirect. Sexually transmitted diseases such as syphilis and gonorrhea illustrate spread by direct contact. The term **contagious disease** had been used for diseases transmitted by direct contact, distinct from **infectious disease**, signifying all other modes of transmission. This distinction is now not generally employed. Indirect contact may be through the agency of **fomites**, which are inanimate objects such as clothing, pencils or toys which may be contaminated by a pathogen from one person and act as a vehicle for its transmission to another. Pencils shared by school children may act as fomites in the transmission of diphtheria, and face towels in trachoma.

Inhalation: Respiratory infections such as influenza and tuberculosis are transmitted by inhalation of the pathogen. Such microbes are shed by the patients into the environment, in secretions from the nose or throat during sneezing, speaking or coughing. Large drops of such secretions fall to the ground and dry there. Pathogens resistant to drying may remain viable in the dust and act as sources of infection. Small droplets, under 0.1 mm in diameter, evaporate immediately to become minute particles or **droplet nuclei** (usually 1–10 μm in diameter) which remain suspended in the air for long periods, acting as sources of infection.

Ingestion: Intestinal infections are generally acquired by the ingestion of food or drink contaminated by pathogens. Infection transmitted by ingestion may be waterborne (cholera), foodborne (food poisoning) or handborne (dysentery). The importance of fingerborne transmission is being increasingly recognised, not only in the case of pathogens entering through the mouth, but also those that enter through the nose and eyes.

Inoculation: Pathogens, in some instances, may be inoculated directly into the tissues of the host. Tetanus spores implanted in deep wounds, rabies virus deposited subcutaneously by dog bite and arboviruses injected by insect vectors are examples. Infection by inoculation may be iatrogenic when unsterile syringes and surgical equipment are employed. Hepatitis B and the human immunodeficiency virus (HIV) may be transmitted through transfusion of infected blood, or the use of contaminated syringes and needles, particularly among addicts of injectable drugs.

Insects: Insects may act as mechanical or biological vectors of infectious diseases.

Congenital: Some pathogens are able to cross the placental barrier and infect the fetus in utero. This is known as **vertical transmission**. This may result in abortion, miscarriage or stillbirth. Live infants may be born with manifestations of a disease, as in congenital syphilis. Intrauterine infection with the rubella virus, especially in the first trimester of pregnancy, may interfere with organogenesis and lead to congenital malformations. Such infections are known as **teratogenic infections**.

Iatrogenic and laboratory infections: Infection may sometimes be transmitted during administration of injections, lumbar puncture and catheterisation, if meticulous care in asepsis is lacking. Modern methods of treatment such as exchange transfusion, dialysis and organ transplant surgery have increased the possibilities for iatrogenic infections. Laboratory personnel handling infectious material are at risk and special care should be taken to prevent laboratory infection.

The outcome of an infection will depend on the interaction between microbial factors which predispose to pathogenicity and host factors which contribute to resistance.

FACTORS PREDISPOSING TO MICROBIAL PATHOGENICITY

The terms 'pathogenicity' and 'virulence' refer to the ability of a microbe to produce disease or tissue injury but it is important to make a distinction between them. **Pathogenicity** is generally employed to refer to the ability of a microbial species to produce disease, while the term **virulence** is applied to the same property in a strain of microorganism. Thus the species *M.tuberculosis* or the polio virus is referred to as being pathogenic. The pathogenic species *M.tuberculosis* and the polio virus contain strains of varying degrees of virulence including those which are avirulent, such as the vaccine strains. The virulence of a strain is not constant and may undergo spontaneous or induced variation. Enhancement of virulence is known as **exaltation** and can be demonstrated experimentally by serial passage in susceptible hosts. Reduction of virulence is known as **attenuation** and can be achieved by passage through unfavourable hosts, repeated cultures in artificial media, growth in high temperature or in the presence of weak antiseptics, desiccation or prolonged storage in culture.

Virulence is the sum total of several determinants, as detailed below.

Adhesion: The initial event in the pathogenesis of many infections is the attachment of the bacteria to body surfaces. This attachment is not a chance event but a specific reaction between surface receptors on host cells and adhesive structures (ligands) on the surface of bacteria. These adhesive structures are called **adhesins**. Adhesins may occur as organised structures, such as fimbriae or fibrillae and pili, or as colonisation factors. This specific adhesin may account for the tissue tropisms and host specificity exhibited by many pathogens. Adhesins serve as virulence factors, and loss of adhesins often renders the strain avirulent. Adhesins are usually made of protein and are antigenic in nature. Specific immunisation with adhesins has been attempted as a method of prophylaxis in some infections, as for instance against *E.coli* diarrhea in calves and piglets, and gonorrhea in human beings.

Invasiveness: This refers to the ability of a pathogen to spread in the host tissues after establishing infection. Highly invasive pathogens characteristically produce spreading or generalised lesions (for example, streptococcal septicemia following wound infection), while less invasive pathogens cause more localised lesions (for example, staphylococcal abscess). Some pathogens, though capable of causing serious or even fatal diseases, lack invasiveness altogether (for example, the tetanus bacillus which remains confined to the site of entry and produces the disease by elaborating a potent toxin).

Toxigenicity: Bacteria produce two types of toxins— exotoxins and endotoxins.

Exotoxins are heat labile proteins which are secreted by certain species of bacteria and diffuse readily into the surrounding medium. They are highly potent in minute amounts and constitute some of the most poisonous substances known. One mg of tetanus or botulinum toxin is sufficient to kill more than one million guinea pigs and it has been estimated that 3 kg of botulinum toxin can kill all the inhabitants of the world. Treatment of exotoxins with formaldehyde yields toxoids that are nontoxic but retain the ability to induce antibodies (antitoxins). They exhibit specific tissue affinities and pharmacological activities, each toxin producing a typical effect which can be made out by characteristic clinical manifestations or autopsy appearances. Exotoxins are generally formed by Gram-positive bacteria but may also be produced by some Gram-negative organisms such as Shiga's dysentery bacillus, vibrio cholera and enterotoxigenic *E.coli*.

Endotoxins are heat stable lipopolysaccharides (LPS) which form an integral part of the cell wall of Gram-negative bacteria. Their toxicity depends on the lipid component (lipid A). They are not secreted outside the bacterial cell and are released only by the disintegration of the cell wall. They cannot be toxoided. They are poor antigens and their toxicity is not completely neutralised by the homologous antibodies. They are active only in relatively large doses. They do not exhibit specific pharmacological activities. All endotoxins, whether isolated from pathogenic or nonpathogenic bacteria, produce similar effects. Administration of small quantities of endotoxin in susceptible animals causes an elevation of body temperature manifested within 15 minutes and lasting for several hours. The pyrogenic effect of fluids used for intravenous administration is usually due to the presence of endotoxins from contaminant bacteria. Intravenous injections of large doses of endotoxin and massive Gram-negative septicemias cause endotoxic shock marked by fever, leucopenia, thrombocytopenia, significant fall in blood pressure, circulatory collapse and bloody diarrhea leading to death (Tables 8.1 and 8.2).

Plasmids: Genes coding for some virulence characteristics may be plasmidborne. Examples of plasmidborne virulence factors are surface antigens responsible for the colonisation of intestinal mucosa by *E.coli* and enterotoxin production by *E.coli* and *S.aureus*. Multiple drug resistance (R) plasmids increase the severity of clinical disease by their resistance to antibiotic therapy.

Bacteriophages: The classical example of phage-directed virulence is seen in diphtheria. In the diphtheria bacilli, the gene for toxin production is present in beta or other tox+ corynephages.

Table 8.1 *Distinguishing features of exotoxins and endotoxins*

Exotoxins	Endotoxins
Proteins	Lipopolysaccharides
Heat labile	Heat stable
Actively secreted by cells; diffuse into surrounding medium	Form part of cell wall; do not diffuse into surrounding medium
Readily separable from cultures by physical means such as filtration	Obtained only by cell lysis
Action often enzymic	No enzymic action
Specific pharmacological effect for each exotoxin	Effect nonspecific; action common to all endotoxins
Specific tissue affinities	No specific tissue affinity
Active in very minute doses	Active only in very large doses
Highly antigenic	Weakly antigenic
Action specifically neutralised by antibody	Neutralisation by antibody ineffective

Table 8.2 *Biological activities of endotoxins*

Pyrogenicity	Lethal action	Depression of blood pressure
Activation of complement	Intravascular coagulation	Leucopenia
Leucocytosis	Inhibition of glucose and glycogen synthesis in the liver	Stimulation of B lymphocytes
Macrophage inhibition	Interferon release	Induction of prostaglandin synthesis
Clotting of limulus lysate (lysate of amebocytes from horseshoe crab, Limulus polyphemus, used as a test for detection of endotoxins.)		

Communicability: The ability of a parasite to spread from one host to another is known as communicability. This property does not influence the production of disease in an individual host but determines the survival and distribution of a parasite in a community. A correlation need not exist between virulence and communicability. In fact, a highly virulent parasite may not exhibit a high degree of communicability due to its rapidly lethal effect on the host. In general, infections in which the pathogen is shed in secretions, as in respiratory or intestinal diseases, are highly communicable. In some instances, as in hydrophobia, human infection represents a dead end, there being an interruption in the spread of the pathogen to other hosts.

Development of epidemic and pandemic diseases requires the pathogen strain to possess high degrees of virulence and communicability.

Other bacterial products: Some bacterial products other than toxins, though devoid of intrinsic toxicity, may contribute to virulence by inhibiting the mechanisms of host resistance. Pathogenic staphylococci produce a thrombin-like enzyme **coagulase** which prevents phagocytosis by forming a fibrin barrier around the bacteria and walling off the lesion. **Fibrinolysins** promote the spread of infections by breaking down the fibrin barrier in tissues. **Hyaluronidases** split hyaluronic acid which is a component of intercellular connective tissue and thus facilitate the spread of infection along tissue spaces. **Leucocidins** damage polymorphonuclear leucocytes. Many pathogens produce **hemolysins** capable of destroying erythrocytes but their significance in pathogenicity is not clearly understood.

Bacterial appendages: Capsulated bacteria such as pneumococci, *K.pneumoniae* and *H.influenzae* are not readily phagocytosed. Some bacterial surface antigens such as the Vi antigen of *S.Typhi* and K antigens of *E.coli* also help the bacteria to withstand phagocytosis and the lytic activity of complements.

Biofilms: These are well-organised microcolonies of bacteria enclosed in self-produced extracellular polymer matrices known as glycocalyx. They are separated by water channels that remove water and deliver nutrients. They may be classified as adherent, clinging and submerged biofilms.

Biofilms are of two types: monomicrobial biofilms and polymicrobial biofilms.

Pathogenesis: Free-floating bacteria come in contact with medical devices and attach to them with pili. They then aggregate, multiply and secrete exracellular polymers and are encased. Prevention is by using sonication, antibiotics, catheter lock solutions, catheter flushing and removal of the catheter.

Infecting dose: Successful infections require that an adequate number of bacteria should gain entry into the host. The dosage may be estimated as the minimum infecting dose (MID) or minimum lethal dose (MLD) which are, respectively, the minimum number of bacteria required to produce clinical evidence of infection or death, respectively, in a susceptible animal under standard conditions. As animals exhibit considerable individual variation in susceptibility, these doses are more correctly estimated as statistical expressions, ID 50 and LD 50, as the dose required to infect or kill 50 per cent of the animals tested under standard conditions.

Route of infection: Some bacteria, such as streptococci, can initiate infection whatever be the mode of entry. Others can survive and multiply only when introduced by the optimal routes. Cholera vibrios are infective orally but are unable to cause infection when introduced subcutaneously. This difference is probably related to the modes by which different bacteria are able to initiate tissue damage and establish themselves. Bacteria also differ in their sites of election in the host body after introduction into tissues. They also differ in the ability to damage different organs in different species of animals. Tubercle bacilli injected into rabbits cause lesions mainly in the kidneys and infrequently in the liver and spleen, but in guinea pigs the lesions are mainly in the liver and spleen, the kidneys being spared. The reasons for such selective multiplication in tissues are largely obscure, though they may be related to the presence in tissues of substances that may selectively hinder or favour their multiplication.

TYPES OF INFECTIOUS DISEASES

Infectious diseases may be localised or generalised. Localised infections may be superficial or deep-seated.

Generalised infection involves the spread of the infecting agent from the site of entry by contiguity, through tissue spaces or channels, along the lymphatics or through the bloodstream. Circulation of bacteria in the blood is known as **bacteremia**. Transient bacteremia is a frequent event even in healthy individuals and may occur during chewing, brushing of teeth or straining at stools. The bacteria are immediately mopped up by phagocytic cells and are unable to initiate infection. Bacteremia of greater severity and longer duration is seen during generalised infections as in typhoid fever. **Septicemia** is the condition where bacteria circulate and multiply in the blood, form toxic products and cause high, swinging type of fever. **Pyemia** is a condition where pyogenic bacteria produce septicemia with multiple abscesses in the internal organs such as the spleen, liver and kidneys.

Depending on their spread in the community, infectious diseases may be classified into different types.

- An **endemic disease** is one which is constantly present in a particular area. Typhoid fever is endemic in most parts of India.
- An **epidemic** disease is one that spreads rapidly, involving many persons in an area at the same time. Influenza causes annual winter epidemics in cold countries.
- A **pandemic** is an epidemic that spreads through many areas of the world involving very large numbers of people within a short period. Influenza, cholera, plague and enteroviral conjunctivitis are pandemic diseases.
- Epidemics vary in the rapidity of spread. Waterborne diseases such as cholera and hepatitis may cause explosive outbreaks, while diseases which spread by person-to-person contact evolve more slowly. Such creeping or smouldering epidemics, as that of cerebrospinal fever, are termed **prosodemic** diseases.

RECAP

- Infection and immunity involve interaction between the animal body (host) and the infecting microorganism. Parasites are microbes that can establish themselves and multiply in hosts. Pathogens produce disease in the host, commensals do not cause damage to the host, many commensals are facultative pathogens they can produce disease when host resistance is lowered.

- Infections may be classified as primary infection, re-infection, secondary infection, focal infection, cross-infection, endogenous infection and inapparent infection.
- Sources of infection:
  - Humans constitute the commonest source of infection. The parasite may originate from a patient or a carrier. A carrier may be a healthy carrier, convalescent carrier a contact carrier or a paradoxical carrier. The carrier state may be temporary or chronic.
  - Animals may serve as sources of human infection since the pathogen may be capable of infecting both humans and animals. Infectious diseases transmitted from animals to humans are zoonoses,
  - Blood sucking insects (mosquitoes, ticks, mites, flies, fleas, lice) that transmit pathogens to humans (arthropod-borne diseases) are called vectors.
  - Some pathogens can survive in the soil for very long periods,
  - The presence of pathogens in food may be due to external contamination or due to pre-existing infection in meat and other animal products (salmonellosis).
- Infection may be transmitted by direct contact or through fomites, inhalation of droplets, ingestion of food or drink contaminated by pathogens, or directly inoculated into the tissues of the host.
- Pathogenicity is the ability of a microbial species to cause disease, while virulence is the same property in a microbial strain. Virulence is the sum total of several determinants, including:
  - The ability of the organism to adhere to surface receptors, spread in the host tissues and produce toxins, presence of plasmid-borne or bacteriophage-borne genes, and ability of the organism to spread from one host to another.
  - Microbial products other than toxins, that contribute to virulence include coogulase, fibrinolysins, hyaluronidase and leucocidins.
  - Microbial appendages such as capsules and certain surface antigens help the bacteria resist phago-cytosis and the lytic activity of complement.
- Infectious diseases may be localised or generalised.
  - Bacteremia refers to circulation of bacteria in the blood
  - Septicemia refers to the circulation and multiplication of bacteria in the blood with formation of toxic products and production of high fever
  - Pyemia refers to the septicemia produced by pyogenic bacteria, which is accompanied by formation of multiple abscesses in internal organs
- Infectious diseases may be classified into different types depending on their spread in the community as:
  - Endemic, epidemic, pandemic and prosodemic diseases
- Biofilms are well-organised microcolonies of bacteria enclosed in self-produced extracellular polymer matrices known as glycocalyx.

SHORT ANSWERS

1. Methods of transmission of infection
2. Factors contributing to microbial pathogenicity
3. Differences between exotoxins and endotoxins

SHORT NOTES

1. Bacterial virulence
2. Carrier

9 Immunity

INTRODUCTION

The term 'immunity' has traditionally referred to the resistance exhibited by the host towards injury caused by microorganisms and their products. However, protection against infectious diseases is only one of the many consequences of immune response, which in its entirety is concerned with the reaction of the body against any foreign antigen. This state of protection has both less specific and more specific components.

Types

Immunity against infectious diseases is mainly of two types: innate and acquired (adaptive).

Innate (Native) Immunity

(a) Non-specific
  i. Species
  ii. Racial
  iii. Individual

(b) Specific
  i. Species
  ii. Racial
  iii. Individual

Acquired (Adaptive) Immunity

(a) Active
  i. Natural
  ii. Artificial

(b) Passive
  i. Natural
  ii. Artificial

INNATE OR NATIVE IMMUNITY

This provides the first line of defense against infections. It is the resistance to infections that an individual possesses by virtue of his or her genetic and constitutional make-up. It is not affected by prior contact with microorganisms or immunisation. It may be non-specific, when it indicates a degree of resistance to infections in general, or specific, where resistance to a particular pathogen is concerned.

Innate immunity may be considered at the level of the species, race or individual.

Species immunity: This refers to the total or relative refractoriness to a pathogen, shown by all members of a species. For instance, all human beings are totally unsusceptible to plant pathogens and to many animal pathogens such as rinderpest and distemper. This immunity is something a person obtains by virtue of being a part of the human species. The mechanisms of species immunity are not clearly understood but may be due to physiological and biochemical differences between the tissues of the different host species, which determine whether or not a pathogen can multiply in them.

Racial immunity: Within a species, different races may show differences in susceptibility to infection, the classic example of which is the high resistance of Algerian sheep to anthrax. Such racial differences are known to be genetic in origin, and by selection and inbreeding, it is possible to develop, at will, races that possess high degrees of resistance or susceptibility to various pathogens. It is difficult to demonstrate marked differences in immunity in human races, as controlled breeding is not possible. It has been reported that people of African origin in the USA are more susceptible than Caucasians to tuberculosis. But such comparisons are vitiated by external influences such as differences in socioeconomic levels. An interesting instance of genetic resistance to *Plasmodium falciparum* malaria is seen in some parts of Africa and the Mediterranean coast. A hereditary abnormality of red cells (sickling) prevalent in the area confers immunity to infection by the malarial parasite and may have evolved from the survival advantage conferred by it in a malarial environment.

Individual immunity: This is the difference in innate immunity exhibited by different individuals in a race. The genetic basis of individual immunity is evident from studies on the incidence of infectious diseases in twins. It is well documented that homozygous twins exhibit similar degrees of resistance or susceptibility to lepromatous leprosy and tuberculosis. Such correlation is not seen in heterozygous twins.

Factors affecting innate immunity

Age: The very young and the very old are more susceptible to infectious disease than the rest. The fetus in utero is normally protected from maternal infection by the placental barrier. But some pathogens cross this barrier, causing overwhelming infection resulting in fetal death. Some, such as rubella, herpes, cytomegaloviruses and *Toxoplasma gondii*, lead to congenital malformations.

Increased susceptibility in the young may, in some instances, be due to hormonal influence. Tinea capitis caused by *Microsporum audouinii* frequently undergoes spontaneous cure with the onset of puberty. The susceptibility of the vaginal epithelium in prepubertal girls to gonococcal infection is another instance of the effect of sex hormones on resistance.

Some infections like poliomyelitis and chickenpox tend to be more severe in adults than in young children, due to hypersensitivity that causes greater tissue damage. Conversely, hepatitis B virus infections in the newborn are usually asymptomatic because clinical disease requires adequate immune response which is lacking at that age. However, the virus multiplies unrestrained and such neonates end up as chronic viral carriers, often developing late hepatic complications. Older persons are highly susceptible to infections due to the waning of their immune responses and other infirmities like enlarged prostate leading to urinary stasis.

Hormonal influences: Endocrine disorders such as diabetes mellitus, hypothyroidism and adrenal dysfunction are associated with enhanced susceptibility to infection. The high incidence of staphylococcal sepsis in diabetes may be related to the increased level of carbohydrates in tissues. Corticosteroids exert an important influence on the response to infection. They depress the host's resistance by their anti-inflammatory and anti-phagocytic effects and by the suppression of antibody formation and hypersensitivity. They also have a beneficial effect in that they neutralise the harmful effect of bacterial products such as endotoxins. Elevated steroid levels during pregnancy may be related to the heightened susceptibility of pregnant women to many infections.

Nutrition: The relationship between malnutrition and immunity is complex but, in general, both humoral and cell-mediated immune processes are reduced when there is malnutrition. Cell-mediated immune responses such as the Mantoux test become negative in severe protein deficiency, as in kwashiorkor. Malarial infection in the famine stricken may not induce fever but once their nutrition improves, clinical malaria develops.

Mechanisms of innate immunity

Epithelial surfaces: The intact skin and mucous membrane covering the body protect it considerably against invasion by microorganisms. They provide much more than a mechanical barrier. Healthy skin possesses bactericidal activity to which the presence of a high concentration of salt in drying sweat, sebaceous secretions and long chain fatty acids and soaps contribute. When cultures of typhoid bacilli placed on healthy skin and on a glass surface are sampled at intervals, the bacteria on the skin are seen to be killed within minutes, while those on the glass survive for several hours. The bactericidal activity of skin secretions is illustrated by the frequent mycotic and pyogenic infections seen in persons who immerse their hands in soapy water for long periods occupationally.

Though the **skin** frees itself readily of bacteria deposited on it (transients), its reactions are different to the bacterial flora normally resident on it. Resident flora are not easily removed even by washing and application of disinfectants.

The **mucosa** of the respiratory tract has several innate mechanisms of defence. The very architecture of the nose prevents entry of microorganisms to a large extent, the inhaled particles being arrested at or near the nasal orifices. Those that pass beyond are held by the mucus lining the epithelium, and are swept back to the pharynx where they tend to be swallowed or coughed out. The cough reflex is an important defence mechanism of the respiratory tract. The cilia on the respiratory epithelial cells propel particles upwards. Nasal and respiratory secretions contain mucopolysaccharides capable of combining with influenza and certain other viruses. Particles that manage to reach the pulmonary alveoli are ingested by the phagocytic cells present there.

The **mouth** is constantly bathed in saliva which has an inhibitory effect on many microorganisms. Particles deposited in the mouth are swallowed and subjected to the action of the digestive juices. The high acidity of the stomach destroys most microorganisms. The **conjunctiva** is freed of foreign particles by the flushing action of lachrymal secretions. The eyes become susceptible to infection when lachrymal secretions are absent. **Tears** contain the antibacterial substance lysozyme, first described by Fleming (1922). This is a thermolabile, low-molecular-weight, basic protein which acts as a muraminidase. Lysozyme is present in tissue fluids and in nearly all secretions except cerebrospinal fluid, sweat and urine. It acts by splitting certain polysaccharide components of the cell walls of susceptible bacteria. In the concentrations seen in tears and other secretions, lysozyme is active only against some non-pathogenic Gram-positive bacteria. However, it occurs in phagocytic cells in concentrations high enough to be lethal to many pathogens.

The flushing action of **urine** eliminates bacteria from the urethra. Spermine and zinc present in semen carry out antibacterial activity. The acidity of the adult vagina, due to the fermentation of glycogen in the epithelial cells by the resident aciduric bacilli, makes it inhospitable to many pathogens.

Antibacterial substances in blood and tissues: The complement system possesses bactericidal activity and plays an important role in the destruction of pathogenic bacteria that invade the blood and tissues.

Several substances possessing antibacterial properties have been described in blood and tissues.

- **Beta lysin**, a relatively thermostable substance active against anthrax and related bacilli
- **Basic polypeptides** such as leukins extracted from leucocytes and plakins from platelets
- **Acidic substances**, such as lactic acid found in muscle tissue and in the inflammatory zones
- **Lactoperoxidase** in milk possesses antibacterial properties demonstrable experimentally; however, their relevance in the natural context is not clearly understood

- **Interferon** has been shown to be more important than specific antibodies in protection against and recovery from certain acute viral infections. Tissues and body secretions contain other antiviral substances.

Microbial antagonisms: The skin and mucous surfaces have resident bacterial flora which prevent colonisation by pathogens. Alteration of normal resident flora may lead to invasion by extraneous microbes, causing serious diseases such as staphylococcal or clostridial enterocolitis following oral antibiotics. The importance of normal bacterial flora in native immunity is exemplified by the extreme susceptibility of germ-free animals to all types of infections.

Cellular factors: Natural defence against the invasion of blood and tissues by microorganisms and other foreign particles is mediated to a large extent by phagocytic cells which ingest and destroy them. Phagocytic cells, originally discovered by Metchnikoff (1883), were classified by him into microphages and macrophages. **Microphages** are polymorphonuclear leucocytes. **Macrophages** consist of histiocytes which are the wandering ameboid cells seen in tissues, the fixed reticuloendothelial cells and the monocytes in the blood. A major function of the reticuloendothelial system is the removal of foreign particles that enter the body.

Phagocytic cells reach the sites of inflammation in large numbers, attracted by chemotactic substances, and ingest particulate material. Capsulated bacteria, such as *S.pneumoniae*, are not readily phagocytosed except in the presence of opsonins. They are more readily phagocytosed when trapped against a firm surface such as the alveolar wall than when they are free in tissue fluids. Bacteria are phagocytosed into a vacuole (phagosome), which fuses with the lysosomes found in the cell to form the phagolysosome. The bacteria are subjected to the action of the lytic enzymes in the phagolysosome and are destroyed.

Some bacteria, such as brucella and lepra bacilli, resist intracellular digestion and may actively multiply inside the phagocytic cells. Phagocytosis in such instances may actually help to disseminate infection to different parts of the body. The importance of phagocytosis in protection against infection is evidenced by the enhanced susceptibility to infection seen either when the phagocytic cells are depleted, as in agranulocytosis, or when they are functionally deficient, as in chronic granulomatous disease. A class of lymphocytes called natural killer (NK) cells are important in non-specific defence against viral infections and tumours. They selectively kill virus-infected cells and tumour cells. NK cells are activated by interferons.

Inflammation: Tissue injury or irritation, initiated by the entry of pathogens or other irritants, leads to inflammation, which is an important, non-specific defence mechanism. The arterioles at the site constrict initially and then dilate leading to increased blood flow. There is slowing of blood flow and margination of the leucocytes, which escape into the tissues by diapedesis and accumulate in large numbers, attracted by the chemotactic substances released at the site of injury. Microorganisms are phagocytosed and destroyed. There is an outpouring of plasma, which helps to dilute the toxic products present. A fibrin barrier is laid, serving to wall off the site of infection.

Fever: A rise in temperature following infection is a natural defence mechanism. It not only helps to accelerate the physiological processes but may also, in some cases, actually destroy the infecting pathogens. Therapeutic induction of fever was used for the destruction of *Treponema pallidum* in the tissues of syphilitic patients before penicillin became available. Fever stimulates the production of interferon and aids recovery from viral infections.

Acute phase proteins: Infection or injury leads to a sudden increase in the plasma concentration of certain proteins, collectively called acute phase proteins. These include C reactive protein (CRP), mannose binding protein, alpha-1-acid glycoprotein, serum amyloid P component and many others. CRP and some other acute phase proteins activate the alternative pathway of complements. They are believed to enhance host resistance, prevent tissue injury and promote repair of inflammatory lesions.

Toll-like receptors: Many of the molecules involved in innate immunity have the property of pattern recognition, the ability to recognise a given class of molecules. Certain molecules are unique in microbes and never found in multicellular organisms. To recognise these patterns and to destroy the invaders displaying such molecules is a strong feature of innate immunity. Such molecules are a class of cell-associated receptors and known as toll-like receptors. There are 13 different TLRs that recognise pathogens and enhance phagocytosis and lead to inflammation at the site. The factors contributing to innate immunity are listed in Table 9.1.

ACQUIRED OR ADAPTIVE IMMUNITY

The resistance that an individual acquires during life by recognising and selectively eliminating specific foreign molecules is known as acquired immunity. This displays four characteristic features:

- **Antigenic specificity:** The immune system or antibodies can distinguish among antigens, even between two proteins that differ in only one amino acid.
- **Diversity:** The immune system is capable of generating enormous antibody diversity in its recognition molecules, allowing it to reorganise billions of unique structures/patterns on foreign antigens. Genes form the basis of such diversity.
- **Immunologic memory:** The immune system exhibits memory on the second encounter of the same antigen by generating a secondary response which is more specific, heightened and quick.
- **Self/non-self recognition:** Self-tolerance is one of the unique characteristics of the immune system which prevents it from reacting to the body's own molecules while still effectively eliminating foreign antigens. Multiple mechanisms ensure self-tolerance. Failure of these mechanisms may lead to autoimmunity.

TYPES

Active immunity

This is the resistance developed by an individual as a result of an antigenic stimulus. It is also known as **adaptive immunity** as it represents the adaptive response of the host to a specific pathogen or other antigen.

- It involves the active functioning of the host's immune apparatus, leading to the synthesis of antibodies and the production of immunologically active cells.
- It sets in only after a latent period which is required for the immunological machinery to be set in motion.
- During the development of active immunity, there is often a negative phase during which the level of measurable immunity may actually be lower than it was before the antigenic stimulus. This is because the antigen combines with any pre-existing antibody and lowers its level in circulation.
- Once developed, active immunity is long-lasting. If an individual who has been actively immunised against an antigen experiences the same antigen subsequently, the immune response occurs more

Table 9.1 *Non-specific host defense barriers contributing to innate immunity*

Body systems and factors involved	Active component	Effector mechanism
Skin	Squamous cells, salt of sweat glands, sebaceous glands, (long chain fatty acids and lactic acid)	Desquamation, flushing, organic acids, bactericidal pH (3–5) retards bacterial growth
Mouth	Saliva	Bathing, flushing
GI tract	Wall, gastric secretions	Peristalsis, mucus, low pH, flushing
Respiratory tract	Tracheal cilia, coughing reflex	Mucociliary elevator, surfactant, forcible removal
Nasopharynx	Nasal hair, mucus	Mechanical barrier, entrap and swallow
Eye	Tears	Flushing, lysozyme
Circulation and lymphoid organs	Phagocytic cells, NK cells	Phagocytosis, intracellular killing, direct and antibody dependent cytolysis
Serum	Lactoferrin and transferrin, interferons, TNF-α, lysozyme, fibronectin, complement proteins	Iron binding, antiviral proteins, phagocyte activation, peptidoglycan hydrolysis, opsonisation and phagocytosis, enhanced intracellular killing
Cell-associated receptors	Toll-like receptors	Pattern recognition of pathogen and elimination
Acute phase proteins	CRP mannose binding protein, alpha-1 acid glycoprotein	Inflammation
Adult vagina	Acidic pH	Retard bacterial growth
Semen	Spermine and zinc	Antibacterial activity
Urinary system	Acidic pH and flow	Retard bacterial growth, flushing
Breast milk	Antibodies, fibronectin, interferon, lactoferrin, lysozyme, mucin, oligosaccharides	Protection of newborn
Fever	High temperature	Destroys the pathogen

quickly and abundantly than during the first encounter. This is known as **secondary response**.

- Besides the development of humoral and cellular immunity, active immunity is associated with immunological memory.
- Active immunisation is more effective and confers better protection than passive immunisation.

Passive immunity

This is the resistance that is transmitted passively to a recipient in a 'readymade' form. Here the recipient's immune system plays no active role.

- There is no antigenic stimulus; instead, preformed antibodies are administered.
- There is no latent period, protection being effective immediately after passive immunisation.
- There is no negative phase. The immunity is transient, usually lasting for days or weeks, only till the passively transmitted antibodies are metabolised and eliminated.
- No secondary type response occurs in passive immunity. In fact, passive immunity diminishes in effect with repetition. When a foreign antibody is

administered a second time, it is eliminated more rapidly than initially.

- Following the first injection of an antibody such as immune horse serum, the elimination is only by metabolic breakdown but during subsequent injections of horse serum, elimination is much quicker as it combines with antibodies to horse serum that would have been produced following its initial injection. This factor of **immune elimination** limits the usefulness of repeated passive immunisation.
- Passive immunisation is less effective than active immunisation.
- The main advantage of passive immunisation is that it acts immediately and, therefore, can be employed when **'instant' immunity** is desired (Table 9.2).

Types of active immunity:

1. **Natural active immunity** results from either a clinical or an inapparent infection by a microbe. A person who has recovered from an attack of measles develops natural active immunity. The large majority of adults in the developing countries possess natural active immunity to poliomyelitis due to repeated inapparent infections in childhood. Such

Table 9.2 *Comparison of active and passive immunity*

Active immunity	Passive immunity
Produced actively by host's immune system	Received passively. No active host participation
Induced by infection or by immunogens	Readymade antibody transferred
Durable effective protection	Transient, less effective
Immunity effective only after lag period	Immediate immunity
Immunological memory present	No memory
Booster effect on subsequent dose	Subsequent dose less effective
Negative phase may occur	No negative phase
Not applicable in the immunodeficient	Applicable in the immunodeficient

immunity is usually long-lasting but the duration varies with the type of pathogen. The immunity is lifelong following many viral diseases such as chickenpox and measles. In some, such as influenza or the common cold, the immunity appears to be shortlived. Influenza can recur in an individual after a few months or a year but this is not so much due to lack of the immunising capacity of the virus as to its ability to undergo antigenic variation so that immunity following the first infection is not effective against the second infection caused by an antigenically novel virus. In the common cold, the apparent lack of immunity is because the same clinical picture can be caused by infection with a large number of different viruses.

The immunity following bacterial infection is generally less permanent than that following viral infection. Some, such as typhoid fever, induce durable protection. In syphilis, a special type of immunity known as 'premunition' is seen. Here, immunity to re-infection lasts only as long as the original infection remains active. Once the disease is cured, the patient becomes susceptible to the spirochete again. In chancroid, another venereal disease caused by *Haemophilus ducreyi*, there does not appear to be any effective immunity as the patient may develop lesions following re-infection even while the original infection is active.

2. **Artificial active immunity** is the resistance induced by vaccines. Vaccines are preparations of live or killed microorganisms or their products used for immunisation. Examples of vaccines are as follows:

- **Bacterial vaccines**
  - Live (BCG vaccine for tuberculosis)
  - Killed (Cholera vaccine)
  - Subunit (Typhoid Vi antigen)
  - Bacterial products (Tetanus toxoid)

- **Viral vaccines**
  - Live (Oral polio vaccine—Sabin)
  - Killed (Injectable polio vaccine—Salk)
  - Subunit (Hepatitis B vaccine)

Live vaccines initiate infection without causing any injury or disease. The immunity following live vaccine administration therefore parallels that following natural infection though it may be of a lower order. The immunity lasts for several years but booster doses may be necessary. Live vaccines may be administered orally (as with the Sabin vaccine for poliomyelitis) or parenterally (as with the measles vaccine).

Killed vaccines are generally less immunogenic than live vaccines, and protection lasts only for a short period. They have, therefore, to be administered repeatedly, generally at least two doses being required for the production of immunity. The first is known as the **primary dose** and the subsequent doses as **booster doses**. Killed vaccines may be given orally but this route is generally not effective. Parenteral administration provides humoral antibody response, which may be improved by the addition of 'adjuvants' (for example, aluminium phosphate).

Types of passive immunity:

1. **Natural passive immunity** is the resistance passively transferred from mother to baby. In human infants, maternal antibodies are transmitted predominantly through the placenta, while in animals such as pigs, transfer of antibodies occurs mainly orally through the colostrum. The human colostrum, which is also rich in IgA antibodies resistant to intestinal digestion, gives protection to the neonate.

The human fetus acquires some ability to synthesise antibodies (IgM) from about the twentieth week of life but its immunological capacity is still inadequate at birth. It is only by about the age of three months that the infant acquires some measure of immunological independence. Until then, maternal antibodies give passive protection against infectious diseases to the infant. It is for this reason that most pediatric infections are more common after the age of three months than in younger infants.

By active immunisation of mothers during pregnancy, it is possible to improve the quality of passive immunity in the infants. Immunisation of pregnant women with tetanus toxoid is recommended for this purpose in communities in which neonatal tetanus is common.

2. **Artificial passive immunity** is the resistance passively transferred to a recipient by the administration of antibodies. The agents used for this purpose are hyperimmune sera of animal or human origin, convalescent sera and pooled human gamma globulin. These are used for prophylaxis and therapy. Equine hyperimmune sera such as antitetanus serum and ATS prepared from hyperimmunised horses used to be extensively employed. They gave temporary protection but carried the disadvantages of hypersensitivity and immune elimination. Human hyperimmune globulin (for example, tetanus immune globulin, TIG) is free from those complications and also provides more lasting protection. Antisera of animal origin are now recommended only where human preparations are not available (anti–gas gangrene and anti–botulinum sera; antivenoms).

Convalescent sera (sera of patients recovering from infectious diseases) contain high levels of specific antibody. **Pooled human gamma globulin** (gamma globulin from pooled sera of healthy adults) contains antibodies against all common pathogens prevalent in the region. Convalescent sera and pooled human gamma globulin were used for passive immunisation against some viral infections (like viral hepatitis A). Human gamma globulin is also used in the treatment of patients with some immunodeficiencies.

Indications: Passive immunisation is indicated for immediate and temporary protection in a non-immune host faced with the threat of infection. Passive immunisation may also be used for the suppression of active immunity, when the latter may be injurious. An example is the use of Rh immune globulin during delivery to prevent immune response to the Rhesus factor in Rh-negative women with Rh-positive babies.

3. **Combined immunisation**: Sometimes a combination of the active and passive methods of immunisation is used. Ideally, whenever passive immunisation is employed for immediate protection, combined immunisation is to be preferred, as in the protection of a non-immune individual with a tetanus-prone wound. The method is to inject TIG in one arm and the first dose of tetanus toxoid in the other. This is followed by the full course of phased tetanus toxoid injections. TIG provides the protection necessary till active immunity is able to take effect.

Adoptive immunity: A special type of immunisation is the injection of immunologically competent lymphocytes. This is known as adoptive immunity and does not have general application. Instead of whole lymphocytes, an extract of immunologically competent lymphocytes, known as the '**transfer factor**', can be used. This has been attempted in the treatment of certain types of diseases (for example, lepromatous leprosy).

MEASUREMENT OF IMMUNITY

The truly valid measurement of immunity is to test the resistance of an individual to a challenge by the pathogen. This is, however, not applicable since the challenge itself alters the state of immunity. It is, therefore, not possible to measure accurately the level of immunity in an individual. Estimates of immunity are generally made by statistical methods using large numbers of individuals.

A simple method of testing immunity is to relate its level to some convenient indicator, such as demonstration of the specific antibody. This is not always reliable as the immune response to a pathogen consists of the formation of antibodies to several antigens present in it, as also to the production of cellular immunity. The antibodies may be demonstrated by a variety of techniques such as agglutination, precipitation, complement fixation, hemagglutination inhibition, neutralisation, ELISA and others. In the absence of exact information as to which antigen of the pathogen constitutes the **protective antigen**, serological attempts to measure immunity are at best only approximations. In some instances, as in diphtheria where pathogenesis is due to a well-defined antigen (the toxin), the level of immunity can be assayed by in vitro or in vivo (Schick test) methods. Where protection is associated with cell-mediated immunity, skin tests for delayed hypersensitivity and in vitro tests for CMI provide an indication of immunity.

Local immunity

The concept of local immunity, proposed by Besredka (1919–24), has gained importance in the treatment of infections that are localised or where it is operative in combating infection at the site of primary entry of the pathogen. In poliomyelitis, for instance, systemic immunity provided by active immunisation with the killed vaccine neutralises the virus when it enters the bloodstream, but it does not prevent multiplication of the virus at the site of entry (the gut mucosa) and its fecal shedding. This is achieved by the local intestinal immunity acquired either as a result of natural infection or immunisation with the live oral vaccine. In influenza, immunisation with the killed vaccine elicits a humoral antibody response. But the antibody titre in respiratory secretions is often not high enough to prevent infection. Natural infection or the live virus vaccine administered intranasally provides local immunity. A special class of **immunoglobulins (IgA)** forms the main component of local immunity.

One type of IgA antibody called **secretory IgA** is produced locally by plasma cells present on mucosal surfaces or in secretory glands. There appears to be selective transport of such antibodies between the various mucosal surfaces and secretory glands. Thus, following intestinal exposure to an antigen, the specific IgA antibody and the plasma cells forming such an antibody can be demonstrated in breast milk. This indicates the existence of a common **mucosal** or **secretory immune system**.

Herd immunity

This refers to the overall level of immunity in a community and is relevant in the control of epidemic diseases. When a large proportion of individuals in a community *(herd)* are immune to a pathogen, the herd immunity to the pathogen is satisfactory. When herd immunity is low, epidemics are likely to occur on the introduction of a suitable pathogen, due to the presence of large numbers of susceptible individuals in the community. Eradication of communicable diseases depends on the development of a high level of herd immunity rather than on the development of a high level of immunity in individuals.

RECAP

- The term immunity refers to the resistance exhibited by the host towards injury caused by foreign antigens/microorganisms and their products.
- The two fundamental types of immunity are innate and acquired. Each type is, in turn, composed of different subtypes.
- Innate (native) immunity is the resistance to infection which an individual possesses due to his genetic and constitutional make-up. It may be:
  - non-specific, when it protects against many types of infections
  - specific, when it protects against a particular organism
- Important non-specific antimicrobial factors found in blood, secretions and tissues include lysosymes, beta lysin, peroxidase enzymes, interferons and lactoferrin.
- The resistance acquired by an individual during life is known as acquired immunity. It displays four characteristic features: antigenic specificity, diversity, immunologic memory and self/non-self recognition.
- Acquired immunity is of two types: active immunity, where the host produces its own response to foreign antigens to confer protection, and passive immunity, where preformed antibodies are introduced parenterally (not by the oral route but by the intramuscular or intravenous route) into the host to confer protection.
- Local immunity refers to the protection given to a potential site of entry for a pathogen; such immunity prevents entry of the pathogen. This is important in poliomyelitis, where a live vaccine is used to augment the resistance at the level of the gut mucosa, which is the site of entry for the polio virus.

- Herd immunity is the immunity developed in a large proportion (80 per cent) of individuals in a population. This reduces the likelihood of epidemics arising in that community by the pathogen.

ESSAYS

1. What is innate immunity? Elaborate on the mechanisms/factors that contribute to it.
2. Explain the term acquired/adaptive immunity and its characteristic features.

SHORT ANSWERS

1. Types of innate immunity and the factors that affect them
2. Differences between active and passive adaptive immunity
3. Natural and artificial active immunity

SHORT NOTES

1. Innate immunity
2. Adaptive immunity
3. Species and racial immunity
4. Local immunity
5. Herd immunity

10 Antigens

INTRODUCTION

An **antigen** is any substance which, when introduced parenterally into the body, stimulates the production of an antibody with which it reacts specifically and in an observable manner.

The word 'specifically' is important as specificity is the hallmark of all immunological reactions. An antigen introduced into the body reacts only with those particular immunocytes (B or T lymphocytes) which carry the specific marker for that antigen and which produce antibodies or cells complementary to that antigen; still immunological cross-reaction may occur between closely related antigens.

A more accurate definition of antigen would be, substances that can be recognised by B cell receptors (Ig) and T cell receptors (along with the major histocompatibility complex [MHC]). The nature/molecular configurations and properties of an antigen as well as the immune system of the host both play an important role in eliciting an immune response. Both T and B lymphocytes recognise each antigen differently owing to the presence of different antigen recognition sites on each type of lymphocyte. These sites or receptors recognise the different molecular features of an antigen and a response is generated accordingly.

Definitions

Antigens: Molecules that interact specifically with the products of immune response generated by an immunogen, that is, with antibodies, B cell receptors (BCRs) and/or T cell receptors (TCRs).

Immunogen: A substance which induces a detectable immune response (humoral or cellular). Immunogens stimulate the immune reaction, resulting in either the production of antibodies or the activation of T cells, and finally leading to either immune response or immune tolerance.

Antigenicity: The property that allows a substance to combine specifically with antibodies or TCRs, whether or not they are immunogenic. An immunogen can trigger an immune response and act as an antigen in that immune response. Thus, all immunogens are antigens but all antigens are not immunogens.

Immunogenicity: The ability to induce humoral and/or cell-mediated immune response.

TYPES OF ANTIGENS

The two attributes of antigenicity are:

- **Immunogenicity** (induction of an immune response)
- **Immunological reactivity** (specific reaction with antibodies or sensitised cells)

Based on the ability to carry out these two functions, antigens may be classified into different types. A **complete antigen** can induce antibody formation and produce a specific and observable reaction with the antibody so produced.

Haptens are substances that are incapable of inducing antibody formation by themselves but can react specifically with antibodies (in Greek, *haptein* means 'to fasten'). Haptens become immunogenic (capable of inducing antibodies) on combining with a larger molecule carrier. They may be complex or simple: while **complex haptens** can precipitate with specific antibodies, **simple haptens** are non-precipitating. They can inhibit the precipitation of specific antibodies by the corresponding antigen or complex hapten. Complex and simple haptens have been described as polyvalent and univalent, respectively, since it is assumed that precipitation requires the antigen to have two or more antibody combining sites.

Epitope: The smallest unit of antigenicity is known as the **antigenic determinant** or **epitope**. The epitope is that small area on the antigen, usually consisting of four or five amino acids or monosaccharide residues, possessing a specific chemical structure, electrical charge and steric (spatial) configuration. It is capable of sensitising an immunocyte and of reacting with its complementary site on the specific antibody or TCR.

Epitopes may be present as a single linear segment of the primary sequence (**sequential** or **linear epitope**) (Fig. 10.1a) or be formed by being brought together on surface residues from different sites of the peptide chain during its folding into the tertiary structure (**conformational epitope**), as shown in (Fig. 10.1b) T cells recognise sequential epitopes, while B cells identify the tertiary configuration of the conformational epitopes. The combining area on the antibody molecule, corresponding to the epitope, is called the **paratope**. Epitopes and paratopes determine the specificity of immunological reactions. Antigens such as bacteria or viruses carry many different types of epitopes, presenting an **antigenic mosaic**. The presence of the same or similar epitopes on different antigens accounts for one type of antigenic cross-reaction.

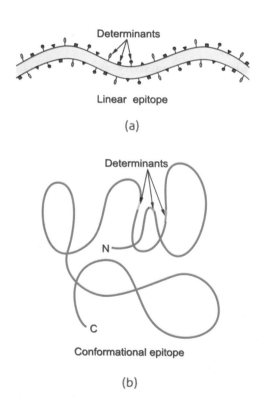

Linear epitope

(a)

Conformational epitope

(b)

Fig. 10.1   Epitopes: (a) linear and (b) conformational

Determinants of antigenicity

A number of properties that make a substance antigenic have been identified, but the exact basis of antigenicity is still not clear.

Size: Antigenicity is related to molecular size. Very large molecules, such as hemocyanins (MW 6.75 million), are highly antigenic and particles with low molecular weight (less than 5000) are non-antigenic or feebly so. Low-molecular-weight substances may be rendered antigenic by adsorbing them on large inert particles such as bentonite or kaolin. Some low-molecular-weight substances (such as picryl chloride, formaldehyde and penicillin) may be antigenic when applied on the skin, probably by combining with tissue proteins. They are haptens of low immunogenicity, effective in some persons only and related to hypersensitivity.

Chemical nature: Most naturally occurring antigens are proteins and polysaccharides. Lipids and nucleic acids are less antigenic. Their antigenicity is enhanced by combining with proteins. A certain degree of structural diversity is required for antigenicity. That probably explains why proteins, which are composed of about 20 different amino acids, are better antigens than polysaccharides, which have only four or five monosaccharide units. However, not all proteins are antigenic. A well-known exception is gelatin, which is non-immunogenic because of its structural instability.

Susceptibility to tissue enzymes: Only substances which are metabolised and are susceptible to the action of tissue enzymes behave as antigens. Antigens introduced into the body are degraded by the host into fragments of appropriate size containing the antigenic determinants. Phagocytosis and intracellular enzymes appear to play an essential role in breaking down antigens into immunogenic fragments. Substances not susceptible to tissue enzymes, such as polystyrene latex, are not antigenic. Substances very rapidly broken down by tissue enzymes are also not antigenic. Synthetic polypeptides, composed of D-amino acids which are not metabolised in the body, are not antigenic, while polypeptides consisting of L-amino acids are antigenic.

Foreignness: Only antigens that are 'foreign' to the individual (non-self) induce an immune response. The animal body contains numerous antigens that induce an immune response when introduced into another individual or species. An individual does not normally mount an immune response against his or her own normal constituent antigens. This was first recognised by Ehrlich, who proposed the concept of 'horror auto-toxicus' (fear of self-poisoning). Tolerance of self-antigens is conditioned by contact with them during the development of the immune apparatus. Breakdown of this homeostatic mechanism results in autoimmunisation and autoimmune disease.

In general, the antigenicity of a substance is related to the degree of its foreignness. Antigens from other individuals of the same species are less antigenic than those from other species. Antigens from related species are less antigenic than those from distant species.

Antigenic specificity: The basis of antigenic specificity is stereochemical, as was first demonstrated by Obermayer and Pick and confirmed by Landsteiner. Using haptens such as atoxyl coupled with protein, it was shown that antigenic specificity is determined by single chemical groupings and even by a single acid radical. The importance of the position of the antigenic determinant group in the antigen molecule was evidenced by the differences in specificity in compounds with the group attached at the **ortho**, **meta** or **para** positions. The influence of spatial configuration of the determinant group was shown by differences in the antigenic specificity of the **dextro**, **levo** and **meso** isomers of substances such as tartaric acid.

Antigenic specificity is not absolute. Cross-reactions can occur between antigens that bear stereochemical similarities. In some instances, apparent cross-reactions may actually be due to the sharing of identical antigenic determinants by different antigens.

The specificity of natural tissue antigens of animals may be considered under different categories as species, iso, auto and organ specificities.

- **Species specificity:** Tissues of all individuals in a species contain species-specific antigens. There exists some degree of cross-reaction between antigens from related species. This immunological relationship parallels their phylogenetic relationship. It has been used in tracing evolutionary relationships between species. It also has forensic applications in the identification of the species from blood and seminal stains. Phylogenetic relationships are reflected in the extent of cross-reactions between antigens from different species that cause hypersensitivity. An individual sensitised to horse serum will react with serum from other equines but may not do so with bovine serum.

- **Isospecificity:** Isoantigens are antigens found in some but not all members of a species. A species may be grouped depending on the presence of different isoantigens in its members. The best examples of isoantigens are the human erythrocyte antigens, based on which individuals can be classified into different blood groups. These are genetically determined. They are of clinical importance in blood transfusion and in isoimmunisation during pregnancy. They were of help in determining disputed paternity cases, but have been supplanted by the more discriminatory DNA fingerprinting tests. Blood groups find application in anthropology.

Histocompatibility antigens are those cellular determinants specific to each individual of a species. They are recognised by genetically different individuals of the same species when attempts are made to transfer or transplant cellular material from one individual to another.

- **Autospecificity:** Autologous or self-antigens are ordinarily non-antigenic but there are exceptions. Sequestrated antigens that are not normally found free in circulation or tissue fluids (such as the eye lens protein normally confined within its capsule) are not recognised as self-antigens. Similarly, antigens that are absent during embryonic life and develop later (such as the sperm) are also not recognised as self-antigens.

- **Organ specificity:** Some organs, such as the brain, kidneys and lens protein of different species, share the same antigen. Such antigens, characteristic of an organ or tissue and found in different species, are called organ-specific antigens. The neuroparalytic complications following anti-rabic vaccination using sheep brain vaccines are a consequence of brain-specific antigens shared by sheep and human beings. The sheep brain antigens induce immunological response in the vaccinees, damaging their nervous tissue.

Heterogenetic (heterophile) specificity: The same or closely related antigens may sometimes occur in different biological species, classes and kingdoms. These are known as heterogenetic or heterophile antigens. For example,

- **Forssman antigen**, a lipid carbohydrate complex widely distributed in many animals, birds, plants and bacteria. It is absent in rabbits, so anti-Forssman antibody can be prepared in these animals.

Other heterophile antigens are responsible for some diagnostic serological reactions in which antigens unrelated to etiological agents are employed (heterophile reaction):

- The **Weil–Felix reaction** in typhus fever
- The **Paul–Bunnell test** in infectious mononucleosis
- The **cold agglutinin test** in primary atypical pneumonia

BIOLOGICAL CLASSES OF ANTIGENS

Depending on their ability to induce antibody formation, antigens are classified into:

- T cell-dependent (TD) antigens
- T cell-independent (TI) antigens

T cell-dependent antigens: Most natural proteins are T-dependent antigens and B cells cannot respond to these antigens without a co-stimulatory signal from the T_H cells. Structurally, these antigens are characterised by a few copies of many different antigenic determinants. These antigens bind to the surface Ig on B cells and are internalised and processed to smaller peptides, which are then expressed on the surface of B cells complexed with MHCII and presented to T cells. Once these complexes are recognised by T_H cells, they secrete cytokines and start expressing the CD40 ligand which interacts with CD40 on the B cells. The T–B interaction and the cytokines provide the stimulus for B cell activation.

T cell-independent antigens: Some antigens can directly stimulate antibody production by B cells, without the apparent participation of T cells. Such antigens are called **TI antigens**. These antigens react with BCRs of innate immunity. Most microbial sugars, lipids and certain nucleic acid are T cell-independent antigens. These are of two types: **type 1 antigens** (endotoxin, lipopolysaccharide [LPS]) are directly mitogenic for B cells and cause **polyclonal** B cell activation; **type 2 antigens** are polymeric compounds like polysaccharides (bacterial cell wall lipopolysaccharide or pneumococcal capsular polysaccharide) or proteins (flagellar proteins). They activate B cells to generate specific antibodies with the help of cytokines, and complement other cells like macrophages, dendritic cells, mast cells and NK cells. Some other differences are mentioned in Table 10.1.

Superantigens: Superantigens are certain protein molecules, such as staphylococcal enterotoxins, that activate very large numbers of T cells irrespective of their antigenic specificy. Superantigens bind outside the antibody binding groove directly to the lateral aspect of the TCR β chain, while conventional antigen fragments bind to the αβ heterodimer groove of the MHC molecules through the V regions of the TCR α and β chains (Fig. 10.2). Microbial superantigens are medium-sized proteins (MW 22–29 kDa) characterised by high resistance to proteases and to denaturation by CD4+ T cells. They cause the release of cytokines (IL-2) which results in massive proliferation of T lymphocytes. This ultimately leads to further release of a variety of cytokines which can have profound effects on the immune system. Some human diseases associated with superantigens are given in Table 10.2.

Table 10.1 *Comparison between T cell-dependent and T cell-independent antigens*

Property	T cell-dependent	T cell-independent
T cell involvement	Yes	No
Antigen interaction	Involves tertiary complex of T cell receptor, Ag, MHC molecule	Involves binary complex of membrane Ig and Ag
Antigen processing by macrophages	Yes	No
Chemical nature of antigen	Mostly soluble protein	Type 1: LPS; Type 2: polymeric proteins and polysaccharide
Degradability	Easily degradable	Type 2: poorly degradable
Complement activation	No	Type 2 Ag causes complement activation
Isotype switching	Yes	Type 1 : no; Type 2 : limited
Immunologic memory	Yes	No
Polyclonal activation	No	Type 1 : yes, Ag in high doses
Effect on antibody production	Full range, IgM, IgG, IgA and IgE	Limited to IgM and IgG3

Table 10.2 *Human diseases associated with superantigens*

Organism	Superantigen	Disease
Staphylococcus aureus	Enterotoxins	Food poisoning Toxic shock syndrome Multiple sclerosis
Group A streptococci	Pyrogenic exotoxins	Shock Psoriasis Rheumatic heart disease
Mycobacterium tuberculosis	Not identified	Tuberculosis
HIV	Nef (negative regulatory factor)	AIDS
Rabies virus	Nucleocapsid protein	Rabies
Epstein–Barr virus	Not identified	B cell lymphoma

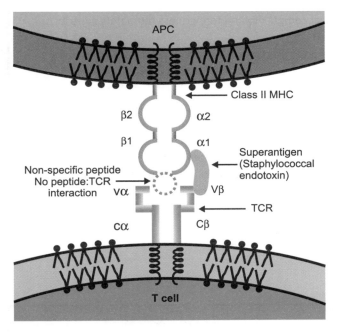

Fig. 10.2 Schematic diagram of a superantigen

Determinants recognised by the innate immune system

The receptors of the adaptive immune system recognise discrete determinants and demonstrate a high degree of specificity, enabling this system to recognise and react to a particular pathogen. In contrast, components of the innate immune system recognise unique molecular patterns which are shared by many related pathogens but not with their host. Hence, immunity has the property of pattern recognition. The broad molecular patterns are called **pathogen associated molecular patterns** or **PAMPs** and the receptors for PAMPs are called **pattern recognition receptors** or **PRRs**. A particular PRR can recognise a molecular pattern that may be present on a number of different pathogens, thereby, enabling the receptor to recognise a variety of different pathogens.

PRRs are divided into three classes:

- **Toll-like receptors (TLRs):** These are transmembrane receptors present on macrophages and dendritic cells. There are 13 different TLRs that recognise pathogens and enhance phagocytosis, and further lead to inflammation at the site.
- **Scavenger receptors:** These include CD-36, CD-68, and SRB-1. These can bind to bacterial cell wall components such as LPS, peptidoglyans as well as infected, injured or apoptotic cells and modified lipoproteins.
- **Mannose receptors:** These receptors on the surface of phagocytes bind mannose-rich glycans, which are the short carbohydrate chains with mannose or fucose as the terminal sugar, commonly found in microbial glycoproteins and glycolipids but rare in those of humans.

RECAP

- A substance that induces an immune response is called an antigen. If the antigen stimulates production of an antibody, it will react specifically, generally in an observable manner, with the antibody. Antigenicity refers to the ability of an antigen to induce an immune response.
- An immunogen is a substance that can induce an immune response but which does not necessarily bind to its specific antibody.
- A hapten is a small molecule which, by itself, is not immunogenic but which can form a complex with a large molecule to induce a specific immune response.
- Most antigens are foreign to the host. They are large molecules, such as proteins and polysaccharides. Small chemical groups on the antigen molecule, called epitopes, constitute the areas that are recognised by antibodies.
- Antigens having molecular properties like size, chemical complexity and foreignness ultimately contribute to activation of the immune system.
- T cell-independent antigens can directly stimulate antibody production by B cells, without the apparent participation of T cells, whereas T cell-dependent antigens require a co-stimulatory signal and cytokines from T_H cells.
- Superantigens are protein molecules that bind outside the antibody binding groove directly to the lateral aspect of the TCR β chain and activate very large numbers of T cells irrespective of their antigenic specificity.
- Toll-like receptors, scavenger receptors and mannose receptors are components of the innate immune system and recognise unique molecular patterns which are shared by many related pathogens but not with their host; hence, they recognise a variety of different pathogens/antigens.

ESSAY

1. Define antigen. Describe the various determinants of antigenicity.

SHORT ANSWERS

1. Differences between T-cell dependent and T-cell independent antigens
2. Factors responsible for the antigenicity of a molecule

SHORT NOTES

1. Haptens
2. Superantigens
3. Epitopes (linear and conformational)
4. Toll-like receptors
5. Mannose receptors

11 Antibodies— Immunoglobulins

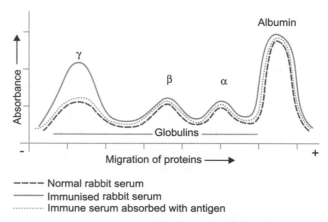

Fig. 11.1 Serum electrophoresis showing γ globulin nature of antibodies

INTRODUCTION

Antibodies are glycoprotein molecules that recognise a particular epitope on an antigen, bind specifically to it and finally facilitate the clearance of that antigen. They are present on the B cell membrane and are secreted by plasma cells. Secreted antibodies circulate in blood, where they eliminate/neutralise the antigen by their effector functions such as phagocytosis, antibody-dependent cell-mediated cytotoxicity (ADCC), opsonisation, etc.

Antibodies have unique structural features and motifs and bind to antigens to destroy them effectively. Sera having high antibody levels following infection or immunisation are called **immune sera**. Fractionation of immune sera by half saturation with ammonium sulphate separates the serum proteins into soluble albumins and insoluble globulins. Globulins can be separated into water soluble pseudoglobulins and insoluble euglobulins. Most antibodies have been found to be euglobulins.

Tiselius (1937) separated serum proteins into albumin and alpha, beta and gamma globulins based on their electrophoretic mobility (Fig. 11.1). Tiselius and Kabat (1938) showed that antibody activity was associ-ated with the gamma globulin fraction. Most antibodies are found in these gamma globulin fractions, and are hence named **immunoglobulins** (Ig).

In 1964, the WHO endorsed the generic term 'immunoglobulin' which was internationally accepted for 'proteins of animal origin endowed with known antibody activity and for certain other proteins related to them by chemical structure'. The definition includes, besides antibody globulins, the abnormal proteins found in myeloma, macroglobulinemia, cryoglobulinemia and the naturally occurring subunits of immunoglobulins. Immunoglobulins are synthesised by plasma cells and to some extent by lymphocytes. They provide a structural and chemical concept, while the term 'antibody' is a biological and functional concept. All antibodies are immunoglobulins, but all immunoglobulins may not be antibodies.

Immunoglobulins constitute 20–25 per cent of total serum proteins. Based on physicochemical and antigenic differences, five classes of immunoglobulins have been recognised: IgG, IgA, IgM, IgD and IgE.

ANTIBODY STRUCTURE

Enzyme digestion

Studies involving cleavage of the immunoglobulin molecule, pioneered by Porter, Edelman, Nisonoff and their colleagues, led to a detailed picture of its structure. Rabbit IgG antibody to egg albumin, digested by papain in the presence of cysteine, splits into two fractions: an insoluble fraction which crystallises in the cold (called *Fc* for **crystallisable**), and a soluble fragment which, while unable to precipitate with egg albumin, can still bind with it. This fragment is called the *Fab* (**antigen binding**) fragment. Each molecule of immunoglobulin is split by papain into three parts, one *Fc* and two *Fab* pieces, having a sedimentation co-efficient of 3.5 S. When treated with pepsin, a 5 S fragment is obtained, which is composed essentially of two *Fab* fragments held together in position. It is bivalent and precipitates with the antigen. This fragment is called *F(ab')$_2$*. The *Fc* portion is digested by pepsin into smaller fragments (Fig. 11.2a). Chemical treatment by mercaptoethanol cleaves the disulphide bonds to its four-subunit structure (Fig. 11.2b).

Immunoglobulin chains

Antibodies or immunoglobulins are glycoprotein molecules consisting of four polypeptide chains:

- Two identical **heavy (large) chains** (H), molecular weight >50 kDa
- Two identical **light (small) chains** (L), molecular weight >25 kDa
- The H chains are structurally and antigenically distinct for each class and are designated by the Greek letter corresponding to the immunoglobulin class.
- The heavy chains are of five types called **alpha** (α), **gamma** (γ), **delta** (δ), **epsilon** (ε) and **mu** (μ) (Table 11.1).
- The L chains are similar in all classes of immunoglobulins.

There are two types of light chains **kappa** (κ) and **lambda** (λ). They are named after Korngold and Lapari who originally described them. A molecule of immunoglobulin may have either kappa or lambda chains, but never both together. In humans, 60 per cent of L chains are kappa and 40 per cent are lambda. Each light chain is bound to a heavy chain by interchain and intrachain disulphide bonds (Fig. 11.3).

The antigen combining site of the molecule is at its amino-terminus. It is composed of both L an H chains. The first 110 amino acids from the N terminal are quite variable in amino acid sequence and this region is called the **variable region**: V$_L$, **variable light chain**; V$_H$, **variable heavy chain**. The sequence beyond the variable region in all antibodies is relatively constant throughout the rest of the molecule and is called the C **constant region**: C$_L$, **constant light chain**; C$_H$, **constant heavy chain**.

Table 11.1   *Immunoglobulin classes and H chains*

Immunoglobulin class	H chain
IgG	γ (gamma)
IgA	α (alpha)
IgM	μ (mu)
IgD	δ (delta)
IgE	ε (epsilon)

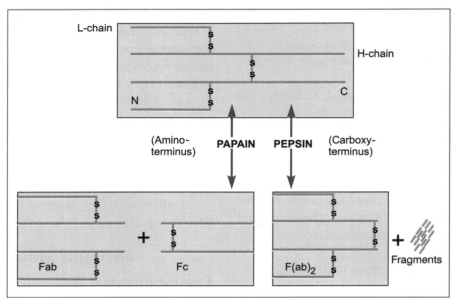

Fig. 11.2   (a) Basic structure of an immunoglobulin molecule and the fragments obtained by cleavage by papain and pepsin

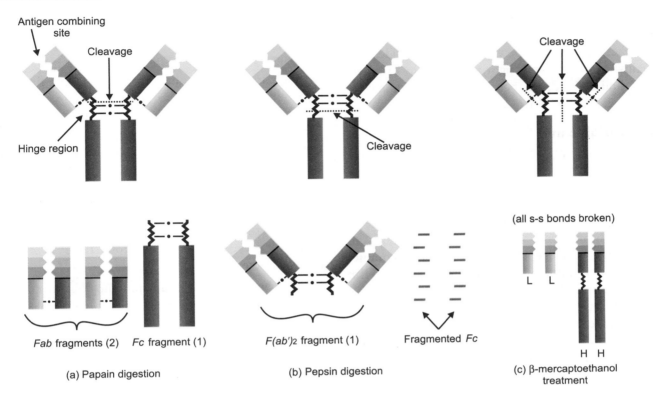

Fig. 11.2 (b) Cleavage of antibody molecule using papain, pepsin and mercaptoethanol

The carbohydrate moieties are linked to the constant region of the H chains. The *amino terminal* variable region of light and heavy chains participates in antigen recognition and the *carboxyl terminal* constant region of heavy chains mediates the effector functions.

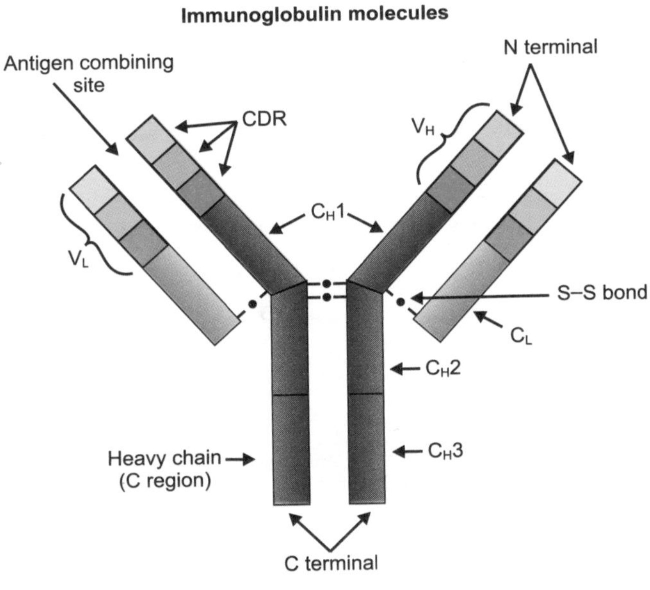

Immunoglobulin molecules

Fig. 11.3 Structure of immunoglobulin molecule

The C region of the light chains does not attach to the cell membrane and does not participate in its effector functions.

Immunoglobulin domains

The L and H chains contain several homologous units of about 110 amino acid residues. Within each unit, an intrachain disulphide bond forms a loop of 60 amino acids, called the domain. The light chain contains one variable domain V_L and one constant domain C_L. The heavy chain contains one variable domain V_H and three or four constant domains, depending on the Ig class: C_H1, C_H2, C_H3, C_H4. X-ray crystallographic analysis has revealed that Ig domains are folded into a characteristic compact structure, known as **immunoglobulin fold**. The structure of the Ig domain is a sandwich of two β-antiparallel pleated sheets stabilised by hydrophobic interactions between them and by disulfide bonds.

The variable and constant domains have a similar structure, except for some subtle differences. For example, the V domain is slightly longer than the C domain; it contains an extra pair of β strands and an extra loop sequence connecting this pair of β strands. The quaternary structure of the immunoglobulin is facilitated by non-covalent interactions between domains across the faces of the β strand.

Interactions occur between two non-identical domains of heavy and light chains; for example, V_H / V_L and C_H1 / C_L and between identical domains as C_H2 / C_H2, C_H3 / C_H3 or C_H4 / C_H4.

Hypervariable and framework regions

In the variable region of the H and L domains, maximum sequence variation is concentrated in a few discrete regions called **hypervariable (HV) regions**; the less variable stretches are termed **framework (FR) regions**. HV regions form the antigen binding site of the antibody molecule which are complementary to the structure of the epitope and are called **complementarity determining regions (CDRs)**. Each *Fab* fragment has six CDRs (three in H and three in L). The wide range of specificity exhibited by antibodies is a function of variations in the length and amino acid composition of six CDRs. The framework region acts as a scaffold support to six CDR loops in each *Fab* fragment. Crystallographic studies suggest that out of the six CDRs, only four mainly make contact with the antigen's epitope.

Constant region domains

C region domains are associated with various biological functions determined by the amino acid sequence of each domain. The presence of C_H1 and C_L domains appears to increase the number of stable V_H and V_L interactions possible, thus contributing to the overall diversity of the antibody molecule.

Hinge region

An extended amino acid sequence between the C_H1 and C_H2 domains is called the hinge region. It is rich in proline and cysteine amino acids and is more flexible. The number of disulphide bonds varies in different classes and subclasses of immunoglobins. The γ, δ and α heavy chains have hinge regions but the μ and ε chains lack it; thus they have an additional domain of 110 amino acids (C_H2/C_H2) with hinge-like features.

IMMUNOGLOBULIN CLASSES

Human sera contain IgG, IgA, IgM, IgD and IgE in descending order of concentration. Table 11.2 lists their characteristics.

IgG: This is the main serum immunoglobulin, constituting about 80 per cent of the total. It has a molecular weight of 150,000 (7 S). IgG may occasionally exist in a polymerised form. It is distributed approximately equally between the intravascular and extravascular compartments. It contains less carbohydrate than other immunoglobulins. It has a half-life of approximately 23 days. The catabolism of IgG is unique in that it varies with its serum concentration. When its level is raised, as in chronic malaria, kala azar or myeloma, the IgG synthesised against a particular antigen will be catabolised rapidly and may result in deficiency of the particular antibody. Conversely, in hypogammaglobulinemia, the IgG given for treatment will be catabolised slowly. The normal serum concentration of IgG is about 8–16 mg per ml.

Table 11.2 *Some properties of immunoglobulin classes*

	IgG	IgA*	IgM	IgD	IgE
Sedimentation co-efficient (S)	7	7	19	7	8
Molecular weight	150,000	160,000	900,000	180,000	190,000
Serum concentration (mg/ml)	12	2	1.2	0.03	0.00004
Half-life (days)	23	6	5	2–8	1–5
Daily production (mg/kg)	34	24	3.3	0.4	0.0023
Intravascular distribution (per cent)	45	42	80	75	50
Carbohydrate (per cent)	3	8	12	13	12
Complement fixation					
Classical	++	–	+++	–	–
Alternative	–	+	–	–	–
Placental transport	+	–	–	–	–
Present in milk	+	+	–	–	–
Selective secretion by					
seromucous glands	–	+	–	–	–
Heat stability (56°C)	+	+	+	+	–

* IgA may occur in 7 S, 9 S and 11 S forms.

IgG is the only maternal immunoglobulin that is normally transported across the placenta and provides natural passive immunity in the newborn. It is not synthesised by the fetus in any significant amount. IgG binds to microorganisms and enhances their phagocytosis. Extracellular killing of target cells coated with IgG antibody is mediated through recognition of the surface *Fc* fragment by K cells bearing the appropriate receptors. Interaction of IgG complexes with platelet *Fc* receptors probably leads to aggregation and vasoactive amine release.

IgG participates in most immunological reactions such as complement fixation, precipitation and neutralisation of toxins and viruses. It may be considered a general purpose antibody, protective against infectious agents active in blood and tissues. Passively administered IgG suppresses homologous antibody synthesis by a feedback process. This property is utilised in the isoimmunisation of women by the administration of anti-Rh(D) IgG during delivery. With most antigens, IgG is a late antibody and makes its appearance after the initial immune response, which is IgM in nature.

It has four **subclasses**: IgG_1, IgG_2, IgG_3 and IgG_4, due to the presence of $\gamma 1$, $\gamma 2$, $\gamma 3$ or $\gamma 4$ H chains. Subtle differences are seen in the sequence of their constant regions. The subclasses differ from one another in the size of the hinge region and the number and position of the interchain disulphide bonds between the heavy chains. All four IgG subclasses are distributed in human serum in the approximate proportions of 65 per cent, 23 per cent, 8 per cent and 4 per cent, respectively.

IgA: IgA is the second most abundant class, constituting about 10–13 per cent of serum immunoglobulins. The normal serum level is 0.6–4.2 mg per ml. It has a half-life of 6–8 days. It is the major immunoglobulin in the colostrum, saliva and tears.

IgA occurs in two forms. **Serum IgA** is principally a monomeric 7 S molecule (MW about 160,000). IgA found on mucosal surfaces and in secretions is a dimer formed by two monomer units joined together at their carboxyterminals by a glycopeptide termed the **J chain** (J for joining). This is called **secretory IgA** (SIgA). **Dimeric SIgA** is synthesised by plasma cells situated near the mucosal or glandular epithelium. The J chain is also produced in the same cells. J chains are also present in other polymeric immunoglobulins such as IgM. The schematic diagrams of all four classes are given in Fig. 11.4.

SIgA contains another glycine-rich polypeptide called the **secretory component** or **secretory piece**. This is not produced by lymphoid cells but by mucosal or glandular epithelial cells. Dimeric IgA binds to a receptor on the surface of the epithelial cells and is endocytosed and transported across the cells to the luminal surface. During this process, a part of the receptor remains attached to the IgA dimer. This part is known as the secretory component. The secretory piece is believed to protect IgA from denaturation by bacterial proteases in sites such as the intestinal mucosa which have rich and varied bacterial flora. SIgA is a much larger molecule than serum IgA (11 S; MW about 400,000).

SIgA is selectively concentrated in secretions and on mucus surfaces forming an 'antibody paste' and is believed to play an important role in local immunity against respiratory and intestinal pathogens. Secretory IgA is relatively resistant to digestive enzymes and reducing agents. IgA antibodies may function by inhibiting the adherence of microorganisms to the surface of mucosal cells by covering the organisms and thereby preventing their entry into body tissues. This is done by cross-linking the multivalent antigen with polymeric IgA, and finally the pathogen is elimi-

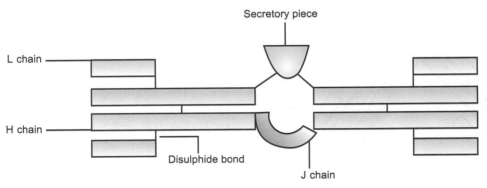

Fig. 11.4 Secretory IgA molecule

nated. Secretory IgA provides an important defense mechanism against bacteria such as salmonella, vibrio cholera and viruses such as polio, influenza, etc. Breast milk rich in IgA helps protect the newborn against infection during the first month of life. IgA does not fix complement but can activate the alternative complement pathway. It promotes phagocytosis and intracellular killing of microorganisms.

Two **IgA subclasses** have been described: **IgA$_1$** and **IgA$_2$**. IgA$_2$ lacks interchain disulphide bonds between the heavy and light chains. Though IgA$_2$ is a minor component of serum IgA, it is the dominant form in the secretions.

IgM: IgM constitutes 5–8 per cent of serum immunoglobulins, with a normal level of 0.5–2 mg per ml. It has a half-life of about five days. It is a heavy molecule (19 S; MW 900,000 to 1,000,000, hence called 'the millionaire molecule'). IgM molecules are polymers of five four-peptide subunits, each bearing an extra C_H domain. As with IgA, polymerisation of the subunits depends on the presence of the J chain. Though the theoretical valency is 10, this is observed only with small haptens. With larger antigens, the effective valency falls to five, probably due to steric hindrance (Fig. 11.5).

Most of IgM (80 per cent) is intravascular in distribution. Phylogenetically, IgM is the oldest immunoglobulin class. It is also the earliest immunoglobulin to be synthesised by the fetus, beginning by about 20 weeks of age. As it is not transported across the

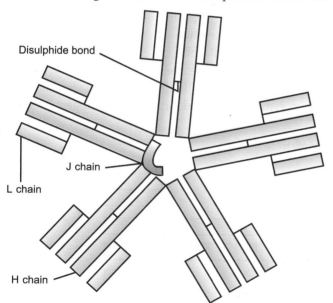

Fig. 11.5 IgM molecule

Disulphide bond

J chain

L chain

H chain

placenta, the presence of IgM in the fetus or newborn indicates intrauterine infection and its detection is useful in the diagnosis of congenital infections such as syphilis, rubella, HIV infection and toxoplasmosis.

IgM antibodies are relatively short-lived, disappearing earlier than IgG. Hence, their demonstration in serum indicates recent infection. Treatment of serum with 0.12 M 2-mercaptoethanol selectively destroys IgM without affecting IgG antibodies. This is a simple method for the differential estimation of IgG and IgM antibodies.

The isohemagglutinins (anti-A, anti-B) and many other natural antibodies to microorganisms are usually IgM, as also antibodies to the typhoid 'O' antigen (endotoxin) and reagin antibodies in syphilis.

The unique structural features of IgM appear particularly suited to the biological role of providing protection against microorganisms and other large antigens that have repeating antigenic determinants on their surface. A single molecule of IgM can bring about immune hemolysis, whereas 1000 IgG molecules are required for the same effect. IgM is also 500–1000 times more effective than IgG in opsonisation, 100 times more effective in bactericidal action and about 20 times in bacterial agglutination. In the neutralisation of toxins and viruses, however, it is less active than IgG. Being largely confined to the intravascular space, IgM is believed to be responsible for protection against blood invasion by microorganisms. IgM deficiency is often associated with septicemias.

Monomeric IgM is the major antibody receptor on the surface of B lymphocytes for antigen recognition.

IgD: IgD resembles IgG structurally. It is present in a concentration of about 3 mg per 100 ml of serum and is mostly intravascular. It has a half-life of about three days. IgD and IgM occur on the surface of unstimulated B lymphocytes and serve as recognition receptors for antigens. Combination of cell membrane–bound IgD or IgM with the corresponding antigen leads to specific stimulation of the B cell—either activation and cloning to produce antibody, or suppression.

IgE: This immunoglobulin was discovered in 1966 by Ishizaka during an investigation of atopic reagin antibodies. It is an 8 S molecule (MW about 190,000), with a half-life of about two days. It resembles IgG structurally. It exhibits unique properties such as heat lability (inactivated at 56°C in one hour) and affinity for the surface of tissue cells (particularly mast cells) of the same species (homocytotropism). It mediates the Prausnitz-Kustner reaction. It is susceptible to mercaptoethanol. It does not pass the placental barrier or fix complement. It is mostly extravascular in distribution. Normal serum contains only traces (a few nanograms per ml) but greatly elevated levels are seen in atopic (type 1 allergic) conditions such as asthma, hay fever and eczema. Children living in insanitary conditions, with a high load of intestinal parasites, have high serum levels of IgE.

IgE is chiefly produced in the linings of the respiratory and intestinal tracts. IgE deficiency has been associated with IgA deficiency in individuals with impaired immunity who present undue susceptibility to infection. IgE is responsible for the anaphylactic type of hypersensitivity. The physiological role of IgE appears to be protection against pathogens by mast cell degranulation and release of inflammatory mediators. It is also believed to have a special role in defence against helminthic infections.

In general, IgG protects the body fluids, IgA the body surfaces and IgM the bloodstream, while IgE mediates reaginic hypersensitivity. IgD is a recognition molecule on the surface of B lymphocytes.

ABNORMAL IMMUNOGLOBULINS

Apart from antibodies, other structurally similar proteins are seen in serum in many pathological processes:

- **Multiple myeloma:** The earliest description of an abnormal immunoglobulin was the discovery by Bence Jones (1847) of the protein that bears his name. The **Bence Jones protein** is typically found in multiple myeloma. It can be identified in urine by its characteristic property of coagulation when heated to 50°C but redissolving at 70°C. Bence Jones proteins are the light chains of immunoglobulins and so may occur as the **kappa** or **lambda** forms. But in any one patient, the chain is either kappa or lambda only, and never both, being uniform in all other respects. This is because myeloma is a plasma cell dyscrasia in which there is unchecked proliferation of one clone of plasma cells, resulting in excessive production of the particular immunoglobulin synthesised by the clone. Such immunoglobulins are, therefore, called **monoclonal**.

Multiple myeloma may affect plasma cells synthesising IgG, IgA, IgD or IgE. Similar involvement of IgM producing cells is known as **Waldenstrom's** **macroglobulinemia**. In this condition, there is excessive production of the respective myeloma proteins (M proteins) and of their light chains (Bence Jones proteins).

- **Heavy chain disease** is a form of paraproteinemia causing lymphoid neoplasia and characterised by the overproduction of the *Fc* parts of the immunoglobulin heavy chains. Three types of heavy chain disease (HCD) are recognised, based upon the class of immunoglobulin heavy chain produced (alpha, gamma, mu) by the malignant cell.

- **Cryoglobulinemia** is a condition in which a gel or precipitate is formed on cooling the serum, which redissolves on warming. It may not always be associated with disease but is often found in myelomas, macroglobulinemias and autoimmune conditions such as systemic lupus erythematosus. Most cryoglobulins consist of IgG, IgM or their mixed precipitates.

Because of the monoclonal nature of Bence Jones and other M proteins, they have been valuable models for the understanding of immunoglobulin structure and function.

Immunoglobulin specificities

Immunoglobulin specificity is of the greatest biological importance in immunology. The antigenic determinants, or epitopes, on immunoglobulin molecules fall into three main categories and are located in characteristic portions of the molecule (Fig. 11.6):

Isotype: Isotypic determinants refer to the genetic variations or differences in the constant region of the heavy chain of the Ig classes and subclasses within a species. Each isotype is encoded by a separate constant region gene, and all members of a species carry the same constant region genes. Within a species, each normal individual will express all isotypes in the serum. Different species inherit different constant region genes and therefore express different isotypes. When an antibody from one species is injected into another, the isotypic determinants will be recognised as foreign, inducing an antibody response to the isotypic determinants.

Allotype: Allotypic determinants refer to multiple alleles that exist for some of the genes and which lead to subtle amino acid differences that occur in some, but not all, members of a species. The sum of the individual allotypic determinants displayed by an antibody

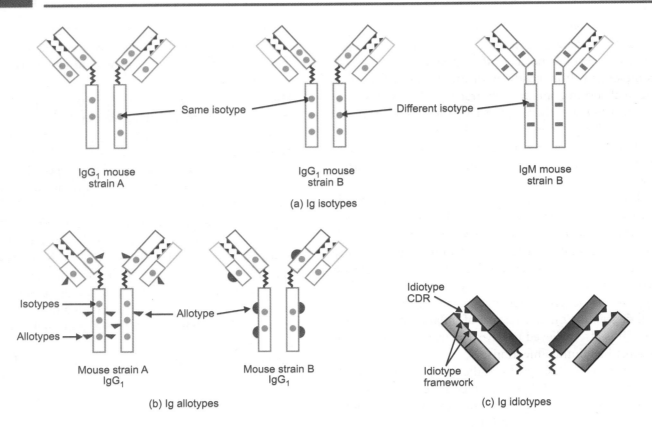

Fig. 11.6 Isotypes, allotypes and idiotypes of antibodies

determines its allotype. In humans, allotypes have been characterised for all four IgG subclasses, for one IgA subclass, and for the kappa light chain. Each of these allotypic determinants represents differences in one to four amino acids that are encoded by different alleles. Antibody to allotypic determinants can be produced by injecting antibodies from one member of a species into another member of the same species who carries different allotypic determinants. Antibody to allotypic determinants is sometimes produced by a mother during pregnancy in response to paternal allotypic determinants on the fetal immunoglobulins. Antibodies to allotypic determinants can also arise from a blood transfusion. To date in the human system, no allotypic markers have been found for γ light chains or μ, δ or ε heavy chains.

Idiotype: Idiotypic determinants arise from the sequence of the heavy and light chain variable regions. Each individual antigenic determinant of the variable region (paratope) is referred to as an idiotope. The sum total of idiotopes on an Ig molecule constitutes its idiotype. An idiotope may be the actual antigen binding site or variable region sequences outside of the antigen binding site. By immunisation with *Fab* fragments, anti-idiotypic antibodies can be produced. These resemble the epitopes of the original antigen. Used as a vaccine, these show protection against the original antigen (pathogen or tumour) in experimental animals. Sequential anti-idiotypic antibody formation is the basis of Jerne's network hypothesis of immune regulation.

ANTIBODY DIVERSITY

One of the important structure–function relationships to antigen recognition is antibody diversity. An individual is capable of making an enormous number of structurally distinct antibodies, each with distinct specificity. The presence of a large number of antibodies that bind different antigens/pathogens is called **antibody diversity**, and the total collection of antibodies with different specificities is called the **antibody repertoire**. This diversity is mainly of genetic origin, where the recombination of different gene segments plays an important role. The genetic mechanisms that can generate such large antibody repertoire occur exclusively in lymphocytes.

Clinical significance

Knowledge of immunoglobulin genes has made it possible to develop engineered antibodies for therapeutic purposes to treat various lymphomas and autoimmune diseases. In human immunodeficiency virus (HIV), the genetic variation and mutability of the virus has created a plethora of constantly changing antigens which generate diverse immune responses. This poses a major challenge in developing an HIV vaccine.

CLASS SWITCHING

On antigen stimulation, the H-chain VDJ unit can join any constant heavy gene segment and express the particular antibody class. This process is called class switching. The exact mechanism is unclear but evidence suggests that the DNA flanking regions/sequences are located 2–3 kb upstream of each constant H-chain gene segment (C_H), except C_δ. These are called switch sites (SS) and are composed of multiple copies of short repeated sequences (GAGCT and TGGGG). Class-specific recombinases bind to switch sites and facilitate recombination. Therefore, the expression of a particular antibody class depends on the specificity of the recombinase proteins expressed.

Class switching depends on the interplay of three factors:

- Switch regions/sites
- Switch recombinase
- Cytokine signals (IL-4)

Clinical significance

Immunoglobulin class switch recombination deficiencies (Ig CSR deficiencies) or hyper IgM syndromes (HIGM) are a group of primary immunodeficiency diseases characterised by defective CD40 signalling of B cells. Affected patients are characterised by low serum levels of IgG and IgA, and normal or elevated levels of IgM, which lead to increased susceptibility to infections such as frequent bacterial infections of the skin and respiratory tract, mucosal ulcers and diarrhea.

RECAP

- An antibody (immunoglobulin) is a glycoprotein molecule formed by the immune system in response to an antigenic stimulus; is found in blood, bodily secretions or on mucous surfaces, and binds to the specific antigen responsible for its production, thereby inactivating it.
- There are five classes of immunoglobulins: IgG, IgM, IgA, IgD and IgE; antibodies of all five classes can combine specifically with antigens.
- IgG constitutes 80–85 per cent of total antibody; it can cross the placenta, fix complement and specifically attach to phagocytes. It provides protection within the body, causes lysis or removal of foreign antigens and neutralises viruses and toxins.
- IgM constitutes 9–10 per cent of total antibody. It fixes complement but is unable to cross the placenta or attach to phagocytes. It provides protection within the body and is especially effective in agglutinating antigens and in inactivating complement.
- IgA constitutes about 10 per cent of total antibody. It is secreted into external secretions (saliva, milk, mucus) and guards mucosal surfaces.
- IgD constitutes 1–3 per cent of total antibody. It serves as an antigen receptor on B lymphocytes, and promotes the development and maturation of the antibody response.
- IgE constitutes just 0.05 per cent of total antibody. It specifically attaches to mast cells and basophils, and is involved in Type I hypersensitivity (allergic and atopic) reactions.

- Abnormal immunoglobulins include Bence Jones proteins in multiple myeloma, overproduction of the *Fc* parts of the immunoglobulin heavy chains in heavy chain disease and cryoglobulins consisting of IgG, IgM or their mixed precipitates in cryoglobulinemia.
- Isotypic (genetic variations or differences in the constant region of the heavy chain), allotypic (multiple alleles exist for some of the genes) and idiotypic (sequence of the heavy and light chain variable regions) antigenic determinants are located on immunoglobulin molecules and play an important role in antibody specificity.
- The presence of a large number of antibodies that bind different antigens/pathogens is called antibody diversity.
- On antigen stimulation, the H-chain VDJ unit can join any constant heavy gene segment and express the particular antibody class. This process is called class switching.

ESSAYS

1. Define antibody. Draw a labelled diagram of an immunoglobulin with its different domains.
2. Describe the various classes of immunoglobulins, their properties and functions.

SHORT ANSWERS

1. The effect of enzymatic (papain and pepsin) digestion on immunoglobulin molecule
2. Structure of the IgM molecule
3. Structure of the IgG molecule
4. Structure of IgA with diagram
5. Abnormal immunoglobulins

SHORT NOTE

1. Isotypes

12 Antigen–Antibody Reactions

INTRODUCTION

Antigens and antibodies, by definition, combine with each other specifically and in an observable manner.

Uses: The **reactions** between antigens and antibodies serve several purposes:

- In the body, they form the basis of antibody-mediated immunity in infectious diseases, or of tissue injury in some types of hypersensitivity and autoimmune diseases.
- In the laboratory, they help in the diagnosis of infections.
- In epidemiological surveys, they assist in the identification of infectious agents and non-infectious antigens such as enzymes and in screening the population for a particular infection.
- In general, these reactions can be used for the detection and quantitation of either antigens or antibodies.

Antigen–antibody reactions in vitro are known as **serological reactions**.

Stages

The reactions between antigens and antibodies occur in three stages:

- **Primary stage:** This is the initial interaction between antigens and antibodies, without any visible effects. This reaction is rapid, occurs even at low temperatures and obeys the general laws of physical chemistry and thermodynamics. The reaction is reversible, the combination between antigen and antibody molecules being affected by weaker intermolecular forces such as Van der Waal's forces, ionic bonds and hydrogen bonding, rather than by the firmer covalent bonding. The primary reaction can be detected by estimating free and bound antigens or antibodies separately in the reaction mixture by a number of physical and chemical methods, including the use of markers such as radioactive isotopes, fluorescent dyes or ferritin.
- **Secondary stage:** In most, but not all, instances, the primary stage is followed by the secondary stage, leading to demonstrable events such as precipitation, agglutination, lysis of cells, killing of live antigens, neutralisation of toxins and other biologically active antigens, fixation of complement, immobilisation of motile organisms and enhancement of phagocytosis. When such reactions were discovered one by one, it was believed that a different type of antibody was responsible for each type of reaction, and the antibodies came to be designated by the reactions they were thought to produce. Thus, the antibody causing agglutination was called **agglutinin,** that causing precipitation **precipitin,** and so on, and the corresponding antigen, **agglutinogen**, **precipitinogen**, and so on. It is true that a single antibody can cause

precipitation, agglutination and most of the other serological reactions and an antigen can stimulate the production of different classes of immunoglobulins which differ in their reaction capacities as well as in other properties (Table 12.1).

- **Tertiary stage**: Some antigen–antibody reactions occurring in vivo initiate chain reactions that lead to neutralisation or destruction of injurious antigens, or to tissue damage. These are tertiary reactions and include humoral immunity against infectious diseases as well as clinical allergy and other immunological diseases.

General features of antigen–antibody reactions

1. The reaction is specific, an antigen combining only with its homologous antibody and vice versa. The specificity, however, is not absolute and 'cross-reactions' may occur due to antigenic similarity or relatedness.
2. Entire molecules, and not fragments, react. When an antigenic determinant present in a large molecule or on a 'carrier' particle reacts with its antibody, whole molecules or particles are agglutinated.
3. There is no denaturation of the antigen or the antibody during the reaction.
4. The combination occurs at the surface. Therefore, it is the surface antigens that are immunologically relevant. Antibodies to the surface antigens of infectious agents are generally protective.
5. The combination is firm but reversible. The firmness of the union is influenced by the affinity and avidity of the reaction:
   - **Affinity** refers to the intensity of attraction between the antigen and antibody molecules. It is a function of the closeness of fit between an epitope and the antigen-combining region of its antibody (paratope). Affinity is a quantitative measure of binding strength between an antibody and an epitope. Low-affinity antibodies bind antigens weakly and tend to dissociate readily,

whereas high-affinity antibodies bind antigens more tightly and remain bound longer.
   - **Avidity** is the strength of the bond after the formation of the antigen–antibody complexes and is a better measure of its binding capacity within biological systems (for example, the reaction of an antibody with antigenic determinants on a virus or bacterial cell) than the affinity of its individual binding sites. Secreted pentameric IgM often has lower affinity than IgG, but the high avidity of IgM, resulting from its higher valence, enables it to bind antigens effectively.
6. Both antigens and antibodies participate in the formation of agglutinates or precipitates.
7. Antigens and antibodies can combine in varying proportions, unlike chemicals with fixed valencies. Both antigens and antibodies are multivalent. Antibodies are generally bivalent, though IgM molecules may have five or ten combining sites. Antigens may have valencies up to the hundreds.

Measurement of antigen and antibody

Many methods are available for the measurement of the antigens and antibodies participating in the primary, secondary and tertiary reactions. Measurement may be in terms of mass (for example, mg nitrogen) or more commonly as units or titre. The **antibody titre** of a serum is the highest dilution of the serum that shows an observable reaction with the antigen in the particular test. The titre of a serum is influenced by the nature and quantity of the antigen and the type and conditions of the test. Antigens may also be titrated against sera.

Two important parameters of serological tests are sensitivity and specificity:
- **Sensitivity** refers to the ability of the test to detect even very minute quantities of antigen or antibody. When a test is highly sensitive, false negative results will be absent or minimal.
- **Specificity** refers to the ability of the test to detect reactions between homologous antigens and antibodies only, and with no other. In a highly specific test, false positive reactions are absent or minimal.

In general, the sensitivity and specificity of a test are in inverse proportion.

Originally, reagents for serological tests were prepared by individual laboratories, leading to batch variation, and lack of reproducibility and comparability. The commercial availability of readymade standardised test

Table 12.1 *Comparative efficiency of the immunoglobulin classes in different serological reactions*

Reaction	IgG	IgM	IgA
Precipitation	Strong	Weak	Variable
Agglutination	Weak	Strong	Moderate
Complement fixation	Strong	Weak	Negative
Lysis	Weak	Strong	Negative

kits has simplified test procedures, improved quality and greatly enlarged their scope and use.

SEROLOGICAL REACTIONS

PRECIPITATION REACTION

Precipitation: When a soluble antigen combines with its antibody in the presence of electrolytes (NaCl) at a suitable temperature and pH, the antigen–antibody complex forms an insoluble precipitate.

Flocculation: When, instead of sedimenting, the precipitate remains suspended as floccules, the reaction is known as **flocculation**. Precipitation can take place in liquid media or in gels such as agar, agarose or polyacrylamide.

Phases: The amount of precipitate formed is greatly influenced by the relative proportions of antigens and antibodies. If increasing quantities of antigens are added to the same amount of antiserum in different tubes, precipitation will be found to occur most rapidly and abundantly in one of the middle tubes in which the antigen and antibody are present in optimal or equivalent proportions. In the preceding tubes in which the antibody is in excess and in the later tubes in which the antigen is in excess, the precipitation will be weak or even absent. For a given antigen–antibody system, the optimal or equivalent ratio will be constant, irrespective of the quantity of the reactants. If the amounts of precipitate in the different tubes are plotted on a graph, the resulting curve will have three phases:

1. **Prozone phenomenon:** This is caused by excess antibody in the test system. Failure of a visible reaction is due to inhibition of lattice formation by the excess antibody.
2. **Zone of equivalence:** Here, the antigen and antibody are in optimum proportions. Lattice formation and visible reactions are enhanced.
3. **Post-zone phenomenon:** This is caused by the presence of excess antigen in the test system. No visible reaction will occur.

The prozone and post-zone phenomena may be corrected by making serial dilutions of serum, thereby reducing the concentration of antigen or antibody in the test serum, and optimising the concentrations of antigen and antibody.

Zoning occurs in agglutination and some other serological reactions. The prozone is of importance in clinical serology, as sera rich in antibody may sometimes give a false negative precipitation or agglutination result, unless several dilutions are tested.

Mechanism of precipitation

Marrack (1934) proposed the lattice hypothesis to explain the mechanism of precipitation. According to this concept, which is supported by considerable experimental evidence and is now widely accepted, multivalent antigens combine with bivalent antibodies in varying proportions, depending on the antigen–antibody ratio in the reacting mixture. Precipitation results when a large lattice is formed consisting of alternating antigen and antibody molecules. This is possible only in the zone of equivalence. In the zones of antigen or antibody excess, the lattice does not enlarge, as the valencies of the antibody and the antigen, respectively, are fully satisfied (Fig. 12.1). The lattice hypothesis holds good for agglutination also.

Applications

The precipitation test may be carried out as a qualitative or quantitative test. It is sensitive in the detection of antigens and as little as 1 μg of protein can be detected. It is relatively less sensitive for the detection of antibodies. Precipitation tests have several applications:
- Forensic application in the identification of blood and seminal stains
- Testing for food adulterants
- Grouping of streptococci by the Lancefield technique
- The VDRL test for syphilis
- To standardise toxins and toxoids
- To test toxigenicity in diphtheria bacilli

The following types of precipitation and flocculation tests are in common use:

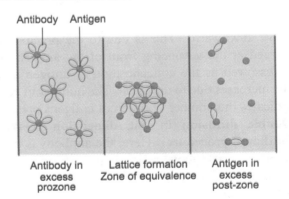

Fig. 12.1 Lattice hypothesis

Ring test: This, the simplest type of precipitation test, consists of layering the antigen solution over a column of antiserum in a narrow tube. A precipitate forms at the junction of the two liquids. Ring tests have only a few clinical applications now. Examples are Ascoli's thermoprecipitin test and the grouping of streptococci by the Lancefield technique.

Slide test: When a drop each of the antigen and the antiserum are placed on a slide and mixed by shaking, floccules appear. The VDRL test for syphilis is an example of slide flocculation.

Tube test: The Kahn test for syphilis is an example of a tube flocculation test. A quantitative tube flocculation test is used for the standardisation of toxins and toxoids. Serial dilutions of the toxin/toxoid are added to the tubes containing a fixed quantity of the antitoxin. The amount of toxin or toxoid that flocculates optimally with one unit of the antitoxin is defined as an Lf dose.

Immunodiffusion (precipitation in gel): There are several advantages in allowing precipitation to occur in a gel rather than in a liquid medium. The reaction is visible as a distinct band of precipitation, which is stable and can be stained for preservation, if necessary. As each antigen–antibody reaction gives rise to a line of precipitation, the number of different antigens in the reacting mixture can be readily observed. Immunodiffusion also indicates identity, cross-reaction and non-identity between different antigens. Immunodiffusion is usually performed in a soft (1%) agar or agarose gel.

Modifications of the immunodiffusion test:

1. **Single diffusion in one dimension (Oudin procedure):** The antibody is incorporated in agar gel in a test tube and the antigen solution is layered over it. The antigen diffuses downward through the agar gel, forming a line of precipitation that appears to move downwards. This is due to the precipitation formed at the advancing front of the antigen, and is dissolved as the concentration of antigen at the site increases due to diffusion. The number of bands indicates the number of different antigens present.

2. **Double diffusion in one dimension (Oakley–Fulthorpe procedure):** Here, the antibody is incorporated in gel, above which is placed a column of plain agar. The antigen is layered on top of this. The antigen and antibody move towards each other through the intervening column of plain agar and

form a band of precipitate where they meet at optimum proportion (Fig. 12.2a).

3. **Single diffusion in two dimensions (Radial immunodiffusion):** Here, the antiserum is incorporated in agar gel poured on a flat surface (slide or petri dish). The antigen is added to the wells cut on the surface of the gel. It diffuses radially from the well and forms ring-shaped bands of precipitation (halos) concentrically around the well. The diameter of the halo gives an estimate of the concentration of the antigen. This method has been used for the estimation of the immunoglobulin classes in sera and for screening sera for antibodies to influenza viruses, among others (Fig. 12.2b).

4. **Double diffusion in two dimensions (Ouchterlony procedure):** This method is most widely employed and helps to compare different antigens and antisera directly. Agar gel is poured on a slide and wells are cut using a template. The antiserum is placed in the central well, and different antigens in the surrounding wells. If two adjacent antigens are identical, the lines of precipitate formed by them will fuse. If they are unrelated, the lines will cross each other. Cross-reaction or partial identity is indicated by spur formation. A special variety of double diffusion in two dimensions is the Elek test for toxigenicity in diphtheria bacilli. When diphtheria bacilli are streaked at right angles to a filter paper strip carrying the antitoxin implanted on a plate of suitable medium, arrowhead-shaped lines of precipitation appear on incubation, if the bacillus is toxigenic (Fig. 12.2c).

6. **Immunoelectrophoresis:** The resolving power of immunodiffusion was greatly enhanced when Grabar and Williams devised the technique of immunoelectrophoresis. This involves the electrophoretic separation of a composite antigen (such as serum) into its constituent proteins, followed by immunodiffusion against its antiserum, resulting in separate precipitin lines, indicating reaction between each individual protein with its antibody. This enables identification and approximate quantitation of the various proteins present in the serum. The technique is performed on agar or agarose gel on a slide, with an antigen well and an antibody trough cut on it. The test serum is placed in the antigen well and electrophoresed for about an hour. Antibody against human serum is then placed in the trough and diffusion allowed to proceed for 18–24 hours. The resulting precipitin lines can be photographed and

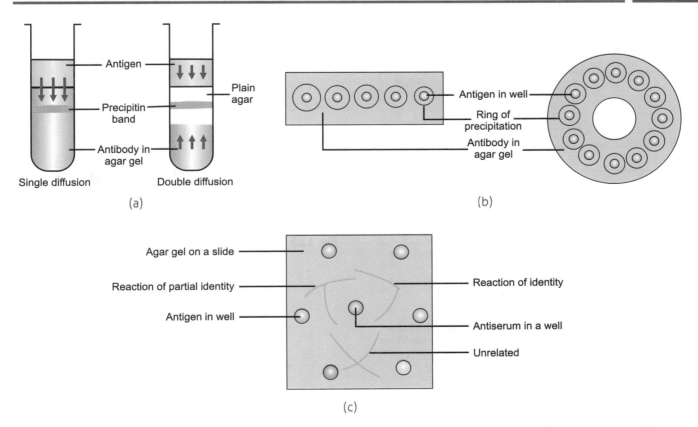

Fig. 12.2 (a) Single and double diffusion in one dimension; (b) Single diffusion in two dimensions; (c) Double diffusion in two dimensions

the slides dried, stained and preserved for record. Over 30 different proteins can be identified by this method in human serum. This is useful for testing for normal and abnormal proteins in serum and urine (Fig. 12.3).

Electroimmunodiffusion: The development of precipitin lines can be speeded up by electrically driving the antigen and antibody with diffusion using various methods in the clinical laboratory as given below.

- **Counterimmunoelectrophoresis (CIE, counter-current immunoelectrophoresis):** This involves simultaneous electrophoresis of the antigen and antibody in gel in opposite directions, resulting in precipitation at a point between them (Fig. 12.4). This method produces visible precipitation lines within 30 minutes and is ten times more sensitive than the standard double diffusion techniques. The clinical applications comprise detecting various antigens such as alpha fetoprotein in serum and specific antigens of cryptococcus and meningococcus in cerebrospinal fluid.

- **One-dimensional single electroimmunodiffusion (rocket electrophoresis):** The main application of this technique is for quantitative estimation of antigens. The antiserum to the antigen to be quantitated is incorporated in agarose and gelled on the glass slide. The antigen, in increasing concentrations, is placed in wells punched in the set gel. The antigen is then electrophoresed into the antibody containing agarose (Fig. 12.5). The pattern of immunoprecipitation resembles a rocket (hence, the name).

- **Two-dimensional electrophoresis:** In Laurell's two-dimensional electrophoresis, the antigen mixture is first electrophoretically separated in a direction perpendicular to that of the final rocket stage. By this method, one can quantitate each of several antigens in a mixture (Fig. 12.6).

AGGLUTINATION REACTION

When a particulate antigen is mixed with its antibody in the presence of electrolytes at a suitable temperature and pH, the particles are clumped or agglutinated.

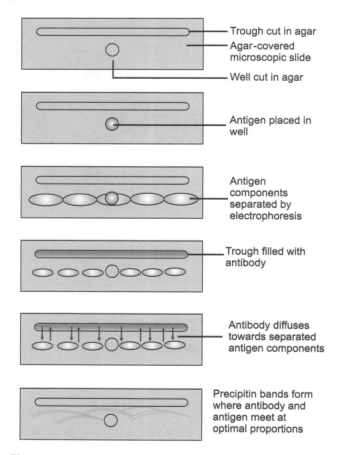

Fig. 12.3   Immunoelectrophoresis

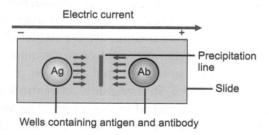

Fig. 12.4   Counterimmunoelectrophoresis

Agglutination is more sensitive than precipitation for the detection of antibodies. The same principles govern agglutination and precipitation. Agglutination occurs optimally when antigens and antibodies react in equivalent proportions. The zone phenomenon may be seen when either an antibody or an antigen is in excess. 'Incomplete' or 'monovalent' antibodies do not cause agglutination, though they combine with the antigen. They may act as 'blocking' antibodies, inhibiting agglutination by the complete antibody added subsequently.

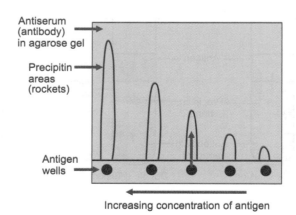

Fig. 12.5   Rocket electrophoresis

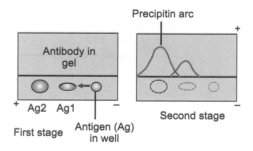

Fig. 12.6   Laurell's two-dimensional electrophoresis

Slide agglutination:

Procedure:

1. When a drop of the appropriate antiserum is added to a smooth, uniform suspension of a particulate antigen in a drop of saline on a slide or tile, agglutination takes place.
2. A positive result is indicated by the clumping together of the particles and the clearing of the drop.
3. The reaction is facilitated by mixing the antigen and the antiserum with a loop or by gently rocking the slide. Depending on the titre of the serum, agglutination may occur instantly or within seconds.
4. Clumping occurring after a minute may be due to drying of the fluid and should be disregarded.
5. It is essential to have on the same slide a control consisting of the antigen suspension in saline, without the antiserum, to ensure that the antigen is not autoagglutinable. Agglutination is usually visible to the unaided eye but may sometimes require confirmation under the microscope.

Uses:

- It is a routine procedure for the identification of many bacterial isolates from clinical specimens.

• It is also the method used for blood grouping and cross-matching.

Tube agglutination: This is a standard quantitative method for the measurement of antibodies. When a fixed volume of a particulate antigen suspension is added to an equal volume of serial dilutions of an antiserum in test tubes, the agglutination titre of the serum can be estimated.

Uses: It is routinely used for the serological diagnosis of typhoid, brucellosis and typhus fever. In the Widal test used in typhoid, two types of antigens are used. The 'H' or flagellar antigen on combining with its antibody forms large, loose, fluffy clumps resembling wisps of cotton wool. The 'O' or somatic antigen forms tight, compact deposits resembling chalk powder. Agglutinated bacilli spread out in a disc-like pattern at the bottom of the tubes.

Complications: The tube agglutination test for brucellosis may be complicated by the **prozone phenomenon.** Several dilutions of the serum should be tested to prevent false negative results due to the prozone of **'blocking' antibodies.** Incomplete or blocking antibodies may be detected by doing the test in hypertonic (5%) saline or albumin saline, or more reliably by the antiglobulin (Coombs) test.

Heterophile agglutination test:
• The **Weil–Felix reaction** for serodiagnosis of typhus fevers is a heterophile agglutination test and is based on the sharing of a common antigen between typhus rickettsiae and some strains of proteus bacilli.
• The *Streptococcus* **MG agglutination test** for the diagnosis of primary atypical pneumonia.
• Examples of agglutination tests using red cells as antigens are the **Paul–Bunnell test** and the cold agglutination test. The former is based on the presence of sheep cell agglutinins in the sera of infectious mononucleosis patients, which are adsorbed by ox red cells but not by guinea pig kidney extract. The cold agglutination test is positive in mycoplasmal (primary atypical) pneumonia. The patient's sera agglutinate human O group erythrocytes at 4°C, the agglutination being reversible at 37°C.

Antiglobulin (Coombs) test: This was devised by Coombs, Mourant and Race (1945) for the detection of anti-Rh antibodies that do not agglutinate Rh-positive erythrocytes in saline.

Principle: When sera containing incomplete anti-Rh antibodies are mixed with Rh-positive red cells, the antibody globulin coats the surface of the erythrocytes, though they are not agglutinated. When such erythrocytes coated with the antibody globulin are washed free of all unattached protein and treated with a rabbit antiserum against human gamma globulin (anti-globulin or Coombs serum), the cells are agglutinated (Fig. 12.7).

Types:
• **Direct Coombs test:** The sensitisation of the erythrocytes with incomplete antibodies takes place in vivo, as in hemolytic disease of the newborn due to Rh incompatibility. When the red cells of erythroblastotic infants are washed free of unattached protein and then mixed with a drop of Coombs serum, agglutination results. The direct Coombs test is often negative in hemolytic disease due to ABO incompatibility.
• **Indirect Coombs test:** Sensitisation of red cells with the antibody globulin is performed in vitro.

Uses: Originally employed for the detection of anti-Rh antibodies, the Coombs test is useful for demonstrating any type of incomplete or non-agglutinating antibody, as, for example, in brucellosis.

Passive agglutination test: The only difference between the requirements for the precipitation and agglutination tests is the physical nature of the antigen. By attaching soluble antigens to the surface of carrier particles, it is possible to convert precipitation tests into agglutination tests, which are more convenient and more sensitive for the detection of antibodies. Such tests are known as passive agglutination tests.

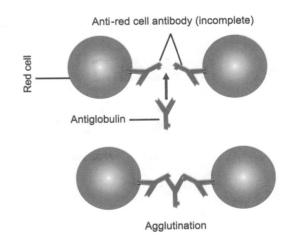

Fig. 12.7   Coombs test

The commonly used carrier particles are red cells, latex particles or bentonite. Human or sheep erythrocytes adsorb a variety of antigens. Polysaccharide antigens may be adsorbed by simple mixing with the cells. For adsorption of protein antigens, tanned red cells are used.

- **Hemagglutination:** A special type of passive hemagglutination test is the **Rose–Waaler test**. In rheumatoid arthritis, an autoantibody (RA factor) appears in the serum, which acts as an antibody to gamma globulin. The RA factor is able to agglutinate red cells coated with globulins. The antigen used for the test is a suspension of sheep erythrocytes sensitised with a subagglutinating dose of rabbit anti–sheep erythrocyte antibody (amboceptor).
- **Latex agglutination test:** Polystyrene latex, which can be manufactured as uniform spherical particles, 0.8–1.0 μm in diameter, can adsorb several types of antigens. Latex agglutination tests (latex fixation tests) are widely employed in the clinical laboratory for the detection of anti-streptolysin O (ASO), C-reactive protein (CRP), RA factor, human chorionic gonadotrophin (HCG) and many other antigens.
- Passive agglutination tests are very sensitive and yield high titres, but may give false positive results. When, instead of the antigen, the antibody is adsorbed to carrier particles in tests for the estimation of antigens, the technique is known as reversed passive agglutination. This method is used to diagnose bacterial antigens like *Legionella*, *Streptococcus pyogenes* and *N.gonorrhoea* in clinical samples.
- **Co-agglutination test:** It is based on agglutination of a specific antibody-sensitised protein A-bearing *Staphylococcus aureus* agglutinating with the soluble bacterial (e.g., Legionella) antigen in the clinical specimen.

COMPLEMENT FIXATION TEST (CFT)

Complement takes part in many immunological reactions and is absorbed during the combination of antigens with their antibodies. In the presence of the appropriate antibodies, complement lyses erythrocytes, kills and, in some cases, lyses bacteria, immobilises motile organisms, promotes phagocytosis and immune adherence and contributes to tissue damage in certain types of hypersensitivity.

Principle: The ability of antigen–antibody complexes to 'fix' complement is made use of in the CFT. This is a very versatile and sensitive test, applicable with various types of antigens and antibodies and capable of detecting as little as 0.04 mg of antibody nitrogen and 0.1 mg of antigen. CFT is a complex procedure consisting of two steps and five reagents—antigen, antibody, complement, sheep erythrocytes and amboceptor (rabbit antibody to sheep red cells). Each of these reagents has to be separately standardised (Fig. 12.8).

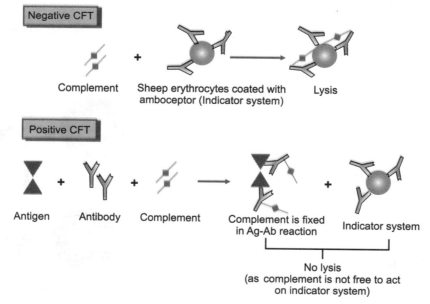

Fig. 12.8   Complement fixation test

Procedure:

1. The antigen may be soluble or particulate. The antiserum should be heated at 56°C (inactivated) for half an hour before the test to destroy any complement activity the serum may have and also to remove some non-specific inhibitors of complement present in some sera (anti-complementary activity).
2. The source of the complement is guinea pig serum. As complement activity is heat labile, the serum should be freshly drawn, or preserved either in the lyophilised or frozen state or with special preservatives, as in Richardson's method.

Standardisation: The guinea pig serum should be titrated for complement activity. One unit or minimum hemolytic dose (MHD) of complement is defined as the highest dilution of the guinea pig serum that lyses one unit volume of washed sheep erythrocytes in the presence of excess hemolysin (amboceptor) within a fixed time (usually 30 or 60 minutes) at a fixed temperature (37°C). The amboceptor should be titrated for hemolytic activity. One MHD of amboceptor is defined as the least amount (or highest dilution) of the inactivated amboceptor that lyses one unit volume of washed sheep erythrocytes in the presence of excess complement within a fixed time (usually 30 or 60 minutes) at a fixed temperature (37°C). The diluent used for the titrations and for CFT is physiological saline with added calcium and magnesium ions.

Wasserman reaction: The classical example of CFT is the Wassermann reaction, formerly the routine method for the serodiagnosis of syphilis.

Procedure:

1. The inactivated serum of the patient is incubated at 37°C for one hour with the Wassermann antigen and a fixed amount (two units) of guinea pig complement. If the serum contains syphilitic antibody, the complement will be utilised during antigen–antibody interaction. If the serum does not contain the antibody, no antigen–antibody reaction occurs and the complement will therefore be left intact.
2. Testing for complement in the post-incubation mixture will thus indicate whether the serum had antibodies or not. This consists of adding sensitised cells (sheep erythrocytes coated with 4 MHD hemolysin), and incubating at 37°C for 30 minutes.

Interpretation of results:

1. Lysis of the erythrocytes indicates that the complement was not fixed in the first step and, therefore, the serum did not have the antibody (**negative CFT**).
2. Absence of erythrocyte lysis indicates that the complement was used up in the first step and, therefore, the serum contained the antibody (**positive CFT**) (Fig. 12.9).

Appropriate controls should be used, including the following:

1. Antigen and serum controls to ensure that they are not anti-complementary
2. Complement control to ensure that the desired amount of complement is added
3. Cell control to observe that sensitised erythrocytes do not undergo lysis in the absence of complement

Indirect complement fixation test: Certain avian (for example, duck, turkey, parrot) and mammalian (for example, horse, cat) sera do not fix guinea pig complement. When such sera are to be tested, the indirect complement fixation test may be employed. Here, the test is set up in duplicate and after the first step, the standard antiserum known to fix the complement is added to one set. If the test serum contained antibody, the antigen would have been used up in the first step and, therefore, the standard antiserum added subsequently would not be able to fix the complement. Therefore, in the indirect test, hemolysis indicates a positive result.

Conglutinating complement absorption test: For systems which do not fix guinea pig complement, an alternative method is the conglutinating complement absorption test. This uses horse complement which is non-hemolytic. The indicator system is sensitised sheep erythrocytes mixed with bovine serum. Bovine serum

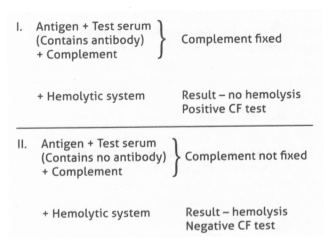

Fig. 12.9 Complement fixation test—Wassermann reaction

contains a beta globulin component called **conglutinin**, which acts as antibody to the complement. Therefore, conglutinin causes agglutination of sensitised sheep erythrocytes (conglutination) if they have combined with the complement. If the horse complement had been used up by the antigen–antibody interaction in the first step, agglutination of sensitised cells will not occur.

Other complement-dependent serological tests: When some bacteria (for example, *Vibrio cholerae, Treponema pallidum*) react with the specific antibody in the presence of complement and particulate materials such as erythrocytes or platelets, the bacteria are aggregated and adhere to the cells. This is known as **immune adherence**. The **immobilisation test** is another complement-dependent reaction. In the *Treponema pallidum* immobilisation test, a highly specific test formerly considered the 'gold standard' for the serodiagnosis of syphilis, the test serum is mixed with a live motile suspension of *T.pallidum* in the presence of the complement. On incubation, the specific antibody inhibits the motility of treponemes. **Cytolytic** or **cytocidal tests** are also complement-dependent. When a suitable live bacterium, such as the cholera vibrio, is mixed with its antibody in the presence of the complement, the bacterium is killed and lysed. This forms the basis of the vibriocidal antibody test for the measurement of anti-cholera antibodies.

NEUTRALISATION TESTS

Virus neutralisation tests: Neutralisation of viruses by their antibodies can be demonstrated in various systems. Neutralisation of bacteriophages can be demonstrated by the plaque inhibition test. When bacteriophages are seeded in appropriate dilution on lawn cultures of susceptible bacteria, plaques of lysis are produced. Specific antiphage serum inhibits plaque formation.

Toxin neutralisation: Bacterial exotoxins are good antigens and induce the formation of neutralising antibodies (antitoxins) which are important clinically, in protection against and recovery from diseases such as diphtheria and tetanus. The toxicity of endotoxins is not neutralised by antisera. Toxin neutralisation can be tested in vivo or in vitro.

Neutralisation tests in animals consist of injecting toxin–antitoxin mixtures and estimating the least amount of antitoxin that prevents death or disease in the animals. With the diphtheria toxin, which, in small doses, causes a cutaneous reaction, neutralisation tests can be done on rabbit skin.

The **Schick test** is based on the ability of circulating antitoxin to neutralise the diphtheria toxin given intradermally, and indicates immunity or susceptibility to the disease. Toxin neutralisation in vitro depends on the inhibition of some demonstrable toxic effect.

Anti-streptolysin O (ASO) test demonstrates that antitoxin present in patient sera neutralises the hemolytic activity of the streptococcal O hemolysin (O, an immunogenic, oxygen-labile hemolytic toxin). When the body is infected with streptococci, it produces antibodies against the various antigens that the streptococci produce. ASO is one such antibody. Raised or rising levels can indicate past or present infection.

Nagler's reaction is a test for the identification of alpha toxin of *Clostridium perfringens* in clinical specimens. This toxin, on addition of antitoxin to cultures grown on agar medium containing egg yolk (as a source of lecithin), prevents visible opacity due to lecithinase action which is normally observed around colonies.

OPSONISATION

The name 'opsonin' was originally given by Wright (1903) to a heat labile substance present in fresh normal sera, which facilitated phagocytosis. This factor was subsequently identified as a complement. A heat-stable serum factor with similar activity was called 'bacteriotropin'. This appears to be a specific antibody. The term opsonin is now generally used to refer to both these factors.

Wright used the '**opsonic index**' to study the progress of resistance during the course of diseases. The opsonic index was defined as the ratio of the phagocytic activity of the patient's blood for a given bacterium, to the phagocytic activity of blood from a normal individual. It was measured by incubating fresh citrated blood with the bacterial suspension at 37°C for 15 minutes and estimating the average number of phagocytosed bacteria per polymorphonuclear leucocyte (phagocytic index) from stained blood films.

RADIOIMMUNOASSAY (RIA)

Besides fluorescent dyes, many other distinctive 'labels' can also be conjugated to antigens and antibodies. The most commonly used labels are radioisotopes and enzymes. A variety of tests have been devised for the measurement of antigens and antibodies using such labelled reactants. The term **binder–ligand assay** has been used for these reactions. The substance (antigen) whose concentration is to be determined is termed the **analyte** or **ligand**. The binding protein (ordinarily, the antibody) which binds to the ligand is called the **binder**. The first reaction of this type was **radioimmunoassay** (RIA) described by Berson and Yallow in 1959. RIA permits the measurement of analytes up to picogram (10^{-12} g) quantities. The importance of RIA was acknowledged when the Nobel Prize was awarded to Yallow for his discovery in 1977.

RIA is a competitive binding assay in which fixed amounts of antibody and radiolabelled antigen react in the presence of unlabelled antigen. The labelled and unlabelled antigens compete for the limited binding sites on the antibody. This competition is determined by the level of the unlabelled (test) antigen present in the patient's serum samples. After the reaction, the antigen is separated into 'free' and 'bound' fractions and their radioactive counts measured. The concentration of the test antigen can be calculated from the ratio of the bound and total antigen labels, using a standard dose–response curve (Fig. 12.10).

For any reacting system, the **standard dose–response** or **calibrating curve** has to be prepared first. This is done by running the reaction with fixed amounts of antibody and labelled antigen, and varying known amounts of unlabelled antigen. The ratios of bound antigen to total antigen (B:T ratio) plotted against the analyte concentrations give the standard calibration curve. The concentration of antigen in the test sample is computed from the B:T ratio of the test by interpolation from the calibration curve. RIA and its modifications have versatile applications in various areas of biology and medicine, including the quantitation of hormones, drugs, tumour markers, IgE and viral antigens (Fig. 12.11).

ENZYME IMMUNOASSAY (EIA)

Enzyme-labelled conjugates were first introduced in 1966 for localisation of antigens in tissues, as an alternative to fluorescent conjugates. In 1971, enzyme-labelled antigens and antibodies were developed as serological reagents for the assay of antibodies and antigens. Their versatility, sensitivity, simplicity, economy and absence of radiation hazard have made EIA the most widely used procedure in clinical serology. The availability of test kits and facility for automation has added to their popularity.

The term enzyme immunoassay includes all assays based on the measurement of enzyme-labelled antigen, hapten or antibody. EIAs are of two basic types:

- **Homogeneous EIA** does not require the bound and free fractions to be separated; the test can thus be completed in one step, with all reagents added simultaneously. This type of EIA can be used only for the assay of haptens such as drugs and not for microbial antigens and antibodies. An example of homogeneous EIA is **enzyme-multiplied immunoassay technique (EMIT)**, which is a simple assay method for small-molecule drugs such as opiates, cocaine, barbiturates or amphetamine in serum.

- **Heterogeneous** EIA requires the separation of the free and bound fractions either by centrifugation or by absorption on solid surfaces and washing. It is therefore a multistep procedure, with reagents

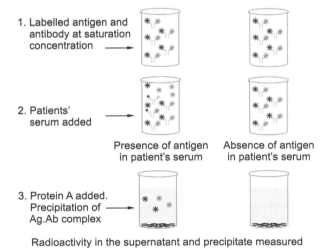

Fig. 12.10 Radioimmunoassay procedure

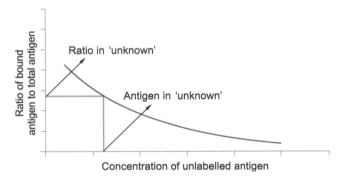

Fig. 12.11 Radioimmunoassay standard curve

added sequentially. The main type of heterogeneous EIA is **ELISA**.

Enzyme-linked immunosorbent assay (ELISA)

ELISA is so named because the technique involves the use of an **immunosorbent,** an absorbing material specific for one of the components of the reaction: the antigen or antibody. This may be a particulate, for example, cellulose or agarose, or a solid phase such as polystyrene, polyvinyl or polycarbonate tubes or microwells, or membranes or discs of polyacrylamide, paper or plastic. ELISA is usually done using 96-well microtitre plates suitable for automation. The principle of the test can be illustrated by outlining its application for the detection of rotavirus antigen in feces.

Procedure

Sandwich ELISA:

1. The wells of a microtitre plate are coated with goat antirotavirus antibody. After thorough washing, the fecal samples to be tested are added and incubated overnight at 4°C or for two hours at 37°C. Suitable positive and negative controls are also set up.
2. The wells are washed and guinea pig antirotavirus antiserum, labelled with alkaline phosphatase, is added and incubated at 37°C for one hour.
3. After washing, a suitable substrate (para-nitrophenyl phosphate) is added and held at room temperature till the positive controls show the development of a yellow colour. The phosphatase enzyme splits the substrate to yield a yellow compound.
4. If the test sample contains rotavirus, it is fixed to the antibody coating the wells. When the enzyme-labelled antibody is added subsequently, it is in turn fixed. The presence of residual enzyme activity, indicated by the development of yellow colour, therefore denotes a positive test (Fig. 12.12).
5. If the sample is negative, there is no significant colour change. An ELISA reader provides quantitative colour recordings which are directly proportional to the quantity of analyte present in the test sample.

Types

- **Indirect ELISA:** The detection of antibody by ELISA can be illustrated by the anti-HIV antibody test. Purified inactivated HIV antigen is adsorbed onto microassay plate wells. Test serum diluted in buffer is added to the well and incubated at 37°C for 30 minutes. The well is then thoroughly washed.

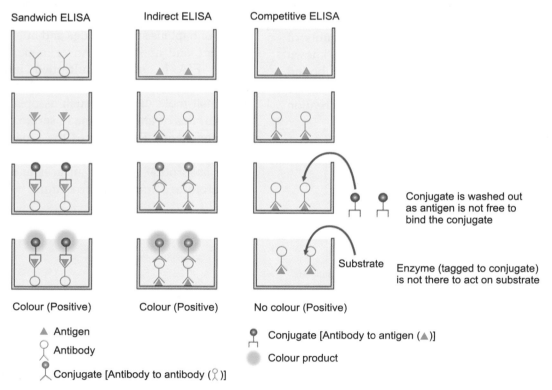

Fig. 12.12   Enzyme-linked immunosorbent assay (ELISA)

If the serum contains anti-HIV antibody, it will form a stable complex with the HIV antigen on the plate. A goat anti-human immunoglobulin antibody conjugated with horseradish peroxidase enzyme is added and incubated for 30 minutes. After thorough washing, the substrate O-phenylene diamine dihydrochloride is added and after 30 minutes, the colour that develops is read using a microassay plate reader. Positive and negative controls should invariably be used with test sera.

- **Competitive ELISA**: Similar to RIA, both the unknown antigen (sample) and the known antigen (standard) compete with each other for a fixed amount of antibody. Competitive ELISA yields an inverse curve, where higher values of antigen in the samples/standards yield a lower amount of colour change. It is normally used for hapten detection.

- **Capture ELISA** and immunometric tests are even more specific. Several variations of the ELISA technique have been developed to provide simple diagnostic tests, including the card and dipstick methods suitable for clinical laboratory and bedside applications.

- **Sandwich ELISA**: It is used for antigen detection in patient sample. The antigen is sandwiched between two layers of antibodies (i.e., capture and detection antibodies).

- **Cylinder or cassette ELISA**: A simple modification of ELISA which has found wide application for testing one or a few samples of sera at a time is the cylinder or cassette ELISA. Here, each specimen is tested in a separate disposable cassette. The test is rapid (10–15 minutes). There is no need for microplate washers or readers. The result is read visually. In-built positive and negative controls are usually provided for validation of the test procedure.

An example of cassette ELISA is the **Dot Blot Assay** used for the detection of HIV type 1 and 2 antibodies. Specific type 1 and 2 antigens are immobilised at separate fixed sites on the nitrocellulose membrane in the cassette.

Procedure: Test serum is added on the membrane and allowed to filter into absorbent material placed below it in the cassette base. Antibody, if present in the serum, will bind to the appropriate antigen. After washing to remove the unbound antibody, enzyme-labelled anti-human immunoglobulin antibody is added. After additional washing to remove the unbound conjugate, a substrate yielding a coloured product is added.

Result: A positive result is indicated by a coloured spot developing at the site of the antigen against which the antibody is present in the serum. Human immunoglobulin immobilised at a spot on the membrane acts as a control for the test procedure, as shown by the development of colour at the site.

Uses of ELISA: ELISA plays a major role in the diagnosis of innumerable diseases. Some examples are given below:

- HIV detection
- Infectious diseases like hepatitis, EBV, cytomegalovirus IgM/IgG, dengue IgG, influenza, TORCH panel, etc.
- Rotavirus detection in fecal specimens and enterotoxin of *E.coli* in feces
- Syphilis IgG/IgM, *H.pylori* IgG and antigen detection
- Food toxins like chloramphenicol, streptomycin, penicillin, aflatoxins, etc.
- Food adulterants including *E.coli*, *Campylobacter* and *Salmonella* antigens
- Mycobacterial antibody detection in tuberculosis
- Human allergen-specific IgE and IgA ELISA

CHEMILUMINESCENCE IMMUNOASSAY (CLIA)

Chemiluminescence refers to a chemical reaction emitting energy in the form of light. Just as radioactive conjugates are employed in RIA, fluorescent conjugates in IFA and enzymes in ELISA, chemiluminescent compounds (such as luminol or acridinium esters) are used in CLIA as the label to provide the signal during the antigen–antibody reaction. The signal (light) can be amplified, measured and the concentration of the analyte calculated. The method has been fully automated and is being increasingly used in laboratories where the volume of work is large.

IMMUNOELECTROBLOT/WESTERN BLOT TECHNIQUES

Immunoelectroblot or western blot techniques combine the sensitivity of enzyme immunoassay with much greater specificity. The technique is a combination of three separate procedures:

1. Separation of ligand–antigen components by poly-acrylamide gel electrophoresis
2. Blotting of the electrophoresed ligand fraction on nitrocellulose membrane strips
3. Enzyme immunoassay (or radioimmunoassay) to:
   - detect antibody in test sera against the various ligand fraction bands
   - probe with known antisera against specific antigen bands

The western blot test, considered to be the definitive/confirmatory test for the serodiagnosis of HIV infection, is an example of the immunoelectroblot technique.

IMMUNOCHROMATOGRAPHIC TESTS

A one-step, qualitative immunochromatographic technique has found wide application in serodiagnosis due to its simplicity, economy and reliability. A description of its use for HBsAg detection illustrates the method.

The test system is a small cassette containing a membrane impregnated with anti-HBsAg antibody colloidal gold dye conjugate. The membrane is exposed at three windows on the cassette. The test serum is dropped into the first window. As the serum travels upstream by capillary action, a coloured band appears at the second window (test site) if the serum contains HBsAg, due to the formation of an HBsAg antibody conjugate complex. This is the positive reaction. Absence of a coloured band at the test site indicates a negative reaction. Simultaneously, a coloured band should appear in every case at the third window, which forms an in-built control, in the absence of which the test is invalid. The test is claimed to be nearly as sensitive and specific as EIA tests.

IMMUNOELECTRON MICROSCOPIC TESTS

Immunoelectron microscopy: When viral particles mixed with specific antisera are observed under the electron microscope, they are seen to be clumped. This finds application in the study of some viruses such as the hepatitis A virus and the viruses causing diarrhea.

Immunoferritin test: Ferritin (an electron-dense substance from horse spleen) can be conjugated with antibody, and such labelled antibody reacting with an antigen can be viewed under the electron microscope.

Immunoenzyme test: Some stable enzymes, such as peroxidase, can be conjugated with antibodies. Tissue sections carrying the corresponding antigens are treated with peroxidase-labelled antisera. The peroxidase bound to the antigen can be visualised under the electron microscope, by microhistochemical methods. Some other enzymes, such as glucose oxidase, phosphatases and tyrosinase, may also be included in immunoenzyme tests.

IMMUNOFLUORESCENCE

Fluorescence is the property of absorbing light rays of one particular wavelength and emitting rays with a different wavelength. Fluorescent dyes show up brightly under ultraviolet light as they convert ultraviolet into visible light. Coons and his colleagues (1942) showed that fluorescent dyes can be conjugated to antibodies and that such labelled antibodies can be used to locate and identify antigens in tissues. This 'fluorescent antibody' or immunofluorescence technique has several diagnostic and research applications (Fig. 12.13).

Direct immunofluorescence test: This can be used for the identification of bacteria, viruses or other antigens, using the specific antiserum labelled with a fluorescent dye. For example, direct immunofluorescence is routinely used as a sensitive method of diagnosing rabies, by detection of the rabies virus antigens in brain smears. A disadvantage of this method is that separate fluorescent conjugates have to be prepared against each antigen to be tested.

Indirect immunofluorescence test: This test overcomes the difficulty mentioned above by using an antiglobulin fluorescent conjugate. An example is the fluorescent treponemal antibody test for the diagnosis of syphilis. Here, a drop of the test serum is placed on a smear of *T.pallidum* on a slide and after incubation, the slide is washed well to remove all free serum, leaving behind only antibody globulin, if present, coated on the surface of the treponemes. The smear is then treated with a fluorescent-labelled antiserum to human gamma globulin. The fluorescent conjugate reacts with the antibody globulin bound to the treponemes. After washing away all the unbound fluorescent conjugate, when the slide is examined under ultraviolet illumination, if the test is positive, the treponemes will be seen as bright objects against a dark background. If the serum

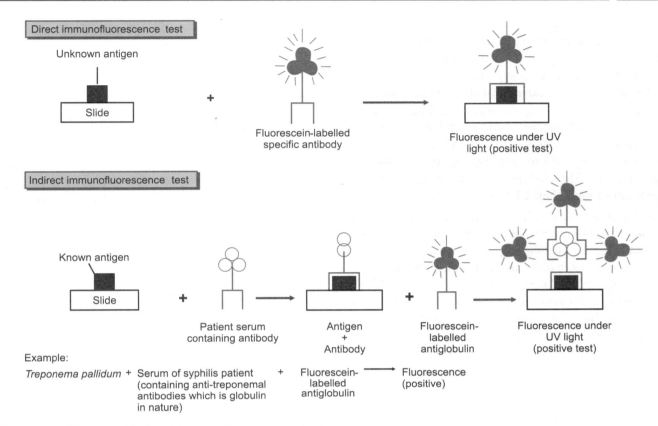

Fig. 12.13 Direct and indirect immunofluorescence tests

does not have anti-treponemal antibody, there will be no globulin coating on the treponemes and therefore they will not take on the fluorescent conjugates. A single anti-human globulin fluorescent conjugate can be employed for detecting human antibodies to any antigen.

Fluorescent dyes may also be conjugated with the complement. Labelled complement is a versatile tool and can be employed for the detection of antigen or antibody. Antigens also take fluorescent labelling but not as well as antibodies do. For detection of antibodies by immunofluorescence, the **sandwich** technique can be used. The antibody is first allowed to react with unlabelled antigen, which is then treated with fluorescent-labelled antibody. A sandwich is thus formed, the antigen being in the middle and the labelled and unlabelled antibodies on either side.

Immunohistochemical technique: By combining the specificity of serology with the localising capacity of histology, immunofluorescence helps in the visualisation of antigen–antibody reactions in situ and is thus called an immunohistochemical technique. The main

disadvantage of the technique is the frequent occurrence of non-specific fluorescence in tissues and other materials. The fluorescent dyes commonly used are fluorescein isothiocynate and rhodamine, exhibiting blue-green and orange-red fluorescence, respectively.

Flow cytometry: This is the fluorescence technique used to identify and enumerate cells bearing a particular antigen(s) or the surface markers by suspending them in a stream of fluid and passing them through an electronic detection apparatus. It allows simultaneous multiparametric analysis of the physical and/or chemical characteristics of up to thousands of particles per second. Different populations of molecules, cells or particles can be differentiated by size and shape using forward and right-angle light scatter. These cells, particles or molecules, can be labelled with different fluorescent labels or with dye-labelled monoclonal antibodies. In this way, we can measure the amounts or isolated individual cells or populations of particular cells from a mixed population.

Here, cells are made to flow in a single cell stream in a flow cell by hydrodynamic focussing. In this, the sample stream containing the cells are focussed by a surrounding layer of sheath fluid. An Argon laser (at 488 nm) is focussed on the cells. Various sensors pick up the laser light reflected by the cells.

The parameters measured by the flow cytometer are forward scatter (FS), a measure of cellular size, side scatter (SS), a measure of the granularity of the cell and fluorescence sensors (FL1–FL8), which measure light emitted by various dyes bound to the cells. The emitted light is directed into various sensors by a combination of filters (Fig. 12.14).

Applications: Multiple parameters—the size, granularity, DNA or RNA content, cellular antigens, receptor levels, etc.,—can be measured using flow cytometry. It is widely used in research and diagnostics, for example, to count blood cells including differential leucocyte count (DLC), to isolate T cell subsets (CD4 and CD8 counts in HIV patients), for diagnosis, treatment and prognosis in cancer (especially leukemias), to study the cell cycle and apoptosis, etc.

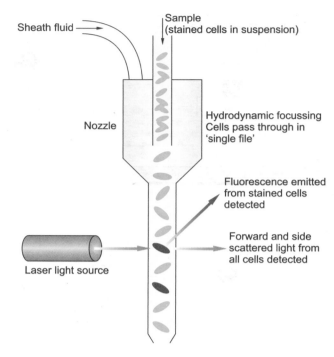

Fig. 12.14   Schematic diagram of a flow cytometer

RECAP

- Antigen–antibody reactions enable us to detect, identify and quantify (measure the concentration) of antigens and antibodies. Since antibodies are present in serum, their study is known as serology.
- Antibodies may be demonstrated by various types of reactions:
  - ❖ In agglutination reactions, specific antibodies (agglutinins) formed in response to the occurrence of particulate antigens in host tissues combine with a homologous antiserum. Agglutination reactions are used for the diagnosis of infections due to salmonellae (Widal test), brucellae (brucella agglutination test), and rickettsiae (Weil–Felix test) and other toxic products elaborated by microorganisms.
  - ❖ In precipitation reactions, the antigen is in a soluble form and, on combination with the antibody, sediments or remains suspended in the form of floccules. Examples of diagnostic precipitation tests include the Kahn and VDRL tests.
  - ❖ In the complement fixation reaction, an antigen combines with its (specific) antibody in the presence of complement, and the antigen–antibody complex adsorbs the complement. This reaction is not visible and requires the use of an indicator (sheep erythrocytes and the specific anti-erythrocyte antibody). Examples include the Wassermann test for syphilis and some tests for the detection of viruses.
  - ❖ In neutralisation tests, the effect of the antigen, toxin or virus is neutralised on mixing with its antibody. Examples include the Schick test for diphtheria toxin, antistreptolysin O (ASO) test for streptococcal O infection, Nagler's reaction for the identification of alpha toxin of *Clostridium perfringens*, *Treponema pallidum* immobilisation (TPI) test for *T. pallidum* in clinical specimens.
  - ❖ In certain viral diseases, the antibody produced prevents the agglutination of certain red blood cells by the specific virus; this hemagglutination inhibition test can be used for the diagnosis of influenza.

- Tests based on the primary interaction between the antibody and antigen are very sensitive and specific. In radioimmunoassay, a radioisotope is used to indicate the presence of an antigen–antibody reaction, while in enzyme immunoassay, the detection system involves the use of an enzyme-labelled antibody. ELISA is the most popular technique for the diagnosis of hepatitis, HIV, rotavirus and many others.
- Immunofluorescence technique involves fluorochrome-labelled antibodies for the diagnosis of syphillis, treponemal infection, etc. in clinical samples and also visualisation of antigen–antibody reactions *in situ* by the immunohistochemical technique.
- Flow cytometry allows simultaneous multiparametric analysis of the physical and/or chemical characteristics of cells. Different populations of cells or particles can be differentiated by size and shape using forward and light scatter, where cells are made to flow in a single cell stream. It is widely used for CD4 and CD8 counts in HIV patients, diagnosis and prognosis in cancer (especially leukemias), study of cell cycle and apoptosis, etc.

ESSAYS

1. Enumerate the types of antigen–antibody reactions and describe the principle and applications of the precipitation reactions.
2. Enumerate the types of antigen–antibody reactions and describe in detail the agglutination test and its use in laboratory diagnosis.

SHORT ANSWERS

1. Precipitation reactions
2. Agglutination test
3. Complement fixation test
4. Neutralisation test
5. Immunoflourescence test
6. Principle and applications of ELISA in clinical microbiology
7. Principle of immunoelectrophoresis
8. Principle of radioimmunoassay; its advantages and disadvantages over ELISA

SHORT NOTES

1. Rocket immunoelectrophoresis
2. Principle of Coombs test (antiglobulin test)
3. Ouchterlony double immunodiffusion technique
4. Two-dimensional electrophoresis
5. Sandwich ELISA
6. Immunoelectroblot/Western blot technique
7. Flow cytometry

13 Complement System

INTRODUCTION

The term complement (C) refers to a system of factors that occurs in normal serum and is activated characteristically by antigen–antibody interaction and which subsequently mediates a number of biologically significant consequences.

Buchner (1889) was the first to observe that the bactericidal effect of serum was destroyed by heating at 55°C for one hour. Pfieffer (1894) discovered that cholera vibrios were lysed when injected intraperitoneally into specifically immunised guinea pigs (bacteriolysis in vivo or **Pfieffer's phenomenon**). Bordet (1895) extended these observations and established that immune bacteriolysis and hemolysis required two factors: a heat stable antibody and a heat labile factor called alexine. This term was replaced by the name **complement,** coined by Ehrlich, because this factor complemented the action of the antibody.

Bordet and Gengou (1901) described the **complement fixation test**, using the hemolytic indicator system, as a sensitive serological reaction. This found wide application, and the Wassermann complement fixation test for syphilis became one of the most popular serological tests. Later, the structural and functional complexities of the complement system were defined and its role as a mediator and amplifier of many immune and inflammatory reactions recognised.

The complement system belongs to the group of biological effector mechanisms (called **triggered enzyme cascades**) which also includes coagulation, and the fibrinolytic and kinin systems. Such biological cascades have distinct advantages. For example, each enzyme in the cascade can activate many molecules of the succeeding component, providing for amplification of the response at each step. Every step has its own control mechanisms so that the cascade can be regulated with precision.

GENERAL PROPERTIES

Complement is present in the sera of all mammals and also in that of most other animals, including birds, amphibians and fish.

- It is a non-specific serological reagent in that the complement from one species can react with antibodies from other species, though the efficiency of reaction is influenced by the taxonomic distance between the species.
- Complement constitutes about 5 per cent of normal serum protein and is not increased as a result of immunisation.

Effect of temperature: Though some of its components are heat stable, complement as a whole is heat labile, its cytolytic activity undergoing spontaneous denaturation slowly at room temperature and being destroyed in 30 minutes at 56°C. A serum, deprived of its complement activity by heating at 56°C for 30 minutes, is then said to be 'inactivated'.

Complement (C) ordinarily does not bind to free antigens or antibodies but only to antibodies that have combined with their antigens. Various terms such as **fixation, binding** and **consumption** have been used to refer to the combination of C with bound immunoglobulin, leading to the activation of the **classical C pathway**.

All classes of Ig do not fix C. Only IgM, IgG3, 1 and 2 (in that order) fix C, but not IgG4, IgA, IgD or IgE.

The site of C binding is located on the *Fc* piece of the Ig molecule (C_H2 domain on IgG, C_H4 on IgM), and is expressed only when Ig is combined with its antigen. The fixation of C is not influenced by the nature of antigens, but only by the class of immunoglobulins.

Components

The complement system consists of at least 30 chemically and immunologically distinct serum proteins which make up the complement components, the properdin system and the control proteins. The biological activities of this system affect both innate and acquired immunity far beyond the earlier concept of antibody-mediated lysis of bacteria and erythrocytes. Initially, the structural proteins were thought to be involved in complement pathways in innate immunity but interactions of cellular receptors with C proteins which control B cell activation play a crucial role in the highly developed acquired immune system.

Fractions: Complement is a complex of **nine** different fractions, **C1 to C9**. The fraction C1 occurs in serum as a calcium ion–dependent complex, which on chelation with EDTA yields three protein subunits called C1q, r and s. Thus C is made up of a total of 11 different proteins. C fractions are named C1 to C9 in the sequence of the cascading reaction, except that C4 comes after C1, before C2.

The model traditionally used to explain C activity in immune cytolysis is the lysis of erythrocyte sensitised by its antibody. The erythrocyte (E) antibody (A) complex is called EA, and when C components are attached to EA, the product is called EAC, followed by the components that have reacted (for example, EAC 14235 or EAC 1–5). When a C component acquires enzymatic or other demonstrable biological activity, it is indicated by a bar over the component number, for example, enzymatically activated C1 is shown as C̄1. Fragments cleaved from C components during the cascade are indicated by small letters (C3a, C3b). Inactivated forms of C components are indicated by the prefix 'i' (iC3b).

COMPLEMENT ACTIVATION

Complement is normally present in the body in an inactive form but when its activity is induced by antigen–antibody combination or other stimuli, C components react in a specific sequence as a cascade. Basically, the **C cascade** is a series of reactions in which the preceding components act as enzymes on the succeeding components, cleaving them into dissimilar fragments. The larger fragments usually join the cascade. The smaller fragments which are released often possess biological effects which contribute to defence mechanisms by various basic **effector mechanisms** including:

- Lysis of cells and bacteria
- Promoting virus neutralisation
- Opsonisation, which promotes phagocytosis of particulate antigens
- Immune clearance, which removes immune complexes from circulation and deposits them in the spleen and liver
- Amplifying the inflammatory process, increasing vascular permeability, inducing smooth muscle contraction and effecting the release of histamine from mast cells, as shown in Fig. 13.1.

PATHWAYS

The C cascade can be triggered off by three parallel but independent mechanisms or pathways which differ only in the initial steps. Once C3 activation occurs, the subsequent steps are common to all pathways; this is called the classical C pathway, alternative or properdin pathway and lectin pathway.

The classical pathway is so called because it was the first one identified. It is a more recently evolved mechanism of specific active immunity, while the alternative pathway and lectin pathway represent a more primitive system of non-specific innate immunity.

Classical Complement pathway

The chain of events in which complement components react in a specific sequence following activation of **C1qrs** and typically culminate in immune cytolysis is known as the classical pathway (Fig. 13.2).

Steps:
1. The first step is the **binding of C1 to the antigen–antibody complex** (traditionally represented as EA). The recognition unit of C1 is C1q, which reacts with the *Fc* piece of bound IgM or IgG. C1q has six combining sites. Effective activation occurs only when C1q is attached to immunoglobulins by at least two of its binding sites. One molecule of IgM or two molecules of IgG can therefore initiate the process. C1q binding in the presence of calcium ions leads to sequential activation of C1r and s.

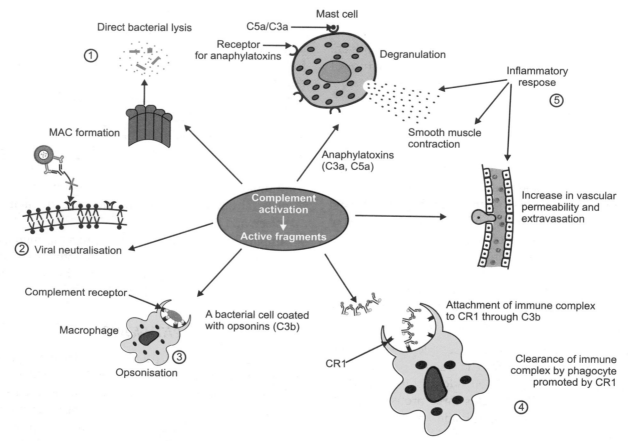

Fig. 13.1   Biological effects of complement activation

2. C$\overline{1s}$ is an esterase (C$\overline{1s}$ esterase), one molecule of which can cleave several molecules of C4, an instance of amplification. C4 is split into C4a, which is an anaphylatoxin, and C4b, which binds to cell membranes along with C1.

3. C$\overline{4b}$ in the presence of magnesium ions cleaves C2 into C2a, which remains linked to cell-bound C$\overline{4b}$, and C2b which is released into the fluid phase. C$\overline{4b2a}$ has enzymatic activity and is referred to as the classical pathway **C3 convertase**.

4. C3 convertase splits C3 into two fragments: C3a which is an anaphylatoxin and C3b which remains cell-bound along with C$\overline{4b2a}$ to form a trimolecular complex C$\overline{4b2a3b}$ which has enzymatic activity and is called C5 convertase.

5. The **membrane attack** phase of complement activity begins at this stage, with C5 convertase cleaving C5 into C5a, an anaphylatoxin which is released into the medium, and C5b which continues with the cascade. C6 and C7 then join together. A heat stable trimolecular complex C$\overline{567}$ is formed, part of which binds

to the cell membrane and prepares it for lysis by C8 and C9 which join the reaction subsequently. Most of C$\overline{567}$ escape and serve to amplify the reaction by adsorbing onto unsensitised '**bystander cells**' and rendering them susceptible to lysis by C8 and C9. The unbound C$\overline{567}$ has chemotactic activity, though the effect is transient due to its rapid inactivation. The mechanism of complement-mediated cytolysis is the production of 'holes', approximately 100 Å in diameter on the cell membrane. This disrupts the osmotic integrity of the membrane, leading to the release of the cell contents.

Although the classical pathway is generally activated by the antigen–antibody complex or aggregated immunoglobulin, activation may also be due to other stimuli, such as DNA, C reactive protein, trypsin-like enzymes or some retroviruses.

Alternative Complement pathway

The central process in the complement cascade is the activation of C3, which is the major component of C.

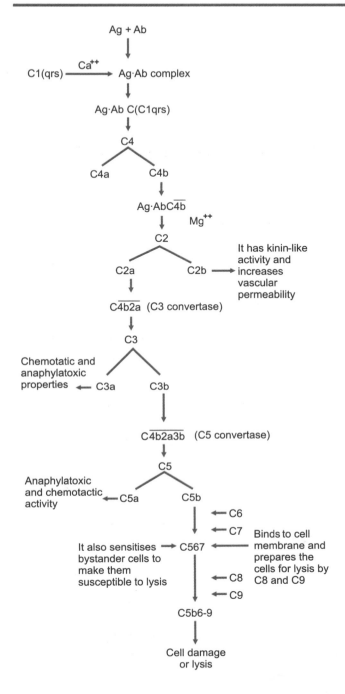

Fig. 13.2 The classical pathway of complement

In the classical pathway, activation of C3 is achieved by C$\overline{4b2a}$ (classical C3 convertase). The activation of C3 without prior participation of C$\overline{4b2a}$ is known as the alternative pathway.

The first example of the alternative pathway was the demonstration by Pillemer (1954) of the 'properdin system' as a group of serum proteins contributing to antimicrobial defence without requiring specific antibodies. The activator in this system was **zymosan**, a polysaccharide from the yeast cell wall, but many other substances can also activate the pathway. These activators include bacterial endotoxins, IgA and D, the cobra venom factor and the nephritic factor (a protein present in the serum of glomerulonephritis patients).

1. The first step in the alternative pathway is the **binding of C3b** to an activator. C3b is continuously generated in small quantities in circulation but in the free state it is rapidly inactivated by serum protein factors H and I.

2. Bound C3b, which is protected from such inactivation, interacts with a serum protein called Factor B (also known as '**C3 proactivator**') to form a magnesium-dependent complex 'C3b,B'.

3. This complex is cleaved by another serum protein Factor D (also called '**C3 proactivator convertase**') into two fragments, Ba and Bb. Fragment Ba is released into the medium. Fragment Bb remains bound to C3b, forming the esterase C$\overline{3b}$, $\overline{Bb}$ complex, which is the alternative pathway C3 convertase. This enzyme is extremely labile. The function of properdin (also called Factor P) is to stabilise the C3 convertase, which hydrolyses C3, leading to further steps in the cascade, as in the classical pathway (Fig. 13.3).

Lectin Complement pathway

Lectins are proteins that recognise and bind to specific carbohydrate targets. Since the lectin that activates complement binds to mannose residues, it is also called **MB lectin** or the **mannan-binding lectin pathway**. This pathway does not depend on antibody for its activation as in the alternate pathway but its mechanism is more like the classical pathway.

The lectin pathway is activated by the binding of mannose binding lectin to mannose residues present on the surfaces of microorganisms like certain *Salmonella*, *Neisseria* and *Listeria* strains, as well as *Cryptococcus neoformans* and *Candida albicans*. MBL is an acute phase protein produced in inflammatory responses. Its function is similar to that of C1q. After MBL binds to the foreign surface of a pathogen, specific proteases (MASP1 and MASP2) bind to it and form the C1-like active complex. Later it causes cleavage and activation of C4 and C2 to produce C5 convertase without the need for specific antibody binding; this represents an innate defense mechanism comparable to the alternate pathway while utilising classical pathway components except the C1 proteins.

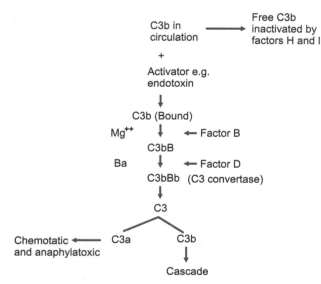

Fig. 13.3   Alternative pathway of complement

The three complement pathways converge at the **membrane attack complex (MAC)** which contains C5b, C6, C7, C8 and C9 proteins after sequential interaction to form this macromolecular structure. This complex forms a large channel through the mem-

brane of a pathogen or target cell, enabling ions and small molecules to diffuse freely across the membrane; hence the cell cannot maintain its osmotic stability and is killed by an influx of water and loss of electrolytes. An overview of all three pathways is represented in Fig. 13.4.

REGULATION OF COMPLEMENT ACTIVATION

Unchecked complement activity can cause not only exhaustion of the complement system but also serious damage to tissues. Several inbuilt control mechanisms regulate the complement cascade at different steps. These are mainly of two kinds: **inhibitors**, which bind to complement components and halt their further function, and **inactivators**, which are enzymes that destroy complement proteins.

Inhibitors:

* Normal serum contains an inhibitor of C1 esterase (**C1sINH**). This heat labile alpha neuraminoglycoprotein also inhibits many other esterases found in blood, such as plasmin, kininogen and the Hageman factor. This does not prevent the normal progress of

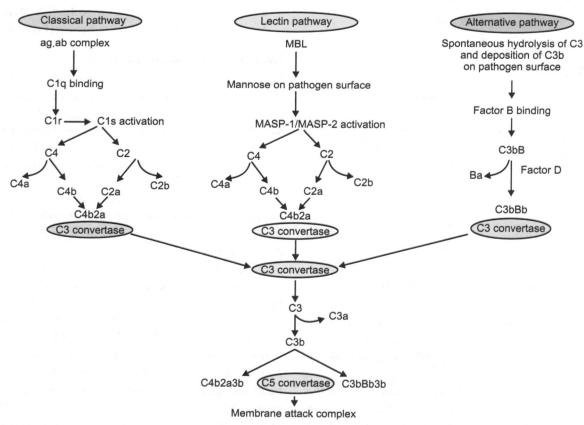

Fig. 13.4   Overview of pathways of complement activation

the complement cascade but checks its autocatalytic prolongation.

- The **S protein** present in normal serum binds to $\overline{C67}$ and modulates the cytolytic action of the membrane attack complex.

Inactivators:

- A serum betaglobulin, called **Factor I** (formerly known as C3b, C4b INAC, conglutinogen activating factor or KAF), provides homeostatic control of C3 activation, particularly by the alternative pathway.
- Another beta globulin **Factor H** acts in concert with Factor I, modulating C3 activation.
- **Anaphylatoxin inactivator** is an alphaglobulin that enzymatically degrades C3a, C4a and C5a which are anaphylatoxins released during the C cascade.
- The **C4 binding protein** controls the activity of cell-bound C4b.

BIOLOGICAL EFFECTS OF COMPLEMENT

Complement mediates immunological membrane damage (cytolysis, bacteriolysis), amplifies the inflammatory response and participates in the pathogenesis of certain hypersensitivity reactions. It exhibits antiviral activity and promotes phagocytosis and immune adherence.

Phagocytosis: An important function of C is to facilitate the uptake and destruction of pathogens by phagocytic cells. This opsonic effect is based on the presence on the surface of phagocytic cells (macrophages, monocytes, neutrophils and others) of complement receptors or CRs. Many such receptors have been identified, such as CR 1, 2, 3, 4 and C1q, which stimulate phagocytosis and removal of immune complexes. The CR 2 receptor on B cells also acts as a receptor for the Epstein–Barr virus (EBV), the causative agent of infectious mononucleosis, and so has a role in the pathogenesis of this condition.

Inflammatory response: C fragments released during the cascade reaction help in amplifying the inflammatory response. C2 kinins are vasoactive amines and increase capillary permeability. C3a and C5a are anaphylatoxic (histamine releasing) and chemotactic. $\overline{C567}$ is chemotactic and also brings about reactive lysis.

Hypersensitivity reactions: C participates in cytotoxic (Type II) and immune complex (Type III) hypersensitivity reactions. The destruction of erythrocytes, following incompatible transfusion and thrombocytopenia in sedormid purpura, are examples of Type II

reactions. C contributes to the pathogenesis of nephrotoxic nephritis, though immunological kidney damage may also occur in its absence. C is required for the production of immune complex diseases such as serum sickness and Arthus reaction.

Autoimmune diseases: Serum C components are decreased in many autoimmune diseases such as systemic lupus erythematosus and rheumatoid arthritis. C also plays a major role in the pathogenesis of autoimmune hemolytic anemia.

Endotoxic shock: Endotoxin is an efficient activator of the alternative C pathway. In endotoxic shock, there is massive C3 fixation and platelet adherence. Large-scale platelet lysis and release of large amounts of platelet factor lead to disseminated intravascular coagulation and thrombocytopenia. Gram-negative septicemias and dengue hemorrhagic syndrome may have a similar pathogenesis. Depletion of C protects against the Shwartzman reaction.

Immune adherence: C bound to antigen–antibody complexes adheres to erythrocytes or to non-primate platelets. This reaction, called immune adherence, contributes to defence against pathogenic microorganisms since such adherent particles are rapidly phagocytosed. C3 and C4 are necessary for immune adherence.

Conglutination: Bovine serum contains an unusual protein called conglutinin (K) which causes clumping of particles or cells coated with C, a process known as conglutination. Conglutinin reacts exclusively with bound C3. Though conglutinin behaves as an antibody to C, it is not an immunoglobulin and requires Ca^{++} for its activity. Antibodies with conglutinin-like activity (immunoconglutinin, IK) can be produced by immunisation with complement coated materials. They may also occur frequently in human beings and other mammals as autoantibodies to fixed C.

The complement system is generally effective in lysing Gram-negative bacteria; however, some Gram-negative bacteria and most Gram-positive bacteria have mechanisms to evade complement-mediated damage, as shown in Table 13.1.

Quantitation of Complement and its components

Complement activity of serum is measured by estimating the highest dilution of serum lysing sheep erythrocytes sensitised by anti-erythrocytic antibody. Estimation of individual complement components also

Table 13.1 *Microbial evasion of complement-mediated damage*

Microbial components	Mechanism of evasion	Examples
	Gram-negative bacteria	
Cell wall lipopolysaccharides (LPS)	Side chains prevent insertion of MAC into bacterial membrane	Resistant strains of *E.coli* and *Salmonella*
Other membrane proteins	MAC interacts with membrane proteins and fails to insert into bacterial membrane	Resistant strains of *Neisseria gonorrhoeae*
Elastase	Anaphylatoxins C3a and C5a are inactivated by microbial elastase	*Pseudomonas aeruginosa*
	Gram-positive bacteria	
Peptidoglycan layer of cell wall	Thick layer prevents MAC from inserting into bacterial membrane	Streptococcus
Bacterial capsule	Provides physical barrier between C3b deposited on bacterial membrane and CR 1 on phagocytic cells	*Streptococcus pneumoniae*
	Other microbes	
Proteins that mimic complement regulatory proteins	Proteins present in various bacteria,viruses , fungi and protozoans inhibit the complement cascade	Vaccinia virus, herpes simplex, Epstein–Barr virus, Toxoplasma cruzi, Candida albicans

Table 13.2 *Clinical syndromes associated with genetic deficiencies of complement components*

Group	Deficiency	Syndrome
I	Cl inhibitor	Hereditary angioneurotic edema
II	Early components of classical pathway C1, C2, C4	SLE and other collagen vascular diseases
III	C3 and its regulatory protein C3b inactivator	Severe recurrent pyogenic infections
IV	C5 to C8	Bacteremia, mainly with Gram-negative diplococci, toxoplasmosis
V	C9	No particular disease

uses hemolytic activity in a system containing an excess of all complement components except the one to be measured. C components can also be quantitated by radial immunodiffusion in agar but this method does not differentiate between active and inactive fractions.

Biosynthesis of Complement

Complement components are synthesised at various sites in the body, such as the intestinal epithelium (C1), macrophages (C2, C4), spleen (C5, C8) and liver (C3, C6, C9). C is, to some extent, an 'acute phase substance' and a rise in C levels (particularly C4, C3, C5 and C6) is observed during the acute phase of inflammation.

DEFICIENCIES OF THE COMPLEMENT SYSTEM

Complete or partial deficiencies of all classical complement components and several of the C inhibitors have been described in humans and animals. Some are associated with severe diseases, while in others clinical manifestations are sporadic. C deficiencies result in the host being unable to efficiently eliminate the microbial antigens or circulating immune complexes. Recurrent bacterial and fungal infections and collagen diseases also occur (Table 13.2).

Deficiency of the C1 inhibitor is associated with **hereditary angioneurotic edema**, a condition characterised by episodic angioedema of the subcutaneous tissues or of the mucosa of the respiratory or alimentary tracts. It may be fatal when the larynx and trachea are affected. The attack is precipitated by local exhaustion of the reduced amount of the C1 inhibitor present, leading to the autocatalytic activation of C1 and the unrestrained breakdown of C4 and C2. The main mediator of the edema appears to be the C2 kinin released. The attack may be treated by infusion of fresh plasma as a source of the inhibitor. Prophylactic administration of epsilon aminocaproic acid (or its analogues) is useful. They are believed to inhibit the activation of plasma enzymes, thus sparing the small amounts of the C1 inhibitor present.

RECAP

- The complement system consists of at least 30 distinct proteins. The major components are C1 through C9, which are numbered in the order of their discovery, not in the order in which they react.
- Some of the proteins of the complement system are inactive enzymes which, once activated, act in sequence one after another in a cascade reaction. Other components perform specific biologic functions.
- The components released after activation often possess various biological effector functions which contribute to defence mechanisms, such as lysis of cells and bacteria, promoting virus neutralisation, opsonisation which promotes phagocytosis of particulate antigens and immune clearance, which removes immune complexes from the circulation.
- Complement can be activated in three ways: a classical pathway, which requires a specific immune reaction for activation, an alternative pathway and lectin pathway, which are antibody independent. These pathways are activated by the reaction of complement proteins with surface molecules of microorganisms.
- The complement destroys invading bacteria and foreign cells by disrupting their cytoplasmic membranes and is also involved in the inflammatory response since it contributes to vascular permeability, stimulates chemotaxis and enhances phagocytosis.
- Complement proteins and protein fragments with receptors on the cells of the immune system control both innate and acquired immune response.
- The direct and indirect complement fixation tests are examples of in vitro diagnostic antigen–antibody reactions.
- Complement deficiencies result in the host being unable to efficiently eliminate the microbial antigens or circulating immune complexes, causing recurrent bacterial and fungal infections.

ESSAYS

1. Describe the basic properties of the complement system and the classical complement pathway.
2. Briefly explain the alternative pathway of the complement system.

SHORT ANSWERS

1. Biological functions mediated by the complement system
2. Activators and inhibitors for regulation of the complement system
3. Classical complement pathway
4. Alternative complement pathway (properidin pathway)
5. Lectin complement pathway

14 Structure and Functions of the Immune System

INTRODUCTION

The lymphoreticular system is a complex organisation of cells of diverse morphology distributed widely in different organs and tissues of the body responsible for immunity. Lymphoreticular cells consist of lymphoid and reticuloendothelial components, with clearly demarcated functions. The lymphoid cells—lymphocytes and plasma cells—are primarily concerned with specific immune response. The phagocytic cells, forming part of the reticuloendothelial system, are primarily concerned with the 'scavenger' functions of eliminating effete cells and foreign particles. They contribute to non-specific immunity by removing microorganisms from blood and tissues. They also play a role in specific immunity, in the afferent and efferent limbs of the immune response.

Types of immune response

The functional anatomy of the lymphoid system can be appreciated on the basis of two types of immune response to an antigen:

1. **Humoral immunity (antibody-mediated, AMI).** It is mediated by antibodies produced by plasma cells and present in blood and other body fluids (hence the name 'humoral' from 'humor', the old term for body fluids).
2. **Cellular immunity:** It is mediated directly by sensitised lymphocytes.

Cells for each of these components develop through separate channels and remain independent, though they may also interact in some instances (Fig. 14.1).

Hematopoiesis: All cells of immunological importance originate from a hematopoietic stem cell (HSC). The details of hematopoiesis are shown in Fig. 14.2.

THE LYMPHOID SYSTEM

The lymphoid system consists of lymphoid organs and cells. The thymus and bone marrow are the **primary lymphoid organs**; the spleen and lymph nodes are the **secondary lymphoid organs**. The **lymphoid cells** consist of lymphocytes and plasma cells (Fig. 14.3).

CENTRAL (PRIMARY) LYMPHOID ORGANS

Thymus

The thymus performs the important function of generating and selecting a repertoire of T cells that will protect the body from infection. In humans, the thymus reaches its maximal relative size just before birth. It continues to grow till about the twelfth year. After puberty, it undergoes spontaneous progressive involution, indicating that it functions best in early life.

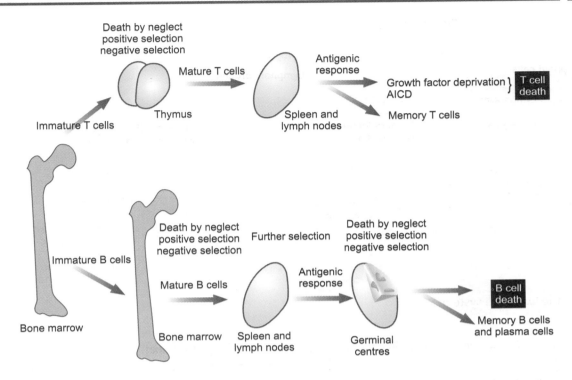

Fig. 14.1   Development of T and B cell systems

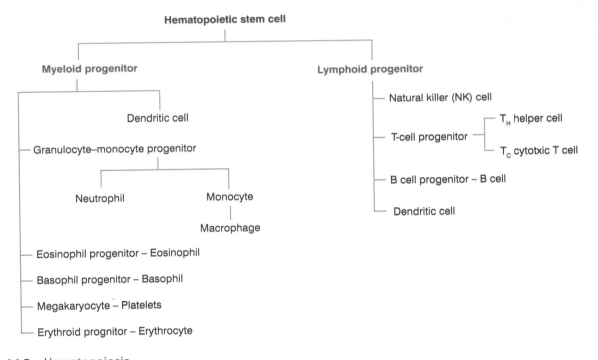

Fig. 14.2   Hematopoiesis

Structure: The thymus is located behind the upper part of the sternum. It has two lobes surrounded by a fibrous capsule. Septa arising from the capsule divide the gland into lobules which are differentiated into an outer cortex and an inner medulla. The cortex is crowded with actively proliferating small lymphocytes. The medulla consists mainly of epithelial cells and mature lymphocytes, in the middle of which are

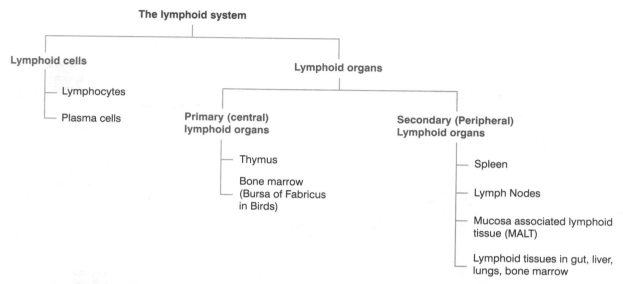

Fig. 14.3   The lymphoid system

Hassall's corpuscles, which are whorl-like aggregations of epithelial cells.

Functions: The primary function of the thymus is the production of thymic lymphocytes. It is the main site for lymphocyte proliferation in the body. However, of the lymphocytes produced, only about one per cent leave the thymus. The rest are destroyed locally. During thymic selection, as thymocytes develop, some T cells with receptors are capable of recognising antigen–MHC complexes. The thymus induces the death of those T cells that cannot recognise the antigen–MHC complexes and those that react with self-antigen–MHC and may cause autoimmune disease.

More than 95 per cent of all thymocytes die by apoptosis in the thymus without ever reaching maturity. In the thymus, the lymphocytes acquire new surface antigens ('**Thy**' antigens). Lymphocytes conditioned in the thymus are called '**thymus (T) dependent** lymphocytes' or '**T cells**'. Unlike in the peripheral organs, lymphocyte proliferation in the thymus is not dependent on antigenic stimulation. In fact, peripheral antigenic stimuli do not lead to any immune response in the thymus. Antigen introduced directly into the thymus may lead to a local immune response. The thymus confers immunological competence on the lymphocytes during their stay in the organ. In the thymus, they are 'educated' to become capable of mounting cell-mediated immune response against appropriate antigens.

Clinical significance:

* **DiGeorge syndrome:** Deficient CMI is seen in congenital aplasia of the thymus in human beings (DiGeorge syndrome) and in mice ('nude mice').
* **Runt disease:** Deficiency of CMI is evident from lymphopenia, deficient graft rejection and the so-called 'runt disease' seen in neonatally thymectomised mice.

Post thymectomy, T lymphocytes are selectively seeded into certain sites in the peripheral lymphatic tissue, being found in the white pulp of the spleen, around the central arterioles, and in the paracortical areas of lymph nodes. These regions have been termed 'thymus dependent' as they are found grossly depleted after neonatal thymectomy. While thymectomy primarily affects the CMI, it also diminishes antibody response to many types of antigens (thymus dependent antigens) such as sheep erythrocytes and bovine serum albumin. Humoral response to other antigens is unaffected.

Bone marrow

In humans and other mammals, the bone marrow is the site of B cell origin and development. Immature B cells originating from lymphoid progenitors proliferate and differentiate within the bone marrow with the help of cytokines. In birds, the Bursa of Fabricius is the primary site for B cell maturation, equivalent to the bone marrow. A selection process within the bone marrow eliminates B cells with self-reactive antibody receptors, as in thymic selection during

T cell maturation. All lymphocytes originate in the bone marrow. While T lymphocytes develop in the thymus, B lymphocytes develop in the bone marrow itself. In the human fetus, Peyer's patches develop and lymphoid cells appear in the spleen and lymph nodes by the 20th week of gestation. From then on the fetus is able to produce IgM and IgD. It receives maternal IgG, but IgA and IgE are not present. At birth, IgM production is enhanced, but the IgG level falls steadily to reach minimum levels by the third month. IgG production then picks up and becomes adequate by 2–3 years. Full immunocompetence is attained only after the first decade of life.

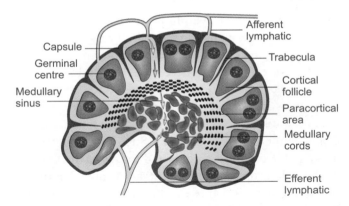

Fig. 14.4 Diagrammatic section of lymph node (arrows indicate the path of lymph flow)

PERIPHERAL (SECONDARY) LYMPHOID ORGANS

Lymph nodes

Lymph nodes are placed along the course of lymphatic vessels and differentiated into an outer cortex and an inner medulla. In the cortex are accumulations of lymphocytes (primary lymphoid follicles) within which germinal centres (secondary follicles) develop during antigenic stimulation. The follicles contain, besides proliferating lymphocytes, dendritic macrophages which capture and process the antigen. In the medulla, the lymphocytes, plasma cells and macrophages are arranged as elongated branching bands (medullary cords). The cortical follicles and medullary cords contain B lymphocytes and constitute the bursa-dependent areas. Between the cortical follicles and medullary cords, there is a broad, ill-defined intermediate zone (paracortical area) which contains T lymphocytes and interdigitating cells. This constitutes the thymus-dependent area. The accumulations of lymphocytes (B and T), dendritic macrophages, plasma cells and interdigitating dendritic cells in different parts are shown in **Fig. 14.4**.

Functions: Lymph nodes act as a filter for lymph, each group of nodes draining a specific part of the body. They phagocytose foreign materials including microorganisms. They help in the proliferation and circulation of T and B cells. They enlarge following local antigenic stimulation.

Spleen

The spleen is the largest of the lymphoid organs. It has a capsule from which trabeculae descend, dividing the

organ into several interconnected compartments. The lymphatic sheath immediately surrounding the central arteriole is the thymus dependent area of the spleen. The perifollicular region, germinal centre and mantle layer form the thymus independent areas (**Fig. 14.5**).

Functions: The spleen serves as the graveyard for effete blood cells, as a reserve tank and settling bed for blood and as a systemic filter for trapping circulating bloodborne foreign particles. The immunological function of the spleen is primarily directed against bloodborne antigens.

Clinical significance: The effects of splenectomy on the immune response depend on the age. In children, splenectomy often leads to increased incidence of **bacterial sepsis** caused primarily by *Streptococcus pneumoniae*, *Neisseria meningitidis* and *Haemophilus influenzae*. In adults, the effects are less adverse and may lead to bacterial infections (**bacteremia**).

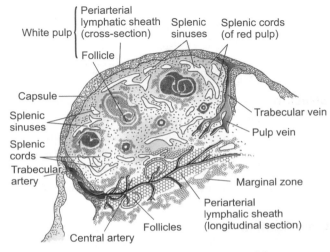

Fig. 14.5 Schematic diagram of splenic architecture

Mucosa associated lymphoid tissue (MALT): The mucosa lining the alimentary, respiratory, genitourinary and other lumina and surfaces are constantly exposed to numerous antigens. These areas are endowed with a rich collection of lymphoid cells, either specialised aggregates like Peyer's patches or scattered isolated lymphoid follicles, collectively called the mucosa associated lymphoid tissue (MALT). Such lymphoid tissues in the gut, from the adenoids and tonsils to the follicles in the colon, are called the **gut associated lymphoid tissue (GALT)** and those in the respiratory tract, the **bronchus associated lymphoid tissue (BALT).**

MALT contains lymphoid as well as phagocytic cells. MALT has functional significance in the body's defense due to its large population of antibody-producing plasma cells, than that of plasma cells in the spleen, lymph nodes and bone marrow. Both B and T cells are present. While the predominant immunoglobulin produced in the mucosa is secretory IgA, other immunoglobulin classes, IgG, IgM and IgE, are also formed locally. There appears to be free traffic of antigen-specific effector lymphocytes between the various mucosal and secretory areas, so that antigenic exposure at one site may cause the production of the specific antibody at the other mucosal and secretory sites. This indicates the existence of a common mucosal or secretory immune system and explains the superiority of oral or nasal immunisation over the parenteral route for many enteric and respiratory infections.

CELLS OF THE LYMPHORETICULAR SYSTEM

Lymphocytes

Lymphocytes constitute 20–40 per cent of the body's white blood cells and 99 per cent of the cells in the lymph. On the basis of function and cell-membrane components, lymphocytes can be broadly subdivided into three types: B cells, T cells and natural killer cells.

Structure: Lymphocytes are small, round cells found in peripheral blood, lymph, lymphoid organs and in many other tissues. The human body contains about 10^{12} lymphocytes, approximately 10^9 of them being renewed daily. Lymphocytes are now recognised as the main cellular elements responsible for immunological response.

Classification: Depending on their life span, they can be classified as short-lived and long-lived lymphocytes. In humans, the short-lived lymphocytes have a life span of about two weeks, while the long-lived cells may last for three years or more, or even for life. Short-lived lymphocytes are the effector cells in immune response, while the long-lived cells act as a storehouse for immunological memory. Long-lived cells are mainly thymus derived.

Lymphocytic recirculation: Lymphopoiesis takes place mainly in the central lymphoid organs where they differentiate and mature before entering circulation and then the peripheral lymphoid organs and tissues, like a policeman on beat patrol. These populations of lymphocytes do not remain distinct but mix together in a process known as 'lymphocyte recirculation'. There is a constant traffic of lymphocytes through the blood, lymph, lymphatic organs and tissues. This recirculation ensures that following introduction of the antigen into any part of the body, lymphocytes of appropriate specificity reach the site during their ceaseless wandering and mount an immune response. A lymphocyte completes one cycle of recirculation in about one or two days. Recirculating lymphocytes can be recruited by the lymphoid tissues whenever necessary. Recirculating lymphocytes are mainly T cells. B cells tend to be more sessile. Chronic thoracic duct drainage will therefore result in selective T cell depletion.

Functions: Both T and B lymphocytes are central cells and play a vital role in generating immune response. A lymphocyte that has been 'educated' by the central lymphoid organs becomes an '**immunologically competent cell' (ICC)**. Mature T and B cells, before they encounter antigens, are called **naïve cells**. Such cells, though not actually engaged in an immunological response, are nevertheless fully qualified to undertake such a responsibility when appropriately stimulated by an antigen. They subserve the following functions: recognition of antigens, storage of immunological memory and immune response to specific antigens.

Lymphocytes have antigen recognition mechanisms on their surface, enabling each cell to recognise only one antigen. The reaction of an immunocompetent cell to its specific antigen may be induction of either 'tolerance' or the immune response. The nature of immune response depends on whether the lymphocyte is a B or T cell. Stimulated T cells produce certain activation products (lymphokines) and induce CMI, while stimulated B cells divide and transform into plasma cells which synthesise immunoglobulins.

A number of surface antigens or markers have been identified on lymphocytes and other leukocytes by means of monoclonal antibodies. These markers reflect the stage of differentiation and functional properties of the cells. Order was introduced at the International Workshops for Leukocyte Differentiation Antigens by comparing the specificities of different antisera. When a cluster of monoclonal antibodies was found to react with a particular antigen, it was defined as a separate marker and given a CD (cluster of differentiation) number. Over 150 CD markers have been identified thus far. Table 14.1 lists a few CD markers, with their cell association for CD4 (helper/inducer) and CD8 (suppressor/cytotoxic) cells.

Difference between T and B cells: The most clear-cut differentiation between T and B cells is by their surface markers, for example, by demonstration of CD3 on T cells and Ig on B cells. Many other tests help in their differentiation (Table 14.2).

- T cells bind to sheep erythrocytes, forming rosettes (SRBC or E rosette) by the CD2 antigen. B cells do not.
- B cells bind to sheep erythrocytes coated with antibody and complement, forming EAC rosettes, due to the presence of a C3 receptor (CR2) on the B cell surface. CR2 also acts as a receptor for the Epstein–Barr virus. T cells do not possess this.
- B cells have immunoglobulin on their surface. Each B cell carries about 10^5 identical Ig molecules on its surface. The first Ig class to appear on the B cell surface is monomeric IgM. Subsequently other classes (IgG, IgA or IgE) may be present, along with IgD. The surface Ig on a B cell will have single antigen specificity. It therefore serves as the antigen recognition unit. T cells do not have surface Ig. Instead

Table 14.1   *A few examples of leukocyte differentiation antigens*

CD number	Cell type association	Former designation
CD1	Thymocytes, Langerhans cells	T6, Leu 6
CD2	T cell SRBC receptor	T11, Leu 5
CD3	T cell antigen receptor complex	T3, Leu 4
CD4	Helper T cell (receptor for HIV)	T4, Leu 3
CD8	Suppressor/Cytotoxic T cells	T8, Leu 2
CD19	B cells	B4, Leu 12

Table 14.2 *Some distinguishing characteristics of T cells, B cells and macrophages*

Property	T cell	B cell	Macrophage
CD3 receptor	+	–	–
Surface immunoglobulins	–	+	–
Receptor for Fc piece of IgG	–	+	–
EAC rosette (C3 receptor; CR2; EBV receptor)	–	+	–
SRBC rosette (CD2; measles receptor)	+	–	–
Thymus-specific antigens	+	–	–
Numerous microvilli, on surface	–	+	–
Blast transformation with:			
a) Anti-CD3	+	–	–
b) Anti-Ig	–	+	–
c) PHA	+	–	–
d) Concanavalin A	+	–	–
e) Endotoxins	–	+	–
Phagocytic action	–	–	+
Adherence to glass surface	–	–	+

they have T cell receptors (TCR) composed of two chains of polypeptides, linked to CD3.

- T cells have thymus-specific antigens, which are absent on B cells.
- T cells undergo blast transformation on treatment with mitogens such as phytohemagglutinin (PHA) or Concanavalin A (Con A), while B cells undergo similar transformation with bacterial endotoxins, *Staphylococcus aureus* (Cowan 1 strain) or EB virus.
- Viewed under the scanning microscope, T cells are generally free of cytoplasmic surface projections, while B cells have an extensively filamentous surface, with numerous microvilli.

T CELL MATURATION

T cell precursors from the yolk sac, fetal liver and bone marrow migrate to the thymus during the embryonic and postnatal stages. The earliest identifiable cells of T lineage are the CD7$^+$ pro-T cells, which acquire CD2 on entering the thymus. They synthesise CD3 in the cytoplasm and become pre-T cells. T cell receptor (TCR) synthesis also takes place.

T cell receptors

TCR is a heterodimer of glycoprotein chains expressed on the T cell surface, which in association with CD3 acts as the antigen recognition unit, analogous to Ig on the surface of B cells. TCR occurs as two pairs of glycoprotein chains, either αβ or γδ. Pre-T cells differentiate into two lineages, expressing either αβ or γδ TCR chains. The large majority of T cells carry αβ TCR (**Fig. 14.6**). The two chains are held together by a disulphide bond near the T cell membrane at the hinge region. TCRs have positive charges in the transmembrane portion and a short cytoplasmic tail. TCR chains contain four separately encoded regions: V or variable, D or diversity, J or joining and C or constant, as in the case of immunoglobulins and hence belong to the immunoglobulin gene superfamily. By re-assortment of these regions, a very wide repertoire of antigen specificities can be formed on the T cell surface (**Fig. 14.7**).

Contact with self-antigens within the thymus leads to the destruction of immature T cells carrying the corresponding TCR. Thus, self-tolerance or elimination of T cells capable of reacting with self-antigens takes place in the thymus. But cells capable of reacting with autoantigens continue to arise throughout life. These

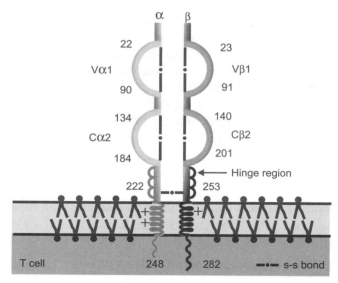

Fig. 14.6 Structure of T cell receptor (TCR)

potentially harmful 'forbidden clones' are deleted by antigen-specific suppressor cells. Immunocompetence against foreign antigens is also developed in the thymus.

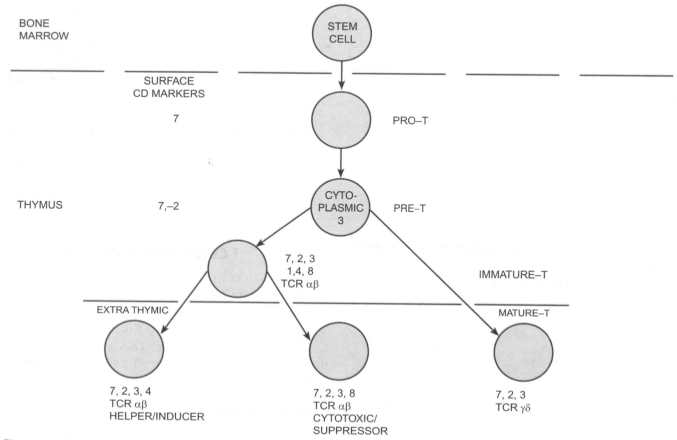

Fig. 14.7 T cell maturation

T cells also develop MHC restriction so that CD8+ cells respond only to foreign antigens presented along with HLA Class I, and CD4+ cells to those presented with HLA Class II molecules. Immature T cells in the thymus exhibit CD7, 2, 3, 1, 4 and 8, besides TCR. On functional maturity, they lose CD1 and differentiate into the two major subsets CD8–4+ or CD4–8+. Mature CD8–4+ TCRαβ cells are helper/inducer cells, inducing B cell differentiation, stimulating proliferation of CD8+ cytotoxic cells, producing lymphokines and regulating certain stages of erythropoiesis. CD4–8+ TCRαβ cells are suppressor/T cytotoxic cells (T_C), inhibiting B cell antibody synthesis and acting as cytotoxic effector cells. T_C cells are activated when they interact with an antigen–class I MHC complex on the surface of an altered self-cell (for example, a virus-infected cell or a tumour cell) in the presence of appropriate cytokines. This activation, which results in proliferation, causes the T_C cell to differentiate into an effector cell called a **cytotoxic T lymphocyte (CTL)**, and hence acquire the ability to recognise and eliminate altered self-cells. Small numbers of CD4+8+ and CD4–8– cells are also present in circulation.

The function of TCR γδ cells is not well understood, but they are believed to be immune surveillance cells on epithelial surfaces and a form of defense against intracellular bacteria and participate in innate immunity and immune response homeostasis.

Sequential antigenic changes characterising T cell maturation enable their easy identification. This has application in defining T cell malignancies. Acute T cell malignancies such as lymphoblastic leukemia and lymphomas involve early T cells, pro-T cells and other immature forms. Chronic T cell malignancies like mycosis fungoides, peripheral T cell lymphomas and HTLV-1-associated adult T cell leukemias involve mature T cells, mainly CD4+ cells.

Types of T cells

Based on their surface markers, target cells and functions, the following T cell categories have been identified. Minor subsets of CD4+ cells and CD8+ cells also exist. **Figure 14.8** shows the major and minor subsets of T cells along with their functions.

T cells are classified as regulatory or effector cells. They may be CD4+ or CD8+ on their surface:
- **Helper/Inducer (T_H) cells**, with a CD4 surface marker and major histocompatibility complex (MHC) class II restriction, generally stimulate and

promote the growth of T cells and macrophages. CD4+ cells can differentiate into T_H cells or T regulatory cells. T_H cells are further differentiated into:
- T_H 1 cells, which produce cytokines, interferon gamma and interleukin-2, which activate macrophage and T cells, promoting cell-mediated immunity, destruction of target cells and killing of intracellular pathogens (tubercle and lepra bacilli)
- T_H 2 cells produce cytokines IL4, 5 and 6 which stimulate B cells to form antibodies
- T_H 17 cells produce cytokine IL17 and promote inflammation, for example, autoimmune diseases (systemic lupus erythematous [SLE] and rheumatic arthritis) and cancer.

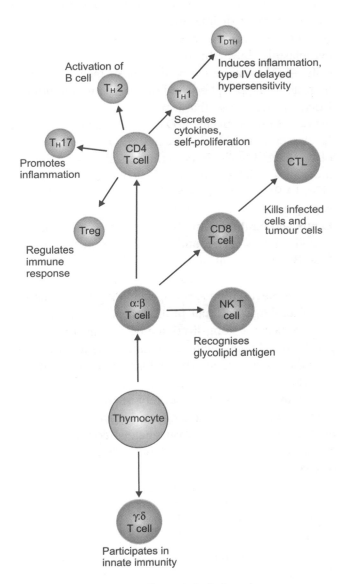

Fig. 14.8 Types of T cells and their functions

- **Treg cells** are CD4+cells and produce cytokine TGF beta. These cells regulate the immune response and tolerance to self-reacting cells.
- **Cytotoxic/Cytolytic T cells (T$_c$)**, with CD8 surface markers and MHC class I restriction, which can kill and lyse target cells carrying new or foreign antigens, including tumour, allograft and virus-infected cells.
- **Memory cells (T$_m$)**, both CD4 and CD8, provide memory and anamnestic immune response.

B CELL MATURATION

B lymphocyte precursors, pro-B cells, develop in the fetal liver during embryonic life and in the bone marrow afterwards continuously throughout life. Rearrangement of immunoglobulin genes takes place on their becoming pre-B cells, which synthesise cytoplasmic IgM. In the next stage—immature B cells—IgM is expressed on the cell surface. These cells migrate to the periphery and undergo immunoglobulin isotype switching so that instead of IgM alone, the cell expresses on its surface IgD as well as one of the other Ig classes—IgM, IgG, IgA or IgE. By re-assortment of Ig genes, B cells develop the capacity to produce Ig molecules which can react with all the possible epitopes (Fig. 14.9). By a process of allelic exclusion, each B cell is programmed to form only one class of Ig, with either **kappa** and **lambda light chain**, possessing specificity to a single epitope alone, and to express it on the cell surface. By contact with self-antigens during development, self-tolerance is developed by clonal deletion or anergy.

On contact with its appropriate antigen, the mature B cell undergoes clonal proliferation. Some activated B cells become long-lived memory cells responsible for the recall phenomenon seen on subsequent contact with the same antigen. The majority of activated B cells are transformed into plasma cells.

Plasma cell is the antibody secreting cell. It is oval, about twice the size of a small lymphocyte, with an eccentrically placed oval nucleus containing large blocks of chromatin located peripherally (**cartwheel appearance**). The cytoplasm is large and contains abundant endoplasmic reticulum and a well-developed Golgi apparatus. It is structurally designed to be an immunoglobulin producing factory. Plasma cells are end cells and have a short life span of two or three days.

A plasma cell makes an antibody of a single specificity, of a single immunoglobulin class and allotype, and of a single light chain type only. An exception is seen in the primary antibody response, when a plasma cell producing IgM initially, may later be switched to IgG production.

After B cells are selected in the germinal centre for those bearing high-affinity membrane Ig for antigen, some B cells differentiate into plasma cells and others become **memory B cells**. These express all isotypes, IgM, IgD, IgG, IgA, and IgE, as compared to naive B cells which express only IgM and IgD. They are characteristically long lived and more readily stimulated than naïve cells and mediate secondary immune response to subsequent encounters with the same antigen.

A separate lineage of B cells, which are predominant in fetal and early neonatal life, express the T cell marker CD5 on their surface and have been named B1 cells. Their progenitor cells move from the fetal

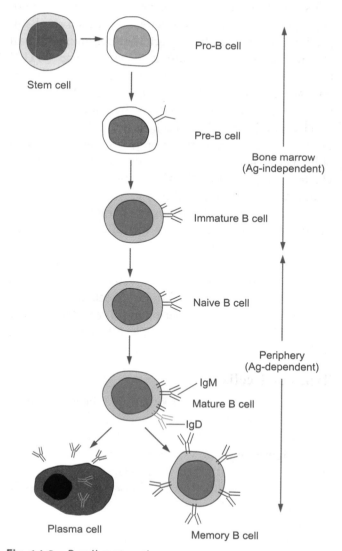

Fig. 14.9 B cell maturation

liver to the peritoneal cavity where they multiply. They secrete low affinity polyreactive IgM antibodies, many of them autoantibodies. They are responsible for the T-independent 'natural' IgM antibacterial antibodies which appear in neonates seemingly without antigenic stimulus. CD5+ B cells may be relevant in the causation of autoimmune conditions.

NULL CELLS

When circulating lymphocytes are classified by their surface markers into T and B cells, about 5–10 per cent of the cells are found to lack features of either type. They are called **null cells**. Because of their morphology, they are also known as **large granular lymphocytes (LGL)**. They are nearly double the size of the small lymphocytes, with indented nuclei and abundant cytoplasm containing several azurophilic granules, composed of mitochondria, ribosomes, endoplasmic reticulum and Golgi apparatus. LGL are a heterogeneous group of cells with differences in their functional and surface marker features. The most important member of this group is the **natural killer (NK) cell**. Others are the **antibody dependent cytotoxic cells (ADCC)** and the **lymphokine activated killer (LAK) cells**. The term NK cell is sometimes used as a common name for all null cells.

Natural killer cells possess spontaneous cytotoxicity towards various target cells, mainly malignant and virus-infected. Their cytotoxicity is not antibody dependent or MHC restricted. NK activity is 'natural' or 'non-immune' as it does not require sensitisation by prior antigenic contact. NK cells therefore form part of the innate immune set-up. They belong to a different lineage from T and B cells and are therefore normally active in 'severe combined immunodeficiency diseases', in which mature T and B cells are absent. They have CD16 and CD56 on their surface. They bind to the glycoprotein receptors on the surface of autologous as well as allogeneic target cells and release several cytolytic factors. One of these, **perforin**, which resembles complement component C9, causes transmembrane pores through which cytotoxic factors, such as the tumour necrosis factor beta, enter the cell and destroy it by **apoptosis** (programmed cell death). NK cell activity is augmented by interferon. They are considered to be important in immune surveillance and natural defence against virus infected and malignant mutant cells.

Antibody dependent cytotoxic cells (ADCC) are a subpopulation of LGLs possessing surface receptors for the *Fc* part of Ig. They are capable of lysing or killing target cells sensitised with IgG antibodies. This antibody-dependent cellular cytotoxicity is distinct from the action of cytotoxic T cells, which are independent of the antibody. ADCC cells were formerly called killer (K) cells but are now classified with NK cells.

Lymphokine activated killer (LAK) cells are NK lymphocytes treated with interleukin-2 (IL2), which are cytotoxic to a wide range of tumour cells without affecting normal cells. LAK cells have shown promise in the treatment of some tumours such as renal cell carcinoma. IL2 also acts as a growth factor for NK cells.

Phagocytic cells

Phagocytosis is phylogenetically the oldest defence mechanism in animals. These cells are specialised in the removal of foreign and autochthonous particles. Phagocytic cells are the mononuclear macrophages (of blood and tissues) and the polymorphonuclear microphages.

Macrophages: The blood macrophages (monocytes) are the largest of the lymphoid cells found in peripheral blood (12–15 μm). The tissue macrophages (histiocytes) are larger (15–20 μm). Mononuclear macrophage cells originate in the bone marrow from precursor cells and become monocytes in about six days. Monocytes in circulation have an approximate half-life of three days. They leave the circulation and reach various tissues to be transformed into macrophages, with morphological and functional features characteristic of the tissues. Tissue macrophages survive for months. Multinucleated cells and epithelioid cells seen in granulomatous inflammatory lesions such as tuberculosis originate from mononuclear macrophage cells. Macrophages have different function to perform and are named according to tissue location; for example, **alveolar macrophages, histiocytes, Kupffer cells, osteoclasts** and **mesangial cells.**

Clinical significance: While phagocytosis is an effective defence against most microorganisms, some (such as the bacilli of typhoid, brucellosis and tuberculosis) resist digestion and may multiply in the cells and be transported in them to other locations.

Macrophages express many surface receptors including Ia proteins, those for the *Fc* part of IgG, activated complement components and various lymphokines.

Mac 1 is a protein antigen found on mouse macrophages. A similar protein on human macrophages has been named the **M1 marker**. This appears closely related to CR3, a cell receptor for C3 components.

Mechanism: Macrophages may participate in several ways in the induction and execution of the specific immune response. They trap the antigen and provide it, in optimal concentration, to the lymphocytes. Too high a concentration of antigen may be tolerogenic, and too low may not be immunogenic. It has also been shown that with some antigens, prior processing by macrophages is an essential prerequisite for induction of antibodies.

The processing and presentation of antigen by the macrophage to T cells requires that both the cells possess surface determinants coded for by the same MHC genes. The T cell can accept the processed antigen only if it is presented by a macrophage carrying on its surface the self-MHC antigens. When the macrophage bears a different MHC antigen, it cannot cooperate with the T cells. This is **MHC restriction.**

Features of activated macrophages:

- The functional efficiency of macrophages can be increased in many ways. They may be 'activated' by lymphokines, complement components or interferon.
- Activated macrophages are not antigen-specific. For example, activated macrophages from animals infected with one microorganism are cytotoxic to tumour cells as well as to many other microorganisms.
- Activated macrophages show morphological and functional changes as compared with unstimulated quiescent macrophages. They are larger, adhere better, spread faster on glass and are more phagocytic.
- They secrete a number of biologically active substances, including hydrolytic enzymes, binding proteins (fibronectin, transferrin), tumour necrosis factor (cachectin), colony stimulating factor (CSF) and interleukin-1 (formerly called the leukocyte activating factor). Interleukin-1 acts as an endogenous pyrogen and also induces synthesis of interleukin-2 by T cells. Interleukin-2 facilitates the activation of T cells.
- When stimulated by cytophilic antibodies and certain lymphokines, macrophages become 'armed'. Such armed macrophages are capable of antigen-specific cytotoxicity, which is important in antitumour activity and graft rejection.

Microphages are the polymorphonuclear leukocytes of the blood—neutrophils, eosinophils and basophils. **Neutrophils** are actively phagocytic and form the predominant cell type in acute inflammation. The phagocytic property of neutrophils is non-specific, except for its augmentation by opsonins. They do not appear to have any role in specific immune processes. **Eosinophilic leukocytes** are found in large numbers in allergic inflammation, parasitic infection and around antigen–antibody complexes. They primarily inhabit tissues rather than the bloodstream. Their distinctive feature is the presence of two types of granules: the small, round, homogeneous ones and the large ovoid ones. The granules contain a variety of hydrolytic enzymes which bring about extracellular killing of large parasites. Eosinophils possess phagocytic activity but only to a limited degree.

Basophil leukocytes are found in the blood and tissues (mast cells). Their cytoplasm has large numbers of prominent basophilic granules containing heparin, histamine, serotonin and other hydrolytic enzymes. Degranulation of mast cells, with release of pharmacologically active agents, constitutes the effector mechanism in anaphylactic and atopic allergy.

Antigen-presenting cells: Activation of both the humoral and cell-mediated branches of the immune system requires cytokines produced by T_H cells. T helper cells can recognise only antigens that are displayed together with class MHC II molecules on the surface of antigen-presenting cells (APCs). These are specialised dendritic cells, macrophages and B lymphocytes.

Dendritic cells: These are the major antigen presenting cells. They are bone marrow–derived cells of a lineage different from the macrophages and T or B lymphocytes. They possess MHC class II expression along with co-stimulatory signals like B7 and CD28 which are necessary for T_H activation. They are called professional antigen presenting cells. They are highly pleomorphic, with a small central body and many long needle-like processes, and are present in peripheral blood and in the peripheral lymphoid organs, particularly in the germinal areas of the spleen and lymph nodes. Dendritic cells are involved in the presentation of antigens to T cells during the primary immune response.

The **B cell** is another antigen presenting cell, particularly during the secondary immune response.

Langerhans cells in the skin possess features of macrophages and dendritic cells. They process and present antigens that reach the dermis.

Abnormalities of immune cells

Abnormalities in immune cells are generally inherited defects found in either specific or non-specific immune mechanisms. Individuals suffering from such abnormalities are susceptible to a variety of infections and the type of infection depends on the nature of the abnormality. These abnormalities are responsible for some specific diseases, as shown in **Table 14.3**.

MAJOR HISTOCOMPATIBILITY COMPLEX (MHC)

The primary function of the immune system is the recognition and elimination of foreign cells and antigens that enter the body. Tissues and organs grafted from one individual to another member of the same species ('allografts') are recognised as foreign and rejected. It was the early work of Gorer in the 1930s on the antigens responsible for allograft rejection in inbred mice that led to the discovery of the major histocompatibility complex (MHC).

Gorer identified two blood group antigen systems in mice: antigen 1 was common to all the strains, antigen 2 was found only in some strains and appeared to be responsible for allograft rejection. This was called the H-2 antigen (H for histocompatibility). The histocompatibility antigens are cell surface antigens that induce an immune response leading to rejection of allografts. The H-2 antigen system was found to be the major histocompatibility antigen for mice and to be coded for by a closely linked multiallelic cluster of genes, called the **major histocompatibility complex**.

The development of congenic (animals which differ only at a single genetic locus) and recombinant strains of mice by Snell enabled the detailed analysis of the various loci of this complex. Dausset pioneered studies on human leukocyte antigens, which were later found to be the major histocompatibility antigens in human beings.

The genetic basis of immune response was proved by Benacerraf and colleagues, who established that the ability to respond immunologically to an antigen was conditioned by specific genes called the **immune response (Ir) genes**. For their work on MHC and the genetic control of immune response, Snell, Dausset and Benacerraf were awarded the Nobel Prize for Medicine in 1980.

Classes of proteins

Early studies on MHC were carried out in mice. However, all species of animals (including human beings) examined subsequently were found to possess a similar complex of genes on a segment of one chromosome pair, coding for three different classes of proteins:

- **Class I proteins** that determine histocompatibility, and the acceptance or rejection of allografts (tissues or organs from different individuals within the same species)
- **Class II proteins** that regulate the immune response
- **Class III proteins** that include some components of the complement system and a few others

The name 'histocompatibility complex' arose because its discovery was based on transplantation experiments. The major antigens determining histocompatibility in human beings are alloantigens, characteristically found on the surface of leukocytes. Human MHC antigens are therefore synonymous with human leukocyte antigens (HLA), and the MHC complex of genes with the HLA complex.

HLA complex

The HLA complex of genes is located on the short arm of chromosome 6 (**Fig. 14.10**). It consists of three separate clusters of genes:

Table 14.3 *Abnormalities of the immune cells, responsible for certain diseases/malfunction*

Abnormality	Disease/Mechanism
Stem cell differentiation	Neutropenia: very few neutrophils
Lack of adhesion to endothelium	Leukocyte adhesion deficiency
Lack of expression of CD18 molecule	
Defective phagocytosis	Chediak Higashi syndrome
Lack of fusion of phagosome with lysosome	
Defective intracellular killing	Chronic granulomatous disease
Defective encoding for NADPH oxidase involved in oxygen-mediated killing	
Defective IFN-g or IL-12 receptors	Failure to activate NADPH oxidase
Congenital aplasia of the thymus	DiGeorge syndrome, Deficient CMI

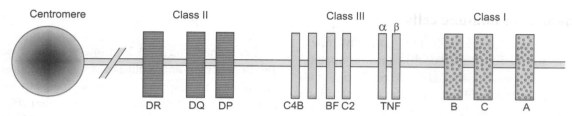

Fig. 14.10   HLA complex loci on chromosome

- **Class I** comprising A, B and C loci
- **Class II** or the D region consisting of the DR, DQ and DP loci
- **Class III** or the complement region containing genes for complement components C2 and C4 of the classical pathway, as well as properdin factor B of the alternative pathway, heat shock proteins and tumour necrosis factors α and β

HLA loci are multiallelic, that is, the gene occupying the locus can be any one of several alternative forms (alleles). As each allele determines a distinct product (antigen), the HLA system is very pleomorphic. For example, at least 24 distinct alleles have been identified at HLA locus A and 50 at B.

HLA molecules: HLA antigens are two-chain glycoprotein molecules anchored on the surface membrane of cells (Fig. 14.11).

- **HLA Class I** molecules consist of a heavy peptide chain (alpha chain) non-covalently linked to a much smaller peptide called beta 2-microglobulin (beta chain). The beta chain has a constant amino acid sequence and is coded for by a gene on chromosome 15. The alpha chain consists of three globoid domains (alpha 1, alpha 2, alpha 3) which protrude from the cell membrane and a small length of transmembrane C terminus reaching into the cytoplasm. The distal domains (alpha 1 and alpha 2) have highly variable amino acid sequences and are folded to form a cavity or groove between them. Protein antigens processed by macrophages or dendritic cells to form small peptides are bound to this groove for presentation to CD8 T cells. The T cell will recognise the antigen only when presented as a complex with the MHC Class I molecule and not otherwise (MHC restriction). When so presented, the CD8 cytotoxic killer cell destroys the target cell (for example, a virus infected cell).

HLA Class I antigens (A, B and C) are found on the surface of virtually all nucleated cells. They are the principal antigens involved in graft rejection and cell-mediated cytolysis. Class I molecules may function as components of hormone receptors.

- **HLA Class II** antigens are more restricted in distribution, being found only on cells of the immune system: macrophages, dendritic cells, activated T cells, and particularly on B cells.

Class II antigens are heterodimers, consisting of an alpha and a beta chain (Fig. 14.12). Each chain has two domains, the proximal domain being the constant region and the distal the variable. The two distal domains (alpha 1, beta 1) constitute the antigen-binding site, for recognition by CD4 lymphocytes, in a fashion similar to the recognition of the Class I antigen peptide complex by CD8 T cells. HLA Class II molecules are primarily responsible for the graft-versus-host response and the mixed leukocyte reaction (MLR).

Both class I and II molecules are members of the immunoglobulin gene superfamily. The immune response (*Ir*) genes which control immunological responses to specific antigens are believed to be situated in the HLA Class II region, probably associated with the DR locus. *Ir* genes have been studied extensively in mice and located in the I region of mouse MHC. They code for Ia (I region associated) antigens consisting of 1A and 1E proteins. However, the relevance of the *Ir* genes in humans is not clear.

- **HLA Class III** molecules are heterogeneous. They include complement components linked to the formation of C3 convertases, heat shock proteins and tumour necrosis factors. They also display polymorphism.

The MHC system was originally identified in the context of transplantation, which is an artificial event. In the natural state, besides serving as cell surface markers that help infected cells to signal cytotoxic and helper T cells, the enormous polymorphism of the MHC helps maximise protection against microbial infections. By increasing the specificity of self-antigens, the MHC

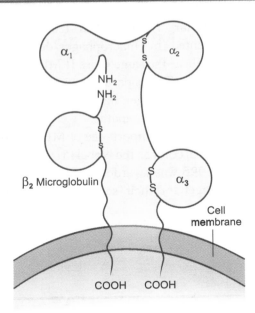

Fig. 14.11 HLA Class I molecule

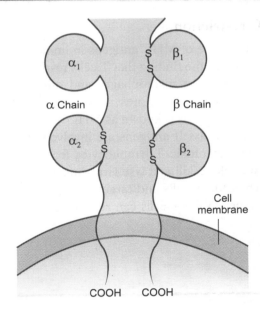

Fig. 14.12 HLA Class II molecule

prevents microbes with related antigenic make-up from sneaking past host immune defences by molecular mimicry. The primary aim of the MHC may be defense against microbes and not against the graft.

MHC has been implicated in a number of non-immunological phenomena such as individual odour, body weight in mice and egg laying in chickens.

HLA typing

Antisera for HLA typing were obtained principally from multiparous women as they tend to have antibodies to the HLA antigens of their husbands, due to sensitisation during pregnancy. Monoclonal antibodies to HLA antigens have been developed. Typing is done serologically by microcytotoxicity, which tests for complement-mediated lysis of peripheral blood lymphocytes with a standard set of typing sera. However, serological typing is not possible for HLA-DR antigens, which are detected by the mixed leukocyte reaction (MLR) and primed lymphocyte typing (PLT), respectively. Genetic methods are being used increasingly for HLA typing in advanced centres. These employ restriction fragment length polymorphism (RFLP) and gene sequence–specific oligonucleotide probe typing.

The HLA antigens coded for by the combination of alleles at each locus on one strand of a chromosome pair represent the haplotype. The complete HLA type of an individual comprises the antigens represented on both strands of the diploid chromosome and so will consist of two haplotypes (for example, HLA-A1, -A2; -B7, -B12; -Cw3, -Dw8; Dw4; -Dw7; -DR1; -DR7; DQw1; -Qw3; -DPw4; -DPw6).

Applications: Due to the extreme pleomorphism of the HLA system, delineation of the HLA type provides a method of typing of individuals that is far more discriminating than blood grouping.

- **Transplantation**: HLA typing is used primarily for testing compatibility between recipients and potential donors before tissue transplantation.
- **Paternity**: It also has applications in disputed paternity.
- **Anthropological studies**: As the prevalence of HLA types varies widely between different human races and ethnic groups, HLA typing is used in anthropological studies. Population studies of HLA polymorphism suggest the origin of the human species in Africa and emigration as different subtypes to other continents.
- **Genetic predisposition to disease**: An association has been observed between HLA types and certain diseases. Such diseases are generally of uncertain origin, associated with immunological abnormalities and exhibit a hereditary tendency. For example, strong association has been found between ankylosing spondylitis and HLA-B27, rheumatoid arthritis and HLA-DR4, and many autoimmune conditions and HLA-DR3.

MHC restriction

The importance of MHC antigens in immune reaction is indicated by the finding that T cells respond to processed antigens on macrophages and other accessory cells only when they are presented along with the self-MHC antigen. This is known as MHC restriction. Both Class I and Class II antigens are involved in this phenomenon. Cytotoxic T lymphocytes from immunised mice are able to kill and lyse virus infected target cells only when the T cells and target cells are of the same MHC type, so the T cells can recognise Class I MHC antigens on the target cells. Helper T cells can accept antigens presented by macrophages/dendritic cells only when they bear the same Class II MHC molecules on the surface. For T cells participating in delayed type hypersensitivity, the antigen has to be presented along with Class II MHC determinants.

In view of the great importance of MHC restriction in immunological control, the Nobel Prize for Medicine for the year 1996 was awarded to Peter Doherty and Rolf Zinkernagel for their seminal contributions in this area.

RECAP

- Hematopoietic stem cell (HSC) is multipotent, differentiates initially into lymphoid progenitor cell or a common myeloid progenitor cell and is committed to a particular cell lineage, for example, erythrocytes, granulocytes, monocytes, mast cells, lymphocytes, etc.
- The lymphoreticular cells consist of lymphoid and reticuloendothelial components:
    - The lymphoid cells (lymphocytes, plasma cells) are primarily concerned with specific immune response.
    - The reticuloendothelial system includes phagocytic cells, which, 'scavenge' effete cells and foreign particles and contribute to non-specific immunity by removing microorganisms.
- The lymphoid system consists of the lymphoid cells and the lymphoid organs. The lymphoid organs may be as follows:
    - Central (primary) lymphoid organs include the bone marrow in humans. All lymphocytes originate in the bone marrow, with T lymphocytes undergoing further differentiation in the thymus and B lymphocytes in the bone marrow.
    - Peripheral (secondary) lymphoid organs: the spleen, lymph nodes and mucosa-associated lymphoid tissue (MALT).
- Lymphocytes are small, round cells and the main cellular elements responsible for immunological processes.
- A lymphocyte that has been 'educated' by the central lymphoid organs becomes an immunocompetent cell. Before they encounter antigens, mature T and B cells are called 'naïve cells', which subserve functions such as recognition of antigen and storage of immunological memory.
- Lymophocytes have antigen recognition mechanisms on their surfaces. When an immunocompetent cell reacts with its specific antigen, there may be induction of 'tolerance' or an immune response.
- Stimulated T cells produce lymphokines and effect cell-mediated immunity. A number of surface antigens or markers on lymphocytes reflect the stage of differentiation and functional properties of the cells. One such marker is the cluster of differentiation (CD) marker (CD4 in helper/inducer T cells, CD8 in suppressor/cytotoxic T cells). All T cells possess CD3 on their surface and B cells have Ig on their surface.
- T cells are classified as regulatory or effector cells. They may be CD4+ or CD8+ on their surface:
    - Helper/Inducer (T_H) cells, with a CD4 surface marker and major histocompatibility complex (MHC) Class II restriction, stimulate the growth of T cells and macrophages and can differentiate into TH cells or T regulatory cells. T_H cells are further differentiated into T_H1, T_H2, T_H17 and Treg cells.

- ❖ Cytotoxic T cells (T$_c$), with CD8 surface markers and MHC Class I restriction, which can kill and lyse target cells including tumour, allograft and virus-infected cells.
  - ❖ Memory T cells (T$_m$), both CD4 and CD8 cells, provide memory and anamnestic immune response.
- B cells undergo maturation in different stages as pro-, pre-, immature and mature B cells.
  - ❖ On contact with its specific antigen, the mature B cell undergoes clonal proliferation to form long-lived memory cells or plasma cells. These are antibody secreting cells, which makes an antibody of a single specificity, of a single immunoglobulin class and allotype and of a single light chain type only.
- Null cells are circulating lymphocytes which possess neither T cell nor B cell markers. They are of three types. Natural killer (NK) cells, antibody dependent cytotoxic cells (ADCC) and lymphokine activated killer (LAK) cells.
- Phagocytic cells consist of mononuclear macrophages (of blood and tissues) and polymorphonuclear microphages and function as an effective defence against most microorganisms.
- Macrophages, dendritic cells and B cells are the major antigen-presenting cells.
- Histocompatibilty antigens are cell surface antigens that induce an immune response leading to rejection of allografts coding for three different classes of proteins:
  - ❖ Class I proteins that determine histocompatibility and acceptance or rejection of allografts
  - ❖ Class II proteins that regulate the immune response
  - ❖ Class III proteins that include some components of the complement system
- Human major histocompatibility complex (MHC) antigens are synonymous with human leukocyte antigens (HLA) and the MHC complex of genes with the HLA complex. The HLA complex of genes consists of three separate clusters of genes: HLA Class I, comprising A, B and C loci; HLA Class II or the D region, consisting of DR, DQ and DP loci; and HLA Class III or the complement region, containing genes for complement components C2 and C4.
- HLA loci are multiallelic and the HLA system is very pleomorphic. HLA antigens are two-chain glycoprotein molecules anchored on the surface membrane of cells.
  - ❖ Class I HLA antigens are found on the surface of virtually all nucleated cells and are involved in graft rejection and cell-mediated cytolysis.
  - ❖ HLA Class II antigens are found only on cells of the immune system (macrophages, dendritic cells, activated T cells, and particularly on B cells).
  - ❖ HLA Class III molecules are heterogenous.
- The MHC system, in the natural state, serves as cell markers that help infected cells to signal cytotoxic and helper T cells. The enormous polymorphism of MHC helps maximise protection against microbial infections.
- HLA typing is done serologically by microcytotoxicity, which tests for complement-mediated lysis of peripheral blood lymphocytes with a standard set of typing sera. It is used primarily for testing compatibility between recipients and potential donors before tissue transplantation. It has applications in disputed paternity and in anthropological studies. An association has been noted between HLA types and certain diseases (HLA-B27 and ankylosing spondylitis; many autoimmune conditions and HLA-DR3).
- T cells respond to processed antigens on the macrophages and other accessory cells only when they are presented along with the self-MHC antigen—the phenomenon of MHC restriction.

SHORT ANSWERS

1. Lymphoid cells and organs of the immune system and their functions
2. Differences between B and T cells and their process of maturation
3. Types of immune response
4. Types of T cells and their functions
5. Virus recognition and elimination by the immune system
6. Classes of Major Histocompatibilty Complex (MHC) and their role in immune cells
7. HLA, its classes and their functions

SHORT NOTES

1. B cells
2. T cells
3. T cell receptor
4. Antigen presenting cells
5. Null cells
6. Phagocytic cells
7. HLA typing and their applications
8. MHC restriction
9. Applications of HLA typing
10. Role of macrophages in immunity

15 Immune Response

INTRODUCTION

The specific reactivity induced in a host by an anti-genic stimulus is known as the **immune response**. In infectious disease, it is generally equated with pro-tection against invading microorganisms. However, the immune response has a much wider scope and includes reactions against any antigen, living or non-living. It may lead to consequences that are beneficial, indifferent or injurious to the host. It also includes the state of specific non-reactivity (tolerance) induced by certain types of antigenic stimuli.

Types

The immune response can be of two types: humoral (antibody-mediated) and cellular (cell-mediated). The two are usually developed together, though at times one or the other may be predominant or exclusive. They usually act in conjunction but sometimes in opposition.

Antibody-mediated immunity (AMI)

- provides primary defence against most extracellular bacterial pathogens,
- helps in defence against viruses that infect through the respiratory or intestinal tracts,
- prevents recurrence of virus infections, and
- participates in the pathogenesis of immediate (types 1, 2 and 3) hypersensitivity and certain autoimmune diseases.

Cell-mediated immunity (CMI)

- protects against fungi, viruses and facultative intra-cellular bacterial pathogens,
- participates in the rejection of homografts and graft-versus-host reaction,
- provides immunological surveillance and immunity against cancer, and
- mediates the pathogenesis of delayed (type 4) hyper-sensitivity and certain autoimmune diseases.

HUMORAL IMMUNE RESPONSE (ANTIBODY-MEDIATED)

Production of antibodies: This consists of three steps:

1. The entry of the antigen, its distribution and fate in the tissues and its contact with appropriate immu-nocompetent cells (called the **afferent limb**).
2. The processing of antigen by cells and control of the process of antibody formation (called the **central functions**).
3. The secretion of antibody, its distribution in tissues and body fluids and the manifestations of its effects (called the **efferent limb**).

Phases: Antibody production follows characteristic phases:

1. **Lag phase,** the stage immediately following anti-genic stimulus during which no antibody is detect-able in circulation
2. **Log phase,** in which the titre of antibodies rises steadily
3. **Plateau** or steady state, when there is equilibrium between antibody synthesis and catabolism
4. **Phase of decline,** during which catabolism exceeds production and the titre falls (Fig. 15.1)

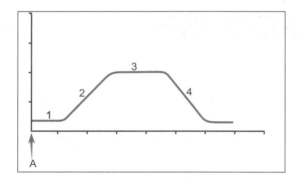

Fig. 15.1   Primary immune response

Primary and secondary responses

Primary response: The antibody response to an initial antigenic stimulus.

Secondary response: The response to subsequent stimuli with the same antigen.

Primary response differs qualitatively and quantitatively from secondary response (**Fig. 15.2**). The differences between primary and secondary responses are given in Table 15.1.

The duration of the lag phase and the persistence of the antibody vary with the nature of the antigen. With some antigens such as diphtheria toxoid, the lag phase

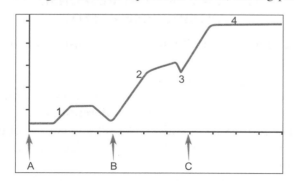

Fig. 15.2   Effect of repeated antigenic stimulus

in the primary response may be as long as 2–3 weeks, while with pneumococcal polysaccharide, antibodies can be detected as early as within a few hours.

Dose: A single injection of an antigen helps more in sensitising or priming the immunocompetent cells producing the particular antibody than in the actual generation of high levels of antibody. Effective levels of antibody are usually induced only by subsequent injections of the antigen. It is for this reason that non-living vaccines are given in multiple doses for active immunisation. The first injection is known as the **priming** dose and subsequent injections as **booster** doses. With live vaccines, a single dose is sufficient as multiplication of the organism in the body provides a continuing antigenic stimulus that acts as both the priming and the booster dose.

When an antigen is injected into an animal already carrying the specific antibody in circulation, a temporary fall in the level of the circulating antibody occurs due to combination of the antigen with the antibody. This has been called the **negative phase**. It is followed by an increase in the titre of the antibody exceeding the initial level.

Fate of antigen in tissues

The manner in which an antigen is dealt with in the body depends on factors such as the physical and chemical nature of the antigen, its dose and route of entry, and whether antigenic stimulus is primary or secondary. Antigens introduced intravenously are rapidly localised in the spleen, liver, bone marrow, kidneys and lungs. They are broken down by the reticuloendothelial cells and excreted in urine, about 70–80 per cent being thus eliminated within one or two days. In contrast, antigens introduced subcutaneously are mainly localised in the draining lymph nodes, only small amounts being found in the spleen.

Table 15.1   *Differences between primary and secondary immune response*

Features	Primary response	Secondary response
Lag period after immunisation	Usually 4–10 days	Usually 1–3 days
Involving B cell	Naive B cell	Memory B cell
Peak response time	7–10 days	3–5 days
Peak antibody response	Depends on antigen	Usually 100–1000 times more than primary response
Isotype generated	In early response IgM predominates	IgG predominates
Antigens	Both thymus dependent and independent	Only thymus dependent
Antibody affinity	Lower	Higher
Immunisation needed	Comparatively high dose of antigens, favourably with adjuvants (protein antigens)	Adjuvants not required

- **Particulate antigens** are removed from circulation in two phases. The first is the **non-immune phase** during which the antigen is engulfed by the phagocytic cells, broken down and eliminated. With the appearance of the specific antibody, the phase of **immune elimination** begins, during which antigen–antibody complexes are formed and rapidly phagocytosed, resulting in accelerated disappearance of the antigen from circulation.

- **Soluble antigens** are removed in three phases— equilibration, metabolism and immune elimination. The phase of **equilibration** consists of diffusion of the antigen to the extravascular spaces. During the **metabolic phase**, the level of the antigen falls due to catabolic decay. During the phase of **immune elimination**, there is rapid elimination of the antigen with the formation of antigen–antibody complexes. Such complexes may cause tissue damage and may be responsible for 'immune complex diseases' such as serum sickness.

The **rate of elimination** of an antigen is related to the rate at which it is metabolised. Protein antigens are generally eliminated within days or weeks, whereas polysaccharides, which are metabolised slowly, persist for months or years. Pneumococcal polysaccharide, for instance, may persist for up to 20 years in humans, following a single injection.

Production of antibodies

Immune response to an antigen is brought about by three types of cells: antigen processing cells (APC— principally macrophages and dendritic cells), T cells and B cells.

- **Antigen processing and presentation**: The first step is the capture and processing of antigens by APC and their presentation, in association with the appropriate MHC molecule, to T cells. While this step is essential for most antigens (T cell–dependent antigens such as proteins and erythrocytes), in the case of T cell–independent antigens, such as polysaccharides and other structurally simple molecules with repeating epitopes, antibody production does not require T cell participation.

- **T and B cell activation**: Only when the processed antigen is presented on the surface of the APC, in association with MHC molecules, to the T cell carrying the receptor (TCR) for the epitope is the T cell able to recognise it. In the case of CD4 (helper T/T_H) cells, the antigen has to be presented complexed with MHC Class II and for CD8 (cytotoxic T/T_C) cells with MHC Class I molecules. B cells, which possess surface Ig and MHC Class II molecules, can also present antigens to T cells, particularly during the secondary response.

The T_H cell requires two signals for activation. The first signal is a combination of the T cell receptor (TCR) with the MHC Class II-complexed antigen. The second signal is interleukin-1 (IL1) which is produced by the APC. The activated T_H cell forms interleukin-2 and other cytokines required for B cell stimulation. These include IL4, IL5 and IL6 which act as B cell activating factor (BCGF) and the the B cell differentiation factor (BCDF). They activate B cells which have combined with their respective antigens to clonally proliferate and differentiate into antibody secreting plasma cells. A small proportion of activated B cells, instead of being transformed into plasma cells, become long-lived memory cells producing a secondary type of response to subsequent contact with the antigen.

Cytotoxic T (CD8/TC) cells are activated when they come into contact with antigens presented along with MHC Class I molecules. They also need a second signal IL2, which is secreted by activated T_H cells. On contact with a target cell carrying the antigen on its surface, the activated T_C cells release cytotoxins that destroy the target, which may be virus infected or tumour cells. Some T_C cells also become memory cells (Fig. 15.3).

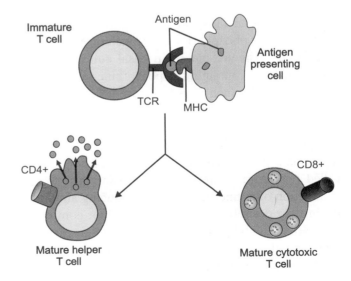

Fig. 15.3 T cell response

Monoclonal antibodies

Principle: A single antibody forming cell or clone produces antibodies directed specifically against a single antigen or antigenic determinant only. However, antibodies produced ordinarily by infection or antigens have multiple epitopes or antigenic determinants, each of which generates separate clones of lymphocytes. This results in antisera containing immunoglobulins of different classes with specificities against different epitopes of the antigen. On the other hand, when a clone of lymphocytes or plasma cells undergoes selective proliferation, as in multiple myeloma, antibodies with single antigenic specificity accumulate. Such antibodies produced by a single clone and directed against a single antigenic determinant are called monoclonal antibodies. Monoclonal antibodies are very useful tools for diagnostic and research techniques.

An ingenious method for the large-scale production of monoclonal antibodies against any desired antigen was developed by Kohler and Milstein in 1975. In recognition of the great importance of this hybridoma technology, the Nobel Prize for Medicine was awarded to them in 1984.

Hybridomas are somatic cell hybrids produced by fusing antibody forming spleen cells with myeloma cells. The resultant hybrid retains the antibody producing capacity of the spleen cell and the ability of the myeloma cells to multiply indefinitely (**Fig. 15.4**).

Technique: Lymphocytes from the spleen of mice immunised with the desired antigen are fused with mouse myeloma cells grown in culture which do not form immunoglobulins and are deficient in the enzyme hypoxanthine phosphoribosyl transferase (HPRT). The fused cells are placed in basal culture medium (HAT medium containing hypoxanthine, aminopterin and thymidine) which does not permit the growth of enzyme deficient myeloma cells. As normal lymphocytes cannot replicate indefinitely, only hybrid cells possessing properties of both the splenic lymphocytes and myeloma cells can grow in culture. These hybrid cells, called hybridomas, are cloned and examined for the production of antibodies. Clones producing antibodies against the desired antigen are selected for continuous cultivation. Such hybridomas can be maintained indefinitely in culture and will continue to form monoclonal antibodies. They may also be injected intraperitoneally in mice and monoclonal antibodies may be obtained by harvesting the ascitic fluid produced.

Hybridomas may be frozen for prolonged storage. The discovery of hybridoma technology for the production of unlimited quantities of identical monoclonal antibodies of the same Ig class, possessing uniform specificity, affinity and other properties, created a revolution in clinical immunology.

Humanised (chimeric) antibodies: Murine monoclonal antibodies, however, proved unsuitable for human therapeutic use because they induced strong antimouse immune response. Moreover, the *Fc* piece of mouse Ig could not initiate effector defence mechanisms in human beings. Various modifications were introduced to improve efficiency. Cleaved *Fab* fragments could be coupled to various active substances like toxins, enzymes, radionuclides or cytotoxic drugs. Mouse monoclonals have been humanised by genetic manipulation to make chimeric antibodies consisting of murine variable regions and human constant regions. Grafting of murine monoclonal CDR loops on a human Ig framework provides a virtually human molecule. (The antigen binding surface of an antibody is composed of six hypervariable loops of amino acids. These are called **complementarity determining regions** or CDRs).

Antibody engineering: Human monoclonal antibodies have subsequently been developed. Genes for particular antibody fragments have been fused to bacteriophage genes. Whole libraries of such antibodies have been built using bacteriophages. Large quantities of the desired antibody can be prepared by infecting bacteria with the appropriate bacteriophage. Such antibody engineering holds great promise for immunotherapy.

Applications:
- Monoclonal antibodies have numerous diagnostic applications for bacterial, viral and other antigens.
- It also has various therapeutic and research applications.
- Monoclonal antibodies against several antigens are now used in immunoflourescence and ELISA kits available commercially.

Factors influencing antibody production

Genetic factors: The immune response is under genetic control and differences in immune response to the same antigen shown by different individuals in a species are determined by genetic differences. The terms '**responder**' and '**non-responder**' are used to describe the individual's capacity to respond to a

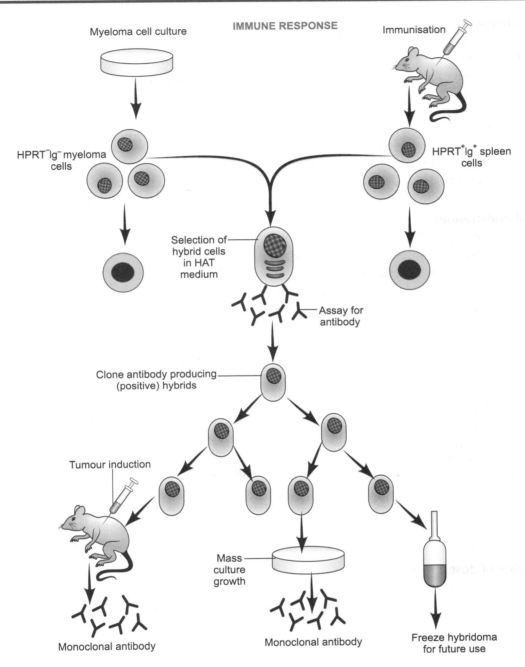

Fig. 15.4   Monoclonal antibody production by hybridoma

particular antigen. The Ir (immune response) genes control this property.

Age: The embryo is immunologically immature. The capacity to produce antibodies starts only with the development and differentiation of lymphoid organs. The age at which embryos acquire immunological competence varies with different species. During embryonic life, the developing lymphoid cells come into contact with all the tissue antigens of the body released by cellular breakdown, so that all the clones of cells that have specificity towards self-antigens are eliminated.

Immunocompetence is not complete at birth, but continues to develop as the infant grows. The infant has to depend on itself for antibody production from 3–6 months of age, by which time the maternal antibodies disappear. However, full competence is acquired only by about 5–7 years for IgG and 10–15 years for IgA.

Nutritional status: Malnutrition affects immune response adversely, though serum components necessary for immunity are conserved selectively till the nutritional deficiency becomes marked. Protein calorie malnutrition suppresses both humoral and cellular immune response, the latter more severely. Deficiencies of amino acids (tryptophan, phenyl alanine, methionine, glycine, isoleucine) and vitamins (vitamin A and B, riboflavin, pyridoxine, pantothenic acid, folic acid) have been shown to cause a decrease in antibody synthesis.

Route of administration: The humoral immune response is better following parenteral administration of antigens than through the oral or nasal routes. Large particulate antigens, such as bacteria or erythrocytes, are more effective when injected into tissues. The route of administration may also influence the type of antibody produced. For production of IgA antibodies, the oral or nasal route is most suitable. Inhalation of pollen antigens induces IgE synthesis, whereas the same antigens given parenterally lead to IgG antibodies. With some antigens the route of administration determines whether tolerance or antibody response results. Injection of protein antigens into the mesenteric vein or intrathymically usually induces tolerance.

With some antigens the site of injection seems relevant. The hepatitis B vaccine is less immunogenic following gluteal injection than following injection into the deltoid. This may be due to the paucity of antigen presenting cells in gluteal fat, delaying presentation of the antigen to T and B cells.

Size and number of doses: Antibody response is, to an extent, dose dependent. An antigen is effective only above a minimum critical dose. Further increase in dose (optimal) enhances the intensity of antibody response. But beyond a certain level, increase in the dose of antigen does not improve the antibody response but may even inhibit it and induce tolerance. Mice injected with 0.5 μg of pneumococcal capsular polysaccharide produced specific antibodies but those injected with 50 μg of the antigen not only failed to form antibodies but did not respond even to subsequent doses of the same antigen. The massive antigenic stimulus appears to swamp the antibody producing system and paralyse it. This phenomenon was designated '**immunological paralysis**' by Felton (1949).

The increased antibody response to a secondary antigenic stimulus has already been noticed. With repeated antigen injections, the antibody response increases progressively, but after a certain stage, no further increase occurs.

Multiple antigens: When two or more antigens are administered simultaneously, the effects may vary. Antibodies may be produced against the different antigens just as though they had been given separately, or antibody response to one or other of the antigens may be enhanced, or the response to one or more of them may be diminished (antigenic competition). When two bacterial vaccines (for example, typhoid and cholera vaccines) are given in a mixed form, the antibody response to each is not influenced by the other. When toxoids are given along with bacterial vaccines (for example, triple vaccine containing diphtheria and tetanus toxoids along with *Bordetella pertussis* vaccine) the response to the toxoid is potentiated. When diphtheria and tetanus toxoids are given together, with one in excess, the response to the other is inhibited. When the triple antigen is given to a person who had earlier received a primary dose of diphtheria toxoid, the response to the tetanus and pertussis antigens will be diminished. Such antigenic competition is important, from a practical point of view, in immunisation with polyvalent antigens. For optimal effect, the nature and relative proportions of the different antigens in a mixture should be carefully adjusted.

Adjuvants: The term adjuvant refers to any substance that enhances the immunogenicity of an antigen. Adjuvants may confer immunogenicity on non-antigenic substances, increase the concentration and persistence of the circulating antibody, induce or enhance the degree of cellular immunity and lead to the production of 'adjuvant diseases' such as allergic disseminated encephalomyelitis. A variety of substances exhibit adjuvant activity.

Repository adjuvants such as aluminium hydroxide or phosphate and incorporation of protein antigens in the water phase of a water-in-oil emulsion (Freund's incomplete adjuvant) delay the release of antigen from the site of injection and prolong the antigenic stimulus. Others such as silica particles, beryllium sulphate and endotoxins activate macrophages. The most potent adjuvant is **Freund's complete adjuvant**, which is the incomplete adjuvant along with a suspension of killed tubercle bacilli. Besides increasing the humoral immune response, it induces a high degree of cellular immunity (delayed hypersensitivity) as well. As it produces a local granuloma, it is unsuitable for human use. The adjuvant effect of the tubercle bacilli is due to a water soluble peptide MDP (muramyl dipeptide) which induces good antibody response without causing granuloma. Given in mineral oil or as liposomes, it also stimulates cell-mediated immunity. Derivatives of MDP are being developed for human use. Gram-negative bacilli show an adjuvant effect due to their lipopolysaccharide fraction. *Bordetella pertussis*, which has, in addition, a lymphocytosis promoting factor acting on both T and B cells, acts as a good adjuvant for diphtheria and tetanus toxoid in the triple vaccine. Other adjuvants commonly used with human vaccines are aluminium hydroxide and phosphate.

Immunosuppressive agents: These inhibit immune responses. They are useful in certain situations like transplantation, when it becomes necessary to prevent graft rejection. Examples are as follows:

- Sub-lethal **whole body irradiation** suppresses antibody response. When antigenic stimulus follows 24 hours after irradiation, antibody production does not occur, whereas if the antigen is administered 2–3 days before irradiation, the antibody response is actually enhanced. The primary response is more radiosensitive than the secondary response.

- **Radiomimetic drugs** are agents with an action resembling that of x-rays. They belong in general to the class of alkylating agents (for example, cyclophosphamide, nitrogen mustard). In human beings, cyclophosphamide given for three days after the antigen completely suppresses the antibody response. It is much less effective when given before the antigen.

- **Corticosteroids** cause depletion of lymphocytes from blood and lymphoid organs. They also stabilise the membranes of cells and lysosomes, inhibiting histamine release and the inflammatory response. Therapeutic doses have little effect on antibody formation in human beings. They inhibit the induction and manifestations of delayed hypersensitivity in humans.

- **Anti-metabolites** are substances that interfere with the synthesis of DNA, RNA or both and thus inhibit the cell division and differentiation necessary for humoral and cellular immune response. They include folic acid antagonists (methotrexate), alkylating agents (cyclophosphamide) and analogues of purine (6-mercaptopurine, azathioprine), cytosine (cytosine arabinoside) and uracil (5-fluorouracil). Many anti-metabolites find clinical application in the prevention of graft rejection.

- The drug most widely used now for immunosuppression is **cyclosporine**, a cyclic polypeptide derived from the soil fungus *Tolypocladium inflatum*. It is not cytotoxic for lymphocytes and has no anti-mitotic activity. It selectively inhibits helper T cell activity. A related drug is rapamycin.

- **Anti-lymphocyte serum (ALS)** is a heterologous antiserum raised against lymphocytes. The antibody prepared against thymus cells is called **anti-thymocyte serum (ATS)**. The corresponding globulin preparations are called **ALG** and **ATG**. They were used to prevent graft rejection. While all other immunosuppressive agents have undesirable side effects, ALS is devoid of any action other than that on lymphocytes. ALS acts primarily against T lymphocytes and therefore specifically on cell-mediated immunity. Humoral antibody response to thymus-independent antigens is unaffected and may even be enhanced. ALS acts only against lymphocytes in circulation and not cells in lymphoid organs. As ALS is a foreign protein, its effect is decreased on repeated administration, which may also lead to serum sickness and other hypersensitivity reactions. Monoclonal antibodies against specific lymphocyte membrane antigens have been prepared.

Effect of antibody: The humoral immune response to an antigen can be suppressed specifically by passive administration of the homologous antibody. The action appears to be by a feedback mechanism. The primary response is more susceptible to inhibition than the secondary response. The antibody may also combine with the antigen and prevent its availability for the immunocompetent cells. The inhibitory effect of a passively administered antibody on the humoral immune response has been applied in the prevention of Rh sensitisation in Rh-negative women carrying an Rh-positive fetus. This is achieved by the administration of anti-Rh globulin immediately after delivery (within 72 hours).

This effect is also relevant in the practice of combined immunisation as in diphtheria and tetanus. In such cases, the toxoid and antitoxin should be given at separate sites. Adsorbed toxoid should be used as the inhibitory effect is much less than with fluid toxoid.

Intravenous administration of immune globulin has been shown to have immunomodulatory effects. It has been used in the treatment of many diseases of presumed immunopathologic origin, such as thrombocytopenias and autoimmune hemolytic anemias.

CELLULAR IMMUNE RESPONSE

The term cell-mediated immunity (CMI) refers to the specific immune responses mediated by effector T cells generated in response to the antigen. Both activated T_H cells and cytotoxic T lymphocytes (CTLs) serve as effector cells in CMI. It refers to the immune responses that do not involve antibodies. For long, the only demonstrable facet of CMI was the phenomenon of delayed hypersensitivity (DH) which resulted in injury rather than protection. Koch (1890) described the exaggerated cutaneous reaction of tuberculous guinea pigs to the intradermal injection of the tubercle bacillus or a protein extract of the bacillus (tuberculin). Thereafter, the tuberculin test became the paradigm for DH.

The term **delayed hypersensitivity** refers to the appearance of a skin lesion 48–72 hours after administration of the antigen. The lesion is an indurated nodule with infiltration by mononuclear cells. DH was found to be immunologically specific but did not have any relation to antibodies and could not be transferred passively by serum. The cellular basis of DH was shown by Landsteiner and Chase (1942) by its passive transfer in guinea pigs through the injection of leucocytes from sensitised donors. With the recognition of the two-component concept of immunity, DH and other types of CMI were found to be mediated by T lymphocytes. A variety of techniques are now available for the detection of CMI, though they lack the sensitivity and precision of antibody assays for humoral immunity.

Scope of cell-mediated immunity (CMI)

Cell-mediated immunity participates in the following immunological functions:
- Delayed hypersensitivity
- Immunity in infectious diseases caused by obligate and facultative intracellular parasites. These include infections with bacteria (for example, tuberculosis, leprosy, listeriosis, brucellosis), fungi (for example, histoplasmosis, coccidioidomycosis, blastomycosis), protozoa (for example, leishmaniasis, trypanosomiasis) and viruses (for example, measles, mumps)
- Transplantation immunity and graft-versus-host reaction
- Immunological surveillance and immunity against cancer
- Pathogenesis of certain autoimmune diseases (for example, thyroiditis, encephalomyelitis)

Induction of cell-mediated immunity (CMI)

The nature of the antigenic stimulus is important in the induction of CMI. It is best developed following infection with intracellular parasites. Killed vaccines and other non-living antigens do not induce CMI unless administered with the Freund type of adjuvants. Only T cell–dependent antigens lead to CMI. The application of certain chemicals on the skin induces DH (Fig. 15.5).

Each T cell bears on its surface a specific receptor (TCR) for one epitope and combines only with antigens carrying that epitope. On contact with the appropriate antigen, T cells undergo blast transformation, clonal proliferation and differentiation into memory cells and effector cells providing CMI. T cells recognise antigens only when presented with MHC molecules. Helper T cells react with antigens presented on the surface of macrophages or other cells, complexed with MHC Class II molecules. They then release biological mediators (cytokines) which activate macrophages, enabling them to kill intracellular parasites. Cytotoxic T cells recognise antigens on the surface of cells (such as virus infected, tumour or allograft cells), in association with MHC Class I molecules, secrete cytokines and destroy the target cells.

Cytokines

Biologically active substances released by activated T lymphocytes were called lymphokines. Similar

Table 15.2 *Examples of lymphokines*

I. Affecting macrophages
a) Migration inhibiting factor (MIF)
b) Macrophage activation/Aggregation factor (MAF)
c) Macrophage chemotactic factor (MCF)
II. Affecting lymphocytes
a) Blastogenic/Mitogenic factor (BF/MF)
b) T cell growth factor (TGF)
c) B cell growth factor (BGF)
III. Affecting granulocytes
a) Chemotactic factor (CF)
b) Colony stimulating factor (CSF)
IV. Affecting cultured cells
a) Lymphotoxin (LT)
b) Interferon (IFN)
c) Tumour necrosis factor (TNF)
V. Others
a) Skin reactive factor (SRF)
b) Transfer factor (TF)

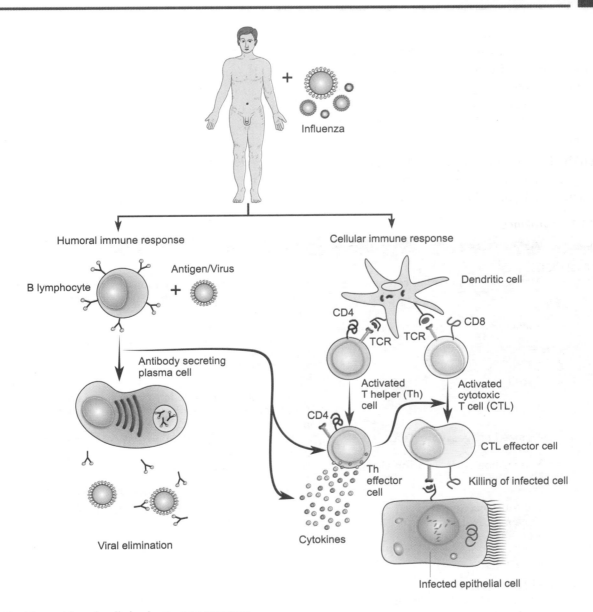

Fig. 15.5 Humoral and cellular immune response

substances produced by monocytes or macrophages were called monokines. Initially they were given names based on their demonstrated biological effect (Table 15.2). As most lymphokines exhibit multiple biological effects and the same effect may be caused by different lymphokines, their names lacked precision. The term **interleukin** was therefore introduced for those products of leucocytes that exert a regulatory influence on other cells. Interferons, growth factors and others were found to have similar effects. Therefore all of them have been grouped under the term cytokines.

Cytokines are peptide mediators or intercellular messengers that regulate immunological, inflammatory and reparative host responses. They are highly potent hormone-like substances, active even at femtomolar (10^{-15}M) concentrations. They differ from endocrine hormones in being produced not by specialised glands but by widely distributed cells (such as lymphocytes, macrophages, platelets and fibroblasts), and acting not systemically but locally near the producing cells (paracrine effect) or directly on the producing cells themselves (autocrine effect). They are, in general, pleiotropic, having multiple effects on the growth and differentiation of various cell types. There is considerable overlap in the effects produced by different cytokines. Cloning of cytokines and the availability of monoclonal antibodies against them have helped to characterise them better (Table 15.3).

The features of some important cytokines are presented below.

Interleukin-1: Originally described as the leucocyte activating factor (LAF) in 1972 and as the B cell activating factor (BAF) in 1974, this cytokine was renamed interleukin-1 (IL1) in 1979. IL1 is a stable polypeptide retaining its activity up to 56°C and between pH 3 and 11. IL1 occurs in two molecular forms, alpha and beta. It is principally secreted by macrophages and monocytes but can be produced by most other nucleated cells as well. Its production is stimulated by antigens, toxins, injury and inflammatory processes and inhibited by cyclosporin A, corticosteroids and prostaglandins.

The immunological effects of IL1 include stimulation of T cells for the production of IL2 and other lym-

Table 15.3 *Cytokines*

Cytokine	Main sources	Major functions
A. INTERLEUKINS		
IL1 (α and β)	Macrophages and other cell types	Proliferation and differentiation of T, B and other cells; pyrogenic; induce acute phase proteins; bone marrow cell proliferation
IL2	T cells	Promote growth and differentiation of T and B cells, cytotoxicity of T and NK cells, secretion of other lymphokines
IL3	T cells	Multi-CSF
IL4	T_H cells	Proliferation of B and cytotoxic T cells; increase IgGl and IgE production; enhance MHC Class II and IgE receptors
IL5	T_H cells	Proliferation of eosinophils, stimulate IgA and IgM production
IL6	T_H, macrophages, fibroblasts	Promote B cell differentiation; IgG production, acute phase proteins
IL7	Spleen, bone marrow stromal cells	B and T cell growth factor
IL8	Macrophages, others	Neutrophil chemotactic factor
IL9	T cell	T cell growth and proliferation
IL10	T, B cells, macrophages	Inhibit IFN production and mononuclear cell functions
IL11	Bone marrow stromal cells	Induce acute phase proteins
IL12	T cells	Activate NK cells
IL13	T cells	Inhibit mononuclear cell functions
IL17	T_H 17 cells	Proinflammatory marker
B. COLONY STIMULATING FACTORS		
GM-CSF	T cells, macrophages, fibroblasts	T cell and macrophage growth stimulation
G-CSF	Fibroblasts, endothelium	Granulocyte growth stimulation
M-CSF	Fibroblasts, endothelium	Macrophage growth stimulation
C. TUMOUR NECROSIS FACTORS		
TNFα	Macrophages, monocytes	Tumour cytotoxicity, lipolysis, wasting, acute phase proteins, phagocytic cell activation, antiviral and antiparasitic effects, endotoxic shock
TNFβ	T cells	Induce other cytokines
D. INTERFERONS		
IFN α	Leucocytes	
IFN β	Fibroblasts	Antiviral activity
IFN γ	T cells	Antiviral, macrophage activation; MHC Class I and II expression on cells
E. OTHERS		
TGF-β	T and B cells	Inhibit T and B cell proliferation and hematopoiesis; promote wound healing
LIF	T cells	Proliferation of stem cells; eosinophil chemotaxis

phokines, B cell proliferation and antibody synthesis, neutrophil chemotaxis and phagocytosis. It mediates a wide range of metabolic, physiological, inflammatory and hematological effects by acting on bone marrow, epithelial and synovial cells, fibroblasts, osteoclasts, hepatocytes, vascular endothelium and other targets. IL1 is an important endogenous pyrogen. Together with the tumour necrosis factor (TNF), it is responsible for many of the hematological changes in septic shock and also enhances the initial meningeal inflammation in bacterial meningitis. Cytokine inhibitors such as dexamethasone have been found to protect against the sequelae of such excessive meningeal inflammation. On the other hand, IL1 has a beneficial effect in severe infections in immunocompromised hosts.

Interleukin-2: The discovery in 1976 of a T cell growth factor (TCGF) produced by activated T cells, which induced T cell proliferation and enabled their maintenance in continuous culture, contributed greatly to the understanding of T cell function. This cytokine, renamed IL2, is a powerful modulator of the immune response. It is the major activator of T and B cells and stimulates cytotoxic T cells and NK cells. It converts some null cells (LGL) into lymphokine activated killer (LAK) cells which can destroy NK-resistant tumour cells. This property has been used in the treatment of certain types of cancer.

Interleukin-3: IL3 is a growth factor for bone marrow stem cells. It stimulates multilineage hematopoiesis and is therefore known also as the multicolony stimulating factor (multi-CSF).

Interleukin-4: Formerly known as the B cell growth factor-1 (BCGF-1), IL4 activates resting B cells and acts as a B cell differentiating factor. It also acts as a growth factor for T cells and mast cells. It enhances the action of cytotoxic T cells. It may have a role in atopic hypersensitivity as it augments IgE synthesis.

Interleukin-5: Formerly known as the B cell growth factor-II, IL5 causes proliferation of activated B cells. It also induces maturation of eosinophils.

Interleukin-6: IL6 is produced by stimulated T and B cells, macrophages and fibroblasts. It induces immunoglobulin synthesis by activated B cells and formation of IL2 receptors on T cells. It has a stimulatory effect on hepatocytes, nerve cells and hematopoietic cells. It acts as an inflammatory response mediator in host defence against infections.

Colony stimulating factor (CSF): These cytokines stimulate the growth and differentiation of pluripotent stem cells in the bone marrow. They have been named after the types of cell colonies they induce in soft agar culture—for example, granulocyte (G), or mononuclear (M) CSF. IL3 which induces growth of all types of hematopoietic cells is known as multi-CSF. In the body they cause other effects also, presumably by inducing cascades of other cytokines. They are responsible for adjusting the rate of production of blood cells according to requirements, for example, the massive granulocyte response seen in pyogenic infections. Colony stimulating factors have clinical applications for treating hematopoietic dysfunctions in infections and malignancies.

Tumour necrosis factor (TNF): The tumour necrosis factor occurs as two types, alpha and beta. A serum factor found to induce hemorrhagic necrosis in certain tumours was named the tumour necrosis factor. The same substance was independently described as cachectin, a serum factor causing the wasting syndrome (cachexia) during chronic infections. This has been renamed TNFα. It is formed principally by activated macrophages and monocytes. It resembles IL1 in possessing a very wide spectrum of biological activities such as participation in the manifestations of endotoxic shock. It exerts an immunomodulatory influence on other cytokines. TNFβ, formerly known as lymphotoxin, is produced principally by T helper cells. Its effects are similar to those of TNFα.

Interferons (IFN): Originally identified as antiviral agents, interferons are now classified as cytokines. There are three classes of IFNs: alpha produced by leucocytes, beta produced by fibroblasts and gamma by T cells activated by antigens, mitogens or exposure to IL2. IFNγ causes many immunological effects, such as macrophage activation, augmentation of neutrophil and monocyte function, and anti-tumour activity.

Other cytokines: The transforming growth factor beta (TGFβ) was so named because of its ability to transform fibroblasts. Besides acting as a growth factor for fibroblasts and promoting wound healing, it also acts as a down-regulator of some immunological and hematological processes.

The leukemia inhibitory factor (LIF), produced by T cells, helps stem cell proliferation and eosinophil chemotaxis.

Cytokine production is regulated by exogenous stimuli such as antigens and mitogens, as well as by endogenous factors such as neuroendocrine hormonal peptides (corticosteroids, endorphins) and products of lipoxygenase and cyclooxygenase pathways. They also regulate each other by positive and negative feedback. A number of cytokines (for example, IL1, 2, 3, colony stimulating factors, interferons) have already found therapeutic application. IL17 is a proinflammatory cytokine that plays an important role in autoimmune disorders. With a better understanding of their properties, it is possible that many cytokines, their agonists and antagonists could eventually be used in the management of inflammatory, infectious, autoimmune and neoplastic conditions.

Detection of cell-mediated immunity (CMI)

The original method for detecting CMI was the skin test for delayed hypersensitivity (for example, the tuberculin test). A number of in vitro correlates of CMI have now become available. These include the lymphocyte transformation test (transformation of cultured sensitised T lymphocytes on contact with the antigen), target cell destruction (killing of cultured cells by T lymphocytes sensitised against them), and the migration inhibiting factor test which is commonly used. As originally described, this consisted of incubating in a culture chamber, packed peritoneal macrophages in a capillary tube. The macrophages migrate to form a lacy, fan-like pattern. If the macrophages are from a guinea pig sensitised to tuberculoprotein, addition of tuberculin to the culture chamber will inhibit the migration (Fig. 15.6). This has been adapted for clinical use by incubating human peripheral leucocytes in capillary tubes in culture chambers. When an antigen to which the individual has CMI is introduced into the culture medium, the leucocytes are prevented from migrating. By comparison with the control, it is possible to make a semi-quantitative assessment of the migration inhibition.

Transfer factor

Passive transfer of CMI was first achieved by the injection of viable leucocytes from sensitised donors. Lawrence (1954) reported the transfer of CMI in humans by the injection of extracts from leucocytes. This extract is known as the 'transfer factor' (TF). The transferred immunity is specific in that CMI can be transferred only to those antigens to which the donor is sensitive.

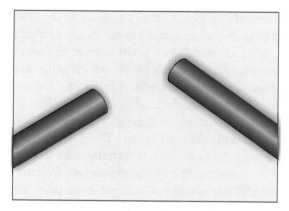

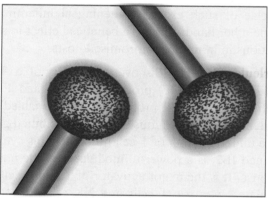

Fig. 15.6 Inhibition of migration of macrophage cells

TF is a dialysable, low-molecular-weight substance (MW 2000–4000), resistant to trypsin, DNAase, RNAase and freeze thawing. It is stable for several years at −20°C and in the lyophilised form at 4°C. It is inactivated at 56°C in 30 minutes. It is not antigenic. Chemically, it appears to be a polypeptide–polynucleotide.

TF is highly potent—an extract from 0.1 ml of packed leucocytes is sufficient for transfer. The transferred CMI is systemic and not local at the injected site. Following TF injection, DH and various in vitro correlates of CMI can be demonstrated in the recipient. Humoral immunity is not transmitted by TF; TF transfers CMI to all the antigens to which the donor is sensitive as a whole. It is possible to transfer CMI from the recipient to another in a serial fashion.

The mechanism of action of TF is not known. TF could be an informational molecule or a specific gene derepressor capable of inducing antigenically uncommitted lymphocytes to produce antigen-specific receptors. TF activity was till recently demonstrable only in humans but it has now been reported in monkeys, guinea pigs and mice.

Applications:

- Used to restore immune capacity in patients with T cell deficiency (Wiskott–Aldrich syndrome)
- Used in the treatment of disseminated infections associated with deficient CMI (lepromatous leprosy, tuberculosis, mucocutaneous candidosis)
- Employed in the treatment of malignant melanoma and may be beneficial in other types of cancer
- Use has been suggested in some autoimmune diseases (systemic lupus erythematosus, rheumatoid arthritis) and diseases of unknown origin (sarcoidosis, multiple sclerosis)

IMMUNOLOGICAL TOLERANCE

Immunological tolerance or immunological unresponsiveness is the condition in which contact with an antigen specifically abolishes the capacity to mount an immune response against that particular antigen when it is administered subsequently. This non-reactivity is specific to the particular antigen, immune reactivity to other antigens being unaffected.

Burnet and Fenner (1949) suggested that the unresponsiveness of individuals to self-antigens was due to contact of the immature immunological system with self-antigens during embryonic life. Any antigen that comes into contact with the immunological system during embryonic life would be recognised as a self-antigen and would not induce any immune response. They postulated that tolerance could be induced against foreign antigens if they were administered during embryonic life. This was proved experimentally by Medawar and his colleagues (1953) using two strains of syngeneic mice. When a skin graft from one inbred strain of mice (CBA) is applied on a mouse of another strain (A), it is rejected. If CBA cells are injected into fetal or newborn strain A mice, however, the latter when they grow up will freely accept skin grafts from CBA mice. The content of the self-antigen appears to have been enlarged by contact with a foreign antigen during embryonic life. This phenomenon is called 'specific immunological tolerance'. Development of tolerance is not confined to the embryo or newborn but can also occur in adults. Tolerance may be total or partial, short-lived or long-lasting.

Factors affecting the induction, degree and duration of tolerance are as follows:

- **Species and immunocompetence of the host:** Rabbits and mice can be rendered tolerant more rapidly than guinea pigs and chickens. Strain differences in tolerance induction are seen within species. The higher the degree of immunocompetence of the host, the more difficult it is to induce tolerance. It is for this reason that embryos and newborns are particularly susceptible to induction of tolerance. Tolerance can be induced in adults in whom immunocompetence is temporarily interrupted by immunosuppressive agents. Induction of tolerance is very difficult in adults already immunised against the antigen.

- **Nature of antigen:** The physical state of the antigen is important. Soluble antigens and haptens are more tolerogenic than particulate antigens. The tolerogenicity of an antigen can be modified by certain procedures. When human gamma globulin is heat aggregated, it is highly immunogenic in mice but is tolerogenic when deaggregated. Solutions of serum proteins centrifuged at high speed separate into tolerogenic supernatant and immunogenic sediment fractions.

- **Dose of the antigen:** The induction of tolerance is dose dependent. There is a threshold dose below which tolerance is not induced. Further increase in dose increases the duration of tolerance. With certain antigens, tolerance can be induced by two types of doses, one high and the other low, with intermediate doses producing immunity instead of tolerance. These are known as 'high zone' and 'low zone' tolerance, respectively. A special type of high zone tolerance is Felton's immunological paralysis. The duration of tolerance is variable. Tolerance can be prolonged by repeated tolerogenic stimuli.

- **Route of administration:** The best route to induce tolerance is that whereby the antigen equilibrates throughout the extra- and intravascular compartments. With antigens that do not equilibrate readily or are rapidly eliminated, the route of choice is intravenous. Certain haptens that are immunogenic in guinea pigs by the intradermal route are tolerogenic orally or intravenously.

Tolerance can be overcome spontaneously or by an injection of cross-reacting immunogens. For example, tolerance to bovine serum albumin in rabbits can be abolished by immunisation with cross-reacting human serum albumin. In general, tolerance to living agents is more lasting than that to non-living substances.

Naturally occurring tolerance is found in certain viral infections such as congenital rubella and cytomegalovirus infections in which there is persistent viremia with decreased ability in the production of neutralising antibodies (persistent tolerant infection).

In lymphocytic choriomeningitis infection in carrier mice, the virus may persist in virtually all the cells and tissues and be transmitted vertically to the offspring without any demonstrable immune response or pathogenic effect. When the tolerance is interrupted by an induction of antibody or an injection of sensitised lymphocytes, disease results.

Mechanism: The mechanism of tolerance is not clear. In specific immunological tolerance in embryonic life, the clones of cells responding to the particular antigen were believed to be annihilated by contact with the antigen. This may not be entirely true, as self-reactive B cells can be found in adults. The more likely mechanism may be elimination of T_H cells, effectively preventing B cell activation. This is the '**central mechanism**' of tolerance induction. In other instances, the mechanism may be an '**afferent block**' in which access of the antigen to immunocompetent cells is interfered with, or an '**efferent block**' in which the antibody synthesised is neutralised or destroyed. T and B lymphocytes appear to possess differing sensitivity to tolerance induction, the former being more susceptible. In general, high doses of antigens induce B cell tolerance and repeated minute doses of antigens induce T cell tolerance.

Tolerance to humoral and cellular types of immunity is usually induced simultaneously. '**Split tolerance**' can also occur where unresponsiveness is established for one parameter of the immune response and not for the other. In guinea pigs, DH to tuberculin can be inhibited, without affecting production of a circulating antibody, by the injection of tuberculoprotein prior to immunisation with BCG.

THEORIES OF IMMUNE RESPONSE

A succession of theories have been put forward from time to time to explain the versatility, specificity, memory and other features of immune response. Theories of immunity fall into two categories: instructive and selective.

The **instructive theories** postulate that an immunocompetent cell is capable of synthesising antibodies of any specificity. The antigen encounters an immunocompetent cell and instructs it to produce the complementary antibody. **Selective theories**, on the contrary, shift the emphasis from the antigen to the immunocompetent cell. They postulate that immunocompetent cells have a restricted immunological range. The antigen exerts only a selective influence by stimulating the appropriate immunocompetent cell to synthesise an antibody.

Side chain theory: This, the first plausible theory of immune response, was proposed by Ehrlich (1900). Cells were considered to have surface 'receptors' capable of reacting with substances having complementary 'side chains'. These receptors anchor nutrients to cells before assimilation. When foreign antigens are introduced, they combine with cell receptors that have a complementary fit. This inactivates the receptors and interferes with the absorption of nutrients. As a compensatory mechanism, there is overproduction of the same type of receptors which circulates in blood as antibodies.

While it explains the specificity of antibody response, this theory had to be abandoned when Landsteiner demonstrated that antibodies could be formed not only against natural antigens but also against various synthetic chemicals.

Direct template theories: Instructive theories were proposed by Breinl and Haurowitz (1930), Alexander (1931) and Mudd (1932). According to these, the antigen (or antigenic determinant) enters antibody forming cells and serves as a 'template' against which antibody molecules are synthesised so that they have combining sites complementary to the antigenic determinant. Pauling (1940) presented a more detailed model suggesting that specificity was determined by the folding of the antibody polypeptide chains to form a tertiary structure fitting the antigenic determinant.

Indirect template theory: According to Burnet and Fenner (1949), the entry of the antigenic determinant into the antibody producing cell induced in it a heritable change. A 'genocopy' of the antigenic determinant was thus incorporated in its genome and transmitted to the progeny cells (indirect template). This theory explained specificity and secondary response but became untenable with advances in the molecular biology of protein synthesis.

Natural selection theory: According to Jerne (1955), about a million globulin (antibody) molecules were formed in embryonic life, which covered the full range of antigenic specificities. These globulins were the 'natural antibodies'. When an antigen was introduced, it combined selectively with the globulin that had the nearest complementary 'fit'. This then homed in on the antibody forming cells and stimulated them to synthesise the same kind of antibody. However, this theory did not explain the fact that immunological memory resides in cells and not in serum.

Clonal selection theory: With the advent of cellular and molecular mechanisms, currently the most relevant and accepted theory is that of clonal selection. Burnet (1957) proposed this theory which shifted immunological specificity to the cellular level.

According to the clonal selection hypothesis, during immunological development, cells capable of reacting with different antigens were formed by a process of somatic mutation. Clones of cells that had immunological reactivity with self-antigens were eliminated during embryonic life. Such clones are called **forbidden clones**. Their persistence or development in later life by somatic mutation could lead to autoimmune processes. Each immunocompetent cell was capable of reacting with one antigen (or a small number of antigens) which could recognise and combine with antigens introduced into the body. The result of the contact with the specific antigen was cellular proliferation to form clones synthesising the antibody.

The clonal selection theory is more widely accepted than other theories, though it is unable to account for all the features of immune response. A variety of modifications and alternative theories have been proposed in recent times but none has succeeded in explaining all that is known of immunity.

As an explanation for the mechanism of regulation of antibody response, Jerne has postulated the **network hypothesis**. The variable region of an immunoglobulin molecule carrying the antigen combining site is different in different antibodies. The distinct amino acid sequences at the antigen combining site and the adjacent parts of the variable region are termed **idiotypes**. The idiotype can, in turn, act as an antigenic determinant and induce anti-idiotypic antibodies. These in turn can induce antibodies to them and so on, forming an idiotype network which is postulated to regulate the amount of antibodies produced and the number of antibody forming cells in action. For his theoretical contribution to antibody formation and regulation of the immune system, Niels K Jerne was awarded the Nobel Prize for Medicine in 1984.

The genetic basis of antibody diversity has been clarified recently. An individual has the capacity to produce an estimated 10^8 different antibody molecules. To have each such antibody molecule coded for by a separate gene would require millions of genes to be set apart for antibody production alone. The discovery of split genes for immunoglobulins demolished the longstanding dogma of 'one gene—one protein' and has important implications in biology, beyond immunology. For this discovery, Susumu Tonegawa was awarded the Nobel Prize for Medicine in 1987.

RECAP

- Two phases are seen in the response of the immune system to an antigen: primary and secondary.
- Primary immune response: when a microorganism (or antigen) is encountered for the first time; the latent period is usually long; response itself may be transient and mild.
- Secondary immune response: when the immune system encounters the same microorganism (antigen) on a second or subsequent occasion; response is more rapid (short latent period), vigorous and prolonged.
- The lymphocytes involved in the specific immune response are of two principal types: B lymphocytes (B cells) and T lymphocytes (T cells).
- B lymphocytes are precursors of the antibody producing cells (plasma cells). The immune response can be of two types—humoral (antibody-mediated) and cellular (cell-mediated).
- The antibodies produced by a single clone and directed against a single antigenic determinant are called monoclonal antibodies. They are very useful tools for diagnostic and research techniques.

- T lymphocytes are responsible for cell-mediated immunity. When a T cell encounters an antigen recognised by the T cell receptors, a number of substances, collectively called lymphokines, are released; these activate macrophages and increase their ability to destroy the pathogens.
- Immunological tolerance or unresponsiveness is the condition in which contact with an antigen specifically abolishes the capacity to mount an immune response against that particular antigen when it is administered subsequently.
- Theories of immunity fall into two categories: instructive and selective. The instructive theories postulate that an immunocompetent cell is capable of synthesising antibodies of any specificity. Selective theories shift the emphasis from the antigen to the immunocompetent cell. They postulate that immunocompetent cells have a restricted immunological range.

SHORT ANSWERS

1. Principle and method of preparation of monoclonal antibodies in the laboratory
2. Types of immune response and their functions

SHORT NOTES

1. Humoral immunity
2. Cell-mediated immunity
3. Primary and secondary response
4. Theories of immune response
5. Cytokines
6. Transfer factor
7. Immunosuppressive agents
8. Immunological tolerance
9. Differences between primary and secondary response
10. Applications of monoclonal antibodies in clinical microbiology
11. Factors that influence antibody production

16 Hypersensitivity

INTRODUCTION

Immunity was originally considered a protective process, helping the body to overcome infectious agents and their toxins. Immune response may sometimes be injurious to the host. Sensitised individuals respond to subsequent antigenic stimuli in an inappropriate or exaggerated manner, leading to tissue damage, disease or even death.

The term **hypersensitivity** refers to the undesirable injurious consequences in the sensitised host, following contact with specific antigens. In the protective process of immunity, the focus of attention is the antigen and what happens to it—for example, killing of a bacterium or neutralisation of a toxin. In hypersensitivity, on the other hand, antigens are of little concern and often, they are innocuous or bland substances such as serum proteins or pollen. Hypersensitivity is concerned with what happens to the host as a result of inappropriate immune reaction.

The term **allergy** refers to all immune processes harmful to the host, such as hypersensitivity and autoimmunity. Allergy is probably most commonly used as a synonym for hypersensitivity. It is sometimes used in a narrow sense to refer to only one type of hypersensitivity, namely atopy.

For induction of hypersensitivity reactions, the host should have had contact with the antigen (allergen). The initial contact sensitises the immune system, leading to priming of the appropriate B or T lymphocytes. This is known as the **sensitising** or **priming dose**. Subsequent contact with the allergen causes manifestations of hypersensitivity. This is known as the **shocking dose**.

Cutaneous anaphylaxis

Clinical Case A 45-year-old farmer was brought to the Emergency department with shortness of breath, pounding sensation in the head and tightness in the chest. He had a history of being stung by bees on two earlier occasions. The clinical diagnosis was of cutaneous anaphylaxis. Intramuscular adrenaline and intravenous antihistamines were administrated. The patient recovered completely by the following day.

CLASSIFICATION OF HYPERSENSITIVITY REACTIONS

Hypersensitivity reactions have been classified traditionally into 'immediate' and 'delayed', based on the time required for a sensitised host to develop clinical reactions on re-exposure to the antigen. The main differences between these types of hypersensitivity reactions are shown in Table 16.1.

Immediate and delayed reactions are subdivided into several distinct clinical types:

Immediate hypersensitivity (B cell or antibody mediated)

- Anaphylaxis
- Atopy
- Antibody-mediated cell damage
- Arthus phenomenon
- Serum sickness

Table 16.1   *Distinguishing features of immediate and delayed types of hypersensitivity*

Immediate hypersensitivity	Delayed hypersensitivity
1. Appears and recedes rapidly	1. Appears slowly, lasts longer
2. Induced by antigens or haptens by any route	2. Antigen or hapten intradermally or with Freund's adjuvant or by skin contact
3. Circulating antibodies present and responsible for reaction; 'antibody mediated' reaction	3. Circulating antibodies may be absent and not responsible for reaction; 'cell mediated' reaction
4. Passive transfer possible with serum	4. Cannnot be transferred with serum; but possible with T cells or transfer factor
5. Desensitisation easy, but short-lived	5. Difficult, but long-lasting

Delayed hypersensitivity (T cell mediated)

- Infection (tuberculin)
- Contact dermatitis

Coombs and Gell (1963) classified hypersensitivity reactions into four types based on the different mechanisms of pathogenesis. Their classification, now widely used, is outlined below:

Type I (anaphylactic, IgE or reagin dependent): Antibodies ('cytotropic' IgE antibodies) are fixed on the surface of tissue cells (mast cells and basophils) in sensitised individuals. The antigen combines with the cell-fixed antibody, leading to release of pharmacologically active substances (vasoactive amines) which produce the clinical reaction.

Type II (cytotoxic): This type of reaction is initiated by IgG (or rarely IgM) antibodies that react either with cell surface or tissue antigens. Cell or tissue damage occurs in the presence of complement or mononuclear cells. Type II reactions are intermediate, between hypersensitivity and autoimmunity. Combination with antibody may, in some instances, cause stimulation instead of damage.

Type III (immune complex diseases): Here the damage is caused by antigen–antibody complexes. These may precipitate in and around small blood vessels, causing damage to cells secondarily, or on membranes, interfering with their function.

Type IV (delayed or cell-mediated hypersensitivity): This is a cell-mediated response. The antigen activates specifically sensitised CD4 and CD8 T cells, leading to the secretion of lymphokines and phagocyte accumulation.

Type V (stimulatory hypersensitivity): Other allergy mediated reactions, where instead of binding to cell surface components, the antibodies recognise and bind to the cell surface receptors. This is a modified form of Type II reaction.

The classification and some of the features of hypersensitivity reactions are shown in Table 16.2. The four types of immunopathogenic mechanisms described are not mutually exclusive. Any given hypersensitive reaction may consist of the components of more than one, or all, of these mechanisms. The pathology and clinical features of such immunological diseases would also be influenced by the contributions of many non-immune body mechanisms such as inflammation, complement, coagulation, fibrinolytic and kininogenic systems, collectively called the **humoral amplification system.**

Table 16.2   *Types of hypersensitivity reactions and their features*

Type of reaction	Clinical syndrome	Time required for manifestation	Mediators
Type I: IgE type	1. Anaphylaxis 2. Atopy	Minutes	IgE: histamine and other pharmacological agents
Type II: Cytolytic and cytotoxic	Antibody mediated damage—thrombocytopenia—agranulocytosis, hemolytic anemia, etc.	Variable: hours to days	IgG: IgM, C
Type III: Immune complex	1. Arthus reaction 2. Serum sickness	Variable: hours to days	IgG: IgM, C, leucocytes
Type IV: Delayed hypersensitivity	1. Tuberculin 2. Contact dermatitis	Hours to days	T cells; lymphokines; macrophages

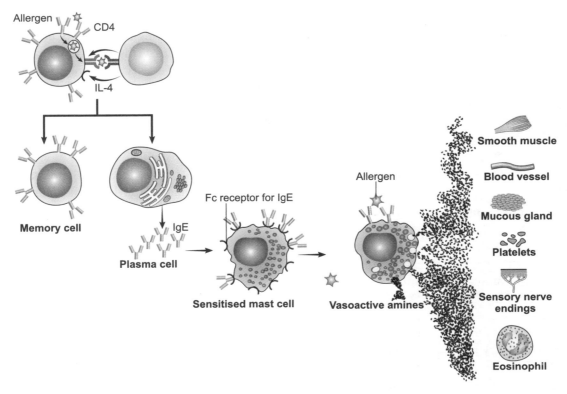

Fig. 16.1 Type I reaction

TYPE I REACTIONS (IgE DEPENDENT)

These occur in two forms: the acute, potentially fatal, systemic form called anaphylaxis and the chronic or recurrent, non-fatal, typically localised form called atopy (Fig. 16.1).

Anaphylaxis

This is the classical immediate hypersensitivity reaction.

Features:

- Antigens and haptens can induce anaphylaxis. There should be an interval of at least 2–3 weeks between the sensitising dose and the shocking dose.
- Once sensitised, the individual remains so for long periods.
- The shocking dose is most effective when injected intravenously, less effective intraperitoneally or subcutaneously and least effective intradermally.
- The shocking antigen must be identical or immunologically closely related to the sensitising antigen.
- The clinical features of anaphylaxis are the same with any antigen but vary between species. The clinical effects are due to smooth muscle contraction and increased vascular permeability.

- The organs affected vary with the species. Tissues or organs predominantly involved in the anaphylactic reaction are known as 'target tissues' or 'shock organs'. Other changes seen in anaphylaxis are edema, decreased coagulability of blood, fall in blood pressure and temperature, leucopenia and thrombocytopenia.

In human beings, fatal anaphylaxis is fortunately rare. Symptoms and signs of anaphylactic shock begin with itching of the scalp and tongue, flushing of the skin over the whole body and difficulty in breathing due to bronchial spasm. Nausea, vomiting, abdominal pain and diarrhea, sometimes with blood in the stool, may be present. Acute hypotension, loss of consciousness and death follow. Human anaphylaxis, once commonly associated with heterologous serum therapy, is now seen mostly following injection of antibiotics or other drugs. Insect stings can also cause anaphylaxis in human beings. Prompt treatment with adrenaline can be life-saving. (0.5 ml of a 1-in-1000 solution, subcutaneously or intramuscularly).

Types:

Cutaneous anaphylaxis: When a small shocking dose of an antigen is administered intradermally to a sensitised host, there will be a local **wheal-and-flare** response (local anaphylaxis). The wheal is a pale, central area of puffiness due to edema, which is surrounded by a flare caused by hyperemia and subsequent erythema. Cutaneous anaphylaxis (skin test for Type I hypersensitivity) is useful in testing for hypersensitivity and in identifying the allergen responsible in atopic diseases. In highly sensitised individuals, even the skin test may lead to serious and even fatal reactions. Hence a syringe loaded with adrenaline should always be kept ready (*Case*).

Passive cutaneous anaphylaxis (PCA): This test developed by Ovary (1952) is an extremely sensitive in vivo method for the detection of antibodies. A small volume of the antibody is injected intradermally into a normal animal. If the antigen, along with a dye such as Evans blue, is injected intravenously 4–24 hours afterwards, there will be immediate blueing at the site of intradermal injection due to vasodilatation and increased capillary permeability (wheal-and-flare reaction). PCA can be used to detect the human IgG antibody which is heterocytotropic (capable of fixing to cells of other species) but not IgE which is homocytotropic (capable of fixing to cells of homologous species only).

Anaphylaxis in vitro: Isolated tissues, such as intestinal or uterine muscle strips from sensitised guinea pigs, held in a bath of Ringer's solution will contract vigorously on addition of the specific antigen to the bath. This is known as the **Schultz–Dale phenomenon**. The reaction is specific and will be elicited only by the antigen to which the animal is sensitive. Tissues from normal animals can be passively sensitised by treatment with serum from sensitised animals.

Mechanism: The immunological basis of hypersensitivity is the cytotropic IgE antibody. Free IgE antibody in circulation is not relevant in anaphylaxis. Thus, an animal with a high titre of circulating antibody may be refractory to shock, while anaphylaxis may be caused by a cell-fixed antibody, even in the absence of detectable circulating antibodies. While in human beings, IgE is the cytophilic antibody, in the guinea pig and mouse the analogous cytophilic antibody is IgG_1.

IgE molecules are bound to surface receptors on mast cells and basophils. These cells carry large numbers of receptors called *Fc* ER receptors, analogous to the TCR receptors on the T cell surface. IgE molecules attach to these receptors by their *Fc* end. Following exposure to the shocking dose, the antigen molecules combine with cell-bound IgE, bridging the gap between adjacent antibody molecules. This cross-linking increases the permeability of the cells to calcium ions and leads to degranulation, releasing biologically active substances contained in the granules.

Pharmacological mediators:

The **primary mediators** are the preformed contents of mast cells and basophils:

- **Histamine:** This is the most important vasoactive amine in human anaphylaxis. Histamine is formed by the decarboxylation of histidine found in the granules of mast cells, basophils and in platelets. Released into the skin, histamine stimulates sensory nerves, producing burning and itching sensations. It causes vasodilatation and hyperemia by an axon reflex (flare effect) and edema by increasing capillary permeability (wheal effect). Histamine induces smooth muscle contraction in diverse tissues and organs.

- **Serotonin (5-hydroxy tryptamine):** This is a base derived by decarboxylation of tryptophan. It is found in the intestinal mucosa, brain tissue and platelets. It causes smooth muscle contraction, increased capillary permeability and vasoconstriction.

- **Chemotactic factors:** The eosinophil chemotactic factors of anaphylaxis (ECF-A) are acidic tetrapeptides released from mast cell granules which are strongly chemotactic for eosinophils. These probably contribute to the eosinophilia accompanying many hypersensitivity states. A high molecular weight chemotactic factor has been identified, which attracts neutrophils (NCF).

- **Enzymatic mediators** such as proteases and hydrolases are also released from mast cell granules.

The **secondary mediators** are newly formed upon stimulation by mast cells, basophils and other leucocytes:

- **Prostaglandins and leukotrienes:** They are derived by two different pathways from arachidonic acid, which is formed from disrupted cell membranes of mast cells and other leucocytes. The lipoxygenase pathway leads to the formation of leukotrienes, while the cyclo-oxygenase pathway leads to prostaglandins and thromboxane. A substance originally demonstrated in lungs, producing slow, sustained contraction of smooth muscles, and therefore termed slow reacting substance of anaphylaxis (SRS-A), has since been identified as a family of leukotrienes (LTB4, C4, D4, E4). Prostaglandin F2α and thromboxane A2 are powerful but transient bronchoconstrictors. Prostaglandins also affect secretion by mucous glands, platelet adhesion, permeability and dilatation of capillaries and the pain threshold.

- **Platelet activating factor (PAF):** PAF is a low-molecular-weight lipid released from basophils which causes aggregation of platelets and release of their vasoactive amines.

Other mediators of anaphylaxis: Several biologically active substances such as the anaphylatoxins released by complement activation and bradykinin and other kinins formed from plasma kininogens.

Anaphylactoid reaction: Intravenous injection of peptone, trypsin and certain other substances provokes a clinical reaction resembling anaphylactic shock. This is termed 'anaphylactoid reaction'. The only difference is that anaphylactoid shock has no immunological basis and is a non-specific mechanism involving the activation of complement and the release of anaphylatoxins.

Atopy

The term atopy (literally out of place or strangeness) was introduced by Coca (1923) to refer to naturally occurring familial hypersensitivities of human beings, typified by hay fever and asthma. The antigens commonly involved in atopy are characteristically inhalants (for example, pollen, house dust) or ingestants (for example, eggs, milk). Some of them are contact allergens to which the skin and conjunctiva may be exposed. These atopens are generally not good antigens when injected parenterally but induce IgE antibodies, formerly termed 'reagin' antibodies. Atopic sensitisation is developed spontaneously following natural contact with atopens. It is difficult to induce atopy artificially.

- Predisposition to atopy is **genetically determined**, probably linked to MHC genotypes. Atopy therefore runs in families. What is inherited is not sensitivity to a particular antigen or a particular atopic syndrome but the tendency to produce IgE antibodies in unusually large quantities.
- All individuals are capable of forming IgE antibodies in small amounts but in atopics, **IgE response is preponderant**. About 10 per cent of persons have this tendency to overproduce IgE.
- **Simpler techniques** such as ELISA and passive agglutination have been used for its demonstration.
- While atopy occurs commonly in human beings, it is not easy to induce it experimentally in animals.

IgE differs from other immunoglobulins. Unlike other antibodies, IgE is heat sensitive and is inactivated at 56°C in 2–4 hours. Heating appears to damage the *Fc* part of the IgE molecule, which is necessary for fixation to cells. The atopic antibody does not pass through the placenta.

Prausnitz–Kustner (PK) reaction: IgE is homocytotropic, that is, species specific. Only human IgE can fix to the surface of human cells. This is the basis of the Prausnitz–Kustner (PK) reaction, which was the original method for detecting atopic antibodies. Prausnitz and Kustner (1921) reported that if serum collected from Kustner, who had atopic hypersensitivity to certain species of cooked fish, was injected intracutaneously into Prausnitz, followed 24 hours later by an intracutaneous injection of a small quantity of the cooked fish antigen into the same site, a wheal-and-flare reaction occurred within a few minutes. As reaginic IgE is homocytotropic, the test has to be carried out on human skin. It carries the risk of transmission of infection and so is no longer used.

Atopic sensitivity is caused by overproduction of IgE antibodies. This is often associated with a deficiency of IgA. This association has led to the suggestion that IgA deficiency may predispose to atopy. In normal individuals, the inhalant and ingestant antigens are dealt with by IgA lining the respiratory and intestinal mucosa and therefore they do not come into contact with potential IgE producing cells. When IgA is deficient, the antigens cause massive stimulation of IgE forming cells, leading to overproduction of IgE.

Symptoms of atopy are caused by the release of pharmacologically active substances following the combination of the antigen and the cell fixed IgE. The clinical expression of atopic reactions is usually determined by the portal of entry of the antigen—conjunctivitis, rhinitis, gastrointestinal symptoms and dermatitis following exposure through the eyes, respiratory tract, intestine or skin, respectively. Sometimes the effects may be at sites remote from the portal of entry, for example, urticaria following ingestion of the allergen. Specific desensitisation (hyposensitisation) is often practised in the treatment of atopy.

TYPE II REACTIONS: CYTOLYTIC AND CYTOTOXIC

These reactions involve a combination of IgG (or rarely IgM) antibodies with the antigenic determi-

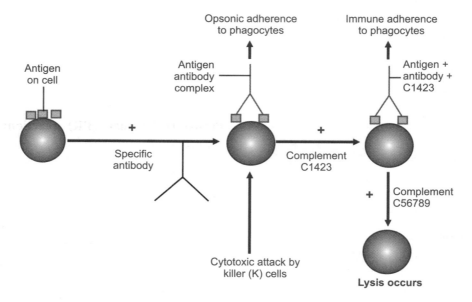

Fig. 16.2 Type II reaction

nants on the surface of cells leading to cytotoxic or cytolytic effects. Examples are lysis of red cells caused by anti-erythrocyte antibodies in autoimmune anemias and hemolytic disease of the newborn. Alternatively, a free antigen or hapten may be absorbed on cell surfaces. Subsequent reaction of the combined antigen or hapten with its corresponding antibody leads to cell damage. Many drugs may behave in this manner, leading to complement-mediated lysis of red cells, leucocytes and platelets, causing hemolytic anemia, agranulocytosis and thrombocytopenic purpura (Fig. 16.2).

TYPE III REACTIONS: IMMUNE COMPLEX DISEASES

The plasma concentration of complement falls due to massive complement activation and fixation by the antigen–antibody complexes. The disease is self-limiting with continued rise in antibody production. The immune complexes become larger and more susceptible to phagocytosis and immune elimination. When all foreign antigen are thus eliminated and free antibodies appear, the symptoms clear without any sequelae.

Arthus reaction

Arthus (1903) observed that when rabbits were repeatedly injected subcutaneously with normal horse serum, the initial injections had no local effect but with later injections, there occurred intense local reaction con-

sisting of edema, induration and hemorrhagic necrosis. This is known as the Arthus reaction and is a local manifestation of generalised hypersensitivity. The tissue damage is due to the formation of antigen–antibody precipitates causing complement activation and release of inflammatory molecules. This leads to increased vascular permeability and infiltration of the site with neutrophils. Leucocyte–platelet thrombi that reduce blood supply and lead to tissue necrosis are formed. The Arthus reaction can be passively transferred with sera containing precipitating antibodies (IgG, IgM) in high titres.

Arthus reaction forms a pathogenic component of many clinical syndromes. For example, intrapulmonary Arthus-like reaction to inhaled antigens, such as thermophilic actinomycetes from mouldy hay or grain, causes farmer's lung and other types of hypersensitivity pneumonitis.

Serum sickness

This is a systemic form of Type III hypersensitivity. As originally described by von Pirquet and Schick (1905), this appears 7–12 days following a single injection of a high concentration of foreign serum such as the diphtheria antitoxin. The clinical syndrome consists of fever, lymphadenopathy, splenomegaly, arthritis, glomerulonephritis, endocarditis, vasculitis, urticarial rashes, abdominal pain, nausea and vomiting. The pathogenesis is the formation of immune

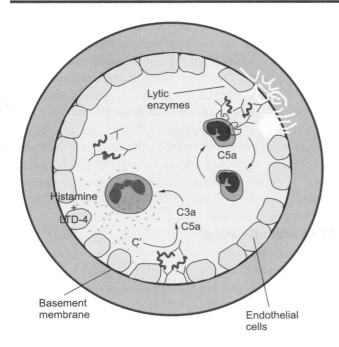

Fig. 16.3 Type III reaction

complexes (consisting of the foreign serum and antibody to it that reaches high enough titres by 7–12 days; **Fig. 16.3**), which get deposited on the endothelial lining of blood vessels in various parts of the body, causing inflammatory infiltration .

Serum sickness differs from other types of hypersensitivity reactions in that a single injection can serve both as the sensitising dose and the shocking dose. As heterologous serum injections are not used often now, the syndrome is currently more commonly seen following injection of penicillin or other antibiotics.

The nephritis and arthritis seen in these conditions may be caused by deposition of immune complexes.

TYPE IV REACTIONS: DELAYED HYPERSENSITIVITY

Type IV hypersensitivity reactions (delayed hypersensitivity) constitute one aspect of cell-mediated immune response. These are typically provoked by intracellular microbial infections or haptens like simple chemicals applied on the skin, evolve slowly and consist of a mixed cellular reaction involving lymphocytes and macrophages in particular. The reaction is not induced by circulating antibodies but by sensitised T cells (T_{dth}, Th_1, Th_2, T_c) which, on contact with the specific antigen, release cytokines that produce biological effects on leucocytes, macrophages and tissue cells. Delayed

hypersensitivity cannot be passively transferred by serum but can be transferred by lymphocytes or the transfer factor. Two types of delayed hypersensitivity are recognised: the tuberculin (infection) type and the contact dermatitis type.

Tuberculin (infection) type

The archetype of delayed hypersensitivity is the tuberculin reaction. When a small dose of tuberculin is injected intradermally in an individual sensitised to tuberculoprotein by prior infection or immunisation, an indurated inflammatory reaction develops at the site within 48–72 hours. In unsensitised individuals, the tuberculin injection provokes no response. The tuberculin test therefore provides a useful indication of the state of delayed hypersensitivity (cell-mediated immunity) to the bacilli. The tuberculin test differs from the skin test for Type I hypersensitivity not only in the longer interval for appearance but also in its morphology and histology.

Tuberculin type hypersensitivity develops in many infections with bacteria, fungi, viruses and parasites, especially when the infection is subacute or chronic and the pathogen intracellular. A similar hypersensitivity is developed in allograft reactions and in many autoimmune diseases.

Cutaneous basophil hypersensitivity

A local reaction resembling the tuberculin response may be produced by the intradermal injection of some protein antigens. This is not a delayed hypersensitivity reaction as it can be passively transferred by serum. Its histology is different from the tuberculin response, being characterised by prominent basophil infiltration. This was formerly known as the Jones–Mote reaction but is now termed cutaneous basophil hypersensitivity. Its significance is not known.

Contact dermatitis type

Delayed hypersensitivity sometimes results from skin contact with a variety of chemicals—metals such as nickel and chromium, simple chemicals like dyes, picryl chloride, dinitrochlorobenzene, drugs such as penicillin, plant allergen (parthenin from parthenium) and toiletries. Sensitisation is particularly liable when contact is with an inflamed area of skin and when the chemical is applied in an oily base. Antibiotic ointments applied on patches of dermatitis frequently provoke sensitisation. The substances involved are in themselves not antigenic but may acquire antigenicity on combination with skin proteins. Sensitisation requires percutaneous absorption. As most of the substances involved are fat soluble, passage along sebaceous glands may be the method of entry of the allergens.

Mechanism: Langerhans' cells of the skin capture locally applied hapten, along with the modified tissue proteins, and migrate to the draining lymph nodes where they present the processed antigen along with MHC molecules to T cells. The sensitised T cells travel to the skin site, where on contacting the antigen they release various lymphokines. Th_1 cells secrete IFNγ and IL2 which activate macrophages and other lymphocytes. Th_2 cells release IL4, IL5, GM-CSF and other factors that lead to an influx of eosinophils and tissue damage. Activated T_c cells mediate the killing of target cells.

Symptoms: Contact with the allergen in a sensitised individual leads to '**contact dermatitis**', the lesions varying from macules and papules to vesicles that break down, leaving behind raw weeping areas typical of acute eczematous dermatitis. Hypersensitivity is detected by the '**patch test**'. The allergen is applied to the skin under an adherent dressing. Sensitivity is indicated by itching appearing in 4–5 hours, and local reaction which may vary from erythema to vesicle or blister formation, after 24–28 hours.

TYPE V REACTIONS (STIMULATORY HYPERSENSITIVITY)

Here, the antibody activates receptor sites and enhances the activity of the cell. A few examples are the 'long-acting thyroid stimulator' (LATS), an antibody against some determinant on thyroid cells, which stimulates excessive secretion of the thyroid hormone; Stevens Johnson syndrome; sulphonamide-induced Morbilliform rash, etc.

SHWARTZMAN REACTION

This is not an immune reaction but rather a perturbation in factors affecting intravascular coagulation. It is traditionally described along with hypersensitivity reactions because of a superficial resemblance.

Shwartzman (1928) observed that if a culture filtrate of *S.* Typhi is injected intradermally in a rabbit, followed 24 hours later by the same filtrate intravenously, a hemorrhagic necrotic lesion develops at the site of the intradermal injection. The intradermal and intravenous injections need not be of the same or even related endotoxins. Culture suspensions or filtrates of a variety of bacteria will sensitise the skin to intravenous injection by an equally wide variety of cultures or filtrates. This absence of specificity and the short interval between the two doses preclude any immunological basis for the reaction.

Dose administration: The initial (preparatory) dose is characteristically an endotoxin. The intravenous (provocative) injection can be a variety of substances: bacterial endotoxins, antigen–antibody complexes, starch, serum, kaolin and others. The preparatory injection causes accumulation of leucocytes which condition the site by releasing lysosomal enzymes damaging capillary walls. Following the provocative dose, there occurs intravascular clotting, the thrombi leading to necrosis of vessel walls and hemorrhage.

If both the injections are given intravenously, the animal dies 12–24 hours after the second dose. An essentially similar phenomenon was described by Sanarelli (1924) in experimental cholera. The reaction is therefore called the Sanarelli–Shwartzman reaction or the generalised Shwartzman reaction.

Mechanism: It has been suggested that mechanisms similar to the Shwartzman reaction may operate in some clinical conditions such as the purpuric rashes of meningococcal septicemia and the acute hemorrhagic adrenal necrosis found in overwhelming infections (**Waterhouse–Friderichsen syndrome**).

Massive activation of complement by the alternative pathway, associated with release of thromboxane A2 and prostaglandins from platelets, may lead to disseminated intravascular coagulation. The mechanism may be the excessive release of cytokines such as the tumour necrosis factor and interleukins 1 and 6 by macrophages and endothelial cells in response to contact with large quantities of lipopolysaccharide endotoxin. Some Gram-positive infections may also cause similar effects. *Staphylococcus aureus* can induce TNF secretion by macrophages and peptidoglycan-mediated platelet aggregation, leading to disseminated intravascular coagulation.

RECAP

- Hypersensitivity reactions are pathologic processes that result from exaggerated (very vigorous) specific interactions between antigens (exogenous or endogenous) and either between humoral antibodies or sensitised lymphocytes, resulting in tissue injury.
- It occurs only if the host has had an earlier contact with the antigen (allergen). The initial or sensitising dose sensitises the immune system, while subsequent contact (shocking dose) with the same antigen (allergen) causes manifestations of hypersensitivity.
- Hypersensitivity reactions can be classified:
  - Based on the duration between exposure to antigen and reaction, into immediate type hypersensitivity and delayed type hypersensitivity
  - Based on the component involved in the reaction, into antibody-mediated hypersensitivity and cell-mediated hypersensitivity
  - Based on Gel and Coombs classification into Type I, Type II, Type III Type IV and Type V
- Type I (immediate, anaphylactic), IgE-mediated hypersensitivity reactions occur within minutes of exposure to the antigen. The cross-linking of mast cell–bound IgE by the allergen causes release of vasoactive substances (histamine, leukotrienes, prostaglandins, etc.) which produce inflammation. Diagnostic tests include total IgE levels, direct skin test, radioallergosorbent test, leucocyte histamine release test, provocative challenge and provocative food testing.
- Clinical conditions resulting from Type I reactions include systemic anaphylaxis, allergic extrinsic asthma, seasonal allergic rhinitis, reactions to the sting of an insect, some reactions to foods and drugs and some cases of urticaria.
- In Type II (cytotoxic) hypersensitivity reactions, antibody binding to cell surface antigens is followed by antibody dependent cell-mediated cytotoxicity by K cells, or complement-mediated lysis. Type II diseases include transfusion reactions, hemolytic disease of the newborn, certain drug allergies caused by cytotoxic T lymphocytes.
- In Type III (immune complex mediated) hypersensitivity reactions, tissue damage occurs due to activation of complement by immune complexes (through the classical pathway). It may result from persistent infection with streptococci, hepatitis B virus, malarial parasites and filarial worms; other examples include glomerulonephritis, alveolitis and certain autoimmune diseases.
- In Type IV (cell-mediated or delayed type) hypersensitivity reactions, symptoms appear at least 24–48 hours after exposure to antigen. There is activation of T cells, release of lymphokines and subsequent influx of macrophages to the site. Allergic contact dermatitis (due to poison ivy) and the skin test for exposure to tubercle bacilli (tuberculin test) are examples.
- In Type V (stimulatory hypersensitivity) reaction, the antibodies recognise and bind to the cell surface receptors. This is a modified form of Type II reaction.

ESSAY

1. Classify hypersensitivity reactions with examples. Describe type I hypersensitivity.

SHORT ANSWERS

1. Anaphylaxis
2. Atopy
3. Praustniz–Kustner reaction
4. Arthus reaction
5. Serum sickness
6. Tuberculin type delayed hypersensitivity
7. Contact dermatitis
8. Shwartzman reaction
9. Delayed hypersensitivity
10. Mediators of anaphylaxis

17 Immunodeficiency Diseases

INTRODUCTION

Immunodeficiency diseases are conditions where the defence mechanisms of the body are impaired, leading to repeated microbial infections of varying severity and sometimes enhanced susceptibility to malignancies. Deficiencies of defence mechanisms may involve specific immune functions—humoral immunity, cell-mediated immunity or both—or non-specific mechanisms such as phagocytosis and complement, which augment and act in conjunction with specific immune processes.

Primary immunodeficiency

Clinical Case A nine-month-old male infant was brought to the hospital with symptoms of fever and difficulty in breathing. The mother reported of two similar episodes in the previous two months. At the age of 12 months, the child was again brought in with an episode of measles, from which he recovered after treatment. At 18 months of age, it was observed that the boy's height and weight were not appropriate to his age. The child was the fourth of unrelated parents. His three sisters enjoyed good health and the parents did not report of them suffering from any repeated infections, unlike the boy.

Tests on the boy showed the serum immunoglobulin IgG to be less than a tenth and IgA and IgM to be less than a hundredth of the normal level. Lymph node biopsy revealed depletion of cells of the bursa-dependent areas. The child was diagnosed with Bruton's disease (X-linked agammaglobulinemia) and was treated with an initial administration of 300 mg of gamma globulin/kg body weight in 3 doses, followed by monthly injections of 100 mg/kg. The child responded well to treatment.

Classification

- **Primary immunodeficiencies** result from abnormalities in the development of immune mechanisms.
- **Secondary immunodeficiencies** are consequences of disease, drugs, nutritional inadequacies and other processes that interfere with the proper functioning of the mature immune system.

PRIMARY IMMUNODEFICIENCIES

The established types of primary immunodeficiency syndromes are listed in Table 17.1. Though primary deficiencies of specific immunity can be conveniently classified as those affecting B cell responses, T cell responses, or both, it must be realised that there is considerable overlap due to the intimate interaction between the B cell and T cell systems. For instance, T cell deficiencies involving helper or suppressor T cells will have a profound effect on antibody response.

DISORDERS OF SPECIFIC IMMUNITY

Humoral immunodeficiencies

X-linked agammaglobulinemia: This syndrome described by Bruton (1952) is the first immunodeficiency disease to have been recognised. It is seen only in male infants.

Manifestations: The disease is not apparent till about six months of age due to the passive protection afforded by maternal antibodies. It presents as recurrent serious infection with pyogenic bacteria, particularly with pneumococci, streptococci, meningococci, *Pseudomonas* and *H.influenzae*. Patients respond normally to viral infections such as measles and chickenpox, though

Table 17.1 *Classification of primary immunodeficiency syndromes*

A. Disorders of specific immunity
 I. Humoral immunodeficiencies (B cell defects)
   a) X-linked agammaglobulinemia
   b) Transient hypogammaglobulinemia of infancy
   c) Common variable immunodeficiency (late onset hypogammaglobulinemia)
   d) Selective immunoglobulin deficiencies (IgA, IgM or IgG subclasses)
   e) Immunodeficiencies with hyper-IgM
   f) Transcobalamin II deficiency
 II. Cellular immunodeficiencies (T cell defects)
   a) Thymic hypoplasia (DiGeorge syndrome)
   b) Chronic mucocutaneous candidosis
   c) Purine nucleoside phosphorylase (PNP) deficiency
 III. Combined immunodeficiencies (B and T cell defects)
   a) Cellular immunodeficiency with abnormal immunoglobulin synthesis (Nezelof syndrome)
   b) Ataxia telangiectasia
   c) Wiskott–Aldrich syndrome
   d) Immunodeficiency with thymoma
   e) Immunodeficiency with short-limbed dwarfism
   f. Episodic lymphopenia with lymphocytotoxin
   g) Severe combined immunodeficiencies
    1. 'Swiss type' agammaglobulinemia
    2. Reticular dysgenesis of de Vaal
    3. Adenosine deaminase (ADA) deficiency

B. Disorders of complement
   a) Complement component deficiencies
   b) Complement inhibitor deficiencies

C. Disorders of phagocytosis
   a) Chronic granulomatous disease
   b) Myeloperoxidase deficiency
   c) Chediak–Higashi syndrome
   d) Leukocyte G6PD deficiency
   e) Job's syndrome
   f) Tuftsin deficiency
   g) Lazy leukocyte syndrome
   h) Hyper-IgE syndrome
   i) Actin binding protein deficiency
   j) Shwachman's disease

there have been reports of paralytic poliomyelitis and progressive encephalitis following immunisation with live virus vaccines or exposure to a wild virus. As a general rule, live microbial vaccines should not be given to children with any type of primary immunodeficiency.

All classes of immunoglobulins are grossly depleted in the serum, the IgG level being less than a tenth, and IgA and IgM less than a hundredth of the normal level. Tonsils and adenoids are atrophic. Lymph node biopsy reveals depletion of cells of the bursa-dependent areas.

Plasma cells and germinal centres are absent even after antigenic stimulation. There is a marked decrease in the proportion of B cells in circulation. Antibody formation does not occur even after injection of antigens.

Cell-mediated immunity CMI is not affected. Delayed hypersensitivity of tuberculin and contact dermatitis types can be demonstrated. Allograft rejection is normal. Arthritis, hemolytic anemia and atopic manifestations are frequently observed. However, the wheal-and-flare response of atopic hypersensitivity cannot be demonstrated.

Management: This consists of maintenance of an adequate level of immunoglobulins. This can be achieved with an initial administration of 300 mg of gamma globulin per kg of body weight in three doses followed by monthly injections of 100 mg per kg. Commercial preparations of gamma globulin contain only traces of IgA and IgM, therefore, whole plasma infusions have been used (*Case*).

Transient hypogammaglobulinemia of infancy: This is due to an abnormal delay in the initiation of IgG synthesis in some infants. Maternal IgG is slowly catabolised in the newborn and reaches a level of 200 mg per 100 ml by the second month. Ordinarily, the infant begins synthesising his/her own IgG by this age. When there is a delay, immunodeficiency occurs. Recurrent otitis media and respiratory infections are the common diseases found in this condition. Spontaneous recovery occurs between 18 and 30 months of age. It may be found in infants of both sexes.

Management: Treatment with gamma globulin may be required in some cases but it is not recommended prophylactically, as it may contribute to prolongation of immunodeficiency by negative feedback inhibition of IgG synthesis.

Common variable immunodeficiency: This common form of immunodeficiency is also known as late onset hypogammaglobulinemia because it usually manifests only by 15–35 years of age. It is characterised by recurrent pyogenic infection and increased incidence of autoimmune disease. Malabsorption and giardiasis are common. The total immunoglobulin level is usually low. B cells may be present in circulation in normal numbers, but they appear defective in their ability to differentiate into plasma cells and secrete immunoglobulins. Increased suppressor T cell and diminished helper T cell activity have been proposed as a cause of this disorder.

Management: Treatment is by administration of gamma globulin preparations intramuscularly or intravenously.

Selective immunoglobulin deficiencies: In these conditions, there is selective deficiency of one or more immunoglobulin classes, while the others remain normal or elevated. These 'dysgammaglobulinemias' are common and have been reported in about one per cent of all patients with recurrent infection.

- Isolated IgA deficiency is the most common condition in this group, with a reported incidence of about 0.2 per cent in normal populations. These patients exhibit increased susceptibility to respiratory infection and steatorrhea. IgA deficiency is often accompanied by atopic disorders. Anti-IgA antibodies are present in many of these patients.
- Selective IgM deficiency has been found to be associated with septicemia. Deficiencies of IgG subclasses have been observed in relation with chronic progressive bronchiectasis.

Management: Preventative antibiotics may be used to help diminish the frequency of recurrent infections. Individuals with IgA deficiency often require a longer course of antibiotics for infections to clear up.

Immunodeficiencies with hyper-IgM: In this group of immunodeficiencies, some of which are X-linked and some inherited as autosomal recessive, low IgA and IgG levels are seen with elevated IgM. The IgM molecules appear to have normal structure and possess antibody activity. Patients show enhanced susceptibility to infections and autoimmune processes such as thrombocytopenia, neutropenia, hemolytic anemia and renal lesions. Some patients develop malignant infiltration with IgM-producing cells. Elevated IgM level with immunodeficiency is sometimes seen in congenital rubella.

Management: Intravenous immunoglobulin (IVIG) therapy has reportedly significantly decreased the frequency of lower respiratory tract and severe infections.

Transcobalamin II deficiency: In this disorder, inherited as an autosomal recessive trait, patients show the metabolic effects of vitamin B12 deficiency including megaloblastic anemia and intestinal villous atrophy. The associated immunological defects are depleted plasma cells, diminished immunoglobulin levels and impaired phagocytosis.

Management: Treatment with vitamin B12 has been reported to restore hematopoietic, gastrointestinal and B cell functions but not phagocytic activity.

Cellular immunodeficiencies

Thymic hypoplasia (DiGeorge syndrome): This is a developmental defect involving the endodermal derivatives of the third and fourth pharyngeal pouches. It leads to aplasia or hypoplasia of the thymus and parathyroid glands. It does not appear to be hereditary and does not show a familial incidence. It is probably due to some intrauterine infection or other complications. It is usually associated with Fallot's tetrology and other anomalies of the heart and the great vessels, and a characteristic facial appearance. Neonatal tetany is present. Patients who survive the neonatal period show enhanced susceptibility to viral, fungal and bacterial infections, which ultimately prove fatal.

The immunodeficiency primarily involves cell-mediated immunity. The thymus-dependent areas of the lymph nodes and spleen are depleted of lymphocytes. Circulating T cells are reduced in number. Delayed hypersensitivity and graft rejection are depressed. The humoral immune mechanism is largely unaffected.

Management: Transplantation of fetal thymus tissue has been reported to restore the immunological function.

Chronic mucocutaneous candidosis: This constitutes an abnormal immunological response to *Candida albicans*. Patients develop severe chronic candidosis of the mucosa, skin and nails. They do not show increased susceptibility to other infections but often have endocrinopathies. CMI to candida is deficient. Delayed hypersensitivity to candida antigens is absent but circulating antibodies to them are high titres. Intracellular killing of candida is defective.

Management: Transfer factor therapy, along with amphotericin B, has been reported to be effective.

Purine nucleoside phosphorylase (PNP) deficiency: The enzyme purine nucleoside phosphorylase is involved in the sequential degradation of purines to hypoxanthine and finally to uric acid. Patients who have PNP deficiency as an autosomal recessive inherited trait show decreased CMI and recurrent or chronic infection. They usually present with hypoplastic anemia and recurrent pneumonia, diarrhea and candidosis. Due to defects in purine degradation, serum uric acid is low and may point to the diagnosis.

Management: Allogeneic hematopoietic stem cell transplantation (HSCT) may be the choice of treatment to restore the immunological functions.

Combined immunodeficiencies

Cellular immunodeficiency with abnormal immunoglobulin synthesis (Nezelof syndrome): The term Nezelof syndrome has been rather loosely applied to a group of disorders, probably of varied origin, where depressed CMI is associated with selectively elevated, decreased or normal levels of immunoglobulin. The consistent features are a marked deficiency of T cell immunity and varying degrees of deficiency of B cell immunity. Patients are susceptible to recurrent fungal, bacterial, viral and protozoal diseases. Abundant plasma cells are seen in the spleen, lymph nodes, intestines and elsewhere in the body. Thymic dysplasia occurs with lymphoid depletion. Autoimmune processes such as hemolytic anemia are common. In spite of normal levels of immunoglobulins, antigenic stimuli do not induce antibody formation.

Management: Histocompatible bone marrow transplantation, transfer factor and thymus transplantation have been used for treatment, with success in some cases. Adequate antimicrobial therapy is essential.

Ataxia telangiectasia: This is a hereditary condition transmitted in the autosomal recessive mode, where combined immunodeficiency is associated with cerebellar ataxia, telangiectasia, ovarian dysgenesis and chromosomal abnormalities. Ataxia and chorioathetoid movements are usually noticed in infancy. Telangiectasia involving the conjunctiva, face and other parts of the body usually appears at five or six years of age. Death occurs due to sinopulmonary infection early in life, or malignancy in the second or third decade. The majority of patients lack serum and secretory IgA and some possess antibody to IgA. IgE deficiency is also frequent. CMI is also defective, resulting in impairment of delayed hypersensitivity and graft rejection.

Management: Transfer factor therapy and fetal thymus transplants have been tried with some benefit.

Wiskott–Aldrich syndrome: This is an X-linked disease characterised by eczema, thrombocytopenic purpura and recurrent infections. Affected boys rarely survive the first decade of life, death being due to infection, hemorrhage or lymphoreticular malignancy. CMI undergoes progressive deterioration associated with cellular depletion of the thymus and the paracortical areas of lymph nodes. Serum IgM level is low but IgG and IgA levels are normal or elevated. Isohemagglutinins are absent in the serum. The humoral defect appears to be a specific inability to respond to polysaccharide antigens.

Management: Bone marrow transplantation and transfer factor therapy have been found to be beneficial.

Immunodeficiency with thymoma: This syndrome, occurring usually in adults, consists of a benign thymic tumour, impaired cell-mediated immunity and agammaglobulinemia. It is frequently accompanied by aplastic anemia. This is of historical importance as one of the experiments of nature which suggested the immunological function of the thymus.

Immunodeficiency with short-limbed dwarfism: The features of this condition are a distinctive form of short-limbed dwarfism, ectodermal dysplasia, thymic defects and enhanced susceptibility to infection. These defects are apparently inherited as autosomal recessives.

Episodic lymphopenia with lymphocytotoxin: In this syndrome, there occurs an episodic but profound depression of T cell function by the action of a circulating complement–dependent lymphocytotoxin. The toxin appears to be an anti-lymphocyte antibody. The patients lack 'immunological memory' so the secondary antibody response is abolished. The disease is familial.

Severe combined immunodeficiencies: These include many syndromes with severe deficiency of both humoral and CMI response. They are inherited in the autosomal recessive mode and the primary defects are at the level of the early precursors of immunocompetent cells in the fetal liver and bone marrow. Many distinct patterns of severe combined immunodeficiency have been described.

In 1958, Swiss workers reported agammaglobulinemia with lymphocytopenia and severe defect in CMI.

- **Swiss-type agammaglobulinemia:** The basic defect is presumed to be at the level of the lymphoid stem cell.
- **Reticular dysgenesis of de Vaal:** Here the defect is at the level of the multipotent hemopoietic stem cell, as a result of which there is total failure of myelopoiesis leading to lymphopenia, neutropenia, thrombocytopenia, anemia and bone marrow aplasia. The most serious form and condition is invariably fatal in the first week of life.
- **Adenosine deaminase (ADA) deficiency:** This is the first immunodeficiency disease associated with

an enzyme deficiency. ADA catalyses the conversion of adenosine to inosine in the purine metabolic pathway. How this deficiency causes immunological impairment is not clear. The range of immunodeficiency varies from complete absence to mild abnormalities in B and T cell function. The condition is associated with chondrocyte abnormalities which can be discerned radiologically.

DISORDERS OF COMPLEMENT

Complement component deficiencies: Genetic deficiencies have been detected for almost all the complement components in human beings. The defects are transmitted as autosomal recessive traits. Hemolytic and other functional activities are completely restored by supplying the deficient factor. Complement component deficiencies have been frequently associated with systemic lupus erythematosus. Recurrent pyogenic infections were found associated with C3 deficiency and neisserial infections with deficiency of C6, C7 and C8.

Complement inhibitor deficiencies: Hereditary angioneurotic edema is due to a genetic deficiency of the C1 inhibitor. This relatively common defect is transmitted as an autosomal dominant trait. The rare deficiency of the C3b inactivator has been associated with chronic recurrent pyogenic lesions.

Management: Androgens, aminocaproic acid and its analogue tranexamic acid have been found useful in the management of this condition.

DISORDERS OF PHAGOCYTOSIS

Phagocytosis may be impaired by intrinsic or extrinsic defects. Intrinsic disorders may be due to defects within the phagocytic cell, such as enzyme deficiencies. Extrinsic disorders may be due to a deficiency of opsonic antibody, complement or other factors promoting phagocytosis, or to the effects of drugs or anti-neutrophil autoantibodies. Phagocytic dysfunction leads to increased susceptibility to infection, ranging from mild recurrent skin infections to overwhelming systemic infection.

Chronic granulomatous disease: This familial disease manifests itself as recurrent infection with low grade pathogens, starting early in life. The progress is chronic and the outcome fatal. Chronic suppurative granulomatous lesions develop in the skin and lymph nodes, along with hepatosplenomegaly, progressive infiltration of lungs and granulomatous septic osteomyelitis. Humoral and cellular immune response are normal.

The bacteria involved in the recurrent infections are catalase-positive pyogenic pathogens such as staphylococci and coliforms. Catalase-negative pathogens such as streptococci and pneumococci are handled normally. Leukocytes from the patients are unable to kill catalase-positive bacteria following phagocytosis. The bacteria multiply in the cells and, being protected from antibodies and antibiotics by their intracellular position, set up chronic suppurative infection. The diminished bactericidal capacity of the phagocytic cells is associated with a decrease of some metabolic processes like oxygen consumption, hexose monophosphate pathway activity and production of hydrogen peroxide. Diminished H_2O_2 production appears to be the main reason for the bactericidal defect. The leukocytes do not undergo degranulation following phagocytosis. Delayed granule rupture and defective release of myeloperoxidase also contribute to inefficient bactericidal activity.

Nitroblue tetrazolium test: Leukocytes from the patients fail to reduce nitroblue tetrazolium (NBT) during phagocytosis. This property has been used as a screening method (NBT test) for the diagnosis of chronic granulomatous disease.

The disease shows two types of inheritance: the more common X-linked type seen in boys and the rare autosomal recessive type seen in girls.

Myeloperoxidase deficiency: In this rare disease, leukocytes have reduced myeloperoxidase. Patients are particularly liable to *Candida albicans* infection.

Chediak–Higashi syndrome: This is a genetic disorder characterised by decreased pigmentation of the skin, eyes and hair, photophobia, nystagmus and giant peroxidise-positive inclusions in the cytoplasm of leukocytes. The inclusions may be the result of autophagocytic activity. The leukocytes possess diminished phagocytic activity. Patients suffer from frequent and severe pyogenic infections.

Leukocyte G6PD deficiency: In this rare disease, leukocytes are deficient in glucose-6-phosphate dehydrogenase and show diminished bactericidal activity after phagocytosis. The condition resembles chronic granulomatous disease in reduced myeloperoxidase activity and susceptibility to microbial agents, but the NBT test may be normal.

Job's syndrome: This is characterised by multiple large 'cold' staphylococcal abscesses containing large quantities of pus, occurring repeatedly on the skin and in various organs, with little inflammatory response. Atopic eczema, chronic nasal discharge and otitis media are common features. Serum immunoglobulins are normal, except for elevated IgE. The pathogenesis of the syndrome is not clear but it is probably a primary defect in phagocytic function.

Tuftsin deficiency: A leukokinin capable of stimulating phagocytosis, discovered at Tufts University, Boston, has been designated 'tuftsin'. Chemically, it is a small tetrapeptide (Thr-Lys-Pro-Arg). Patients with tuftsin deficiency have been reported to be prone to local and systemic bacterial infections.

Lazy leukocyte syndrome: The basic defect here is in chemotaxis and neutrophil mobility. The bone marrow has the normal number of neutrophils but there is peripheral neutropenia, with poor leukocyte response to chemical and inflammatory stimulation. Patients show increased susceptibility to bacterial infection, with recurrent stomatitis, gingivitis and otitis.

Hyper-IgE syndrome: These patients, of both sexes, have early onset eczema and recurrent bacterial infections such as abscess, pneumonia and secondary infection of eczema. The organisms responsible include *Staphylococcus aureus* and *Streptococcus pyogenes*. Cellular and humoral immune mechanisms are normal but serum IgE levels are usually more than ten times the normal level.

Actin binding protein deficiency: Frequent infection and slow mobility of leukocytes results from the defective actin binding protein in these patients.

Shwachman's disease: In this condition, frequent infections are found together with decreased neutrophil mobility, pancreatic malfunction and bone abnormalities.

SECONDARY IMMUNODEFICIENCIES

A variety of factors such as malnutrition, malignancy, infection, metabolic disorders and cytotoxic drugs may lead to deficits in specific and non-specific immunity. AIDS is a secondary immunodeficiency. Secondary immunodeficiencies are therefore much more common than primary deficiencies.

Humoral deficiency:
- B cells are depleted, as in lymphoid malignancy, particularly in chronic lymphatic leukemia;
- Immunoglobulin catabolism is increased as in nephrotic syndrome;
- Excessive loss of serum protein occurs, as in exfoliative skin disease and in protein-losing enteropathies
- Excessive production of abnormal immunoglobulins occurs, as in multiple myeloma.

Cell-mediated immunity deficiency:
- CMI is depressed in lymphoreticular malignancies, as in Hodgkin's disease;
- Obstruction to lymph circulation or lymphorrheas;
- The thymus-dependent areas of lymph nodes are infiltrated with non-lymphoid cells, as in lepromatous leprosy
- Transiently, following certain viral infections such as measles.

Nutritional deprivation affects both types of immune response adversely. Ageing also causes waning in the efficiency of acquired immunity. Immunodeficiency follows the intentional or unintentional administration of immunosuppressive agents.

RECAP

- Immunodeficiency diseases are conditions in which the body's defence mechanisms are impaired, resulting in repeated microbial infections of variable severity and, sometimes, enhanced susceptibility to malignancies.

- Deficiencies of defence mechanisms may involve specific immune functions, namely humoral and/or cell-mediated immunity, or non-specific mechanisms (phagocytosis, complement) which augment specific immune processes. Immunodeficiencies may be primary or secondary.
- Primary immunodeficiencies result from abnormalities in the development of immune mechanisms and comprise the following:
  - Disorders of specific immunity, such as B cell defects or humoral immunodeficiencies (X-linked agammaglobulinemia, transient hypogammaglobulinemia of infancy, common variable immunodeficiency, selective immunoglobulin deficiencies)
  - T cell defects or cellular immunodeficiencies (thymic hypoplasia, chronic mucocutaneous candidosis)
  - Combined B and T cell defects or combined immunodeficiencies (cellular immunodeficiency with abnormal immunoglobulin synthesis, ataxia telangiectasia, Wiskott–Aldrich syndrome, severe combined immunodeficiencies)
  - Disorders of complement (deficiencies of complement components, deficiencies of complement inhibitor)
  - Disorders of phagocytosis (chronic granulomatous disease, myeloperoxidase deficiency, Chediak–Higashi syndrome, leukocyte glucose-6-phosphate deficiency, Job's syndrome, tuftsin deficiency)
- Secondary immunodeficiencies arise when infections, drugs, nutritional inadequacies, metabolic disorders and malignancies lead to defects in specific and non-specific immunity. Secondary immunodeficiencies are more common than primary immunodeficiencies.
- Secondary immunodeficiencies occur due to certain infections (acquired immunodeficiency syndrome), nutritional deprivation (kwashiorkor), use of certain drugs (immunosuppressive agents, corticosteroids), metabolic disorders (protein losing enteropathies) and malignancies (chronic lymphocytic leukemia, multiple myeloma, Hodgkin's disease).

SHORT NOTES

1. Primary immunodeficiency disorders
2. Secondary immunodeficiencies
3. Humoral immunodeficiency disorders
4. Cellular immunodeficiencies
5. Combined B and T cell defects
6. Chronic granulomatous disease
7. Chronic mucocutaneous candidosis
8. Nezelof syndrome
9. Severe combined immunodeficiencies
10. Disorders of phagocytosis

18 Autoimmunity

Systemic lupus erythematosus

Clinical Case A 27-year-old woman was referred to the rheumatology clinic with a history of pain and swelling in the joints of her hand and a rash over her cheeks. Immunoflourescent test for antinuclear antibodies (ANA) showed a homogenous pattern—anti-ds DNA antibody was positive. LE cells were demonstrated on bone marrow biopsy. A diagnosis of systemic lupus erythematosus (SLE) was made. The patient was treated with low-dose corticosteroids and showed improvement.

INTRODUCTION

Autoimmunity is a condition in which structural or functional damage is produced by the action of immunologically competent cells or antibodies against the normal components of the body. Autoimmunity literally means 'protection against self' but it actually implies 'injury to self.' Ehrlich (1901) observed that goats produce antibodies against erythrocytes from other goats but not against their own, and postulated the concept of **'horror autotoxicus'**.

Criteria were proposed for proving the authenticity of putative autoimmune diseases. It may be proper to restrict the term 'autoimmune disease' to those where autoimmune processes, humoral or cellular, are shown to be responsible for the pathogenesis, rather than merely associated. Diseases of autoimmune origin usually exhibit the following **features**:

- Elevated levels of immunoglobulins
- Demonstrable autoantibodies
- Deposition of immunoglobulins or their derivatives at sites of election, such as renal glomeruli
- Accumulation of lymphocytes and plasma cells at the sites of lesion
- Benefit from corticosteroid or other immunosuppressive therapy
- The occurrence of more than one type of autoimmune lesion in an individual
- A genetic predisposition towards autoimmunity
- Higher incidence among females
- Chronicity, usually non-reversible

MECHANISMS OF AUTOIMMUNITY

Antigenic alterations: Cells or tissues may undergo antigenic alteration as a result of physical, chemical and biological influences. Such altered or **'neoantigens'** may elicit an immune response. Neoantigens can arise by physical agents such as irradiation, photosensitivity and cold allergy. Drug-induced anemias, leucopenias and thrombocytopenias often have an autoimmune basis. Infectious microorganisms, particularly viruses and other intracellular pathogens, may induce alteration of cell antigens. Viral infections, such as infectious mononucleosis, are known to often precede autoimmune disease. Bacterial enzymes also induce alteration of cell antigens. Neuraminidases formed by myxoviruses and many bacteria act on erythrocytes releasing the T antigen. Neoantigens may also arise by mutation. Such mutant cells may be immunogenic.

Sequestered antigens: Certain self-antigens are present in closed systems and are not accessible to the immune apparatus. These are known as sequestered antigens. An example is the lens antigen of the eye. The lens protein is enclosed in its capsule and does not circulate in blood. Hence immunological tolerance against this antigen is not established during fetal life. When the antigen leaks out, following a penetrating injury, it may induce an immune response, causing damage to the lens of the other eye.

An example of 'sequestration in time' is seen with sperm antigens. As spermatozoa develop only with puberty, the antigen cannot induce tolerance during fetal life. The sperm antigen is therefore not recognised as self, and when it enters circulation it is immunogenic. This is believed to explain the pathogenesis of orchitis following mumps. The virus damages the basement membrane of seminiferous tubules, leading to leakage of sperms and initiation of an immune response, resulting in orchitis.

Cross-reacting foreign antigens: The fortuitous similarity between some foreign and self-antigens is the basis of the 'cross-reacting antigen' theory of autoimmunity. Organ-specific antigens are present in several species. Injection of heterologous organ-specific antigens may induce an immune response, damaging the particular organ or tissue in the host.

An example is the neurological injury that used to be a complication of antirabic immunisation in humans with the neural vaccine of infected sheep brain tissue. Its injection elicits an immune response against sheep brain antigens. This may damage the individual's nerve tissue due to cross-reaction between human and sheep brain antigens.

Streptococcal M proteins and the heart muscle share antigenic characteristics. The immune response induced by repeated streptococcal infection can therefore damage the heart. Nephritogenic strains of streptococci possess antigens found in the renal glomeruli. Infection with such strains may lead to glomerulonephritis due to antigenic sharing.

Molecular mimicry: A related type of autoimmunisation is 'molecular mimicry' which is due to the presence in some infecting microorganisms and self-antigens, of epitopes with identical peptide sequences (instead of similarities in 'cross-reactions'). Examples of such homologous sequences are seen in arthritogenic *Shigella flexneri* and HLA-B27, *Mycobacterium tuberculosis* and joint membranes, Coxsackie B and myocardium.

Polyclonal B cell activation: In this hypothesis, while an antigen generally activates only its corresponding B cell, certain stimuli non-specifically turn on multiple B cell clones. Such stimuli include chemicals (for example, 2-mercaptoethanol), bacterial products (PPD, lipopolysaccharide), enzymes (trypsin), antibiotics (nystatin) and infections with some bacteria (mycoplasma), viruses (EB virus) and parasites (malaria). Multiple non-specific antibodies form during some infectious diseases, such as

anti-human erythrocyte cold antibodies in mycoplasma pneumonia and anti–sheep erythrocyte antibodies in infectious mononucleosis. These polyclonal antibodies are IgM in nature, similar to the 'natural antibodies' produced by CD5+ B cells.

Forbidden clones: Breakdown of immunological homeostasis may lead to cessation of tolerance and the emergence of forbidden clones of immunocompetent cells capable of mounting immune response against self-antigens. Autoimmunisation may result when tolerance to a self-antigen is abrogated, as for instance by the injection of the self-antigen with Freund's adjuvant.

Altered T or B cell function: Enhanced helper T cell and decreased suppressor T cell functions have been suggested as causes of autoimmunity. Defects in the thymus, in stem cell development and macrophage function have also been postulated as causes.

Defects in the idiotype–anti-idiotype network have also been said to lead to autoimmunity. Genetic factors such as defective *Ir* or immunoglobulin genes have also been postulated. In spite of so many different possible mechanisms proposed, their actual role in autoimmunity, if any, has not been established.

CLASSIFICATION OF AUTOIMMUNE DISEASES

Based on the site of involvement and nature of the lesions, autoimmune diseases may be classified as hemocytolytic, localised (or organ specific), and systemic (or non-organ specific).

Hemocytolytic autoimmune diseases

Autoimmune hemolytic anemias: Autoantibodies against erythrocytes are demonstrable in this condition. Serologically, two groups of autoimmune anemias can be distinguished, characterised by 'cold' and 'warm' antibodies, respectively.

The **cold autoantibodies** are, generally, complete agglutinating antibodies belonging to the IgM class and agglutinate erythrocytes at 4°C but not at 37°C. This condition, which used to frequently accompany syphilitic infection, is seldom seen nowadays. Cold agglutinins are also seen in primary atypical pneumonia, trypanosomiasis and black water fever.

Warm autoantibodies are generally incomplete, non-agglutinating antibodies usually belonging to the IgG class and frequently seen in patients taking certain drugs such as sulphonamides, antibiotics and alpha methyldopa.

In autoimmune anemias, the red cells coated with antibodies are prematurely destroyed in the spleen and liver. Complement-dependent intravascular hemolysis appears to be a rare event.

Autoimmune thrombocytopenia: Autoantibodies directed against platelets occur in idiopathic thrombocytopenic purpura. Sedormid purpura is an instance of immune response against drug-induced neoantigens on platelets.

Autoimmune leucopenia: Non-agglutinating anti-leucocyte antibodies can be demonstrated in the serum of patients with systemic lupus erythematosus and rheumatoid arthritis.

Localised (organ-specific) autoimmune diseases

Hashimoto's disease (lymphadenoid goitre): Hashimoto's disease occurs more frequently in females and is associated with enlargement of the thyroid gland and symptoms of hypothyroidism or frank myxedema. Histologically, the glandular structure is replaced by lymphoid tissue consisting of lymphocytes, histiocytes and plasma cells. Antibodies with different specificities have been found in this condition. They include antibodies that react with thyroglobulin, a second acinar colloid, microsomal antigen and a thyroid cell surface component.

Thyrotoxicosis (Graves' disease): Most patients with thyrotoxicosis possess antibodies to thyroglobulin. Lymphocytic infiltration is common in thyrotoxic glands. The immunological basis of thyrotoxicosis is supported by the identification of the '**long-acting thyroid stimulator' (LATS)** which is an IgG antibody to the thyroid membrane antigen. Combination of LATS with the surface membrane of thyroid cells seems to stimulate excessive hormone secretion.

Addison's disease: The immunological basis of Addison's disease is suggested by lymphocytic infiltration of the adrenal glands and the presence of circulating antibodies directed against the cells of the zona glomerulosa.

Autoimmune orchitis: Lymphocytic infiltration of the testes and circulating antibodies to the sperms and germinal cells can be demonstrated in this condition. This condition sometimes follows mumps orchitis.

Myasthenia gravis: In this disease, there is abnormal fatiguability of muscles due to malfunction of the myoneural junction. An antibody against the acetyl choline receptor on myoneural junctions of striated muscles is present in these patients. This prevents acetyl choline from combining with its receptor, and impairs muscular contraction. The thymus shows lymphoid hyperplasia and numerous germinal centres. Infants born to affected mothers show symptoms of the disease but recover spontaneously by the age of two months, coinciding with the disappearance of maternal antibodies. This suggests that the pathogenic factor in neonatal myasthenia may be the autoantibody passively acquired from the mother.

Autoimmune diseases of the eye: Two types of autoimmune disease are seen in the eye. Cataract surgery sometimes leads to intraocular inflammation caused by autoimmune response to the lens protein. This is known as **phacoanaphylaxis**. Perforating injuries of the eye, particularly those involving the iris or ciliary bodies, are often followed by **sympathetic ophthalmia** in the opposite eye.

Pernicious anemia: Two types of autoantibodies are present in this condition. The first is directed against the parietal cells of the gastric mucosa. This is believed to cause achlorhydria and atrophic gastritis. The second is directed against the intrinsic factor and prevents absorption of vitamin B12 either by blocking its attachment to the gastric intrinsic factor or by binding to the B_{12} intrinsic factor complex and interfering with its uptake by the intestinal mucosa.

Autoimmune diseases of the nervous system: The 'neuroparalytic accidents' following rabies vaccination represent injury to the nervous system by the immune response against the sheep nerve tissue in the vaccine, which cross-reacts with human nerve tissue. Idiopathic polyneuritis (Guillain–Barré syndrome) is considered an autoimmune response against the peripheral nervous tissue.

Autoimmune diseases of the skin: Three serious diseases of the skin are considered to have an autoimmune basis. Pemphigus vulgaris may be caused by an antibody to the intercellular adhesion protein desmoglein. In bullous pemphigoid, antibodies directed against the dermal epithelial junction have been demonstrated. Specific antibodies in dermatitis herpetiformis have not been identified.

Systemic (non–organ specific) autoimmune diseases

This group includes conditions characterised by immune response against a variety of self-antigens and damage to several organs and tissue systems.

Systemic lupus erythematosus: This is a chronic, multisystem disease with remissions and exacerbations, terminating fatally. Patients have a variety of autoantibodies directed against cell nuclei, intracytoplasmic cell constituents, immunoglobulins, thyroid and other organ-specific antigens. Biological false positive reaction is seen in standard tests for syphilis.

The first immunological feature identified in SLE was the **LE cell phenomenon** described in 1948. The LE cell is a neutrophil containing a large, pale, homogeneous body (**LE body**) almost filling the cytoplasm. The LE body is the immunologically damaged nucleus of a leucocyte. Sometimes, instead of being intracellular, the LE body can be seen free, surrounded by a rosette of neutrophils (*Case*).

Immunofluorescent tests for antinuclear antibodies (ANA) show up different patterns of staining, such as homogeneous (diffuse), peripheral (outline), speckled and nucleolar. They are sensitive but not specific for SLE, as they may be positive in many other autoimmune conditions, viral infections, chronic inflammatory processes, etc.

Anti-DNA antibodies are tested by RIA or ELISA. Three major types of these antibodies are seen—those reacting with single-stranded (ss), double-stranded (ds) and both ss and ds DNA. Of these, high titre anti-ds DNA antibody is relatively specific for SLE. Another SLE-specific antibody is the anti-sm antibody.

Rheumatoid arthritis: This is a symmetric polyarthritis with muscle wasting and subcutaneous nodules, commonly associated with serositis, myocarditis, vasculitis and other disseminated lesions. It is found more commonly in women. The synovial membranes of the affected joints are swollen and edematous, with dense infiltration of lymphocytes and plasma cells. A striking feature is the presence of a circulating autoantibody called the 'rheumatoid factor' (**RF**). This is usually a 19-s IgM, though IgG and IgA RF have also been demonstrated. RF acts as an antibody against the *Fc* fragment of immunoglobulins.

RF is detected by agglutination tests using, as antigens, particles coated with globulins. In the Rose–Waaler test, the original technique for the detection of RF, sheep erythrocytes coated with a subagglutinating dose of anti-erythrocyte antibody (amboceptor) are used as the antigen in an agglutination test. In modifications of the test, latex and bentonite are used as the carrier particles for IgG. Antinuclear antibodies are frequently found in rheumatoid arthritis.

Polyarteritis nodosa: This is a necrotising angiitis involving medium-sized arteries, ending fatally due to coronary thrombosis, cerebral hemorrhage or gastrointestinal bleeding. Polyarteritis is seen as a component of serum sickness and other toxic complex diseases. Though it has been suggested that polyarteritis nodosa may be an autoimmune disease, the autoantibody responsible has not been identified.

Sjogren's syndrome: This is a triad of conjunctivitis sicca, dryness of the mouth, with or without salivary gland enlargement, and rheumatoid arthritis. The syndrome may occur in association with other collagen diseases. Antinuclear antibodies and rheumatoid factor commonly occur in sera.

PATHOGENESIS OF AUTOIMMUNE DISEASE

Many diseases are considered to be of autoimmune origin, based on their association with cellular or humoral immune response against self-antigens. Autoantibodies are more easily detected than cellular autosensitisation. However, the mere presence of autoantibodies during the course of a disease does not prove their causative role. Autoantibody formation may be a result of tissue injury and the antibody may help in promoting immune elimination of the damaged cell or tissue elements.

Antibodies may cause damage by the cytolytic or cytotoxic (type 2) and toxic complex (type 3) reactions. They are obviously important in hemocytolytic autoimmune diseases. Another mechanism of autoimmune tissue damage is by sensitised T lymphocytes (type 4 reaction). It is likely that humoral and cellular immune responses may act synergistically in the production of some autoimmune diseases. For example, experimental orchitis can be induced only when both types of immune response are operative.

Once initiated, most autoimmune responses tend to be self perpetuating. Their progress can be arrested by immunosuppressive therapy, though the degree of response to such therapy varies in different diseases.

Other recent therapies include vaccination with T cells specific for a given autoantigen, administration of synthetic blocking peptides that compete with autoantigen for binding to MHC molecules and few monoclonal antibodies to self-antigen responsible for autoimmune reactions. etc.

RECAP

- Autoimmune disorders are those in which the immune system produces auto (self) antibodies to endogenous (self) antigens, resulting in tissue injury.
- Usually the body displays immunological tolerance, wherein the individual's immune system 'tolerates' its own 'self' antigens, and is able to differentiate between 'self' and 'non-self' antigens. Autoimmunity occurs when this tolerance is lost, and the immune system attacks its own tissues. Autoimmune reactions may be mounted by antibody and T cell responses.
- Self-antigens may be intracellular components, receptors, cell membrane components, extracellular components, plasma proteins or hormones; depending on the location of the self-antigen, the disease may be localised to a single organ or may affect multiple sites.
- Autoimmunity may involve antigenic alterations, sequestration, cross-reacting foreign antigens, molecular mimicry or forbidden clones of self-antigens and hence mount the immune response against self-antigens.
- Examples of autoimmune diseases are renal injury (nephritis) associated with systemic lupus erythematosus, orchitis following mumps virus infection, pernicious anemia, thyrotoxicosis (Graves' disease) and Hashimoto's thyroiditis.
- The common treatment is immunosuppressants but recently other approaches like monoclonal antibodies and vaccination with specific T cells against self-antigens are also being studied.

SHORT NOTES

1. Molecular mimicry
2. Sequestered antigens in autoimmunity
3. Localised (organ-specific) autoimmune disease
4. Hashimoto's disease
5. Systemic lupus erythematosus (SLE)
6. Rheumatoid arthritis
7. Grave's disease
8. Myasthenia gravis

19 Immunology of Transplantation and Malignancy

IMMUNOLOGY OF TRANSPLANTATION

When, as a result of disease or injury, an organ or tissue becomes irreparably damaged, or when an organ is congenitally defective or absent, transplantation or grafting becomes necessary for the restoration of function. The tissue or organ transplanted is known as the **transplant** or **graft**. The individual from whom the transplant is obtained is known as the **donor** and the individual to whom it is applied, the **recipient**.

Allograft rejection

Clinical Case A 38-year-old man with end-stage renal failure due to chronic glomerulonephritis was given a cadaveric kidney transplant. His major blood group was A, the donor kidney was also of blood group A, and was matched for one DR and four of the six ABC antigens. The patient was put on immunosuppressive therapy.

On the third post-operative day, his urea and creatinine levels decreased appreciably. But on the seventh post-operative day, his graft became tender and the creatinine level increased. A clinical diagnosis of acute rejection was confirmed on finding lymphocytic infiltration in the renal cortex biopsy. The patient was started on intravenous corticosteroids and improved 24 hours later. Oral steroids were continued.

Classification of transplants

Transplants may be classified in various ways:

- Based on the **organ or tissue transplanted**, they are classified as kidney, heart, skin transplant, and so on.
- Based on the **anatomical site of origin** of the transplant and the **site of its placement**, grafts are classified as
  - **Orthotopic**: Grafts are applied in anatomically 'normal' sites, as in skin grafts.
  - **Heterotopic**: Grafts are placed in anatomically 'abnormal' sites, as when thyroid tissue is transplanted in a subcutaneous pocket.
- Transplants may be of **fresh tissues and organs** or of **stored** ones. It may be of **living or dead materials**.
  - **Vital grafts**: Live grafts, such as the kidney or heart, which are expected to survive and function physiologically in the recipient.
  - **Structural (static) grafts**: Non-living transplants like bone or artery which merely provide a scaffolding on which new tissue is laid by the recipient.
- Based on the **genetic (and antigenic) relationship** between the donor and the recipient.

Types of grafts

Autograft: An organ or tissue taken from an individual and grafted on him/herself

Isograft: A graft taken from an individual and placed on another individual of the same genetic constitution. Examples: Grafts made between identical twins or between syngeneic members of highly inbred strains of animals.

Allograft (formerly homograft): Grafts between two genetically non-identical members of the same species

Xenograft (formerly heterograft): Grafts between members of different species

The allograft reaction

When a skin graft from an animal (such as a rabbit) is applied on a genetically unrelated animal of the same species, the graft appears to be accepted initially. The graft is vascularised and seems morphologically and functionally healthy during the first two or three days. However, by about the fourth day, inflammation becomes evident and the graft is invaded by lymphocytes and macrophages. The blood vessels within the graft are occluded by thrombi, the vascularity diminishes and the graft undergoes ischemic necrosis. With extending necrosis, the graft assumes a scab-like appearance and sloughs off by the tenth day. This sequence of events resulting in the rejection of the allograft is known as the **first set response** (also 'first set rejection or reaction').

If, in an animal that has rejected a graft by the first set response, another graft from the same donor is applied, it will be rejected in an accelerated fashion. This accelerated allograft rejection is known as the **second set response**.

Mechanism of allograft rejection: The immunological basis of graft rejection is evident from the specificity of the second set response. Accelerated rejection is seen only if the second graft is from the same donor as the first. Application of a skin graft from another donor will evoke only the first set response.

An allograft will be accepted if the animal is rendered immunologically tolerant. The method of transferring immunity by means of lymphoid cells is known as **adoptive immunisation.**

Transplantation immunity is predominantly cell mediated:

- The **first set response** is brought about almost exclusively by T lymphocytes. Humoral antibodies are also produced during allograft rejection. They can be detected by a variety of methods including hemagglutination, lymphocytotoxicity, complement fixation and immunofluorescence.
- Antibodies are formed more rapidly and abundantly during **second set response** than during primary rejection. Antibodies are believed to participate in the second set response along with cell-mediated

immunity. When a graft is applied to an animal possessing the specific antibodies in high titres, hyperacute rejection takes place. The graft remains pale and is rejected within hours without even an attempt at vascularisation. This is known as the **white graft response**. This type of hyperacute rejection is sometimes seen in human recipients of kidney transplants, who may possess pre-existing antibodies as a result of prior transplantation, transfusion or pregnancy.

Humoral antibodies may sometimes act in opposition to cell-mediated immunity, by inhibiting graft rejection. This phenomenon, called **immunological enhancement** was originally described by Kaliss in tumour transplants. If the recipient is pretreated with one or more injections of killed donor tissue and the transplant applied subsequently, it survives much longer than in control animals. The enhancing effect can be passively transferred to normal animals by an injection of serum from immunised animals, showing that the effect is due to humoral antibodies.

The antibodies may bring about the enhancing effect in various ways. They may combine with the antigens released from the graft so that they are unable to initiate an immune response (**afferent inhibition**). The antibodies may combine with the lymphoid cells of appropriate specificity and, by a negative feedback influence, render them incapable of responding to the antigens of the graft (**central inhibition**). They may also cause **efferent inhibition** by coating the surface of cells in the graft so that sensitised lymphocytes are kept out of contact with them.

Allograft immunity is a generalised response directed against all the antigens of the donor. A recipient sensitised by a skin graft will reject by the second set response not only another skin graft but also any other organ or tissue graft from the same donor (Fig. 19.1).

Histocompatibility antigens

Immune response against transplants depends on the presence of antigens in the grafted tissue that are absent in the recipient and hence recognised as foreign. Therefore, if the recipient possesses all the antigens present in the graft, there will be no immune response, and consequently no graft rejection, even when the donor and recipient are not syngeneic. The first generation (F_1) hybrids between two inbred strains possess antigens representative of both the parent strains and

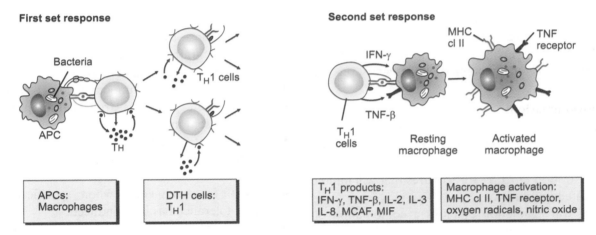

Fig. 19.1   Allograft reaction

will therefore accept grafts from either of the parental strains. If the two parental strains have genotypes AA and BB, respectively, the F_1 hybrid will be of genotype AB. It can therefore accept tissues with genotype AA as well as BB, as it possesses both alleles. Transplantation in the reverse direction (from F_1 to parent) will not succeed as strain AA will react against antigen B and strain BB against antigen A.

While transplants between members of a highly inbred strain of animals are successful, an exception is seen when the donor is a male and the recipient a female. Such grafts are rejected as the grafted male tissue (XY) will have antigens determined by the Y chromosome which will be absent in the female (XX) recipient. Grafts from the female to the male will succeed. This unilateral sex-linked histoincompatibility is known as the **Eichwald–Silmser effect**.

Antigens that participate in graft rejection are called **transplantation or histocompatibility antigens**. The term 'major histocompatibility system' refers to a system of cell antigens that exert a decisive influence on the fate of allografts. The major histocompatibility system in human beings is the human leucocyte antigen (HLA) system (*Case*).

Histocompatibility testing

Blood grouping: ABO blood group antigen compatibility is important in transplantation.

HLA compatibility: Next to ABO blood group compatibility, the most important factor in allograft survival is HLA compatibility. This is tested by HLA typing and tissue matching. HLA typing identifies the HLA antigens expressed on the surface of leucocytes.

Methods of HLA typing:

- **Microcyto-toxicity test:** Lymphocyte suspensions are added to microwells of tissue typing trays pre-dispensed with a panel of HLA typing sera, each containing alloantibodies to a specific HLA antigen, and incubated with complement. Cells carrying antigens corresponding to the HLA antiserum are killed by complement-mediated membrane damage. These can be detected by the addition of eosin or trypan blue which stains only dead cells. The lymphocyte is presumed to have HLA antigens corresponding to the specificities of all the antisera that have caused cell death, as indicated by the staining.

  Antisera for HLA typing were originally obtained from multigravidae, placental fluid and from multiple blood transfusion recipients, who have antibodies against mismatched paternal or donor HLA antigens. These are now being replaced by monoclonal antibodies.

- **Molecular methods:** More discriminating molecular methods have been developed for tissue typing. These include **restriction fragment length polymorphism (RFLP) with Southern blotting** and **polymerase chain reaction (PCR) amplification** using sequence-specific primers.

- **Tissue matching:** Once a set of HLA-compatible donors is available (commonly, siblings of the patient), the best among them can be chosen by tissue matching. This is done by the mixed lymphocyte reaction or culture (MLR, MLC). It depends on the fact that T lymphocytes in culture, when exposed to HLA incompatible antigens, will undergo blast transformation, the intensity of the reaction being a measure of the antigenic disparity between the donor and recipient lymphocytes. This is a one-way test in which donor lymphocytes are killed and only recipient lymphocytes are permitted to be transformed in response to the incompatible antigens on the donor cells.

Immunosuppression: As allograft rejection is an immunological process, immunosuppression will inhibit it. This can be achieved in experimental animals by neonatal thymectomy, chronic lymphatic drainage or administration of ALS—procedures that will inhibit cell-mediated immunity.

Clinical transplantation employs a combination of immunosuppressive drugs, including steroids, azathioprene and the fungal metabolite cyclosporin A, which is currently the most effective agent.

Priviledged sites: There appear to be certain privileged sites where allografts are permitted to survive, safe from immunological attack. The fetus can be considered an intrauterine allograft as it contains antigens foreign to the mother. Why the fetus is exempt from rejection is not clear, though many explanations have been offered. The placenta acts as an immunological barrier by generating a locally immunosuppressive hormone. Major histocompatibility complex (MHC) antigens are present only in low density on trophoblastic cells and the cell membranes are relatively resistant to attack by T or K cells. Antigen shedding by the fetus blocks the aggressive T cells or antibodies by an enhancement effect. An incomplete mucopolysaccharide barrier rich in sialic acid surrounds the trophoblastic cells, protecting them from cytotoxic lymphocytes. The high concentration of alpha fetoprotein in fetal blood may also be a factor, as it has immunosuppressive properties, which may protect the fetus against immunological damage from any maternal leucocytes entering fetal circulation.

Any site that is impenetrable to immunocompetent cells (for example, cartilage) is an immunologically privileged site. Areas where a lymphatic drainage system is absent, such as the brain or hamster cheek pouch, or ineffective, such as the testes, can accept allografts without rejection. Lack of vascularity at the site also prevents graft rejection. This is the reason for the success of corneal transplants.

Graft-versus-host reaction

Graft rejection is due to the reaction of the host to the grafted tissue (host-versus-graft response).

The contrary situation, in which the graft mounts an immune response against the antigens of the host, is known as the graft-versus-host (GVH) reaction. This occurs when the following conditions are present:
- The graft contains immunocompetent T cells.
- The recipient possesses transplantation antigens that are absent in the graft.
- The recipient must not reject the graft.

Examples of situations leading to the GVH reaction are:
- Allograft in a recipient in whom specific immunological tolerance has been induced.
- Adult lymphocytes injected into an immunologically deficient recipient. The immunological deficiency may be due to immaturity (newborn) or immunosuppression.
- F_1 hybrid receiving a transplant from any one parental strain.

The main clinical features of the GVH reaction in animals are retardation of growth, emaciation, diarrhea, hepatosplenomegaly, lymphoid atrophy and anemia, terminating fatally. The syndrome has been called **runt disease**.

Clinical transplantation: Organ/tissue transplantation is being performed for various illnesses in India and the world. Although, the frequency of cornea, kidney, skin, heart, lung, liver and bone marrow transplants is increasing, the availability of organ donors is a challenge which might be solved in the future by xenograft transplants.

IMMUNOLOGY OF MALIGNANCY

When a cell undergoes malignant transformation, it acquires new surface antigens. It may also lose some normal antigens. This makes a tumour antigenically different from the normal tissues of the host. A tumour can, therefore, be considered an allograft and be expected to induce an immune response.

Clinical evidence of immune response in malignancy

Several clinical observations indicate the presence of an immune response that prevents, arrests and occasionally cures malignancies.

Spontaneous regression: Instances of spontaneous regression of established tumours have been reported, especially with neuroblastoma and malignant melanoma. Based on the analogy of the role played by the immune response in recovery from infections, it is believed that recovery from malignancy may also represent an immune process.

Chemotherapy cures: Dramatic cures sometimes follow chemotherapy of choriocarcinoma and Burkitt's lymphoma. Even a single dose of a cytotoxic drug may, on occasion, result in a complete cure. Again, in some types of tumours, such as hypernephroma with pulmonary metastases, removal of the primary tumour often leads to regression of the metastases. These observations suggest that once a large mass of tumour has been removed, mopping up operations can be effected by the immune process. The immune response appears to be effective only when the tumour is below a 'critical mass'.

Overcome defence mechanisms: There is a higher prevalence of certain types of cancers observed unexpectedly at autopsy than their clinical incidence would suggest. This indicates that the immune system is able to deal with malignant cells as they arise and that only some of them overcome the defence mechanisms and develop into clinical cancer.

Cellular response: Histological evidence of immune response against malignancy is provided by the presence of lymphocytes, plasma cells and macrophages infiltrating tumours. The cellular response resembles that seen in the allograft reaction. Tumours showing such cellular infiltration have a better prognosis than those that do not.

Immunodeficiency states: If the immune system plays a natural role in preventing tumour development, a high incidence of malignancy should be expected in immune deficiency states. This is indeed so. Increased incidence of cancer, particularly lymphoreticular malignancies, is found in congenital immunodeficiency states, in AIDS and in patients undergoing chronic immunosuppressive therapy.

Tumour antigens

Tumor-specific antigens: These antigens are present in malignant cells but absent in the corresponding normal cells of the host. They induce an immune response when the tumour is transplanted in syngeneic animals. Such antigens which induce rejection of tumour transplants in immunised hosts are termed **tumour-specific transplantation antigens** (TSTA) or **tumour associated transplantation antigens** (TATA).

In chemically induced tumours, the TSTA is tumour specific. Different tumours possess different TSTA, even though induced by the same carcinogen. In contrast, the TSTA of virus-induced tumours is virus specific in that all tumours produced by one virus will possess the same antigen, even if the tumours occur in different animal strains or species.

Tumour-associated antigens: This type of antigen is found in some tumours and may also present in a few normal cells:

- **Oncofetal antigens** are **fetal antigens** which are found in embryonic and malignant cells but not in normal adult cells. The best known examples are alpha fetoprotein in hepatomas. Their synthesis represents a de-differentiation of malignant cells into more primitive forms.
- The **carcinoembryonic antigen** is a glycoprotein that can be detected in the serum of many patients with carcinoma of the colon, particularly in the presence of metastases. However, it also appears in some other conditions such as alcoholic cirrhosis, and hence its diagnostic value is limited. Alpha fetoprotein is an alpha globulin secreted by normal embryonic hepatocytes. Its serum level drops sharply after birth and is hardly detectable in adults. High levels are present in hepatic carcinoma, in which condition it is of diagnostic value.
- **Differentiation antigens** include those such as the prostate-specific antigen (PSA), whose level is higher in patients of prostate cancer and has been used as a diagnostic indicator. Similarly CA125 (cancer/carbohydrate antigen 125) is widely used as a diagnostic and prognostic marker for ovarian cancer.

Immune response in malignancy

Both humoral and cellular responses can be demonstrated in malignancy. Anti-TSTA antibodies can be demonstrated by indirect membrane immunofluorescence. Delayed hypersensitivity to tumour antigens can be detected by skin testing with tumour cell extracts. Cell-mediated immunity can be demonstrated by the stimulation of DNA synthesis and lymphokine production by the patient's leucocytes on exposure to the tumour antigens. The lymphocytes from the patients are cytotoxic to the cultured tumour cells.

CMI is believed to be the mechanism of host defence against malignancy. The humoral response may not be relevant, or may even be detrimental, due to its facilitating tumour growth by the process of enhancement.

Immunological surveillance

The concept of immunological surveillance was developed by Lewis Thomas in the 1950s. It postulates that the primary function of cell-mediated immunity is to 'seek and destroy' malignant cells that arise by somatic mutation. Such malignant mutations are believed to occur frequently and would develop into tumours but for the constant vigilance of the immune system. Inefficiency of the surveillance mechanism, either as a result of ageing or in congenital or acquired immunodeficiencies, leads to increased incidence of cancer. While this hypothesis is attractive, it may perhaps represent an oversimplification of a complex situation.

Mechanisms: If immunological surveillance is effective, cancer should not occur. The development of tumours represents a lapse in surveillance. The mechanisms of such lapses are not clear but several possibilities have been suggested:

- Due to the very fast **rate of proliferation** of malignant cells, they may be able to 'sneak through' before the development of an effective immune response and, once they reach a certain mass, may be beyond the power of immunological attack.
- **Circulating tumour antigens** may act as a **'smoke-screen'**, coating the lymphoid cells and preventing them from acting on the tumour cells. The tumour antigens on malignant cells may be inaccessible to sensitised cells, being covered by some antigenically neutral substance. Humoral antibodies may cause immunological enhancement. 'Blocking' activity has been demonstrated in humoral factors. This may be due to the circulating antigen, antibody or antigen–antibody complexes.
- Some tumours may be of **low immunogenicity** or may form cytokines, like transforming growth factor β (TGF-β) which suppresses CMI.
- Tumour cells frequently express **low levels of class I MHC molecules** and hence may not be recognised by CD8+ CTLs for destruction. Further, poor immunogenicity and co-stimulatory signals may lead to clonal anergy.

Immunotherapy of cancer

Different approaches have been used for the immunotherapy of cancer—passive, active and adoptive immunotherapy, specific and non-specific.

Passive immunotherapy: Was the earliest method. A special type of serotherapy has been found beneficial in experimental tumours. Appropriate antisera that possess 'de-blocking' activity in vitro have been found to cause regression of tumours, apparently by neutralising the circulating tumour antigens and permitting the sensitised lymphocytes to act on tumour cells. Monoclonal antibodies to tumour antigens may play a role as carriers in transporting cytotoxic or radioactive drugs specifically to the tumour cells.

Specific active immunotherapy: By the injection of tumour cell 'vaccines' was tried early in the last century but was given up as unprofitable. The method has been modified recently by using purified tumour cell membrane antigens and tumour cells treated with neuraminidase to increase their immunogenic potential.

Non-specific active immunotherapy: Uses BCG and non-living *Corynebacterium parvum*. Mathe, the leading proponent of cancer immunotherapy, reported very good results in acute leukemia, following combined treatment with BCG and allogeneic or autochthonous leukemia blast cells. Intralesional BCG in malignant melanoma has been reported to induce complete remission in a high percentage of patients. It has also been used against the intradermal recurrence of breast cancer following mastectomy. Dinitrochlorobenzene has been used in the treatment of squamous and basal cell carcinoma of the skin. Glucan, a pyran copolymer derived from microorganisms, and levamisole, originally introduced as an anthelmintic, have been used to stimulate CMI and macrophage function. Interferons have been employed in the treatment of leukemias.

Specific adoptive immunotherapy: Has been attempted with lymphocytes, transfer factor and 'immune RNA'. The donors have been persons cured of their neoplasms or specifically immunised against the patient's tumour. Lymphokine activated killer (LAK) cells obtained by treatment of the natural killer cells with interleukin-2 have been found useful in the treatment of certain malignancies, such as renal carcinomas.

Immunotherapy is ineffective in the presence of a large mass of tumour cells. Its role appears to be important in getting rid of the residual malignant cells after the gross tumour has been removed. The best results in the treatment of cancer apparently follow an integrated approach to therapy, combining surgery, radiotherapy, chemotherapy and immunotherapy.

RECAP

- Transplants may be classified based on the organs or tissue transplanted, the anatomical site of origin of the transplant and its placement. Based on the genetic relationships, transplants can be classified as:
  - autograft (taken from an individual and grafted on himself/herself)
  - isograft (between individuals of the same genetic constitution, like identical twins)
  - allograft (between two genetically non-identical members of the same species)
  - xenograft (between members of different species)
- First set response refers to the sequence of events resulting in the rejection of an allograft. In second set response, there is accelerated rejection of another graft from the same donor.
- An allograft will be accepted if the host is rendered immunologically tolerant. Adoptive immunisation is the process of transferring immunity by means of lymphoid cells.
- Transplantation immunity is predominantly cell mediated. The first set response is brought about almost exclusively by T lymphocytes, while in the second set response, antibodies participate along with cell-mediated immunity.
- Immunological enhancement is a phenomenon wherein pre-existing antibodies prevent CMI from causing graft rejection.
- Histocompatibility (transplantation) antigens participate in graft rejection. Major histocompatibility system refers to a system of cell antigens that exerts a decisive influence on the fate of allografts. The human leucocyte antigen (HLA) system is the major histocompatibility system in humans.
- The three classes of HLA antigens are I, II and III. HLA class I antigens (A, B, C) are the principal antigens involved in graft rejection and cell-mediated cytolysis.
- The most important factors favouring allograft survival are the ABO blood group antigens and the HLA antigens. HLA compatibility is tested for by HLA typing and tissue matching.
- Any site that is impenetrable to immunocompetent cells (cartilage) is an immunologically privileged site. Graft rejection is prevented in areas where there is no lymphatic drainage (brain) or where there is lack of vascularity (cornea).
- In the graft-versus-host (GVH) reaction, the graft mounts an immune response against the antigens of the host.
- When a cell undergoes malignant transformation, it acquires new surface antigens and may also lose some antigens, making it antigenically different from the normal tissues of the host.
- Tumour-specific antigens are present in malignant cells but absent in the corresponding normal cells of the host such as tumour-specific transplantation antigens (TSTA).
- Tumour-associated antigens are found in some tumours and may also present in a few normal cells such as fetal antigens, which are found in embryonic and malignant cells but not in normal adult cells, alpha fetoprotein in hepatomas, carcinoembryonic antigen in colonic cancers and CA125 in ovarian cancers.
- Both humoral and cellular responses can be demonstrated in malignancy; cell-mediated immunity is the probable mechanism of host defence against malignancy.
- Lapses in immune surveillance allow tumours to emerge; may result in proliferation of malignant cells, inaccessibility of tumour antigens on malignant cells to immunocompetent cells, lowered cell-mediated and humoral immune responses.
- Different approaches have been attempted in the immunotherapy of cancer:
  - Passive immunotherapy, using antisera against TSTA, was found to be of no use.
  - Monoclonal antibodies to tumour antigens have been used as carriers to transport cytotoxic or radio-active drugs specifically to tumour cells.
  - Non-specific active immunotherapy uses BCG and non-living *Corynebacterium parvum*.

❖ Specific adoptive immunotherapy with lymphocytes, transfer factor and 'immune RNA'. LAK cells, have been found useful in the treatment of certain malignancies. Immunotherapy is ineffective in the presence of a large mass of tumour cells.

SHORT ANSWERS

1. Features of an allograft reaction
2. Graft-versus-host reaction

SHORT NOTES

1. Histocompatibilty antigens
2. Methods of HLA typing
3. Graft-versus-host reaction
4. Tumour antigens
5. Immune surveillance
6. Immunotherapy in cancer

20 Immunohematology

INTRODUCTION

Blood was considered the essence of life and was believed to cure diverse diseases and restore youth and vitality to the aged. Blood transfusion became scientifically feasible only after the discovery of blood groups by Landsteiner.

History

In his original experiment, Landsteiner (1900) cross-tested serum from himself and five of his colleagues against their red blood cells. Three distinct patterns of agglutination were observed. Cells which failed to agglutinate with any of the serum samples were designated group O, while cells agglutinating in the two different patterns were called groups A and B, respectively. The fourth group AB was described later by his pupils von Decastallo and Sturli (1902). In 1930, Landsteiner was awarded the Nobel Prize for his discovery of human blood groups.

The **ABO system** is the most important of all blood group systems and its discovery made blood transfusion possible.

ABO BLOOD GROUP SYSTEM

The ABO system contains four blood groups and is determined by the presence or absence of two distinct antigens, A and B, on the surface of erythrocytes.

The four groups are also distinguished by the presence or absence of two distinct isoantibodies in the serum. The serum contains the isoantibodies specific for the antigen that is absent in the red cell. The serum of a group A individual has anti-B antibody, group B has anti-A and group O both anti-A and anti-B, while in group AB both anti-A and anti-B are absent (Table 20.1).

Blood group antigens are inherited according to simple Mendelian laws. Their synthesis is determined by allelomorphic genes A, B and O. Genes A and B give rise to the corresponding antigens, but O is an amorph and does not produce any antigen. The frequency of ABO distribution differs in different people. Group O is the most common and AB the rarest. In India, the distribution is approximately: O – 40 per cent, A – 22 per cent, B – 33 per cent and AB – 5 per cent.

Anti-A and anti-B isoantibodies appear in the serum of infants by the age of six months and persist thereafter. These are called 'natural' antibodies because they seem to arise from genetic control without any appar-

Table 20.1 *Distribution of ABO antigens and antibodies in red cells and serum*

	Red cells		Serum	
Group	Antigen present	Agglutinated by serum of group	Antibody present	Agglutinates cells of group
A	A	B, O	Anti-B	B, AB
B	B	A, O	Anti-A	A, AB
AB	A and B	A, B, O	None	None
O	None	None	Anti-A and anti-B	A, B, AB

ent antigenic stimulation. Natural anti-A and anti-B antibodies are IgM saline agglutinating antibodies reacting optimally between 4°C and 18°C but which are less active at 37°C. Immune isoantibodies may develop following ABO incompatible pregnancy or transfusion. Immune isoantibodies are 'albumin agglutinating' IgG antibodies reacting optimally at 37°C and acting as hemolysins in the presence of complement. They are clinically more important than natural IgM antibodies and may cause more severe transfusion reactions.

H antigen: Red cells of all ABO groups possess a common antigen, the H antigen or H substance which is a precursor to the formation of A and B antigens. The amount of the H antigen is related to the ABO group of the cell, group O cells having the most and AB the least amount. Due to its universal distribution, the H antigen is not ordinarily important in grouping or blood transfusion. Bhende et al. (1952) from Bombay reported a very rare instance in which A and B antigens as well as H antigens were absent from red cells. This is known as '**Bombay**' or **OH blood**. Such individuals have anti-A, anti-B and anti-H antibodies and their sera are incompatible with all red cells except of those with the same rare blood group.

RH BLOOD GROUP SYSTEM

Levine and Stetson (1939) demonstrated a new type of antibody in the serum of a woman who had developed severe reactions following transfusion of her husband's ABO-compatible blood. She had recently delivered a stillborn infant with hemolytic disease. They suggested that the woman may have been sensitised by some antigen inherited by the fetus from its father. The 'new type' of antibody described by Levine and Stetson was identified as the **anti-Rh factor antibody**. Landsteiner and Wiener (1940) identified in the red cells of the majority of persons tested, an antigen that reacted with rabbit antiserum to Rhesus monkey erythrocytes. This antigen was called the 'Rhesus' or Rh factor. Levine and colleagues (1941) proved that Rh sensitisation was the cause of hemolytic disease of the newborn.

Rh typing:
- For routine purposes, the typing of persons as Rh positive or negative depends on the presence or absence of **antigen D (Rho)** on red cells and hence can be accomplished by testing with anti-D (anti-Rh) serum. This is because D is the most powerful Rh antigen and accounts for the vast majority of Rh incompatibility

reactions. The distribution of Rh positives differs in different races. Among people of European descent, about 85 per cent are Rh positive and 15 per cent negative. Among Indians, approximately 93 per cent are Rh positive and 7 per cent negative.
- A variant of D is known as Du. Red cells of the **Du subtype** react with some but not all anti-D sera. Though Du cells may not be agglutinated by anti-D sera, they absorb the antibody on their surface. The Du subtype can therefore be detected by reacting red cells with anti-D serum and then performing a direct Coombs test. For the purpose of blood donation, Du cells are considered Rh positive. But when a Du individual requires transfusion, it is advisable to use Rh-negative blood because he or she is capable of being immunised by standard Rh-positive blood.

There are no natural anti-Rh antibodies in the serum. They arise only as a result of Rh incompatible pregnancy or transfusion.

OTHER BLOOD GROUP SYSTEMS

The **Lewis blood group system** consists of two antigens, Le^a and Le^b. It differs from other blood group systems in that the antigens are present primarily in the plasma and saliva.

In the **MN system**, using rabbit antisera, persons were originally classified into three groups—M, N and MN. An antigen, S, was later added to this system. This system has expanded to include at least 28 antigens.

Blood group systems other than ABO and Rh are of little clinical importance as they do not usually cause transfusion reactions or hemolytic disease. They have applications in genetics, anthropology, tissue typing and forensic medicine. As blood group antigens are inherited from the parents, they are often useful in settling cases of disputed paternity.

MEDICAL APPLICATIONS OF BLOOD GROUPS

Blood transfusion

The existence of several different blood group antigens makes it almost impossible to obtain perfectly matched blood for transfusion. But in routine transfusion practice, only the ABO and Rh antigens are relevant. The other antigens are too weak to be of importance.

Choice of donor: Safety in blood transfusion requires that the following conditions be satisfied in choosing a donor:

- The recipient's plasma should not contain any antibody that will damage the donor's erythrocytes.
- The donor plasma should not have any antibody that will damage the recipient's red cells.
- The donor red cells should not have any antigen that is lacking in the recipient. If the transfused cells possess a 'foreign antigen', it will stimulate an immune response in the recipient.

Ideally, the donor and recipient should belong to the same ABO group. It used to be held that O group cells could be transfused to recipients of any group as they possessed neither the A nor the B antigen. Hence the O group was designated as the 'universal donor'. The anti-A and anti-B antibodies in the transfused O blood group do not ordinarily cause any damage to the red cells of A or B group recipients because they will be rendered ineffective by dilution in the recipient's plasma. But some O group plasma may contain isoantibodies in high titres (1:200 or above) so that damage to recipient cells may result. This is known as the **dangerous O group**.

Due to the absence of isoantibodies in plasma, the AB group persons were designated 'universal recipients'. AB group donors may not always be available due to their rarity. In such cases, group A blood is safer than group B, because the anti-A antibody is usually more potent than the anti-B antibody.

Rh compatibility is important only when the recipient is Rh negative. An Rh-positive person may safely receive either Rh-positive or -negative blood. But an Rh-negative individual receiving Rh-positive blood may form antibodies against the Rh antigen. A subsequent transfusion with Rh-positive blood may then cause an adverse reaction. An additional risk in women is Rh sensitisation leading to hemolytic disease of the newborn. Therefore it is particularly important that Rh-negative women who are not past childbearing age receive only Rh-negative blood.

Cross-matching: Besides ABO grouping and Rh typing of the donor and recipient, it is invariably necessary before transfusion to perform cross-matching to ensure that the donor's blood is compatible with the recipient's blood.

Method: The routine procedure used in most blood banks is a rapid cross-match by the tile or slide method. This is done in two parts—the major cross-match where the donor red cells are tested against the recipient's serum, and the minor cross-match where

the recipient's cells are tested against the donor serum. One drop of a 5% suspension of donor red cells in saline is added to a drop of the recipient's serum on a porcelain tile or glass slide, mixed and observed for agglutination. Though in most cases agglutination occurs early, it may sometimes be delayed. The result is to be read, macroscopically and under low-power microscope, after incubation in a moist chamber for 10–15 minutes at room temperature. In the minor cross-match, the same is repeated using recipient cells and donor serum. Only the major cross-match is done ordinarily.

Coombs cross-match: The saline slide test does not detect Rh and other minor incompatibilities. The most discriminating method is the Coombs cross-match where washed donor cells and recipient serum are incubated in a water bath at 37°C for two hours and a direct Coombs test is done. This detects all incompatibilities, including incomplete antibodies.

Hemolytic disease of the newborn

When an Rh-negative woman carries an Rh-positive fetus, she may be sensitised against the Rh antigen by the passage of fetal red cells into maternal circulation. Minor transplacental leaks may occur any time during pregnancy but it is during delivery that fetal cells enter maternal circulation in large numbers. The mother is usually sensitised only at the first delivery and, consequently, the first child escapes damage (except where the woman has been sensitised already by prior Rh-incompatible transfusion). During a subsequent pregnancy, Rh antibodies of the IgG class pass from the mother to the fetus and damage its erythrocytes. This is the pathogenesis of hemolytic disease of the newborn. The clinical features may vary from a mere accentuation of physiological jaundice in the newborn to erythroblastosis fetalis or intrauterine death due to hydrops fetalis. Hemolytic disease does not affect all the offspring of Rh-incompatible unions.

Immunological unresponsiveness to the Rh antigen: Not every Rh-negative individual forms Rh- antibodies following antigenic stimulation. Some fail to do so even after repeated injection of Rh-positive cells. They are called non-responders. The reason for this immunological unresponsiveness is not known.

Fetomaternal ABO incompatibility: Rh immunisation is more likely to result when the mother and fetus possess the same ABO group. When Rh and ABO incompatibility co-exist, Rh sensitisation in the mother is rare. In this situation the fetal cells entering maternal circulation are believed to be destroyed rapidly by the ABO antibodies before they can induce Rh antibodies.

Number of pregnancies: The first child usually escapes disease because sensitisation occurs only during its delivery. The risk to the infant increases with each successive pregnancy.

Zygosity of the father: An individual may be homozygous or heterozygous with respect to the D antigen. When the father is homozygous, all his children will be Rh positive. When he is heterozygous, half his children will be Rh positive.

Detection of Rh antibodies

Most Rh antibodies are of the IgG class, and being 'incomplete antibodies', they do not agglutinate Rh-positive cells in saline. A minority are complete (saline agglutinating) antibodies of the IgM class. These are not relevant in the pathogenesis of hemolytic disease as they do not traverse the placenta.

IgG anti-D antibodies may be detected by the following techniques: (1) using a colloid medium such as 20 per cent bovine serum albumin; (2) using red cells treated with enzymes such as trypsin, pepsin, ficin or bromelin and (3) by the **indirect Coombs test**. The last is the most sensitive method.

Identification of Rh incompatibility

Rh typing should form part of routine antenatal examination. When the woman is Rh negative, and her partner Rh positive, fetal complications should be expected. Women with Rh-incompatible pregnancies should be screened for Rh antibodies by the indirect Coombs test at 32–34 weeks of pregnancy and at monthly intervals thereafter.

When hemolytic disease is diagnosed antepartum, intrauterine transfusion with Rh-negative blood may be indicated. Red cells introduced into the fetal peritoneal cavity will find their way into circulation and will survive normally. Premature delivery followed by transfusion may be necessary in some cases. When a baby is born with hemolytic disease, exchange transfusion with Rh-negative, ABO-compatible blood is the treatment of choice.

ABO hemolytic disease

Maternofetal ABO incompatibility is very common and in a proportion of these, hemolytic disease occurs in the newborn. In persons of blood group A or B, natural antibodies are IgM in nature and so do not cross the placenta to harm the fetus. However, in persons of blood group O, the isoantibodies are predominantly IgG in nature. Hence ABO hemolytic disease is seen largely in O group mothers, bearing A or B group fetuses. As ABO hemolytic disease is due to naturally occurring maternal isoantibodies, it may occur even in the firstborn, without prior immunisation. ABO hemolytic disease is much milder than Rh disease, probably because erythrocytes of the newborn have fewer A or B antigenic sites as compared to adult erythrocytes. The direct Coombs test is therefore often negative in this condition, while the indirect Coombs test (neonatal serum with type-specific adult erythrocytes) is more commonly positive. Peripheral blood smear characteristically shows spherocytosis.

Complications of incompatible blood transfusion:

- The red cells may undergo clumping and intravascular hemolysis or they may be coated by antibodies, engulfed by phagocytes, removed from circulation and subjected to extravascular lysis.
- It may be accompanied by symptoms such as shivering, tingling sensation, excruciating headache, constricting precordial discomfort and severe lumbar pain. Hypotension, cold clammy skin, cyanosis, feeble pulse and other signs of collapse may be seen. Jaundice, hematuria, oliguria and anuria may follow.

Some transfusion reactions may be due to immunological processes other than blood group incompatibility. Rigor, urticaria and other manifestations often occur when the recipient is hypersensitive to some allergen present in the donor's blood. Serious reactions follow when hemolysed or contaminated blood is transfused.

Complications following blood transfusion of infectious origin: Transfusion of blood contaminated by **bacteria** may lead to endotoxic shock or septicemia. Gross contamination can be recognised in most cases by inspection of the blood before transfusion.

The most important infections transmitted at present by blood transfusion are the **HIV and hepatitis viruses**. Several cases of transfusion-induced AIDS have occurred before HIV-screening of donors became mandatory. However, screening may not detect HIV-infected donors during the window period when they are infectious. Hepatitis B, C, D and possibly others can be transmitted by transfusion. Screening for the hepatitis B surface antigen can exclude most HBV carriers but the available serological tests against other hepatitis viruses are not quite satisfactory.

Despite diligent screening, there exists a small risk (about 1 in 300,000) of **transfusion-associated HIV, HBV** and **HCV** infections. The variant CJD prion is another risk in endemic areas like the UK where it is mandatory to screen donors for the prion.

Cytomegalovirus transmitted by transfusion may cause an infectious mononucleosis–like syndrome. **Syphilis** may be transmitted by transfusion of fresh blood from an infectious donor but not if the blood has been stored for three days or more before transfusion. **Malaria** too is transmissible by transfusion.

Red cell suspensions contaminated with certain bacteria, such as *Pseudomonas aeruginosa*, become agglutinable by all blood group sera and even by normal human sera. This, known as the **Thomsen–Freidenreich phenomenon**, is due to the unmasking of a hidden antigen normally present on all human erythrocytes. This is called the **T antigen**. Anti-T agglutinins are normally present in human sera. Such panagglutinability of red cells has occasionally been observed in persons suffering from systemic bacterial infections.

Several investigators have attempted to correlate blood group and susceptibility to certain diseases. It has been shown that duodenal ulcer is more frequent in persons of blood group O than in others. An association has also been established between group A and cancer of the stomach.

RECAP

- Twenty-eight blood group systems are currently recognised, but the ABO and Rh systems are the most important. Blood group systems are inherited according to Mendelian laws of inheritance.
- The ABO system consists of four groups, namely A, B, AB and O. This system is based on the presence or absence of two distinct antigens on the surface of the erythrocytes, A and B. Thus, for example the red cells of group A carry antigen A.
- The serum of a particular group carries antibodies specific for the antigen that is absent on the red cell:
  - ❖ The serum of group A individuals has antibody against the antigen that is absent on the red cell, that is, anti-B antibody; group B individuals have anti-A antibody; group O individuals have anti-A and anti-B antibody; whereas Group AB individuals possess neither anti-A nor anti-B antibody.
- Blood grouping for ABO groups is done by agglutination tests.
- It is essential to administer blood of the same group as that of the recipient. Before blood transfusions, besides ABO grouping and Rh typing of the donor and recipient, it is necessary to perform cross-matching to ensure that the donor's blood is compatible with the recipient's blood.
- In an emergency, group O blood can be given, since group O RBCs carry no antigens. Group O individuals are termed universal donors. Group AB individuals have neither anti-A nor anti-B antibodies in their serum, they can accept blood of any of the four groups, and hence are termed universal recipients.
- In India, about 93 per cent of individuals have the Rh antigen on their red blood cells (Rh positive). If an Rh-negative mother conceives a fetus that has Rh-positive red blood cells, anti-Rh antibodies from maternal circulation may pass into fetal circulation, damaging fetal red blood cells; erythroblastosis fetalis or even intrauterine death may occur. This usually does not happen with the first pregnancy but only with subsequent pregnancies.
- Blood transfusion of infectious origin by bacteria may lead to endotoxic shock or septicemia, HIV, HBV and HCV infections, malaria, etc.

ESSAY

1. List the different ABO blood groups and explain the Rh blood group system.

SHORT ANSWER

1. Complications of infected blood transfusion

SHORT NOTES

1. Hemolytic disease of the newborn
2. Methods of Rh antibody detection
3. Rh compatibility

21 Staphylococcus

INTRODUCTION

Staphylococci are Gram-positive cocci that occur in grape-like clusters and are ubiquitous. There are more than 45 species known, of which many are part of the normal commensal flora of humans. *Staphylococcus aureus* is the most important human pathogen, commonly causing localised suppurative lesions in humans but can cause disseminated infections (*Case* 1). Their ability to develop resistance to penicillin and other antibiotics enhances their importance as a human pathogen. Other clinically important species, such as *S.epidermidis*, *S.lugdenensis*, *S.haemolyticus* and *S.hominis*, mostly cause healthcare-associated infections in a compromised host. *S.saprophyticus* is a cause of urinary tract infections in young women. These are collectively known as **coagulase-negative staphylococci** (CoNS) to differentiate them from **coagulase-positive** *S.aureus*. *S.aureus* and *S.epidermidis* are the two important species causing infections in humans. They are differentiated by the characteristics shown in **Table 21.1**.

Staphylococci were first observed in human pyogenic lesions by von Recklinghausen in 1871 and Sir Alexander Ogston gave it the name Staphylococcus (*staphyle* in Greek, meaning 'bunch of grapes'; *kokkos* meaning a berry). Most staphylococcal strains from pyogenic lesions were found to produce golden-yellow colonies, because of which Rosenbach (1884) named them *S.aureus*.

STAPHYLOCOCCUS AUREUS

Morphology

Staphylococci are spherical cocci, approximately 1 μm in diameter, arranged characteristically in grape-

---

Staphylococcus aureus

Clinical Case 1   A 56-year-old man developed a skin abrasion on the hand while working in a garden. After four days, he noticed swelling and inflammation over the area of abrasion, followed by swelling of the hand. There was a purulent discharge from the lesion after another two days. A Gram stain of the discharge and culture on blood agar were positive for Gram-positive cocci in clusters. The patient was found to have a strong family history of diabetes and so he was investigated for this, as the possibility of spread to deeper tissues and the bloodstream existed. On further testing, this bacteria was identified as *S.aureus* and antimicrobial susceptibility showed resistance to penicillin and sensitivity to cloxacillin.

Clinical Case 2   A 15-year-old boy returned from a birthday party and began vomiting 6–7 hours later. There was no fever and the boy passed loose stools. The next morning, he rang up his school to inform them that he could not come that day, when the teachers let him know that six other children who had attended the party had reported a similar illness. On further questioning, the common dish that all the affected children had consumed was found to be a pineapple pastry. This pastry was recovered and the cream tested positive for *S.aureus*. Further investigations found that a specimen obtained from the nose of the cook was positive for *S.aureus*. Both were ascertained to be the same type by phage typing and pulse field gel electrophoresis; this indicated a common source.

Table 21.1 *Differences between* S.aureus *and* S.epidermidis

Test	S.aureus	S.epidermidis
Coagulase	+	–
Mannitol fermentation	+	–
Heat-stable nuclease	+	–
Phenolphthalein phosphatase	+	–
Beta hemolyis on blood agar	+	–
Golden-yellow pigment	+	–
Sensitivity to lysostaphin	+	–

like clusters (Fig. 21.1). Cluster formation is due to cell division occurring in three planes, with daughter cells tending to remain in close proximity. They are non-motile and non-sporing. A few strains possess microscopically visible capsules, particularly in young cultures. Many apparently non-capsulated strains have small amounts of capsular material on the surface. They stain readily with aniline dyes and are uniformly Gram-positive. Under the influence of penicillin and certain chemicals, they may change to **L forms.**

The other human pathogen *S.saprophyticus* is similar to *S.epidermidis*, except that the former is resistant to novobiocin, whereas the latter is not.

Resistance

Staphylococci are among the more resistant non-sporing bacteria.

They are uniformly resistant to lysozymes but are generally sensitive to lysostaphin—a mixture of enzymes produced by a particular strain of *S.epidermidis*.

Staphylococci were uniformly sensitive to penicillin in the pre-antibiotic era, with very few strains capable of producing penicillinase. Soon after penicillin came to be used clinically, resistant strains began to emerge, first in hospitals and then in the community at large.

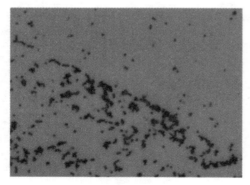

Fig. 21.1 *Staphylococcus aureus* in Gram stain

Types of resistance

Beta-lactamase-mediated: This is mediated through production of β-lactamase or **penicillinase**, which inactivates penicillin by splitting the beta lactam ring. These are inducible enzymes which are plasmid-mediated. They can be transmitted by transduction or conjugation. Penicillinase-producing strains remain sensitive to penicillinase-resistant penicillins such as methicillin and cloxacillin while the β-lactamase-producing strains are sensitive to beta lactamase inhibitor combinations like amoxicillin-clavulanic acid.

Altered target site PBP2a: Alterations in the penicillin-binding protein PBP2a and changes in **bacterial surface receptors** reduces binding affinity of beta lactam antibiotics to cells. This mechanism imparts resistance to all beta lactam antibiotics and has been named **methicillin-resistant S.aureus (MRSA)** as it was found to be resistant to penicillinase-resistant penicillins like methicillin and oxacillin. Majority of these strains also show resistance to other antibiotics like erythromycins, tetracyclines, aminoglycosides and cause outbreaks of hospital infection.

MRSA: This mechanism is regulated by a set of chromosomal genes called **staphylococcal cassette chromosomal *mec* genes (SCC *mec*)**, especially the *mec* A gene. Based on the type of these genes, the MRSA strains are divided as

- **Hospital-acquired MRSA (HA MRSA)**: SCC *mec* has Types I, II and III mainly and are multidrug-resistant.
- **Community-acquired MRSA (CA MRSA)**: SCC *mec* is Type IV mainly. These strains are less resistant, more likely to produce PVL toxin and more transmissible.

Tolerance to penicillin: Development of tolerance to penicillin, by which the bacterium is only inhibited but not killed by the antibiotic, is seen. It is demonstrated by a large difference in the minimum inhibitory concentration (MIC) and minimum bactericidal concentration (MBC) of penicillin in vitro.

Vancomycin resistance (VRSA): The strains showing resistance to vancomycin have started to emerge in some parts of the world. These strains have been shown to be harbouring both *van* A and *mec* A genes. This is the cause of major therapeutic challenges worldwide as they remain susceptible only to linezolid as of now.

Vancomycin intermediate resistance (VISA): These strains fall into the decreased category of susceptibility to vancomycin by the in vitro microdilution tests. They do not carry any resistance genes, but have a thickened cell wall. They have been isolated from patients who are on prolonged vancomycin treatment but show clinical failure to treatment with vancomycin. Terms like **hVISA** have been used for the heterogeneously resistant population of *S.aureus* which is a likely step towards full VISA development.

Pathogenicity and virulence

Staphylococci produce two types of diseases: **infections** and **intoxications**. In the former, the cocci gain access to damaged skin, mucosal or tissue sites, colonise by adhering to cells or extracellular matrix, evade host defence mechanisms and multiply and cause tissue damage. In intoxications, the disease is caused by the bacterial toxins produced either in the infected host or preformed in vitro.

Regulation of virulence factors: A number of staphylococcal factors, both cell-associated and extracellular, have been identified, which may influence virulence. The production of virulence factors is regulated by complex regulatory mechanisms through a set of genes whose expression is determined by the binding of the ligands, host receptors and the environment.

The **virulence factors** described include the following:

Cell-associated factors
Cell-associated polymers
- The cell wall **polysaccharide peptidoglycan** confers rigidity and structural integrity to the bacterial cell. It activates the complement and induces release of inflammatory cytokines.
- **Teichoic acid**, an antigenic component of the cell wall, facilitates adhesion of the cocci to the host cell surface and protects them from complement-mediated opsonisation.
- The **capsular polysaccharide** surrounding the cell wall inhibits opsonisation.

Cell surface proteins:
- **Protein A**, present in most *S.aureus* strains, has many biological properties, including chemotactic, anti-phagocytic and anti-complementary effects. It also induces platelet damage and hypersensitivity. Protein A binds to the *Fc* terminal of IgG molecules (except IgG3), leaving the *Fab* region free to combine with its specific antigen. Protein-A-bearing staphylococci coated with any IgG antiserum will be agglutinated if mixed with the corresponding antigen. This procedure, known as **co-agglutination**, has many applications such as streptococcal grouping and gonococcal typing. Protein A is a B cell mitogen. It has also been used as a ligand for isolation of IgG.
- **Clumping factor**, another surface protein, is the '**bound coagulase**' which is responsible for the slide coagulase test.
- Staphylococci possess **protein receptors** for many mammalian proteins such as fibronectin, fibrinogen, IgG and C1q. These facilitate staphylococcal adhesion to host cells and tissues.

Extracellular enzymes
- **Coagulase:** This is an enzyme which brings about clotting of human or rabbit plasma. It acts with a coagulase-reacting factor (CRF) present in plasma, binding to prothrombin and converting fibrinogen to fibrin. It is the basis of the tube coagulase test.
- **Lipid hydrolases**: Staphylococci produce a number of lipases which help them infect the skin and subcutaneous tissues.
- **Hyaluronidase:** It breaks down the connective tissue. Staphylokinase (fibrinolysin), fatty-acid-modifying enzymes and proteases help in initiation and spread of infection.
- **Nuclease**: A heat-stable DNase is a characteristic component of *S.aureus*, which helps in the identification of the organism.

Toxins
Cytolytic toxins are membrane-active substances, consisting of four hemolysins and a leucocidin:
- **Alpha hemolysin** (alpha toxin, lysin) is the most important among them. It is a protein inactivated at 70°C, but reactivated paradoxically at 100°C. This is because at 60–70°C, the toxin combines with a heat labile inhibitor which is denatured at 100°C, leaving the toxin free. Alpha toxin lyses rabbit erythrocytes, but is less active against sheep and human red cells. It is also leucocidal, cytotoxic, dermonecrotic (on intradermal inoculation in rabbits), neurotoxic and lethal (on intravenous inoculation in rabbits). It is toxic to macrophages, lysosomes, muscle tissues, the renal cortex and the circulatory system.
- **Beta hemolysin** is a sphingomyelinase, hemolytic for sheep cells, but not for human or rabbit cells. It exhibits a **hot–cold phenomenon**, the hemolysis being initiated at 37°C, but becoming evident only after chilling.

- **Gamma hemolysin** is composed of two separate proteins, both of which are necessary for hemolytic activity.
- **Delta hemolysin** has a detergent-like effect on the cell membranes of erythrocytes, leucocytes, macrophages and platelets.

Panton–Valentine Leucocidin (called **PVL**) is also a two-component toxin, like gamma lysin, being composed of the S and F components. Such bi-component, membrane-active toxins have been grouped as **synergohymenotropic toxins**. The interest in PVL has been renewed because of its increased association with CA MRSA.

Enterotoxin is responsible for the manifestations of staphylococcal food poisoning—nausea, vomiting and diarrhea 2–6 hours after consuming food contaminated by the preformed toxin. The toxin is relatively heat-stable, resisting 100°C for 10 to 40 minutes depending on the concentration of the toxin and the nature of the medium. About two-thirds of S.aureus strains, growing in carbohydrate and protein foods, secrete the toxin. Meat and fish or milk and milk products cooked and left at room temperature after contamination with staphylococci, for enough time for the toxin to accumulate, are the common items responsible. The source of infection is usually a food handler who is a carrier. The illness is usually self-limited, with recovery in a day or so (*Case 2*). Eight antigenic types of enterotoxin are currently known, named *A, B, C$_{1-3}$, D, E* and *H*. They are formed by toxigenic strains, singly or in combination. The toxin is believed to act directly on the autonomic nervous system to cause the illness, rather than on the gastrointestinal mucosa. The toxin is antigenic and neutralised by the specific antitoxin. Type A toxin is responsible for most cases. Sensitive serological tests such as latex agglutination and ELISA are available for detection of the toxin.

The toxin is potent—micrograms can cause illness. Some cases of post-antibiotic diarrhea are caused by enterotoxin-forming staphylococci. The toxin also exhibits pyrogenic, mitogenic, hypotensive, thrombocytopenic and cytotoxic effects.

Toxic shock syndrome toxin (TSST) is a potentially fatal multisystem disease presenting with fever, hypotension, myalgia, vomiting, diarrhea, mucosal hyperemia and an erythematous rash which desquamates subsequently. This is associated with infection of mucosal or sequestered sites by toxic shock syndrome toxin (TSST)-producing *S.aureus* strains usually belonging to bacteriophage group I. TSST type 1 (formerly known as enterotoxin type F or pyrogenic exotoxin C) is most often responsible, though enterotoxins B or C may also cause the syndrome.

TSST-1 antibody is seen in convalescents. This is protective and its absence is a factor in the pathogenesis of the condition. Though tampon-related TSS is now rare, the syndrome occurs in other infections of the skin, mucosa and other sites and also in some surgical wounds.

Staphylococcal enterotoxins and TSST-1 are **superantigens** which are potent activators of T lymphocytes. Being Vβ-restricted T cell mitogens, such superantigens stimulate very large numbers of T cells, without relation to their epitope specificity. This leads to an excessive and dysregulated immune response, with release of cytokines interleukins 1 and 2, tumour necrosis factor and interferon gamma. This explains the multisystem involvement and florid manifestations in staphylococcal food poisoning and TSS.

Exfoliative (epidermolytic) toxin, also known as ET or 'exfoliatin', is responsible for the **staphylococcal scalded skin syndrome (SSSS)**, an exfoliative skin disease in which the outer layer of the epidermis gets separated from the underlying tissues. The severe form of SSSS is known as Ritter's disease in the newborn and toxic epidermal necrolysis in older patients. Milder forms are pemphigus neonatorum and bullous impetigo.

STAPHYLOCOCCAL DISEASES

Staphylococcal infections are among the most common bacterial infections and range from the trivial to the fatal. They are characteristically **localised pyogenic lesions**, in contrast to the spreading nature of streptococcal infections.

The **common pyogenic staphylococcal infections** are as follows (*Case 1*):

- **Skin and soft tissue:** Folliculitis, furuncle (boil), abscess (particularly breast abscess), wound infection, carbuncle, impetigo, paronychia, less often cellulitis
- **Musculoskeletal:** Osteomyelitis, arthritis, bursitis, pyomyositis
- **Respiratory:** Tonsillitis, pharyngitis, sinusitis, otitis, bronchopneumonia, lung abscess, empyema, rarely pneumonia
- **Central nervous system:** Abscess, meningitis, intracranial thrombophlebitis

- **Endovascular:** Bacteremia, septicemia, pyemia, endocarditis
- **Urinary:** Staphylococci are uncommon in routine urinary tract infections, though they do cause infection in association with local instrumentation, implants or diabetes. Urinary isolates of staphylococci are to be considered significant even with low colony counts, as they may be related to bacteremia.

The **common toxin-mediated staphylococcal diseases** are as follows (*Case 2*):
- Food poisoning
- Toxic shock syndrome
- Scalded skin syndrome (as described above)

Epidemiology

Sites: Staphylococci are primary parasites of human beings and animals, colonising the skin, skin glands and mucous membranes.

Source: The most common sources of infection are human patients and carriers, animals and inanimate objects being less important. Patients with superficial infections and respiratory infections disseminate large numbers of staphylococci into the environment. About 10–30 per cent of healthy persons carry staphylococci in the nose and about 10 per cent in the perineum and also on the hair. Vaginal carriage is about 5–10 per cent, which rises greatly during menses, a factor relevant in the pathogenesis of TSS related to menstruation.

Staphylococcal carriage starts early in life, colonisation of the umbilical stump being very common in babies born in hospitals.

Shedders
Some carriers, called 'shedders', disseminate very large numbers of cocci for prolonged periods. The cocci shed by patients and carriers contaminate fomites such as handkerchiefs, bed linen and blankets and may persist on them for days or weeks.

Staphylococci may also come from infected domestic animals such as cows.

Staphylococcal disease may follow endogenous or exogenous infection. The modes of transmission may be by contact, direct or through fomites, by dust or by airborne droplets.

Healthcare-associated infections by staphylococci deserve special attention because of their frequency and because they are caused by strains resistant to various antibiotics.

Epidemic methicillin-resistant *S.aureus* strains, also called **EMRSA**, get easily disseminated in a hospital environment and are responsible for post-operative wound infections and other cross-infections in the hospital. They are multidrug-resistant most of the time. **HAMRSA** and **CAMRSA** (described above) are a public health concern now as the division between the two is getting blurred and both the types are circulating in community as well as hospitals.

Outbreaks: MRSA are notorious in causing outbreaks in hospitals. Such events need to be identified early in order to undertake interventions for early control.

Outbreak control measures: Measures for the control of staphylococcal infection in hospitals include:
- **Standard precautions** are the mainstay of control measures (described in Chapter 69, Healthcare-associated Infections). Hand washing, the oldest, simplest and most effective method of checking hospital cross-infections, unfortunately is often neglected.
- Isolation of patients with open staphylococcal lesions
- Detection of staphylococcal lesions among surgeons, nurses and other hospital staff and keeping them away from work till the lesions are healed
- Following strict aseptic techniques in theatres
- Source identification and control of the chain of transmission

Carriers, if found as a source of an outbreak, should be treated.

Treatment
For nasal carriers, treatment with local application of **muprocin** is required. **Chlorhexidine** may be needed in some carriers or colonisers as a small number of strains have shown resistance to muprocin. In resistant cases posing major problems, rifampicin along with another oral antibiotic may be effective in the long-term suppression or elimination of the carrier state.

Source: Identification is done by typing of bacteria. The methods used for typing are described below.

Typing methods

Typing may be done if the information is desired for epidemiological purposes.

Methods for typing bacterial strains can be
- Phenotypic: based on phenotypic characters like antibiograms, phage types, biotypes, etc.
- Genotypic: based on the genetic composition like rRNA or pulse field gel electrophoresis (PFGE).

Phenotypic–bacteriophage typing: Staphylococci may be typed based on their susceptibility to bacteriophages. An internationally accepted set of phages is used for typing. Staphylococcal phage typing is done by a pattern method (Fig. 21.2). For example, in India, the phage typing centre at Maulana Azad Medical College, New Delhi, had found that Phage group III was predominantly found amongst MRSA strains whereas MSSA from the community belonged to phage group NA (phage type 81). However, this method has many limitations.

Not all cultures are typeable by this procedure, and the phage susceptibility patterns of circulating strains vary by time and locality. Hence, phages in the reference set require periodic revision. Due to the availability of molecular methods now, phage typing is no longer used.

Molecular typing: Due to lack of discriminatory power of phenotyping methods, molecular typing is currently being carried out. For example, DNA fingerprinting using **RFLP**, **ribotyping** and **PCR-based** methods is used. **PFGE** and sequence-based typing methods **(MLST)** are now used in outbreak investigations as they are more discriminatory.

Details of methods are described in Chapter 7.

Laboratory diagnosis

1. Specimen: The specimens to be collected depend on the type of lesion (for example, pus from suppurative lesions, sputum from respiratory infections). In food poisoning, feces and the remains of suspected food should be collected. For the detection of carriers, the nasal swab is the usual specimen. Swabs from the perineum, pieces of hair and the umbilical stump may be necessary in special situations.

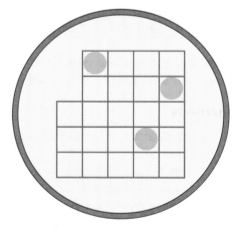

Fig. 21.2 Bacteriophage typing of staphylococci

2. Microscopy: Direct microscopy with Gram-stained smears is useful in the case of pus, where cocci in clusters may be seen. This is of no value for specimens like sputum where mixed bacterial flora are normally present.

3. Culture: Diagnosis may readily be made by culture. The specimens are plated on **blood agar**. Staphylococcal colonies appear after overnight incubation. Specimens where staphylococci are expected to be scanty and outnumbered by other bacteria (for example, swabs from carriers, feces in food poisoning cases) are inoculated on selective media like **Ludlam's** or **salt-milk agar** or **Robertson's cooked meat medium** containing 10% sodium chloride. Smears are examined from the cultures and the coagulase test carried out when staphylococci are isolated.

Cultural characteristics

Solid medium: They grow readily on ordinary media within a temperature range of 10°C to 42°C, the optimum being 37°C, and a pH of 7.4–7.6. They are aerobes and facultative anaerobes.

- On **nutrient agar**, after incubation for 24 hours, the colonies are large (2–4 mm in diameter), circular, convex, smooth, shiny, opaque and easily emulsifiable. Most strains produce golden-yellow pigment, though some may be white, orange or yellow. The pigment does not diffuse into the medium. Pigment production occurs optimally at 22°C and only in aerobic cultures. Pigment production is enhanced when 1% glycerol monoacetate or milk is incorporated in the medium. On nutrient agar slope, confluent growth presents a characteristic 'oil-paint' appearance.

- On **blood agar**, the colonies are similar to those on nutrient agar. Most strains are hemolytic, especially when incubated under 20–25% carbon dioxide. **Hemolysis** is marked on rabbit or sheep blood and weak on horse blood agar. For primary isolation, sheep blood agar is recommended. Human blood should not be used as it may contain antibodies or other inhibitors (Fig. 21.3).

- On **MacConkey agar**, they produce smaller colonies that appear pink due to lactose fermentation.

Liquid media: The growth appears as uniform turbidity.

Selective media: These may be needed for isolating *S. aureus* from specimens such as feces containing other bacteria. These include media containing 8–10% NaCl (**salt-milk agar, salt broth**), lithium chloride and tellurite (**Ludlam's medium**) and polymyxin.

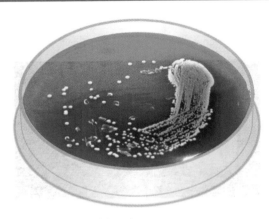

Fig. 21.3 Growth on blood agar

Strains of **S.aureus** subspecies **anaerobius** initially grow under anaerobic conditions but become aerotolerant on subculture.

4. Identification:

Biochemical reactions

Coagulase test: The coagulase test can be done using two methods: tube and slide (Table 21.2).

- The **tube coagulase test** detects free coagulase (extracellular product) of *S. aureus*. About 0.1 ml of a young broth culture or agar culture suspension of the isolate is added to about 0.5 ml of human or rabbit plasma in a narrow test tube. EDTA, oxalate or heparin may be used as the anticoagulant for preparing the plasma. Citrate is not recommended because it may be utilised by some contaminant bacteria, causing false positive results. Positive and negative controls are also set up. The tubes are incubated in a water bath at 37°C for 3–6 hours. If positive, the plasma clots and does not flow when the tube is tilted. Continued incubation is not recommended as the clot may be lysed by the fibrinolysin formed by some strains (Fig. 21.4a).

- The **slide test** detects bound coagulase (clumping factor) but can be positive for some of the CoNS. For the slide test, the isolate is emulsified in a drop of saline on a slide. After checking for absence of autoagglutination, a drop of human or rabbit plasma is added to the emulsion and mixed. Prompt clumping of the cocci indicates a positive test. Positive and negative controls are also set up (Fig. 21.4b).

Other biochemical tests: They are catalase-positive (unlike streptococci) and usually hydrolyse urea, reduce nitrates to nitrites, liquefy gelatin and are MR- and VP-positive but indole-negative.

5. Antimicrobial susceptibility tests

These should be performed as a guide to treatment. This is important as staphylococci readily develop resistance to drugs.

❖ **Detection of MRSA**

This is done by **cefoxitin disc diffusion agar** as per the present international guidelines. Cefoxitin resistance correlates with the presence of *mec* A gene.

Some strains called **borderline resistance S.aureus (BORSA)** have been found to be missed by cefoxitin susceptibility test and may need to be tested under special incubation conditions using **oxacillin screen** agar.

D-test

This is used to detect inducible clindamycin resistance where clindamycin disc is placed near erythromycin disc. If the zone of inhibition shows flattening towards erythromycin disc, the test is positive. In such situations, clindamycin should be reported as resistant, as clinical resistance is likely to be induced while the patient is on treatment.

❖ **Vancomycin susceptibility**

The current recommendation is to test using only the MIC for determining the susceptibility of *S.aureus*.

The guidelines on antimicrobial susceptibility tests are regularly revised and need to be consulted regularly. The interpretations need to be revised accordingly (details in Chapter 67).

6. Serological tests:
These may sometimes help in the diagnosis of hidden deep infections. Their relevance is limited. They are not widely available and are not used for diagnosis generally.

Table 21.2 *Difference between tube coagulase and slide coagulase tests*

Tube coagulase	Slide coagulase
Free coagulase: There is activation of plasma coagulase-reacting factor (CRP) found in the rabbit plasma, to from a coagulase-CRP complex. This complex, in turn, reacts with fibrinogen to produce the fibrin clot.	**Clumping factor:** It is bound to the bacterial cell wall and reacts directly with fibrinogen resulting in alternation of fibrinogen which precipitates on the staphylococcal cell, causing the cells to clump when a bacterial suspension is mixed with plasma. This does not require coagulase-reacting factor.

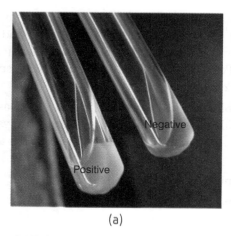

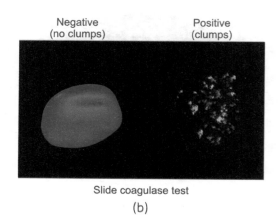

Slide coagulase test

(a)   (b)

Fig. 21.4   (a) Tube coagulase test: positive and negative; (b) Slide coagulase test: negative and positive

7. Molecular diagnosis: These tests are described under typing methods and are used to detect the spread of a strain during suspected outbreaks.

Treatment

As drug resistance is very common among staphylococci, the appropriate antibiotic should be chosen based on antibiotic sensitivity tests.

Benzyl penicillin is the most effective antibiotic, if the strain is non-penicillinase-producing.

Cloxacillin: Methicillin was the first compound developed to combat resistance due to penicillinase (beta lactamase) production by staphylococci. Due to limitations in clinical use of methicillin, cloxacillins are used instead against penicillinase-producing strains.

Vancomycin or teicoplanin: Wherever MRSA strains are detected, vancomycin is the drug of choice. Strains resistant to vancomycin and teicoplanin are still not common and not yet reported from India.

Linezoid is the treatment of choice for patients infected with VRSA.

For mild superficial lesions, systemic antibiotics may not be necessary. Topical application of drugs not used systemically, such as bacitracin, chlorhexidine or mupirocin, may be sufficient.

OTHER COAGULASE-POSITIVE STAPHYLOCOCCI

Besides *S.aureus*, there are other coagulase-positive staphylococci, for example, *S.intermedius* and *S.hyicus*. These are animal parasites and do not infect humans.

COAGULASE-NEGATIVE STAPHYLOCOCCI

Coagulase-negative staphylococci constitute a major component of the normal flora of the human body. Some species can produce human infections—*S.epidermidis*, *S.haemolyticus* and *S.lugdonensis*, especially in device-associated and healthcare-associated infections.

S.epidermidis is the most common cause of CoNS infections in humans. It is invariably present on normal human skin. It can cause disease when the host defences are breached. It is a common cause of **stitch abscess**. It has a predilection for growth on implanted foreign bodies such as artificial heart valves, shunts, intravascular catheters and prosthetic appliances, leading to bacteremia. Hospital strains of *S.epidermidis* are usually multidrug-resistant. It can cause cystitis and central-line-associated bloodstream infection (BSI). Endocarditis may be caused, particularly in drug addicts.

> **Biofilm formation** is an important factor in the pathogenesis of infections by *S.epidermidis*. It is an extracellular polysaccharide matrix which protects bacteria from antibacterial agents and helps in colonisation and resistance of infections.

S.saprophyticus may be present on normal human skin and the periurethral area and can cause urinary tract infection, particularly in sexually active young women. The infecting strains are usually sensitive to most common antibiotics, except nalidixic acid. *S.saprophyticus* is identified by its novobiocin resistance.

MICROCOCCI

These are Gram-positive cocci which can be mistaken for *S.aureus* in culture but are larger and mostly in pairs, tetrads or irregular clusters (Fig. 21.5). In cultures, they form smaller colonies. They are catalase- and modified oxidase-positive and oxidative in Hugh and Leifson's oxidation–fermentation test. They are ordinarily non-pathogenic but can rarely cause infections in an immunocompromised host.

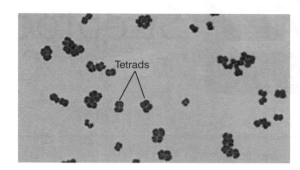

Fig. 21.5 Micrococci

RECAP

- *Staphylococcus* are Gram-positive cocci, non-motile, facultative anaerobes, and catalase-positive.
- The coagulase test is used to broadly demarcate staphylococci into coagulase-positive (*Staphylococcus aureus*) and coagulase-negative (*Staphylococcus epidermidis*, *Staphylococcus saprophyticus*, among others) species.
- *Staphylococcus aureus* is a major pathogen causing suppurative infections.
- They possess many virulence factors— cellular and extracellular—enzymes and toxins that cause various lesions based on its ability to invade breaks in the body's defences,
- *Staphylococcus epidermidis* forms biofilms on medical devices and causes infections associated with implants such as central venous catheters, cerebrospinal fluid shunts and intraocular lenses.
- Staphylococci are usually susceptible to penicillinase-resistant penicillins, such as methicillin and cloxacillin, and to aminoglycosides and macrolides.
- Methicillin-resistant HAMRSA and CAMRSA, VRSA and VISA are posing major therapeutic challenge in treatment of these infections.

ESSAYS

1. Describe the virulence factors of *Staphylococcus aureus* and their mechanism of action.
2. What is toxic shock syndrome? Describe its etiology and pathogenesis.

SHORT ANSWERS

1. Co-agglutination (definition)
2. Differences between *Staphylococcus aureus* and *Staphylococcus epidermidis*

SHORT NOTES

1. Principle and interpretation of the coagulase test
2. MRSA
3. Staphylococcal food poisoning

22 Streptococcus

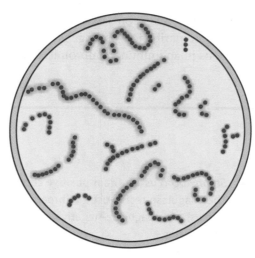

Fig. 22.1 Streptococci (Gram-positive cocci in chains)

Ogston (1881) isolated them from acute abscesses, distinguished them from staphylococci and established their pathogenicity by animal inoculation. Rosenbach (1884) isolated the cocci from human suppurative lesions and gave them the name *Streptococcus pyogenes*.

Classification

Several systems of classification (as shown in the box below) have been used in medical bacteriology.

Classification of streptococci is based on several characteristics:
1. Hemolysis on blood agar
   ❖ α hemolyis
   ❖ β hemolyis
   ❖ No hemolysis
2. Cell wall antigen (group-specific carbohydrate or Lancefield antigen)
   ❖ Group A-H and K-V
3. Biochemical reactions
   ❖ Viridans streptococci
4. Growth conditions
   ❖ Facultative anaerobes, e.g., *S.pyogenes*
   ❖ Strict anaerobes, e.g., Peptostreptococcus
(Classification of *Streptococcus pneumoniae* based on capsular polysaccharide is discussed in Chapter 23.)

INTRODUCTION

Streptococci are Gram-positive cocci arranged in chains or pairs (Fig. 22.1). They are part of the normal flora of humans and animals. Some of them are human pathogens. The most important streptococci are *Streptococcus pyogenes* which cause pyogenic infections, with a characteristic tendency to spread, as opposed to staphylococcal lesions, which are typically localised. It is also responsible for the non-suppurative lesions, acute rheumatic fever and glomerulonephritis which occur as sequelae to infection.

Cocci in chains were first seen in erysipelas and wound infections by Billroth (1874), who called them streptococci (*streptos*, meaning twisted or coiled).

Based on hemolysis on blood agar

Aerobic and facultative anaerobic streptococci are classified on the basis of their hemolytic properties. Brown (1919) categorised them into three varieties based on their growth on 5% horse blood agar.

- **Alpha (α) hemolytic streptococci**

  These produce a greenish discolouration with partial hemolysis around the colonies. The zone of lysis is small (1 or 2 mm wide) with indefinite margins, and unlysed erythrocytes can be made out microscopically within this zone. Viridans streptococci are known to produce α hemolysis. Most alpha hemolytic streptococci are normal commensals in the throat, and may cause opportunistic infections rarely. (Pneumococcus [*S.pneumoniae*] is also an alpha hemolytic streptococcus.)

- **Beta (β) hemolytic streptococci**

  These produce a sharply defined, clear, colourless zone of hemolysis, 2–4 mm wide, within which red cells are completely lysed. The term 'hemolytic streptococci' applies strictly only to beta hemolytic strains. Most pathogenic streptococci belong to this group.

- **Non-hemolytic streptococci**

  These do not produce hemolysis in the medium and include mostly the fecal streptococci which are classified as the **Enterococcus** species.

Based on carbohydrate antigen or Lancefield groups

Hemolytic streptococci were classified by Lancefield (1933) serologically into groups based on the nature of a carbohydrate (C) antigen on the cell wall. These are known as **Lancefield groups**, twenty of which have been identified so far and named **A–H and K–V (without I and J)**.

(*Streptococcus pneumoniae* is another important streptococci where classification is based on capsular polysaccharide and is discussed in a separate chapter.)

Griffith typing is used for further classification of *S.pyogenes*, belonging to Lancefield's group A. Based on the M proteins on the cell surface, they are subdivided into M types. About 80 types of *S.pyogenes* have been recognised so far (types M1, M2, M3 and so on).

Table 22.1 shows the medically important streptococci and their characteristics.

Table 22.1   *Medically important streptococci and their characteristics*

Species or common name	Lancefield group	Hemolysis	Habitat in human hosts	Laboratory tests	Common diseases caused
S.pyogenes	A	Beta	Throat, skin	Bacitracin-sensitive; PYR test-positive; Ribose not fermented	Upper respiratory tract infections, pyoderma, rheumatic fever, glomerulonephritis
S.agalactiae	B	Beta	Female genital tract, rectum	CAMP test, hippurate hydrolysis	Neonatal meningitis, septicemia
S.equisimilis	C	Beta	Throat	Ribose and trehalose fermentation	Pharyngitis, endocarditis
S.anginosus	A, C, F, G, untypable	Beta (alpha or non-hemolytic gamma)	Throat, colon, female genital tract	Group A strains, bacitracin-resistant, PYR-negative; minute colony variants of other groups	Pyogenic infections
Enterococcus sp (*S.faecalis* and other enterococci)	D	Gamma (alpha, beta)	Colon	Growth in 6.5% NaCl; PYR-positive	Urinary tract infections, endocarditis, suppurative infections
Non-enterococcal Group D species (*S.bovis*)	D	Gamma	Colon	No growth in 6.5% NaCl	Endocarditis
Viridans streptococci (many species)	Not typed	Alpha (gamma)	Mouth, colon, female genital tract	Optochin-resistant, species classification on biochemical properties	Endocarditis (*S.sanguis*); dental caries (*S.mutans*)

Based on biochemical tests

This is more commonly used to differentiate the members of viridans group of streptococci.

Based on oxygen requirement
- Facultative anaerobe
- Obligate anaerobe

STREPTOCOCCUS PYOGENES

VIRULENCE FACTORS AND PATHOGENICITY

The diseases caused by *S.pyogenes* can be suppurative or non-suppurative, which include the sequelae to post-streptococcal infections.

S.pyogenes produces pyogenic infections with a **tendency to spread** locally, along lymphatics and through the bloodstream.

Virulence factors

Cell-wall associated factors

1. **Capsule:** The capsule, when present, inhibits phagocytosis. It is not antigenic in human beings. The cell wall is composed of an outer layer of protein and lipoteichoic acid, a middle layer of group-specific carbohydrate and an inner layer of peptidoglycan. The peptidoglycan (mucoprotein) is responsible for cell wall rigidity. It also has some biological properties such as pyrogenic and thrombolytic activity.

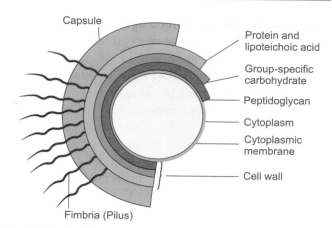

Fig. 22.2 Antigenic structure of *S.pyogenes*

2. **Carbohydrate antigen:** On the basis of the C carbohydrate antigen, *S.pyogenes* is classified under Lancefield group A. This antigen shows cross-reactivity with some human tissues (see post-streptococcal infection sequelae). As this antigen is an integral part of the cell wall, it has to be extracted for grouping by a precipitation test with group antisera. For the test, streptococci are grown in Todd–Hewitt broth and extracted with hydrochloric acid (Lancefield's acid extraction method), formamide (Fuller's method), by an enzyme produced by *Streptomyces albus* (Maxted's method) or by autoclaving (Rantz and Randall's method). The extract and the specific antisera are allowed to react in capillary tubes. Precipitation occurs within five minutes at the interface between the extract

---

Streptococcus pyogenes

Clinical Case 1 A seven-year-old girl presented with severe sore throat and fever up to 39°C for the past three days, with difficulty in swallowing. She did not complain of coryza or earache. On examination, she was found to have bilateral tender submandibular lymphadenopathy, enlarged tonsils and pharyngeal exudates. A culture of the throat swab was performed and, pending results, she was started on oral penicillin. The culture after 24 hours was positive for beta hemolytic colonies, which were shown to be Gram-positive cocci in short chains, on smear examination. They were sensitive to penicillin. The girl was diagnosed with streptococcal pharyngitis.

Clinical Case 2 A nine-year-old girl had developed fever and sore throat, and group A streptococci had been cultured from her throat. Three weeks later, she developed pain and tender swelling of both knees and ankles; a palpable effusion of the right knee was drained, which yielded straw-coloured fluid. Culture of the aspirate was negative. Simultaneously, the girl began experiencing shortness of breath. Physical examination and chest x-ray suggested mild congestive heart failure. The girl was diagnosed with acute rheumatic fever with reactive poststreptococcal arthritis. On follow-up after one year, a murmur was audible at the cardiac apex suggestive of rheumatic heart disease (RHD).

Clinical Case 3 A seven-year-old boy developed skin infection (pyoderma), but his mother did not seek medical help. A week later, he passed dark-coloured urine. Four days later, he developed pitting edema in both ankles. On examination, the boy was found to have elevated blood pressure, 4+ proteinuria, red blood cell casts and elevated serum creatinine. He was diagnosed with acute post-streptococcal glomerulonephritis.

and the homologous antiserum. Grouping may also be done by agar gel precipitation.

3. **Protein antigen:** Several protein antigens have been identified in the outer part of the cell wall. *S.pyogenes* can be typed based on:

- **M proteins**: This is the most important protein used for typing as well as for virulence. It acts as a virulence factor by inhibiting phagocytosis. It is antigenic. The antibody to the M protein promotes phagocytosis of the coccus and is therefore protective. The M protein is heat- and acid-stable but susceptible to tryptic digestion. It can be extracted by Lancefield's acid extraction method and typing is done with type-specific sera. About 80 M protein types have been recognised.

- **T proteins**: The T protein is an acid-labile, trypsin-resistant antigen present in many serotypes of *S.pyogenes*. It may be specific but many different M types possess the same T antigen. It is usually demonstrated by the slide agglutination test using trypsin-treated whole streptococci.

- **R proteins**: Some types of *S.pyogenes* (2, 3, 28 and 48) and some strains of groups B, C and G contain a third antigen, the R protein. The T and R proteins have no relation to virulence. A non-type-specific protein, associated with the M protein, known as the **M-associated protein (MAP)**, has been identified.

4. **Pili (fimbria):** These hair-like structures project through the capsule of group A streptococci (GAS). The pili consist partly of M proteins and are covered with lipoteichoic acid which is important in the attachment of streptococci to epithelial cells.

Figure 22.2 illustrates the disposition of the various antigens in *S.pyogenes*.

Antigenic cross-reactivity: Various structural components of *S.pyogenes* exhibit antigenic cross-reaction with different tissues of the human body. Antigenic relationships have been demonstrated between capsular hyaluronic acid and human synovial fluid; cell wall proteins and myocardium; group A carbohydrates and cardiac valves; cytoplasmic membrane antigens and vascular intima; and peptidoglycans and skin antigens. It has been postulated that these antigenic cross-reactions may account for some of the manifestations of rheumatic fever and other streptococcal diseases, the tissue damage being of an immunological nature.

Toxins

Hemolysins

Streptococci produce two hemolysins, streptolysin 'O' and 'S'. Streptolysin O is so called because it is oxygen-labile. It is inactive in the oxidised form but may be reactivated by treatment with mild reducing agents. On blood agar, streptolysin O activity is seen only in the subsurface and not on the surface cultures. It may be obtained in the active state by growing streptococci in broth containing reducing agents such as sodium hydrosulphite. It is also heat labile. It appears to be an important virulence factor. It is lethal on intravenous injection into animals and has specific cardiotoxic activity. It also has leucotoxic activity. In its biological action, streptolysin O resembles the oxygen-labile hemolysins of *C.perfringens*, *C.tetani* and *S.pneumoniae*.

- **Streptolysin O** is antigenic, and anti-streptolysin O appears in sera following streptococcal infection. Estimation of this antibody (**ASO titre**) is a standard serological procedure for the diagnosis of past infection with *S.pyogenes*. This streptolysin is inhibited by cholesterol but not by normal sera. Following certain chemical treatments or bacterial contamination, sera may develop inhibitory activity due to some changes in the lipoproteins. Such sera are unfit for the ASO test. Because of the complexity of the hemolysis inhibition test, the ASO test is now done by the serological method of latex agglutination. An ASO titre in excess of 200 units is considered significant and suggests either recent or recurrent infection with streptococci.

- **Streptolysin S** is an oxygen-stable hemolysin and is responsible for the hemolysis seen around streptococcal colonies on the surface of blood agar plates. It is called streptolysin S as it is soluble in serum. It is a protein but is not antigenic. Convalescent sera do not neutralise streptolysin S activity. It is inhibited non-specifically by serum lipoproteins. Streptolysin S and O are produced by groups A, C and G also.

Streptococcal pyrogenic exotoxin (SPE)

SPE is also called erythrogenic or Dick or scarlatinal toxin. This toxin was named 'erythrogenic' because its intradermal injection into susceptible individuals produced an erythematous reaction. This test was used to identify children susceptible to scarlet fever, a type of acute pharyngitis with extensive erythematous rash, caused by the *S.pyogenes* strains producing this toxin.

It is of historical interest now.

Types of SPEs: Three types of SPEs have been identified—**A**, **B** and **C**. Types A and C are coded for by bacteriophage genes, while type B gene is chromosomal.

Superantigens: SPEs are 'superantigens' (like staphylococcal enterotoxins and the TSS toxin), which are T cell mitogens that induce a massive release of inflammatory cytokines, causing tissue damage, fever and shock.

Streptokinase (fibrinolysin)

This toxin promotes the lysis of human fibrin clots by activating a plasma precursor (plasminogen). It is an **antigenic** protein, and neutralising antibodies appear in convalescent sera. Antistreptokinase antibodies provide retrospective evidence of streptococcal infection. Fibrinolysin appears to play a biological role in streptococcal infections by breaking down the fibrin barrier around the lesions and facilitating the spread of infection. Streptokinase is given intravenously for the treatment of early myocardial infarction and other thromboembolic disorders.

Deoxyribonucleases (streptodornase, DNase)

These cause depolymerisation of DNA. Pyogenic exudates contain large amounts of DNA, derived from the **nuclei** of necrotic cells. Streptodornase helps to liquefy the thick pus and may be responsible for the thin serous character of streptococcal exudates. This property has been applied therapeutically in liquefying localised collections of thick exudates, as in empyema. A preparation containing streptokinase and streptodornase is available for this purpose.

Types of DNases: Four antigenically distinct DNases, **A**, **B**, **C** and **D**, have been recognised, of which type B is the most antigenic in human beings. Demonstration of **anti-DNase B antibody** is useful in the retrospective diagnosis of *S.pyogenes* infection, particularly in skin infections, where ASO titres may be low. Streptodornase B and D also possess ribonuclease activity.

Nicotinamide adenine dinucleotidase (NADase)

NADase was formerly diphosphopyridine nucleotidase, DPNase. This acts on the co-enzyme NAD and liberates nicotinamide from the molecule. It is antigenic and is specifically neutralised by the antibody in convalescent sera. The biological significance of NADase is not known, though it is believed to be leucotoxic.

Hyaluronidase

This enzyme breaks down the hyaluronic acid of the tissues. This might favour the spread of infection along the intercellular spaces. Streptococci possess a hyaluronic acid capsule and also synthesise a hyaluronidase—a seemingly self-destructive process. It has, however, been found that strains that form hyaluronidase in large quantities (M types 4 and 22) are non-capsulated. The enzyme is antigenic and specific antibodies appear in convalescent sera.

Serum opacity factor (SOF)

Some M types of *S.pyogenes* produce a lipoproteinase which results in opacity when applied to agar gel containing horse or swine serum. This is known as serum opacity factor (SOF). This is a virulence determinant of the organism.

Other enzymes

Many strains also produce proteinase, phosphatase, esterases, amylase, *N*-acetyl glucosaminidase, neuraminidase and other toxins or enzymes. It is not known whether, and to what extent, these contribute to pathogenesis.

Pathogenicity of streptococcal diseases

Suppurative diseases

1. **Respiratory infections**: The primary site of invasion of the human body by *S.pyogenes* is the throat. Sore throat is the most common streptococcal disease. It may be localised as tonsillitis or may involve the pharynx more diffusely (**pharyngitis**) as described (*Case* 1). Virulent group A streptococci adhere to the pharyngeal epithelium by means of the lipoteichoic acid covering the surface pili. The glycoprotein fibronectin on the epithelial cells serves as the receptor to the lipoteichoic acid ligand. Tonsillitis is more common in older children and adults than in younger children, who commonly develop diffuse pharyngitis. Localisation is believed to be favoured by hypersensitivity due to prior contact.

   From the throat, streptococci may spread to the surrounding tissues, leading to suppurative complications such as otitis media, mastoiditis, quinsy, Ludwig's angina and suppurative adenitis. It may rarely lead to meningitis. Streptococcal pneumonia seldom follows throat infection but may occur as a complication of influenza or other respiratory viral diseases.

2. **Skin and soft tissue infections**: *S.pyogenes* causes a variety of suppurative infections of the skin, including infections of wounds or burns, with a predilection to produce lymphangitis and cellulitis. Infection of minor abrasions may at times lead to fatal septicemia.

The two typical streptococcal infections of the skin are erysipelas and impetigo:

- **Erysipelas** is a diffuse infection involving the superficial lymphatics. The affected skin, which is red, swollen and indurated, is sharply demarcated from the surrounding healthy area. While erysipelas is rare and seen only in older patients, impetigo is found mainly in young children.

- **Impetigo** is caused by *S.pyogenes* belonging to a limited number of serotypes, usually the higher numbered M types, instead of the lower numbered M types which cause throat infections. Impetigo and streptococcal infection of scabies lesions are the main causes of acute glomerulonephritis in children in the tropics.

In **pyoderma**, antibody response to streptolysin O is not high and ASO estimation does not have as much clinical significance as in pharyngeal infections. Antibody to DNase B and hyaluronidase are more useful in the retrospective diagnosis of pyoderma antecedent to acute glomerulonephritis.

3. **Necrotising fasciitis**: Streptococcal subcutaneous infections range from **cellulitis** to **necrotising fasciitis**. The latter condition is more commonly caused by a mixed aerobic and anaerobic bacterial infection, but some strains of *S.pyogenes* (more particularly **M types 1 and 3 forming pyrogenic exotoxin A**) may alone be responsible. **Small outbreaks in the UK and the USA have caused much alarm because of their severity and high fatality.** These strains have earned notoriety under the name 'flesh-eating bacteria'. In such cases, extensive necrosis of subcutaneous and muscular tissues and adjacent fascia is associated with a severe systemic illness—a toxic shock-like syndrome with disseminated intravascular coagulation and multiple system failure. *S.pyogenes* can be isolated from the affected site and rising titres of antistreptolysin and anti-DNase B demonstrated. Though the isolates are penicillin-sensitive in vitro, treatment with penicillin may not be effective.

Vancomycin is the drug of choice in life-threatening infections.

4. **Toxic shock syndrome**: Soft tissue infections with some M types of *S.pyogenes* (1, 3, 12, 28) may sometimes cause a toxic shock syndrome resembling staphylococcal TSS. **Streptococcal TSS** and necrotising fasciitis occur in persons not immune to the infecting M types.

5. **Genital infections**: Both aerobic and anaerobic streptococci are normal inhabitants of the female genitalia.

S.pyogenes was an important cause of death due to **puerperal sepsis**, with the infection usually being exogenous, in the pre-antibiotic era. The emphatic demonstration by Semmelweis in 1847 that hospital outbreaks of puerperal fever could be prevented by the simple measure of handwashing by those attending the labour wards remains a landmark in clinical microbiology.

Puerperal fever is caused currently due to endogenous infection with anaerobic streptococci.

6. **Other suppurative infections**: *S.pyogenes* may cause abscesses in internal organs such as the brain, lungs, liver and kidneys, and also septicemia and pyemia.

Non-suppurative diseases

S.pyogenes infections lead to two important non-suppurative post-streptococcal sequelae:

- **Acute rheumatic fever**: A typical case is described in *case* 2.

- **Post-streptococcal glomerulonephritis**: A typical case is described in *case* 3. These complications ensue 1–4 weeks after the acute infection. The organism may not be detectable when sequelae sets in. The two post-streptococcal sequelae differ in their natural history in a number of respects.

The important features of the two are presented in Table 22.2.

Pathogenesis of non-suppurative post-streptococcal sequelae: The pathogenesis of these complications is not clearly understood. The essential lesion in rheumatic fever is carditis, including connective tissue degeneration of the heart valves and inflammatory myocardial lesions characterised by **Aschoff nodules**. Typically, rheumatic fever follows persistent or repeated streptococcal throat infections with a strong antibody response to some '**rheumatogenic strains**'. The lesions

Table 22.2   *Comparison of rheumatic fever and post-streptococcal glomerulonephritis*

Point of comparison	Acute rheumatic fever	Post-streptococcal glomerulonephritis
Primary site of infection	Throat	Throat or skin
Prior sensitisation	Essential	Not necessary
Serotype of *S.pyogenes*	Any	Pyodermal types 49, 53–55, 59–61 and pharyngitis strains 1 and 12
Immune response	Marked	Moderate
Complement level	Unaffected	Lowered
Genetic susceptibility	Present	Not known
Repeated attacks	Common	Absent
Penicillin prophylaxis	Essential	Not indicated
Course	Progressive or static	Spontaneous resolution
Prognosis	Variable	Good

are believed to be the result of hypersensitivity to some streptococcal component. It has also been suggested that an element of autoimmunity may be involved, and antigenic cross-reactions have been demonstrated between streptococci and heart tissues. Features of rheumatic fever have been produced experimentally in rabbits by repeated infection with *S.pyogenes* and in mice by injection of sonic lysates of the cocci.

While rheumatic fever may follow infection with any serotype of *S.pyogenes*, nephritis is caused by only a few 'nephritogenic' types. In the tropics, skin infections are perhaps more important in this respect than throat infections. The nephritis is usually a self-limited episode that resolves without any permanent damage. The pathogenesis may be due to antigenic cross-reactions between the glomerular membrane antigen and cell membranes of nephritogenic streptococci, or more often it may be an immune complex disease. This condition has been produced in monkeys and rabbits by repeated infection with type 12 *S.pyogenes*.

Epidemiology

S.pyogenes colonises the human upper respiratory tract—throat, nasopharynx and nose—of patients and carriers. Carrier rates of up to 20 per cent have been observed. Symptomless infection is common and helps maintain the organism in the community.

Spread: Transmission of infection is either by direct contact or through contaminated fingers, dust or fomites. In the tropics, streptococcal infection of the skin is common and may be spread by non-biting insects, particularly the eye gnat *Hippelates*.

Streptococcal infections of the respiratory tract are more frequent in children at 5–8 years of age than in children below the age of two years or in adults. They are common in winter in the temperate countries. No seasonal distribution has been identified in the tropics. **Crowding is an important factor in the transmission of infection. Outbreaks of infection may occur in closed communities such as boarding schools or army camps.**

Immunity: Immunity is type-specific and appears to be associated with the antibody to the M protein. Re-infections occur because of the multiplicity of serotypes.

Typing

MTR protein-based typing of *S.pyogenes* is required only for epidemiological purposes and may be done by precipitation or agglutination techniques using specific antisera.

Emm Typing

A non-serologic typing system for GAS is based on M-types (1–81) sequencing the 5' end of the M protein (*emm*) gene by a molecular-based typing system.

Laboratory diagnosis

In acute infections, diagnosis is established by culture, while in the non-suppurative complications, diagnosis is mainly based on the demonstration of antibodies.

1. Specimen

Throat swab, pus swab or exudates are collected. In rheumatic fever and glomerulonephritis, serum is collected for serology. For cultures, swabs should be collected under vision from the affected site cultured immediately.

Transport media: If the sample cannot be transported immediately, **Pike's medium** (blood agar containing

1 in 1,000,000 crystal violet and 1 in 16,000 sodium azide) is used as transport media.

2. Microscopy

Presumptive information may be obtained by an examination of Gram-stained films from pus. The presence of Gram-positive cocci in chains is indicative of streptococcal infection. **However, smears are of no value in infections of the throat or genitalia, where streptococci may form part of the resident flora.**

The individual cocci are spherical or oval, 0.5–1.0 μm in diameter. They are arranged in chains. Chain formation is due to the cocci dividing in one plane only and the daughter cells failing to separate completely (*S.salivarius* forms the longest chains).

3. Culture

The specimen is plated on 5% sheep **blood agar** and incubated at 37°C (range 22–42°C), anaerobically or under 5–10% CO_2, as hemolysis develops better under these conditions. It is exacting in nutritive requirements with growth occurring only in media containing fermentable carbohydrates or enriched with blood or serum.

- On **blood agar**, after incubation for 24 hours, the colonies are small (0.5–1.0 mm), circular, semitransparent, low, convex discs with an area of clear hemolysis around them. Growth and hemolysis are promoted by 5–10% CO_2 (Figs 22.3 and 22.4). Virulent strains, on fresh isolation from lesions, produce a **'matt'** (finely granular) colony, while avirulent strains form **'glossy'** colonies. Strains with well-marked capsules produce 'mucoid' colonies, corresponding in virulence to the matt type.
- In **liquid media**, such as glucose or serum broth, growth occurs as a granular turbidity with a powdery deposit without any surface pellicle. The organism can be stored for a long period of time in **Robertson's cooked meat** medium.
- **Selective media with crystal violet:** *S.pyogenes* is resistant to crystal violet more than many other bacteria, including *S.aureus*. Crystal violet (1 mg/L), nalidixic acid (15 mg/L) and colistin sulphate (10 mg/L) added to blood agar provide a good selective medium for the isolation of streptococci, including pneumococci from specimen where mixed flora is expected.

Fig. 22.3   Blood agar: showing beta hemolysis

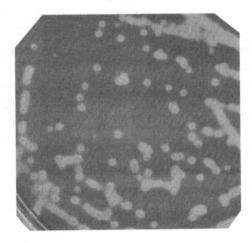

Fig. 22.4   Blood agar: *S.pyogenes* magnified to show small colonies surrounded by zones of clear hemolysis

4. Identification

Streptococci are non-motile and non-sporing. Some strains of *S.pyogenes* and some group C strains have capsules composed of hyaluronic acid, while polysaccharide capsules are encountered in members of groups B and D. These capsules are best seen in very young cultures.

- **Antigen detection:** Rapid diagnostic test kits for the detection of streptococcal group A antigen from throat swabs are available commercially using specific antisera. The tests can be completed in 1–4 hours and are nearly as specific as cultures, though less sensitive.
- **Bacitracin sensitivity:** A convenient method for the identification of *S.pyogenes* is based on Maxted's observation that they are more sensitive to bacitracin than other streptococci. A filter paper disc of 0.04 U is applied on the surface of an inoculated blood agar.

After incubation, a wide zone of inhibition is seen with *S.pyogenes*, but not with other streptococci.

Biochemical reactions

Streptococci ferment several sugars producing acid but no gas. They are catalase-negative and are not soluble in 10% bile, unlike pneumococci. Hydrolysis of pyrrolidonyl-beta-naphthylamide (PYR test) and failure to ferment ribose help differentiate *S.pyogenes* from other streptococci.

Serology

In rheumatic fever and glomerulonephritis, a retrospective diagnosis of streptococcal infection may be established by demonstrating high levels of antibody to streptococcal toxins.

- **Antistreptolysin O (ASO):** The standard test is antistreptolysin O titration. ASO titres higher than 200 are indicative of prior streptococcal infection. The upper limit may vary with age, being higher in children than adults. High levels are usually found in acute rheumatic fever but in glomerulonephritis, titres are often low.
- **Antideoxyribonuclease B (anti-DNase B):** This is an antibody to DNase. Titres higher than 300 are taken as significant. Anti-DNase B and antihyaluronidase tests are very useful for the retrospective diagnosis of streptococcal pyoderma, for which ASO is of much less value.
- **Streptozyme test:** It is a passive slide hemagglutination test using erythrocytes sensitised with a crude preparation of extracellular antigens of streptococci. It is a convenient, sensitive and specific screening test. It becomes positive after nearly all types of streptococcal infections, whether of the throat or the skin.

Antimicrobial susceptibility

Streptococcus group A are uniformly susceptible to penicillin. However, clinical failures are being reported following penicillin therapy. Hence, monitoring MIC to penicillin is advisable in referral centres. Strains resistant to cotimoxazole and erythromycin have been reported and, therefore, antimicrobial susceptibility is required.

Treatment

All beta hemolytic group A streptococci are sensitive to **penicillin G,** and most are sensitive to **erythromycin.** In patients allergic to penicillin, erythromycin or **cephalexin** may be used. Tetracyclines and sulphonamides are not recommended. Antimicrobial drugs have no effect on established glomerulonephritis and rheumatic fever.

Bacitracin has been used for local application on skin lesions.

Prophylaxis

The indication for prophylaxis in streptococcal infections is directed at prevention of rheumatic fever. This is achieved by long-term administration of penicillin in children who have developed early signs of rheumatic fever. This prevents streptococcal re-infection and further damage to the heart. Antibiotic prophylaxis is not useful for glomerulonephritis as this complication follows a single streptococcal infection, and re-infections do not occur.

OTHER HEMOLYTIC STREPTOCOCCI

Besides *S.pyogenes*, streptococci belonging to groups B, C, D, F, G and rarely H, K, O and R may also cause human infection. Of these, B, C and G are more common.

Group B Streptococci (GBS)

Streptococcus agalactiae

Streptococcus agalactiae is an important human pathogen responsible for several infections. These are also important pathogens of cattle, producing bovine mastitis.

Human infections include the following:

Neonatal infections

From the 1960s, group B streptococcus has assumed great clinical importance as the single most common cause of neonatal meningitis in the West. Infection in the newborn is classified as the:

- **Early onset type**, occurring within a week of birth
- **Late onset type**, developing between the second and twelfth weeks of life

The more common early onset type presents as meningitis or septicemia, and is often fatal. Infection is acquired from the maternal vagina during birth. In the late onset type, infection is more often obtained from the environment and presents as septicemia.

Other group B infections in neonates include arthritis, osteomyelitis, conjunctivitis, respiratory infections, peritonitis, omphalitis and endocarditis.

Infections in adults

Group B streptococci may also cause infections in non-pregnant adults, especially in an immunocompromised host. Common infections are sepsis, skin and soft tissue infections, respiratory tract infections, and urinary tract infection in women.

Human pathogenic group B strains possess a polysaccharide capsule which appears to confer virulence. Nine capsular serotypes have been identified, antibodies to which confer type-specific protection.

Identification

On blood agar, the colonies show beta hemolysis, as in the case of GAS.

Their ability to hydrolyse hippurate acts as a presumptive identification method. They may be identified by the **CAMP test** (Christie, Atkins and Munch–Peterson), which can be demonstrated as an accentuated zone of hemolysis when *S.agalactiae* is inoculated perpendicular to a streak of *S.aureus* (*Staphylococcus plazens* streak producing beta lysin) grown on blood agar (Fig. 22.5).

Group C

Streptococci of this group are predominantly animal pathogens. Group C strains isolated from human sources usually belong to the *S.equisimilis* species. It can cause upper respiratory infections, as well as deep infections such as endocarditis, osteomyelitis, brain abscess, pneumonia and puerperal sepsis. Strains are often tolerant to penicillin and serious infections may not respond to penicillin treatment. The addition of gentamicin is recommended in serious cases. It resembles *S.pyogenes* in fermenting trehalose but differs in fermenting ribose. It produces streptolysin O, strep-tokinase (antigenically distinct from that produced by *S.pyogenes*) and other extracellular substances. *S.equisimilis* is the source of **streptokinase** used for **thrombolytic** therapy in patients.

Group F

These grow poorly on blood agar unless incubated under CO_2. They have been called the '**minute streptococci**'. They are sometimes found in suppurative lesions. One member of this group is **Streptococcus MG** which is an alphalytic strain isolated from cases of primary atypical pneumonia. Demonstration of agglutinins to Streptococcus MG in the sera of patients had been used as a diagnostic test for **primary atypical pneumonia.**

Group G

These are commensals in the throats of human beings, monkeys and dogs. They may occasionally cause tonsillitis, endocarditis and urinary infections in human beings.

Group D

Most of the members are not human pathogens except *Streptococcus bovis*. It resides in the gastrointestinal tract. They are identified by their ability to grow on bile and cause esculin hydrolysis but do not grow in 6.5% NaCl (to differentiate from enterococci). Members of this group are generally susceptible to penicillins. They may cause urinary infection or endocarditis.

Other groups

Groups H and K sometimes cause infective endocarditis. Group O is isolated mainly from the healthy human throat and may cause acute tonsillitis and endocarditis. Group R strains are natural pathogens of pigs. They have been reported from occasional cases of meningitis, septicemia and respiratory infection in persons in contact with infected pigs or contaminated meat.

Enterococcus species

The *Enterococcus* group (enterococci or fecal streptococci) has been reclassified as a separate genus called *Enterococcus* and contains different species, for example, *E.faecalis*, *E.faecium* and *E.durans*. Enterococci possess several distinctive features that distinguish them from streptococci (Table 22.3). They can grow in the presence of 40% bile, 6.5% sodium chloride, at pH 9.6, at 45°C and in 0.1% methylene blue milk.

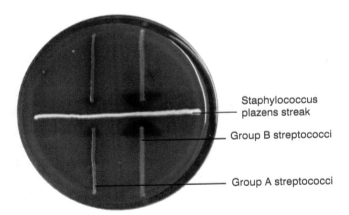

Staphylococcus plazens streak

Group B streptococci

Group A streptococci

Fig. 22. 5   CAMP test

Table 22.3   *Distinctive features that distinguish Enterococci from Streptococci*

Characteristics	Enterococci	Streptococci
Shape	Oval cocci, sometimes at an angle to each other	Spherical
Length of chain	Short chains	Long chains
Growth on sheep blood agar	Generally non-hemolytic	Usually beta or alpha hemolytic
Growth on MacConkey medium	Tiny magenta pink colonies	Usually do not grow on MacConkey medium
Heat tolerance	Survive at 60°C for 30 minutes	Do not survive at this temperaure

- On MacConkey medium, they produce tiny magenta-pink colonies.
- They are relatively heat-resistant, surviving at 60°C for 30 minutes.
- They typically appear as pairs of oval cocci, the cells in a pair arranged at an angle to each other (Fig. 22.6).
- They are usually non-hemolytic, though some strains may show alpha or beta hemolysis.

Identification of the *Enterococcus* species is made on biochemical grounds. *E.faecalis* is the enterococcus most often isolated from human sources. It can be identified by its ability to ferment mannitol, sucrose, sorbitol and esculin, and to grow on tellurite blood agar producing black colonies. *Enterococcus faecium* is also being frequently isolated from clinical specimens.

Enterococci are present in the intestine, genital tract and saliva. They are frequently isolated from cases of urinary tract infection and wound infection. They may also cause endocarditis, infection of the biliary tract, septicemia and intra-abdominal abscess complicating diverticulitis and peritonitis.

Antimicrobial resistance: Strains resistant to penicillin and other antibiotics occur frequently, so it is essential to perform antibiotic sensitivity for proper therapy. Enterococci are intrinsically resistant to cephalosporins and offer low-level resistance to some aminoglycosides; therefore, they require testing with high-level gentamicin discs in clinical laboratories.

In penicillin-sensitive strains, synergism occurs with combination treatment with penicillin and aminoglycoside. However, if the strain shows high-level resistance to aminoglycosides, this synergism does not occur. The choice of drug for infections due to such strains is vancomycin. Recently, **VRE (vancomycin-resistant enterococci)** have begun to emerge. The phenotypes responsible for vancomycin resistance could be Van A, B, C, D and E. The mechanism is the alteration of D-alanyl-D-alanine chain in the cell wall.

Viridans group

This group, formerly called Streptococcus viridans, is a miscellany of streptococci normally resident in the mouth and upper respiratory tract, and typically producing greening (alpha lysis) on blood agar—hence, the name viridans.

Some of them may be non-hemolytic. They cannot be categorised under the Lancefield antigenic groups. However, based on sugar fermentation, cell wall composition and production of dextrans and levans, they have been classified into many species, for example, *S.mitis, S.mutans, S.salivarius* and *S.sanguis*.

Infections: They are ordinarily non-pathogenic but can, on occasion, cause disease. In persons with pre-existing cardiac lesions, they may cause **sub-acute bacterial endocarditis (SABE)**, *S.sanguis* being most often responsible. Following tooth extraction or other dental procedures, they cause transient bacteremia and get implanted on damaged or prosthetic valves or in a congenitally diseased heart, and grow to form vegetation. **Prophylactic antibiotic cover is advisable in such persons before tooth extraction or similar procedures.** While Viridans streptococci are generally

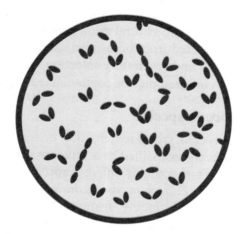

Fig. 22.6   *Enterococcus:* Oval cells arranged in pairs at an angle, or in short chains.

penicillin-sensitive, some strains may be resistant. It is, therefore, essential that in endocarditis, the causative strain is isolated and its antibiotic sensitivity determined so that appropriate antibiotics in adequate bactericidal concentration can be employed for treatment.

Streptococcus mutans is an alpha hemolytic streptococcus which is part of the normal flora of the oral cavity. This Gram-positive coccus is commonly found in the mouth, from where it can spread to cause dental caries or endocarditis in individuals with risk factors (dental extraction in people with damaged heart valves). The bacterium has a polysaccharide coat (glycocalyx) that allows it to stick to teeth and also to damaged heart valves; it can invade the bloodstream. It also produces acid from sugar in saliva, and this promotes erosion of tooth enamel. Normal body defences are usually adequate to prevent disease. In microscopy, Gram-positive cocci in chains are noted. It cannot be grouped by the Lancefield scheme and is resistant to optochin and bile. Disease due to this bacterium can be prevented by maintenance of good oral hygiene and by regular dental check-up; prophylactic antibiotics may be needed prior to major dental work on people with damaged heart valves.

Nutritionally variant streptococci

They are also called **nutritionally deficient streptococci or NVS**. They need pyridoxal or cysteine for their growth on blood agar. They are part of the normal flora but can be responsible for infective endocarditis, especially **culture-negative infective endocarditis** or **brain abscess.**

RECAP

- Bacteria belonging to the genus *Streptococcus* are Gram-positive, oxidase- and catalase-negative, and facultative anaerobes. They occur in pairs or short and long chains. Some are nutritionally fastidious (require enriched media such as blood for growth).
- Hemolytic activity has been used as a preliminary criterion for classifying some streptococci thus: alpha hemolytic, beta hemolytic or non-hemolytic (gamma hemolytic).
- *Streptococcus pyogenes* is responsible for many human diseases, which are partly attributable to actual infection by the organisms (for example, pharyngitis, impetigo, pyogenic infection), from the release of bacterial toxins (scarlet fever) and from immunological cross-reactions associated with streptococcal antigens (glomerulonephritis, rheumatic fever).
- Virulence factors include M protein and lipoteichoic acid, which help the bacteria to bind to cells, enzymes (hyaluronidase) which aid tissue spread, and toxins (erythrogenic toxin) which act as a superantigen. The isolate can be subtyped based on its M protein. Antibody to streptolysin can be estimated. Penicillin is often given for pharyngitis and skin infections to prevent more serious sequelae.
- *Streptococcus agalactiae* (group B beta hemolytic streptococci) can be found as normal flora of the vagina; hence, neonatal infection may occur during vaginal birth. It causes neonatal septicemia, pneumonia and meningitis, and also infection of mothers during birth.
- *Streptococcus mutans* is an alpha hemolytic streptococcus which is part of the normal flora of the oral cavity. This Gram-positive coccus is commonly found in the mouth, from where it can spread to cause dental caries or endocarditis in individuals with risk factors (dental extraction in people with damaged heart valves).
- The genus *Enterococcus* was formerly grouped under streptococci. Enterococci are part of the normal commensal flora of the gastrointestinal tract. *Enterococcus faecalis* is the commonest clinical isolate. Infection and disease are usually hospital-acquired and include urinary tract infections, abdominal and pelvic wound infections and bacteremia. These can grow on media containing bile and esculin. Increasing isolation of vancomycin-resistant enterococci is a worrying trend.

- Nutritionally deficient Streptococci or NVS produce infective endocarditis or brain abscess. They require pyridoxal for growth.

ESSAYS

1. Classify streptococci and write a note on their pathogenesis.
2. Enumerate the virulence factors of streptococci and explain the laboratory diagnosis of streptococcal sore throat.
3. Draw a diagram of the cell wall of *Streptococcus pyogenes*. Explain the relevance of the cell wall antigens to virulence and classification.
4. Explain the pathogenesis and laboratory diagnosis of *Streptococcus pyogenes*.

SHORT ANSWERS

1. Name the Viridans streptococci and list the diseases caused by them.
2. Classification of streptococci
3. Diseases caused by streptococci
4. Toxins of streptococci

SHORT NOTES

1. Post-streptococcal complications (non-suppurative complications)
2. Laboratory diagnosis of rheumatic fever
3. Streptococcus viridans
4. Endotoxins

23 Pneumococcus

INTRODUCTION

Streptococcus pneumoniae is a Gram-positive, lanceolate-shaped diplococcus (commonly referred to as *Pneumococci*). It differs from other streptococci chiefly in its morphology, bile solubility, optochin sensitivity and possession of a specific polysaccharide capsule. These are normal inhabitants of the human upper respiratory tract. They are the single most prevalent bacterial agents in pneumonia and in otitis media in children. They can also cause sinusitis, bronchitis, bacteremia, meningitis and other infections.

S.pneumoniae were first noticed in 1881 by Pasteur and Sternberg independently. But the relationship between the organism and pneumonia was established only later by Fraenkel and Weichselbaum independently in 1886.

Morphology

S.pneumococci are typically small (1 μm), slightly elongated cocci, with one end broad or rounded and the other pointed, presenting a flame-shaped or lanceolate appearance. They occur in pairs (diplococci), with the broad ends in apposition, the long axis of the coccus parallel to the line joining the two cocci in a pair. They are capsulated, the capsule enclosing each pair. The capsules are best seen in material taken directly from exudates and may be lost on repeated cultivation. In culture, the typical morphology may not be apparent and the cocci are more rounded, tending to occur in short chains. They are non-motile and non-sporing.

They are readily stained with aniline dyes and are Gram positive (Fig. 23.1). The capsule may be demonstrated as a clear halo in India ink preparations or may be stained directly by special techniques (Fig. 23.2).

Streptococcus pneumoniae

Clinical Case 1 A 60-year-old man was brought in with a history of high-grade fever with chills and rigors for the previous two days. He also had mild chest pain and productive cough. The sputum was submitted for investigations. X-ray chest showed consolidation in the right lower lobe. The direct smear observed after Gram staining showed pus cells with Gram-positive, lanceolate-shaped diplococci. Sputum culture after 24 hours was positive for a Gram-positive bacteria growing as greenish colonies on blood agar. The patient was diagnosed with pneumococcal pneumonia. Antibiotic susceptibility after another 24 hours showed the organism to be sensitive to penicillin, to which he responded.

Clinical Case 2 A five-year-old child was brought to the Emergency department with a history of seizures following high-grade fever. He had also had 1–2 episodes of projectile vomiting. On examination in the hospital, he was found to have altered sensorium and neck rigidity, and Kernig's sign was positive. A lumbar puncture was done. CSF cytology showed high counts of polymorphs, biochemistry showed low glucose and raised proteins, and Gram smear showed the presence of Gram-positive diplococci, some of them inside the polymorphs. The culture was positive for alpha hemolytic colonies on sheep blood agar which had the typical 'draughtsman colonies' appearance, and were catalase negative and optochin sensitive, suggestive of *S.pneumoniae*. The patient was started on penicillin and responded to treatment.

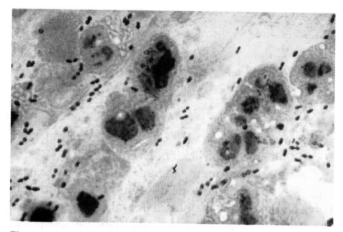

Fig. 23.1 Gram-stained smear of sputum containing Gram-positive diplococci

Fig. 23.2 *S.pneumoniae*; India ink preparation to show capsules

Cultural characteristics

S.pneumoniae have complex growth requirements and grow only in enriched media. They are aerobes and facultative anaerobes, the optimum temperature being 37°C (range 25–42°C) and pH 7.8 (range 6.5–8.3). Growth is improved by 5–10% CO_2.

- On **blood agar**, after incubation for 18 hours, the colonies are small (0.5–1 mm), dome-shaped and glistening, with an area of green discolouration (**alpha hemolysis**) around them, resembling colonies of viridans streptococci. On further incubation the colonies become flat with raised edges and central umbonation, so that concentric rings are seen on the surface when viewed from above (**draughtsman** or carrom coin appearance;). Some strains that develop abundant capsular material (types 3 and 7) form large mucoid colonies.

Under anaerobic conditions, colonies on blood agar are surrounded by a zone of beta hemolysis due to oxygen-labile hemolysin O.

- In **liquid media** such as glucose broth, growth occurs as uniform turbidity. The cocci readily undergo autolysis in cultures due to the activity of intracellular enzymes. Autolysis is enhanced by bile salts, sodium lauryl sulphate and other surface-active agents. Heat-killed cultures do not undergo autolysis.

Biochemical reactions

S.pneumoniae are catalase and oxidase negative. They ferment several sugars, forming only acid. Fermentation is tested in **Hiss's serum sugars**. Fermentation of inulin is a useful test for differentiating them from streptococci, as the latter do not ferment it (Table 23.1).

Bile solubility test: *S.pneumoniae* are bile soluble. If a few drops of 10% sodium deoxycholate solution are added to 1 ml of an overnight broth culture, the culture clears due to lysis of the cocci. Alternatively, if a loopful of 10% deoxycholate solution is placed on an *S.pneumoniae* colony on blood agar, the colony lyses within a few minutes. Bile solubility is a constant property of *S.pneumoniae* and hence is of diagnostic importance. The test should be carried out at neutral pH using deoxycholate and live young cells in saline suspension (Fig. 23.3).

Principle: The bile solubility test is based on the presence in the *S.pneumoniae* of an autolytic amidase that cleaves the bond between alanine and muramic acid in the peptidoglycan. The amidase is activated by surface-active agents such as bile or bile salts, resulting in lysis of the organisms.

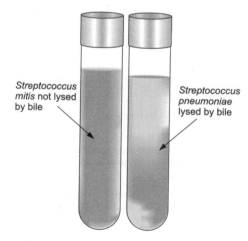

Streptococcus mitis not lysed by bile

Streptococcus pneumoniae lysed by bile

Fig. 23.3 Bile solubility test

Table 23.1 *Differentiation between* S.pneumoniae *and Viridans streptococci*

	S.pneumoniae	Viridans streptococci
Morphology	Capsulated, lanceolate diplococci	Non-capsulated, oval or round cells in chains
Quellung test	Positive	Negative
Colonies on blood agar	Initially dome-shaped, later,'draughtsman' colonies	Dome-shaped
Growth in liquid media	Uniform turbidity	Granular turbidity, powdery deposit
Bile solubility	Positive	Negative
Inulin fermentation	Positive	Negative
Optochin sensitivity	Positive	Negative
Intraperitoneal inoculation in mice	Fatal infection	Non-pathogenic

Resistance

S.pneumoniae are delicate organisms and are readily destroyed by heat (thermal death point 52°C for 15 minutes) and antiseptics. In culture, they die on prolonged incubation, perhaps due to an accumulation of toxic peroxides. Strains may be maintained on semisolid blood agar or by lyophilisation.

They are sensitive to most antibiotics, beta lactams being the drugs of choice. Almost all strains were sensitive to 0.05 mg penicillin till 1967, when resistant strains began to appear.

Optochin sensitivity: The sensitivity of *S.pneumoniae* to optochin (ethyl hydrocuprein) 1/500,000 is useful in differentiating them from streptococci. When a disc impregnated with optochin is applied on a plate of blood agar inoculated with *S.pneumoniae*, a wide zone of inhibition appears on incubation (Fig. 23.4).

Antigenic properties

Capsule: The most important antigen of the *S.pneumoniae* is the type-specific capsular polysaccharide. As this polysaccharide diffuses into the culture medium or infective exudates and tissues, it is also called the '**specific soluble substance**' (SSS). *S.pneumoniae* are classified based on the antigenic nature of the capsular polysaccharide, and now more than 90 different serotypes are recognised, named 1, 2, 3 and so on.

Serotyping based on capsular antigens may be carried out by:

● **Agglutination** of the cocci with the type-specific antiserum

● **Precipitation** of the SSS with the specific serum

● By the capsule swelling or '**quellung' reaction** (quellung = swelling), described by Neufeld (1902). Here, a suspension of *S.pneumoniae* is mixed on a slide with a drop of the type-specific antiserum and a loopful of methylene blue solution. In the presence of the homologous antiserum, the capsule becomes apparently swollen, sharply delineated and refractile. The quellung test can be done directly with sputum from acute pneumonia cases. It used to be a routine bedside procedure in the past when the specific antiserum was used for the treatment of pneumonia (Fig. 23.5).

● **PCR-based tests** have shown higher sensitivity in the detection of infections, especially meningitis as it can detect the presence of a small number of the specific DNA sequences of the bacteria which cannot be cultured by conventional methods due to the administration of prior antibiotics or because of a smaller bacterial load in the body fluids.

Other antigens: *S.pneumoniae* contain other antigens as well—a nucleoprotein deep inside the cell and a somatic 'C' carbohydrate antigen, both of which are species specific.

An abnormal protein (beta globulin) that precipitates with the somatic 'C' antigen of *S.pneumoniae* appears in the acute phase sera of pneumonia but disap-

Fig. 23.4 *S.pneumoniae* colonies sensitive to optochin

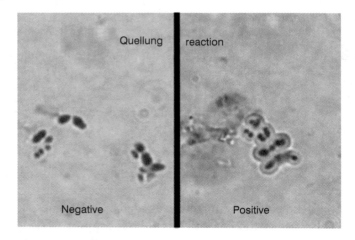

Fig. 23.5 Quellung reaction

pears during convalescence. It also occurs in some other pathological conditions. This is known as the **C-reactive protein (CRP)**. Its apparent antibody-like relationship to the 'C' antigen of *S.pneumoniae* is only fortuitous. It is not an antibody produced as a result of pneumococcal infection. It is an 'acute phase' substance, produced in hepatocytes. Its production is stimulated by bacterial infections, inflammation, malignancies and tissue destruction. It disappears when the inflammatory reactions subside.

Variation

On repeated subculture, *S.pneumoniae* undergo **smooth-to-rough (S–R) variation**. In the R form, the colonies are rough and the cocci are non-capsulated, autoagglutinable and avirulent. R forms arise as spontaneous mutants and outgrow the parental S forms in artificial culture; in tissues, such R mutants are eliminated by phagocytosis.

Rough *S.pneumoniae* derived from the capsulated cells of one serotype may be made to produce capsules of the same or different serotypes, on treatment with DNA from the respective serotypes of *S.pneumoniae*. This **transformation**, which may be demonstrated in vivo or in vitro, was discovered by Griffith (1928) and is of considerable historical interest as the first demonstration of genetic exchange of information in bacteria.

Toxins and other virulence factors

The virulence of *S.pneumoniae* depends on:
- The **capsular polysaccharide**, because of its acidic and hydrophilic properties, protects the cocci from phagocytosis. Capsulated *S.pneumoniae* are not phagocytosed efficiently in fluid media or exudates. They are, however, susceptible to 'surface phagocytosis', being engulfed against a firm surface, such as a fibrin clot or epithelium.

  The enhanced virulence of type 3 *S.pneumoniae* is due to the abundance of its capsular material. Non-capsulated strains are avirulent. The antibody to the capsular polysaccharide affords protection against infection.
- **Pneumolysin**, a membrane damaging toxin produced by *S.pneumoniae*, has cytotoxic and complement activating properties and so may be a virulence factor. It is immunogenic. Pneumolysin-negative mutants show reduced virulence in experimental animals.
- **Autolysins:** Pneumococcal autolysins, by releasing bacterial components in infected tissues, may also contribute to virulence.

S.pneumoniae produce an oxygen labile hemolysin and a leucocidin but these are weak and make no contribution to virulence

Pathogenicity

Experimentally, fatal infection can be produced in mice or rabbits by intraperitoneal inoculation of *S.pneumoniae*. Death occurs in 1–3 days, and *S.pneumoniae* can be demonstrated in large numbers in the peritoneal exudate and heart blood.

S.pneumoniae colonise the human nasopharynx and may cause infection of the middle ear, paranasal sinuses and respiratory tract by direct spread. Infection of the meninges may also occur, by contiguity or through blood. Pneumococcal bacteremia may also lead to distant infections in the heart, peritoneum or joints. Infection is commonly endogenous, but exogenous infection may also occur, especially with highly virulent strains.

S.pneumoniae are one of the most common bacteria causing pneumonia, both **lobar** and **bronchopneumonia**. They also cause acute tracheobronchitis and empyema (*Case* 1).

Aspiration of nasopharyngeal secretions containing *S.pneumoniae* into the lower respiratory tract is a common event and may occur even in sleep. Normal mucosal defence mechanisms such as entrapment, expulsion and the cough reflex, aided by the ciliary escalator effect, prevent the establishment of infection. When the normal defences are compromised by viral infection, anesthesia, chilling or other factors, *S.pneumoniae* multiply, penetrate the bronchial mucosa and spread through the lung along the peribronchial tissues and lymphatics. Bacteremia is common during the early stage of lobar pneumonia. Toxemia is due to diffusion of the capsular polysaccharide into blood and tissues. The fall in temperature by crisis and relief of symptoms coincide with the neutralisation of SSS by anticapsular antibodies.

Bronchopneumonia is almost always a secondary infection. This may be caused by any serotype of *S.pneumoniae*. The damage to the respiratory epithelium and excessive bronchial secretions caused by the primary infection facilitate the invasion of *S.pneumoniae* along the bronchial tree. Bronchopneumonia is frequently a terminal event in aged and debilitated patients.

S.pneumoniae are commonly associated with acute exacerbations in **chronic bronchitis**. The copious respiratory secretions in chronic bronchitis aid pneumococcal invasion. Another bacterium commonly associated with this condition is *Haemophilus influenzae*.

Meningitis is the most serious of pneumococcal infections. It is usually secondary to other pneumococcal infections such as pneumonia, otitis media, sinusitis or conjunctivitis but in a proportion of cases, other foci of infection may not be demonstrable. Pneumococcal meningitis occurs at all ages. Untreated cases are almost invariably fatal. Even with antibiotic therapy, the case fatality rate is about 25 per cent (*Case* 2).

S.pneumoniae may also produce **suppurative lesions** in other parts of the body—empyema, pericarditis, otitis media, sinusitis, conjunctivitis, suppurative arthritis and peritonitis. It is also responsible for ocular infections like keratitis and dacryocystitis.

Epidemiology

The source of human infection is the respiratory tract of carriers and, less often, of patients. *S.pneumoniae* occur in the throats of approximately half the population sampled at any one time. They are transmitted by contaminated droplets or droplet nuclei. Dissemination is facilitated by crowding.

Infection usually leads only to pharyngeal carriage. Disease results only when host resistance is lowered by contributory factors such as respiratory viral infections, pulmonary congestion, stress, malnutrition, immunodeficiency or alcoholism. Splenectomy and sickle cell disease are important predisposing conditions.

S.pneumoniae serotypes vary greatly in virulence. The case fatality rates of pneumonia may vary according to the virulence of the infecting serotype. Type 3 is the most virulent. The commonest pneumococcal infections are otitis media and sinusitis. Prior respiratory infection or allergy causing congestion and blockage predispose to these conditions. Serotypes 6, 14, 19F and 23F are commonly encountered in these conditions in the West.

In adults, types 1–8 are responsible for about 75 per cent of cases of pneumococcal pneumonia and for more than 50 per cent of all fatalities due to pneumococcal bacteremia. In children, types 6, 14, 19 and 23 are frequent causes.

In India, lobar pneumonia is usually a sporadic disease but epidemics may occur among closed communities, as in army camps. The incidence of bronchopneumonia increases when an epidemic of influenza or other viral infection of the respiratory tract occurs. Cases are more common in winter and affect the two extreme age groups more often.

Laboratory diagnosis

The clinical diagnosis of pneumonia is easy but as the disease may be caused by several different microorganisms, etiological diagnosis should be made by laboratory tests. This is of great importance in treatment.

1. Specimen: Sputum, CSF, blood for culture and urine are used for antigen detection.

2. Microscopy: In the acute phase of lobar pneumonia, the rusty sputum contains *S.pneumoniae* in large numbers, with hardly any other kind of bacterium. They may be demonstrated by Gram stain. In acute otitis media, *S.pneumoniae* may be demonstrated in the fluid aspirated from the middle ear. In meningitis, presumptive diagnosis may be made from Gram-stained films of CSF. Gram-positive diplococci can be seen both inside the polymorphs and extracellularly.

3. Culture: The sputum, after homogenisation if necessary, is inoculated on **blood agar plates** and incubated at 37°C under 5–10% CO_2. Growth occurs after overnight incubation. Isolation from respiratory secretions is facilitated by using blood agar containing gentamicin 5 µg/ml.

Blood culture: In the acute stage of pneumonia, the organism may be obtained from blood culture in glucose broth. Isolation of *S.pneumoniae* from blood indicates a bad prognosis.

4. Mouse inoculation: In specimens where *S.pneumoniae* are expected to be scanty, isolation may be obtained by intraperitoneal inoculation in mice, even if cultures are negative. Inoculated mice die in 1–3 days, and *S.pneumoniae* may be demonstrated in the peritoneal exudate and heart blood. The test may be negative with occasional strains that are avirulent for mice (type 14 strains).

5. Antigen detection: Although diagnosis is confirmed by culture in meningitis, in cases which are negative by culture, it may be possible to establish the diagnosis by demonstrating the SSS in **CSF** by precipitation with antisera or the latex agglutination test.

Capsular polysaccharide can be demonstrated in blood, urine and cerebrospinal fluid by counterimmunoelectrophoresis. Now, an immunochromatography-based test is available for the detection of polysaccharide antigen in **urine**.

6. Biomarkers: **CRP testing**, by passive agglutination using latex particles coated with anti-CRP antibody, is a routine diagnostic procedure. **Procalcitonin** is another biomarker which is elevated in invasive pneumococcal disease, and the levels are monitored to determine prognosis and response to treatment,

7. Molecular methods: PCR-based methods have much potential where the patient has taken antibiotics.

Prophylaxis

Immunity is type specific and associated with antibodies to the capsular polysaccharide. The existence of some 90 serotypes makes a complete polyvalent vaccine impracticable.

- A **polyvalent polysaccharide vaccine** representing the capsular antigens of the 23 most prevalent serotypes has been stated to give 80–90 per cent protection. It is not meant for general use, but only in persons at enhanced risk of pneumococcal infection such as those with absent or dysfunctional spleen, sickle cell disease, celiac disease, chronic renal, lung, heart and liver diseases, diabetes mellitus and immunodeficiencies including HIV infection. It is not recommended in children under the age of two years and those with lymphoreticular malignancies and immunosuppressive therapy.
- A **7-valent conjugate vaccine** (conjugated to the CRM197 protein of *C.diphtheriae*) is now available which can be used in children from two months to two years. However, protection would depend on whether the serotypes included in the vaccine are also prevalent in the community where the vaccine is used.

Treatment

The antibiotic of choice is parenteral penicillin in severe cases and amoxycillin in milder ones, provided the infecting strain is penicillin sensitive. Many penicillin-resistant strains are also resistant to other antibiotics like erythromycin and tetracycline. The resistance may be intermediate (MIC 1 μg) or high (2 μg or more) and due to mutation or gene transfer. The mode of resistance is not production of beta lactamase, but alteration in the penicillin binding proteins on the bacterial surface. Such strains are also resistant to multiple drugs. A drug-resistant *S.pneumoniae* (DRSP) strain originating in Spain has spread to most parts of the world, posing problems in treatment.

A third-generation cephalosporin is indicated in such cases. Vancomycin is to be reserved for life-threatening illnesses with highly resistant strains.

RECAP

- *Streptococcus pneumoniae* causes pneumococcal pneumonia, especially in the elderly and the very young, pneumococcal meningitis and pneumococcal keratitis and dacryocystitis.
- A major virulence factor is the polysaccharide capsule (> 90 types) that inhibits phagocytosis by polymorphonuclear leucocytes in blood, leading to invasion of the bloodstream and cerebrospinal fluid. Pneumolysin (a toxin) is also a virulence factor.
- *S.pneumoniae* occur as lanceolate-shaped, Gram-positive diplococci in sputum, blood and CSF. They are alpha hemolytic on blood agar. The bacterium is susceptible to optochin and to bile. Capsule swelling (the quellung phenomenon) occurs when the bacterium is mixed with a specific antibody.
- A vaccine with the 23 most common serotypes of capsular polysaccharides can protect the elderly. Now a conjugate vaccine is also available for children below the age of two years.
- Antibiotics are used to treat infections. Resistance to beta lactams (penicillins, cephalosporins) is on the rise.

ESSAYS

1. Describe the culture and identification of *Streptococcus pneumoniae*.
2. Describe the laboratory diagnosis of streptococcal pneumonia.
3. Describe the antigenic properties of the capsule and methods of typing.
4. Enumerate the organisms causing meningitis and write the laboratory diagnosis of meningitis.

SHORT ANSWERS

1. Quellung reaction
2. Virulence factors of *S.pneumoniae*
3. Bile solubility test
4. Optochin sensitivity

SHORT NOTES

1. Biochemical test for the identification of *S.pneumoniae*
2. Vaccines against *S.pneumoniae*

24 Neisseria

INTRODUCTION

The genus *Neisseria* consists of Gram-negative, aerobic, non-sporulating, non-motile, oxidase-positive cocci arranged typically in pairs (diplococci). It contains two important pathogens, *Neisseria meningitidis* and *Neisseria gonorrhoeae*. These strict human pathogens are Gram-negative, diplococci, oxidase-positive and fastidious in growth requirements.

The intracellular presence of these bacteria inside polymorphs in patient samples is a characteristic finding. The important difference is the presence of a polysaccharide capsule in *N.meningitidis* and of plasmids including those imparting antibiotic resistance in *N.gonorrhoeae*. Both can be differentiated by biochemical tests using serum sugars.

The genus contains many other species such as *N.lactamica* that occur as commensals in the mouth or upper respiratory tract and *Moraxella catarrhalis* which can cause respiratory tract infections in compromised hosts.

N.meningitidis causes meningococcal meningitis (formerly known as cerebrospinal fever) which may occur sporadically, as localised outbreaks, epidemics or as septicemia. It was first described and isolated in 1887 by Weichselbaum from the spinal fluid of a patient.

NEISSERIA MENINGITIDIS

Morphology

Meningococci are Gram-negative, oval or spherical cocci, 0.6 μm–0.8 μm in size, arranged typically in pairs, with the adjacent sides flattened (Fig. 24.1). The long axis of the coccus is at right angles to a line joining the two cocci in a pair. Considerable variation occurs in

Fig. 24.1 *N.meningitidis* in cerebrospinal fluid. Inset: Enlarged view showing flat adjacent sides of Gram-negative diplococci.

Neisseria meningitidis

Clinical Case 1 A seven-year-old boy presented to the emergency department with high-grade fever since the previous day. He complained of headache, was disoriented and had projectile vomiting. On examination, the neck was found to be rigid and Kernig's sign was positive. A lumbar puncture was carried out along with complete blood counts and serum biochemistry. Cytology showed polymorphs at $1000/mm^3$, protein 250 mg/dL and glucose 20 mg/dL. Blood glucose levels were normal. On Gram stain, Gram-negative cocci were seen in pairs, most of them inside polymorphs. The latex agglutination test was positive for *N.menigitidis* antigen, confirming the diagnosis of meningitis. The patient responded to antimicrobial treatment. Vaccination was advised for the patient's siblings along with chemoprophylaxis.

size, shape and staining properties, especially in older cultures, due to autolysis. In smears from lesions, the cocci are more regular and generally intracellular. They are non-motile. Most fresh isolates are capsulated.

Cultural characteristics

Meningococci have exacting growth requirements and do not grow on ordinary media. Growth occurs on media enriched with blood, serum or ascitic fluid, which promote growth by neutralising certain inhibiting substances in culture media rather than by providing additional nutrition.

They are aerobes but growth is facilitated by 5–10% CO_2 and high humidity. The optimum temperature for growth is 35–36°C and optimum pH 7.4–7.6.

On **solid media**, after incubation for 24 hours, the colonies are small (about 1 mm in diameter) translucent, round, convex, bluish grey, with a smooth glistening surface and with entire edges. The colonies are typically lenticular in shape, butyrous in consistency and easily emulsifiable. Weak hemolysis occurs on **blood agar**. Smooth and rough types of colonies are found. Growth is poor in **liquid media**, producing a granular turbidity with little or no surface growth.

Blood agar, chocolate agar, Thayer–Martin medium and Mueller–Hinton starch casein hydrolysate agar are used to culture meningococci.

Selective media: Modified Thayer–Martin medium (with vancomycin, colistin and nystatin) may be used as selective media to isolate meningococcus from carriers during an epidemic.

Biochemical reactions

They are catalase- and oxidase-positive. The prompt oxidase reaction helps in the identification of *Neisseria* (both meningococcus and gonococcus) in mixed cultures.

Oxidase test: When a freshly prepared 1% solution of oxidase reagent (tetramethyl paraphenylene diamine hydrochloride) is poured on the culture media, the neisseria colonies turn deep purple. Subcultures should be made immediately as the organism dies on prolonged exposure to the reagent. The test may also be performed by rubbing a little of the growth with a loop on a strip of filter paper moistened with the oxidase reagent (**Kovac's method**). A deep purple colour appears immediately.

Indole and hydrogen sulphide are not produced and nitrates are not reduced. Glucose and maltose are utilised, but not sucrose or lactose, producing acid but no gas (gonococci acidify glucose but not maltose). Acid formation by neisseriae is weak, being oxidative, and therefore best tested on peptone serum agar slopes containing the sugar and indicator.

Antigenic properties and classification

- **Serogroups:** Meningococci are capsulated, unlike other neisseriae. Based on their capsular polysaccharide antigens, they are classified into at least 13 serogroups, of which groups A, B C, X, Y and W-135 are the most important. Group A is usually associated with epidemics and group C with localised outbreaks, while group B causes both epidemics and outbreaks. Groups 29-E, W-135 and Y also frequently cause meningitis. Any serogroup may colonise the nasopharynx, but these six groups account for most cases of meningitis.
- **Serotypes:** Serogroups are further classified into serotypes and subtypes based on the outer membrane proteins and about 20 serotypes have been identified.

Resistance

Meningococci are very delicate organisms, being highly susceptible to heat, dessication, alterations in pH and to disinfectants. They were uniformly sensitive to penicillin and other antibiotics, but resistant strains have emerged and become common in many areas.

Pathogenicity

Meningococcal disease can present as cerebrospinal meningitis and meningococcal septicemia. A typical presentation of pyogenic meningitis is given in *clinical case* 1. Meningococci are strict human parasites inhabiting the nasopharynx. Infection is usually asymptomatic. In some, local inflammation ensues, with rhinitis and pharyngitis. Dissemination occurs only in a small proportion.

Meningitis

The cocci spread from the nasopharynx to the meninges by travelling directly along the perineural sheath of the olfactory nerve, through the cribriform plate to the subarachnoid space, or more probably, through the bloodstream. On reaching the central nervous system, a suppurative lesion of the meninges is set up, involving the surface of the spinal cord as well as the base and cortex of the brain. The cocci are invariably found in spinal fluid, especially intracellular in leucocytes. Case fatality is variable but may be as high as 80 per cent in untreated cases. Survivors may have sequelae such as blindness and deafness. Some cases develop chronic or recurrent meningitis.

Meningococcemia

This presents as acute fever with chills, malaise and prostration. Typically, a petechial rash occurs early in the disease. Meningococci may be isolated from the petechial lesions. Metastatic involvement of the joints, ears, eyes, lungs and adrenals may occur. About 10 per cent develop pneumonia. A few develop fulminant meningococcemia (formerly called **Waterhouse–Friderichsen syndrome**) which is an overwhelming and usually fatal condition, characterised by shock, disseminated intravascular coagulation and multisystem failure. Rarely, chronic meningococcemia may be seen. Meningococcal disease is favoured by deficiency of the terminal complement components (C5–C9).

Pathogenesis

This appears to be due to the endotoxin lipopolysaccharide released by autolysis. The vascular endothelium is particularly sensitive to the endotoxin. All major inflammatory cascade systems as well as cytokines and nitric oxide are triggered and upregulated. In fulminant cases, adrenal hemorrhage and profound shock are present.

Epidemiology

Natural infection is limited to human beings. The human nasopharynx is the only reservoir of the meningococcus. Asymptomatic nasopharyngeal carriers rarely contract the illness but serve to infect their contacts. Transmission is essentially by airborne droplets or less often by fomites. During inter-epidemic periods, the carrier rate is about 5–10 per cent. An increase in carrier rate heralds the onset of an epidemic. During epidemics, the carrier rates in closed communities may go up to 90 per cent. Meningitis is common in children between the ages of three months and five years. Epidemics usually occur in semi-closed communities living in crowded conditions, as in jails and ships formerly, and in army camps in recent times.

Prevalence of meningitis is highest in the 'meningitis belt of Africa' stretching from Ethiopia to Senegal. Frequent epidemics have occurred here. One of the largest was in 1996, when 150,000 cases and 15,000 deaths were reported. In India, serogroup A is the most common cause of epidemics and endemic infections.

Laboratory diagnosis

It is necessary to establish the specific cause in purulent meningitis for proper treatment. The primary agents causing purulent bacterial meningitis (pyogenic meningitis) are *N.meningitidis*, *S.pneumoniae* and *Haemophilus influenzae*. In meningococcal meningitis, the cocci are present in large numbers in spinal fluid and, in the early stages, in the blood as well. Isolation of meningococci from the nasopharynx helps in the detection of carriers. Other important causative agents of neonatal meningitis are group B streptococci, staphylococci, *Escherichia coli* and *Listeria monocytogenes*.

1. Specimens

Cerebrospinal fluid, blood, nasopharyngeal swab and skin scrapings from petechial lesions are the specimens collected depending on the clinical presentation.

2. Examination of CSF

The fluid will be under pressure and turbid, with a large number of pus cells. For bacteriological examination, if a sufficient quantity is available, the CSF is divided into three portions:

- **One portion** is centrifuged and Gram-stained smears are prepared from the deposit. Meningococci will be seen mainly inside polymorphs but often extracellularly also. This presumptive diagnosis is sufficient to start antibiotic treatment. The supernatant will contain meningococcal antigens, which may be demonstrated by latex agglutination or counter-immunoelectrophoresis using meningococcal antisera. Similar tests are also available for *S.pneumoniae*, *H.influenzae* type b and group B streptococcus antigens. Antigen detection is particularly useful in partially treated patients in whom smear and culture tests may be negative.

- The **second portion** of the CSF is inoculated on blood agar or chocolate agar plates and incubated at 35–36°C under 5–10% CO_2. Colonies appear after 18–24 hours and may be identified by morphology and biochemical reactions. It must be remembered that morphologically similar organisms such as *N.flavescens*, *N.flava* and *Acinetobacter* may also occasionally cause purulent meningitis. The isolated meningococcus may be grouped, if required, by agglutination with the appropriate sera.
- The **third portion** of the CSF is incubated overnight, either as it is or after adding an equal volume of glucose broth, and then subcultured on chocolate agar. This method may sometimes succeed where direct plating fails.

3. Blood culture
In meningococcemia and in early cases of meningitis, blood culture is often positive. Cultures should be incubated for 4–7 days, with daily subcultures. Meningococcal antigens can be found in the blood in active disease.

4. Nasopharyngeal swab
This is useful for the detection of carriers. Sampling should be done without contamination with saliva. The swab should be held in a suitable transport medium (for example, Stuart's) till it is plated.

5. Petechial lesions
Meningococci may sometimes be demonstrated in petechial lesions by microscopy and culture.

6. Autopsy
At autopsy, specimens may be collected from the meninges, lateral ventricles or the surface of the brain and spinal cord for smear and culture. Meningococci may die if specimens are not collected within twelve hours of the death of the patient.

7. Serology
Retrospective evidence of meningococcal infection may be obtained by detection of antibodies to the polysaccharide antigen.

8. Molecular diagnosis
Group-specific diagnosis of infection can be made by detection of meningococcal DNA sequence in CSF or blood by PCR amplification.

Treatment
Prompt treatment is essential to ensure recovery without sequelae. Sulphonamides, once the mainstay, are not used now due to widespread resistance. Intravenous penicillin G is the treatment of choice. Chloramphenicol is equally effective. One of the third-generation cephalosporins (ceftriaxone, ceftazidime) may be used for initiation of treatment before the cause of meningitis is known.

After the initial course, eradicative therapy is to be given with rifampicin or ciprofloxacin to free the nasopharynx of the cocci and prevent the carrier state.

Prophylaxis
Sulphonamides are not effective due to resistance. Penicillin is unable to eradicate the carrier state. Rifampicin or ciprofloxacin is recommended for chemoprophylaxis. As attack rates are very high in the household or close contacts of meningococcal patients, they should be provided with chemoprophylaxis.

Monovalent and polyvalent vaccines containing the capsular polysaccharides of groups A, C, W-135 and Y are available. The vaccines induce good immunity after a single dose in older children and adults but are of little value in children below the age of two years as the polysaccharide antigen is T-cell-independent. Immunity is group-specific. There is no group B vaccine available at present.

Conjugate vaccines are now available, where the polysaccharide antigen is conjugated to the diphtheria toxoid which makes the vaccine immunogenic for children below the age of two years.

NEISSERIA GONORRHOEAE

N.gonorrhoeae causes the venereal disease gonorrhea. The gonococcus was first described in gonorrheal pus by Neisser in 1879. Bumm, in 1885, cultured the coc-

Clinical Case 2   A 20-year-old man presented with urethral discharge and dysuria for the previous two days. His history revealed that he had had unprotected sex with a commercial sex worker seven days before. On examination of a smear of the pus, Gram-negative diplococci were found inside polymorphs. The culture on Thayer–Martin medium was positive and a diagnosis of gonorrhoea was made. The patient responded to suitable antibiotics.

cus and proved its pathogenicity by inoculating human volunteers.

Morphology

In smears from the urethral discharge in acute gonorrhea, the organism appears as a diplococcus with the adjacent sides concave, being typically kidney-shaped. It is found predominantly within the polymorphs, some cells containing as many as a hundred cocci.

Gonococci possess pili on their surface. Pili facilitate adhesion of the cocci to mucosal surfaces and promote virulence by inhibiting phagocytosis. Piliated gonococci agglutinate human red blood cells but not those of other mammals. The hemagglutination is not inhibited by mannose.

Cultural characteristics

Gonococci are more difficult to grow than meningococci. They are aerobic but may grow anaerobically also. Growth occurs best at pH 7.2–7.6 and at a temperature of 35–36°C. It is essential to provide 5–10% CO_2. They grow well on **chocolate agar** and **Mueller–Hinton** agar. The selective media for *N.gonorrhoeae* is modified Thayer–Martin medium (with vancomycin, colistin and nystatin). This medium inhibits most contaminants including non-pathogenic *Neisseria* and is used to inoculate **urethral and endocervical swabs.**

Colonies are small, round, translucent, convex or slightly umbonate, with a finely granular surface and lobate margins. They are soft and easily emulsifiable. Four types of colonies have been recognised: T1 to T4. Types 1 and 2 form small brown colonies. The cocci are piliated, autoagglutinable and virulent. Types 3 and 4 form larger, granular, non-pigmented colonies. T3 and T4 cocci are non-piliated, form smooth suspensions and are avirulent. Fresh isolates from acute cases of gonorrhea generally form T1 and T2 colonies. On serial subculture, they change to T3 or T4 colonial morphology. T1 and T2 types are also known as P+ and P++, respectively, while T3 and T4 are known as P-.

Biochemical reactions

Gonococci resemble meningococci except that they acidify only glucose and not maltose in serum sugars while meningococci acidify both.

Rapid carbohydrate utilisation test (RCUT): This is a rapid sugar fermentation test that has now been recommended. It is based on the presence of preformed enzymes in the bacteria and is not dependent on the growth of bacteria in the sugar media. This is rapid and more sensitive and specific.

Antigenic properties

Gonococci are antigenically heterogeneous. They are capable of changing their surface structures in vitro. They probably do so in vivo as well, to avoid host defence. The **surface structures** include the following:

- **Pili,** which are hair-like structures several micrometres long, and act as virulence factors by promoting attachment to host cells and inhibiting phagocytosis. Pili are composed of repeating peptide subunits (pilins) consisting of conserved (constant) and variable regions. Pili undergo antigenic and phase variation.
- The trilaminar **outer membrane** of gonococci contains many different proteins. Protein I is the major constituent and shows antigenic diversity, which helps in typing gonococcal strains. Protein I of a single strain is antigenically constant, though it shows considerable heterogeneity among different strains. It has two types, IA and IB. Any one strain carries only IA or IB but not both. Using monoclonal antibodies to protein I epitopes, gonococci can be classified into several serovars, A1–24 and B1–32.
- Proteins I and III act as ligands attaching the coccus to the host cells. They also form transmembrane channels (porins) which play a role in the exchange of molecules across the outer membrane. Protein II is related to the opacity of the gonococcal colonies and so is called the **'opacity-associated' (OPA) outer membrane protein.** Strains with the OPA protein form opaque colonies and those lacking it

form transparent colonies. A strain may express 0–3 serological varieties of the OPA protein at a time. OPA may be responsible for attachment to the host cells and also for the clumping of cocci seen in urethral exudate smears.

- The outer membrane also contains **endotoxins** which may be responsible for the toxicity in gonococcal infections. It is a lipooligosaccharide as compared to the lipopolysaccharide of Enterobacteriaceae.
- Many other proteins with poorly defined roles in pathogenicity have been described. Both gonococci and meningococci produce **IgA1 protease** that splits and inactivates IgA.

Resistance

The gonococcus is a very delicate organism, readily killed by heat, drying and antiseptics. It is a strict parasite and dies in 1–2 hours in exudates outside the body. In cultures, the coccus dies in 3–4 days but survives in slant cultures at 35°C if kept in sterile paraffin oil. Cultures may be preserved for years if frozen quickly and stored at −70°C.

Gonococci contain several plasmids. About 95 per cent of the strains have a small cryptic plasmid of unknown function. Two other transmissible plasmids contain genes that code for beta lactamase which causes resistance to penicillin.

Pathogenicity

Gonorrhea is a venereal disease that has been known since ancient times. The name gonorrhea (meaning flow of seed) was first employed by Galen in 130 AD. In the acute stage, diagnosis can be established readily but chronic cases sometimes present great difficulties.

Spread: The disease is acquired by sexual contact. The first step in infection is adhesion of gonococci to the urethra or other mucosal surfaces. Pili are involved in this adhesion. Adhesion is rapid and firm so that micturition after exposure offers no protection against infection. The cocci penetrate through the intercellular spaces and reach the subepithelial connective tissue by the third day of infection. The incubation period is 2–8 days. In men, the disease starts as acute urethritis with a mucopurulent discharge containing gonococci in large numbers (*Case* 2). The infection extends along the urethra to the prostate, seminal vesicles and epididymis. Chronic urethritis may lead to stricture formation. The infection may spread to the periurethral tissues, causing abscesses and multiple discharging sinuses (**watercan perineum**).

In women, the initial infection involves the urethra and cervix uteri. The vaginal mucosa is not usually affected in adults because the stratified squamous epithelium is resistant to infection by the cocci and also because of the acid pH of vaginal secretions. (Vulvovaginitis occurs in prepubertal girls). The infection may extend to Bartholin's glands, the endometrium and the Fallopian tubes. Pelvic inflammatory disease and salpingitis may lead to sterility. Rarely, peritonitis may develop with perihepatic inflammation (**Fitz-Hugh–Curtis syndrome**). Clinical disease is, as a rule, less severe in women, many of whom may carry gonococci in the cervix without any symptoms. Asymptomatic carriage of gonococci is rare in men.

Disseminated gonococcal infection (DGI) is a severe form of systemic illness.

Proctitis occurs in both sexes. It may develop by direct contiguous spread in women but in men is usually the result of anal sex.

Conjunctivitis may occur, usually due to autoinoculation by the patient's fingers.

Blood invasion may occur from the primary site of infection and may lead to metastatic lesions such as arthritis, ulcerative endocarditis and, very rarely, meningitis. Occasional cases of pyemia have been reported.

Ophthalmia neonatorum, a non-venereal infection, is gonococcal ophthalmia in the newborn, which results from direct infection during passage through the birth canal.

Gonococcal bacteremia leads to skin lesions, especially hemorrhagic papules and pustules on the hands, forearm, feet and legs, and to tenosynovitis and suppurative arthritis, usually of the knees, ankles and wrists.

Epidemiology

Gonorrhea is an exclusively human disease, there being no natural infection in animals. The only source of infection is a human carrier or, less often, a patient. The existence of asymptomatic carriage in women makes them a reservoir, serving to perpetuate infection among their male contacts. The mode of infection is almost exclusively venereal. The only non-venereal infection is ophthalmia neonatorum. Once very common, this has been controlled by the practice of instilling 1% silver nitrate solution into the eyes of all newborn babies (**Crede's method**).

The incidence of gonorrhoea has been rising steeply all over the world. The recent increase in antimicrobial resistance has also affected the treatment and control of infection.

Fomites do not play any significant role, as the cocci die rapidly outside the human body.

Laboratory diagnosis

1. Specimen

Discharge or urethral swab, endocervical swab: The meatus is cleaned with a gauze soaked in saline and a sample of the discharge collected with a platinum loop for culture, or directly on slide for smears. In women, besides the urethral discharge, cervical swabs should also be collected. This should be done carefully, using a speculum. High vaginal swabs are not satisfactory. In chronic infections, there may not be any urethral discharge. The 'morning drop' of secretion may be examined or some exudate may be obtained after prostatic massage. It may also be possible to demonstrate gonococci in the centrifuged deposits of **urine** in cases where no urethral discharge is available.

2. Microscopy

In acute gonorrhoea, the urethral discharge contains gonococci in large numbers (Fig. 24.2). Demonstration of intracellular, Gram-negative diplococci in stained smears provides presumptive evidence of gonorrhea in men. It has to be emphasised that diagnosis of gonorrhea by smear examination is unreliable in women as some of the normal genital flora have essentially similar morphology. The use of fluorescent antibody techniques for the identification of gonococci in smears has increased the sensitivity and specificity of diagnosis by microscopy.

3. Culture

For culture, specimens should be inoculated immediately on collection. If this is not possible, specimens should be collected with charcoal impregnated swabs and sent to the laboratory in **Stuart's transport medium**. In acute gonorrhea, cultures can be obtained readily on chocolate agar or Mueller–Hinton agar incubated at 35–36°C under 5–10% CO_2. In chronic cases, where mixed infection is common and in the examination of lesions such as proctitis, however, it is better to use a selective medium such as **Thayer–Martin**. Growth is identified by morphology and biochemical reactions.

4. Serology

Serological tests like the complement fixation test have been used with varying degrees of success. Many other serological tests have been attempted, including precipitation, passive agglutination, immunofluorescence, and radioimmunoassay using whole-cell lysate, pilus protein and lipopolysaccharide antigens. However, no serological test has been found useful for routine diagnostic purposes.

5. Molecular methods

It may not be possible to obtain gonococci in culture from some chronic cases or from patients with metastatic lesions such as arthritis. PCR molecular methods have improved the sensitivity of the assay.

Treatment

When penicillin was introduced, all strains were highly sensitive (MIC 0.005 unit/ml). From 1957, strains with decreased susceptibility (MIC higher than 0.1 unit/ml) became common. As patients infected with such strains did not respond to the usual doses of penicillin, very large doses, 2.4–4.8 million units, were used. From 1976, gonococci producing beta lactamase (penicillinase) have appeared, rendering penicillin treatment ineffective. These penicillinase-producing *N.gonorrhoeae* (PPNG) have spread widely.

The Centers for Disease Control and Prevention, USA, in 1993, recommended the following schedule for uncomplicated gonorrhea: ceftriaxone 125 mg sin-

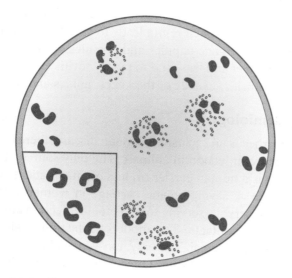

Fig. 24.2 Gonococci in urethral pus. Inset: Enlarged view to show kidney-shaped Gram-negative diplococci with adjacent surfaces concave.

gle IM dose or ciprofloxacin 500 mg (or ofloxacin 400 mg) single oral dose. Since 2006, due to increase in ciprofloxacin resistance, the dosage is ceftriaxone 125 mg IM single dose, with 1 g azithromycin single dose or with doxycycline 100 mg twice a day for 7 days. The regimen is costly but works very well against gonococci and the frequently co-existing chlamydial infection.

Prophylaxis

Control of gonorrhea consists of early detection of cases, contact tracing, health education and other general measures. As even clinical disease does not confer any immunity, vaccination has no place in prophylaxis.

NON-GONOCOCCAL (NON-SPECIFIC) URETHRITIS

Along with an increase in the incidence of gonorrhea, there has also been an increase, in recent years, of cases of chronic urethritis where gonococci cannot be demonstrated. This has been called non-gonococcal or non-specific urethritis. In some of these, urethritis forms part of a syndrome consisting of conjunctivitis and arthritis in addition (**Reiter's syndrome**). Some of these cases may be due to gonococcal infection, the cocci persisting as L forms and hence undetectable by routine tests. The majority of such cases are, however, the result of infections of diverse origin. The most important of these are *C.trachomatis, Ureaplasma urealyticum* and *Mycoplasma hominis*. Herpes virus and cytomegalovirus may also account for some cases. Urethritis may also be caused by other bacteria (for example, *Gardnerella vaginalis, Acinetobacter lwoffi, Ac.calcoaceticus*), fungi (*Candida albicans*), protozoa (*Trichomonas vaginalis*), or even by mechanical or chemical irritation. As etiological diagnosis is seldom achieved, the management of this syndrome is difficult.

COMMENSAL NEISSERIAE

Several species of neisseriae inhabit the normal respiratory tract. The characteristic features of some of the common species are listed in Table 24.1. Their pathogenic significance is uncertain though some of them (for example, *N.flavescens, N.catarrhalis*) have been reported occasionally as having caused meningitis. *N.catarrhalis* is now classified as *Moraxella* (*Branhamella*) *catarrhalis*. It is an opportunistic pathogen capable of causing laryngitis, bronchopneumonia, meningitis, sinusitis and middle ear disease.

N.lactamica, frequently isolated from the nasopharynx, is closely related to meningococci, though it is virtually avirulent. It differs from pathogenic neisseriae in being positive in the ONPG test for beta galactosidase. Nasopharyngeal colonisation by *N.lactamica* in young children may be responsible for the presence in them of antibodies protective against meningococcal infection.

Table 24.1 *Differential characteristics of Neisseriae*

Species	Colonies	Growth		Fermentation			Serological classification
		On nutrient agar	At 22°C	Glucose	Maltose	Sucrose	
N.menigitidis	Round, smooth, shiny, creamy consistency	–	–	A	A	–	Thirteen antigenic groups
N.gonorrhoeae	Same as above, but smaller and more opalescent	–	–	A	–	–	Antigenically heterogeneous
N.flavescens	Resemble meningococcus but pigmented yellow	+	+	–	–	–	Antigenically distinct homogeneous group
N.sicca	Small, dry, opaque, wrinkled, brittle	+	+	A	A	A	Autoagglutinable
N.catarrhalis (Branhamella catarrhalis)	Variable, smooth and translucent or adherent and opaque, not easily emulsifiable	+	+	–	–	–	Autoagglutinable

RECAP

- Bacteria belonging to the genus *Neisseria* are Gram-negative cocci occurring in pairs. The two important pathogenic species are *Neisseria meningitidis* and *Neisseria gonorrhoeae*.
- Non-pathogenic species of *Neisseria* can occur as commensals.
- *Neisseria meningitidis* and *Neisseria gonorrhoeae* are more difficult to grow (fastidious), and require enriched culture media and an atmosphere with high humidity and enhanced carbon dioxide concentration for isolation from specimens.
- *Neisseria meningitidis* (meningococcus) is a common cause of meningitis.
- *Neisseria gonorrhoeae* (gonococcus) causes gonorrhoea.

ESSAYS

1. List the organisms causing pyogenic meningitis and describe the laboratory diagnosis of meningococcal meningitis.
2. List the organisms causing STI and describe the laboratory diagnosis of *N.gonorrhoeae*.
3. Explain the virulence factors of *N.gonorrhoeae* and write the laboratory diagnosis.

SHORT ANSWERS

1. Four differences between *N.meningitidis* and *N.gonorrhoeae*
2. Media used for gonococcus

SHORT NOTES

1. Serotypes of *N.meningitidis* and the epidemiology in India
2. Antibiotic resistance in *N.gonorrhoeae*
3. Chemoprophylaxis of meningococcal meningitis

25 Corynebacterium

INTRODUCTION

Corynebacteria are Gram-positive, non-acid fast, non-motile rods with irregularly stained segments, due to the presence of granules in some species. They frequently show club-shaped swellings—hence, the name *Corynebacterium* (from *coryne*, meaning club).

The most important member of the genus is *C.diphtheriae,* the causative agent of diphtheria (*case*). The disease was first recognised as a clinical entity by Bretonneau (1826) who called it 'diphtherite' (from *diph-*

theros, meaning leather). The name is derived from the tough, leathery pseudomembrane formed in the disease.

The diphtheria bacillus was first observed and described by Klebs (1883) but was first cultivated by Loeffler (1884). It is hence known as the Klebs–Loeffler bacillus or KLB. Loeffler studied the effect of the bacillus in experimental animals and concluded that the disease was due to some diffusible product of the bacillus. Roux and Yersin (1888) discovered the diphtheria exotoxin and established its pathogenic effect. The antitoxin was described by von Behring (1890).

CORYNEBACTERIUM DIPHTHERIAE

Morphology

The diphtheria bacillus is a slender rod with a tendency to clubbing at one or both ends. The bacilli are pleomorphic, measuring approximately 3–6 μm $\times$ 0.6–0.8 μm. They are non-sporing, non-capsulated and non-motile. They are Gram-positive but tend to be decolourised easily. They possess polymetaphosphate granules that serve as storage granules and are called **volutin** or **Babes–Ernst granules or metachromatic granules**. These give the bacilli a beaded appearance when stained with aniline dyes. The bacilli are arranged in characteristic pairs, palisades (resembling the stakes of a fence) or small groups. They often appear at various angles to each other, resembling the letters V or L. This has been called the **Chinese letter** or **cuneiform** arrangement, due to incomplete separation of the daughter cells after binary fission.

Corynebacterium diphtheriae

Clinical Case   A five-year-old child presented to the pediatrics outpatient department with a history of pain in the throat and difficulty in swallowing. He had had low-grade fever for the past two days. On examination, he was found to have cervical lymphadenopathy, and the tonsillar pillars were covered by a grey-white discharge. His vaccination card showed that the child's immunisation was not complete. A throat swab was collected and submitted for microscopy and culture. Albert's stain showed the presence of rod-shaped bacteria, green in colour, with bluish-black granules. A diagnosis of diphtheria was made and the child was started on penicillin followed by passive immunisation with diphtheria antitoxin. Prophylactic antibiotics were also prescribed to close siblings and with an advice to complete vaccination.

Antigenic structure

Diphtheria bacilli are antigenically heterogeneous. Based on colonial and other characteristics, *C.diphtheriae* have been typed as gravis, intermedius and mitis. By agglutination, gravis strains have been classified into 13 antigenic types, intermedius into 4 and mitis into 40 types. Gravis strains of types I and III have been reported to be common in Great Britain, type II worldwide, type IV mainly in Egypt and type V in the USA. No connection has been established between type-specificity and other characters.

Pathogenicity

Toxin

Virulent strains of diphtheria bacilli produce a very powerful exotoxin (Table 25.1). The pathogenic effects of the bacillus are due to the toxin. Almost all strains of gravis and intermedius (about 95–99 per cent) are toxigenic, while only about 80–85 per cent of mitis strains are so.

The proportions vary with the origin of the cultures tested. Strains of all three types are invariably virulent when isolated from acute cases. Avirulent strains are common among convalescents, contacts and carriers, particularly in those with extrafaucial infection.

There is considerable variation in the amount of toxin produced by the different strains, some producing it abundantly and others only poorly, but the toxins produced by all strains of the diphtheria bacilli are qualitatively similar. The standard strain almost universally used for toxin production is the **Park–Williams 8 strain**, which has been variously described as a mitis (Topley and Wilson) and intermedius (Cruickshank).

Properties: The diphtheria toxin is a protein and has been crystallised. It has a molecular weight of about 62,000. It is extremely potent and the lethal dose for a 250 g guinea pig is 0.0001 mg. It consists of two fragments, **A and B**, of MW 24,000 and 38,000, respectively. Both fragments are necessary for the toxic effect. When released by the bacterium, the toxin is inactive because the active site on fragment A is masked. Activation is probably accomplished by proteases present in the culture medium and infected tissues (Table 25.1). All the enzymatic activity of the toxin is present in fragment A. Fragment B is responsible for binding the toxin to the cells. The antibody to fragment B protects by preventing the binding of the toxin to the cells. The toxin is labile. Prolonged storage, incuba-

tion at 37°C for 4–6 weeks, treatment with 0.2–0.4% formalin or acid pH converts it to toxoid. **Toxoid is a toxin that has lost its toxicity but not its antigenicity.** It is capable of inducing antitoxin antibodies and is used as a vaccine candidate.

The **factors affecting toxin production** are as follows:

- The toxigenicity of the diphtheria bacillus depends on the intracellular presence of **corynephages (tox+)**, which act as the genetic determinant controlling toxin production. Non-toxigenic strains may be rendered toxigenic by infecting them with **beta** or some other phage. This is known as **lysogenic** or **phage conversion**. The toxigenicity remains only as long as the bacillus is lysogenic. When the bacillus is cured of its phage, as by growing it in the presence of antiphage serum, it loses its toxigenic capacity.
- Toxin production is also influenced by the concentration of **iron** in the medium. The optimum level of iron for toxin production is 0.1 mg/l, while a concentration of 0.5 mg/l inhibits the formation of toxin.

Mechanism of action: The diphtheria toxin acts by inhibiting protein synthesis. Specifically, fragment B helps in binding and fragment A inhibits polypeptide chain elongation in the presence of nicotinamide adenine dinucleotide by inactivating the elongation factor, EF-2. It has a special affinity for certain tissues such as the myocardium, adrenals and nerve endings.

Clinical features

The incubation period in diphtheria is commonly 3–4 days but may on occasion be as short as one day. In carriers, the incubation period may be very prolonged. The site of infection may be:

Table 25.1 *Characteristics of diphtheria toxin*

Lethal dose	0.1 µg/kg
Structure	2 subunits
	a) A-Active domain—responsible for action
	b) B-Binding domain—trigger entry host cell
Host cell receptor	CD9 and HBEGF-like precursor
Mechanism	Entry by receptor method endocytosis
	Action—inhibits protein synthesis by inactivating EF2
	(Similar action demonstrated by exotoxin of *Psuedomonas aeruginosa*)

- Otitic
- Nasal
- Genital: vulval, vaginal or prepucial
- Pharyngeal (most common)
- Laryngeal
- Conjunctival
- Cutaneous

Pharyngeal diphtheria is the most common type and may vary from mild catarrhal inflammation to very widespread involvement (*Case*). According to the **clinical severity**, diphtheria may be classified as:

- **Malignant** or **hypertoxic** in which there is severe toxemia with marked adenitis (bull neck). Death is due to circulatory failure. There is a high incidence of paralytic sequelae in those who recover.
- **Septic**, which leads to ulceration, cellulitis and even gangrene around the pseudomembrane.
- **Hemorrhagic**, which is characterised by bleeding from the edge of the membrane, epistaxis, conjunctival hemorrhage, purpura and generalised bleeding tendency.

Common complications are:

- **Asphyxia** due to mechanical obstruction of the respiratory passage by the pseudomembrane, for which an emergency tracheostomy may become necessary.
- **Acute circulatory failure**, which may be peripheral or cardiac.
- **Post-diphtheritic paralysis**, which typically occurs in the third or fourth week of the disease; palatine and ciliary, but not papillary, paralysis is characteristic, and spontaneous recovery is the rule.
- **Toxemia,** in which the bacilli remain confined to the site of entry, where they multiply and form the toxin, which is absorbed and produce toxic damage to the heart (myocarditis), kidney (tubular necrosis), liver and adrenal glands.
- **Local necrotic changes**, leading to fibrinous exudates; these, together with the disintegrating epithelial cells, leucocytes, erythrocytes and bacteria, constitute the pseudomembrane, which is characteristic of diphtheritic infection.
- **Mechanical**, caused by the membrane.
- **Non-toxigenic strains,** which may cause infection even in immunised individuals, as immunity with the toxoid does not confer antibacterial immunity. Such infection is mild, though pseudomembrane formation may sometimes occur.

Cutaneous diphtheria: In the tropics, diphtheria bacilli infect the skin more often than the respiratory tract. Toxigenic diphtheria bacilli may persist in the skin for over three years. Cutaneous infections may stimulate natural immunity to diphtheria but may also lead to **pharyngeal diphtheria** in non-immune contacts. Cutaneous infections are usually secondary to pre-existing skin lesions. Sometimes, diphtheritic whitlow or ulcer may occur. Cutaneous infections are commonly caused by non-toxigenic strains of the diphtheria bacilli. Fomites do not seem to play an important role, though in special situations, toys and pencils may act as vehicles of infection.

Typing

Typing methods are used to determine the transcontinental spread. This has become important because infection can be introduced from the countries where outbreaks continue to occur in children into countries that have been able to contain the infection, but adolescent and adult population are still susceptible to the infections.

Typing methods

- **Biotyping:** This is done based on biochemical tests, mostly using automated systems.
- **Ribotyping:** This is presently considered to be the most useful method to type the strains of *C.diptheriae*.
- **Molecular methods** like **Pulse Field Gel Electrophoresis (PFGE), Random Amplification of Polymorphic DNA (RAPD)** or **Amplified Fragment Length Polymorphism (AFLP)** are the other molecular methods used for typing.
- **Bacteriophage typing:** About 15 bacteriophage types have been described. Types I and III are mitis, IV and VI intermedius, VII avirulent gravis and the remainder virulent gravis. The phage types are apparently stable. A system of bacteriocin (diphthericin) typing has also been described. Other methods of typing include bacterial polypeptide analysis, DNA restriction patterns and hybridisation with DNA probes. However, due to poor discriminatory power, this is not used any longer.

Laboratory diagnosis

Laboratory confirmation of diphtheria is necessary for the initiation of control measures and for epidemiological purposes but not for the treatment of individual cases. Specific treatment should be instituted **immediately** on suspicion of diphtheria without waiting for laboratory tests. Any delay may be fatal.

1. Specimen

Preferably, two dacron swabs from the lesions are collected under vision, using a tongue depressor from the lesion. The area under the visible membrane should be sampled.

2. Microscopy

Stained smear examination: Smears are stained with methylene blue or one of the special stains.

Neisser's or **Albert's stain:** This stain will show the bacilli with metachromatic granules and in the typical arrangement (Fig. 25.1), Albert's stain may show delicate green bacilli with purple-blue metachromatic granules. The granules are often situated at the poles of the bacilli and are called **polar bodies**.

By Gram stain, the granules are more strongly Gram-positive than the rest of the bacterial cell.

Loeffler's methylene blue: The granules take up a bluish-purple colour and are, hence, called **metachromatic granules.** However, the bacilli may not always be demonstrable in smears from the lesion; confident differentiation from some commensal corynebacteria normally found in the throat may also be difficult.

Gram- or Leishman-stained smear: This is done to rule out Vincent's spirochetes and fusiform bacilli, responsible for Vincent's angina which clinically resembles diphtheria.

Immunofluorescence: Diphtheria bacilli may be identified in smears by **direct immunofluorescence test.** This is more specific as the smear is stained with specific antibody.

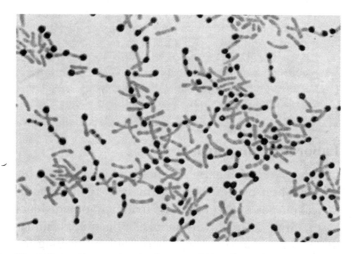

Fig. 25.1 Corynebacterium on Albert's stain

3. Isolation by culture

Enrichment with blood, serum or egg is necessary for good growth, as it is scanty on ordinary media. The optimum temperature for growth is 37°C (range 15–40°C) and the optimum pH is 7.2. *C.diphtheriae* is an aerobe and a facultative anaerobe.

The usual media employed for the cultivation of the diphtheria bacillus are:

Loeffler's serum slope: Growth is rapid on Loeffler's serum slope. The colonies can be visualised in 6–8 hours. Colonies appear at first as small, circular white opaque discs but enlarge on continued incubation and may acquire a distinct yellow tint.

Tellurite blood agar: Several modifications of tellurite blood agar have been utilised, such as **McLeod's** and **Hoyle's** media. Tellurite (0.04%) inhibits the growth of most other bacteria, acting as a selective agent. Diphtheria bacilli reduce tellurite to metallic tellurium, which is incorporated in the colonies, giving them a grey or black colour. The growth of diphtheria bacilli may be delayed on the tellurite medium and colonies may take two days to appear. **Plates will have to be incubated for at least two days before being considered negative, as growth may sometimes be delayed**. The tellurite medium is particularly important in the isolation of diphtheria bacilli from convalescents, contacts and carriers, as in these cases they may be outnumbered by other bacteria.

Based on colonial morphology on the tellurite medium and other properties, McLeod classified diphtheria bacilli into three types: **gravis, intermedius** and **mitis.** Table 25.2 lists the characteristics of the three types.

Sheep blood agar: This is required to differentiate colonies from streptococcal or staphylococcal pharyngitis, which may simulate diphtheria. If the swab cannot be inoculated promptly, it should be kept moistened with sterile serum so that the bacilli remain viable. The serum slope may show growth in 4–8 hours but, if negative, will have to be incubated for 24 hours.

4. Biochemical reactions

Hiss's serum sugars: Diphtheria bacilli ferment glucose, galactose, maltose and dextrin with the production of acid but without gas; they do not ferment lactose, mannitol or sucrose. Some strains of virulent diphtheria bacilli have been found to ferment sucrose. It is necessary to use Hiss's serum sugars for fermenta-

Table 25.2 *Type differentiation of diphtheria bacilli*

	Gravis	Intermedius	Mitis
Morphology	Usually short rods, with uniform staining, few or no granules. Some degree of pleomorphism, with irregularly barred, snow-shoe and tear-drop forms	Long barred forms with clubbed ends; poor granulation, very pleomorphic	Long, curved, pleomorphic rods with prominent granules
Colony on tellurite blood agar	In 18 hours, colony is 1–2 mm in size, with greyish-black centre, paler, semitranslucent periphery and commencing crenation of edge. In 2–3 days, 3–5 mm in size, flat colony with raised dark centre and crenated edge with radial striation—'**daisy head**' colony	18-hour colony, small, 1 mm in size, misty. Does not enlarge in 48 hours, dull granular centre with smoother, more glistening periphery and a lighter ring near the edge—'**frog's egg**' colony	Size variable, shiny black. In 2–3 days, colonies become flat, with a central elevation—'**poached egg**' colony
Consistency of colonies	Like 'cold margarine', brittle, moves as a whole on the plate, not easily picked out or emulsifiable	Intermediate between gravis and mitis	Soft, buttery, easily emulsifiable
Hemolysis	Variable	Non-hemolytic	Usually hemolytic
Growth in broth	Surface pellicle, granular deposit, little or no turbidity	Turbidity in 24 hours, clearing in 48 hours, with fine granular sediment	Diffuse turbidity with soft pellicle later
Glycogen and starch fermentation	Positive	Negative	Negative

tion tests. Proteolytic activity is absent. They do not hydrolyse urea or form phosphatase.

5. Demonstration of toxicity (virulence testing)

Any isolate of the diphtheria bacillus should be tested for toxigenicity for the bacteriological diagnosis to be complete. Virulence testing may be by the in vivo or in vitro methods.

In vivo tests

- **Subcutaneous test:** The growth from an overnight culture on Loeffler's slope is emulsified in 2–4 ml of broth and 0.8 ml of the emulsion injected subcutaneously into two guinea pigs, one of which has been protected with 500 units of the diphtheria antitoxin 18–24 hours before. If the strain is virulent, the unprotected animal will die within four days. The method is not usually employed as it results in death of the animals.

- **Intracutaneous test:** The broth emulsion of the culture is inoculated intracutaneously into two guinea pigs (or rabbits) so that each receives 0.1 ml in two different sites. One animal acts as the control and should have received 500 units of antitoxin the previous day. The other is given 50 units of antitoxin intraperitoneally four hours after the skin test, in order to prevent death. Toxigenicity

is indicated by inflammatory reaction at the site of injection, progressing to necrosis in 48–72 hours in the test animal and no change in the control animal. An advantage in the intracutaneous test is that the animals do not die. As many as ten strains can be tested at a time on a rabbit.

In vitro tests

- **Elek's gel precipitation test:** A rectangular strip of filter paper impregnated with diphtheria antitoxin (1000 units/ml) is placed on the surface of a 20% normal horse serum agar in a petri dish while the medium is still fluid. If horse serum is not available, sheep or rabbit serum may be used. When the agar has set, the surface is dried and narrow streaks of the strains are made at right angles to the filter paper strip. **Positive and negative controls should be tested.** The plate is incubated at 37°C for 24–48 hours. Toxins produced by the bacterial growth will diffuse in the agar and, where it meets the antitoxin at optimum concentration, will produce a line of precipitation (Fig. 25.2). The presence of such arrowhead lines of precipitates indicates that the strain is toxigenic. No precipitate will form in the case of non-toxigenic strains. This test is very convenient and economical but some brands of peptone and some samples of serum do not give satisfactory results.

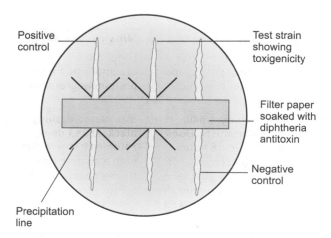

Fig. 25.2 Elek's gel precipitation test

Tissue culture test: The toxigenicity of diphtheria bacilli can be demonstrated by incorporating the strains in the agar overlay of cell culture monolayers. The toxin produced diffuses into the cells below and causes lysis of the cells.

PCR: Polymerase chain reaction for detection of Toxin gene *(tox)* has been developed to detect the presence of genes coding for the toxin, in clinical isolates.

ELISA: The test may be done to detect toxin from the patient's isolate using antitoxin and enzyme-substrate system.

Epidemiology

Faucial diphtheria was formerly an important pediatric disease all over the world but following the development of effective prophylactics and mass immunisation, the disease has been virtually eradicated from most advanced countries. In developing countries where childhood immunisation programmes have been implemented effectively, diphtheria has become rare but in others it continues to be a serious problem. In India, it is included in the universal immunisation programme for infants.

Gravis, intermedius and **mitis** were originally proposed to relate to the clinical severity of the disease produced by the three types—gravis, causing the most serious, and mitis the mildest variety, with intermedius being responsible for disease of intermediate severity. However, this association is not constant.

- The gravis and intermedius types are associated with high case fatality rates, while mitis infections are less lethal.

- Paralytic complications are most common in gravis, hemorrhagic complications in gravis and intermedius, and obstructive lesions in the air passage in mitis infections.
- In general, mitis is the predominant strain in endemic areas, while gravis and intermedius tend to be epidemic. The mitis type is abler than the more virulent types to establish a commensal relationship with the host.
- Wide variations have been noted in the frequency of the different types in different places at different times.

Evidence shows that the gravis and, to a lesser extent, the intermedius strains are able to spread more readily than mitis in populations naturally immune or artificially immunised. Table 25.2 lists the characteristics of the three types. The prolonged and extensive epidemic of diphtheria in parts of the erstwhile Soviet Union in the 1990s, involving several thousands, with a mortality rate of up to 20 per cent is a warning of what can befall countries that neglect immunisation and let living conditions deteriorate.

Age: In endemic areas, it is mainly a disease of childhood. It is rare in the first year of life due to the passive immunity obtained from the mother, reaches a peak between 2 and 5 years, falls slowly between 5 and 10 years, and rapidly between 10 and 15 years with only very low incidence afterwards because of active immunity acquired by repeated subclinical infections.

Asymptomatic carriers who outnumber cases by a hundredfold or more in endemic areas are the most important sources of infection. In the temperate regions, carriage is mainly in the nose and throat. Nasal carriers harbour the bacilli for longer periods than pharyngeal carriers.

In nature, diphtheria is virtually confined to human beings, though cows may on occasion be found to have diphtheritic infection of the udder. The infection in such cases is invariably transmitted by the milker. The infection may be spread through the milk of infected cows.

Prophylaxis

Protective immunity

Diptheria is a disease which is due to the toxin and not the invasion of the pathogen. Therefore, the protective immunity is dependent on the levels of antitoxin antibodies present in circulation. The objective of immunisation is to increase protective levels of antitoxins in circulation. The susceptibility of an individual is tested by determining the antitoxic level using the following tests.

- **In vivo Schick**: This is a neutralisation-based skin test introduced in 1913. This test is no longer in use.
- **In vitro assays**: The circulating antitoxin level can also be determined by serological tests such as passive hemagglutination or by neutralisation in cell culture. **Antitoxin levels of more than 0.1 IU/per ml of blood is considered an index of protective antibody level.**

Vaccines

Diphtheria can be controlled by immunisation. Three methods of immunisation are available: active, passive and combined. Of these, only active immunisation can provide herd immunity and lead to eradication of the disease. Passive and combined immunisation can provide emergency protection to susceptible individuals exposed to risk.

Active immunisation: Diphtheria immunisation is done using a killed vaccine. Currently, two preparations are available for active immunisation:

- **Formol toxoid** (also known as fluid toxoid) is prepared by incubating the toxin with formalin.
- **Adsorbed toxoid** is purified toxoid adsorbed onto insoluble aluminium phosphate, less often the hydroxide. It is much more immunogenic than formol toxoid.

Dosage: Diphtheria toxoid is usually given in children as a trivalent preparation containing tetanus toxoid and pertussis vaccine, as the **DTP, DPT or triple vaccine**. For young children, diphtheria toxoid is given in a dose of 10–25 Lf (limit of flocculation) units to all recommended individuals.

Schedule: The schedule of primary immunisation of infants and children consists of three doses of DPT given at intervals of at least four weeks, preferably six weeks or more, followed by a fourth dose about a year afterwards. A further booster dose is given at school entry.

Adult immunisation: Smaller doses (1–2 Lf units) are used for older children and adults to minimise adverse reactions. In toxoid preparations, the lower dose of toxoid is indicated by the small letter 'd' and the full dose by capital 'D'. For example, the tetanus diphtheria vaccine for adults containing low-dose diphtheria toxoid is referred to as 'Td'.

Some **side effects** or adverse reactions which might occur after vaccination are injection site reactions (redness, warmth, swelling, tenderness, itching, pain, hives, and rash), fever, drowsiness, fretfulness, vomiting, anorexia, persistent crying (in infants), and rarely, convulsions.

Passive immunisation: This is an emergency measure to be used when susceptible persons are exposed to infection, as when a case of diphtheria is admitted to general pediatric wards. It consists of the subcutaneous administration of 500–1000 units of antitoxin (antidiphtheritic serum, ADS). As this is a horse serum, precaution against hypersensitivity should be observed.

Combined immunisation: This consists of administration of the first dose of adsorbed toxoid on one arm, while ADS is given on the other arm, to be continued for the full course of active immunisation. Ideally, all cases that receive ADS prophylactically should receive combined immunisation.

> **Chemoprophylaxis**
> This is sometimes given to the susceptible close contacts of a diphtheria patient, with erythromycin along with the booster dose of vaccine.

Treatment

Specific treatment of diphtheria consists of antitoxic and antibiotic therapy. **Antitoxin** should be given immediately when diphtheria is suspected, as the fatality rate increases with delay in starting antitoxic treatment. **The recommended dose is 20,000–100,000 units for serious cases, half the dose being given intravenously**. Antitoxin treatment is generally not indicated in cutaneous diphtheria as the causative strains are usually non-toxigenic.

C.diphtheriae is sensitive to **penicillin** and can be cleared from the throat within a few days by penicillin treatment. Diphtheria patients are given a course of penicillin though it only supplements and does not replace antitoxin therapy.

Erythromycin is more active than penicillin in the treatment of **carriers.**

OTHER PATHOGENIC CORYNEBACTERIA

These can be divided into lipophilic and non-lipophilic based on the improved growth on adding lipid to the medium.

NON-LIPOPHILIC CORYNEBACTERIA

Corynebacterium ulcerans

This bacillus is related to *C.diphtheriae* and can cause diphtheria-like lesions. It resembles the gravis type of the diphtheria bacillus but it liquefies gelatin, ferments trehalose slowly and does not reduce nitrate to nitrite. It produces two types of toxins, one probably identical to the diphtheria toxin and the other resembling the toxin of **C.pseudotuberculosis**. It is pathogenic to guinea pigs, the lesions produced resembling those caused by *C.diphtheriae*. It has been found to cause infection in cows, and human infections may be transmitted through cow's milk. It is sensitive to erythromycin. Diphtheria antitoxin is protective. It has been suggested that **C.ulcerans** be considered a subgroup of diphtheria bacilli rather than a separate species.

Erythrasma, a localised infection of the stratum corneum usually affecting the axilla and groin, is **caused by C.minutissimum** which produces superficial skin lesions. This is a lipophilic corynebacterium and can be grown readily in media containing 20% fetal calf serum.

LIPOPHILIC CORYNEBACTERIA

Corynebacterium jeikeium

C.jeikeium is one of the most important members of this group and can cause cutaneous and bloodstream infections with high mortality rate. This is often seen in immunocompromised hosts. This organism is usually multidrug-resistant, responding only to vancomycin. It is increasingly being associated with infective endocarditis.

Arcanobacterium (formerly Corynebacterium) haemolyticum

These bacteria can cause pharyngitis and skin ulcers.

DIPHTHEROIDS

Corynebacteria resembling *C.diphtheriae* occur as normal commensals in the throat, skin, conjunctiva and other areas. These may sometimes be mistaken for diphtheria bacilli and are called diphtheroids. In general, diphtheroids stain more uniformly than diphtheria bacilli, possess few or no metachromatic granules and tend to be arranged in parallel rows (palisades) rather than in a cuneiform pattern. However, some diphtheroids may be indistinguishable from diphtheria bacilli microscopically. Differentiation is by biochemical reactions and more reliably by virulence tests. The common diphtheroids are *C.pseudodiphtheriticum* (*C.hofmannii*) found in the throat and *C.xerosis* found in the conjunctival sac. The former is urease-positive and does not ferment glucose, while the latter is urease-negative and ferments glucose. Both are pyrazinamidase-positive, unlike diphtheria bacilli.

OTHER CORYNEFORM BACTERIA

Besides the genus *Corynebacterium*, a number of other genera of coryneform bacteria have been defined. Among them, the genus *Propionibacterium* is of medical interest. This is because three species, *P.acnes*, *P.granulosum* and *P.avidum*, are constantly present on human skin. They are anaerobic and aerotolerant, growing well in media containing lipid. *P.acnes* is often isolated from acne lesions but its pathogenic role is uncertain.

Corynebacterium parvum, which is frequently used as an immunomodulator, is a mixture of the *Propionibacterium* species.

Important diseases and species of corynebacteria are summarised in Table 25.3.

Table 25.3   *Important diseases and species of Corynebacterium*

Agent	Disease produced
C.diphtheria	Toxigenic strains—diphtheria
	Nontoxigenic strains—bacteremia, endocarditis
C.ulcerans	Diphtheria by toxigenic strains
C.pseudotuberculosis	Diphtheria by toxigenic strains
C.striatum	Healthcare-associated infections
C.urealyticum	Urinary tract infections
C.jeikeium	Bacteremia in immunocompromised hosts
Arcanobacterium hemolyticum	Pharyngitis; wound infections; septicemia

RECAP

- *Corynebacteria* are non-motile, aerobic, Gram-positive bacilli, some species being commensals in the human body.
- *Corynebacterium diphtheriae* causes diphtheria in the upper respiratory tract. Skin infections may occur due to toxigenic and non-toxigenic strains in individuals in poor socioeconomic circumstances.
- The bacterium attaches to the back of the throat of (mainly) children. This is followed by secretion of the diphtheria toxin, which kills cells and causes inflammation and fibrin accumulation, leading to the formation of the characteristic pseudomembrane (which may break off and lead to asphyxiation of the child).
- *Corynebacterium diphtheriae* grows slowly on selective media containing tellurite (colonies appear black) but rapidly on enriched media such as Loeffler's serum slope.
- Toxin production can be detected by Elek's gel precipitation test.
- Active immunisation during childhood with the diphtheria toxoid stimulates the production of neutralising antibodies that protect against the effects of active toxin secreted during infection.
- Other pathogenic corynebacteria include *C.pseudotuberculosis*, *C.ulcerans*, *C.minutissimum* and *Corynebacterium jeikeium (Lipophilic bacteria)*.
- Diphtheroids resembling *C.diphtheriae* occur as normal commensals in the throat, skin, conjunctiva and other areas.

ESSAYS

1. Describe the morphology, cultural characteristics and pathogenesis of *Corynebacterium diphtheriae*, and add a note on prophylactic treatment.
2. What are the organisms that cause sore throat? Explain the pathogenesis and laboratory diagnosis of diphtheriae.

SHORT ANSWERS

1. Cultivation of *C.diphtheriae*
2. Diseases caused by the *Corynebacteria* species
3. Elek's test/virulence test for diphtheria
4. Laboratory diagnosis of diphtheria
5. Mechanism of action and detection of the diphtheria toxin

SHORT NOTES

1. Metachromatic granules
2. Diphtheria toxin
3. DPT vaccine

26 Bacillus

25% NaCl. Their spores are ubiquitous, being found in the soil, dust, water and air and constitute the commonest contaminants in bacteriological culture media.

Bacillus anthracis, the causative agent of anthrax (*Case*) is the major pathogenic species. Anthrax is primarily a disease of cattle and sheep, and less often of horses and swine.

B.cereus can cause food-borne gastroenteritis. Some species may be responsible for opportunistic infections.

Considerable historical interest is attached to the anthrax bacillus. It was the first pathogenic bacterium to be observed under the microscope (Pollender 1849), the first communicable disease shown to be transmitted by inoculation of infected blood (Davaine 1850), the first bacillus to be isolated in pure culture and shown to possess spores (Koch 1876) and the first bacterium used for the preparation of an attenuated vaccine (Pasteur 1881).

INTRODUCTION

The spore-forming, Gram-positive, rod-shaped bacteria are classified into two genera, aerobic **Bacilli** and anaerobic **Clostridia**.

GENUS *BACILLUS*

The genus consists of aerobic bacilli forming heat-resistant spores. Members of this group exhibit great diversity in their properties. The genus includes psychrophilic, mesophilic and thermophilic species, the maximum temperatures for vegetative growth ranging from about 25°C to above 75°C and the minimum from about 5°C to 45°C. Their salt tolerance varies from less than 2% to

BACILLUS ANTHRACIS

Morphology

The anthrax bacillus is one of the largest of pathogenic bacteria, measuring 3–10 × 1–1.6 µm. It is Gram-positive, but tends to be decolourised easily so as to appear Gram-variable, or even Gram-negative. It is non-acid fast. It is **non-motile**, unlike most other members of this genus. In tissues, it is found singly, in pairs or in short chains, the entire chain being surrounded by a capsule.

Spores

Sporulation occurs under unfavourable conditions for growth. Oxygen is required for sporulation, but not for

---

Bacillus anthracis

Clinical Case   A 45-year-old cowherd presented with a black eschar on the left hand. There was extensive swelling around the ulcer but it was not painful. There were few vesicular lesions surrounding the ulcer. He gave a history of handling a dead animal on his farm. The fluid from the vesicle was positive for Gram-positive bacilli. Culture was positive for *Bacillus anthracis*, establishing a diagnosis of cutaneous anthrax. The patient responded to ciprofloxacin.

germination. Spores are central or subterminal, elliptical or oval in shape, and are of the same width as the bacillary body so that they do not cause bulging of the vegetative cell.

The spores are highly resistant to physical and chemical agents. They have been isolated from naturally infected soil after as long as 60 years. They resist dry heat at 140°C for 1–3 hours and boiling for 10 minutes. **Spores are formed in culture or in the soil but never in the animal body during life**. The optimum temperature for sporulation is 25–30°C. Destruction of the spores in animal products imported into non-endemic countries is achieved by 'duckering' in which formaldehyde is used as a 2% solution at 30–40°C for 20 minutes for disinfection of wool and as 0.25% at 60°C for six hours for animal hair and bristles.

In contrast, the **vegetative bacilli** are not particularly resistant and are destroyed at 60°C in 30 minutes. In the carcasses of animals which have died of anthrax, the bacilli remain viable in the bone marrow for a week and in the skin for two weeks. Normal heat fixation of smears may not kill the bacilli in blood films.

Pathogenicity

Two **virulence factors** have been identified in the pathogenesis:

Capsule

The **capsule** is polypeptide in nature, being composed of a polymer of d(−) glutamic acid. It is plasmid-borne. It aids virulence by inhibiting phagocytosis. Loss of the plasmid leads to loss of virulence and is the mechanism for attenuation and making of anthrax spore vaccine (Sterne strain). Capsules are not formed under ordinary conditions of culture but only if the media contains added bicarbonate or if incubated under 10–25% CO_2. If grown in media containing serum, albumin, charcoal or starch, capsule formation may occur in the absence of CO_2.

Anthrax toxin

The **anthrax toxin**, which is also encoded by a separate plasmid, was identified by the finding that injecting the sterile plasma of guinea pigs dying of anthrax into healthy guinea pigs killed them. Death of experimental animals could be prevented by immune serum. Loss of this plasmid renders the strain avirulent and is believed to have been the basis for the original anthrax vaccine developed by Pasteur.

The toxin is a complex of **three fractions.** They are not toxic individually but the whole complex produces local edema and generalised shock. These three factors have been characterised and cloned.

- **Protective antigen factor (PA or Factor II):** PA is the fraction that binds to the receptors on the target cell surface, and, in turn, provides attachment sites for Factor I or Factor III, facilitating their entry into the cell. The antibody to PA is protective because it blocks the first step in toxin activity, namely, its binding to target cells.
- **Edema factor (OF or Factor I):** OF is an adenyl cyclase which is activated only inside the target cells, leading to intracellular accumulation of cyclic AMP. This is believed to be responsible for the edema and other biological effects of the toxin.
- **Lethal factor (LF or Factor III):** Entry of LF into the target cell causes cell death but the mechanism of action is not known.

ANTHRAX

Anthrax is a zoonotic infection. Animals are infected by ingestion of the spores present in the soil. Direct spread from animal to animal is rare. The disease is generally a fatal septicemia but may sometimes be localised, resembling the cutaneous disease in human beings. Infected animals shed large numbers of bacilli in discharges from the mouth, nose and rectum. These sporulate in the soil and remain as the source of infection. The spores remain viable for many years.

Human anthrax is contracted from animals, directly or indirectly. The disease may be cutaneous, pulmonary or intestinal, all types leading to fatal septicemia or meningitis.

Clinical features

Cutaneous anthrax

- This follows entry of the infection through the skin. The face, neck, hands, arms and back are the usual sites.
- The lesion starts as a papule 1–3 days after infection and becomes vesicular, containing fluid which may be clear or bloodstained (*Case*).
- The whole area is congested and edematous, and several satellite lesions filled with serum or yellow fluid are arranged around a central necrotic lesion (Fig. 26.1) which is covered by a black **eschar.** (The

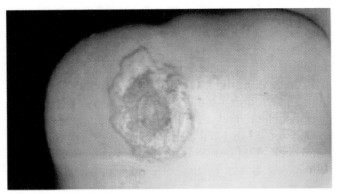

Fig. 26.1 Cutaneous lesions

name *anthrax*, which means coal, comes from the black colour of the eschar.)
- The lesion is called a **malignant pustule**.
- The disease used to be common in dock workers carrying loads of hides and skins on their bare backs and, hence, was known as the **hide porter's disease**.
- Cutaneous anthrax generally resolves spontaneously, but 10–20 per cent of untreated patients may develop fatal septicemia or meningitis.

Pulmonary anthrax
- This is called the **wool-sorter's disease** because it used to be common among workers in wool factories, due to inhalation of spores from infected wool.
- This is a hemorrhagic pneumonia with a high fatality rate.
- Hemorrhagic meningitis may occur as a complication.

Intestinal anthrax
- This is rare and occurs mainly in primitive communities who eat the carcasses of animals dying of anthrax.
- A violent enteritis with bloody diarrhea occurs, with high case fatality.

Anthrax meningitis or meningoencephalitis
This is a fatal infection which occures when the organisms enter the CNS via the bloodstream. The CSF is characteristically hemorrhagic and the condition may be mistaken for cerebrovascular accident.

Human anthrax may be **industrial** or non-industrial (agricultural). The former is found in workers in industries such as meat packing or wool factories. **Non-industrial anthrax** is often an occupational disease among those who associate frequently with animals,

such as veterinarians, butchers and farmers. It may also be found in the general population. Cutaneous anthrax used to be caused by shaving brushes made with animal hair. *Stomoxys calcitrans* and other biting insects may occasionally transmit infection mechanically.

Epidemiology

Anthrax is enzootic in India, the number of animals infected running into the tens of thousands annually. An epizootic of anthrax in sheep has been active near the Andhra Pradesh–Tamil Nadu border, causing many cutaneous and meningoencephalitic human infections, with high mortality rate. There have been outbreaks in Karnataka and West Bengal. Anthrax infection in human beings provides permanent immunity and second attacks are extremely rare.

The disease is rare in some countries such as Britain, where infection is imported through contaminated hides, bone meal fertiliser and other animal products.

> **Bioterrorism**
> *B.anthracis* is a potential tool in biological warfare and was used for the same in 2001, when it was sent by mail to various destinations in the USA, causing disease and death in many persons.

Laboratory diagnosis

Biosafety
Biosafety procedures in laboratories are very important. When an animal is suspected to have died of anthrax, autopsy is not permissible, as the spilt blood will lead to contamination of the soil. **Biosafety level II/III cabinets** are mandatory to handle such specimens.

Anthrax may be diagnosed by:

1. Specimen
- Clinical specimen: This can be fluid or pus from the lesion in cutaneous anthrax, pleural fluid, blood or CSF in inhalational or associated sepsis, and stool in case of gastrointestinal (GI) anthrax.
- In animals: An ear may be cut off from the carcass and sent to the laboratory. Alternatively, swabs soaked in blood or several blood smears may be sent.

2. Microscopy
Demonstration of Gram-positive bacilli with the morphology of anthrax bacilli, and with the characteristic spore stain (from culture isolates), can help in diagnosis. The spores do not stain by ordinary methods but can be stained differentially by special techniques:

- **M'Fadyean's reaction by polychrome methylene blue**: When blood films containing anthrax bacilli are stained with **polychrome methylene blue** for a few seconds and examined under the microscope, an amorphous purplish material is noticed around the bacilli. This represents the capsular material and is characteristic of the anthrax bacillus. This is called **M'Fadyean's reaction** and is employed for the presumptive diagnosis of anthrax in animals.
- **Sudan black B stain**: Fat globules may be made out within the bacilli.
- **Immunofluorescent microscopy** can confirm the identification.

Smears from cultures show that the bacilli are arranged end to end in long chains. The ends of the bacilli are truncated or often concave and somewhat swollen so that a chain of bacilli presents a '**bamboo stick**' appearance (Fig. 26.2).

3. Culture

Isolation of the bacillus is easy and can be done on nutrient agar, blood agar, gelatine stab culture or selective medium containing 0.05 to 0.50 units of penicillin per ml. It is an aerobe and a facultative anaerobe, with a temperature range for growth of 12–45°C (optimum 35–37°C).

- On **agar plates,** irregularly round colonies are formed, 2–3 mm in diameter, raised, dull, opaque, greyish white, with a frosted glass appearance. Under the low-power microscope, the edge of the colony is composed of long, interlacing chains of bacilli, resembling locks of matted hair. This is called the **Medusa head appearance** (Fig. 26.3). This should

Fig. 26.3 Medusa head appearance of colony on nutrient agar

not be attempted in the laboratory as the cultures are highly infectious due to the presence of spores.
- Virulent capsulated strains form rough cultures, while avirulent or attenuated strains form smooth colonies.
- On **gelatin stab culture,** a characteristic '**inverted fir tree**' appearance is seen, with slow liquefaction commencing from the top (Fig. 26.4). On blood agar, the colonies are non-hemolytic, though occasional strains produce a narrow zone of hemolysis. In broth, growth occurs as floccular deposits, with little or no turbidity.
- On **solid medium** containing 0.05–0.50 units of penicillin/ml, when *B.anthracis* is grown, in 3–6 hours, the cells become large and spherical, and

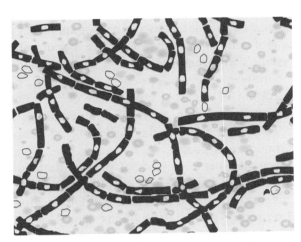

Fig. 26.2 Bamboo stick appearance on Gram staining from cultures

Fig. 26.4 Inverted fir tree appearance in gelatin stab culture

occur in chains on the surface of the agar, resembling a string of pearls. This '**string of pearls reaction**' clearly differentiates *B.anthracis* from *B.cereus* and other aerobic spore bearers. Another useful test of differentiation is the susceptibility of *B.anthracis* to gamma phage.

- A **selective medium (PLET medium)**, consisting of polymyxin, lysozyme, ethylene diamine tetraacetic acid (EDTA) and thallous acetate added to heart infusion agar, has been devised to isolate *B.anthracis* from mixtures containing other spore-bearing bacilli.

4. Biochemical reactions

Glucose, maltose and sucrose are fermented, producing acid but no gas. Nitrates are reduced to nitrites. Catalase is formed. However, these are not very useful for confirmation.

5. Animal inoculation

Experimentally, most animals are susceptible, including guinea pigs, rabbits and mice.

The anthrax bacillus can often be isolated from contaminated tissues by applying them over the shaven skin of a guinea pig. Following the subcutaneous inoculation of a culture into a guinea pig, the animal dies in 24–72 hours, showing a local, gelatinous, hemorrhagic edema at the site of inoculation, extensive subcutaneous congestion and, characteristically, an enlarged, dark red, friable spleen. The blood is dark red and coagulates less firmly than normally. The bacilli are found in large numbers in the local lesion, heart blood and spleen (more than 10^8 bacilli/ml). The bacilli are seen confined to the interior of the capillaries, where their numbers may be so great as to obstruct the flow of blood.

6. Serological demonstration

Diagnosis may be established by Ascoli's thermoprecipitin test by demonstration of the anthrax antigen in tissue extracts. **Direct fluorescent antibody test (DFA)** for capsule-specific staining and for polysaccharide cell wall antigen are now available.

7. Serology for antibodies

Acute and convalescent phase sera should be obtained, since antibodies to the organism can be demonstrated by gel diffusion, complement fixation, antigen-coated tanned red cell agglutination and ELISA techniques.

8. Molecular methods

For further confirmation, **PCR with specific primers** can be carried out.

9. Molecular typing

For epidemiological studies and strain characterisation, **MLVA (Multiple-Locus Variable number tandem repeat analysis)** or **AFLP (Amplified Fragment Length Polymorphism)** can be used. This can help in tracking the source in case of an outbreak or to monitor the spread of infection across the globe.

CDC guidelines for identification after bioterrorism threat

After the bioterrorism incidents in the USA in 2001, the **Centres for Disease Control and Prevention (CDC)** prepared **guidelines** for the identification of the anthrax bacillus.

> Any large Gram-positive bacillus with the general morphology and cultural features of anthrax—non-motile, non-hemolytic on blood agar and catalase positive—can be given a presumptive report of anthrax.

For initial confirmation, lysis by gamma phage and direct fluorescent antibody test (DFA) for capsule-specific staining and for polysaccharide cell wall antigen are sufficient.

Prophylaxis

1. Hygiene and biosafety

Prevention of human anthrax is mainly by general methods such as improvement of factory hygiene and proper sterilisation of animal products like hides and wool. Carcasses of animals suspected to have died of anthrax are buried deep in quicklime or cremated to prevent soil contamination.

2. Immunisation

Vaccines are available and used more commonly for prevention of anthrax in animals by active immunisation.

- **Pasteur's anthrax vaccine**: It is of great historical importance. It was Pasteur's convincing demonstration of the protective effect of his anthrax vaccine in a public experiment at Pouilly-le-Fort in 1881 that marked the beginning of scientific immunoprophylaxis.
- **Sterne vaccine**: It consists of spores of attenuated strains of a non-capsulated, avirulent, mutant strain. This was also used for humans but not any more.
- **Mazzucchi vaccine**: It contains spores of stable, attenuated Carbazoo strain in 2% saponin.
- **Anthrax Vaccine Adsorbed (AVA) vaccine for human use**: AVA BioThrax is a vaccine for human

use obtained from the culture of *B.anthracis* having the protective antigen.

Pre-exposure: Five doses to be given only to high risk people who are likely to be exposed followed by boosters.

Post-exposure: It is given after exposure to inhalation anthrax along with antibiotics.

Treatment

CDC has issued updated guidelines on anthrax post-exposure (PEP) and treatment

Recommendations include the following:

1. Uncomplicated cutaneous anthrax can be treated with a single oral agent—fluoroquinolones or doxycycline for 7–14 days.
2. For patients suspected to have systemic anthrax, antitoxin should be added to combination antimicrobial drug treatment.
3. Antitoxin (antibody against protective antigen) is used with antibiotics
   - Human anthrax immunoglobulin (Anthrasil)
   - Monoclonal antibodies to protective antigen— Obiltoxaximab or Roxibacumab

   These are indicated in severe cases with systemic involvement, such as inhalational anthrax as antibiotics have no effect on the toxin once it is formed.
4. Anthrax meningitis should include at least three antimicrobial drugs including clindamycin and a full 60 days of antibiotic treatment, regardless of their vaccine strains.
5. **Post-exposure prophylaxis (PEP)** for inhalation anthrax in adults—ciprofloxacin and doxycycline are first-line treatments for 60 days along with vaccine (AVABioThrax).

ANTHRACOID BACILLI

Many members of the genus *Bacillus*, other than the anthrax bacillus, have occasionally caused human infections. Of them, the most important is *B.cereus*, which from 1970 has been recognised as a frequent cause of food-borne gastroenteritis. It has also been associated with septicemia, meningitis, endocarditis, pneumonia, wound infections and other suppurative lesions, particularly as an opportunist pathogen. *B.subtilis*, *B.licheniformis* and a few other species have also occasionally been isolated from such lesions. These and a large number and variety of non-pathogenic, aerobic, spore-bearing bacilli that appear as common contaminants in cultures and have a general resemblance to the anthrax bacilli have been collectively called **pseudoanthrax** or **anthracoid bacilli**. Table 26.1 lists the main differentiating features between them.

Table 26.1 *Differentiating features between anthrax and anthracoid bacilli*

S.No	Anthrax bacilli	Anthracoid bacilli
1	Non-motile	Generally motile
2	Capsulated	Non-capsulated
3	Grow in long chains	Grow in short chains
4	Medusa head colony	Not present
5	No growth in penicillin agar (10 units/ml)	Grow usually
6	Hemolysis absent or weak	Usually well-marked
7	Inverted fir tree growth and slow gelatin liquefaction	Rapid liquefaction
8	No turbidity in broth	Turbidity usual
9	Salicin fermentation negative	Usually positive
10	No growth at 45°C	Usually grows
11	Growth inhibited by chloral hydrate	Not inhibited
12	Susceptible to gamma phage	Not susceptible
13	Pathogenic to laboratory animals	Not pathogenic

BACILLUS CEREUS

B.cereus has become an important cause of food poisoning. It is widely distributed in nature and may be readily isolated from soil, vegetables and a wide variety of foods including milk, cereals, spices, meat and poultry. *B.cereus* is generally motile but non-motile strains may occur. It resembles *B.anthracis*, except that it is not capsulated and not susceptible to gamma phage and does not react with anthrax fluorescent antibody conjugate. The animal pathogenicity test is also used to differentiate between the two.

Patterns of food-borne disease

Two types of food poisoning have been associated with *B.cereus*:

1. Diarrheic type
2. Emetic type

- The **diarrheal type** is associated with a **wide range of foods** including cooked meat and vegetables. It is characterised by diarrhea and abdominal pain, 8–16 hours after ingestion of contaminated foods. Vomiting is rare. *B.cereus* is not found in large numbers in fecal specimens from these patients. The diarrheal disease is **mostly** caused by serotypes 2, 6, 8, 9, 10 or 12.

- The **emetic type** is associated almost exclusively with the **consumption of cooked rice**, usually fried rice from Chinese restaurants. The illness is characterised by acute nausea and vomiting 1–5 hours after the meal. Diarrhea is not common. *B.cereus* is present in large numbers in the cooked rice and fecal samples from these patients. This is caused by serotypes 1, 3 or 5. The emetic toxin is produced only when *B.cereus* is grown in rice but not in other media.

Two mechanisms of action have been described for the enterotoxin of *B.cereus*, one involving stimulation of the cyclic adenosine monophosphate (cAMP) system and the other independent of it.

Diagnosis

A special mannitol – egg yolk – phenol red – poly-myxin agar (**MYPA**) medium is useful in isolating *B.cereus* from feces and other sources. *B.cereus* produces lecithinase and ferments glucose but not mannitol. **For diagnosis, the presence of 10^5 or more bacteria per gram of stool is diagnostic, as anything less than that may be present as normal flora in the gut.**

Treatment

Both types of illness are mild and self-limiting, requiring no specific treatment.

BACILLUS SPECIES AS STERILISATION INDICATORS (CONTROLS)

Many *Bacillus* species are used as biological indictors in sterilisation controls (see Chapter 3 on disinfection and sterilisation).

RECAP

- Bacteria of the genus *Bacillus* are ubiquitous organisms found in the soil, water, airborne dust and even human intestines. These aerobic, Gram-positive bacilli form spores and are catalase-positive. *B.anthracis* is non-motile, but other species, including *Bacillus cereus*, are motile.
- *Bacillus anthracis* and *Bacillus cereus* cause significant pathology.
- *Bacillus anthracis* causes anthrax, a zoonotic infection. Anthrax manifests as cutaneous type (black lesion, 'eschar'), pulmonary type or gastrointestinal type.
- Diagnosis is by microscopy—for example, staining with characteristic M'Fadyean's reaction—is employed for the presumptive diagnosis of anthrax in animals.
- In culture on blood agar plates, large, spreading, grey-white, non-hemolytic colonies with irregular margins are formed (Medusa head colonies). Under the microscope, these organisms are non-motile and appear to have square ends and to be attached by a joint to other cells (bamboo stick appearance).
- For control, protect against exposure to spores in hides of domestic livestock (goats). Deep burial in lime pits or burning of animal carcasses is recommended.
- Exposed persons must be treated with ciprofloxacin or doxycycline; vaccinate against PA where exposure is a risk. Antitoxin is indicated in severe disease.
- *Bacillus cereus* occurs worldwide. It causes food poisoning, manifested by vomiting and diarrhea.
- The enterotoxin may be preformed in stool, causing emetic type of presentation, or produced in the intestines, causing diarrheal type of illness.
- The presence of 10^5 or more bacteria per gram of stool is diagnostic as less than that may be present as normal flora in the gut.
- Control is by proper preparation of food. Vegetative bacterial cells are killed by heating. However, spores withstand boiling for more than one hour.

ESSAYS

1. What are zoonotic diseases? Give examples. Explain the epidemiology and laboratory diagnosis of any one bacterial zoonotic disease.
2. Describe the laboratory diagnosis of anthrax.
3. Describe the pathogenesis of food poisoning due to *B.cereus*.

SHORT ANSWERS

1. Four differentiating features of *B.anthracis* and other *Bacillius* species
2. M'Fadyean reaction
3. Virulence factors of *B.anthracis*

SHORT NOTES

1. Malignant pustule
2. Diseases caused by the *Bacillus* species

27 Anaerobic Bacteria I: Clostridium

INTRODUCTION

The genus *Clostridium* consists of Gram-positive, anaerobic, **spore-forming bacilli**. The genus contains bacteria responsible for **gas gangrene** (*see clinical case*), **food poisoning, tetanus and botulism**. Some of the pathogens, for example, *C.perfringens* and *C.tetani*, are found normally in human and animal intestines. Intestinal clostridia rapidly invade the blood and tissues of the host after death and initiate decomposition of the cadaver. Most species are saprophytes found in soil, water, decomposing plant and animal matter.

Classification

- **Molecular:** Currently based on 16SrRNA gene sequences, 19 clusters are identified, of which clinically relevant species belong to cluster 1.

Clostridium perfringens

Clinical Case A 50-year-old man had a road traffic accident while travelling in a remote village area. He sustained multiple fractures with open wounds in the left leg. After being brought to the nearest hospital two days later, he was found to be in shock. The wound was contaminated with soil and blood; the local muscles appeared to have been crushed. He was started on supportive therapy and antibiotics, but after two days, the edema and pain at the site increased and a serous discharge developed. When the area around the wound was palpated, crepitations were felt. Microscopic examination of the wound discharge showed the presence of thick, brick-shaped, Gram-positive bacilli along with Gram-positive cocci. Based on a provisional diagnosis of gas gangrene, immediate surgical treatment was carried out. The exudate was also inoculated into Robertson's cooked meat medium and cultured for anerobic bacteria. *Clostridium perfringens* and peptostreptococci grew in the culture. Extensive excision of the local area had to be carried out to prevent further spread.

- **Phenotypic:** However, conventional classification based on morphology, culture and biochemicals is commonly used in laboratories.

Morphology

Clostridia are highly pleomorphic, usually 3–8 × 0.4–1.2 µm in size, Gram-positive rods. Cells are often Gram-variable in older cultures (as also seen in the genus *Bacillus*). Long filaments and involution forms are common. Clostridia are motile with peritrichate flagella, with few exceptions such as *C.perfringens* and *C.tetani* type VI which are non-motile. Motility is slow and has been described as 'stately'. *C.perfringens* and *C.butyricum* are capsulated, while others are not.

Spores

The spores are wider than the bacillary bodies, giving the bacillus a swollen appearance, resembling a spindle—hence, the name *Clostridium* (from *kloster*, meaning spindle). Spore formation occurs with varying frequency in different species, most spores being wider than the bacillary body (Fig. 27.1). Some (such as *C.sporogenes*) sporulate readily while others (such as *C.perfringens*) do so inconstantly. Sporulation also takes place in the animal body. The shape and position of spores vary in different species and these are of use in the identification and classification of clostridia. Spores may be:

- **Central or equatorial**, giving the bacillus a spindle shape (*C.bifermentans*)

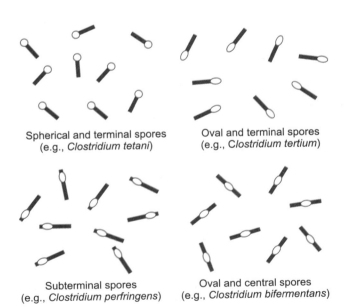

Spherical and terminal spores
(e.g., *Clostridium tetani*)

Oval and terminal spores
(e.g., *Clostridium tertium*)

Subterminal spores
(e.g., *Clostridium perfringens*)

Oval and central spores
(e.g., *Clostridium bifermentans*)

Fig. 27.1   Types of spores

- **Subterminal**, the bacillus appearing club-shaped (*C.perfringens*)
- **Oval and terminal**, resembling a tennis racket (*C.tertium*)
- **Spherical and terminal**, giving a drumstick appearance (*C.tetani*)

Resistance in spores: The spores exhibit a pronounced but variable resistance to heat, drying and disinfectants. The vegetative cells of clostridia do not differ from those of non-sporing bacilli in their resistance to physical and chemical agents.

Spores of *C.botulinum* survive boiling after 3–4 hours and, even at 105°C, they are not killed completely in less than 100 minutes. Spores of most strains of *C.perfringens* are destroyed by boiling for less than five minutes but spores of some type A strains that cause food poisoning survive for several hours. *C.tetani* spores persist for years in dried earth. Spores of some strains of *C.tetani* resist boiling for 15–90 minutes, though in most cases, they are destroyed within five minutes. All species are **killed by autoclaving** at 121°C within 20 minutes.

Disinfectants: Spores are particularly resistant to phenolic disinfectants. Formaldehyde is not very active and spores may sometimes survive immersion in a 2% solution for up to five days. Halogens are effective and 1% aqueous iodine solution kills spores within three hours. Glutaraldehyde (2% at pH 7.5–8.5) is very effective in killing the spores.

Cultural characteristics

Clostridia are anaerobic. The sensitivity to oxygen varies in different species. Some (for example, *C.novyi*) are exacting anaerobes and die on exposure to oxygen, while others (for example, *C.histolyticum*) are aerotolerant and may even grow aerobically. **Of greater importance than the absence of oxygen, is the provision of a sufficiently low redox potential (Eh) in the medium.** This can be achieved by adding reducing substances such as unsaturated fatty acids, ascorbic acid, glutathione, cysteine, thioglycolic acid, alkaline glucose, sulphites or metallic iron. A small concentration of CO_2 appears to enhance growth. The optimum temperature for pathogenic clostridia is 37°C. Some saprophytic clostridia are thermophilic while others are psychrophilic. The optimum pH required for growth is 7–7.4.

Growth is relatively slow on solid media. Colonial characteristics are variable. Some species are hemolytic on **blood agar**.

Robertson's cooked meat broth is a very useful medium. It contains unsaturated fatty acids which take up oxygen, the reaction being catalysed by hematin in the meat, and also sulphydryl compounds which bring about a reduced oxidation reduction (OR) potential. Clostridia grow in the medium, rendering the broth turbid. Most species produce gas. The saccharolytic species turns meat pink, while proteolytic species turn it black, producing foul and pervasive odours.

Production of acid, clot and gas can be detected in **litmus milk medium**.

Many methods have been adopted for the classification of clostridia. These include morphological features such as the shape and position of spores and biochemical features such as saccharolytic and proteolytic capacities (Table 27.1). Clostridia of medical importance may also be categorised based on the diseases they produce (see below).

Pathogenicity

Clostridia can produce disease only when the conditions are appropriate. Their invasive powers are limited:

- **Exotoxin**: Pathogenic clostridia form powerful exotoxins. *C.botulinum* bacilli are virtually non-invasive and non-infectious. Botulism is caused by the ingestion of preformed toxin in food.
- **Invasive**: *C.tetani* has little invasive property and is confined to the primary site of lodgement. Tetanus results from the action of the potent exotoxin it produces.
- **Invasive toxin**: *C.perfringens*, besides being toxigenic, is also invasive and can spread along tissues and even cause septicemia.

CLOSTRIDIUM PERFRINGENS

(*C.welchii, Bacillus aerogenes capsulatus, B.phlegmonis emphysematosae*)

C.perfringens is a normal inhabitant of the large intestine of humans and animals. It is found in the feces and contaminates the skin of the perineum, buttocks and thighs. The spores are commonly found in soil, dust and air.

The bacillus was originally cultivated by Achalme (1891) but was first described in detail by Welch and Nuttall (1892), who isolated it from the blood and organs of a cadaver.

This is the most important of the clostridia causing **gas gangrene**. It also produces food poisoning and necrotic enteritis in human beings and many serious diseases in animals.

Spores: Spores are usually destroyed within five minutes by boiling but those of the 'food poisoning' strains of type A and certain type C strains resist boiling for 1–3 hours. Autoclaving at 121°C for 15 minutes is lethal. Spores are resistant to the antiseptics and disinfectants in common use.

Pathogenicity

Virulence factors

C.perfringens strains are classified into five types, A to E, based on the toxins they produce. Typing is done by neutralisation tests with specific antitoxins by intracutaneous injections in guinea pigs or intravenous injection in mice.

Toxins: *C.perfringens* is one of the most prolific of toxin-producing bacteria, forming at least 12 distinct toxins, besides many other enzymes and biologically

Table 27.1   *A morphological and biochemical classification of clostridia*

Position of spores	Both proteolytic and saccharolytic		Slightly proteolytic but not saccharolytic	Saccharolytic but not proteolytic	Neither proteolytic nor saccharolytic
	Proteolytic predominating	Saccharolytic predominating			
Central or subterminal	C.bifermentans C.botulinum A, B, F C.histolyticum C.sordelli C.sporogenes	C.perfringens C.septicum C.chauvoei C.novyi		C.fallax C.botulinum C, D, E	
Oval and terminal Spherical and terminal	— —	C.difficile —	— C.tetani	C.tertium C.tetanomorphum C.sphenoides	C.cochlearum

active soluble substances. The four 'major toxins', alpha, beta, epsilon and iota, are predominantly responsible for pathogenicity (Table 27.2).

Major toxins

- The **alpha (α) toxin** is produced by all types of *C.perfringens* and most abundantly by type A strains. This is the most important toxin biologically and is responsible for the profound toxemia of gas gangrene. It is lethal, dermonecrotic and hemolytic. It is a phospholipidase (lecithinase C) which, in the presence of Ca^{++} and Mg^{++} ions, splits lecithin into phosphoryl choline and diglyceride. This reaction is seen as opalescence in **serum** or **egg yolk media** and is specifically neutralised by the antitoxin as described under **Nagler's reaction.**
- **Beta (β), epsilon (ε)** and **iota (ι) toxins** have lethal and necrotising properties.

Minor toxins

- **Gamma (γ)** and **eta (η) toxins** have minor lethal action.
- **Delta (δ) toxin** has a lethal effect and is hemolytic for the red cells of even-toed ungulates (sheep, goats, pigs, cattle).
- **Theta (θ) toxin** is an oxygen-labile hemolysin antigenically related to streptolysin O. It is also lethal and a general cytolytic toxin.
- **Kappa (κ) toxin** is a collagenase.
- **Lambda (λ) toxin** is a proteinase and gelatinase.
- **mu (μ) toxin** is a hyaluronidase,
- **nu (ν) toxin** is a deoxyribonuclease.

Enzymes: Besides the toxins, *C.perfringens* also produces other soluble substances. These include:

- Enzymes that destroy the blood group substance, A and H

- A neuraminidase which destroys myxovirus receptors on red blood cells
- A substance that renders red blood cells panagglutinable by exposing their T antigens
- A hemagglutinin active against the red blood cells of human beings and most animals
- A fibrinolysin
- A hemolysin distinct from the alpha, theta and delta toxins
- Histamine
- A **bursting factor** which has a specific action on muscle tissue and may be responsible for the characteristic muscle lesions in gas gangrene
- A **circulating factor** which can cause an increase in the adrenaline sensitivity of the capillary bed and also inhibit phagocytosis

Clinical manifestations

C.perfringens produces the following human infections:

Gas gangrene

C.perfringens type A is the predominant agent causing gas gangrene. It may occur as the sole causative agent but is more commonly seen in association with other clostridia as well as non-clostridial anaerobes and even aerobes. All clostridial wound infections do not result in gas gangrene. More commonly, they lead only to wound contamination or anaerobic cellulitis. It is only when muscle tissues are invaded that gas gangrene (**anaerobic myositis**) results.

Food poisoning

Some strains of type A can produce food poisoning. They are characterised by marked heat resistance of their spores and the feeble production of alpha and theta

Table 27.2 *Toxins produced by* C.perfringens *types*

Type	Pathogenicity	Major toxins				Minor toxins							
		α	β	ε	ι	γ	δ	η	θ	κ	λ	μ	ν
A.	Gas gangrene: wound infections, septicemia	+++	−	−	−	−	−	±	±	±	−	±	±
	Food poisoning	+++	−	−	−	−	−	−	±	±	−	±	++
B.	Lamb dysentery	+++	+++	++	−	+	±	−	++	−	+++	+++	++
C.	Enteritis in animals Enteritis necroticans in human beings	+++	+++	−	−	−	−	−	+++	+++	−	−	±
		+++	++	−	−	++	−	−	−	−	−	−	+++
D.	Enterotoxemia of sheep	+++	−	+++	−	−	−	−	++	++	++	±	±
E.	Doubtful pathogen of sheep and cattle	+++	−	−	+++	−	−	−	++	++	++	±	±

toxins. They have been shown to produce a **heat labile enterotoxin** which, like the enterotoxins of *V.cholerae* and enterotoxigenic *E.coli*, leads to fluid accumulation in the rabbit ileal loop.

Food poisoning by *C.perfringens* is usually caused by a cold or warmed up meat dish. When contaminated meat is cooked, the spores in the interior may survive. During storage or warming, they germinate and multiply in the anaerobic environment of the cooked meat. Large numbers of clostridia may thus be consumed, which may pass unharmed by gastric acid due to the high protein content of the meat and reach the intestines where they produce the enterotoxin. After an incubation period of 8–24 hours, abdominal pain, diarrhea and vomiting set in. **Diagnosis** is made by isolating heat-resistant *C.perfringens* type A from feces and food. As this may be present in normal intestine, isolation from feces, except in large numbers, is not meaningful. Isolation from food has to be attempted by direct plating on selective media, as the bacillus is present in food mainly as vegetative cells.

Treatment: The illness is self-limiting and recovery occurs in 24–48 hours.

Gangrenous appendicitis

C.perfringens **type A** (and **occasionally type D**) strains have been isolated from gangrenous appendicitis. Demonstration of antitoxin in these patients and the beneficial effects of the administration of antitoxin also suggest the causative role of the bacillus in this condition. It has been proposed that the toxemia and shock in some cases of intestinal obstruction and peritonitis may be due to the toxins of *C.perfringens*.

Necrotising enteritis

This is a severe and often fatal enteritis. It is caused by *C.perfringens* **type C** strains with heat-resistant spores which germinate in the intestine producing beta toxin, causing mucosal necrosis. The evocative name 'pigbel' is New Guinea pidgin for abdominal pain and diarrhea following unaccustomed feasting on pig meat along with trypsin inhibitors like sweet potatoes. Immunisation with the type C toxoid has been shown to protect against this condition.

Biliary tract infection

C.perfringens has been reported to produce two rare but serious infections of the biliary tract: **acute emphysematous cholecystitis** and **post-cholecystectomy septicemia.**

Endogenous gas gangrene of intra-abdominal origin

Gas gangrene of the abdominal wall has been reported as an infrequent complication of abdominal surgery. The infection is endogenous, the organism being derived from the gut and contaminating the abdominal wall during surgery. Gas gangrene of the thigh as a result of infection tracking from the abdomen has also been reported.

Brain abscess and meningitis

Brain abscess and meningitis due to *C.perfringens* have been reported very rarely.

Panophthalmitis

Panophthalmitis due to *C.perfringens* has occasionally followed penetrating eye injuries.

Thoracic infections

Clostridial infection of the chest cavity may follow penetrating wounds of the thorax. This is more often seen in battle casualties than in civilian situations.

Urogenital infections

Infection of the urinary tract may occasionally follow surgical procedures such as nephrectomy. Clostridial infection of the uterus is a serious and not infrequent condition, commonly associated with septic abortion. Septicemia is common in this condition.

CLOSTRIDIUM SEPTICUM

This bacteria was first described by Pasteur and Joubert (1887) and called *Vibrion septique*. It is a pleomorphic bacillus, about $3–8 \times 0.6$ μm in size, forming oval, central or subterminal spores. It is motile by peritrichate flagella. Growth occurs anaerobically on ordinary media. The colonies are initially irregular and transparent, turning opaque on continued incubation. Hemolysis occurs on horse blood agar. Growth is promoted by glucose. It is saccharolytic and produces abundant gas.

Virulence factors

Six groups have been recognised, based on somatic and flagellar antigens.

- *C.septicum* produces at least four distinct toxins. The alpha toxin is hemolytic, dermonecrotic and lethal, the beta toxin is a leucotoxic deoxyribonuclease, the gamma toxin a hyaluronidase and the delta toxin an oxygen-labile hemolysin.

- It produces a fibrinolysin.

C.septicum is found in the soil or in animal intestines. It is associated with gas gangrene in humans, usually in association with other clostridia. It also causes 'braxy' in sheep and 'malignant edema' in cattle and sheep.

CLOSTRIDIUM NOVYI (C.OEDEMATIENS)

This is a large, stout, pleomorphic, Gram-positive bacillus with large, oval, subterminal spores. It is widely distributed in soil. It is a strict anaerobe, readily inactivated on exposure to air. Four types (A to D) are recognised, based on the production of toxins. **Only type A is of medical importance, as it causes gas gangrene.** Gas gangrene caused by *C.novyi* is characterised by high mortality and large amounts of edema fluid with little or no observable gas in infected tissue. Other types produce veterinary disease. There was a lethal outbreak of *C.novyi* type A infection among heroin addicts in Britain in 2000.

CLOSTRIDIUM HISTOLYTICUM

This is an actively proteolytic clostridium, forming oval, subterminal, bulging spores. This is aerotolerant and some growth may occur even in aerobic cultures. It forms at least five distinct toxins. It is infrequently associated with **gas gangrene in humans**.

GAS GANGRENE

Oakley (1954) defined gas gangrene as a rapidly spreading, edematous myonecrosis, occurring characteristically in association with severe wounds of extensive muscle masses contaminated with pathogenic clostridia, particularly *C.perfringens*. The disease has been referred to in the past as malignant edema. Other descriptive terms are **anaerobic (clostridial) myositis** and **clostridial myonecrosis (Fig. 27.2)**.

Gas gangrene is characteristically a disease of war, in which extensive wounds with heavy contamination are very common. In civilian life, the disease generally follows road accidents or other types of injury involving crushing of large muscle mass. Rarely, it may follow surgical operations.

Fig. 27.2 Gas gangrene of the lower limb showing edema and discoloured skin

Polymicrobial etiology

The bacteriology of gas gangrene is varied. Rarely is this due to infection by a single clostridium. Generally, several species of clostridia are found in association with anaerobic streptococci and facultative anaerobes such as *E.coli*, proteus and staphylococci. Among the pathogenic clostridia, **C.perfringens** is the most frequently encountered (approximately 60 per cent), with **C.novyi and C.septicum** next (20–40 per cent) and **C.histolyticum** less often. Other clostridia usually found are *C.sporogenes, C.fallax, C.bifermentans, C.sordellii, C.aerofoetidum* and *C.tertium*. These may not be pathogenic by themselves.

Pathogenesis

The infection can be exogenous or endogenous:
- **Exogenous:** Clostridia usually enter the wound along with implanted foreign particles such as soil (particularly manured or cultivated soil), road dust, bits of clothing or shrapnel. They may also be present on normal skin, especially on the perineum and thighs.
- **Endogenous:** Infection may be seen after clean surgical procedures (especially amputations for vascular disease) and even injections (especially adrenaline).

MacLennan has distinguished three types of anaerobic wound infections:
- **Simple wound contamination** with no invasion of the underlying tissue, resulting in little more than some delay in wound healing.
- **Anaerobic cellulitis** in which clostridia invade the fascial planes, with minimal toxin production and no invasion of muscle tissues. The disease is gradual in onset and may vary from a limited 'gas abscess' to extensive involvement of a limb.

- **Anaerobic myositis** or gas gangrene, which is the most serious, associated with clostridial invasion of healthy muscle tissues and abundant formation of exotoxins.

Gas gangrene results only if the conditions favourable for clostridial multiplication exist in the wound. The most important of these is low oxygen tension. The ionised calcium salts and silicic acid in the soil cause necrosis. Crushing tissue or tearing of the arteries produces anoxia of the muscle. Extravasation of blood increases the pressure on the capillaries, reducing blood supply still further. The Eh and pH of the damaged tissues fall, and these changes along with the chemical changes that occur within the damaged and anoxic muscles, including breakdown of carbohydrates and liberation of amino acids from proteins, provide ideal pabulum for the proliferation of anaerobes. Extravasated hemoglobin and myohemoglobin are reduced and cease to act as oxygen carriers. As a result, aerobic oxidation is halted and anaerobic reduction of pyruvate to lactate leads to a further fall in Eh.

The clostridia multiply and elaborate toxins which cause further tissue damage. The lecithinases damage cell membranes and increase capillary permeability, leading to extravasation and increased tension in the affected muscles, causing further anoxic damage. The hemolytic anemia and hemoglobinuria seen in *C.perfringens* infections are due to the lysis of erythrocytes by the alpha toxin. The collagenases destroy collagen barriers in the tissues and hyaluronidases break down the intercellular substances, furthering invasive spread by the clostridia. The abundant production of gas reduces blood supply still further by pressure effects, extending the area of anoxic damage. It thus becomes possible for the infection to spread from the original site, making the lesion a progressive one.

Clinical presentation

The incubation period may be as short as seven hours or as long as six weeks after the wound was created, the average being 10–48 hours with *C.perfringens*, 2–3 days with *C.septicum* and 5–6 days with *C.novyi* infection. The disease develops with increasing pain, tenderness and edema of the affected part along with systemic signs of toxemia. There is a thin, watery discharge from the wound, which later becomes profuse and serosanguinous. Accumulation of gas makes the tissues crepitant (*Case*). In untreated cases, the disease process extends rapidly and inexorably. Profound tox-

emia and prostration develop and death occurs due to circulatory failure.

Laboratory diagnosis

The diagnosis of gas gangrene must be made primarily on clinical grounds, and the function of the laboratory is only to provide confirmation of the clinical diagnosis and identification and enumeration of the infecting organisms. **The mere presence of clostridia in wounds does not constitute gas gangrene.**

> Bacteriological examination also helps to differentiate gas gangrene from anaerobic streptococcal myositis, which may be indistinguishable from it clinically in the early stages. (In the latter, Gram-stained films show large numbers of streptococci and pus cells but not bacilli, contrasting with the scanty pus cells and diverse bacterial flora seen in films from gas gangrene.)

1. Specimens
- **Films from the muscles** at the edge of the affected area, from the tissue in the necrotic area and from the exudate in the deeper parts of the wound
- Exudates from the parts where infection appears to be most active and from the depths of the wound may be collected with a capillary pipette or a swab (which must be soaked in the exudate).
- Necrotic tissue and muscle fragments
- **Blood cultures** may be required as they are often positive, especially in *C.perfringens* and *C.septicum* infections. However, *C.perfringens* bacteremia may occur without gas gangrene.

2. Microscopic examination
Gram-stained films provide presumptive information about the species of clostridia present and their relative numbers. The presence of large numbers of **regularly brick-shaped, Gram-positive bacilli without spores** is strongly suggestive of *C.perfringens* infection (Fig. 27.3). 'Citron bodies' and boat- or leaf-shaped pleomorphic bacilli with irregular staining suggest *C.septicum*. Large bacilli with oval, subterminal spores indicate *C.novyi*. Slender bacilli with round, terminal spores may be *C.tetani* or *C.tetanomorphum*.

3. Culture
It is an anaerobe but can also grow under microaerophilic conditions. Oxygen is not actively toxic to the bacillus and cultures do not die on exposure to air, as happens with some fastidious anaerobes. It grows over a pH range of 5.5–8.0 and temperature range of

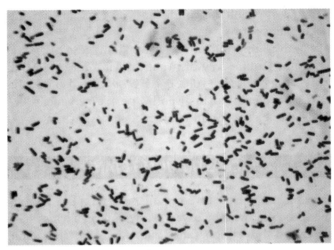

Fig. 27.3 Gram stain of *Clostridium perfringens* in gas gangrene: note the absence of spores

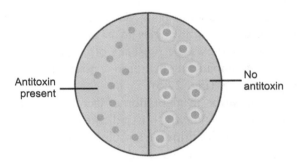

Fig. 27.4 Nagler's reaction

20–50°C. Though usually grown at 37°C, a temperature of 45°C is optimal for many strains. The generation time at this temperature may be as short as ten minutes. This property can be utilised for obtaining pure cultures of *C.perfringens*.

Aerobic and anaerobic cultures are made on:

- **Fresh and heated blood agar**: The colonies on overnight incubation on rabbit, sheep or human blood agar, show **target hemolysis**, resulting from a narrow zone of complete hemolysis due to theta toxin and a much wider zone of incomplete hemolysis due to the alpha toxin. This double zone pattern of hemolysis may fade on longer incubation.
- **Gram stain** shows plump, Gram-positive bacillus with straight, parallel sides and rounded or truncated ends, about 4–6 × 1 μm in size, usually occurring singly or in chains or small bundles. It is pleomorphic, and filamentous and involution forms are common. It is capsulated and non-motile. Spores are central or subterminal but are rarely seen in artificial culture or in material from pathological lesions, and their absence is one of the characteristic morphological features of *C.perfringens*.
- A plate of **serum or egg yolk agar**, with *C.perfringens* antitoxin spread on one half, is used for the **Nagler's reaction** (Fig. 27.4).

Nagler's reaction: When *C.perfringens* is grown on a medium containing 6% agar, 5% Fildes' peptic digest of sheep blood and 20% human serum, with the antitoxin spread on one half of the plate, colonies on the other half without the antitoxin will be surrounded by a zone of opacity. There will be no opacity around the colonies on the half of the plate with the antitoxin, due to the specific neutralisation of the alpha toxin. This specific lecithinase effect, known as the **Nagler's reaction**, is a useful test for the rapid detection of *C.perfringens* in clinical specimens. The incorporation of neomycin sulphate in the medium makes it more selective, inhibiting coliforms and aerobic spore bearers. Human serum may be replaced by 5% egg yolk. The opalescence in the egg yolk media may be produced by other lecithinase-forming bacteria also (*C.novyi, C.bifermentans*, some vibrios, some aerobic spore bearers). In the case of these bacteria, the reaction is not neutralised by the *C.perfringens* antitoxin, except with *C.bifermentans* which produces a serologically related lecithinase.

The alpha toxin is hemolytic for the red cells of most species, except horse and goat, due to its action on the phospholipids on the erythrocyte membranes. Lysis is of the hot–cold variety, being best seen after incubation at 37°C followed by cooling at 4°C. The toxin is relatively heat-stable and is only partially inactivated by boiling for five minutes.

- **Robertson's cooked meat medium**: This is the most commonly used medium serving as transport as well as culture media. The meat is turned pink but is not digested. The culture has an acid reaction and a sour odour. Four tubes of Robertson's cooked meat broth are inoculated and heated at 100°C for 5, 10, 15 and 20 minutes, incubated and subcultured on blood agar plates after 24–48 hours, to differentiate the organisms with heat-resistant spores. Robertson's cooked meat broth inoculated with mixtures of *C.perfringens* and other bacteria and incubated at 45°C for 4–6 hours serves as enrichment. Subcultures from this transferred to blood agar plates yield pure or predominant growth of *C.perfringens*.

The **reverse CAMP test** is used to identify *C.perfringens*; in this test, *C.perfringens* is streaked over the centre of the plate. *Streptococcus agalactiae* is streaked at right angles to it. A positive reverse CAMP test shows the presence of an arrow-shaped zone of enhanced hemolysis pointing towards *C.perfringens* (Fig. 27.5).

- In **litmus milk**, fermentation of lactose leads to the formation of acid, which is indicated by the change in colour of the litmus from blue to red. The acid coagulates the casein (acid clot) and the clotted milk is disrupted due to vigorous gas production. The paraffin plug is pushed up and shreds of clot are seen sticking to the sides of the tube. This is known as **stormy clot formation**.

Biochemical reactions: In *C. perfringens*, glucose, maltose, lactose and sucrose are fermented with the production of acid and gas. It is indole-negative, MR-positive and VP-negative. H_2S is formed abundantly. Most strains reduce nitrates.

Prophylaxis and treatment

- **Surgery** is the most important prophylactic and therapeutic measure in gas gangrene. All damaged tissue should be removed promptly and the wounds irrigated to remove blood clots, necrotic tissue and foreign materials. In established gas gangrene, uncompromising excision of all affected parts may be life-saving. Where facilities exist, **hyperbaric oxygen** may be beneficial in treatment.
- **Antibiotics** are effective in prophylaxis, in combination with surgical methods. The drug of choice **is metronidazole given intravenously** before surgery and repeated every eight hours for 24 hours. As mixed aerobic and anaerobic infections are usual, it should be combined with clindamycin and cephalosporins.
- **Passive immunisation** with 'anti–gas gangrene serum' (equine polyvalent antitoxin in a dose of 10,000 IU *C.perfringens*, 10,000 IU *C.novyi* and 5,000 IU *C.septicum* antitoxin given IM or in emergencies IV) used to be the common practice in prophylaxis.

CLOSTRIDIUM TETANI

C.tetani is the causative organism of tetanus. Tetanus has been known since very early times, having been described by Hippocrates and Aretaeus. The final proof of the etiological role of the bacillus in tetanus was furnished by Kitasato (1889) who isolated it in pure culture and reproduced the disease in animals by inoculation of pure cultures.

C.tetani is widely distributed in soil and in the intestines of humans and animals. It is ubiquitous and has been recovered from a wide variety of other sources, including street and hospital dust, cotton wool, plaster of Paris, bandages, catgut, talc, wall plaster and clothing. It may occur as an apparently harmless contaminant in wounds.

Morphology

It is a Gram-positive, slender bacillus, about 4–8 × 0.5 μm in size, though there may be considerable variation in length. It has a straight axis, parallel sides and rounded ends. It occurs singly and occasionally in chains. The spores are spherical, terminal and bulging, giving the bacillus the characteristic '**drumstick**' **appearance** (Fig. 27.6). The morphology of the spore

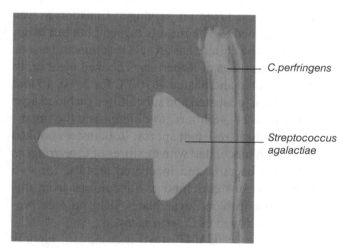

C.perfringens

Streptococcus agalactiae

Fig. 27.5 Reverse CAMP test.

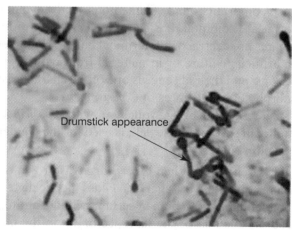

Drumstick appearance

Fig. 27.6 *C.tetani*: drumstick appearance on Gram stain

depends on its stage of development and the young spore may be oval rather than spherical. It is non-capsulated and motile by peritrichate flagella. Young cultures are strongly Gram-positive but older cells show variable staining and may even be Gram-negative.

Spores

Spores can survive in soil for years.

Resistance

The resistance of tetanus spores to heat appears to be subject to strain differences. Most are killed by boiling for 10–15 minutes but some resist boiling for up to three hours. When destruction of spores is to be ensured, autoclaving at 121°C for 20 minutes is recommended. On the other hand, when heat is applied to free cultures of *C.tetani* from non-sporing contaminants, it is important not to exceed 80°C for 10 minutes, as even this mild treatment can cause considerable destruction. They are resistant to most antiseptics.

Disinfectants

They are not destroyed by 5% phenol or 0.1% mercuric chloride solution in two weeks or more. Iodine (1% aqueous solution) and hydrogen peroxide (10 volumes) kill the spores within a few hours.

Classification

Ten serological types have been recognised based on agglutination (**types I to X**). Type VI contains non-flagellated strains. All other types possess type-specific flagellar antigens. All the types produce the same toxin, which is neutralised by antitoxin produced against any one type.

Pathogenicity

C.tetani has little invasive power. Washed spores injected into experimental animals do not germinate and are destroyed by phagocytes. Germination and toxin production occur only if favourable conditions exist, such as reduced OR potential, devitalised tissues, foreign bodies or concurrent infection. The toxin produced locally is absorbed by the motor nerve endings and transported to the central nervous system intra-axonally. The toxin is specifically and avidly fixed by gangliosides of the grey matter of the nervous tissue.

Toxins

C.tetani produces at least two distinct toxins—**a hemolysin (tetanolysin)** and a powerful **neurotoxin (tetanospasmin).** The two are antigenically and pharmacologically distinct and their production is mutually independent. A third toxin, a non-spasmogenic, peripherally active neurotoxin, has been identified. It is not known whether this plays any role in the pathogenesis of tetanus.

Tetanospasmin: This is the toxin responsible for tetanus. It is oxygen-stable but relatively heat labile, being inactivated at 65°C in five minutes. It is plasmid-coded. It gets toxoided spontaneously or in the presence of low concentrations of formaldehyde. It is a good antigen and is specifically neutralised by the antitoxin. The toxin has been crystallised. It is a simple protein composed of a single polypeptide chain. On being released from the bacillus, it autolyses to form a heterodimer consisting of a heavy chain (93,000 MW) and a light chain (52,000 MW) joined by a disulphide bond. The tetanus and botulinum toxins resemble each other in their amino acid sequences.

- **Mechanism of action:** Tetanospasmin resembles **strychnine** in its effects. The tetanus toxin specifically blocks synaptic inhibition in the spinal cord, presumably at inhibitory terminals that use glycine and GABA as neurotransmitters. The toxin acts **pre-synaptically**, unlike strychnine which acts post-synaptically. The abolition of spinal inhibition causes uncontrolled spread of impulses initiated anywhere in the central nervous system. This results in muscle rigidity and spasms due to the simultaneous contraction of agonists and antagonists, in the absence of reciprocal inhibition.

- **Lethal dose:** The purified toxin is active in extremely small amounts and has a minimum lethal dose (MLD) for mice of about $50–75 \times 10^{-6}$ mg. The amount of toxin produced depends on the strain of the bacillus and the type of culture medium used. Its MLD for human beings is about 130 nanograms. There is considerable variation in the susceptibility of different species of animals to the toxin. The horse is the most susceptible. Guinea pigs, mice, goats and rabbits are susceptible in that descending order. Birds and reptiles are highly resistant. Frogs, which are normally insusceptible, may be rendered susceptible by elevating their body temperature.

Tetanolysin: This is a heat labile, oxygen-labile hemolysin, antigenically related to the oxygen-labile hemolysins of *C.perfringens*, *C.novyi* and *S.pyogenes*. It is not relevant in the pathogenesis of tetanus.

TETANUS

Tetanus is characterised by **tonic muscular spasms**, usually commencing at the site of infection and, in all but the mildest cases, becoming generalised, involving the whole of the somatic muscular system.

Etiology: Most frequently, the disease follows injury, sometimes too trivial to be noticed. Puncture wounds are particularly vulnerable as they favour the growth of the anaerobic bacillus. Rarely, it may follow surgical operations, usually due to lapses in asepsis. Sometimes, the disease may be due to local suppuration, such as otitis media (**otogenic tetanus**). Tetanus used to be an important complication of septic abortion. Unhygienic practices, such as application of cow dung on the umbilical stump or rituals such as ear boring or circumcision often led to tetanus in the past. Tetanus may also be caused by unsterile injections.

Incubation period: This is variable, from two days to several weeks, but is commonly 6–12 days. This is influenced by several factors, such as the site and nature of the wound, the dose and toxigenicity of the contaminating organism and the immune status of the patient. The incubation period is of prognostic significance, the prognosis being grave when it is short. Of similar significance is the interval between the appearance of the first symptom of the disease, usually trismus, and the onset of spasms (period of onset).

Mortality: Tetanus was a serious disease with a high rate of mortality, 80–90 per cent, before specific treatment became available. Even with proper treatment, the case fatality rate varies from 15 to 50 per cent. Tetanus neonatorum and uterine tetanus have very high fatality rates (70–100 per cent), while otogenic tetanus is much less serious.

Incidence: Tetanus is common in the developing countries, warm climate, and in rural areas where the soil is made fertile with organic manure, where human and animal populations live in close association and where unhygienic practices are common and medical facilities poor.

Neonatal tetanus: In rural India, tetanus was a common cause of death, particularly in the newborn. However, universal immunisation of infants and expectant mothers has reduced the incidence of maternal and neonatal tetanus to a large extent.

Laboratory diagnosis

Cultural characteristics

Biochemical reactions: *C.tetani* has feeble proteolytic but no saccharolytic properties. It does not ferment any sugar. It is indole-positive, MR- and VP-negative and does not produce H_2S. Nitrate is not reduced. Gelatin liquefaction occurs very slowly. A greenish fluorescence is produced on media containing neutral red (as on MacConkey medium).

The diagnosis of tetanus should always be made on clinical grounds. Laboratory tests are not usually helpful. Laboratory diagnosis may be made by demonstration of *C.tetani* by microscopy, culture or toxigenicity tests.

Specimen

Necrotic tissue may be collected from the site of injury.

1. **Microscopy:** It is unreliable and demonstration of the typical 'drumstick' bacilli in wounds in itself is not diagnostic of tetanus. The bacilli may be present in some wounds without tetanus developing. It may be indistinguishable from *C.tetanomorphum* and *C.sphenoides*.

2. **Culture:** It is an obligatory anaerobe that grows only in the absence of oxygen. The optimum temperature is 37°C and pH 7.4. It grows on ordinary media. Growth is improved by blood and serum but not by glucose. Isolation is more likely from excised bits of tissue from the necrotic depths of wounds than from wound swabs.

   - **Swarming:** *C.tetani* produces **swarming growth.** An extremely fine, translucent film of growth is produced that is practically invisible, except at the delicately filamentous advancing edge. This property enables the separation of *C.tetani* from mixed cultures, which may be detected on the opposite half of the plate after 1–2 days of anaerobic incubation. The incorporation of polymyxin B, to which other clostridia are resistant, makes the medium selective for *C.tetani*.

   - **Fildes technique:** If the water of condensation at the bottom of a slope of nutrient agar is inoculated with the mixed bacterial culture, after incubation anaerobically for 24 hours, subcultures from the top of the tube will yield a pure growth of the tetanus bacillus.

   - **Deep agar shake cultures:** The colonies appear as spherical fluffy balls, 1–3 mm in diameter, made up of filaments with a radial arrangement.

In **gelatin stab cultures**, a fir tree type of growth occurs, with slow liquefaction. It grows well in **Robertson's cooked meat broth**, with turbidity and some gas formation. The meat is not digested but is turned black on prolonged incubation. On **blood agar**, α hemolysis is produced, which later develops into β hemolysis, due to the production of hemolysin (**tetanolysin**).

3. **Toxigenicity testing**
   - **In vitro:** For **in vitro** detection of toxin, blood agar plates (with 4% agar to inhibit swarming) with tetanus antitoxin (1500 units per ml) spread over one half of the plate are used. The *C.tetani* strains are stab-inoculated on each half of the plate, and incubated anaerobically for two days. Toxigenic *C.tetani* strains show hemolysis around the colonies, only on the half without the antitoxin. Hemolysis is inhibited by the antitoxin on the other half. This indicates the production only of tetanolysin and not necessarily of tetanospasmin, which is the pathogenic toxin.
   - **In vivo:** In vivo toxigenicity is best tested in animals. A 2–4-day-old cooked meat culture (0.2 ml) is inoculated into the root of the tail of a mouse. A second mouse that has received a dose of tetanus antitoxin (1000 units) an hour earlier serves as the control. Symptoms develop in the test animal (non-immunised) in 12–24 hours, beginning with stiffness in the tail. Rigidity proceeds to the leg on the inoculated side, the opposite leg, trunk and forelimbs, in that order. The animal dies within two days.

Prophylaxis and treatment

Tetanus is a preventable disease. As the spores are ubiquitous, wound contamination is unavoidable. As the disease is caused by the action of the toxin, the most reliable method of prevention is to build up active immunity by immunisation of children universally, and booster doses when appropriate.

The nature of prophylaxis depends largely on the type of the wound and the immune status of the patient. The prophylactic methods available are:

- **Surgical** prophylaxis aims at removing foreign bodies, necrotic tissue and blood clots, to prevent an anaerobic environment favourable for the tetanus bacillus. The extent of surgical treatment may vary from simple cleansing to radical excision, depending on the type of the wound.

- **Antibiotic** prophylaxis aims at destroying or inhibiting tetanus bacilli and pyogenic bacteria in wounds so that the production of toxin is prevented. Antibiotics have no action on the toxin. Hence, antibiotic prophylaxis does not replace immunisation but serves as a useful adjunct.

- **Metronidazole** and **penicillin** are recommended in the treatment of tetanus. Metronidazole in doses of 500 mg is given every four hours for seven days. Alternatively, **long-acting penicillin injection** may be given. Antibiotics are to be started before wound toilet.

- **Bacitracin** or **neomycin** may be applied locally.

Immunisation

- **Passive immunisation** is by injection of tetanus antitoxin. **Anti-tetanus serum (ATS)** from hyperimmune horses was originally used. However, equine ATS carried two disadvantages common in the use of any heterologous serum: **'immune elimination'** and **hypersensitivity**. The half-life of ATS in human beings is normally about seven days but in persons previously injected with horse serum, it is eliminated much more quickly because it combines with pre-existing antibodies. Prior sensitisation also leads to type III hypersensitivity reactions, which may range from mild local reactions to serum sickness. Infrequently, fatal anaphylaxis (type I hypersensitivity) may also occur. **It is obligatory that a test for hypersensitivity be done prior to administration of ATS.**

  Human anti-tetanus immunoglobulin (TIG) provides passive immunity without the risk of hypersensitivity. This is effective in smaller doses (250 units) and has a longer half-life (3–5 weeks). As TIG is prepared by immunisation of human volunteers, its availability is limited.

  Passive immunisation is an emergency procedure to be used only once.

- **Active immunisation** is the most effective method of prophylaxis whereby tetanus following unnoticed injuries can also be prevented. This is achieved by spaced injections of formol toxoid, which is available either as **'plain toxoid'**, or adsorbed on aluminium hydroxide or phosphate. The **adsorbed toxoid** is a better antigen. The tetanus toxoid is given alone or with the diphtheria toxoid and the pertussis vaccine as the **'triple vaccine'**, in which the pertussis vaccine acts as an adjuvant also.

Dosage: A course of immunisation consists of three doses of tetanus toxoid given intramuscularly, with an interval of 4–6 weeks between the first two injections and the third dose given six months later (or according to the recommendations of the National Immunisation Programme). A full course of immunisation confers immunity for a period of at least ten years. A '**booster dose**' of toxoid is recommended after ten years. A booster dose of toxoid is given if penetrating injury occurs three years or more after the full course of immunisation. ATS or TIG should not be given to an immunised individual. Too frequent injection of toxoid should be avoided as hypersensitivity reactions may occur occasionally.

- **Combined immunisation** consists of administering to a non-immune person exposed to the risk of tetanus a TIG injection at one site, along with the first dose of toxoid at the contralateral site, followed by the second and third doses of toxoid at monthly intervals. It is important to use adsorbed toxoid since the immune response to plain toxoid may be inhibited by TIG. Ideally, combined immunisation should be used whenever passive immunisation is called for.

Table 27.3 shows the recommended integrated prophylaxis of tetanus following injury.

Treatment

Tetanus patients should be treated in hospitals, preferably in special units. Isolation is necessary to protect them from noise and light which may provoke convulsions.

Supportive therapy consists of **ensuring quiet environment, controlling spasms and autonomic dysfunctions with sedatives and muscle relaxants, maintaining airway by tracheostomy with intermit-** tent positive pressure respiration and attention to feeding.

Human TIG: 10,000 IU suitably diluted may be given by slow IV infusion, followed, if needed, by another 5,000 IU later. Even though TIG may not neutralise the toxin already bound to the nervous tissue, it can inactivate the unbound toxin and any further toxin that may be produced.

Antibacterial therapy with penicillin or metronidazole should be started at once and continued for a week or more. Patients recovering from tetanus should receive a full course of **active immunisation**, as an attack of the disease does not confer immunity. Second attacks of tetanus have been recorded.

CLOSTRIDIUM BOTULINUM

C.botulinum causes **botulism**, a paralytic disease that usually presents as a form of food poisoning. The name botulism is derived from the sausage (from *botulus*, which is Latin for sausage) formerly associated with this type of food poisoning. *C.botulinum* was first isolated by van Ermengem (1896) from a piece of ham that caused an outbreak of botulism. The bacillus is a widely distributed saprophyte, occurring in virgin soil, vegetables, hay, silage, animal manure and sea mud.

Morphology

C.botulinum is motile by peritrichate flagella, producing subterminal, oval, bulging spores.

Spores

Spores are heat- and radiation-resistant, surviving several hours at 100°C and for up to 10 minutes at

Table 27.3 *Tetanus prophylaxis in the wounded*

Nature of wound	Immune status of the person		
	Immune	*Partially immune*	*Non-immune*
Clean (wound toilet performed within six hours)	Toxoid × 1*	Toxoid × 1	Toxoid × 3
Contaminated (soil or other foreign or necrotic material present)	Toxoid × 1*	Toxoid × 1 TIG antibiotics	Toxoid × 3 TIG antibiotics
Infected	Toxoid × 1* antibiotics	Toxoid × 1 TIG antibiotics	Toxoid × 3 TIG antibiotics

Note: Immune—Patient has had a full course of three injections of toxoid.
Partially immune—Patient has had two injections of toxoid.
Non-immune—Patient has had one or no injection of toxoid, or immunisation status is not known.
TIG—Tetanus Immune Globulin
*The toxoid needs to be given only if three years or more have elapsed after active immunisation or the last booster injection.

120°C. Spores of the non-proteolytic types B, E and F are much less resistant to heat.

Classification

Eight types of *C.botulinum* strains have been identified (**A, B, C1, C2, D, E, F** and **G**) based on the immunological difference in the toxins produced by them. The toxins produced by the different types are identical in their pharmacological activity but are neutralised only by the homologous antiserum. An exception is the C2 toxin, which shows enterotoxic activity, while the others are neurotoxins.

Pathogenicity

C.botulinum is non-invasive and virtually non-infectious. Its pathogenicity is due to the action of its toxin, the manifestations of which are collectively called botulism.

Toxin

Exotoxin: *C.botulinum* produces a powerful exotoxin that is responsible for its pathogenicity. **The toxin differs from other exotoxins in that it is not released during the life of the organism. It is produced intracellularly and appears in the medium only on cell death and autolysis.** It is believed to be synthesised initially as a non-toxic protoxin or progenitor toxin. Trypsin and other proteolytic enzymes activate the progenitor toxin to produce active toxin.

The toxin has been isolated as a pure crystalline protein which is probably the most toxic substance known. It has a MW of 70,000 and the lethal dose for mice is 0.000,000,033 mg. The lethal dose for human beings is probably 1–2 μg. It is a neurotoxin and acts slowly, taking several hours to kill. **It is one of the most potent toxins known to mankind.**

The toxin is relatively stable, being inactivated only after 30–40 minutes at 80°C and 10 minutes at 100°C. Food suspected to be contaminated with the botulinum toxin can be rendered completely safe by pressure cooking or boiling for 20 minutes. It resists digestion and is absorbed through the small intestines in active form. It acts by blocking the production or release of acetylcholine at the synapses and neuromuscular junctions. Onset is marked by diplopia, dysphagia and dysarthria due to cranial nerve involvement. A symmetric descending paralysis is the characteristic pattern, ending in death by respiratory paralysis.

Clinical uses of toxins: A small quantity of *C.botulinum* type A toxin injected into a muscle selectively weakens it by blocking the release of acetylcholine at the neuromuscular junction. Muscles so injected atrophy but recover in 2–4 months as new terminal axon sprouts form and restore transmission. Intramuscular injection of the toxin, first used to treat strabismus, is now recognised as a safe and effective symptomatic therapy for many neuromuscular diseases.

The botulinum toxin can be toxoided. It is specifically neutralised by its antitoxin and is a good antigen. The toxins produced by the different types of *C.botulinum* appear to be identical, except for immunological differences. Toxin production appears to be determined by the presence of bacteriophages, at least in types C and D.

BOTULISM

Clinical types

Food-borne botulism is caused by the ingestion of preformed toxin. The types of the bacillus and the nature of the food responsible vary in different regions. Human disease is usually caused by types A, B, E and very rarely F. Types C and D are usually associated with outbreaks in cattle and wild fowl. Type G has been associated with sudden death in a few patients. The source of botulism is usually preserved food—meat and meat products in Europe, canned vegetables in America and fish in Japan. Type E is associated with fish and other seafood. Proteolytic varieties of *C.botulinum* can digest food, which then appears spoiled. The cans are often inflated and show bubbles on opening. Non-proteolytic varieties leave food unchanged.

Symptoms usually begin 12–36 hours after ingestion of food. No vomiting or diarrhoea is present. Coma or delirium may supervene. Death is due to respiratory failure and occurs 1–7 days after onset. Case fatality varies at 25–70 per cent.

Wound botulism is a very rare condition resulting from wound infection with *C.botulinum*. Toxin is produced at the site of infection and is absorbed. The symptoms are those of food-borne botulism except for the gastrointestinal components which are absent. Type A has been responsible for most of the cases studied.

Infant botulism was recognised as a clinical entity in 1976. This is a toxico-infection. *C.botulinum* spores are ingested in food, get established in the gut and produce the toxin. Cases occur in infants below six months. Older children and adults are not susceptible. The manifestations are constipation, poor feeding, lethargy, weakness, pooled oral secretions, weak or altered cry, floppiness and loss of head control. Patients excrete toxin and spores in their feces. Toxin is not generally demonstrable in blood. Degrees of severity vary from very mild illness to fatal disease. Some cases of sudden infant death syndrome have been found to be due to infant botulism. Honey has been incriminated as a likely food item through which the bacillus enters the gut.

Management consists of supportive care and assisted feeding. Antitoxins and antibiotics are not indicated.

Laboratory diagnosis

Microscopy

Diagnosis may be confirmed by demonstration of the bacillus or the toxin in food or feces. Gram-positive sporing bacilli may be demonstrated in smears made from the food. *C.botulinum* may be isolated from the food or the patient's feces.

Animal inoculation: The food is macerated in sterile saline, and the filtrate inoculated into mice or guinea pigs intraperitoneally. Control animals protected by polyvalent antitoxin remain healthy.

Cultural characteristics

It is a strict anaerobe. Optimum temperature is 35°C but some strains may grow even at 1–5°C. Good growth occurs on ordinary media. Surface colonies are large, irregular and semitransparent, with a fimbriate border. Biochemical reactions vary in different types. Spores are produced consistently when grown in alkaline glucose gelatin media at 20–25°C. They are not usually produced at higher temperatures.

Prevention and treatment

As most cases of botulism follow consumption of inadequately canned or preserved food, control can be achieved by **proper canning and preservation.**

When an **outbreak** occurs, a **prophylactic dose of antitoxin** should be given intramuscularly to all who consumed the food article.

Active immunisation has been shown to be effective. If immunisation is needed, as in laboratory workers exposed to the risk, two injections of aluminium sulphate adsorbed toxoid may be given at an interval of ten weeks, followed by a booster a year later. Antitoxin may be tried for treatment. Polyvalent antiserum to types A, B and E may be administered as soon as a clinical diagnosis is made.

Supportive therapy with maintenance of respiration is of equal or greater importance.

CLOSTRIDIUM DIFFICILE

C.difficile was first isolated in 1935 from the feces of newborn infants. It was so named because of the unusual difficulty in isolating it. It is a long, slender, Gram-positive bacillus with a pronounced tendency to lose its Gram reaction. Spores are large, oval and sub-terminal. It is non-hemolytic, saccharolytic and weakly proteolytic. It was not considered pathogenic till 1977 when it was found to be responsible for antibiotic-associated colitis. *C.difficile* is an opportunistic organism that rarely causes disease and does so only when normal flora is lost. There appears to be little protective immunity following infection.

PSEUDOMEMBRANOUS COLITIS

C.difficile causes acute colitis with bloody or watery diarrhea and pseudomembranous colitis. *C.difficile* is the most common cause of healthcare-associated diarrhea in many developed countries following the use of broad-spectrum antibiotics like clindamycin, ampicillin or fluoroquinolones to which the organism is resistant.

Pathogenesis

Two high-molecular-weight **exotoxins, A and B**, are involved in the pathogenesis of the condition. Toxin A is a potent enterotoxin which attaches to gut receptors; and it may also be cytotoxic. Toxin B is a cytotoxin. The strains can produce either or both toxins. Toxin genes are present on a chromosomal pathogenicity island.

Diagnosis

- Direct examination of colon by endoscopy to look for microabscesses
- Culture on a selective media
- Detection of toxins A and/or B in stool by ELISA is the mainstay of diagnosis
- Demonstrating the toxin in the feces of patients by its characteristic effect on Hep-2 or and human diploid cell cultures

- The toxin is specifically neutralised by the *C.sordelli* antitoxin
- Molecular methods to detect genes for toxin A or B

Treatment and prevention

The disease is prevented by **restricting the use of antibiotics associated with *C.difficile* outbreaks.**

The condition is treated by discontinuing the antibiotic causing the disease and instituting **vancomycin or metronidazole.**

> **Fecal transplant**
> Recent interest has been generated to treat ulcerative colitis by fecal transplants. Some success has been noted. Further studies need to be done to expand the role of fecal transplants to restore normal flora.

ANTIBIOTIC-ASSOCIATED DIARRHEA

This is seen in patients on prolonged antibiotic use and is mainly due to the alteration of normal flora. About 20–25% of cases are due to *C.difficile* but other anaerobic infections are also implicated in the causation.

RECAP

- Members of the genus *Clostridium* are rod-shaped bacteria which usually exhibit motility, are usually spore-forming, catalase-negative, obligatory anaerobes which are Gram-positive. Clostridia are naturally found in soil and water, animal and human excreta and animal products.
- *Clostridium botulinum* causes botulism (food poisoning), infant botulism and wound botulism:
  - In adult botulism, spores in the soil contaminate food (vegetables) that is inadequately sterilised.
  - In infant botulism, bacterial spores from contaminated honey used to sweeten cow's milk or formula germinate in the child's gut.
- For diagnosis, Gram-positive square rods with swollen subterminal spores can be cultured anaerobically on blood agar, using contaminated food as the specimen. The specific toxin may be detected in food to confirm the cause of the disease.
- *Clostridium perfringens* (*Clostridium welchii*) causes gas gangrene and clostridial food poisoning:
  - In gas gangrene, spores from the soil contaminate open wounds in which spores may germinate, if there is an anaerobic environment, and produce toxins.
  - In food poisoning, spores in contaminated meat germinate following mild heating; if this occurs in an anaerobic environment (packaged foods), organisms grow rapidly producing enterotoxin.
- *C.perfringens* may also be part of the normal flora of the gastrointestinal tract, serving as a source of infection when the normal flora is suppressed (by antibiotics).
- For diagnosis, specimens collected will depend on the presentation of the disease:
  - In direct microscopy, organisms are Gram-positive bacilli with subterminal spores.
  - On blood agar, organisms cause a double zone of hemolysis.
  - Toxins can be detected in feces in food poisoning.
- *Clostridium tetani* from the soil may contaminate wounds; it causes tetanus (lockjaw). Spores in the soil are typically introduced through a puncture wound deep in the tissues. The anaerobic environment of the deep tissues allows the spores to germinate, and the bacilli release the tetanus toxin.
- Diagnosis is by demonstrating Gram-positive bacilli with terminal spores (drumstick appearance) in specimens from the wound.
- Tetanus can be prevented by active and passive immunisation.
- *Clostridium difficile* causes bloody diarrhea and pseudomembranous colitis. *C.difficile* is the most common cause of nosocomial diarrhea.

- *C.difficile* causes pseudomembranous colitis. It can be diagnosed by detecting toxins A and/or B from stools using enzyme immunoassays. The disease is prevented by restricting the use of antibiotics associated with *C.difficile* outbreaks; treatment is by discontinuing the antibiotic causing the disease and starting vancomycin or metronidazole.

ESSAYS

1. Explain the pathogenesis and laboratory diagnosis of gas gangrene.
2. Describe the pathogenesis and laboratory diagnosis of tetanus and outline the prophylactic measures.

SHORT ANSWERS

1. Antibiotic-associated diarrhea
2. Food-borne poisoning due to *Clostridium perfringens*
3. Pathogenesis of gas gangrene
4. Pathogenesis of tetanus

SHORT NOTES

1. Nagler's reaction
2. Reverse CAMP test
2. Virulence factors of *C.perfringens*
3. Virulence factors of *C.tetani*
4. Types and pathogenesis of botulism

28 Anaerobic Bacteria II: Non-sporing Anaerobes

INTRODUCTION

Anaerobic bacteria outnumber aerobic bacteria in many habitats, including most sites of the human body, especially the gastrointestinal tract. Even in such seemingly aerobic locations as the mouth and skin, anaerobic bacteria are ten to thirty times more frequent than aerobes. In the human intestines, they outnumber aerobic bacteria by a thousandfold. The number of anaerobes present has been estimated to be 10^4–10^5/ml in the small intestine, 10^8/ml in saliva and 10^{11}/g in the colon.

Anaerobic bacteria differ widely in the degree of anaerobiosis required for their growth. Some species fail to grow if the atmosphere contains as little as 0.03% oxygen (obligatory), while at the other extreme, some are aerotolerant and may grow sparsely on the surface of aerobic plates (facultative). Consequently, the techniques employed for the propagation and study of anaerobes vary in complexity. Several anaerobes occur in soil and water which may be of industrial and agricultural importance (for example, methanobacteria and butyrivibrios).

Classification

Depending on DNA base composition and analysis of the fatty acid end products of metabolism, **medically important anaerobes** may be broadly classified as follows:

I.   Cocci
     A. Gram-positive
        Peptostreptococcus
        Peptococcus
     B. Gram-negative
        Veillonella

II. Bacilli
     1. Endospore forming
        Clostridia
     2. Non-sporing
     A. Gram-positive
        Eubacterium
        Propionibacterium
        Lactobacillus
        Mobiluncus
        Bifidobacterium
        Actinomyces
     B. Gram-negative
        Bacteroides
        Prevotella
        Porphyromonas
        Fusobacterium
        Leptotrichia

III. Spirochetes
     Treponema
     Borrelia

ANAEROBIC COCCI

Anaerobic cocci represent a heterogeneous collection of cocci and can be divided into the Gram-positive and Gram-negative groups.

Gram-positive cocci

Peptostreptococcus: These have been classified into the genera *Peptostreptococcus*. They are cocci of small size (0.2–2.5 μm). Many of them are aerotolerant and grow well under 10% CO_2 in an aerobic atmosphere.

They are normal inhabitants of the vagina, intestines and mouth. They may cause several clinical infections such as puerperal sepsis and other genital infections, wound infections, gangrenous appendicitis, urinary tract infections, osteomyelitis and abscesses in the brain, lungs and other internal organs. They are often seen in large numbers in pus from suppurative lesions, so a Gram-stained smear may be helpful in diagnosis. Infections are usually mixed, the cocci being present along with clostridia or anaerobic Gram-negative bacilli. *Peptostreptococcus anaerobius* is most often responsible for puerperal sepsis and *Pst.magnus* for abscesses. *Pst.asaccharolyticus*, *Pst.tetradius* and *Pst. prevoti* are some other species commonly present in clinical specimens.

Gram-negative cocci

Veillonellae: These are Gram-negative cocci of varying sizes occurring as diplococci, short chains or groups. They are normal inhabitants of the mouth, and intestinal and genital tracts. *Veillonella parvula* has been reported from clinical specimens but its pathogenic role is uncertain.

All anaerobic cocci are generally sensitive to penicillin, chloramphenicol and metronidazole, and resistant to streptomycin and gentamicin.

NON-SPORING ANAEROBIC GRAM-POSITIVE BACILLI

This group contains many genera, of which the medically relevant are *Eubacterium*, *Propionibacterium*, *Lactobacillus*, *Mobiluncus* and *Bifidobacterium*.

Other genera in this group, *Actinomyces* and *Arachnia*, are dealt with elsewhere.

- Members of the genus *Eubacterium* are strictly anaerobic and grow very slowly. They are part of the normal mouth and intestinal flora. Some species (*E.brachy*, *E.timidum*, *E.nodatum*) are commonly seen in periodontitis. *E.lentum* is commonly isolated from non-oral clinical specimens.

- *Propionibacterium* is constantly present on the skin. *P.acnes* is a common contaminant in blood and CSF cultures.
- *Lactobacillus* is present in the mouth, intestines and, typically, in the adult vagina (**Doderlein's bacilli**). It is generally non-pathogenic, though *L.catenaforme* has been associated with bronchopulmonary infections.
- *Bifidobacterium* is a pleomorphic rod that shows true and false branching. It is present in large numbers in the intestines and in the mouth.
- *Mobiluncus* species are motile, curved, anaerobic bacilli that may appear as Gram-variable rods. *M.mulieris* and *M.curtisii* have been isolated from the vagina in **bacterial vaginosis**, along with *Gardnerella vaginalis*.

Bacterial vaginosis is a polymicrobial infection characterised by a thin, malodorous vaginal discharge. Its '**rotten fish**' smell is accentuated when it is mixed with a drop of KOH solution. The vaginal pH is more than 4.5. Clue cells (epithelial cells whose surface is covered by adherent bacilli) are seen in stained or unstained films. Diagnosis is made by Nugent's score which is based on the morphotypes of bacteria seen on examining the gram-stained smear from discharge.

ANAEROBIC GRAM-NEGATIVE BACILLI

Clinical Case A 65-year-old diabetic woman developed seizures and presented to neurosurgery with a provisional diagnosis of a space-occupying lesion. On further investigation, it was diagnosed as a brain abscess. The patient underwent an operation and the pus was sent to the laboratory in a sealed vial filled with carbon dioxide. Microscopic examination showed the presence of Gram-positive cocci and a few fine Gram-negative bacilli. Culture from Robertson's cooked meat medium was positive for peptostreptococci and *Bacteroides fragilis*. The patient responded to treatment with amoxicillin/sulbactam and metronidazole.

Medically important anaerobic Gram-negative bacilli belong to the family Bacteroidaceae and are classified into the genera *Bacteroides*, *Porphyromonas*, *Prevotella*, *Fusobacterium* and *Leptotrichia*.

Bacteroides

This genus comprises the most common anaerobes isolated from clinical specimens. They are non-sporing, non-motile, strict anaerobes, usually very pleomorphic, appearing as slender rods, branching forms or coccobacilli, seen singly, in pairs or in short chains. They grow well on media such as brain-heart infusion agar in an anaerobic atmosphere containing 10% CO_2. They possess capsular polysaccharides which appear to be virulence factors, and antibodies to them can be detected in patients. They are normal inhabitants of the intestinal, respiratory and female genital tracts. The *Bacteroides* species is susceptible to metronidazole and usually to clindamycin and chloramphenicol. *B.melaninogenicus* is susceptible to penicillin, but *B.fragilis* is not susceptible to penicillin.

B.fragilis is the most frequent of the non-sporing anaerobes isolated from clinical specimens. It is often recovered from blood, pleural and peritoneal fluids, CSF, brain abscesses, wounds and urogenital infections.

Porphyromonas

Previously classified under *Bacteroides*, the asaccharolytic pigmented species have been separated as the genus *Porphyromonas*, containing *P.gingivalis*—responsible for periodontal disease, *P.endodontalis*—causing dental root canal infections and other species.

Prevotella

Previously classified under *Bacteroides*, the moderately saccharolytic species inhibited by 20% bile have been placed in the genus *Prevotella*, containing *P.melaninogenica*, *P.buccalis*, *P.denticola* and others.

P.melaninogenica is easy to recognise because of the black or brown colour of the colonies (Fig. 28.1). The colour is not due to the melanin pigment, as was once thought, but due to a hemin derivative. It has been isolated from various infections including lung or liver abscess, mastoiditis, intestinal lesions and lesions of the mouth and gums. Cultures of *P.melaninogenica* and even dressings from wounds infected with the bacillus produce a characteristic red fluorescence when exposed to ultraviolet light.

Fusobacterium

This contains long, thin or spindle-shaped bacilli with pointed ends. *F.nucleatum* is a normal inhabitant of the mouth and is found in oral infection and pleuropulmonary sepsis. *F.necrophorum* produces a wide range of exotoxins and has been responsible for liver abscess and other abdominal infections in animals and less often in humans.

Leptotrichia

This contains a single species, *L.buccalis* which was formerly known as Vincent's fusiform bacillus or *Fusobacterium fusiforme*. They are long, straight or slightly curved rods, often with pointed ends. They are part of the normal oral flora and are seen in acute necrotising lesions in the mouth. A common condition is **Vincent's angina**, which may resemble diphtheria, with the inflamed pharyngeal mucosa showing a greyish membrane which peels easily. Stained smears show large fusiform and spiral *Borrelia* bacilli.

ANAEROBIC INFECTIONS

Anaerobic infections are usually endogenous and are caused by tissue invasion by bacteria normally resident on the respective body surfaces. Anaerobic bacteria are normally present on the skin, mouth, nasopharynx and upper respiratory tract, intestines and vagina (Table 28.1).

Characteristics of anaerobic infections:
- Anaerobic infections generally follow some **precipitating factor** such as trauma, tissue necrosis, impaired circulation, hematoma formation or the presence of foreign bodies.
- Diabetes, malnutrition, malignancy or prolonged treatment with aminoglycoside antibiotics may act as **predisposing factors**.
- They are typically **polymicrobial**, more than one anaerobe being responsible besides aerobic bacteria (*Case*).
- While the infection is usually localised, general **dissemination** may occur by bacteremia.

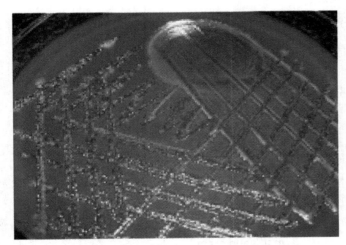

Fig. 28.1 *P.melaninogenica* on anaerobic blood agar

Table 28.1   *Normal anaerobic flora of the human body*

Anaerobe	Skin	Mouth–nasopharynx	Intestine	Vagina
Clostridium			++	
Actinomyces		+		
Bifidobacterium		+	++	+
Propionibacterium	++			
Bacteroides fragilis			++	
P.melaninogenica		++	+	++
Fusobacterium		++	+	
Gram-positive cocci		++	++	++
Gram-negative cocci		++	+	++
Spirochetes		+		

❖ Some **clinical features** suggest the presence of anaerobic infection.

❖ **Pus** produced by anaerobes is characteristically putrid, with a pervasive, nauseating odour. However, there may be exceptions; infections solely due to *B.fragilis* may be free of this smell.

❖ Pronounced **cellulitis** is a common feature of anaerobic wound infections.

❖ Toxemia and fever are not marked.

Table 28.2 lists the common sites and types of anaerobic infections and the bacteria responsible.

Laboratory diagnosis

1. Specimen: As anaerobes form part of the normal flora of the skin and mucous surfaces, their isolation from specimens has to be interpreted cautiously. The mere presence of an anaerobe does not prove its causal role. Specimens should be collected in such a manner as to avoid resident flora. For example, the sputum is unsatisfactory for culture from a suspected case of lung abscess; only material collected by aspiration would be acceptable. Wound swabs are generally unsatisfactory

Table 28.2   *Common anaerobic infections and the bacteria responsible*

Site and type of infection	Bacteria commonly responsible
Central nervous system: Brain abscess	*B.fragilis; Peptostreptococcus*
Ear, nose, throat: Chronic sinusitis, otitis media, mastoiditis, orbital cellulitis	Fusobacteria (aerobes frequently responsible)
Mouth and jaw: Ulcerative gingivitis (Vincent's) Dental abscess, cellulitis Abscess and sinus of jaw	Fusobacteria, spirochetes Mouth anaerobes, *Actinomyces*, other mouth anaerobes
Respiratory: Aspiration pneumonia, lung abscess, bronchiectasis, empyema	Fusobacteria, *P.melaninogenica,* anaerobic cocci; *B.fragilis* rarely
Abdominal: Subphrenic, hepatic abscess; appendicitis, peritonitis; ischiorectal abscess; wound infection after colorectal surgery	*B.fragilis*
Female genitalia: Wound infection following genital surgery; puerperal sepsis; tubo-ovarian abscess, Bartholin's abscess, septic abortion	*P.melaninogenica,* anaerobic cocci; *B.fragilis* Genital anaerobes and *C.perfringens*
Skin and soft tissue: Infected sebaceous cyst Breast abscess, axillary abscess Cellulitis, diabetic ulcer, gangrene	Anaerobic cocci Anaerobic cocci; *P.melaninogenica* (*S.aureus* commonest cause) *B.fragilis* and others

but where they are to be used, they should be sent in a transport medium.

2. Transport: As some anaerobes die on exposure to oxygen, care should be exercised to minimise contact with air during collection, transport and handling of specimens. Transport and culture is done using different methods to ensure anaerobic atmosphere during transport.

Methods of anaerobiosis:

- Pus and other fluids may be collected in sealed vials **gassed out with carbon dioxide,**
- In small bottles with **airtight caps filled to capacity** to remove air and transported quickly.
- **Robertson's cooked meat medium (RCM)**—discussed in Chapter 5.
- **PRAS** (pre-reduced anaerobic sterilised) transport medium is a commercially available transport system. These contain tubes gassed out with nitrogen and fitted tightly with butyl stoppers.
- **Stuart's transport medium**

3. Microscopy: In the laboratory, exposure should be kept to the minimum. Examination of a Gram-stained smear is useful. Pus in anaerobic infection usually shows a large variety of different organisms and numerous pus cells. Rarely, as in brain abscess, is only one type of organism seen.

4. Ultraviolet examination: Examination of the specimen under ultraviolet light may show the bright red fluorescence of *P.melaninogenica*.

5. Gas liquid chromatography of the specimen may yield presumptive information on the types of anaerobes present.

6. Culture: Several special media have been described for anaerobes.

- Freshly prepared blood agar with neomycin, yeast extract, hemin and vitamin K is adequate for routine diagnostic work. Plates are incubated at 37°C in an anaerobic jar, with 10% CO_2. Parallel aerobic cultures should always be set up. This is necessary as a control for the growth on anaerobic plates and also because, in most anaerobic infections, aerobic bacteria are also involved.
- The **Gaspak system** provides a convenient method of routine anaerobic cultures. Plates are examined after 24 or 48 hours. Some anaerobes, such as fusobacteria, require longer periods of incubation.

Treatment

Penicillin, clindamycin and metronidazole are the most active drugs against anaerobes. The exception is the *Bacteroides* species where resistance to penicillin and clindamycin has been reported. Amoxicillin/clavulanic acid or ampicillin/sulbactam combinations or carbapenems can be given. In case of abscess formation, surgical drainage has to be carried out along with antibiotics.

RECAP

- Many anaerobic bacteria cause disease in human beings, but the majority are normal commensals.
- Anaerobic cocci represent a heterogeneous collection of cocci broadly divided into the Gram-positive and Gram-negative groups:
  - The anaerobic Gram-positive *Peptostreptococcus* is a normal inhabitant of the vagina, intestines and mouth.
  - Anaerobic Gram-positive bacilli include *Eubacterium*, *Propionibacterium*, *Lactobacillus*, *Bifidobacterium* and *Mobiluncus*. *Propionibacterium acnes* is present on the skin and has been implicated in late post-operative endophthalmitis. *Lactobacillus* is present in the mouth, intestines and, typically, in the adult vagina; it is generally non-pathogenic. The *Mobiluncus* species are motile, curved anaerobic bacilli that may appear as Gram-variable rods; they have been isolated from the vagina in bacterial vaginosis, along with *Gardnerella vaginalis*.
  - Medically important anaerobic Gram-negative bacilli of this family include the *Bacteroides* and *Fusobacterium* species.

- Transport of clinical specimens and cultures requires special conditions and media so that the specimen is not exposed to oxygen.

ESSAYS

1. Describe the transport and culture of clinical samples for anaerobes.
2. Describe the laboratory diagnosis of anaerobic infections.

SHORT NOTES

1. Bacteroides
2. Antimicrobial treatment for anaerobic infections

29 Enterobacteriaceae I: Coliforms—Proteus

INTRODUCTION

Members of Enterobacteriaceae are a group of non-sporing, non-acid fast, Gram-negative bacilli that are found in the gut of man and animals. They belong to a complex family that exhibit general morphological and biochemical similarities. Members of this family may or may not be capsulated and are motile by peritrichate flagella, or are non-motile. They are aerobic, facultatively anaerobic and grow readily in ordinary media. They ferment glucose, producing acid and gas or acid only, reduce nitrates to nitrites and form catalase but not oxidase. Within the family, they vary widely in their biochemical and antigenic properties.

Classification

The oldest method to classify these bacteria was based on their action on lactose in MacConkey medium.

- **Lactose fermenters** (e.g., *Escherichia* and *Klebsiella*)
- **Non-lactose fermenters** (e.g., *Salmonella*, *Shigella* and *Proteus*)

This scheme has practical value in diagnostic bacteriology. The majority of commensal intestinal bacilli are lactose fermenters (LF), formerly called **coliform bacilli**. They grow as pink colonies. The major intestinal pathogens *Salmonella* and *Shigella* are non-lactose fermenters (NLF) and grow as pale colonies (except *Shigella sonnei* which is a late lactose fermenter). A small group of late lactose fermenters are called **paracolon bacilli**.

Currently, they are grouped together based on similar DNA base compositions and a number of common morphological and biochemical properties. Three widely used systems for the classification of Enterobacteriaceae are:

- **Bergey's** classification
- **Kauffmann and White's classification applied to Salmonella** (see Chapter 31)
- **Edwards–Ewing** classification (see Table 29.1)

They have certain differences while the general approach is the same. The family is first classified into its major subdivision group or tribe. Each tribe consists of one or more genera and each genus consists of one or more subgenera and species. The species

Table 29.1 *Enterobacteriaceae: classification by Edwards and Ewing*

	Tribes	Genus
I	Escherichiae	*Escherichia, Shigella*
II	Edwardsiellae	*Edwardsiella*
III	Salmonellae	*Salmonella*
IV	Citrobacteriaceae	*Citrobacter*
V	Klebsielleae	*Klebsiella, Enterobacter Serratia, Hafnia* and *Pantoea*
VI	Proteae	*Proteus, Providencia, Morganella*
VII	Yersinieae	*Yersinia*
VIII	Erwinieae	*Erwinia*

are further classified into types—biotypes, serotypes, bacteriophage types and colicin types.

ENTEROBACTERIACEAE

The genus *Yersinia*, which includes the plague bacillus, has been placed in the family Enterobacteriaceae. Due to the different disease entity, plague, caused by *Y.pestis*, it is dealt with in Chapter 34.

TRIBE: *ESCHERICHIAE*

Escherichia coli

This genus is named after Escherich who was the first to describe the colon bacillus under the name *Bacterium coli commune* (1885). Presently, one major group, *Escherichia coli* is the recognised human enteric flora, which is further subdivided into biotypes and serotypes. A few other species have been described in the genus but they are of little medical importance

They include *E.fergusonii, E.hermanii* and *E.vulneris.* These have been isolated infrequently from clinical specimens.

Unlike other coliforms, *E.coli* is a parasite living only in the human or animal intestine. Voided in feces, it remains viable in the environment only for a few days. Detection of thermotolerant *E.coli* in drinking water, therefore, is taken as evidence of fecal contamination.

Morphology

E.coli is a Gram-negative, straight rod measuring 1–3 μm × 0.4–0.7 μm, arranged singly or in pairs. It is motile by peritrichate flagella, though some strains may be non-motile. Capsules and fimbriae are found in some virulent strains.

Cultural characteristics

It grows aerobically and is a facultative anaerobe. The temperature range is 10–40°C (optimum 37°C).
- In **ordinary media,** it grows well. Colonies are large, greyish white, moist, smooth, opaque or partially translucent and discoid. This description applies to the **smooth (S)** form seen on fresh isolation, which is easily emulsifiable in saline. The **rough (R)** forms give rise to colonies with an irregular dull surface and are often autoagglutinable in saline. The smooth to rough (S → R) variation occurs as a result of repeated subcultures and is associated with loss of surface antigens and virulence. Many pathogenic isolates have polysaccharide capsules. Some strains may occur in the '**mucoid**' form.
- On **blood agar,** many strains, especially those associated with infection, are hemolytic.
- On **MacConkey medium** (Fig. 29.1), colonies are bright pink due to lactose fermentation.
- On **selective media,** growth is largely inhibited, such as **DCA** or **SS agar** used for the isolation of salmonellae and shigellae.
- In **broth**, growth occurs with uniform turbidity and a heavy deposit, which disperses completely on shaking.

Biochemical reactions

Glucose, lactose, mannitol, maltose and several other carbohydrates are fermented with the production of acid and gas. Typical strains do not ferment sucrose.

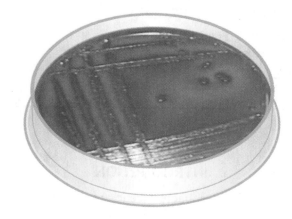

Fig. 29.1 MacConkey agar with smooth, pink colonies of *Escherichia coli*

--- *Escherichia coli* ---

Clinical Case 1 A 25-year-old woman consulted her family physician, complaining of frequency of urination and dysuria. After two days of no relief, followed by fever with chills for the last 24 hours, she visited the outpatient department of a hospital. Microscopic analysis of urine in the laboratory showed the presence of pus cells of >1 per high-power field in an uncentrifuged specimen, and no casts. Urine culture by semi-quantitative method grew >105/CFU/ml of lactose-fermenting colonies. These were identified as *E.coli,* and based on antimicrobial susceptibility, the patient was treated with ciprofloxacin.

IMViC test: Four biochemical tests widely employed in the classification of Enterobacteriaceae are (i) indole, (ii) methyl red (MR), (iii) Voges–Proskauer (VP) and (iv) citrate utilisation, generally referred to by the mnemonic IMViC.

E.coli is indole- and MR-positive, and VP– and citrate-negative (IMViC + + – –). Gelatin is not liquified, H_2S is not formed, urea is not split and growth does not occur in the KCN medium (Table 29.2).

Antigenic structure

Serotyping or antigenic typing of *E.coli* is based on three antigens: somatic antigen O, flagellar antigen H and capsular antigen K. In addition, it also has fimbrial or F antigens. The antigenic pattern of a strain is based on the numerical type of the antigen it carries (e.g., O111: K58: H2).

- **O antigen (somatic antigen):** Thus far, around 170 types of O antigens have been recognised (denoted as 1,2,3, to 170). These are lipopolysaccharides that are heat-stable. They may cross-react with O antigens of few other members of Enterobacteriaceae. O antigens are associated with virulence of the organism. The normal colon strains belong to the 'early' O groups (1, 2, 3, 4, etc.), while the enteropathogenic strains belong to the 'later' O groups (26, 55, 86, 111, etc.). They are typed by slide agglutination using specific antisera. The K antigen may sometimes mask the O antigen and render the strain non-agglutinable. This can be overcome by boiling the cultures prior to agglutination.
- **H antigen (Flagellar antigen):** Thus far, 75 H antigens have been recognised. The expression of this antigen is better in a semisolid agar. These

Table 29.2 *Enterobacteriaceae: Important distinguishing features of the different genera*

	Escherichia	Edwardsiella	Citrobacter	Salmonella¹	Shigella²	Klebsiella	Enterobacter	Hafnia	Serratia	Proteus	Morganella	Providencia
Motility	+	+	+	+	–	–	+	+	+	+	+	+
Gas from glucose	+	+	+	+	–	+	+	+	d	d	+	+
Acid from lactose	+	–	+	–	–	+	+	–	–	–	–	–
Acid from sucrose	d	–	d	–	–	+	+	–	+	d	–	d
Growth in KCN	–	–	+	d	–	+	+	+	+	+	+	+
Indole	+	+	d	–	d	–	–	–	–	d	+	+
MR	+	+	+	+	+	–	–	–	–	+	+	+
VP	–	–	–	–	–	+	+	+	+	–	–	–
Citrate	–	–	+	+	–	+	+	+	+	d	d	d
H_2S	–	+	+	+	–	–	–	–	–	+	–	–
Urease	–	–	–	–	–	+	d	–	–	+	+	d
Phenylalanine deaminase (PPA)	–	–	–	–	–	–	–	–	–	+	+	+
Arginine dehydrolase	d	–	d	+	–	–	d	–	–	–	–	–
Lysine decarboxylase	+	+	–	+	–	d	d	+	+	–	–	–
Ornithine decarboxylase	d	+	d	+	d	–	+	+	+	d	+	–

(d = results different in different species or strains.)
Important exceptions:
¹*S.typhi* does not produce gas from sugars.
²*S.sonnei* ferments lactose and sucrose late

antigens are heat labile. The H antigens are more specific as cross-reactions amongst other members of Enterobacteriaceae are very rare.

- **K antigen (Capsular antigens)**: About 100 K antigens have been recognised till date. This is an acidic polysaccharide antigen located in the **'envelope'** or microcapsule (K is for *kapsel*, the German word for capsule). It encloses the **O antigen** and renders the strain non-agglutinable by the O antiserum. It may also contribute to virulence by inhibiting phagocytosis. K antigens are currently classified into two groups, I and II. Several different serotypes of *E.coli* are found in the normal intestine. Most of them do not have K antigens.

- **F antigens**: Fimbriae are important **virulence factors**. They are heat labile and get detached when the organism is heated to 100°C. They may be plasmid or chromosomally determined. Plasmid-coded fimbriae are found only in small numbers and mediate mannose-resistant hemagglutinins. They have been shown to act as virulence factors. Chromosomally coded fimbriae cause mannose-sensitive hemagglutination and are not associated with virulence.

Virulence factors

Two types of virulence factors have been recognised in *E.coli*: surface antigens and toxins.

Surface antigens

- **Antigen**: The somatic lipopolysaccharide O antigen exerts endotoxic activity. It also protects the organism from phagocytosis and the bactericidal effects of complements. The envelope or K antigens also offer protection against phagocytosis and antibacterial factors in normal serum. These activities are neutralised by the presence of antibodies to the O and K antigens. Strains of *E.coli* responsible for neonatal meningitis and septicemia carry the KI envelope antigen which resembles the group B antigen of meningococci.

    Fimbriae are important in initial attachment and colonisation.

- **Colonisation factor antigens (CFA)** occur in enterotoxigenic *E.coli* causing human diarrhea. Fimbriae are also important for adherence of the organism in urinary tract infection.

- **P fimbria,** seen in uropathogenic strains, binds specifically to the P blood group substance on human erythrocytes and uroepithelial cells.

Toxins: *E.coli* produces two kinds of exotoxins: hemolysins and enterotoxins.

- **Hemolysins** do not appear to be relevant in pathogenesis though they are produced more commonly by virulent strains than by avirulent strains.

- **CNF1** (cytotoxic necrotising factor-1) and **Siderophores** are virulence factors in uropathogenic *E.coli* and are important components of biofilm production and adhesion.

- **Enterotoxins** are important in the pathogenesis of diarrhea. Three distinct types of *E.coli* enterotoxins have been identified: **heat labile toxin (LT), heat-stable toxin (ST)** and **verotoxin (VT),** also known as **Shiga-like toxin (SLT).**

- **Heat labile toxin (LT)** of *E.coli* (discovered in 1956 by De and colleagues in isolates from adult diarrhea cases in Kolkata). *E.coli* LT resembles the cholera toxin in its structure, antigenic properties and mode of action. It is a complex of polypeptide subunits—each unit consisting of one subunit A (A for **active**) and five subunits B (B for **binding**). The toxin binds to the GM1 ganglioside receptor on intestinal epithelial cells by means of subunit B, following which subunit A is activated to yield two fragments: A1 and A2. The A1 fragment activates adenyl cyclase in the enterocyte to form cyclic adenosine 5' monophosphate (cAMP), leading to increased outflow of water and electrolytes into the gut lumen, with consequent watery diarrhea. Though the mechanism of action of LT and cholera toxin (CT) is the same, the latter is about a hundred times more potent than the former. LT is a powerful antigen and can be detected by a number of serological as well as biological tests (Table 29.3).

- **Heat-stable toxin (ST)** of *E.coli* was first identified in 1970 and comprises low molecular weight polypeptides which are poorly antigenic. Two types of ST are known, ST_A (or ST I, which is soluble in methanol) and ST_B (or ST II, insoluble in methanol).

    ST_A acts by activation of cyclic guanosine monophosphate (cGMP) in the intestine. It acts very rapidly and induces fluid accumulation in the intestines of infant mice within four hours of intragastric administration. This infant mouse test is the standard method for demonstration of ST_A.

    ST_B causes fluid accumulation in young piglets (up to nine weeks), but not in infant mice. The mode of action is not known though it is not through cAMP or cGMP. ST genes are carried on plasmids

Table 29.3   *Methods for detection of ETEC enterotoxins*

Assay	LT	ST
In vivo tests		
Ligated rabbit ileal loop		
Read at 6 hours	±	+
Read at 18 hours	+	–
Infant rabbit bowel	+	+
Infant mouse intragastric (4 hours)	–	+
Adult rabbit skin (vascular permeability factor)	+	–
In vitro tests		
Tissue culture tests		
Rounding of Y1 mouse adrenal cells		
Elongation of Chinese hamster ovary (CHO) cells	+	–
Serological tests		
ELISA	+	(ST ELISA with monoclonal antibody
Passive agglutination tests, passive immune hemolysis, precipitin (Eiken's) test	+	– +
Genetic tests		
DNA probes	+	

which may also carry other genes, such as for LT and genes for drug resistance. However, the ST_A and ST_B genes are not carried on the same plasmid.

- **E.coli verocytotoxin or verotoxin** is so named because of its cytotoxic effect on Vero cells (cell line derived from African green monkey kidney cells). It is also known as Shiga-like toxin (SLT) because of its similarity to *Shigella dysenteriae* type 1 toxin, in its physical, antigenic and biological properties. It acts by inhibition of protein synthesis. Besides cytotoxicity in Vero and HeLa cells, VT also shows enterotoxicity in rabbit ileal loops, like the Shiga toxin. VT is also composed of A and B subunits. The genes appear to be phage-encoded. An antigenically different VT, called VT_2 has been identified, which is not neutralised by the Shiga antitoxin, unlike VT_1.

Clinical infections

Four main types of clinical syndromes are caused by *E.coli*:

- Urinary tract infection
- Diarrhea
- Septicemia, neonatal sepsis and neonatal meningitis
- Pyogenic infections

Urinary tract infection: *E.coli* and other coliforms account for the large majority of naturally acquired urinary tract infections (UTI). The *E.coli* serotypes commonly responsible for community-acquired UTI (*Case* 1) are those normally found in the gut of the person, O groups 1, 2, 4, 6, 7, etc. Those acquired in the hospital, following instrumentation, are more often caused by bacteria such as *Pseudomonas* and *Proteus*.

Infection may be precipitated by urinary obstruction due to prostatic enlargement, calculi or pregnancy. About 5–7 per cent of pregnant women have been reported to have **asymptomatic bacteriuria,** which if undetected and untreated, may lead to symptomatic infection later in pregnancy, pyelonephritis and hypertension in pregnant women, leading to prematurity and perinatal death of the fetus.

While infections of the lower urinary tract may be due to 'ascending infections' caused by gut flora, pyelonephritis is probably due to hematogenous spread. Strains carrying K antigens are more commonly responsible for pyelonephritis, while most isolates from cystitis lack K antigens. The P pili-positive *E.coli* are generally **uropathogenic.**

Laboratory diagnosis: Bacteriological diagnosis of UTI is done by demonstrating '**significant bacteriuria**' using quantitative cultures developed by Kass. This is based on the fact that normal urine is sterile, but during voiding may become contaminated with genital commensals. The counts in the contaminated urine would be lower than that caused by an infection. A count of 100,000 bacteria per ml is considered 'significant' (suggesting infection) in a sample collected by voiding.

Specimen:

- **A clean-voided midstream sample of urine is cultured.** In **men,** midstream urine is collected after the prepuce is retracted and the glans penis cleaned with wet cotton. In **women,** anogenital toilet is important and should consist of careful cleaning with water. Urine should be passed keeping the labia separated using the fingers. The first portion of voided urine that flushes out commensal bacteria from the anterior urethra is not collected. The next portion of urine (**midstream sample**) is collected directly into a sterile wide-mouthed container and transported to the laboratory without delay. Urine is a good medium for the growth of coliforms and other urinary commensals, which will vitiate the results of quantitative culture if processing is delayed. If a delay of more than 1–2 hours is unavoidable, the specimen can be refrigerated for up to four hours.
- **Suprapubic aspiration**
- **Catheterised patients:** Urine culture from catheterised patients is not recommended, except immediately after introducing a catheter, urine may be collected from the port.

Counts of 10,000 bacteria or less per ml are due to contamination during voiding and are not significant unless the patient is on antibacterial or diuretic. In Gram-positive organisms like *S.aureus*, lower counts may be significant.

Methods of urine culture

❖ Quantitative culture: Serial tenfold dilutions of urine are tested by the pour plate or surface culture methods and the exact bacterial count per millilitre of urine is counted. This, however, is too complicated for routine diagnostic work.

❖ Semi-quantitative techniques are more convenient and used in routine clinical laboratories. It employs a standard loop which transfers a fixed volume of urine. One loopful of urine is placed on a non-inhibitory medium (blood agar) and another loopful on an indicator medium (MacConkey). The former gives a quantitative measurement of bacteriuria, while the latter enables presumptive diagnosis of the bacterium. The isolates are identified by their properties.

Antimicrobial susceptibility test: *E.coli* and other common urinary pathogens develop drug resistance frequently. Isolates are often resistant to multiple antibiotics, which are transferable.

Screening test for UTI: Several screening techniques have been introduced for the rapid presumptive diagnosis of significant bacteriuria:

- **Griess nitrite test:** The presence of nitrite, detectable by a simple colourimetric test, indicates the presence of nitrate-reducing bacteria in urine; normal urine does not contain nitrites.
- **Catalase test:** The presence of catalase as evidenced by frothing on addition of hydrogen peroxide indicates bacteriuria, though a positive result is also obtained in hematuria.
- **Triphenyl tetrazolium chloride (TTC) test:** This is a dye reduction test signifying respiratory activity of growing bacteria causing urinary tract infection.
- Microscopic demonstration of bacteria in **Gram-stained films** of uncentrifuged urine.
- **Dip slide culture methods:** Agar-coated slides are immersed in urine or even exposed to the stream of urine during voiding, incubated and the growth estimated by colony counting or by colour change of indicators in the medium.

None of the screening methods is as sensitive or reliable as a culture.

Localisation of UTI: This is based on the assumption that bacteria coated with specific antibodies are present in the urine only when the kidneys are infected and not when the infection is confined to the bladder. Antibody-coated bacteria are detected by immunofluorescence using fluorescent-tagged antihuman globulin or by staphylococcal co-agglutination.

Treatment: Treatment of uncomplicated UTI caused by antibiotic-susceptible *E.coli* is with Cotrimoxazole 500/125 mg BD for 3–5 days or Ciprofloxacin 500 mg BD for 3–5 days.

However, treatment would depend on the susceptibility pattern of the clinical isolate.

Diarrhea: From 1885, when Escherich first isolated the bacillus from the feces of infants with enteritis, *E.coli* had been suspected to be a causative agent of diarrhea. In 1945, Bray established the causative role of a specific type of *E.coli* (subsequently recognised as type 0111) during a hospital outbreak of childhood diarrhea in London. Soon, many other enteropathogenic serotypes of *E.coli* came to be recognised as being responsible for diarrhea (Table 29.4).

Currently, six different types of diarrheagenic *E.coli* are recognised:

- Enteropathogenic

Table 29.4 *Properties and symptoms of diarrheagenic E.coli*

Toxins	Properties	Symptoms	Site of intestine involved	Serotypes of E.coli secreting the toxin	Diagnostic test
EPEC	EAF protein Intimin protein (coded by *eae* gene)	Watery diarrhea in adults and infantile diarrhea	Upper small intestine	026:B6, 055:B5, 0111:B4	Detection of genes coding for *LEE* or *EAF* by PCR
ETEC	LT ST Non-invasive	Watery diarrhea, traveller's diarrhea	Small intestine	06, 08, 015, 025, 0167, etc.	Both ST and LT can be detected by PCR
EIEC	Invasive	Mucoid, may be bloody	Colon and small intestine	028 ac, 0112 ac, 0152, 0154, etc.	Invasion assays of HeLa and Hep2. PCR
EHEC	Shiga or Verotoxin	Very watery and bloody	Colon	O157:H7 O26:H1 O111	RT-PCR and conventional PCR
EAEC	ST-like toxin or a plasmid-encoded enterotoxin	Acute or persistent diarrhea	—	Most are O-untypeable	
DAEC	Less well-established as pathogens				

- ETEC – Enterotoxigenic
- EIEC – Enteroinvasive
- EHEC – Enterohemorrhagic
- EAEC – Enteroaggregative
- DAEC – Diffusely adherent *E.coli*

Enteropathogenic *E.coli* (EPEC): These have been associated mainly with diarrhea in infants and children usually occurring as institutional outbreaks, occasionally causing sporadic diarrhea in children and less often in adults.

EPEC are identified by their O antigens (for example, 026:B6, 055:B5, 0111:B4 and so on). These can be identified by slide agglutination of the colonies obtained on culture using polyvalent and monovalent EPEC O antisera.

The pathogenesis of EPEC diarrhea is not fully understood. EPEC are non-invasive and do not produce enterotoxins. In infantile enteritis, a plasmid-encoded protein, EPEC adherence factor (**EAF**) has been incriminated with adherence. Another mechanism is by adherence to the enterocyte membrane. This activity is regulated by chromosomally coded locus of enterocyte effacement (**LEE**). This is a pathogenicity island by an intimin protein coded for by *eae* gene. This results in disruption of the brush border microvilli.

Enterotoxigenic *E.coli* (ETEC): Diarrhea caused by ETEC is of two epidemiological types.

- **Endemic in developing countries** of the tropics, seen in all age groups. Its severity varies from mild

watery diarrhea to a fatal disease indistinguishable from cholera.
- '**Traveller's diarrhea**' seen in persons from non-endemic areas visiting endemic areas. ETEC serotypes responsible for diarrhea are mostly 06, 08, 015, 025, 027, 0167.

It primarily adheres to intestinal mucosa by fimbriae called **colonisation factor antigens**, of which several types have been identified (CFA I, II, III, IV). ETEC produce enterotoxins which may be either LT or ST or both (described under virulence factors).

Diagnosis of ETEC diarrhea depends on demonstration of the enterotoxins in *E.coli* isolates by any of the methods listed in Table 29.3.

Enteroinvasive *E.coli* (EIEC): These resemble the '**Alkalescens–Dispar Group**'. They have been termed enteroinvasive *E.coli* because they have the capacity to invade interstitial epithelial cells in vivo resembling shigellosis. This ability to penetrate cells is determined by a large plasmid, detection of which can also be a diagnostic test. EIEC strains usually belong to serogroups 028 ac, 0112 ac, 0124, 0136, 0143, 0114, 0152, 0154.

Molecular serotyping of clinical isolates is presently used to diagnose EIEC infection. HeLa or HEp-2 cell invasion in culture can also be used as a diagnostic test. Mucopurulent keratoconjunctivitis in guinea pigs (Sereny's test) as a diagnostic test is no longer used.

Enterohemorrhagic *E.coli* (EHEC): These strains produce two potent toxins, verocytotoxin (VT) or Shiga-like toxin (SLT). They can give rise to diarrhea ranging in severity from mild diarrhea to fatal hemorrhagic colitis and hemorrhagic uremic syndrome (HUS), particularly in young children and the elderly. The primary target appears to be the vascular endothelial cells. This may explain the pathogenesis of HUS, in which a characteristic renal lesion is capillary microangiopathy. *E.coli* serotype O157: H7 is associated with EHEC diarrhoea and its complications. O26: H1 also belongs to this category.

Laboratory diagnosis of VTEC diarrhea can be made by detecting VT in feces directly or in culture isolates. Sensitivity can be considerably increased by using conventional or real-time PCR with specific DNA probes for the VT_1 and VT_2 genes. VT can be detected by its cytotoxic effects on Vero or HeLa cells. Most VTEC strains belong to the serotype O157:H7 which does not ferment sorbitol, unlike most *E.coli* strains. So, the use of sorbitol MacConkey medium helps in screening for O:157 VTEC.

Enteroaggregative *E.coli* (EAEC): These strains are so named because they appear aggregated in a 'stacked brick' formation on HEp-2 cells or glass. They have been associated with persistent diarrhea, especially in developing countries. Most of them are O-untypable, but many are H-typable.

Diffusely adherent *E.coli* (DAEC): This is less well established as pathogens.

Pyogenic infections: *E.coli* form the most common cause of intraabdominal infections, such as peritonitis and abscesses resulting from spillage of bowel contents. They also cause pyogenic infections in the perianal area. They are an important cause of neonatal meningitis.

Septicemia: Bloodstream invasion by *E.coli* may lead to fatal conditions like septic shock and 'systemic inflammatory response syndrome' (SIRS). As *E.coli* commonly show multiple drug resistance, antibiotic sensitivity testing of strains is important in treatment.

TRIBE: *EDWARDSIELLAE*

Edwardsiella tarda

This genus includes the species *Edwardsiella tarda* which has the general properties of Enterobacteriaceae. It is a motile rod, with weak fermentative powers. The name *tarda* refers to its tardy or weak fermentation of carbohydrates. It ferments glucose and maltose only with indole and H_2S production, citrate utilisation and decarboxylation of lysine and ornithine.

E.tarda is a normal intestinal inhabitant of snakes and other cold-blooded animals. It has been cultured from normal and diarrheaic human feces. Its pathogenic role is uncertain. *E.tarda* has been isolated from wounds, urine, blood and from CSF in cases of fatal meningitis.

TRIBE: *CITROBACTERIACEAE*

Citrobacter diversus and *Citrobacter freundii*

These are motile bacilli which utilise citrate, grow in KCN medium, produce H_2S and may or may not be late lactose fermenters. Three species are recognised: *Citro freundii* (with typical reactions), and *C.koseri* (formerly *C.diversus*) and *C.amalonaticus* which do not form H_2S. *C.freundii* strains were formerly classified as the '**Bethesda–Ballerup group**'. They exhibit extensive antigenic sharing with salmonellae. This may cause confusion in the diagnostic laboratory. Some strains (for example, the Bhatnagar strain) have a Vi antigen serologically identical to the antigen of *S.typhi* and *S.paratyphi* C. These may be used for the estimation of Vi antibodies or for raising Vi antisera.

Citrobacter is a normal intestinal inhabitant. It may cause infections of the urinary tract, gall bladder, middle ear and meninges.

TRIBE: KLEBSIELLAE

Morphology

This genus consists of non-motile rods, which are capsulated short, plump and straight, measuring about

---

Klebsiella pneumoniae

Clinical Case 2 An adult male was admitted to the ICU following a road traffic accident. He was put on a ventilator due to respiratory distress. On the third day, his condition worsened with symptoms of high fever and pneumonia. A blood culture yielded growth of lactose-fermenting mucoid colonies, identified as *Klebsiella pneumoniae*. They were multidrug-resistant, being sensitive only to imipenem and piperacillin-tazobactam. He was started on imipenem.

1–2 μm × 0.5–1.8 μm in size. The mucopolysaccharide capsule is often prominent and can be made out even in Gram-stained smears as halos around the rods. Klebsiellae are widely distributed in nature, occurring both as commensals in the intestines and as saprophytes in soil and water.

Classification

Their classification has undergone various modifications. They have been classified into three species based on biochemical reactions, and into over 80 serotypes based on the K antigens (Table 29.5).

Klebsiella pneumoniae

(Friedlander's bacillus, Bacillus mucosus capsulatus)
This bacillus was first isolated by Friedlander (1883) from fatal cases of pneumonia.

Cultural characteristics
They grow well on ordinary media, forming large, dome-shaped, mucoid colonies of varying degrees of stickiness. On MacConkey agar, they grow as lactose-forming colonies. Fresh clinical isolates are often very mucoid, almost flowing down the surface of the medium.

Biochemical reactions
Klebsiellae ferment carbohydrates (glucose, lactose, sucrose and mannitol) with the production of acid and abundant gas. The IMViC reaction is −−++). Biochemically variant strains are common. They can be differentiated based on the reactions mentioned below. *K.pneumoniae* subspecies *aerogenes* is the commonest clinical isolate.

Pathogenicity
It is the second most populous member of the aerobic bacterial flora of the human intestine. Currently, it is an important cause of healthcare-associated infections, sometimes replacing *E.coli* in some centres. Common infections associated with *K.pneumoniae* are pneumonia, urinary infection, septicemia, several pyogenic infections and, very rarely, diarrhea.

Pneumonia due to Klebsiella is a serious disease with high case fatality (*Case 2*):
- It occurs in middle-aged or older persons with risk factors such as alcoholism, chronic bronchopulmonary disease or diabetes mellitus.
- The disease is characterised by massive mucoid inflammatory exudate of lobar or lobular distribution, involving one or more lobes of the lung.
- Necrosis and abscess formation are more frequent than in pneumococcal pneumonia.
- Serotypes 1, 2 and 3 are usually responsible for pneumonia. Positive blood cultures can be obtained in about 25 per cent of the cases.

K.pneumoniae is a frequent cause of urinary infection, often causing catheter-associated UTI (CAUTI). As most strains are resistant to antibiotics, treatment poses serious problems. It also causes pyogenic infections such as abscesses, meningitis and septicemia. Mortality is high in neonatal sepsis caused by *Klebsiella pneumoniae*, as mostly multidrug-resistant strains cause these infections.

Diagnosis
Diagnosis is made by culturing appropriate specimens and identifying the isolate by biochemical reactions. Antibiotic sensitivity must be done. Many strains carry plasmids determining multiple drug resistance.

K.ozaenae is a bacillus associated with ozena, a disease characterised by foul-smelling nasal discharge. Identification is difficult due to wide variations in the biochemical reactions of individual strains. *K.ozaenae* belongs to capsular types 3–6.

K.rhinoscleromatis causes rhinoscleroma, a chronic granulomatous hypertrophy of the nose prevalent in southeastern Europe, India and in Central America.

Table 29.5 *Differentiation of* Klebsiella *species*

	K.pneumoniae	K.ozaenae	K.rhinoscleromatis
Gas from glucose	+	d	−
Acid from lactose	+	d	−
MR	−	+	+
VP	+	−	−
Citrate	+	d	−
Urease	+	d	−
Malonate	+	−	+
Lysine	+	d	−

The bacilli are seen intracellularly in lesions. It can be identified by biochemical reactions and belongs to capsular type 3.

The species *K.oxytoca* may rarely be isolated from clinical specimens.

Treatment

For bloodstream infections, emperic treament is done. 4.5 g of Piperacillin+Tazobactam every six hours or 3 g of Cefoperazone-sulbactam every 12 hours or Aminoglycoside, e.g., amikacin 20 mg/kg/day must be given.

Carbapenems like Imipenem and Meropenem must be given in resistant isolates and critically ill patients.

ENTEROBACTER CLOACAE AND ENTEROBACTER AGGLOMERANS

Formerly known as *Aerobacter*, these are motile, capsulated, lactose-fermenting rods which are indole- and MR-negative and VP- and citrate-positive. Two clinically relevant species are *E.cloacae* and *E.aerogenes* (Table 29.6).

They are normally found in feces, sewage, soil and water and rarely in urine, pus and other pathological materials. They may be responsible for healthcare-associated infections.

HAFNIA ALVEI

This is a motile, non-lactose fermenting bacillus which is indole- and MR-negative and VP- and citrate-positive. Biochemical reactions are best evident at 22°C; at 37°C, they may be negative or irregular. Only one genus is recognised—*H.alvei*. It is found in human and animal feces, sewage, soil and water, and is rarely isolated from clinical specimens.

SERRATIA MARCESCENS

Serratia forms characteristic pink, red or magenta, non-diffusible pigment called **prodigiosin** which is formed optimally at room temperature. Only one species is of

Table 29.6 *Differentiation between* E.cloacae *and* E.aerogenes

	E.cloacae	*E.aerogenes*
Gas from glycerol	–	+
Aesculin hydrolysis	–	+
Lysine decarboxylase	–	+
Arginine dihydrolase	+	+

medical importance—*S.marcescens* ('*Bacillus prodigiosus*'). It is pleomorphic, with minute coccobacillary and rod forms. It is a saprophyte found in water, soil and food. It may grow in sputum after collection and may be mistaken for hemoptysis because of the pigment formed ('pseudohemoptysis'). Healthcare-associated infections due to *S.marcescens* are being reported with increasing frequency. They have been reported to contaminate IV fluids, surgical instruments and antiseptic solutions. The bacillus has been associated with meningitis, endocarditis, septicemia, peritonitis, respiratory infection and many other conditions. Multiple drug resistance is common in hospital strains.

TRIBE: *PROTEEAE*

Proteus mirabilis and *Proteus vulgaris*

Proteus is a group of bacilli (Fig. 29.2) that constitute the tribe Proteeae, which are non-lactose fermenters and are not considered as coliform bacilli. However, they are also normal intestinal commensals and opportunistic pathogens like coliforms. The name *Proteus* refers to their pleomorphism, after the Greek god Proteus who could assume any shape.

The tribe Proteeae is classified into three genera: *Proteus*, *Morganella* and *Providencia*. Most of them, except for some *Providencia* strains, produce a powerful enzyme, urease, which rapidly hydrolyses urea to ammonia and carbon dioxide.

PPA Reaction: A characteristic feature which distinguishes Proteeae from other enterobacteria is the presence, in all members of the tribe, of the enzyme phenyl alanine deaminase which converts phenyl alanine to phenyl pyruvic acid (PPA reaction). All of them, with few exceptions, are Gram-negative, non-capsulated, pleomorphic, motile rods.

Fig. 29.2 Swarming of *Proteus* on blood agar

Proteeae
- Resistant to KCN
- Degrade tyrosine
- Fail to acidify lactose, dulcitol or malonate
- Do not form arginine or lysine decarboxylase or beta galactosidase
- MR-positive and VP-negative

The main differentiating features of medically important species of the *Proteus* bacilli are shown in Table 29.7.

Weil–Felix reaction: These bacilli possess somatic O and flagellar H antigens, which form the basis of Weil–Felix reaction for the diagnosis of few rickettsial infections. This is used as a diagnostic test due to cross-reaction of these antigens (heterophile antigens) with some Rickettsiae. However, this test is not widely recommended now. Three non-motile *Proteus* strains—OX2, OX19 and OXK—are used in the agglutination test.

Proteus species are widely distributed in nature as saprophytes. They are found in decomposing animal matter, sewage, manured soil, human and animal feces. They are frequently present on moist areas (perineal and axillary regions, and anterior urethra). They are opportunistic pathogens, often nosocomial, commonly responsible for urinary and septic infections. The genus *Proteus* contains two medically important species—*Pr.mirabilis*, which is an important urinary and nosocomial pathogen, and *Pr. vulgaris* which is found much less commonly in human infections. A characteristic putrid odour described as **'fishy' or 'seminal' odour** is produced in cultures.

Swarming: *Pr.mirabilis* and *Pr.vulgaris* swarm on solid culture media. Discrete colonies are seen in young cultures but thereafter actively motile cells spread on the surface of the plate in successive waves to form a thin filmy layer in concentric circles. This poses a problem in the laboratory, when mixed growth is obtained from clinical samples. Several methods have been used to inhibit swarming: namely, increasing the concentration of agar to 6%, incorporating chloral hydrate (1:500), sodium azide (1:500), alcohol (5–6%), sulphonamide, and surface active agents or boric acid (1:1000) in the medium. Swarming does not occur on MacConkey medium due to the presence of bile. Smooth, colourless colonies are formed on this medium.

The genus *Morganella* has only one species, *M.morganii*. It is commonly found in human and animal feces and causes urinary infection infrequently. Nosocomial wound infections also occur. It does not swarm in culture.

The genus *Providencia* contains three species which are associated with infections:
- *P.alcalifaciens* is sometimes seen in normal human feces but far more frequently in **diarrheal stools,** though its role in the disease is uncertain.
- *P.stuartii* is a common cause of **urinary infection** and infection in **burns.**
- *P.rettgerii* is part of the normal fecal flora of reptiles and amphibians, and sometimes causes **nosocomial infections** of the urinary tract, wounds, burns and blood.

Resistance to disinfectants and antiseptics: *Providencia*, particularly *P.stuartii,* is resistant to disinfectants such as chlorhexidine, cetrimide, benzalkonium chloride and heavy metal compounds such as silver sulphonamide. This is especially a problem in burns units, where it is a major cause of post-burn infection. It is sensitive to phenol and glutaraldehyde.

Treatment: *Proteus* species are resistant to many of the common antibiotics. An exception is *Pr.mirabilis* which is sensitive to ampicillin and cephalosporins. Amikacin and ciprofloxacin are generally effective in treatment of infections due to Providencia.

TRIBE: *ERWINIEAE*

Erwinia herbicola

These are anaerogenic bacilli forming a yellowish pigment, usually found in soil and causing plant infections. *E.herbicola* has occasionally been isolated from respiratory and urinary tract infections in immunocompromised or hospitalised patients.

Table 29.7 *Biochemical features of the genera* Proteus, Morganella *and* Providencia

Test	Pr. mirabilis	Pr. vulgaris	Morg. morganii	Prov. alcalifaciens	Prov. stuartii	Prov. rettgeri
Urease	+	+	+	–	±	+
Ornithine decarboxylase	+	–	+	–	–	–
Indole	–	+	+	+	+	+
Fermentation of adonitol	–	–	–	+	±	±
Fermentation of trehalose	+	±	±	–	+	–

RECAP

- *Escherichia coli* is an aerobe and a facultatively anaerobic, motile, Gram-negative rod found as normal commensal of the intestine. It is oxidase-negative and catalase-positive. The organisms form pink lactose-fermenting colonies on MacConkey agar.
- *E.coli* causes diarrhea or urinary tract infection (UTI), meningitis and respiratory tract infection.
- Virulence factors include the 'P' pili in UTI; K1 capsule (neonatal meningitis); labile and/or stable toxins (LT and ST) in enterotoxigenic *E.coli* (ETEC) gastrointestinal disease; adherence factor and enterocyte effacement factor in enteropathogenic *E.coli* (EPEC) disease; invasiveness in enteroinvasive *E.coli* (EIEC); Shiga-like toxin in enterohemorrhagic *E.coli* (EHEC).
- Identification is based on biochemical reaction: IMViC ++ - -, urease-negative.
- Members of the genus *Klebsiella* are facultatively anaerobic, non-motile, Gram-negative bacilli which are oxidase-negative and catalase-positive. The organisms form pink colonies (lactose-fermenting) on MacConkey agar.
- They are associated with multidrug-resistant nosocomial infections, urinary tract infections, septicemia, chest infections and meningitis.
- Other lactose-fermenting members of Enterobacteriaceae are *Enterobacter*, *Edwardsiella*, *Citrobacter* and *Serratia*. They may cause opportunistic infections in debilitated or immunocompromised patients; this is difficult to treat because the bacteria tend to develop resistance to a wide range of antimicrobial substances.
- Members of the genus *Proteus* are non-lactose fermenting, facultatively anaerobic, motile, Gram-negative bacilli which are oxidase-negative and catalase-positive. They are usually capable of utilising citrate as their sole carbon source and exhibit swarming on nutrient and blood agar. They are commensals of the intestine and cause urinary tract and wound infections.
- Members of the genus *Morganella* and *Providencia* belong to tribe Proteeae. Like other members of Enterobacteriaceae, they may be found in the hospital environment and cause urinary tract and wound infections.

ESSAYS

1. Enumerate the bacteria causing UTI and describe the laboratory diagnosis of UTI.
2. Enumerate the organisms causing diarrhea. Describe the pathogenesis and diagnosis of diarrheagenic *E.coli*.

SHORT NOTES

1. Laboratory diagnosis of UTI
2. Virulence factors of *E.coli*
3. Significant bacteriuria (definition)
4. Swarming of proteus and its inhibition
5. Uropathogenic *E.coli*
6. EPEC
7. EIEC

Enterobacteriaceae II: Shigella

INTRODUCTION

Dysentery is a clinical condition of multiple origin, characterised by the frequent passage of bloodstained, mucopurulent stools. The two common types of dysentery are bacillary and amebic. The causative agents of bacillary dysentery belong to the genus *Shigella*, so named after Shiga, who in 1896 isolated the first member of this genus from epidemic dysentery in Japan. Some other bacilli, such as enteroinvasive *E.coli*, *Vibrio parahaemolytius* and *Campylobacter*, can also produce the clinical picture of dysentery.

Shigella

Clinical Case A 40-year-old man had travelled to a peripheral village in southern India where he stayed for three days. After returning, he developed abdominal cramps with mild fever which was followed by increased frequency of stools with blood and mucus. He visited the hospital where a stool sample was sent to the Microbiology lab. On microscopic examination, plenty of pus cells were found and culture was positive for non-lactose fermenting bacteria on MacConkey agar which agglutinated with *Shigella flexneri* antisera. No antibiotics were given at this time and only supportive therapy was provided.

Morphology

Shigellae are short, Gram-negative rods, about 0.5×1–3 μm in size. They are non-motile, non-sporing and non-capsulated. Fimbriae may be present.

Cultural characteristics

They are aerobes and facultative anaerobes, with a growth temperature range of 10–40°C and optima of 37°C and pH 7.4. They grow on ordinary media but less readily than other enterobacteria. After overnight incubation, colonies are small, about 2 mm in diameter, circular, convex, smooth and translucent. Occasionally on primary isolation and frequently in subcultures, a proportion of the colonies may be of the rough type. Colonies on MacConkey agar are colourless due to the absence of lactose fermentation. An exception is *S.sonnei* which ferments lactose late and forms pale pink colonies. Deoxycholate citrate agar (DCA) and xylose lysine deoxycholate (XLD) is a useful selective medium (in which shigella do not have a black centre as against *Salmonella* which appears red with a black centre). Growth is inhibited on Wilson and Blair bismuth sulphite medium.

Resistance

Shigellae are not especially resistant. They are killed at 56°C in one hour and by 1% phenol in 30 minutes. In ice they last for 1–6 months. They remain viable in moist environments for days, but die rapidly on drying. In feces, they die within a few hours due to the acidity produced by the growth of coliforms. *S.sonnei* is in general more resistant than other shigella species.

Biochemical reactions

Shigellae are MR positive and reduce nitrates to nitrites. They cannot utilise citrate as the sole source of carbon, do not form H_2S and are inhibited by KCN. Catalase is produced, except by *S.dysenteriae* type 1. Glucose is fermented with the production of acid, without gas, except for the Newcastle and Manchester biotypes of *S.flexneri* type 6, and some strains of *S.boydii* types

13 and 14, which form gas. Fermentation of mannitol is of importance in classification and shigellae have traditionally been divided into mannitol fermenting and non-fermenting species. *S.flexneri*, *S.boydii* and *S.sonnei* ferment mannitol, while *S.dysenteriae* does not. Exceptions are not infrequent. Lactose and sucrose are not fermented, except by *S.sonnei* which ferments them late. Adonitol, inositol and salicin are not fermented (Table 30.1).

Antigenic structure

Shigellae possess one or more 'major' antigens and a large number of 'minor' somatic O antigens. Some strains possess K antigens. These are not relevant in typing but may sometimes interfere with agglutination by O antisera. Fimbrial antigens are also present. In general, the antigenic structure of shigellae is simple, compared to the complex structure of salmonellae. There is considerable antigenic sharing between some members of the genus as well as between shigellae and *E.coli*. Common fimbrial antigens may also occur, particularly in *S.flexneri*. It is, therefore, important that the identification of shigellae be made by a combination of antigenic and biochemical properties and not by slide agglutination alone.

Classification

Shigellae are classified into four species or subgroups based on a combination of biochemical and serological characteristics. Serotypes are distinguished within the species.

S.dysenteriae (subgroup A): This species of mannitol non-fermenting bacilli consists of ten serotypes. Type 1 is the bacillus originally described by Shiga (*S.shigae*). It is indole negative and is the only member of the family that is always **catalase negative**. (*S.schmitzi* and *S.sonnei* are invariably catalase posi-

tive, while among other shigella species, some strains may be catalase negative.)

S.dysenteriae type 1 forms a toxin (Shiga toxin), the earliest example of an exotoxin produced by a Gram-negative bacillus. Three types of toxic activity have been demonstrated in shigella culture filtrates:

- **Neurotoxicity**, demonstrable by paralysis and death on injection into mice or rabbits. Though known as 'neurotoxin', the primary site of its action appears to be not the nervous tissue but the blood vessels, mainly of the central nervous system, with the neurological effects being secondary.
- **Enterotoxicity**, with induction of fluid accumulation in ligated rabbit ileal loop. Two new shigella enterotoxins have been identified, designated ShET-1 and -2, the former confined to *S.flexneri* 2a and the latter more widespread.
- **Cytotoxicity**, causing cytopathic changes in cultured Vero cells. This appears to be the same as verotoxin 1 (or Shiga-like toxin) produced by certain strains of *E.coli* (VTEC). The toxin consists of binding (B) and active (A) subunits. Subunit A is divided into two fragments, A1 and A2. Fragment A1 appears to inactivate host cell 60 S ribosome, interfering with protein synthesis.

S.dysenteriae type 2 (*S.schmitzi*) forms indole and ferments sorbitol and rhamnose. Serotypes 3–7 were described by Large and Sachs in India and hence used to be known as the Large–Sachs group. Three further serotypes have been described, making a total of ten.

S.flexneri (subgroup B): This group is named after Flexner, who described the first of the mannitol fermenting shigellae from the Philippines (1900). This group is biochemically heterogeneous and antigenically the most complex among shigellae. Based on type-specific and group-specific antigens, they have been

Table 30.1 *Distinguishing features of the* Shigella *species*

Subgroup	A	B	C	D
Species	S.dysenteriae	S.flexneri	S.boydii	S.sonnei
Mannitol	–	A	A	A
Lactose	–	–	–	A Late
Sucrose	–	–	–	A Late
Dulcitol	–	–	d	–
Indole	d	d	d	–
Ornithine decarboxylase	–	–	–	+
Serotypes	10	6 + variants	15	Only one

A = Acid d = Variable

classified into six serotypes (1–6) and several subtypes (1a; 1b; 2a, 2b; 3a, 3b, 3c, 4a, 4b, 5a, 5b). In addition, two antigenic 'variants' called X and Y are recognised, which lack the type-specific antigens. Serotype 6 is always indole negative and occurs in three biotypes, some of which form gas from sugars (Table 30.2).

S.boydii (subgroup C): This group consists of dysentery bacilli that resemble *S.flexneri* biochemically but not antigenically. The group is named after Boyd, who first described these strains from India (1931). Fifteen serotypes have been identified. *S.boydii* are isolated least frequently from cases of bacillary dysentery.

S.sonnei (subgroup D): This bacillus, first described by Sonne (1915) in Denmark, ferments lactose and sucrose late. It is indole negative. It is antigenically homogeneous but may occur in two forms, phase I and phase II, the latter forming colonies that are larger, flatter and more irregular. On subculture, phase I produces both types of colonies but phase II is considered to be a loss variation. Organisms in phase II may be isolated from patients but are more common in convalescents and carriers.

S.sonnei causes the mildest form of bacillary dysentery. In many cases, the disease may only be a mild diarrhea. However, *S.sonnei* infection persists as the most common shigellosis in advanced countries. *S.sonnei* is serologically homogeneous and is classified by colicin typing tnto 26 types.

Pathogenicity

Shigellae cause bacillary dysentery. Infection occurs by ingestion. The minimum infective dose is low—as few as 10–100 bacilli are capable of initiating the disease, probably because they survive gastric acidity better than other enterobacteria.

Invasive property: Their pathogenic mechanisms resemble those of enteroinvasive *E.coli*. Organisms bind to M cells and invade the lamina propria, then the neighbouring enterocytes from the bottom (basolateral surface). Bacteria grow and induce actin polymerisation that pushes organisms laterally into neighbouring cells, where they continue to spread, causing cell death and inflammation. Inflammatory reaction develops with capillary thrombosis, leading to necrosis of patches of epithelium, which slough off, leaving behind transverse superficial ulcers. Bacteremia may occur in severe infections, particularly in malnourished children and in AIDS.

The invasive property of the bacillus can be demonstrated by its ability to penetrate cultured HeLa or HEp-2 cells or by the Congo red binding test. Invasive property is related to the presence in the bacillus of large plasmids (M.W. 140 × 106) coding for the outer membrane protein responsible for cell penetration. These proteins are called '**virulence marker antigens**' (VMA). Detection of VMA by ELISA serves as a virulence test for Shigellae, as for enteroinvasive *E.coli*.

Exotoxin: Though *S.dysenteriae* type 1 forms an exotoxin, it appears to be much less important in pathogenesis than the ability of the bacillus to penetrate and multiply in colonic mucosa. Non-toxigenic mutants can still cause dysentery but not non-invasive ones. It is also known as **shiga toxin or verotoxin** which is similar to EHEC verotoxin. It acts by inhibition of protein synthesis. It has A and B subunits. They can be tested by toxicity in vero cell lines.

Endotoxin: This may be due to the LPS of Gram-negative cell wall.

Bacillary dysentery: This disease has a short incubation period (1–7 days, usually 48 hours):

- The **onset** and **clinical course** are variable and are largely determined by the virulence of the infecting strain.
- The main **clinical features** are frequent passage of loose, scanty feces containing blood and mucus, along with abdominal cramps and tenesmus (*Case*).
- Fever and vomiting may be present.
- **Complications** are most often seen in infection with *S.dysenteriae* type 1 and include arthritis, toxic neuritis, conjunctivitis, parotitis and, in children, intussusception.
- **Hemolytic uremic syndrome** may occur as a complication in severe cases.
- The **severity** of the disease may vary from acute fulminating dysentery to mild diarrhea.

As the term bacillary dysentery refers only to the more severe cases, the term **shigellosis** has been

Table 30.2 *Biotypes of* S.flexneri *type 6*

Biotype	Fermentation of	
	Glucose	Mannitol
Boyd 88	A	A
Manchester	AG	AG
Newcastle	A or AG	–
A=Acid	AG=Acid and Gas	

employed to include the whole spectrum of diseases caused by shigellae.

Epidemiology

Human beings are the only natural hosts for shigellae. Epidemics of bacillary dysentery have always accompanied wars and often influenced their outcome. Epidemics in civilian communities are associated with poverty and lack of sanitation.

The only source of infection is human beings—cases, or less often, carriers. Chronic carriage is rare, the bacilli disappearing from feces within a few weeks, except in some malnourished children or AIDS patients. Shigellae exhibit a high rate of secondary household transmission. The **modes of transmission** may be as follows:

- **Direct**, through contaminated fingers: 'hand-to-mouth' infection
- Through **fomites** such as door handles, water taps and lavatory seats
- Through **water**
- Through **contaminated food or drink**; shigellosis, especially *S.sonnei* infection, may occur as food poisoning
- Through **flies** which may transmit the infection as mechanical vectors
- In young male homosexuals as part of the **gay bowel syndrome**

Shigellosis is worldwide in distribution but epidemiologically there are a number of differences in the nature and extent of the infection in affluent and poor countries. Where environmental sanitation is good, shigellosis is mainly seen in young children and in special situations like mental hospitals, and *S.sonnei* is the predominant infecting agent. In countries where environmental sanitation is poor, endemic shigellosis is found in all age groups and is caused by all species. In India, *S.flexneri* has been the predominant species, having formed 50–85 per cent of isolates in different series. *S.dysenteriae* (8–25 per cent) and *S.sonnei* (2–24 per cent) are the next. *S.boydii* (0–8 per cent) has been isolated least frequently.

The picture has changed in recent years. After a long period of quiescence, *S.dysenteriae* type I suddenly appeared in an extensive and virulent epidemic form in Central America in 1968. In 1973, a similar outbreak started in Bangladesh and later in Sri Lanka. Several localised outbreaks were observed in India from 1974, followed by extensive epidemics in various states from the early 1980s. The epidemic strains showed plasmid-borne multiple drug resistance.

Laboratory diagnosis

1. Specimen: Diagnosis is made by isolating the bacillus from feces. Fresh feces should be inoculated without delay or transported in a suitable medium such as **Sachs' buffered glycerol saline** or **Gram-negative broth**, pH 7.0–7.4, which are less inhibitory for *Shigella*.

- **Gram-negative broth** is a selective broth used for culturing shigella from stool specimens. It contains sodium deoxycholate to inhibit Gram-positive bacteria and early replication of non-enteric Gram-negative pathogens. It should be subcultured 6–8 hours after incubation. **Rectal swabs are not satisfactory**.

  Enrichment media like **selenite F broth or Salmonella Shigella (SS) broth** can be used for selecting out the pathogens though they are better for *Salmonella*.

2. Microscopy: It shows plenty of pus cells.

3. Culture: For inoculation, it is best to use mucus flakes if they are present in the sample.

- **MacConkey** and **DCA** or **XLD** plates are inoculated. After overnight incubation at 37°C, the plates are inspected for pale or pink-coloured colonies, which are identified by biochemical reactions. Any non-motile bacillus that is urease, citrate, H_2S and KCN negative should be further investigated by biochemical tests. Identification is confirmed by slide agglutination with polyvalent and monovalent sera.
- Another selective medium used for isolation is the **SS agar** where colonies are colourless.
- **Hektoen enteric (HE) agar** also contains bile salts as inhibitory agents and some dyes, due to which colonies appear green, with colour fading to the periphery.

4. Serology: Demonstration of antibodies in sera is not useful.

Treatment

Uncomplicated shigellosis is a self-limiting condition in which the patient usually recovers spontaneously in a few days. However, in acute cases, particularly in infants and young children, dehydration has to be corrected promptly. Oral rehydration is adequate in most cases.

Routine antibacterial treatment is not indicated in dysentery. Multiple drug resistant plasmids are widely prevalent in shigellae. Indiscriminate antibiotic treatment will only worsen the problem of drug resistance in intestinal bacteria. Antibiotics should therefore be limited to severe or toxic cases, and to the very young, debilitated and the aged. The choice of antibiotic should be based on the sensitivity of the prevailing strain. Many strains are still susceptible to nalidixic acid or norfloxacin and other fluoroquinolones.

Control

Control consists essentially in improving personal and environmental sanitation. Antibiotics have no place in prophylaxis. No effective vaccine is available.

RECAP

- *Shigella* is a genus of the family Enterobacteriaceae, which comprises rod-shaped bacteria that are non-motile, facultatively anaerobic, usually catalase positive and oxidase negative, and Gram negative.
- The species can be distinguished biochemically and on the basis of serotypes. The four main species are *Shigella dysenteriae*, *Shigella flexneri*, *Shigella sonnei* and *Shigella boydii*.
- These bacteria are highly infectious, as 10–100 organisms can initiate disease. Humans are the only reservoir.
- The *Shigella* species causes dysentery.
- Organisms bind to M cells and invade the lamina propria, causing cell death and inflammation, leaving behind transverse superficial ulcers.
- *S.dysenteriae* type I also produces an exotoxin.
- The disease is prevented by proper hygiene and food handling. Antibiotics are used to reduce transmission as this is a serious invasive disease.

ESSAY

1. Describe the laboratory diagnosis of bacillary dysentery.

SHORT ANSWERS

1. Shigellosis
2. Bacillary dysentery

SHORT NOTES

1. Selective media for shigella
2. Enrichment media for shigella
3. Classification of shigella
4. Sereny's test

31 Enterobacteriaceae III: Salmonella

INTRODUCTION

The genus *Salmonella* consists of bacilli that parasitise the intestines of a large number of vertebrate species and infect human beings, leading to enteric fever, gastroenteritis, septicemia with or without focal suppuration, and the carrier state.

The most important member of the genus is *Salmonella* Typhi, the causative agent of typhoid fever. The typhoid bacillus was first observed by Eberth (1880) in the mesenteric nodes and spleen of fatal cases of typhoid fever and was isolated by Gaffky (1884).

It came to be known as the Eberth–Gaffky bacillus or *Eberthella typhi*. Salmon and Smith (1885) described a bacillus which was believed to cause hog cholera (mistakenly, as it is a viral disease). This bacillus, later called *S.cholerae-suis,*, was the first of a series of similar organisms to be isolated from animals and human beings, the genus *Salmonella*. It was subsequently realised that the typhoid bacillus also belonged to this group, in spite of minor biochemical differences, and it was redesignated *S.*Typhi, the genus *Eberthella* having been abolished.

Salmonellae currently comprise above 2000 serotypes or species, all of them potentially pathogenic. For practical and clinical purposes, Salmonellae may be divided into two groups:

- **Typhoidal**: The enteric fever group, consisting of the typhoid and paratyphoid bacilli that are exclusively or primarily human parasites; and
- **Non-typhoidal**: The food poisoning group, which essentially comprises animal parasites but which can also infect human beings, producing gastroenteritis, septicemia or localised infections.

Morphology

Salmonellae are Gram-negative rods, about 1–3 × 0.5 μm in size. They are motile with peritrichate flag-

---

Salmonella

Clinical Case A 10-year-old boy was admitted to the Pediatrics ward with a history of remittent fever which increased gradually in a step-ladder pattern over the previous 10 days. He had taken antipyretics and ciprofloxacin, prescribed by a local private practitioner. At presentation to the hospital, he complained of lack of appetite, pain in the abdomen and lethargy. On examination, he was found to have fever with anemia and hepatosplenomegaly. A blood sample was obtained for culture and serology. His blood culture was positive for *Salmonella* typhi and the Widal test was negative. However, the IgM antibody test for *S.*Typhi was positive. His isolate was resistant to ciprofloxacin and so he was treated with ceftriaxone. He responded after 10 days of therapy.

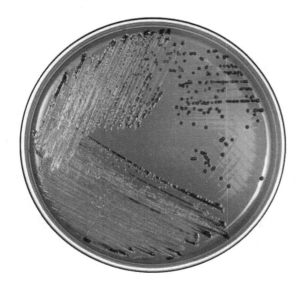

Fig. 31.1 Salmonella on XLD media

ella, except for *S.*Gallinarum and *S.*Pullorum, which are always non-motile. Non-motile mutants of other types may sometimes be found. They do not form capsules or spores but may possess fimbriae.

Cultural characteristics

Salmonellae are aerobic and facultatively anaerobic, growing readily on simple media over a pH range of 6–8 and temperature 15–41°C (optimum 37°C). Colonies are large, 2–3 mm in diameter, circular, low convex and smooth. They are more translucent than coliform colonies. On **MacConkey agar**, they grow as non-lactose fermenting colonies. On **deoxycholate citrate** media and **XLD** (xylose lysine deoxycholate), colonies show black heads due to H_2S production (Fig. 31.1). On the **Wilson** and **Blair** bismuth sulphite medium, jet black colonies with a metallic sheen are formed due to the production of H_2S. *S.*Paratyphi A and other species that do not form H_2S produce green colonies.

Selenite F and **tetrathionate** broth are commonly employed as enrichment media.

Biochemical reactions

Salmonellae ferment glucose, mannitol and maltose, forming acid and gas. An important exception is *S.*Typhi, which is anaerogenic. Lactose, sucrose and salicin are not fermented. Indole is not produced. They are MR positive, VP negative and citrate positive. *S.*Typhi and a few other salmonellae do not grow in Simmons' citrate medium as they need tryptophan

Table 31.1 *Biochemical characteristics of typhoid and paratyphoid bacilli*

	Glucose	*Xylose*	*d-Tartrate*	*Mucate*
*S.*Typhi	A	d	A	d
*S.*Paratyphi A	AG	–	–	–
*S.*Paratyphi B	AG	AG	–	AG
*S.*Paratyphi C	AG	AG	AG	–

as the growth factor. Urea is not hydrolysed. H_2S is produced, except by *S.*Paratyphi A, *S.*Choleraesuis and some other species.

The enteric fever group may be classified biochemically (Table 31.1).

Resistance

The bacilli are killed at 55°C in one hour or at 60°C in 15 minutes. Boiling or chlorination of water and pasteurisation of milk destroys the bacilli. In polluted water and soil, they survive for weeks and in ice for months. Cultures may be viable for years if prevented from drying. They are killed within five minutes by mercuric chloride (1:500) or 5% phenol.

Classification and nomenclature

Kauffmann–White scheme: Salmonella has traditionally been named and identified using the Kauffmann–White scheme. Inclusion in the genus is based on common biochemical properties. Classification within the genus takes place by antigenic characterisation. This scheme depends on the identification, by agglutination, of the structural formulae of the O and H antigens of the strains (Table 31.2).

This is also used for the identification of isolates. According to this, salmonellae are initially classified into serological groups, based on the presence of distinctive O antigen factors, which are designated 1, 2, 3, etc. Strains possessing factor 2 belong to group A, factor 4 to group B, factor 9 to group D and so on. Within each group, differentiation of serotypes is by identification of phase 1 and 2 flagellar antigens. Earlier serogroups were designated by capital letters, A to Z, and as more were added, they were assigned numbers—currently 51–67. Within each group, differentiation of serotypes is by identification of phase 1 and 2 flagellar antigens. Sometimes, serotypes may have to be further differentiated. Thus, *S.*Gallinarum and *S.*Pullorum cannot be distinguished serologically but can be identified by biochemical reactions.

Table 31.2   *Kaufmann–White scheme: Illustrative examples**

Serogroups	Serotype	Antigen O	Antigen H	
			Phase I	*Phase II*
A	S.paratyphi A	1, 2, 12	a	–
B	S.paratyphi B	1, 4, 5, 12	b	1, 2
	S.typhimurium	1, 4, 5, 12	i	1, 2
	S.chester	4, 5, 12	e, h	e, n, x
C1	S.paratyphi C	6, 7, (Vi)	c	1, 5
	S.cholerae-suis	6, 7	c	1, 5
C2	S.muenchen	6, 8	d	1, 2
D	S.typhi	9, 12, (Vi)	d	–
	S.enteritidis	1, 9, 12	g, m	–
	S.gallinarum	1, 9, 12	–	–
E1	S.anatum	3, B	e, h	1, 6

*As the Kauffman–White scheme was created before modifications in nomenclature, this table has retained the earlier style. However, in the text, current nomenclature is used.

(*S*.Gallinarum is anaerogenic and ferments dulcitol, unlike *S*.Pullorum.) Important pathogens such as *S*.Typhi, *S*.paratyphi A and B, and *S*.typhimurium can be further typed for epidemiological purposes by phage susceptibility, biochemical properties, antibiogram and molecular typing.

The classification and nomenclature of salmonellae has undergone modification over the years. Modern taxonomical techniques have shown that all the members of the genus Salmonellae are very closely related in a genetic, phylogenetic and evolutionary sense. Variations in properties such as antigenic structure, biochemical reactions and host preferences exhibited by different strains can therefore be considered as intraspecies divergences.

DNA hybridisation studies have shown that there are two species in the genus *Salmonella*:

1. **Species enterica** – which is further divided into six subspecies

   I   – *S.enterica* subsp. *enterica*

   II   – *S.enterica* subsp. *salamae*

   IIIa – *S.enterica* subsp. *arizonae*

   IIIb – *S.enterica* subsp. *diarizonae*

   IV   – *S.enterica* subsp. *houtenae*

   VI   – *S.enterica* subsp. *indica*

   Most human infections are caused by subspecies *enterica* and rarely by *arizonae*.

2. **Species bongori** (earlier subspecies V)

All these species are further divided into more than 2500 serovars or serotypes. The salmonella serotype is unique in that each serotype is considered as a species. The genus name is given followed by the word 'serotype' and then the serotype name, for example,

Salmonella typhi is written as **Salmonella enterica subspecies enterica serovar Typhi** or in short, *Salmonella* Typhi or *S*.Typhi (the serovar is not written in italics and also starts with a capital letter). The nomenclature system is based on recommendations from the WHO Collaborating Centre.

Antigenic structure

Salmonellae possess the following antigens based on which they are classified and identified:

- Flagellar antigen H
- Somatic antigen O
- Surface antigen Vi, found in some species

Several strains carry fimbriae. Fimbrial antigens are not important in identification but may cause confusion due to their non-specific nature and widespread prevalence among enterobacteria.

H antigen: This antigen present on the flagella is a heat labile protein. It is destroyed by boiling or by treatment with alcohol but not by formaldehyde. When mixed with antisera, H suspensions agglutinate rapidly, producing large, loose, fluffy clumps. The H antigen is strongly immunogenic and induces antibody formation rapidly and in high titres following infection or immunisation. The flagellar antigen is of a dual nature, occurring in one of two phases.

O antigen: The somatic O antigen is a phospholipid–protein–polysaccharide complex which forms an integral part of the cell wall. It is identical to endotoxin. It can be extracted from the bacterial cell by treatment with trichloracetic acid, as first shown by Boivin (and therefore called the **Boivin antigen**). Treatment with phenol splits off the protein moiety, removing the antigenicity but retaining the toxicity of the complex.

The O antigen is unaffected by boiling, alcohol or weak acids. When mixed with antisera, O antigen suspensions form compact, chalky, granular clumps. O agglutination takes place more slowly and at a higher optimum temperature (50–55°C) than H agglutination (37°C). The antibody to the O antigen is cross-reactive while that to the H antigen is a more reliable indicator.

The O antigen is not a single factor but a mosaic of two or more antigenic factors. Salmonellae are classified into a number of groups based on the presence of characteristic O antigens on the bacterial surface.

Vi antigen: Many strains of S. Typhi fail to agglutinate with the O antiserum when freshly isolated. This is due to the presence of a surface polysaccharide antigen enveloping the O antigen. Felix and Pitt, who first described this antigen, believed that it was related to virulence and gave it the name Vi antigen. It is analogous to the K antigens of coliforms. It is heat labile. Bacilli that are not agglutinable with the O antiserum become agglutinable after boiling or heating at 60°C for one hour. It is also destroyed by N HCl and 0.5 N NaOH. It is unaffected by alcohol or 0.2% formaldehyde.

Originally observed in S. Typhi, the Vi antigen with similar antigenic specificity is present in S. Paratyphi C and S. Dublin, as well as in certain strains of *Citrobacter* (the Bethesda–Ballerup group). The Vi antigen tends to be lost on serial subculture. The Vi polysaccharide acts as a virulence factor by inhibiting phagocytosis, resisting complement activation and bacterial lysis by the alternative pathway and peroxidase mediated killing. In human volunteer experiments, strains possessing the Vi antigen were found to cause clinical disease more consistently than those lacking it.

The Vi antigen is poorly immunogenic and only low titres of antibody are produced following infection. No Vi antibody is induced by the phenolised vaccine, though low titres are produced by the alcoholised vaccine. The protective efficacy of the Vi antigen is demonstrated by the success of the purified Vi vaccine for typhoid now in routine use. Detection of the Vi antibody is not helpful for diagnosis and hence the Vi antigen is not employed in the Widal test. The antibody disappears early in convalescence. Its persistence indicates the development of the carrier state. The Vi antigen affords a method of epidemiological typing of S. Typhi strains based on specific Vi bacteriophages.

Antigenic variations

The antigens of salmonellae undergo phenotypic and genotypic variation:

H–O variation: This variation is associated with the loss of flagella. When salmonellae are grown on agar containing phenol (1:800), flagella are inhibited. This change is phenotypic and temporary. Flagella reappear when the strain is subcultured on media without phenol. Rarely, salmonellae may lose their flagella by mutation. A stable non-motile mutant of S. Typhi is the 901-O strain which is widely employed for the preparation of O-agglutinable bacterial suspensions. Generally, the loss of flagella is not total and only a diminution in the number of flagella and the quantity of the H antigen occurs. Flagellated cells are found in small numbers in such cultures. To obtain a population of motile cells rich in H antigen from such cultures, selection may be carried out by using Craigie's tube (Fig. 31.2). This consists of a wide tube containing soft agar (0.2%) at the centre of which is embedded a short, narrow tube open at both ends in such a way that it projects above the agar. The strain is inoculated carefully into the inner tube. After incubation, subcultures withdrawn from the top of the agar outside the central tube will yield a population of motile cells. Instead of Craigie's tube, a U-tube of soft agar may be employed, inoculation being made into one limb and subculture taken from the other.

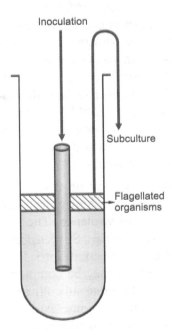

Fig. 31.2 Craigie's tube

Phase variation: The flagellar antigens of most salmonellae occur in one of two phases, that is, the flagella may exhibit one or the other of two alternative sets of antigens, defined by two separate sets of genes in the bacterial genome. Phase 1 antigens are either specific for a species or shared by a few species only. Hence it is called the 'specific' phase. Phase 2 antigens are widely shared and hence this is called the 'non-specific' or 'group' phase. Phase 1 antigens are designated a, b, c, d, etc., and after z, as z1, z2, etc. Phase 2 antigens are far fewer and are termed 1, 2, etc. In some species, antigens belonging to Phase 1 may occur as Phase 2 antigens (for example, e, n, x, z15). Strains that possess both phases are called **diphasic**. Some, like S. Typhi, occur only in Phase 1 and are called **monophasic**.

A culture will contain cells with the flagellar antigens of both phases, but generally one or the other phase will predominate so that the culture is agglutinated only by one of the phase antisera. For serotyping of *Salmonella* isolates, it may be necessary to identify the flagellar antigens of both phases. A culture in Phase 1 can be converted to Phase 2 by passing it through a Craigie's tube containing specific Phase 1 antiserum, and the reverse conversion achieved by using Phase 2 antiserum.

V–W variation: Fresh isolates of S. Typhi generally carry a surface layer of Vi antigen that completely masks the O antigen. Such bacilli are agglutinable with the Vi antiserum but not with the O antiserum. This is called the **V form**. After a number of subcultures, the Vi antigen is completely lost. Such cultures are not agglutinable with the Vi antiserum but readily agglutinable with the O antiserum. This is called the **W form**. Intermediate stages during the loss of the Vi antigen, when the bacillus is agglutinable with both Vi and O antisera, are called **VW forms**.

Other Vi-containing bacilli such as S. Paratyphi C and S. Dublin seldom have the O antigen completely masked by the Vi antigen.

S–R variation: The smooth-to-rough variation is associated with a change in colony morphology and loss of the O antigen and of virulence. The colony becomes large, rough and irregular. Suspensions in saline are autoagglutinable. Conversion into R forms occurs by mutation. R forms may be common in laboratory strains maintained by serial subcultivation. S–R variation may be prevented to some extent by maintaining cultures on Dorset's egg media in the cold, or ideally by lyophilisation.

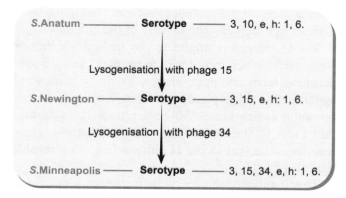

Fig. 31.3 Phage conversion of *Salmonella* serotypes

Mucoid colonies, associated with the development of a new mucoid or 'M' antigen, have been described with S. Paratyphi B and some other species.

Variations in the O antigen: Changes in the structural formulae of the O antigen may be induced by lysogenisation with some converting phages, resulting in the alteration of serotypes. Thus, S. Anatum is converted into S. Newington by one phage and the latter into S. Minneapolis by another phage (Fig. 31.3).

Pathogenicity

Salmonellae are strict parasites of animals or humans. S. Typhi, S. Paratyphi A and usually, but not invariably, S. Paratyphi B are confined to human beings. Other salmonellae are parasitic in various animals—domestic animals, rodents, reptiles—and birds. Some species are host adapted, S. Abortus-equi found only in horses, S. Abortus-ovis in sheep and S. Gallinarum in poultry. Others such as S. Typhimurium have a wide host range, affecting animals, birds and humans. Infection in animals may vary from an asymptomatic condition to fatal and sometimes epizootic disease. S. Typhimurium and S. Enteritidis cause fatal septicemia in rats and mice.

Salmonellae cause the following clinical syndromes in humans:
- Enteric fever
- Gastroenteritis or food poisoning
- Septicemia, with or without local suppurative lesions

ENTERIC FEVER

The term enteric fever includes typhoid fever caused by S. Typhi and paratyphoid fever caused by S. Paratyphi A, B and C.

Typhoid fever was once prevalent all over the world and was not well demarcated from other prolonged fevers. A detailed study of the disease was presented by Bretonneau (1826), who identified the intestinal lesions. The name typhoid was given by Louis (1829) to distinguish it from typhus fever. Budd (1856) pointed out that the disease was transmitted through the excreta of patients. Eberth (1880) described the typhoid bacillus and Gaffky (1884) isolated it in pure culture. Its causative role was confirmed by Metchnikoff and Besredka (1900) by infecting apes experimentally. S. Paratyphi A was isolated by Gwyn (1898), S. Paratyphi B (S. schottmulleri) by Achard and Bensaude (1896) and S. Paratyphi C (S. hirschfeldii) by Uhlenhuth and Hubener (1908) from cases resembling typhoid fever.

The infection is acquired by ingestion. In human volunteer experiments, the ID50 was found to be about 10^3 to 10^6 bacilli. On reaching the gut, the bacilli attach themselves to the microvilli of the ileal mucosa and penetrate to the lamina propria and submucosa. They are phagocytosed there by polymorphs and macrophages. The ability to resist intracellular killing and to multiply within these cells is a measure of their virulence. The genes responsible for this reside on a 'pathogenicity island'. They enter the mesenteric lymph nodes, where they multiply and, via the thoracic duct, enter the bloodstream. Transient bacteremia follows, during which the bacilli are seeded in the liver, gall bladder, spleen, bone marrow, lymph nodes, lungs and kidneys, where further multiplication takes place. Towards the end of the incubation period, there occurs massive bacteremia from these sites of multiplication, heralding the onset of clinical disease.

As bile is a good culture medium for the bacillus, it multiplies abundantly in the gall bladder and is discharged continuously into the intestine where it involves Peyer's patches and the lymphoid follicles of the ileum. These become inflamed, undergo necrosis and slough off, leaving behind the characteristic typhoid ulcers. Ulceration of the bowel leads to the two major complications of the disease—intestinal perforation and hemorrhage. During the 3–4 weeks that normally constitute the course of the disease, the intestinal lesions undergo healing.

Clinical course

The incubation period is usually 7–14 days but may range 3–56 days and appears to be related to the dose of infection. The clinical course may vary from mild undifferentiated pyrexia (ambulant typhoid) to a rapidly fatal disease (*Case*).

- **Onset** is usually gradual, with headache, malaise, anorexia, a coated tongue and abdominal discomfort with either constipation or diarrhea.
- The typical features are **step-ladder pyrexia**, with relative bradycardia and toxemia.
- A soft, **palpable spleen** is a constant finding. Hepatomegaly is also common.
- 'Rose spots' that fade on pressure appear on the skin during the second or third week but are seldom noticeable in dark-skinned patients.

Complications

The most important complications are intestinal perforation, hemorrhage and circulatory collapse. Some degree of bronchitis or bronchopneumonia is always found. Some develop psychoses, deafness or meningitis. Cholecystitis, arthritis, abscesses, periosteitis, nephritis, hemolytic anemia, venous thromboses and peripheral neuritis are other complications. Osteomyelitis is a rare sequel.

Convalescence is slow. In about 5–10 per cent of cases, relapse occurs during convalescence. The relapse rate is higher in patients treated early with chloramphenicol (15–20 per cent).

S. Paratyphi A and B cause paratyphoid fever which resembles typhoid fever but is generally milder. S. Paratyphi C may also cause paratyphoid fever but more often it leads to frank septicemia with suppurative complications. Other salmonellae have on occasion been reported to cause enteric fever. These have included S. Dublin, S. Barielly, S. Sendai, S. Enteritidis, S. Typhimurium, S. Eastbourne, S. Saintpaul, S. Oranienburg and S. Panama. Infection with *Alkaligenes faecalis* may sometimes cause a similar clinical picture.

Epidemiology

Typhoid fever has been virtually eliminated in the developed countries during the past several decades, mainly as a result of improvements in water supply and sanitation, but it continues to be endemic in the resource limited nations of the world. The control of paratyphoid fever has not been so successful. The distribution of paratyphoid bacilli shows marked geographical differences. S. Paratyphi A is prevalent in India and other Asian countries, Eastern Europe and South America,

S.Paratyphi B in Western Europe, Britain and North America and *S*.Paratyphi C in Eastern Europe and Guyana.

Enteric fever is endemic in all parts of India. An incidence of 500–980 per 100,000 population has been reported in different studies varying with age and geographical area. Worldwide, 22 million cases are estimated to occur annually, with 600,000 deaths (highest concentration in Asia)! The proportion of typhoid to paratyphoid A is about 10:1. Paratyphoid B is rare and C very rare. The disease occurs at all ages but is probably most common in the age group of 5–20 years. The age incidence is related to the endemicity of the disease and the level of sanitation.

Carriers: The source of infection is a patient or, far more frequently, a carrier. Patients who continue to shed typhoid bacilli in feces for three weeks to three months after clinical cure are called **convalescent carriers**. Those who shed the bacilli for more than three months but less than a year are called **temporary carriers** and those who shed the bacilli for over a year are called **chronic carriers**. About 2–4 per cent of patients become chronic carriers. Development of the carrier state is more common in women and in the older age groups (over 40 years). Some persons may become carriers following inapparent infection (symptomless excretor). The shedding of bacilli is usually intermittent. The bacilli persist in the gall bladder or kidneys and are eliminated in the feces (fecal carrier) or urine (urinary carrier), respectively. Urinary carriage is less frequent and is generally associated with some urinary lesion such as calculi or schistosomiasis.

Food handlers or cooks who become carriers are particularly dangerous. The best known of such typhoid carriers was Mary Mallon ('**Typhoid Mary**'), a New York cook who, over a period of 15 years, caused at least seven outbreaks affecting over 200 persons.

Carriers occur with paratyphoid bacilli also. While *S*.Paratyphi A occurs only in human beings, *S*.Paratyphi B can infect animals such as dogs or cows, which may act as sources of human disease.

Typhoid fever occurs in two epidemiological types. The first is **endemic** or **residual typhoid** that occurs throughout the year though seasonal variations may sometimes be apparent. The second is **epidemic** typhoid, which may occur in endemic or non-endemic areas. Typhoid epidemics are water-, milk- or food-borne.

Laboratory diagnosis

Bacteriological diagnosis of enteric fever consists of isolation of the bacilli from the patient and the demonstration of antibodies in his/her serum.

1. Specimen: Blood is collected for culture, as is urine and stool. Serum is obtained for the Widal test. The choice of specimen depends on the duration of illness (Fig. 31.4).

2. Blood culture: A positive blood culture is diagnostic. Bacteremia occurs early in the disease and blood cultures are positive in approximately 90 per cent of cases in the first week of fever. Blood culture is positive in approximately 75 per cent of cases in the second week, 60 per cent in the third week and 25 per cent thereafter till the subsidence of pyrexia. Blood cultures rapidly become negative on treatment with antibiotics.

Method: About 5–10 ml of blood is collected by venipuncture and inoculated into a culture bottle containing 50–100 ml of 0.5 per cent bile broth along with a standard blood culture media (Fig. 31.5). Blood contains substances that inhibit the growth of the bacilli and hence it is essential that the broth be taken in sufficient quantity to provide at 1:10 dilution of blood. The addition of liqoid (sodium polyanethol sulphonate) counteracts the bactericidal action of blood.

After overnight incubation at 37°C, the bile broth is subcultured on MacConkey agar. Pale non-lactose fermenting colonies that may appear on this medium are further characterised by biochemical tests.

Subculture repetition: If the first culture is negative, subculture should be repeated and culture declared

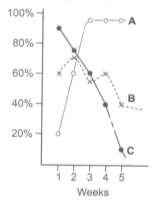

Fig. 31.4 Laboratory diagnosis of typhoid fever. The approximate percentages of tests found positive during different stages of the disease (weeks 1–5). A. Widal agglutination. B. Feces culture. C. Blood culture.

negative only after incubation for 10 days. To eliminate the risk of contamination during repeated subcultures, and also for economy and safety, **Castaneda's method** of culture may be adopted. In this, a double medium is used. The bottle of bile broth has an agar slant on one side. After inoculation of blood, the bottle is incubated in the upright position. For subculture, the bottle is merely tilted so that the broth runs over the surface of the agar. It is reincubated in the upright position. If salmonellae are present, colonies will appear on the slant.

Serotyping by slide agglutination: A loopful of the growth from an agar slope is emulsified in two drops of saline on a slide. One emulsion acts as a control to show that the strain is not autoagglutinable. If *S.* Typhi is suspected (that is, when no gas is formed from glucose), a loopful of typhoid O antiserum (factor 9/group D) is added to one drop of bacterial emulsion on the slide, and agglutination looked for after rocking the slide gently. Prompt agglutination indicates that the isolate belongs to Salmonella group D. Its identity as *S.* Typhi is established by agglutination with the flagellar antiserum (anti-d serum). Quite often, fresh isolates of *S.* Typhi are in the V form and do not agglutinate with the O antiserum. Such strains may be tested for agglutination against the anti-Vi serum. Alternatively, the growth is scraped off in a small amount of saline, boiled for 20 minutes and tested for agglutination with the O antiserum. Where the isolate is a non-typhoid Salmonella (producing gas from sugars), it is tested for agglutination with O and H antisera for groups A, B and C. For identification of unusual serotypes, the help of the **National Salmonella Reference Centre** should be sought. In India it is located at the Central Research Institute, Kasauli. The reference centre for salmonellae of animal origin is at the Indian Veterinary Research Institute, Izatnagar.

3. Clot culture: An alternative to blood culture, in clot culture, 5 ml of blood is withdrawn from the patient into a sterile test tube and allowed to clot. The serum is pipetted off and used for the Widal test. The clot is broken up with a sterile glass rod and added to a bottle of bile broth. The incorporation of streptokinase (100 units per ml) in the broth facilitates lysis of the clot. Clot cultures yield a higher rate of isolation than blood cultures as the bactericidal action of the serum is obviated. Another advantage is that a sample of serum also becomes available. Even though agglutinins may be absent in the early stages of the disease, the Widal test provides a baseline titre against which the results of tests performed later may be evaluated.

4. Feces culture: Salmonellae are shed in feces throughout the course of the disease and even in convalescence, with varying frequency. Hence, fecal cultures are almost as valuable as blood cultures in diagnosis. A positive fecal culture, however, may occur in carriers as well as in patients. The use of enrichment and selective media and repeated sampling increase the rate of isolation. Fecal culture is particularly valuable in patients on antibiotics as the drug does not eliminate the bacilli from the gut as rapidly as it does from blood.

Fecal samples are plated directly on **MacConkey, DCA** or **XLD** and **Wilson–Blair media**. The last is highly selective and should be plated heavily. On MacConkey and DCA media, salmonellae appear as pale colonies and on XLD, they appear pink with a black centre (Fig. 31.1). On the Wilson–Blair medium, *S.* Typhi forms large black colonies, with a metallic sheen. *S.* Paratyphi A produces green colonies due to the absence of H_2S production.

For enrichment, specimens are inoculated into one tube each of selenite and tetrathionate broth, and incubated for 12–18 hours before subculture onto plates.

5. Urine culture: Salmonellae are shed in urine irregularly and infrequently. Hence, urine culture is less useful than the culture of blood or feces. Cultures are generally positive only in the second and third weeks and then only in about 25 per cent of cases. Repeated sampling improves the rate of isolation. Clean voided urine samples are centrifuged and the deposit inocu-

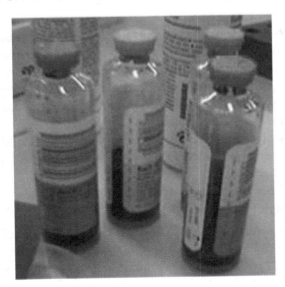

Fig. 31.5   Blood culture bottles

lated into enrichment and selective media, as for fecal culture.

6. Other materials for culture: Isolation may be obtained from several other sources but they are not usually employed. **Bone marrow** culture is valuable as it is positive in most cases even when blood cultures are negative. Culture of **bile** obtained by duodenal aspiration is usually positive and may be employed for the detection of carriers. Other materials which may yield isolation at times are rose spots, pus from suppurative lesions, CSF and sputum. At autopsy, cultures may be obtained from the gall bladder, liver, spleen and mesenteric lymph nodes.

7. Serology:

Widal reaction: This is a test for the measurement of H and O agglutinins for typhoid and paratyphoid bacilli in the patient's sera.

Two types of tubes are generally used for the test:
- A narrow tube with a conical bottom (**Dreyer's agglutination tube**) for H agglutination
- A short round-bottomed tube (**Felix tube**) for O agglutination

Procedure: Equal volumes (0.4 ml) of serial dilutions of the serum (from 1/10 to 1/640) and the H and O antigens are mixed in Dreyer's and Felix agglutination tubes, respectively, and incubated in a water bath at 37°C overnight. Some workers recommend incubation at 50–55°C for two hours, followed by overnight incubation at room temperature. Control tubes containing the antigen and normal saline are set to check for autoagglutination. The agglutination titres of the serum are read. H agglutination leads to the formation of loose, cotton-woolly clumps, while O agglutination is seen as a disc-like pattern at the bottom of the tube. In both, the supernatant fluid is rendered clear.

The antigens used in the test are the H and O antigens of *S*. Typhi and the H antigens of *S*. Paratyphi A and B. The paratyphoid O antigens are not employed as they cross-react with the typhoid O antigen due to their sharing of factor 12. The H agglutinable suspension is prepared by adding 0.1% formalin to a 24-hour broth culture or saline suspension of an agar culture. For preparing the O suspension, the bacillus is cultured on phenol agar (1:800) and the growth scraped off in a small volume of saline. It is mixed with 20 times its volume of absolute alcohol, heated at 40–50°C for 30 minutes, centrifuged and the deposit re-suspended in saline to the appropriate density. Chloroform may

be added as a preservative. It is important to use standard smooth strains for antigen preparation. The strains usually used are *S*. Typhi 901, 'O' and 'H'. Each batch of antigen should be compared with a standard. Readymade Widal kits of stained antigens available commercially are now widely used.

Interpretation of results: The results of the Widal test should be interpreted taking into account the following:
- The agglutination titre will depend on the **stage** of the disease. Agglutinins usually appear by the end of the first week, so blood taken earlier may give a negative result. The titre increases steadily till the third or fourth week, after which it declines gradually.
- Demonstration of a **rise in titre** of antibodies by testing two or more serum samples is more meaningful than a single test. If the first sample is taken late in the disease, a rise may not be demonstrable. Instead, a fall in titre may be seen in some cases.
- The results of a **single test** should be interpreted with caution. It is necessary to obtain information on the distribution of antibody levels in 'normal population' in different areas to determine the cut-off titre.
- Agglutinins may be present on account of prior disease, inapparent infection or **immunisation**. Therefore, the mere presence of agglutinin in the Widal test should not be taken as proof of typhoid fever.
- **H agglutinins** persist longer than **O agglutinins**. Serum from an individual immunised with the TAB vaccine will generally have antibodies to *S*. Typhi and *S*. Paratyphi A and B, while in case of infection antibodies will be seen only against the infecting species.
- Persons who have had prior infection or immunisation may develop an **anamnestic response** during an unrelated fever. This may be differentiated by repetition of the test after a week. The anamnestic response shows only a transient rise, while in enteric fever the rise is sustained.
- Bacterial suspensions used as antigens should be **free from fimbria**. False positive results may occur otherwise.
- Cases treated early with **antibiotics** may show poor agglutinin response.

IgM detection kits: They can be useful in the diagnosis of infection in the initial weeks in a primary infection when a single serum sample is available. They detect IgM antibodies to lipolpolysaccharide or outer membrane protein antigens.

8. PCR-based tests: These are also sensitive but not widely available.

9. Demonstration of circulating antigen: Typhoid bacillus antigens are consistently present in the blood in the early phase of the disease, and also in the urine of patients. The antigen can be demonstrated by sensitised **staphylococcal coagglutination** test. *S.aureus* (**Cowan I strain**) which contains protein A is stabilised with formaldehyde and coated with *S.*Typhi antibody. When a 1% suspension of such sensitised staphylococcal cells is mixed on a slide with serum from patients in the first week of typhoid fever, the typhoid antigen present in the serum combines with the antibody attached to staphylococcal cells, producing visible agglutination within two minutes. The test is rapid, sensitive and specific but is not positive after the first week of the disease.

10. Other laboratory tests: A white cell count is useful. Leucopenia with relative lymphocytosis is seen. Eosinophils are said to be absent but in the tropics, with a high incidence of helminthic infestation, eosinophils are usually present.

Diagnosis of carriers

The detection of carriers is important for epidemiological and public health purposes. Laboratory tests are also useful in screening food handlers and cooks to detect the carrier state.

- Identification of fecal carriers is by **isolation** of the bacillus from feces or from bile. The frequency and intensity of bacillary shedding vary widely and it is essential, therefore, to test repeated samples. Cholagogue purgatives increase the chance of isolation. For the detection of urinary carriers, repeated urine cultures should be carried out.
- The **Widal reaction** is of no value in the detection of carriers in endemic countries. Demonstration of antibodies to Vi antigens has been claimed to indicate the carrier state. While this is useful as a screening test, confirmation should be made by culture.
- The tracing of carriers in cities may be accomplished by the '**sewer-swab**' technique. Gauze pads left in sewers and drains are cultured, and by tracing positive swabs, one may be led to the house harbouring a carrier.
- Another technique of isolating salmonellae from sewage is by **filtration through Millipore membranes** and culturing the membranes on highly selective media such as Wilson and Blair media.

Typing methods

Bacteriophage typing: Intraspecies classification of *S.*Typhi for epidemiological purposes was made possible by bacteriophage typing, first developed by Craigie and Yen (1937). They found that a bacteriophage acting on the Vi antigen of the typhoid bacillus (Vi phage II) was highly adaptable. As phage typing of *S.*Typhi depends on the presence of Vi antigens, a proportion of strains (Vi negative) will be **untypeable**. The phage type is stable. Apart from helping in tracing the source of epidemics, phage typing also provides information on the trends and patterns in the epidemiology of typhoid at the local, national and international levels. The **National Salmonella Phage Typing Centre** for India is located at the Lady Hardinge Medical College, New Delhi. Among *S.*Typhi phage types, A and E1 are more common in India, while among the *S.*Paratyphi A phage, types 1 and 2 are the most common. However the lack of discriminatory power limits the utility of phage typing as an epidemiological tool.

Antibiogram: This is also a stable typing method but lacks discriminatory power.

Molecular methods: Currently, more discriminating genotyping methods like pulse field gel electrophoresis, multilocus enzyme electrophoresis, IS-200 profiling and random amplified polymorphic DNA analysis have been employed for epidemiological typing.

Prophylaxis

Typhoid fever can be effectively controlled by:

General measures, such as improvements in sanitation and provision of protected water supply. Many developed countries have been able to eliminate the risk by these measures, but occasional outbreaks do appear due to unforeseen lapses.

Vaccines:

- **TAB vaccine:** Specific prophylaxis with the heat killed typhoid bacillus vaccine was developed and successfully field tested by Almroth Wright during the Boer war in South Africa. The TAB vaccine which came into general use later contained *S.*Typhi, 1000 million and *S.*Paratyphi A and B, 750 million each per ml killed by heating at 50–60°C and preserved in 0.5 % phenol.

  Dose schedule: The vaccine is given in two doses of 0.5 ml subcutaneously at an interval of 4–6 weeks. Local and general reactions lasting one or two days are quite frequent. Such reactions may be avoided if the vaccine is administered in a dose of 0.1 ml intradermally. In non-endemic areas, vaccination is recommended for troops, medical and paramedical personnel. In endemic areas, vaccination is recommended for all children in whom a single dose might give adequate protection, which may be maintained for several years by the booster effect of repeated natural subclinical infections. The killed vaccines do not provide cell-mediated immunity.

- **Live oral vaccine:** A live oral vaccine has been introduced after successful field trials. The live oral vaccine (**typhoral**) is a stable mutant of *S.*Typhi strain Ty2 1a, lacking the enzyme UDP-galactose-4-epimerase (Gal E mutant). On ingestion, it initiates infection but 'self-destructs' after four or five cell divisions, and therefore cannot induce any illness.

  Dose: The vaccine is an enteric-coated capsule containing 10^9 viable lyophilised mutant bacilli. The course consists of one capsule orally, taken an hour before food, with a glass of water or milk, on Days 1, 3 and 5. No antibiotic should be taken during this period.

- **Vi vaccine:** The injectable vaccine (typhim-Vi) contains purified Vi polysaccharide antigen (25 µg per dose) from *S.*Typhi strain Ty2. It is given as a single subcutaneous or intramuscular injection, which causes only minimal local reaction.

  Both the oral and Vi vaccines are recommended only for those over five years of age, the same dose being used for children and adults. In both cases, protection is stated to commence 2–3 weeks after administration and lasts for at least three years, after which a booster may be given. Both vaccines are effective and only their relatively high cost stands in the way of their wider use.

  Typhoid bacilli are primarily intracellular parasites, and cell-mediated immunity rather than humoral antibodies may be more relevant in protection against the disease. Cell-mediated immunity develops during the course of the disease. Cellular immunity to the typhoid bacillus is common in populations in endemic areas. Absence of CMI has been claimed to indicate susceptibility. The killed vaccines currently used do not stimulate CMI.

Treatment

Specific antibacterial therapy for enteric fever became available only in 1948 with the introduction of chloram-

phenicol, which continued as the sheet anchor against the disease till the 1970s, when resistance became common. Ampicillin, amoxycillin and cotrimoxazole were the other drugs found useful in the treatment of typhoid fever but current strains show resistance to these also. At present, ciprofloxacin is the drug of choice or, in case of resistance, ceftriaxone is given.

Carriers: While antibacterial therapy has been effective in the treatment of cases, it has been disappointing in the treatment of carriers. A combination of antibacterial therapy along with the vaccine has been tried for the eradication of the carrier state. This combination has also been used to prevent relapses. Elimination of the carrier state may require heroic measures such as cholecystectomy, pyelolithotomy or nephrectomy.

Drug resistance

Though occasional resistant strains had been identified in the laboratory, resistance to chloramphenicol did not pose any problem in typhoid fever till 1972, when resistant strains emerged in Mexico and in Kerala (India).

In India, chloramphenicol-resistant typhoid fever appeared in epidemic form first in Calicut (Kerala) in early 1972. It became endemic and was confined to Kerala till 1978. Subsequently such strains carrying drug resistant plasmids appeared in many other parts of India. Though resistant to chloramphenicol, such strains were initially sensitive to ampicillin, amoxycillin, cotrimoxazole and furazolidone, which were successfully used for treatment. By late 1980s, typhoid bacillus strains resistant to many or all of these drugs began to spread to most parts of India. The drugs useful in the treatment of such multiresistant typhoid cases were the later fluoroquinolones (such as ciprofloxacin, pefloxacin, oflaxacin) and the third-generation cephalosporins (such as ceftazidime, ceftrioxone, cefotaxime). Furazolidone is still active against most isolates. Now several isolates of typhoid bacilli are once again sensitive to chloramphenicol.

SALMONELLA GASTROENTERITIS

Salmonella gastroenteritis (more appropriately enterocolitis) or food poisoning is generally a zoonotic disease, the source of infection being animal products. It may be caused by any salmonella called non-typhoidal salmonellae. In most parts of the world, *S.*Typhimurium is the most common species. Some other common species are *S. Enteritidis, S. Haldar, S. Heidelberg, S. Agona, S. Virchow, S. Seftenberg, S. Indiana, S. Newport* and *S. Anatum.*

Sources of infection

Human infection results from the ingestion of contaminated food. The most frequent sources of salmonella food poisoning are poultry, meat, milk and milk products. Of great concern are eggs and egg products. Salmonellae can enter through the shell if eggs are left on contaminated chicken feed or feces, and grow inside. Human carriers do occur but their role is minimal when considered in relation to the magnitude of infection from animals. Even salads and other uncooked vegetables may cause infection if contaminated by manure or by handling. Food contamination may also result from the droppings of rats, lizards or other small animals. Gastroenteritis may occur without food poisoning, as in cross-infection in hospitals.

Pathogenesis

Clinically, the disease develops after a short incubation period of 24 hours or less, with diarrhea, vomiting, abdominal pain and fever.

- It may vary in severity from the passage of one or two loose stools to an acute cholera-like disease.
- It usually subsides in 2–4 days, but in some cases, a more prolonged enteritis develops, with passage of mucus and pus in feces, resembling dysentery.
- In a few, typhoidal or septicemic type of fever may develop.

Laboratory diagnosis

This is made by **isolating** the salmonella from the feces. In outbreaks of food poisoning, the causative article of food can often be identified by taking a proper history. Isolation of salmonellae from the article of food confirms the diagnosis.

Control of salmonella food poisoning requires the prevention of food contamination. Food may become contaminated at various levels, from natural infection in the animal or bird, to contamination of the prepared food. Proper cooking of food destroys salmonellae.

While enteric fever is a major problem only in developing countries, salmonella food poisoning is largely a problem for developed nations. This is due to the differences in food habits and living conditions between them and also because food production, packaging, storage and marketing have become industries in the developed countries while they still remain agricultural in the developing world.

Treatment of uncomplicated, non-invasive salmonellosis is symptomatic. Antibiotics should not be used. Not only do they not hasten recovery but they may also increase the period of fecal shedding of the bacilli. However, for serious invasive cases, antibiotic treatment is needed.

SALMONELLA SEPTICEMIA

Certain salmonellae, *S. Choleraesuis* in particular, may cause septicemic disease with focal suppurative lesions, such as osteomyelitis, deep abscesses, endocarditis, pneumonia and meningitis. Antecedent gastroenteritis may or may not be present. The case fatality may be as high as 25 per cent.

Salmonellae may be isolated from blood or from pus from the suppurative lesion. Feces culture may also sometimes be positive. Septicemic salmonellosis should be treated with chloramphenicol or other appropriate antibiotics as determined by sensitivity tests.

MULTIRESISTANT SALMONELLAE

R factors conferring multiple drug resistance have become widely disseminated among salmonellae. The clinical significance of this phenomenon was first observed during studies of human and veterinary infections with drug-resistant *S. Typhimurium* phage type 29 in England in the 1960s. Human infections were initially gastroenteritis due to spread from infected animals, through food. Subsequently, some salmonellae appear to have changed their ecology in some ways. From being responsible for zoonotic infections only, as in the past, some multiresistant salmonellae have now become important agents of hospital cross-infections. Such nosocomial salmonellosis manifests, particularly in neonates, as septicemia, meningitis and suppurative lesions. Diarrhea may not always be present.

In India, several hospital outbreaks of neonatal septicemia caused by multiresistant salmonellae have occurred in recent years. Mortality in neonates is very high unless early treatment is started with antibiotics to which the infecting strain is sensitive.

RECAP

- The genus *Salmonella* belongs to the family Enterobacteriaceae. It is a Gram-negative, facultatively anaerobic, motile bacillus that is catalase positive and oxidase negative.
- Many serologically distinct species exist. These species have now been unified into one common species, *Salmonella enterica*, with the previously separate species now being referred to as serovars.
- The serovars causing typhoid fever include *Salmonella enterica* serovar Typhi, *Salmonella enterica* serovar Paratyphi A and *Salmonella enterica* serovar Paratyphi B.
- The *Salmonella* species responsible for enteric fever are spread only from human to human. Water contaminated with feces is a common source, especially during natural disasters when the quality of drinking water is compromised.
- For diagnosis, samples of feces or blood are cultured and identified by biochemical characteristics and by slide agglutination tests using reference antibody to the O, H, and Vi (capsular polysaccharide) antigens.
- Some patients become carriers, harbouring the bacteria in their tissues without symptoms and passing organisms in their feces for years.
- Enteric fever can be prevented by proper personal hygiene, consumption of safe drinking water and vaccines. Antibiotics are needed to treat sick individuals and to eliminate the carrier state. There is currently a live oral vaccine available for immunisation.
- The Salmonella species responsible for food poisoning are transmitted by ingestion of food contaminated with feces from infected animals or humans; eggs and poultry are the most common animal sources.
- There are many serovars implicated in food poisoning, the prominent ones being *Salmonella enterica* serovar Typhimurium and *Salmonella enterica* serovar Enteritidis.
- The disease is prevented by good hygiene (hand washing) and by elimination of animal reservoirs.

ESSAYS

1. Classify enterobacteria. Give an account of the morphology, cultural characteristics and pathogenicity of *S.* Typhi.
2. Enumerate the organisms causing PUO and explain the pathogenesis and laboratory diagnosis of enteric fever.

SHORT ANSWERS

1. Slide agglutination for the identification of salmonella
2. Detection of typhoid carriers
3. Media used for the culture and identification of salmonella
4. Widal test

SHORT NOTES

1. Vi antigen in *S.* Typhi
2. Non-typhoidal *Salmonella*

32 Vibrio

Vibrio cholerae

Clinical Case A 10-year-old child from a suburban slum presented to the Pediatric Emergency department during the monsoons complaining of profuse diarrhea—frequency of 10–15 times for the previous two days—and vomiting 2–3 times the previous day. There was no history of fever, abdominal pain or passage of blood in stools. The child complained of decreased urine output, intense thirst and leg cramps. On examination, he was found to be moderately dehydrated. On further questioning, the family mentioned that some of the other residents of the slum were also suffering from a similar condition. The stool on gross examination had a characteristic 'rice water' appearance, and was sent for direct microscopy and culture. Hanging drop examination was positive for bacteria showing darting motility. The culture was positive for *Vibrio cholerae*. Management included rehydration and the child improved.

INTRODUCTION

Vibrios are Gram-negative, curved bacilli that are actively motile by means of a polar flagellum. The name 'vibrio' is derived from the characteristic vibratory motility (from *vibrare,* meaning to vibrate). They are non-sporing and non-capsulated. Vibrios are present in marine environments and surface waters worldwide. The most important member of the genus is *Vibrio cholerae,* the causative agent of cholera. Filippo Pacini first identified, described and named the organism as *Vibrio cholerae* from cholera patients in Florence, Italy, in 1854. Later in 1883, Robert Koch isolated the organism from cholera patients in Egypt.

VIBRIO CHOLERAE

Morphology

The cholera vibrio is a short, curved, cylindrical rod, about 1.5×0.2–0.4 μm in size, with rounded or slightly pointed ends. The cell is typically comma shaped (Fig. 32.1). Pleomorphism is frequent in old cultures. In stained films of mucus flakes from acute cholera cases, the vibrios are seen arranged in parallel rows, described by Koch as having a '**fish in stream**' appearance. It is actively motile, with a single sheathed polar flagellum. The motility is of the darting type, and

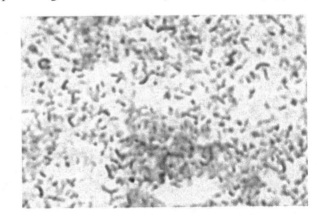

Fig. 32.1 *Vibrio cholerae:* comma-shaped gram-negative rods

can be seen when an acute cholera stool or a young culture is examined under the microscope. The actively motile vibrios suggest a 'swarm of gnats'. The vibrios stain readily with aniline dyes and are Gram negative and non–acid fast.

Cultural characteristics

Vibrio cholerae is aerobic, growth being scanty and slow anaerobically. It grows within a temperature range of 16–40°C (optimum 37°C). Growth is better in an alkaline medium, the range of pH being 6.4–9.6 (optimum 8.2). NaCl (0.5–1%) is required for optimal growth, though high concentrations (6% and above) are inhibitory. Therefore, they are halotolerant (unlike *Vibrio parahaemolyticus* which is halophilic and needs a higher concentration of NaCl).

Ordinary media: It grows well on ordinary media.

- On **nutrient agar**, after overnight growth, colonies are moist, translucent, round discs, about 1–2 mm in diameter, with a bluish tinge in transmitted light. The growth has a distinctive odour.
- On **MacConkey agar**, the colonies are colourless at first but become reddish on prolonged incubation due to the late fermentation of lactose.
- On **blood agar**, colonies are initially surrounded by a zone of greening, which later becomes clear due to hemodigestion.
- In **Gelatin stab** culture, infundibuliform (funnel-shaped) or napiform (turnip-shaped) liquefaction occurs in three days at 22°C.
- In **peptone water**, growth occurs in about six hours as a fine surface pellicle, which on shaking breaks up into membranous pieces. Turbidity and a powdery deposit develop on continued incubation.

Special media: A number of special media have been employed for the cultivation of cholera vibrios. They may be classified as follows:

- **Holding or transport media:**
  - A simple modified form of the **Venkatraman–Ramakrishnan (VR)** medium is prepared by dissolving 20 g crude sea salt and 5 g peptone in one litre of distilled water and adjusting the pH to 8.6–8.8. It is dispensed in screw-capped bottles in quantities of 10–15 ml. About 1–3 ml of stool must be added to each bottle. In this medium, vibrios do not multiply but remain viable for several weeks.
  - The **Cary–Blair medium** is a buffered solution of sodium chloride, sodium thioglycollate, disodium phosphate and calcium chloride at a pH 8.4. It is a suitable transport medium for *Salmonella* and *Shigella* as well as for vibrios.
  - **Autoclaved sea water** also serves as a holding medium.
- **Enrichment media**:
  - Alkaline peptone water at a pH of 8.6
  - Monsur's taurocholate tellurite peptone water at a pH of 9.2

Both are good transport and enrichment media.

- **Plating media:**
  - **Alkaline bile salt agar (BSA)** at pH 8.2 is a simple medium that has stood the test of time and is still widely used. The colonies are similar to those on nutrient agar.
  - In Monsur's gelatin taurocholate trypticase tellurite agar **(GTTA)**, cholera vibrios produce small, translucent colonies with a greyish black centre and a turbid halo. The colonies become 3–4 mm in size in 48 hours.
  - The **thiosulphate citrate bile salt sucrose (TCBS)** medium, containing thiosulphate, citrate, bile salts and sucrose, is available commercially and is very widely used at present. Cholera vibrios produce large yellow convex colonies which may become green on continued incubation.

Identification: Vibrio colonies may be identified by the '**string test**'. A loopful of the growth is mixed with a drop of 0.5% sodium deoxycholate in saline on a slide. If the test is positive, the suspension loses its turbidity, becomes mucoid and forms a 'string' when the loop is drawn slowly away from the suspension (Fig. 32.2).

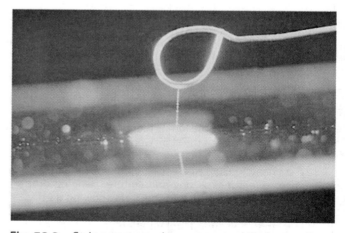

Fig. 32.2 String test used to separate *Vibrio* spp. from *Aeromonas* spp. and *P.shigelloides*

Biochemical reactions

Carbohydrate metabolism is fermentative, producing acid, but no gas. Cholera vibrios ferment glucose, mannitol, maltose, mannose and sucrose but not inositol, arabinose or lactose, though lactose may be split very slowly. Indole is formed and nitrates are reduced to nitrites. These two properties contribute to the 'cholera red reaction' which is tested by adding a few drops of concentrated sulphuric acid to a 24-hour peptone water culture (Fig. 32.3). With cholera vibrios, a reddish pink colour develops due to the formation of nitroso-indole. Catalase and oxidase tests are positive. Methyl red and urease tests are negative. Vibrios decarboxylate lysine and ornithine but do not utilise arginine. Gelatin is liquefied. Vibrios elaborate several enzymes including collagenase, elastase, chitinase, nucleotidase, decarboxylase, lipase, mucinase and neuraminidase (receptor destroying enzyme).

Resistance

Cholera vibrios are susceptible to heat, drying and acids, but resist high alkalinity. They are destroyed at 55°C in 15 minutes. Dried on linen or thread, they survive for 1–3 days but die in about three hours on cover slips. Survival in water is influenced by its pH, temperature, salinity, presence of organic pollution and other factors. In general, the El Tor vibrio survives longer than the classical cholera vibrio. In the laboratory, vibrios survive for months in sterile sea water, and this has been suggested as a method for the survival of vibrios in nature. In grossly contaminated waters, such as those of the river Ganga, the vibrios do not survive for any length of time, due to the apparently large amounts of vibriophages present. They survive in clean tap water for thirty days. In untreated night soil, they may survive for several days. Vibrios are susceptible to common disinfectants.

On fruits, they survive for 1–5 days at room temperature and for a week in the refrigerator. In general, food materials left at room temperature do not act as an important source of infection for longer than a day or two but those stored in the cold may harbour vibrios for more than two weeks.

They are killed in a few minutes in the gastric juice of normal acidity but may survive for 24 hours in achlorhydric gastric juice.

Classification

In the past, many oxidase-positive, motile, curved rods were rather loosely grouped as vibrios. However, precise criteria have been laid down for differentiating vibrios from related genera (Table 32.1).

Heiberg (1934) classified vibrios into six groups based on the fermentation of mannose, sucrose and arabinose. Two more groups were added later. Cholera vibrios belong to Group I (Table 32.2).

A **serological classification** was introduced by **Gardner** and **Venkatraman** (1935). Cholera and biochemically similar vibrios possessing a common flagellar (H) antigen were classified as Group A vibrios, and the rest as Group B vibrios comprising a

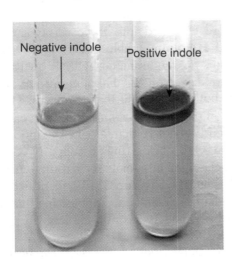

Negative indole   Positive indole

Fig. 32.3   Cholera red reaction

Table 32.1   *Differentiation of vibrios from allied genera*

Genus	Oxidation–Fermentation (Hugh–Liefson Test)		Utilisation of amino acids			String test
	Oxidation	Fermentation	Lysine	Arginine	Ornithine	
Vibrio	+	+1	+	–	+	+
Aeromonas	+	+2	–	+	–	V
Pseudomonas	+	–	V	V	V	–
Plesiomonas	+	+	+	+	+	–
1 = no gas produced; 2 = gas may or may not be produced; V = reaction variable						

Table 32.2 *Heiberg grouping of vibrios*

Group	Fermentation of mannose	Sucrose	Arabinose
I	A	A	–
II	–	A	–
III	A	A	A
IV	–	A	A
V	A	–	–
VI	–	–	–
VII	A	–	A
VIII	–	–	A

heterogeneous collection. Based on the major somatic (O) antigen, Group A vibrios were classified into 'subgroups' (now called O serogroups or serovars), 139 of which are currently known (Table 32.3). All isolates from epidemic cholera (till 1992) belonged to serogroup O-1. Therefore, in the diagnostic laboratory, Group O-1 antiserum (commonly called cholera non-differential serum) came to be used for identifying pathogenic cholera vibrios (referred to as **agglutinable vibrios**). Other vibrio isolates which were not agglutinated by the O-1 antiserum came to be called **non-agglutinable** or **NAG vibrios**. They were considered non-pathogenic and hence also called **non-cholera vibrios (NCV)**.

Table 32.3 *Gardner and Venkatraman's classification (updated)*

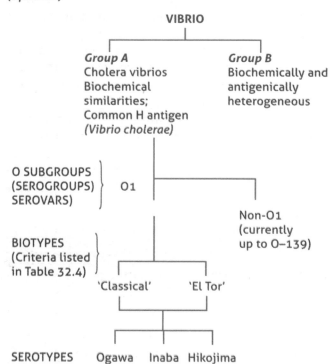

Both these terms are not strictly appropriate. Though NAG vibrios are not agglutinable by the O-1 antiserum, they are readily agglutinated by their specific antisera. The term non-cholera vibrio is not correct either as some of them can cause a disease clinically indistinguishable from cholera. However, by and large, NAG vibrios are non-pathogenic and commonly isolated from environmental sources and healthy human intestines.

While all isolates from epidemic cholera belonged to Group O-1, called **classical *V.cholera***, not all members of the group were capable of causing clinical cholera. The first such members which acquired prominence were the vibrios isolated by Gottschlich (1905) from six Haj pilgrims at the Tor quarantine station on the Sinai Peninsula. These came to be called the **El Tor vibrios**. They were identical to cholera vibrios in all laboratory tests except that they were hemolytic to sheep erythrocytes and gave a positive Voges–Proskauer reaction. In 1937, El Tor vibrios were recognised as endemic in Celebes (Sulawesi), Indonesia, causing a choleraic disease (Table 32.4).

Serotypes: Based on minor surface antigenic characteristics, both classical and El Tor biotypes of cholera vibrios were classified into three serotypes: **Ogawa**, **Inaba** and **Hikojima** (Table 32.5). The Ogawa and Inaba strains are agglutinated by their own respective specific sera only, while the Hikojima strains are agglutinated by both Ogawa and Inaba antisera. There is no difference in pathogenicity among the three serotypes. Serotyping is only of epidemiological significance.

The non–O-1 vibrios (the so-called **NAG vibrios**) have been classified into many serogroups, currently up to 139. The latest serogroup O-139, identified in 1992, causes epidemics of cholera, emphasising that they can no longer be considered as non-cholera vibrios.

Table 32.4 *Differentiation between classical cholera and El Tor vibrios*

Test	Classical cholera	El Tor
Hemolysis	–	+
Voges–Proskauer	–	+
Chick erythrocyte agglutination	–	+
Polymyxin B sensitivity	+	–
Group IV phage susceptibility	+	–
El Tor phage 5 susceptibility	–	+

Table 32.5 *O serotypes of cholera vibrios*

Serotype	O antigens
Ogawa	AB
Inaba	AC
Hikojima	ABC

Modern taxonomical criteria, particularly DNA studies, have led to the recognition that all the cholera vibrios that belong to Gardner and Venkatraman's Group A and share similar biochemical properties and a common H antigen are so closely related that they constitute a single species *Vibrio cholerae,* which can be classified into serogroups (or serovars), biotypes and serotypes. Accordingly, current nomenclature will be indicative of all these features, as, for example, *V.cholerae* serovar O1, biotype El Tor, serotype Ogawa.

Phage typing: Further classification can be done by phage typing. Phage typing schemes have been standardised for classical and El Tor biotypes as well as for O-139 vibrios. New molecular methods like ribotyping have added further refinements to strain typing.

Division of **halophilic** and **non-halophilic** vibrios is based on the requirement of sodium chloride (halophilic: *V.parahemolyticus, V.alginolyticus, V.vulnificus*; non-halophilic: *Vibrio cholera*).

CHOLERA

Cholera is an acute diarrheal disease caused by *V.cholerae.* In its most severe form, it presents as profuse, painless, watery diarrhea and copious effortless vomiting; this may lead to hypovolemic shock and death in less than 24 hours. In treated cases, the disease may last 4–6 days, during which the patient may pass a total volume of liquid stool equal to twice his body weight.

- All the clinical features of severe cholera result from this massive loss of fluid and electrolytes.
- The cholera stool is typically a colourless watery fluid with flecks of mucus, said to resemble water in which rice has been washed (hence called 'rice water stools'). It has a characteristic inoffensive sweetish odour. In composition, it is a bicarbonate-rich isotonic electrolyte solution, with little protein. Its outpouring leads to diminution of extracellular fluid volume, hemoconcentration, hypokalemia, base-deficit acidosis and shock (*Case*).
- The common **complications** are muscular cramps, renal failure, pulmonary edema, cardiac arrhythmias and paralytic ileus.

- The **clinical severity** of cholera varies widely, from the rapidly fatal disease to a transient asymptomatic colonisation of the intestine by the vibrios.
- The **incidence** of mild and asymptomatic infections is more with El Tor vibrios than with the classical cholera vibrios.
- The **incubation period** varies from less than 24 hours to about five days. The clinical illness may begin slowly with mild diarrhea and vomiting in 1–3 days or abruptly with sudden massive diarrhea.

Pathogenesis

Natural infection with cholera occurs only in humans. The vibrios enter orally through contaminated water or food. Vibrios are highly susceptible to acids, and gastric acidity provides an effective barrier against small doses of cholera vibrios. It has been shown that 10^6 pathogenic vibrios administered to fasting normochlorhydric volunteers, without food or buffer, did not produce infection, while the same dose given along with food or sodium bicarbonate caused clinical cholera in 80–100 per cent of them. Achlorhydria predisposes to cholera in the field. A number of animal models have been developed which have helped in understanding the pathogenic mechanisms in cholera. The first of these was the rabbit ileal loop model of De and Chatterjee (1953). Injection of cholera culture or culture filtrate into the **ligated ileal loop** caused fluid accumulation and ballooning.

Mechanism of action: In the small intestine, vibrios can cross the protective layer of mucus and reach the epithelial cells by chemotaxis, motility, mucinase and other proteolytic enzymes. A hemagglutinin-protease (formerly known as cholera lectin) cleaves mucus and fibronectin. It also helps in releasing vibrios bound to bowel mucosa, facilitating their spread to other parts of the intestine and also their fecal shedding. Adhesion to the epithelial surface and colonisation may be facilitated by special fimbria such as the toxin co-regulated pilus (TCP). Throughout the course of infection, the vibrios remain attached to the epithelium but do not damage or invade the cells. The changes induced are biochemical rather than histological.

Enterotoxin: Vibrios multiplying on the intestinal epithelium produce an enterotoxin called cholera toxin or CT which is very similar to the heat labile toxin (LT) of *E.coli* in structural, chemical, biological and antigenic properties, though CT is far more potent than

LT in biological activity. CT production is determined by a filamentous phage integrated with the bacterial chromosome. It can also replicate as a plasmid which can be transmitted to non-toxigenic strains, rendering them toxigenic. CT, TCP and other virulence factors are regulated by the ToxR gene product, **ToxR protein.**

The toxin molecule of approximately 84,000 MW consists of 1 A and 5 B subunits. The **B (binding) units** attach to the GM_1 ganglioside receptors on the surface of jejunal epithelial cells. The **A (active) subunit**, on being transported into the enterocyte, dissociates into two fragments: A_1 and A_2. The A_2 fragment only links biologically active A_1 to the B subunit. The A_1 fragment causes prolonged activation of cellular adenylate cyclase and accumulation of cAMP, leading to outpouring into the small intestinal lumen, of large quantities of water and electrolytes and the consequent watery diarrhea. The fluid secreted is isotonic with plasma but contains much more of potassium and bicarbonate. The toxin also inhibits intestinal absorption of sodium and chloride. All clinical manifestations and complications in cholera result from the massive water and electrolyte depletion thus caused.

CT also exhibits other biological effects which can be used for its detection and estimation. These include activation of lipolysis in rat testicular tissue, elongation of Chinese hamster ovary (CHO) cells in culture and histological changes in adrenal tumour (Y_1) cell culture and Vero cells. It also increases skin capillary permeability, and so has been called the '**permeability factor**' (**PF**). It can be demonstrated by the '**skin blueing test**'—CT is injected intradermally in rabbits or guinea pigs and pontamine sky blue injected intravenously afterwards; the site of toxin injection becomes blue. CT can also be estimated by ELISA. CT is antigenic and induces production of neutralising antitoxins. CT can be toxoided.

Cholera vibrios also possess the lipopolysaccharide O antigen (LPS, endotoxin), as in Gram-negative intestinal bacilli. This apparently plays no role in the pathogenesis of cholera but is responsible for the immunity induced by killed vaccines. It may cause the fatal illness produced experimentally by peritoneal inoculation in mice.

Epidemiology

Cholera can occur in many forms: sporadic, endemic, epidemic or pandemic. India, more specifically the large deltaic area of the rivers Ganga and Brahmaputra in Bengal, is its homeland, where it has been known since ancient times. Till early in the nineteenth century, cholera was virtually confined to India, periodically causing large epidemics in different parts of the country.

From 1817 to 1923, cholera caused by the **classical biotype** spread from Bengal in six separate pandemic waves involving most parts of the world. The seventh pandemic originated in Sulawesi (Celebes), Indonesia, in 1961, caused by the **El Tor biotype,** which replaced the classical biotype. After spreading to Hong Kong and the Philippines, it spread steadily westwards, invading India in 1964. In January 1991, the pandemic reached Peru, thus encircling the globe in thirty years. The seventh pandemic was different from the others. It was the first to have originated from outside the Indian subcontinent. It was also the first to have been caused by the El Tor biotype.

The severity of illness was much less, with a large proportion of mild and asymptomatic infections. Mortality was low and the carrier rate high. El Tor vibrios tended to remain endemic in many new geographic areas, causing periodic epidemics. The El Tor vibrio has proved to be much hardier than the classical vibrios, capable of surviving in the environment for much longer. Thus, in India the classical vibrio was hardly ever encountered after the El Tor epidemic took root, though in Bangladesh, the classical vibrio staged a comeback.

An event of great significance was the sudden emergence of non–O-1 *V.cholerae* (formerly NAG vibrio) as the cause of epidemic cholera (eighth pandemic). In October 1992, a new non–O-1 vibrio was isolated from a cholera outbreak in Madras (Chennai). Similar outbreaks soon followed in different parts of India. By January 1993, the new strain had become epidemic in Bangladesh as well. In the affected areas, this strain replaced the El Tor vibrios as the epidemic and environmental serovar. It also showed a tendency to be more invasive, causing bacteremic illness in some.

The new epidemic strain was designated **serovar O-139 (or O-139 Bengal).** Unlike the O-1 cholera vibrio, the O-139 vibrio is capsulated. As it possessed novel surface antigens, the O-1 strain vaccines could not protect against O-139 infection. There was no natural antibody against the strain in any human population then. It was therefore considered likely that the O-139 strain would initiate the next pandemic of cholera. The new strain continued spreading, eastwards to the Southeast Asian countries, and westwards to Pakistan, China and some parts of Europe. But surprisingly, by

1994, the El Tor strain regained its dominance and the threat of an O-139 pandemic diminished. Both O-1 El Tor and O-139 began to co-exist in endemic areas but are now declining.

Cholera is an exclusively human disease and thus the infection originates from the patients. Some of the infected persons may excrete the bacteria for up to 10 days or intermittently for a longer time. These can serve as a source of infection.

Infection is acquired through fecally contaminated water or food. Direct person-to-person spread by contact may not be common, but hand contamination of stored drinking water has been shown to be an important method of domestic spread of infection. Large-scale movement of persons, as occurs during fairs and festivals, has traditionally been associated with the spread of cholera.

The persistence of the vibrio during the inter-epidemic periods was a matter of controversy. In the endemic areas, it may be maintained by continuous transmission of subclinical or mild infection. It is now known that the natural habitat of cholera vibrios is the saline waters of coastal seas and brackish estuaries, where they can persist for long periods, particularly in association with small crustaceans such as copepods, crabs or plankton. When conditions become unfavourable, they become dormant and unculturable. Drinking contaminated water or vegetables washed with contaminated water can lead to epidemics in humans. Cycles of transmission are perpetuated when bacteria are shed into water sources by fecal contamination.

A significant difference in susceptibility to cholera has been reported in relation to blood groups, group O persons being the most susceptible and group AB the least. The reason for this is not known.

Laboratory diagnosis

1. Specimen:

- **Stool**, collected in the acute stage of the disease, before the administration of antibiotics, is the most useful specimen for laboratory diagnosis. Isolation of cholera vibrios from such stools is a simple matter as they are present in very large numbers—10^6–10^9 vibrios per ml. The specimen is best collected by introducing a lubricated catheter into the rectum and letting the liquid stool flow directly into a screw-capped container.
- **Rectal swabs** may be used, provided they are made with good quality cotton wool, absorbing about 0.1–0.2 ml of fluid. They are useful in collecting specimens from convalescents who no longer have watery diarrhea. In such cases, the swabs should be moistened with transport medium before sampling.
- Collection of stools from pans is not recommended.
- Vomitus is not useful.

2. Transport: As cholera vibrios may die in a few hours at tropical temperatures, it is necessary to preserve the specimen at 4°C or in some appropriate holding medium. Stool samples may be preserved in VR fluid or Cary–Blair medium for long periods. If the specimen can reach the laboratory in a few hours, it may be transported in enrichment media such as alkaline peptone water or Monsur's medium, thus saving the time required for isolation. If transport media are not available, strips of blotting paper may be soaked in the watery stool and sent to the laboratory packed in plastic envelopes. Whenever possible, specimens should be plated at the bedside and the inoculated plates sent to the laboratory.

3. Microscopy: Diagnosis by direct microscopic examination of cholera stool is not recommended as the results are not reliable. For **rapid diagnosis**, the characteristic darting motility of the vibrio and its inhibition by antiserum can be demonstrated under the dark field or phase contrast microscope using cholera stool from acute cases or more reliably after enrichment for six hours.

Demonstration of vibrios in stools by direct immunofluorescence is not useful.

4. Culture: On arrival in the laboratory, the specimens sent in **enrichment media** should be incubated for 6–8 hours including transit time. The specimens sent in holding media should be inoculated into enrichment media, to be incubated for 6–8 hours before being streaked on a selective and a non-selective medium. It is also desirable to do direct plating before enrichment. The **plating media** used vary in different laboratories but the media usually employed are bile salt agar, MacConkey agar for non-selective and TCBS agar for selective plates. The plates should not be older than 3–5 days and should be dried well before streaking. It is possible to identify vibrio colonies on non-selective media after incubation for 4–5 hours by examination under a stereoscope with oblique illumination. Generally, the plates are examined after overnight incubation at 37°C.

5. Identification:

- **Slide agglutination:** Colonies suggestive of vibrios should be picked with a straight wire and tested by slide agglutination with cholera O subgroup I serum (cholera non-differential serum). If positive, agglutination may be repeated using specific Ogawa and Inaba sera for serotyping. Hikojima strains will agglutinate equally well with Ogawa and Inaba sera. If agglutination is negative with one colony, it is essential to repeat the test with at least five more colonies, as agglutinable and non–O-1 vibrios may co-exist in the same specimen. If slide agglutination is positive, the isolate is further tested by biochemicals for differentiation between El Tor and classical cholera vibrios. A report can be sent at this stage, usually the day after the specimen is received. If no vibrios are isolated, a second cycle of enrichment and plating may succeed in some cases.

  Isolates of vibrios that are not agglutinated by the O subgroup I serum should not be ignored as non–O-1 vibrios are known to produce cholera-like disease. An antiserum to the H antigen which is shared by all cholera vibrios has been found to be a useful reagent. Any vibrio which is agglutinated by this H antiserum, but not by the O-1 serum is considered to be non–O-1 cholera vibrio. Specific antiserum against O-139 is available. In a fully equipped laboratory, diagnostic tests in cholera and other diarrheal diseases should consist of a battery of tests designed to isolate other known pathogens also.

- **Biochemical reactions:** The isolate may then be subjected to detailed study, if desired, including an oxidase test, utilisation of amino acids, lysine, arginine and ornithine, fermentation of sugars including sucrose, mannose and arabinose, hemolysis, VP, polymyxin B sensitivity and susceptibility to cholera phage IV. The strain may be sent to the International Reference Centre for vibrio phage typing at the **National Institute of Cholera and Enteric Disease** (NICED) at Kolkata.

6. Serology: Serological examination is not used in the diagnosis of cases though it may be helpful in assessing the prevalence of cholera in an area. The tests available are agglutination using live or killed vibrio suspensions, indirect hemagglutination, vibriocidal test and antitoxin assay. Of these, the complement-dependent vibriocidal antibody test is the most useful.

7. Testing of water samples: For examination of water samples for vibrios, **enrichment or filtration** methods may be employed. In the former, 900 ml of water is added to 100 ml tenfold concentrated peptone water at pH 9.2, incubated at 37°C for 6–8 hours and a second enrichment done before plating on selective media. For the filtration technique, the water to be tested should be filtered through the Millipore membrane filter; it is then placed directly on the surface of a selective medium and incubated. Colonies appear after overnight incubation. Sewage should be diluted in saline, filtered through gauze and treated as for water.

Immunity

In cholera, the vibrios remain confined to the intestine, where they multiply and elaborate the enterotoxin which is responsible for the disease. Immunity, therefore, may be directed against the bacterium or against the toxin—antibacterial or antitoxic. Natural infection confers some amount of immunity but it does not seem to last for more than 6–12 months and re-infections are known after this period.

Immunisation with killed vaccines induces only antibacterial immunity. The protective effect of these vaccines, especially purified somatic antigens used as vaccines, though short-lived, proves that antibacterial immunity can provide protection against infection. The protection appears to be serotype specific but not biotype specific.

Immunity may be local, in the intestine or systemic. The appearance of local antibodies in the intestine has been known for a long time. These are known as co-proantibodies as they appear in the feces. They consist of IgG, IgM and IgA.

Prophylaxis

The prevention of cholera essentially requires general measures such as provision of protected water supply and improvement of environmental sanitation. As these are not easily attainable, vaccination continues to be the most widely used method of prevention in endemic areas.

Vaccines:

- **Parentral:** The vaccines used traditionally are killed suspensions containing 8000 million *V.cholerae* per ml, composed of equal numbers of Ogawa and Inaba serotypes, given by subcutaneous or intramuscular injection. Many laboratories employ classical cholera and El Tor vibrios in equal numbers in the vaccine. Strain O-139 vaccine has also been prepared. Several controlled field trials in endemic areas have shown that the protection afforded by it does not exceed 50–60 per cent; the duration of protection is only 3–6 months Also, injectable vaccines do not provide any local immunity in the intestinal mucosa. They are also unacceptably reactogenic. Hence attention has been directed to oral vaccines.

- **Oral vaccines**: Two types of oral vaccines have been tried recently:
  - **Killed oral whole cell vaccines** with and without the inclusion of the B subunit of CT
  - **Live oral vaccines** with classical, El Tor and O-139 strains, with their toxin genes deleted. While the results have been promising, problems remain to be solved before they are cleared for general use. An ideal cholera vaccine is yet to be found.

Treatment

The treatment of cholera consists essentially of the prompt and adequate replacement of lost fluid and electrolytes. Oral administration of fluid containing glucose and electrolytes, either alone or supplemented by intravenous fluids, is a highly successful and freely available method of treating cholera. Cereal-based preparations are equally effective and are usually more acceptable. Antibacterial therapy is of secondary importance. Oral tetracycline was recommended for reducing the period of vibrio excretion and the need for parenteral fluids. Initially, cholera vibrios were uniformly susceptible to all antibiotics active against Gram-negative bacilli, but since 1979, multiple drug resistant strains have become increasingly common.

VIBRIO MIMICUS

So named because it closely resembles cholera vibrios in biochemical features, *V.mimicus* can be differentiated by its failure to ferment sucrose. Like *V.cholerae*, it grows best at low salt concentrations (0.5–1.0%). It has been responsible for many sporadic cases of diarrheal disease on the Gulf Coast of the USA. Infection is acquired by eating seafood, especially oysters. The disease is self-limiting. Clinical manifestations resemble those caused by *V.parahaemolyticus*.

HALOPHILIC VIBRIOS

Vibrios that have a high requirement of sodium chloride are known as halophilic vibrios. Their natural habitat is sea water and marine life. Some halophilic vibrios have been known to cause human disease—*V.parahaemolyticus, V.alginolyticus* and *V.vulnificus*.

VIBRIO PARAHAEMOLYTICUS

V.parahaemolyticus is an enteropathogenic halophilic vibrio originally isolated in 1951 in Japan as the causative agent of an outbreak of food poisoning caused by sea fish. Gastroenteritis due to this vibrio has since been identified in several countries and it is now considered an important cause of food poisoning throughout the world. It inhabits the coastal seas, where it is found in fish arthropods such as shrimps and crabs, and molluscs such as oysters. In Kolkata, it has also been found in small pond fish.

In morphology, it resembles the cholera vibrio, except that it is capsulated, shows bipolar staining and has a tendency to pleomorphism, especially when grown on 3% salt agar and in old cultures. Unlike other vibrios, it produces peritrichous flagella when grown on solid media. Polar flagella are formed in liquid cultures.

It grows only in media containing NaCl. It can tolerate salt concentrations up to 8% but not 10%. The optimum salt concentration is 2–4%. On TCBS agar, the colonies are green with an opaque, raised centre and flat translucent periphery (note that *V.cholera* colonies are yellow in colour). The string test is positive.

It is oxidase, catalase, nitrate, indole and citrate positive. Glucose, maltose, mannitol, mannose and arabinose are fermented producing acid only. Lactose, sucrose, salicin, xylose, adonitol, inositol and sorbitol are not fermented.

It is killed at 60°C in 15 minutes. It does not grow at 4°C but can survive refrigeration and freezing. Drying destroys it. It dies in distilled water or vinegar in a few minutes.

Three antigenic components have been recognised: somatic O, capsular K and flagellar H antigens. Serotyping is based on the O and K antigens; 12 O groups have been recognised and 59 distinct K antigens.

Not all strains of *V.parahaemolyticus* are pathogenic for human beings. Strains isolated from environmental sources (such as water, fish, crabs or oysters) are nearly always non-hemolytic when grown on a special high salt blood agar (**Wagatsuma agar**), while strains from human patients are almost always hemolytic. This is called the **Kanagawa phenomenon** and is due to a heat stable hemolysin. The significance of this hemolysis is not known but it is used as a laboratory test for pathogenicity, **Kanagawa-positive strains** being considered pathogenic for human beings and negative strains non-pathogenic. No enterotoxin has been identified. The vibrio is believed to cause enteritis by invasion of the intestinal epithelium.

V.parahaemolyticus causes food poisoning associated with marine food. It also causes acute diarrhea, unassociated with food poisoning. Abdominal pain, diarrhea, vomiting and fever are the usual signs. Feces contain cellular exudate and often also blood. Dehydration is of moderate degree and recovery occurs in 1–3 days. Cases are more common in summer, and in adults than in children. In Kolkata, *V.parahaemolyticus* could be isolated from 5–10 per cent of diarrhea cases admitted to the Infectious Diseases Hospital. *V.parahaemolyticus* is common in sea fish in some other parts of India but human cases are much less frequent.

VIBRIO ALGINOLYTICUS

This halophilic vibrio resembles *V.parahaemolyticus* in many respects and was formerly considered a biotype of the latter. It has higher salt tolerance, is VP positive and ferments sucrose (Table 32.6). It is frequently found in sea fish. Its status as a human pathogen is uncertain. It has been associated with infections of the eyes, ears and wounds in human beings exposed to sea water.

VIBRIO VULNIFICUS

V.vulnificus, previously known as L+ vibrio or *Beneckea vulnifica*, is a marine vibrio of medical importance.

Table 32.6 *Some characteristics of* V.parahaemolyticus *and* V.alginolyticus

	V.parahaemolyticus	*V.alginolyticus*
Indole	+	+
VP	–	+
Nitrate reduction	+	+
Urease	–	–
Sucrose fermentation	–	+
Swarming	–	+
Growth in 0% NaCl	–	–
7% NaCl	+	+
10% NaCl	–	+

It is VP negative and ferments lactose but not sucrose. It has a salt tolerance of less than 8%. It causes two types of illness. The first is wound infection following contact of open wounds with sea water. The second type occurs in compromised hosts, particularly those with liver disease. Following ingestion of the vibrio, usually in oysters, it penetrates the gut mucosa without causing gastrointestinal manifestations and enters the bloodstream, rapidly leading to septicemia with high mortality.

AEROMONAS AND PLESIOMONAS

Besides the genus *Vibrio*, the family Vibrionaceae also contains the genera *Aeromonas* and *Plesiomonas*, some members of which have been associated with human lesions.

Aeromonas hydrophila, originally isolated from frogs, in which it causes the 'red leg disease', has been reported from many cases of diarrhea and from some pyogenic lesions in human beings. *Plesiomonas shigelloides* also has been reported from diarrheal disease. Both these are oxidase-positive, polar-flagellated, Gram-negative rods and may be mistaken for vibrios. They may be differentiated from vibrios by biochemical tests such as utilisation of amino acids.

RECAP

- Members of the genus *Vibrio* are Gram-negative, curved bacilli which exhibit motility, are facultative anaerobes and positive by the catalase and oxidase tests. *Vibrio cholerae* is the most important cause of human disease and causes cholera. *Vibrio parahaemolyticus* and *Vibrio vulnificus* are also sometimes implicated in human infections.
- *V.cholerae* possess O-1 or O-139 somatic antigens, and O-1 isolates are subtyped as AB (Inaba), AC (Ogama) or ABC (Hikojima) and as two biovars, classical and El Tor.
- For diagnosis of cholera, the stool is examined for darting motility which is reduced by adding specific antiserum.
- Vibrios grow on selective culture media such as thiosulphate-citrate-bile salts-sucrose (TCBS) agar to obtain yellow colonies.
- Cholera can be prevented by proper treatment of drinking water.
- Cholera is treated with rehydration therapy and, in severe cases, with tetracycline or doxycycline to shorten the course of the disease.
- *Vibrio parahaemolyticus* is halophilic (has an exceptionally high requirement for sodium chloride) and is found in prawns and other seafood. It also produces an enterotoxin but its effect is much milder than that of cholera.
- Other vibrios (*Vibrio vulnificus*) occasionally cause human disease, including traumatic wound infections and, rarely, eye infections.

ESSAYS

1. Classify vibrio. Write about the morphology, pathogenesis and laboratory diagnosis of cholera.
2. Describe the laboratory diagnosis of cholera.
3. Explain the pathogenesis of cholera.
4. Describe the epidemiology of cholera in India.

SHORT ANSWERS

1. Kanagawa phenomenon
2. O-139 *V.cholerae*
3. Cholera vaccines

SHORT NOTES

1. Cholera toxin
2. Halophilic vibrios
3. Differences between classical and El Tor vibrios
4. Selective media for vibrios
5. VR medium
6. String test

33 Pseudomonas

Pseudomonas aeruginosa

Clinical Case A three-year-old boy presented with a history of repeated respiratory tract infections with productive cough. On examination, signs suggestive of acute bronchitis and respiratory distress were found. Further investigations showed that the sweat test was positive for high sodium chloride concentration, suggestive of cystic fibrosis. Culture of sputum showed growth of non–lactose fermenting colonies with a mucoid colony character, which were oxidase positive. These were identified as *B.cepacia*.

INTRODUCTION

Pseudomonas is a large group of aerobic, non-sporing, Gram-negative bacilli, motile by polar flagella. They are ubiquitous, mostly saprophytic, being found in water, soil or other moist environments. Some of them are pathogenic to plants, insects and reptiles. A few cause human infection, typically opportunistic.

Based on molecular analysis, pseudomonads have been re-classified and many former *Pseudomonas* species re-allocated to new genera such as *Burkholderia*, *Stenotrophomonas* and others.

PSEUDOMONAS AERUGINOSA
(FORMERLY *P.PYOCYANEA: BACILLUS PYOCYANEUS*)

Morphology

It is a slender, Gram-negative bacillus, 1.5–3 × 0.5 μm in size, actively motile by a polar flagellum. Clinical isolates are often piliated. It is non-capsulated but many strains have a mucoid slime layer. Mucoid strains, particularly isolates from cystic fibrosis patients, have an abundance of extracellular polysaccharides composed of alginate polymers (*Case*). This forms a loose capsule (glycocalyx) in which microcolonies of the bacillus are enmeshed and protected from host defences.

Cultural characteristics

It is an obligate aerobe. Growth occurs at a wide range of temperatures, 6–42°C, the optimum being 37°C.

- **Ordinary media:** It grows well producing large, opaque, irregular colonies, with a distinctive, musty, mawkish or earthy smell.
- **Nutrient agar:** Iridescent patches with a metallic sheen are seen in cultures with crystals beneath the patches.
- **MacConkey medium:** It forms non–lactose fermenting colonies.
- **Blood agar:** Many strains are hemolytic on blood agar.
- **Broth:** It forms a dense turbidity with a surface pellicle.

Pigment production: *P.aeruginosa* produces a number of pigments, the best known being **pyocyanin** and **fluorescein**. Pyocyanin is a bluish-green phenazine pigment soluble in water and chloroform. Fluorescein (pyoverdin) is a greenish-yellow pigment soluble in water but not in chloroform. In old cultures it may be oxidised to a yellowish-brown pigment. Pyocyanin is produced only by *P.aeruginosa* but fluorescein may be produced by many other species. Other pigments produced are **pyorubin** (red) and **pyomelanin** (brown) in various combinations. Some strains may be non-pigmented. It is not known whether the pigments have any role in pathogenesis. Some of the pigments, particularly pyocyanin, inhibit the growth of many other bacteria and may therefore contribute to *P.aeruginosa* emerging as the dominant bacterium in mixed infections (Fig. 33.1).

Biochemical reactions

The metabolism is oxidative and non-fermentative. It is catalase positive, oxidase positive and motile. Glucose is utilised oxidatively, forming only acid. Peptone water sugars are unsuitable for detecting this weak acid production and therefore Hugh and Leifson's medium with glucose is used to test an oxidative attack on sugars. Nitrates are reduced to nitrites and further to gaseous nitrogen; the arginine dihydrolase test is positive.

Classification

As *P.aeruginosa* has become a very important cause of hospital infections, its classification and typing is essential for epidemiological purposes. Serotyping, bacteriocin (pyocin, aeruginosin) typing and bacteriophage typing were used but are being replaced by molecular methods due to lack of discriminatory power. Typing with pulse field gel electrophoresis is a more reliable method.

Fig. 33.1 *P.aeruginosa* showing pigment production (pyocyanin)

Resistance

The bacillus is not particularly heat resistant, being killed at 55°C in one hour, but exhibits a high degree of resistance to chemical agents. It is resistant to the common antiseptics and disinfectants such as quaternary ammonium compounds, chloroxylenol and hexachlorophane and may even grow profusely in bottles of such antiseptic lotions kept for use in hospitals. Indeed, *P.aeruginosa* can grow in **dettol** or **cetrimide selective medium**. It is sensitive to acids, beta glutaraldehyde, silver salts and strong phenolic disinfectants. Its susceptibility to silver has been applied clinically in the use of silver sulphonamide compounds as topical cream in burns.

Epidemiology

The importance of the bacillus as a disease causing agent was not adequately recognised till recently, when it established itself as one of the most troublesome agents causing nosocomial infections.

Community acquired: In the community outside the hospital, the most common infection caused by *P.aeruginosa* is suppurative otitis, which is chronic though not disabling. It is also a common cause of respiratory tract infection in cystic fibrosis patients.

Healthcare associated: In the hospital, it may cause localised or generalised infections. Localised lesions are commonly infections of wounds and bedsores, eye infections and urinary infections following catheterisation. *P.aeruginosa* is the most common and serious cause of infection in burns. It is also one of the agents responsible for iatrogenic meningitis following lumbar puncture. It frequently causes post-tracheostomy pulmonary infection. Septicemia and endocarditis may occur in patients who are debilitated due to concomitant infection, malignancy or immunosuppressive therapy. Ecthyma gangrenosum and many other types of skin lesions have been described, occurring either alone or as part of generalised infection, mainly in patients with leukemia and other types of malignancy. Infection of the nail bed is not uncommon following excessive exposure of hands to detergents and water.

The pre-eminent role of *P.aeruginosa* in hospital infection is due to its resistance to common antibiotics and antiseptics, and its ability to establish itself widely in hospitals. Being an extremely adaptable organism, it can survive and multiply even with minimal nutrients, if moisture is available. Equipment such as respirators and endoscopes, articles such as bed pans and medicines such as lotions, ointments and eye drops and even stocks of distilled water or plants and flowers may be frequently contaminated. *P.aeruginosa* is present on the skin of the axilla and perineum in some persons. Fecal carriage is not common but may be frequent following oral antibiotic treatment or hospitalisation.

Pathogenicity

'**Blue pus**' was known as a surgical entity long before Gessard (1882) isolated *P.aeruginosa* from such cases. The term aeruginosa means verdigris, which is bluish-green in colour, and pyocyanea is a literal translation of 'blue pus'.

The mechanisms of pathogenesis are not clearly understood. Several toxic extracellular products have been identified:

- **Exotoxin A** has a mechanism of action similar to that of the diphtheria toxin. It also has A active and B binding subunits and inhibits protein synthesis. Good antibody response to exotoxin A is considered a favourable sign in severe infections with *P.aeruginosa*.
- Other extracellular enzymes and toxins include **proteases, elastases, hemolysins** and **enterotoxin**.
- The **slime layer** acts as a capsule in enhancing virulence. In addition, the ability to form biofilms promotes infection.

Factors promoting infection:
- Breach in primary body defences
- Bacterial pili (favour adhesion)
- Bacterial exoproducts (elastase, exotoxin A, exoenzyme S)
- Lipopolysaccharide (cell wall) and the alginate glycocalyx
- The ability to form biofilms

Laboratory diagnosis

The bacterium grows readily on most media. Identification of pigmented strains of the bacillus from clinical specimens is easy. But about 10 per cent of isolates may be non-pigmented. Prompt oxidase reaction and arginine hydrolysis help in their identification. It may be necessary to use selective media such as cetrimide agar for isolation from feces or other samples with mixed flora. Species identification is done by biochemical tests.

As *P.aeruginosa* is a frequent contaminant and coloniser in the hospital setting, isolation of the bacillus from a specimen should not always be taken as proof of its etiological role. Repeated isolation and clinical correlation helps confirm the diagnosis.

Control

Prevention of *P.aeruginosa* cross-infection in hospitals requires constant vigilance and strict attention to asepsis.

Treatment

Specific antibacterial therapy constitutes only one aspect of the management of serious pseudomonas infections.

Resistance to antimicrobials: Antibiotic treatment options are limited as the strains in the hospital are multidrug resistant and now even pan-drug resistant. Standard precautions and contact isolation are important aspects of preventing the spread of infection in the wards. Treatment of the underlying disease, correction of granulopenia and appropriate supportive therapy need attention.

Occasional opportunist infections may be caused by a few other species, such as *P.fluorescens, P.putida* and *P.stutzeri*.

Stenotrophomonas maltophila
(formerly *Pseudomonas maltophila*)

This is a saprophyte and opportunistic pathogen that causes wound infection, urinary tract infection and septicemia in healthcare settings. It is usually oxidase negative and acidifies maltose in addition to glucose, lactose and sucrose. The organism is sensitive to cotrimoxazole and resistant to carbapenems.

Burkholderia cepacia
(formerly *Pseudomonas cepacia*)

B.cepacia is increasingly being recognised as an opportunist environmental pathogen, particularly in those with cystic fibrosis or chronic granulomatous disease, in whom it causes fatal necrotising pneumonia. It is nutritionally very versatile. It can grow in many common disinfectants and can even use penicillin G as its sole source of carbon! It is oxidase positive and acidifies mannitol, sorbitol and sucrose. It can cause urinary, respiratory and wound infections, peritonitis, endocarditis and septicemia. It is inherently resistant to most antibiotics.

GLANDERS

Burkholderia mallei
(formerly *Pseudomonas mallei*)

It is the causative agent of glanders (*malleus*, in Latin), a disease primarily of equine animals—horses, mules and asses—but capable of being transmitted to other animals and to human beings. The bacillus was discovered by Loeffler and Schutz (1882).

Burkholderia mallei is a slender, non-motile, Gram-negative bacillus, 2–5 × 0.5 µm in size, staining irregularly and often having a beaded appearance. It is an aerobe and facultative anaerobe, growing on ordinary media under a wide temperature range. Colonies which are small and translucent initially become yellowish and opaque on ageing. It is quite inactive biochemically, attacking only glucose.

Human infection is usually **occupational**, found among ostlers, grooms and veterinarians.

- It may be acute or chronic and is protean in character, with localisation in the respiratory tract, skin or subcutaneous tissues.
- In acute glanders, there is fever, mucopurulent nasal discharge and severe prostration. The fatality rate is high.
- While human infection is acquired only rarely from infected animals, laboratory cultures are highly infectious and *B.mallei* is one of the most dangerous bacteria to work with.

MELIOIDOSIS

Burkholderia pseudomallei
(formerly *Pseudomonas pseudomallei*)

This is the causative agent of melioidosis, a glanders-like disease, epizootic in rodents in Southeast Asia, India and North Australia. (The name is derived from *melis*, a disease of asses [glanders], and *eidos*, meaning resemblance). The disease was first described in human beings by Whitmore and Krishnaswami (1912) in Rangoon. Whitmore (1913) isolated the bacillus. It resembles *B.mallei* but differs in being motile, liquefying gelatin and forming acid from several sugars. Two thermolabile exotoxins, one lethal and the other necrotising, have been identified in culture filtrates.

Infection is usually acquired by contamination of abrasion wounds with soil and water containing the organism; underlying disease (like diabetes mellitus) may increase the risk. It may take many years before the infection becomes manifest. The human disease may take two forms:

- **Acute**: It may be a generalised infection presenting as acute septicemia, a subacute typhoid-like disease or pneumonia and hemoptysis resembling tuberculosis. Acute melioidosis has a high case fatality rate.
- **Chronic**: In chronic form, there may be multiple caseous or suppurative foci, with abscess formation in the skin and subcutaneous tissues, bones and internal organs.

Serological evidence indicates that inapparent infection is common in endemic areas. Long latency and reactivation may occur as the bacillus can survive intracellularly in the reticuloendothelial system. The bacillus has been isolated from water and soil in endemic areas. It is a soil saprophyte that causes infection in rodents and humans accidentally. Human infection occurs commonly through skin abrasions or by inhalation.

Diagnosis may be made by demonstration of the bacillus in (Fig. 33.2) exudates by microscopy (small, irregularly staining, Gram-negative bacilli, showing typical bipolar '**safety-pin appearance**' with methylene blue stain), isolation by culture from sputum, pus, blood or urine, or by serology (ELISA for IgM and IgG antibody, indirect hemagglutination). A PCR test has also been developed.

Ceftazidime is the drug of choice, along with cotrimoxazole, tetracycline, amoxycillin clavulanate or chloramphenicol. Prolonged **treatment** for many months may be necessary.

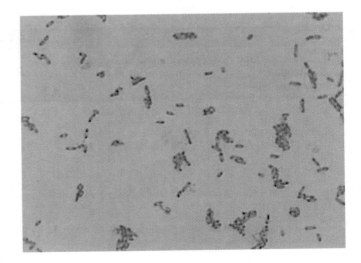

Fig. 33.2   Melioidosis: safety pin appearance

RECAP

- Members of the genus *Pseudomonas* are rod-shaped bacteria which exhibit motility, are catalase and oxidase positive, Gram negative and are obligate aerobes.
- Some species produce pigments, some of which are fluorescent.
- The most important pathogenic species is *Pseudomonas aeruginosa*; other pathogens are *Burkholderia cepacia* (the cause of cepacia disease), *Burkholderia mallei* (the cause of glanders) and *Burkholderia pseudomallei* (the cause of melioidosis).
- *Pseudomonas aeruginosa* causes opportunistic infections of the lung (in cystic fibrosis), and nosocomial infections.
- Factors promoting infection by *Pseudomonas aeruginosa* are bacterial, exotoxin A, lipopolysaccharide (cell wall) and the alginate glycocalyx. The ability to form biofilms is also a virulence factor.
- For diagnosis, culture of colonies shows the presence of blue pyocyanin and/or yellow pyoverdin. The bacteria are Gram-negative rods, motile by polar flagella, oxidase and catalase positive and capable of growing at 42°C.
- *Burkholderia cepacia* can cause severe infections in patients of cystic fibrosis.
- Melioidosis is a pyogenic or granulomatous infection caused by *Burkholderia pseudomallei*.
- Glanders is a disease of animals that can be transmitted to humans; it is caused by *Burkholderia mallei*.

SHORT ANSWERS

1. Antibiotic resistance in *Pseudomonas aeruginosa*
2. Role of *Pseudomonas aeruginosa* in hospital infections
3. *Burkholderia* infections

SHORT NOTES

1. Virulence factors of *Pseudomonas aeruginosa*
2. Glanders
3. Melioidosis

34 Yersinia, Pasteurella, Francisella

GENUS YERSINIA

YERSINIA PESTIS
Morphology
Cultural characteristics
Biochemical reactions
Resistance
Antigens, toxins and other virulence factors
PLAGUE
Yersiniosis

GENUS PASTEURELLA
PASTEURELLA MULTOCIDA

GENUS FRANCISELLA
FRANCISELLA TULARENSIS

--- **Yersinia pestis** ---

Clinical Case   A 45-year-old farmer from a village in upper Himachal Pradesh was brought in shock to the Emergency department of a nearby referral hospital. Relatives informed the attending doctor that the farmer had had sudden onset of fever with difficulty in breathing about two days earlier and hemoptysis subsequently. X-ray at admission showed extensive bronchopneumonia and the patient died despite supportive therapy and antibiotics (gentamicin and doxycycline). He was diagnosed with pneumonic plague as the village had occasionally been referring patients with bubonic plague. His sputum on Wayson stain showed bipolar staining bacilli identified as *Yersinia pestis*. While this patient was being transferred from the village, a close household contact also developed similar symptoms. He was immediately started on specific antibiotics and supportive therapy and recovered.

INTRODUCTION

The Gram-negative, short bacilli that are primary pathogens of rodents have been divided into three genera: *Yersinia*, *Pasteurella* and *Francisella* (Table 34.1).

GENUS YERSINIA

YERSINIA PESTIS

The genus *Yersinia* is assigned to the family Enterobacteriaceae. The medically important species include *Y.pestis* (the causative agent of plague), *Y.pseudotuberculosis* (a primary pathogen of rodents) and *Y.enterocolitica* (which causes enteric and systemic diseases in animals and humans). The plague bacillus was discovered independently and simultaneously by Yersin and Kitasato (1894) in Hong Kong at the beginning of the last pandemic of the disease.

Morphology

Y.pestis is a short, plump, ovoid, Gram-negative bacillus, about 1.5×0.7 μm in size, with rounded ends and convex sides, arranged singly, in short chains or in small groups. In smears stained with Giemsa or methylene blue, it shows bipolar staining (safety pin

Table 34.1   *Some differentiating features of* Yersinia *and* Pasteurella

	Y.pestis	Y.pseudotuberculosis	Y.enterocolitica	P.multocida
Motility at 22°C	−	+	+	−
Growth on MacConkey agar	+	+	+	−
Acid from sucrose	+	−	+	+
Acid from maltose	−	+	+	−
Indole	+	−	+	+
Oxidase	−	−	−	+
Urease	−	+	+	−
Ornithine decarboxylase	−	−	+	+

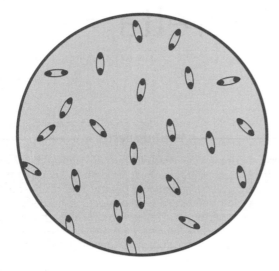

Fig. 34.1   Smear of *Y.pestis* with bipolar staining

appearance) with the two ends densely stained and a clear central area (Fig. 34.1). Pleomorphism is very common and in old cultures, involution forms are seen—coccoid, club-shaped, filamentous and giant forms. Pleomorphism is characteristically enhanced in media containing 3% NaCl. The bacillus is surrounded by a slime layer (envelope or capsule). It is non-motile, non-sporing and non–acid fast.

Cultural characteristics

The plague bacillus is aerobic and facultatively anaerobic. Growth occurs over a wide range of pH (pH 5–9.6, optimum pH 7.2) and temperature (range 2–45°C). The optimum temperature for growth (unlike most pathogens) is 27°C but the envelope develops best at 37°C.

It is not nutritionally exacting and grows on basal media.

- On **nutrient** agar, colonies are small, delicate, transparent discs, becoming opaque on continued incubation.
- Colonies on **blood agar** or other hemin-containing media are dark brown due to the absorption of the hemin pigment.
- Colourless colonies are formed on **MacConkey agar**.
- In **broth**, a flocculent growth occurs at the bottom and along the sides of the tube, with little or no turbidity. A delicate pellicle may form later. If grown in a flask of broth with oil or ghee (clarified butter) floated on top (**ghee broth**), a characteristic growth occurs which hangs down into the broth from the surface, resembling stalactites (**stalactite growth**).

Biochemical reactions

Glucose, maltose and mannitol but not lactose, sucrose and rhamnose are fermented with the production of acid but no gas. Indole is not produced. It is MR positive and VP and citrate negative, catalase positive and esculin positive and oxidase and urease negative. Gelatin is not liquefied.

Resistance

The plague bacillus is easily destroyed by exposure to heat, sunlight, drying and chemical disinfectants. It is destroyed by heat at 55°C or by 0.5% phenol in 15 minutes. It remains viable for long periods in cold, moist environments. It can survive for several months, and even multiply, in the soil of rodent burrows. All strains are lysed by a specific antiplague bacteriophage at 22°C.

Antigens, toxins and other virulence factors

Plague bacilli are antigenically homogeneous and serotypes do not exist. The antigenic structure is complex. At least 20 antigens have been detected by gel diffusion and biochemical analysis. Many of them have been claimed to be virulence factors. They include the following:

- A heat labile protein envelope antigen (**Fraction I** or **F-I**), best formed in cultures incubated at 37°C. It inhibits phagocytosis and is generally present only in virulent strains. This plasmid encoded antigen has been considered a virulence determinant, but occasional strains deficient in the F-I antigen have been isolated from fatal human cases. The antibody to this antigen is protective in mice.
- Two antigens designated **V** and **W** and always produced together have been considered to be virulence factors as they inhibit phagocytosis and intracellular killing of the bacillus. Production of these antigens is plasmid mediated.
- Virulent strains produce a **bacteriocin (Pesticin I), coagulase** and **fibrinolysin**. Pesticin I inhibits strains of *Y.pseudotuberculosis*, *Y.enterocolitica* and *E.coli*.
- The term '**plague toxin**' refers to at least two classes of toxin found in culture filtrates or cell lysates. The first is the **endotoxin**, a lipopolysaccharide similar to the endotoxins of enteric bacilli. The second is a protein called **murine toxins** active in rats and mice but its role in humans is not known.

- Virulence also appears to be associated with an **unidentified surface component** which absorbs hemin and basic aromatic dyes in culture media to form coloured colonies.
- Virulence has also been associated with the ability to synthesise **purine**.

PLAGUE

Plague is an ancient scourge of humans. Central Asia or the Himalayas is believed to have been the original home of the plague, from where it spread causing epidemics and pandemics. The bubonic plague in 542 AD is believed to have been caused by *Y.pestis var antiqua*. In the fourteenth century, pandemic plague known as the **'black death'** was caused by *Y.pestis var medievalis*.

It is believed to have killed a quarter of all humans. The disease was quiescent in the eighteenth and nineteenth centuries and confined to endemic foci. The last pandemic which started in Hong Kong in 1894 and which spread throughout the world was caused by *Y.pestis var orientalis* (Table 34.2).

Plague survives in several scattered natural foci in many parts of the world (Fig. 34.2) among wild rodents, occasionally causing infection in human contacts.

Indian scenario: India was one of the countries worst hit by this pandemic. Plague reached Bombay in 1896 and spread all over the country during the next few years, causing more than 10 million deaths by 1918. It gradually receded thereafter, though occasional cases continued to be reported in endemic foci till 1967.

Table 34.2   *Biotypes of* Yersinia pestis

Variety	Glycerol fermentation	Nitrate reduction	Geographical distribution
Y.pestis var orientalis	–	+	Primary foci in India, Myanmar, and China. Causative agent of 1894 pandemic. Responsible for wild plague in western USA, South America, South Africa
Y.pestis var antiqua	+	+	Transbaikalia, Mongolia, Manchuria, perhaps responsible for Justinian plague
Y.pestis var medievalis	+	–	Southeast Russia

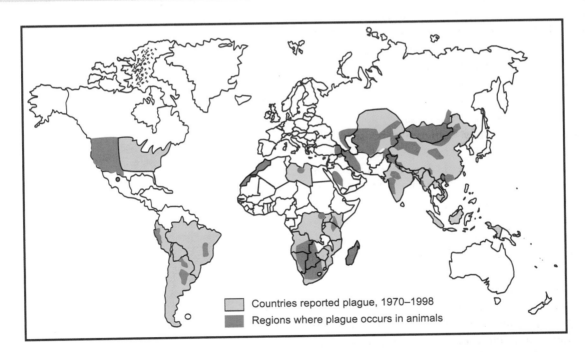

Countries reported plague, 1970–1998
Regions where plague occurs in animals

Fig. 34.2   World distribution of plague, 1998

No further plague cases were seen in India till 1994, when in August a non-fatal outbreak of bubonic plague was reported in Maharashtra (Beed district). In September, pneumonic plague was reported in Surat and adjoining areas of Gujarat and Maharashtra, causing much panic and consternation. A few cases were reported from different parts of North India as well, probably caused by the exodus of people from the affected areas. During the outbreak which subsided in two months, there were over 6000 suspected plague cases and 60 deaths. In February 2002, plague struck again, causing a short outbreak near Simla, claiming four lives.

In India, at least **four foci** of plague are known. One is the region near Kolar at the trijunction of Tamil Nadu, Andhra Pradesh and Karnataka. The second is the Beed–Latur belt in Maharashtra from where the Surat epidemic emanated. The third is in Rhoru in Himachal Pradesh where the 2002 outbreak took place, and the fourth is a small pocket in Uttaranchal.

Types: In human beings, plague occurs in three main forms: bubonic, pneumonic and septicemic.

In **bubonic plague**, after an incubation period of 2–5 days, the lymph nodes draining the site of entry of the bacillus become infected. In some, the infection remains localised at the site of the flea bite, with only minor constitutional symptoms (pestis minor). As the plague bacillus usually enters through flea bites on the legs, the inguinal nodes are involved and hence the name 'bubonic' (bubon meaning groin). The glands become enlarged and suppurate. The bacilli enter the bloodstream and produce septicemia. Sometimes there are hemorrhages into the skin and mucosa. Disseminated intravascular coagulation is common and may lead to gangrene of the skin, fingers and penis. Case fatality in untreated cases may be 30–90 per cent.

Pneumonic plague may sometimes be seen during epidemics of bubonic plague. Rarely, primary pneumonic plague may occur in epidemic form, as happened in Manchuria in 1910–1912, causing some 60,000 deaths. Pneumonic plague is spread by droplet infection. The bacilli spread through the lungs producing hemorrhagic pneumonia. Cyanosis is very prominent. The bloody mucoid sputum that is coughed out contains bacilli in enormous numbers. Pneumonic plague is highly infectious and in untreated patients, almost invariably fatal (*Case*).

Septicemic plague is usually the terminal event in the bubonic or pneumonic plague but may sometimes occur primarily. Meningitic involvement may occur rarely. Human carriers have not been recorded but asymptomatic oropharyngeal infection has been observed in some contacts.

Epidemiology: Plague is a zoonotic disease. The plague bacillus is naturally parasitic in rodents. Infection is transmitted among them by rat fleas. The fleas acquire the infection by feeding on infected rodents. In the flea, the bacilli multiply in the stomach to such an extent that they block the proventriculus. The interval between the ingestion of infected blood and blocking in the proventriculus is the **extrinsic incubation period**, which is usually about two weeks in *Xenopsylla cheopis*. When such a 'blocked' flea bites another rodent, it cannot suck in blood because the bacterial mass blocks the passage mechanically. Blood, mixed with the bacteria, is regurgitated into the bite, transmitting the infection. Infection may also be transferred by contamination of the bite wound with the feces of infected fleas. When a diseased rat dies (rat fall), the fleas leave the carcass and, in the absence of another rat, may bite human beings, causing bubonic plague.

Several species of fleas may act as vectors, the most important being *Xenopsylla cheopis*, *X.astia* and *Ceratophyllus fasciatus*. **X.cheopis, the predominant species in North India** is a more efficient vector than the South Indian species *X.astia*. This has contributed to the more extensive nature of plague outbreaks in the North as compared to those in South India. Plague epidemics generally occur in the cool, humid seasons that favour the multiplication of fleas, leading to a high **'flea index'** (mean number of fleas per rat). Fleas do not thrive in hot, dry weather, and the transmission of infection is interrupted.

Studies of the various governmental Plague Commissions in Bombay, during the early years of the twentieth century, helped clarify the epidemiology of plague. It was found that plague produced epizootics first in *Rattus norvegicus* (sewer rat). When their number dwindled, the disease passed to the domestic rat, *R.rattus*. It was from the domestic rat that the infection spread to human beings.

Two natural cycles of plague exist, the domestic and the wild:

- The term '**urban or domestic plague**' refers to plague that is intimately associated with human beings and the rodents living with them, possessing a definite potential for producing epidemics.
- '**Wild or sylvatic plague**' occurs in nature and in wild rodents, independent of human beings.

The rodents involved vary in different regions. Over 200 species and subspecies are involved. **In India, the gerbil (*Tatera indica*) and the bandicoot are infected.** Human infection may occur during skinning and handling of carcasses of infected wild animals. Carnivores, including cats and dogs, can get infected by eating infected rodents or through their fleas. Clinical plague is seldom seen in dogs, but may develop in cats. Human infection from inhalation of respiratory droplets from infected cats has been reported.

In **enzootic foci**, plague may persist for long periods. Infected fleas may survive for over a year. The bacilli can remain alive and even multiply in the soil of abandoned rodent burrows. They can infect new rodents that may reoccupy such burrows. This may account for the long period of quiescence and subsequent re-emergence characteristic of plague. Attenuated strains of plague bacilli have been isolated from natural foci. They may regain virulence when the plague becomes active. Eradication of plague is an unlikely prospect as it is a disease of rodents that live in burrows and of the fleas that live on them. Only when human beings or domestic animals trespass on these natural foci do human infections set in.

In the 1990s, there was a re-emergence of plague in countries where it had ceased to be noticed for many years. This took place in developing and developed countries—India and China in Asia, Malawi and Zimbabwe in Africa, the erstwhile USSR in Europe and in the USA.

Laboratory diagnosis: The laboratory should be able to diagnose plague in humans and also in rodents, as timely detection of infection in rats may help prevent epidemic spread.

In humans:

1. **Specimen:** For bubonic plague, the buboes are collected; in pneumonic plague, sputum is collected; and in septicemic plague, blood is collected.

2. **Direct demonstration:** In human bubonic plague, the bacilli may be readily demonstrated in buboes by microscopy, culture or animal inoculation. Blood cultures are often positive. In pneumonic plague, the bacilli can be demonstrated in sputum by microscopy, culture or animal inoculation.
   - **Microscopically** smears from the bubo stained with methylene blue (**Wayson stain**) show the bipolar stained bacilli (Fig. 34.3). The fluorescent

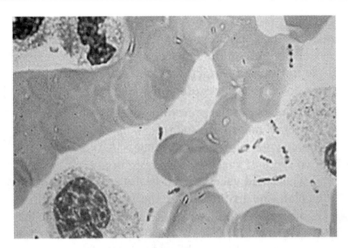

Fig. 34.3 Bubo smears in Wayson stain

antibody technique may be used to identify plague bacilli in the impression films of the tissues by demonstrating the F-I antigen. Bacilli in bubo show considerable pleomorphism. Bacilli may be demonstrated microscopically in spleen smears and heart blood.
   - **Culture:** Cultures may be made from the buboes, spleen, heart blood and particularly, from bone marrow in decomposed carcasses.
   - **Animal inoculation:** In badly putrefied carcasses, microscopy and culture may not be successful. The putrefied tissue rubbed on the shaven abdomen of a guinea pig can infect the animal.

3. **Serological tests:** These are sometimes useful in diagnosis. Antibodies to the F-I antigen may be detected by passive hemagglutination. Rise in titre of antibodies in paired sera or titre of 128 or above in a single serum sample can be considered positive. IgG and IgM ELISA tests and a rapid dipstick assay have now been developed using the F-I antigen.

4. **Molecular methods:**
   - **Clinical material and fleas:** PCR is a rapid and sensitive method for presumptive diagnosis of plague.

In rats: A rat which died of plague may carry infected fleas and should be handled with care. Pouring kerosene oil over the carcass is a simple method of eliminating the fleas. In the laboratory, the carcass should be dipped in 3% lysol to destroy ectoparasites.

On autopsy, buboes are usually present in the cervical region. They are hard and can be moved under the skin. On section, the bubo may show congestion, hemorrhagic points or grey necrosis. The liver is mottled, with red, yellow or grey stippling. The spleen is enlarged, and moulded over the stomach, with granules or nodules on the surface. A characteristic feature is pleural effusion which may be clear, abundant and straw coloured or, less often, bloodstained.

Prophylaxis: In the prevention of domestic plague:
- **General measures** such as control of fleas and rodents are of great importance.
- Two types of **vaccines** have been in use:
  - The **killed vaccine** used in India (prepared at the Haffkine Institute, Mumbai) is a whole-culture antigen. A virulent strain of the plague bacillus is grown in casein hydrolysate broth for 2–4 weeks at 32°C and killed by 0.05% formaldehyde and preserved with phenyl mercuric nitrate. The vaccine is given subcutaneously, two doses at an interval of 1–3 months, followed by a third six months later. Vaccination gives some protection against bubonic plague but not against pneumonic plague. Protection does not last for more than six months. In contrast, an attack of plague provides more lasting immunity. The vaccine is recommended only for those exposed occupationally or otherwise to infection, such as a plague laboratory or hospital personnel and troops deployed in known plague areas. It is of no value in plague outbreaks, and mass vaccination is not advised.
  - The **live vaccine** is no longer recommended.
- **Chemoprophylaxis:** A person exposed to a definite risk of infection, whether vaccinated or not, should be given chemoprophylaxis—cotrimoxazole or tetracycline orally for at least five days.

Treatment: Early treatment with antibiotics has reduced plague mortality from 30–100 per cent to 5–10 per cent. Streptomycin, doxycycline and chloramphenicol are effective. Plague bacillus strains carrying plasmid-borne resistance to multiple antibiotics were reported from Madagascar in 1995. These have the potential to spread and pose a great threat.

Yersiniosis

The term yersiniosis denotes infections with yersiniae other than *Y.pestis*. These include zoonotic infections by *Y.pseudotuberculosis* and *Y.enterocolitica*, which appear to be acquired accidentally from disease cycles of wild or domestic animals.

Yersinia pseudotuberculosis: This bacillus closely resembles the plague bacillus but can be distinguished by its relatively poor growth on MacConkey agar, motility at 22°C (but not at 37°C), production of urease, fermentation of rhamnose and melibiose and failure to be lysed by the antiplague bacteriophage at 22°C. Distinction between *Y.pseudotuberculosis* and *Y.pestis* becomes important when the former is isolated from rats.

Y.pseudotuberculosis is antigenically heterogeneous, six serological groups and many serotypes being distinguished based on somatic and flagellar antigens. It shows antigenic cross-relationships with *Y.pestis* as well as salmonellae.

For **diagnosis**, blood, stool and lymph node aspirate are obtained for culture on standard media such as blood agar at 30–35°C with or without cold enrichment and characterisation of Gram-negative rods (motile at 25°C and non-motile at 37°C).

The natural mode of infection in animals is probably through the alimentary tract. In infected guinea pigs, the liver, spleen and lungs show multiple nodules resembling tuberculosis lesions (hence the name pseudotuberculosis).

Yersinia enterocolitica: This bacillus resembles *Y.pseudotuberculosis* in being motile at 22°C but differs from it in fermenting sucrose and cellobiose and decarboxylating ornithine. It does not ferment rhamnose or melibiose. Many strains give a positive VP test and form indole. Six biotypes have been identified based on cultural and biochemical characteristics. The antigenic structure of *Y.enterocolitica* is distinct from that of *Y.psuedotuberculosis*. More than 60 O serotypes have been reported. Most human isolates belong to serotypes 03, 08 and 09. Serological cross-reactions between serotype 09 and brucella strains occur.

Y.enterocolitica has been isolated from a wide range of domestic and wild animals and, in recent years, is increasingly being reported from human clinical material.

Human diseases are of three types:
1. The first occurs in young children as **self-limiting gastroenteritis** or **enterocolitis** which may be inflammatory or non-inflammatory;
2. The second is **mesenteric adenitis** and **inflammatory terminal ileitis** in older children that may mimic appendicitis; and
3. The third is a **systemic disease** typically seen in adults, often characterised by bacteremia, meningitis, arthralgia or erythema nodosum. Persons belonging

to the HLA-B 27 group are prone to develop reactive arthritis.

For **diagnosis**, a sample of feces is cultured on standard (MacConkey agar) or selective agar (often with cold enrichment) for isolation of Gram-negative rods, which are motile at 25°C and non-motile at 37°C.

GENUS *PASTEURELLA*

PASTEURELLA MULTOCIDA

The genus *Pasteurella* contains several related bacteria causing hemorrhagic septicemia in different species of animals and occasionally producing local and systemic infections in human beings, grouped under a common species named *P.multocida*. One of these, *P.aviseptica*, is the chicken cholera bacillus used by Pasteur for the development of the first attenuated bacterial vaccine; hence the name Pasteurella.

A group of related bacteria isolated from hemorrhagic septicemia in a variety of animals and birds had, in the past, been named according to their species of origin—*P.boviseptica, lepiseptica, aviseptica*, etc. Though they show some degree of host specificity, they are so alike in other respects that they are now considered as strains of a single species designated *P.multocida*.

P.multocida is a non-motile, Gram-negative bacillus generally resembling *Yersinia* but differing in being oxidase positive, producing indole and failing to grow on MacConkey agar.

The bacillus is often carried in the upper respiratory tract of a variety of animals such as dogs, cats, rats, cattle and sheep. It may sometimes occur as a commensal in the human respiratory tract. Human infection is rare but may occur following **animal bites** or trauma. The clinical manifestations may be local suppuration following animal bites (wound infection, cellulitis, abscess, osteomyelitis), meningitis following head injury, respiratory tract infection (pneumonia, bronchitis, sinusitis) or appendicitis and appendicial abscess.

The bacillus is sensitive to tetracycline and streptomycin, and most strains to penicillin as well.

GENUS *FRANCISELLA*

FRANCISELLA TULARENSIS

The genus *Francisella,* consisting of *F.tularensis,* is named after Francis for his pioneering studies on tularemia, caused by this bacillus. This is the causative agent of tularemia, a disease of rabbits and other rodents, originally described in Tulare County, California. Infection is transmitted by ticks and several other arthropod vectors. Human infection may occur by direct contact with infected rodents such as rabbits or through tick bites. It can also be acquired by ingestion of contaminated meat or water and inhalation of infective aerosols.

It is a minute, capsulated, non-motile, Gram-negative bacillus, about $0.3–0.7 \times 0.2$ µm in size. It resembles mycoplasma in being filterable and in multiplying by filament formation and budding, besides binary fission. In infected animals, it acts as an intracellular parasite, being found in large masses inside liver and spleen cells. It has fastidious growth requirements, and special media such as Francis' blood dextrose cystine agar have to be employed for its isolation. Minute transparent colonies appear after incubation for 3–5 days.

Strains of *S.tularensis* have been subdivided into biotypes based on their virulence and epidemiological behaviour. Highly virulent strains are found only in North America, while strains of low virulence are seen in Europe and Asia as well.

In human beings, **tularemia** may present as local ulceration with lymphadenitis, a typhoid-like fever with glandular enlargement or an influenza-like respiratory infection:

- The disease may also be water-borne, as a result of water pollution by the excreta of infected rodents.
- The bacillus is highly infectious and laboratory infection has been quite common.
- Diagnosis may be made by culture or by inoculation into guinea pigs or mice.
- Agglutinating antibodies may be demonstrated in sera from patients.

An attenuated vaccine is available which can be administered by scarification to persons who are subject to high risk of infection.

RECAP

- *Yersinia* are Gram-negative bacilli that are facultative anerobes, positive by the catalase test and negative by the oxides test.
- *Yersinia pestis* is found worldwide, but outbreaks of plague occur in Asia and Africa. Plague is a zoonotic infection in humans, who become accidental hosts when they come into contact with infected rodents or their fleas. Fleas (*Xenopsylla cheopis*) transmit bacteria among rodents.
- *Yersinia pestis* causes plague, which manifests in one of three forms: bubonic plague, which is a potentially fatal infection of the lymph nodes; pneumonic plague, which is a lethal, highly contagious infection of the lungs; and septicemic plague, which is a lethal blood-borne infection.
- Two types of cycles are known: urban (rats) and rural or sylvatic (ground squirrels, prairie dogs).
- For diagnosis, material is aspirated from the bubo for demonstration of bacilli showing bipolar staining using Wayson or methylene blue stain. Alternatively, florescent antibody technique can be used to demonstrate bacilli from impression smears.
- Isolation by culture from material from bubos, spleen and heart blood can be done on MacConkey and blood agar. The patient's serum can be used to detect antibody to the F-1 antigen.
- Infected individuals can be treated with streptomycin for 10 days. Chemoprophylaxis with doxycycline can be given to travellers who face the risk of exposure.
- *Yersinia pseudotuberculosis* is found in domestic animals and birds, but zoonotic infection in humans is rare.
- *Yersinia enterocolitica* is found worldwide in a variety of domesticated animals but is more common in northern Europe than elsewhere as a cause of diarrhea in humans.
- *Pasteurella* are Gram-negative bacilli that do not exhibit motility, do not form spores, are positive for the catalase and oxidase tests, and are facultative anaerobes. The important pathogenic species is *Pasteurella multocida*.
- *Francisella tularensis* is a Gram-negative bacillus that is non-motile, pleomorphic in morphology, and fastidious in nutritional requirements. It causes tularemia, a zoonotic, plague-like infection of the reticuloendothelial system.

ESSAYS

1. What are zoonotic diseases? Give examples. Explain the epidemiology and laboratory diagnosis of *Yersinia pestis*.
2. Describe the clinical spectrum and the laboratory diagnosis of plague.

SHORT ANSWERS

1. Virulence factors of *Yersinia pestis*
2. Epidemiology of plague in India

SHORT NOTES

1. *Yersinia enterocolitica*
2. Diseases by *Y.pestis*
3. *Pasteurella multocida*
4. *Francisella tularensis*

35 Haemophilus

INTRODUCTION

The genus *Haemophilus* contains small, non-motile, non-sporing, oxidase-positive, pleomorphic, Gram-negative bacilli that are parasitic on human beings and animals. They are characterised by their requirement of one or both of two accessory growth factors (X and V) present in blood (*haemophilus,* meaning blood loving) (Table 35.1). *H.influenzae* is the first free-living organism whose complete genome has been sequenced.

Pfeiffer (1892) observed that a small, Gram-negative bacillus was 'constantly present' in the sputum of patients from the influenza pandemic of 1889–92 and mistakenly proposed this as the causative agent of human influenza. This came to be known as the '**influenza bacillus**' (**Pfeiffer's bacillus**), later renamed

Haemophilus influenzae. The causal relationship between this bacillus and human influenza could not be substantiated and was finally disproved when Smith, Andrewes and Laidlaw (1933) isolated the influenza virus.

Haemophilus influenzae

Clinical Case   A six-month-old child was brought to the Pediatrics Outpatient department with the chief complaint of fever, inability to feed and seizures since the morning. On examination, the child was found to have altered sensorium and neck rigidity. A lumbar puncture was carried out and CSF sent for cytology, biochemistry and microbiological examination. The cytology and biochemistry results were suggestive of pyogenic meningitis. Microscopic examination revealed the presence of polymorphs along with Gram-negative coccobacilli. Antigen detection by latex agglutination was positive for *Haemophilus influenzae* type b and the culture on the next day showed a growth on chocolate agar identified as *H.influenzae*. The child responded to treatment with ceftriaxone.

HAEMOPHILUS INFLUENZAE

Morphology

H.influenzae is a small (1.0×0.3 μm), Gram-negative, non-motile, non-sporing bacillus, exhibiting considerable pleomorphism. In sputum, it usually occurs as clusters of coccobacillary forms, while in CSF from meningitis cases, long, bacillary and filamentous forms predominate. Cells from young cultures (18–24 hours) are usually coccobacillary, while older cultures are distinctly pleomorphic. Strains isolated from acute infections are often capsulated.

Cultural characteristics

The bacillus has fastidious growth requirements. The accessory growth factors, named X and V, present in blood are essential for growth.

The **X factor** is hemin or other porphyrins required for the synthesis of cytochrome and other heme

Table 35.1   *Growth characteristics of the* Haemophilus *species*

Species	Growth requirements			Hemolysis on horse blood agar
	X	V	CO$_2$	
H.influenzae	+	+	−	−
H.aegyptius	+	+	−	−
H.ducreyi	+	−	Variable	Variable
H.parainfluenzae	−	+	−	−
H.haemolyticus	+	+	−	+
H.parahaemolyticus	−	+	−	+
H.aphrophilus	+	−	+	−
H.paraphrophilus	−	+	+	−

enzymes such as catalase and peroxidase involved in aerobic respiration. It is heat stable.

The **V factor** is a co-enzyme, nicotinamide adenine dinucleotide (NAD) or NAD phosphate (NADP) which acts as a hydrogen acceptor in the metabolism of the cell. It is heat labile, being destroyed at 120°C in a few minutes. It is present in red blood cells and in many other animal and plant cells. It is synthesised by some fungi and bacteria (for example, *S.aureus*) in excess of their requirements and released into the surrounding medium.

It is aerobic but grows anaerobically also. The optimum temperature is 37°C. It does not grow below 20°C. Some strains require 10% CO$_2$, especially for primary isolation from the clinical specimen. It grows on blood agar if a source of the V factor is also provided. When *S.aureus* is streaked across a plate of blood agar on which a specimen containing *H.influenzae* has been inoculated, after overnight incubation, the colonies of *H.influenzae* will be large and well developed alongside the streak of staphylococcus, and smaller farther away. This phenomenon is called **satellitism** and demonstrates the dependence of *H.influenzae* on the V factor, which is available in high concentrations near staphylococcal growth and in smaller quantities away from it. This is a routine test in clinical bacteriology for the identification of *H.influenzae* (Fig. 35.1).

Biochemical reactions

Glucose and xylose are fermented with acid production but not lactose, sucrose and mannitol. Catalase and oxidase reactions are positive. Nitrates are reduced to nitrites. **Biotyping** has been done on the basis of indole production, and urease and ornithine decarboxylase activity. Eight biotypes have been identified,

of which biotype I is most frequently responsible for meningitis.

Resistance

H.influenzae is a delicate bacterium, destroyed by heating (55°C for 30 minutes), refrigeration (0–4°C), drying and disinfectants. Cultures may be preserved for about a month on chocolate agar slopes in screw-capped bottles. For long-term preservation, the culture may be lyophilised.

Antigenic properties

There are three main surface antigens:
- The major antigenic determinant of capsulated strains is the **capsular polysaccharide** based on which *H.influenzae* strains have been classified by Pittman into six capsular types—a to f. Typing is done by agglutination using commercial kits for the identification of *H.influenzae* type b (Hib). Capsular typing is of medical importance as about 95 per cent

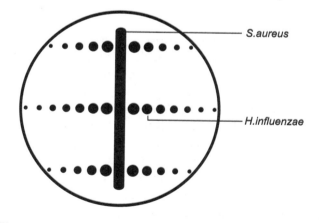

Fig. 35.1   *H.influenzae* on blood agar showing satellitism around *S.aureus* streaks

of *H.influenzae* isolates from acute invasive infections such as meningitis belong to type b.

The type b capsular polysaccharide has a unique chemical structure, containing the pentose sugars ribose and ribitol instead of hexoses and hexosamines as in the other five serotypes. The capsular **polyribosyl ribitol phosphate (PRP) antigen of Hib** induces IgG, IgM and IgA antibodies which are bactericidal, opsonic and protective. Hib PRP is therefore employed for immunisation. Hib capsular antigen shows cross-reaction with the capsular antigens of some Gram-positive and Gram-negative bacteria.

H.influenzae strains lacking a capsule cannot be typed and are called **non-typeable strains**. After Hib, the non-typeable strains are the most relevant in clinical infections.

- The **outer membrane protein antigens (OMP)** show considerable variation. OMP antigens of Hib have been classified into at least 13 subtypes.
- *H.influenzae* **lipooligosaccharides (LOS)** are antigenically complex. OMP and LOS subtyping may be of epidemiological value.

Pathogenicity

H.influenzae is an exclusively human pathogen. Diseases caused by *H.influenzae* may be categorised into two groups:

- **Invasive:** In this group, the bacillus acts as a primary pathogen, causing acute invasive infections. The bacilli spread through blood, being protected from phagocytes by their capsule. Haemophilus meningitis is the most important infection in this group, others being laryngoepiglottitis, conjunctivitis, bacteremia, pneumonia, arthritis, endocarditis and pericarditis. These infections are usually seen in children and are caused by the capsulated strains, type b accounting for most cases.
- **Non-invasive:** In this group, the bacillus spreads by local invasion along mucosal surfaces and causes secondary or superadded infections, usually of the respiratory tract. These include otitis media, sinusitis and exacerbations of chronic bronchitis and bronchiectasis. These are usually seen in adults and are often caused by the non-capsulated strains.

Clinical presentation

Meningitis: This is the most serious disease produced by *H.influenzae*, with case fatality rates up to 90 per cent in the untreated. The bacilli reach the meninges from the nasopharynx through the bloodstream. The disease is more common in children between two months and three years of age. This age incidence has been correlated with the absence of bactericidal anti-PRP antibodies. Older children develop immunity as a result of subclinical infection. It has been reported that in the tropics, non–type b strains may be responsible for meningitis more often than in the temperate zones (*Case*).

Laryngoepiglottitis (croup): This is an acute inflammation of the epiglottis, with obstructive laryngitis, seen in children above two years. Untreated cases may be fatal within hours. Tracheostomy is often necessary to relieve respiratory obstruction caused by the grossly enlarged uvula. This condition is always associated with bacteremia, and blood cultures are usually positive.

Pneumonia: Haemophilus pneumonia typically occurs in infants and is accompanied by empyema and sometimes meningitis as well. In older children and adults, the picture is of lobar pneumonia. While these are primary infections due to capsulated strains, bronchopneumonia may occur as a secondary infection with the non-capsulated strains. *H.influenzae* was a frequent cause of fatal pneumonia in the pandemic of influenza in 1918–19 but this association has not been found later.

Suppurative lesions: Suppurative lesions such as arthritis, endocarditis and pericarditis may result from hematogenous dissemination. Otitis media occurs by direct spread from the nasopharynx. Cellulitis, particularly in the buccal and periorbital areas, is seen in young children.

Bronchitis: *H.influenzae* is an important pathogen associated with pneumococci in acute exacerbations of chronic bronchitis and bronchiectasis.

Laboratory diagnosis

1. Specimen: **CSF, blood** or **sputum** is collected depending on the site of infection. As the bacillus is very sensitive to low temperatures, specimens should never be refrigerated before inoculation.

2. Microscopy: In meningitis, the presence in CSF of pleomorphic, Gram-negative bacilli should arouse the suspicion of *H.influenzae* infection.

3. Direct antigen detection: The capsular polysaccharide antigen may be present in CSF in meningitis and in urine in systemic infection.

Its demonstration by latex particle agglutination is useful in rapid diagnosis.

4. Culture: For isolation, CSF should be plated promptly on any of the following culture media:

- **Chocolate agar**: When blood agar is heated to 80–90°C for 15–20 minutes, the V factor is released from within the erythrocytes.
- **Blood agar** with *Staphylococcus aureus* streaked across the plate, as in Fig. 35.1
- **Nutrient agar** with discs of X and V factors
- **Levinthal's medium:** Clear transparent media prepared by boiling and filtering a mixture of blood and nutrient broth. Iridescence may be demonstrated on Levinthal's medium. Capsulated strains produce translucent colonies with a distinctive iridescence on Levinthal's agar.
- **Fildes' agar:** By adding a peptic digest of blood to nutrient agar. Fildes' agar is best for primary isolation of *H.influenzae* and gives copious growth.

The media should be incubated in an environment of 5–10% CO_2 and high humidity After overnight incubation at 37°C, small opaque colonies of Gram–negative, short, oxidase-positive cocci appear. Typing may be done by slide agglutinatiom using specific antisera.

Blood cultures are often positive in cases of laryngoepiglottitis and pneumonia. Cultures may be done in standard blood culture bottles as the patient's blood affords sufficient enrichment.

Isolation from sputum requires special care as commensal flora may overgrow the pathogen. Sputum should be homogenised by treatment with pancreatin or by shaking with sterile water and glass beads for 15–30 minutes. Culturing several samples of sputum from the patient increases the rate of isolation.

Treatment

Cefotaxime or ceftazidime is the drug of choice for the treatment of haemophilus meningitis. Ampicillin and cotrimoxazole were popular for respiratory infections, but as plasmid-borne resistance to these drugs is now common, amoxycillin–clavulanate or clarithromycin is more effective.

Epidemiology

There is considerable similarity between the epidemiology of *H.influenzae* and *S.pneumoniae*. Both are indigenous to human beings, primarily parasitic in the upper respiratory tract. Infection is transmitted by the respiratory route. Carriage in the upper respiratory tract is common, particularly in young children, but such strains are usually non-capsulated and not responsible for acute invasive infection. Maternal antibodies are protective and can be transmitted from mother to child. Non-immunised children between six months and two years of age become susceptible when maternal antibody wanes. Immunity is type specific. With the increased use of the Hib vaccine, immunity to type b disease is on the rise.

Prevention

As the large majority of serious infections are caused by type b strains, active immunisation with the **Hib PRP** vaccine is indicated. Purified PRP is immunogenic in older children and adults. However, in common with other polysaccharide antigens, PRP is poorly immunogenic in children below the age of two years. Its immunogenicity has been improved by coupling with protein carriers like diphtheria and tetanus toxoids or meningococcus outer membrane protein. These are called **conjugate vaccines**. Such conjugate Hib PRP vaccines are available for use in young children and can be given along with DPT immunisation.

Young household contacts of patients with systemic *H.influenzae* infection are at increased risk of infection. Rifampicin given for four days prevents secondary infection in contacts and also eradicates the carrier state.

HAEMOPHILUS AEGYPTIUS

Even before Pfeiffer described the 'influenza bacillus', Koch (1883) had observed a small bacillus in conjunctivitis cases in Egypt. It was first cultivated by Weeks (1887) in New York and came to be known as the Koch–Weeks bacillus. Recent DNA studies have shown that the bacillus is identical to non-capsulated *H.influenzae*. Therefore, it is now named *H.influenzae* biotype *aegypticus*. It belongs to *H.influenzae* biotype III. It is worldwide in distribution and causes a highly contagious form of conjunctivitis ('**pink eye**'). It is especially common in the tropics and subtropics and may occur in epidemic form. It responds to local sulphonamides or gentamicin.

It has also been identified as the causative agent of **Brazilian purpuric fever (BPF)**, in which conjunctivitis proceeds to fulminant septicemia in infants and children with high fatality. First recognised in Brazil in 1984, BPF is now endemic in South America.

HAEMOPHILUS DUCREYI

Ducrey (1890) demonstrated this bacillus in chancroid lesions and, by inoculation into the skin on the forearm, was able to transmit the lesion through several generations.

Chancroid or **soft sore** is a venereal disease characterised by tender non-indurated irregular ulcers on the genitalia. This infection remains localised, spreading only to the regional lymph nodes which are enlarged and painful. Autoinoculation lesions may be produced by contact. There is no immunity following infection but hypersensitivity results, which can be demonstrated by intradermal inoculation of killed bacilli.

H.ducreyi is a short, ovoid bacillus (1–1.5 μm × 0.6 mm) with a tendency to occur in end-to-end pairs or short chains. It is Gram negative but may often appear Gram positive and frequently shows bipolar staining. The bacilli may be arranged in small groups or whorls or in parallel chains, giving a '**school of fish**' or '**rail road track**' appearance.

Primary isolation is difficult. It can be grown on fresh clotted rabbit blood. Smears made after 24–48 hours' incubation show tangled chains of bacilli. It may also be grown on the chorioallantoic membrane of the chick embryo. On chocolate agar, enriched with IsoVitaleX and fetal calf serum, and containing vancomycin as a selective agent, *H.ducreyi* forms small, grey translucent colonies after incubation at 35°C under 10% CO_2 and high humidity in 2–8 days.

The species is antigenically homogeneous and cultures may be identified by agglutination with the antiserum. Intradermal inoculation of the culture into rabbits produces a local ulcerative lesion.

H.ducreyi is susceptible to sulphonamides and many antibiotics. Cases resistant to sulphonamides and tetracyclines have been reported. Erythromycin, cotrimoxazole, ciprofloxacin or ceftriaxone may be used for treatment.

HAEMOPHILUS PARAINFLUENZAE

This differs from *H.influenzae* in requiring only the V factor and not the X factor. It is a commensal in the upper respiratory tract and has been reported to cause subacute bacterial endocarditis, urethritis and acute pharyngitis.

HAEMOPHILUS HAEMOLYTICUS

This actively hemolytic species occurs as a commensal in the upper respiratory tract. Colonies on blood agar may be mistaken for those of hemolytic streptococci. It requires both X and V factors, and is not pathogenic. Strains that do not require the X factor have been designated *H.parahaemolyticus*.

HAEMOPHILUS APHROPHILUS

It requires the X factor but not the V factor. Its name refers to its high CO_2 requirement for optimal growth. It has been reported to cause bacterial endocarditis, brain abscess, sinusitis, pneumonia and abscesses elsewhere. Similar strains requiring the V factor but not the X factor have been termed *H.paraphrophilus*.

HACEK GROUP BACTERIA

The acronym HACEK refers to a group of fastidious slow-growing bacteria, normally resident in the mouth, which can sometimes cause severe infections, particularly endocarditis. The group includes the *Haemophilus* species (*parainfluenzae, aphrophilus, paraphrophilus*), *Actinobacillus actinomycetemcomitans, Cardiobacterium hominis, Eikenella corrodens* and *Kingella kingae*. Blood cultures from HACEK patients take 7–30 days to become positive. Antibiotic sensitivity tests are essential for effective therapy as drug resistance is very common.

RECAP

- Members of the genus *Haemophilus* are Gram-negative coccobacilli that are non-motile, facultative anaerobes, positive by the catalase and oxidase tests. They require either hemin (X factor) or co-enzyme 1 (V factor) or both for growth. This can be demonstrated by satellitism.
- *Haemophilus influenzae* is the most important species; *Haemophilus ducreyi* and other species may also cause disease in humans.
- The organism can be typed serologically according to capsular antigens, and type b (Hib) is often involved in acute infections. Encapsulated type b strains cause meningitis, epiglottitis in children below the age of two years, conjunctivitis and cellulitis.
- Non-encapsulated strains of *H.influenzae* are often found in the healthy respiratory tract, but can cause middle ear infections in children and pneumonia in compromised adults.
- For diagnosis, samples of blood or CSF are inoculated onto chocolate agar or other media containing X and V factors. *H.influenzae* colonies exhibit satellitism on blood agar plates when grown in the vicinity of *Staphylococcus aureus* colonies.
- Detection of Hib capsular polysaccharide in CSF by latex agglutination is a means of establishing rapid diagnosis of *H.influenzae* meningitis.
- Routine childhood vaccination with Hib conjugate vaccine has almost eliminated invasive Hib disease in developed nations.
- *Haemophilus influenzae* biogroup *aegyptius* causes a purulent conjunctivitis.
- *Haemophilus ducreyi* causes soft chancre (chancroid). This disease is sexually transmitted and manifests as a painful, ulcerative lesion on the genitalia. Such ulcers may predispose to the acquisition of infection with HIV.
- Various other species of *Haemophilus*, including *H.parainfluenzae*, *H.aphrophilus* and *H.paraphrophilus*, are occasionally implicated in infective endocarditis.
- HACEK is a group of fastidious, slow-growing bacteria that can cause severe infections, particularly endocarditis. Blood cultures from such patients take 7–30 days to become positive.

ESSAY

1. Enumerate the organisms causing meningitis and describe the laboratory diagnosis of *H.influenzae* meningitis.

SHORT ANSWERS

1. Satellitism in *H.influenzae*
2. Methods of culture and identification of *H.influenzae*
3. Pathogenesis and identification of *H.ducreyi*

SHORT NOTES

1. Hib vaccines
2. Koch–Weeks bacillus

36 | Bordetella

INTRODUCTION

The genus *Bordetella* is named after Jules Bordet, who along with Octave Gengou, identified the small ovoid bacillus in the sputum of children suffering from whooping cough (1900) and succeeded in cultivating it in a complex medium (1906). The bacillus is now known as *Bordetella pertussis* (pertussis meaning intense cough). A related bacillus, *B.parapertussis,* was isolated from mild cases of whooping cough (1937). *B.bronchiseptica*, originally isolated from dogs with bronchopneumonia (1911),

---

Bordetella pertussis

Clinical Case A four-month-old child was brought from a peripheral centre in a remote rural area with complaints of severe cough for the past 10–12 days and apnea during the bouts, followed by vomiting. In between the child slept comfortably. Blood counts were raised, with lymphocytosis. There was no history of any injection given since birth. A nasopharyngeal swab collected and subjected to culture on a selective medium was positive for *B.pertussis*. A diagnosis of whooping cough was made. In the hospital, the child responded to antibiotics and supportive care.

---

may occasionally infect human beings, producing a condition resembling pertussis. It has been suggested that *B.bronchiseptica* represents the ancestral form from which the other two species evolved. The fourth member of the genus is *B.avium* which causes respiratory disease in turkeys.

BORDETELLA PERTUSSIS

Morphology

B.pertussis is a small, ovoid coccobacillus (mean length 0.5 μm). In primary cultures, cells are of uniform size and shape, but on subculture they may become longer and thread-like. It is non-motile and non-sporing. It is capsulated but tends to lose the capsule on repeated cultivation. The capsule can be demonstrated by special stains but does not swell in the presence of the antiserum. In culture films, the bacilli tend to be arranged in loose clumps, with clear spaces in between giving a '**thumb print**' appearance. Freshly isolated strains of *B.pertussis* have fimbriae.

It is Gram negative. Bipolar metachromatic granules may be demonstrated on staining with toluidine blue.

Cultural characteristics

It is an obligate aerobe. No growth occurs anaerobically. It grows best at 35–36°C. Complex media are necessary for primary isolation. The medium in common use is the **Bordet–Gengou glycerine-potato-blood agar** or the **Regan–Lowe media**. Blood is required not to provide additional nutritive factors but rather to neutralise inhibitory materials formed during bacterial growth. Charcoal or ion exchange resins incorporated in culture media may serve the same purpose. **Charcoal blood agar** is a useful medium. It does not grow on simple media like nutrient agar.

Growth is slow. After incubation for 48–72 hours, colonies on the Bordet–Gengou medium are small, dome-shaped, smooth, opaque, viscid, greyish white, refractile and glistening, resembling '**bisected pearls**' or '**mercury drops**' (Fig. 36.1). Colonies are surrounded

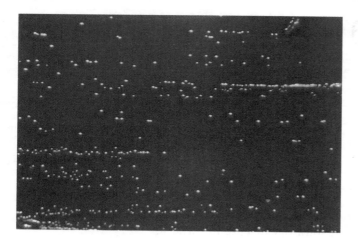

Fig. 36.1   Growth of *B.pertussis* on Regan–Lowe media

by a hazy zone of hemolysis. Confluent growth presents an '**aluminium paint**' appearance.

Biochemical reactions

It is biochemically inactive. It does not ferment sugars, form indole, reduce nitrates, utilise citrate or split urea. It produces oxidase and usually catalase also.

Resistance

It is a delicate organism, being killed readily by heat (55°C for 30 minutes), drying and disinfectants. But unlike *H.influenzae,* it retains viability at low temperatures (0–4°C). Outside the body, *B.pertussis* in dried droplets is said to survive for five days on glass, three days on cloth and a few hours on paper.

Virulence factors

Agglutinogens: Bordetellae carry surface agglutinogens associated with fimbriae. They are classified into various types based on the agglutinogens they carry. As strains causing infection belong to types 1, 2 and 3, it is essential that pertussis vaccine strains contain factors 1, 2 and 3. Factor-specific antibodies are present in the sera of convalescent and immunised persons. Agglutinogens promote virulence by helping bacteria to attach to respiratory epithelial cells. They are useful in serotyping strains and in epidemiological studies.

Pertussis toxin (PT):   This is present only in *B.pertussis.* It plays an important role in the pathogenesis of whooping cough. PT is expressed on the surface of the bacillus and secreted into the surrounding medium. The toxin exhibits diverse biological and biochemical activities, which formerly had been believed to be caused by different substances that had been named accordingly. Examples are the **lymphocytosis producing factor (LPF)**, causing profound lymphocytosis in pertussis patients as well as in experimental animals; and two effects seen only in experimental animals, but not in patients, such as the **histamine sensitising factor (HSF)** responsible for heightened sensitivity to histamine in experimental animals, and the **islet activating protein (IAP)** inducing excessive insulin secretion by the pancreatic islet cells. It is now known that all these are manifestations of the pertussis toxin.

PT is a 117,000-molecular weight hexamer protein composed of six subunits with an A–B structure (A being the enzymatically active moiety and B the binding component). It can be toxoided. PT toxoid is the major component of acellular pertussis vaccines. Antibody to PT can protect mice against intranasal, intraperitoneal or intracerebral challenge.

Filamentous hemagglutinin (FHA):   This is one of the three hemagglutinins produced by *B.pertussis,* the others being PT and a lipid factor. Purified FHA appears as a filamentous structure in the electron microscope and hence the name. It is present on the bacillary surface and is readily shed. It adheres to the cilia of the respiratory epithelium and to erythrocytes. Besides facilitating adhesion of *B.pertussis* to respiratory epithelium, FHA and PT hemagglutinins also promote secondary infection by coating other bacteria such as *Haemophilus influenzae* and *S.pneumoniae* and assisting their binding to respiratory epithelium. This phenomenon has been termed **piracy of adhesins.** Antibodies to FHA are protective and FHA is used in acellular pertussis vaccines along with PT and pertactin.

Pertactin: Pertactin is an outer membrane protein (OMP) antigen present in all virulent strains of *B.pertussis.* Antibody to pertactin can be seen in the blood of children after infection or immunisation. Pertactin is included in acellular pertussis vaccines.

Adenylate cyclase (AC):   Known as the AC toxin (ACT), it acts by catalysing the production of cAMP by various types of cells.

Heat labile toxin (HLT):   It is a cytoplasmic protein present in all bordetellae. It is dermonecrotic and lethal in mice. Its pathogenic role is not known.

Tracheal cytotoxin (TCT):   It is a low-molecular-weight peptidoglycan which induces ciliary damage in hamster trachea. Its role in disease is not known.

Lipopolysaccharide (LPS): LPS or the **heat stable toxin** is present in all bordetellae and exhibits features of Gram-negative bacterial endotoxins. It is present in the whole-cell pertussis vaccine but is not considered to be a protective antigen.

Pathogenicity

B.pertussis is an obligate human parasite and is responsible for whooping cough or pertussis in humans (*Case*).

- In humans, after an **incubation period** of about 1–2 weeks, the disease takes a protracted course comprising **three stages**: catarrhal, paroxysmal and convalescent, each lasting approximately two weeks.
- **Onset** is insidious, with low-grade fever, catarrhal symptoms and a dry, irritating cough.
- **Clinical diagnosis** in the **catarrhal stage** is difficult. This is unfortunate as this is the stage at which the disease can be arrested by antibiotic treatment. This is also the stage of maximum infectivity.
- As the catarrhal stage advances to the **paroxysmal stage**, the cough increases in intensity and comes on in distinctive bouts. During the paroxysm, the patient experiences violent spasms of continuous coughing, followed by a long in-rush of air into the almost empty lungs, with a characteristic whoop (hence the name).
- The paroxysmal stage is followed by **convalescence**, during which the frequency and severity of coughing gradually decrease.

  The disease usually lasts 6–8 weeks though in some it may be very protracted.

Complications may be:
- Due to **pressure effects** during the violent bouts of coughing (subconjunctival hemorrhage, subcutaneous emphysema)
- **Respiratory** (bronchopneumonia, lung collapse), or
- **Neurological** (convulsions, coma). Respiratory complications are self-limited, the atelectasis resolving spontaneously, but the neurological complications may result in permanent sequelae such as epilepsy, paralysis, retardation, blindness or deafness

The infection is limited to the respiratory tract and the bacilli do not invade the bloodstream. In the initial stages, the bacilli are confined to the nasopharynx, trachea and bronchi. Clumps of bacilli may be seen enmeshed in the cilia of the respiratory epithelium. As the disease progresses, inflammation extends into the lungs, producing diffuse bronchopneumonia with desquamation of the alveolar epithelium.

Epidemiology

Whooping cough is predominantly a pediatric disease, the incidence and mortality being highest in the first year of life. Maternal antibodies do not seem to give protection against the disease. Immunisation should, therefore, be started early. The disease is more common in females than in males at all ages. It is worldwide in distribution. It occurs in epidemic form periodically but the disease is never absent from any community.

The source of infection is the patient in the early stages of the disease. Infection is transmitted by droplets and fomites contaminated with oropharyngeal secretions. Whooping cough is one of the most infectious of bacterial diseases and non-immune contacts seldom escape the disease.

The secondary attack rates are highest in close household contacts. In adolescents and adults, the disease is often atypical and may present as bronchitis. They may serve as a source of infection for infants and children. Chronic carriers are not known. Natural infection confers protection though it may not be permanent, and second attacks have been reported.

With universal immunisation, childhood pertussis is on the decline, but adolescent pertussis is on the rise due to waning of immunity at that age. Booster immunisation if not taken makes adults prone to infection.

B.pertussis causes 95 per cent of whooping cough cases. About 5 per cent are caused by *B.parapertussis*. This is generally a milder disease and the incidence varies in different countries. Very infrequently, whooping cough may be caused by *B.bronchiseptica*. A clinical syndrome resembling whooping cough (**pseudo-whooping cough**) may also be produced by some other respiratory pathogens, such as adenoviruses and *Mycoplasma pneumoniae*.

Laboratory diagnosis

The bacilli are present in the upper respiratory tract most abundantly in the early stages of the disease. They may be demonstrated by microscopy or more reliably by culture. In the paroxysmal stage, the bacilli are scanty and during convalescence they are not demonstrable. Antibodies develop late and help only in retrospective diagnosis.

1. Collection and transport of specimen: Respiratory samples can be collected by per-nasal swab, post-nasal swab or using the cough plate method. Some fatty acids present in cotton may inhibit growth of the bacilli and so it is preferable to use dacron or calcium alginate swabs for specimen collection. The swabs are to be plated without delay, or transported in a 0.25–0.5-ml casamino acid solution, at pH 7.2, in modified Stuart's medium or Mischulow's charcoal agar.

- **Per-nasal or nasopharyngeal swab:** Here, a swab on a flexible nichrome wire is passed along the floor of the nasal cavity and material is collected from the pharyngeal wall. Nasopharyngeal aspirate collected through a soft catheter attached to a syringe is a better source. It can be used for PCR also. Specimens collected in this manner are the most effective and best suited for diagnostic procedures

- **Post-nasal (per-oral) swab:** Secretions from the posterior pharyngeal wall are collected with a cotton swab on a bent wire passed through the mouth. Salivary contamination should be avoided. West's post-nasal swab may be conveniently employed.

- **Cough plate method:** Here, a culture plate is held about 10–15 cm in front of the patient's mouth during a bout of spontaneous or induced coughing so that droplets of respiratory exudates impinge directly on the medium. This has the advantage that specimens are directly inoculated at the bedside.

2. Microscopy: Microscopic diagnosis depends on demonstration of the bacilli in respiratory secretions by the fluorescent antibody technique.

3. Culture: The medium employed is the glycerine-potato-blood agar of Bordet and Gengou or one of its modifications. Regan–Lowe is used more commonly with cephalosporins to inhibit the normal upper respiratory flora. Plates are incubated in high humidity at 35–36°C. Colonies appear in 48–72 hours. Identification is confirmed by microscopy and slide agglutination. Bacterial growth can be confirmed by direct immunofluorescence using specific antisera or biochemicals listed in Table 36.1.

4. Polymerase chain reaction (PCR): PCR-based tests are more sensitive and more commonly used now as the culture yield is poor in pertussis.

5. Serology: Serological diagnosis is not helpful and is not used routinely for diagnosis. Rise in antibody titre may be demonstrated in paired serum samples by agglutination, gel precipitation or complement fixation tests. As antibodies appear late, the second sample of serum should be collected some weeks after onset of the disease.

6. Other laboratory parameters: Blood changes in the disease are distinctive and helpful in diagnosis. Marked leucocytosis occurs, with relative lymphocytosis (total leucocytic counts 20,000–30,000 per mm³ with 60–80 per cent lymphocytes). The erythrocyte sedimentation rate is not increased, except when secondary infection is present.

Treatment

B.pertussis is susceptible to several antibiotics (except penicillin) but antimicrobial therapy is beneficial only if initiated within the first ten days of the disease. Erythromycin or one of the newer macrolides is the drug of choice. Chloramphenicol and cotrimoxazole are also useful.

Table 36.1 *Differentiating features of the* Bordetella *species*

	B.pertussis	*B.parapertussis*	*B.bronchiseptica*	*B.avium*
Motility	–	–	+	+
Growth on nutrient agar	–	+	+	+
Growth on Bordet–Gengou medium (days)	3–6	1–2	1	1
Urease	–	+	+	–
Nitrate to nitrite	–	–	+	–
Citrate utilisation	–	V	+	V
Oxidase	+	–	+	+
Toxins:				
HLT and TCT	+	+	+	+
ACT	+	+	+	–
PT	+	–	–	–
V = Variable				

Prophylaxis

Preventing the spread of infection by isolation of cases is seldom practicable, as infectivity is highest in the earliest stage of the disease when clinical diagnosis is not easy. Neutralising antibodies to the toxin and adhesins of *B.pertussis* are thought to contribute to protection; cell-mediated immunity probably confers long-term protection.

Whole-cell killed vaccine: Specific immunisation with killed *B.pertussis* vaccine has been found very effective. It is of utmost importance that a smooth Phase I strain be used for vaccine production. The method of inactivation should be such that antigenic potency is unaffected. Detoxication with 0.2% merthiolate during several months' storage at 4°C has been recommended as a satisfactory procedure. The alum-absorbed vaccine provides better and more sustained protection and less reaction than the plain vaccines. Pertussis vaccine is usually administered in combination with diphtheria and tetanus toxoid (triple vaccine). Not only is this more convenient, but *B.pertussis* also acts as an adjuvant for the toxoids, producing better antibody response.

In view of the high incidence and severity of the disease in newborns, it is advisable to start immunisation as early as possible. Three injections at intervals of 4–6 weeks are to be given before the age of six months, followed by a booster at the end of the first year of life.

Children under four years who are contacts of patients should receive a **booster** even if they had been previously immunised. They should also receive chemoprophylaxis with erythromycin. Non-immunised contacts should receive erythromycin prophylaxis for 10 days after contact with the patient has ceased. Pertussis vaccination may induce reactions ranging from local soreness and fever, to shock, convulsions and encephalopathy. Provocation poliomyelitis is a rare complication.

Complications: Factors contributing to toxicity or post-vaccinal encephalopathy have not been defined. The latter complication is estimated to occur in 1 in 5–10 million injections. Estimated neurological complications of natural disease have the range of 1.5–14 per cent in hospitalised cases; a third of these recover, a third have sequelae and a third die or have severe defects.

If severe complications such as encephalopathy, seizures, shock or hyperpyrexia develop following the vaccine, subsequent doses of the vaccine are contraindicated. Routine pertussis vaccination is not advisable after the age of seven years as adverse reactions are likely.

Acellular vaccine: Acellular vaccines containing the protective components of the pertussis bacillus (PT, FHA, agglutinogens 1, 2, 3 and pertactin), first developed in Japan, are now used in most countries as they cause far fewer reactions, particularly in older children.

Both whole-cell and acellular vaccines have a protection rate of about 90 per cent. With whole-cell vaccines, the protection declines to 50 per cent in about five years and is absent after 12 years. Even fully immunised subjects may develop pertussis but the disease will be very mild in them.

BORDETELLA PARAPERTUSSIS

This is an infrequent cause of whooping cough. The disease is mild. The pertussis vaccine does not protect against *B.parapertussis* infection.

B.parapertussis is readily distinguished from *B.pertussis* by its ability to grow on nutrient agar with the production of a brown, diffusible pigment after two days. It also grows more rapidly than *B.pertussis* on charcoal blood agar, and is agglutinated more strongly by parapertussis than by pertussis antiserum. It usually causes less severe illness than *B.pertussis* and is uncommon in most countries.

BORDETELLA BRONCHISEPTICA

This is motile by peritrichate flagella. It is antigenically related to *B.pertussis* and *Brucella abortus*. It occurs naturally in the respiratory tract of several species of animals. It has been found to cause a very small proportion (0.1 per cent) of cases of whooping cough.

RECAP

- Members of the genus *Bordetella* are Gram-negative, rod-shaped bacteria which are aerobes, non-motile and catalase positive. *Bordetella pertussis* is by far the most important species.
- *B.pertussis* causes whooping cough. It attaches to the nasopharynx, and then grows and spreads to the ciliated cells of the bronchial tree. The bacterium can secrete toxins that lead to cell damage and accumulation of fluid, which induces the paroxysmal cough.
- For diagnosis, nasopharyngeal swabs or aspirates are collected. Bacteria can be cultured on charcoal agar or Bordet–Gengou medium to yield characteristic bisected pearl colonies.
- Erythromycin is given to treat active cases. Vaccination of infants and children is done as part of routine childhood immunisation, and the bacterium forms a component of the 'triple antigen' (diphtheria–pertussis–tetanus).
- In recent years, acellular vaccines have also become available. Aggressive vaccination to achieve herd immunity has resulted in a fall in the incidence of the disease.

SHORT ANSWER

1. Collection and transport of samples from a patient of pertussis

---

SHORT NOTES

1. Acellular pertussis vaccine
2. DPT vaccine
3. Cough plate method

37 Brucella

Brucella

Clinical Case A 50-year-old farmer presented with a history of intermittent fever for the previous three weeks. He complained of loss of appetite and nausea but there were no other specific complaints. The farmer attended to his cattle and sold the milk at the market nearby. On examination, no specific signs for the fever were found. Detailed laboratory testing revealed only anemia. Given his occupational history, blood culture in brucella broth in a biphasic culture bottle and standard agglutination test (SAT) for antibodies were carried out. The culture at this time was negative but SAT titres were >1:1280, suggestive of brucellosis. (Please note the clinical presentation with non-specific signs and symptoms. Diagnosis depends on a high degree of suspicion in a patient of pyrexia of unknown origin with a suggestive occupational history and on ordering specific tests for brucellosis). The patient responded to a course of doxycycline and streptomycin

---

INTRODUCTION AND HISTORY

The genus *Brucella* consists of very small, non-motile, aerobic, Gram-negative coccobacilli that grow poorly on ordinary media and have little or no fermentative powers. They are strict parasites of animals and may also infect humans.

Brucellosis is a **zoonosis**, primarily affecting goats, sheep, cattle, buffaloes, pigs and other animals and transmitted to humans by contact with infected animals or through their products. The human disease was recognised along the Mediterranean littoral from very early times and has been known under various names, such as Mediterranean fever, **Malta fever** and **undulant fever**.

A British army doctor, David Bruce (1886), isolated a small microorganism from the spleen of fatal cases in Malta and transmitted the disease to monkeys experimentally. This was named *Brucella melitensis* (*Brucella* after Bruce, *melitensis* after Melita, the Roman name for Malta). A Maltese bacteriologist Zammit (1905) showed that *B.melitensis* was transmitted to humans by goat's milk. Bang (1897) described *B.abortus*, the cause of contagious abortion in cattle. The third major species in the genus, *B.suis*, was isolated by Traum (1914) from pigs in the USA. These three species cause human brucellosis.

Other species causing animal infections include *B.canis*, isolated from cases of canine abortion, *B.ovis* from abortion in sheep and *B.neotomae* from desert wood rats. *B.canis* may occasionally cause a mild human disease, but the other two are not pathogenic for humans.

Morphology

Brucellae are coccobacilli or short rods, 0.5–0.7 × 0.6–1.5 μm in size, arranged singly or in short chains. The cells are so small that they may be mistaken for cocci, as was done by Bruce who called them *Micrococcus melitensis*. In older cultures, irregular forms appear. They are non-motile, non-capsulated and non-sporing. They are Gram negative and non–acid fast. Bipolar staining is not uncommon.

Cultural characteristics

Brucellae are strict aerobes and do not grow anaerobically. *B.abortus* is capnophilic, many strains requiring 5–10% CO_2 for growth. The optimum temperature is 37°C (range 20–40°C) and pH 6.6–7.4.

- **Simple media**: Growth is slow and scanty. Liver infusion media were widely used for the cultivation of brucellae. The media currently employed are serum dextrose agar, serum potato infusion agar, trypticase soy agar or tryptose agar. The addition of bacitracin, polymyxin and cycloheximide to the above media makes them selective.
- **Liquid media**: Growth is uniform, and a powdery or viscous deposit is formed in old cultures.
- **Solid media**: Colonies are small, moist, translucent and glistening. Mucoid, smooth and rough types of colonies appear, associated with changes in antigenic structure and virulence.

Erythritol has an especially stimulating effect on the growth of brucellae.

Biochemical reactions

No carbohydrates are ordinarily fermented, though they possess oxidative capacity. Brucellae are catalase positive, oxidase positive (except for *B.neotomae* and *B.ovis* which are negative) and urease positive. Nitrates are reduced to nitrites. Citrate is not utilised. Indole is not produced and MR and VP tests are negative.

Resistance

Brucellae are destroyed by heat at 60°C in 10 minutes and by 1% phenol in 15 minutes. They are killed by pasteurisation. They may survive in soil and manure for several weeks. They remain viable for 10 days in refrigerated milk, one month in ice cream, four months in butter and for varying periods in cheese depending on its pH. They may also survive for many weeks in meat. They are sensitive to direct sunlight and acid, and tend to die in buttermilk. *B.melitensis* may stay alive for six days in urine, six weeks in dust and ten weeks in water.

Antigenic structure

The somatic antigens of brucellae contain two main antigenic determinants, A and M, which are present in different amounts in the three major species. *B.abortus* contains about 20 times as much A as M; *B.melitensis* about 20 times as much M as A. *B.suis* has an intermediate antigenic pattern. Absorption of the minor antigenic component from an antiserum will leave most of the major antibody component, and such absorbed A and M monospecific sera are useful for species identification by the agglutination test. The species identifi-

cation of brucella strains is not, however, so straightforward and strains that behave biochemically as *abortus* and serologically as *melitensis* and vice versa are often seen. Species and biotype identification depends on a variety of other factors besides antigenic structure (Table 37.1).

Antigenic cross-reactions exist between brucellae and *Vibrio cholerae* and persons receiving the cholera vaccine may develop brucella agglutinins lasting for about three years. Antigenic cross-reactions also exist with *Escherichia coli* O:116; O:157, Salmonella serotypes group N (O:30 antigen Kauffman and White), *Pseudomonas maltophilia*, *Yersinia enterocolitica* and *Francisella tularensis*. A superficial L antigen resembling the *Salmonella* Vi antigen has been described.

Classification

Brucellae may be classified into different species, based on their CO_2 requirements, H_2S production, sensitivity to dyes (basic fuchsin and thionin), agglutination by monospecific sera, phage lysis and oxidative metabolic tests with amino acids and carbohydrates. The two main species are *B.melitensis* and *B.abortus*. Many biotypes have been recognised in these species.

B.suis strains that produce H_2S are known as 'American' strains and those that do not as 'Danish' strains.

Brucella bacteriophage

Several bacteriophages that lyse the *Brucella* strains have been isolated. These phages are serologically similar. The Tblisi (Tb) phage has been designated as the reference phage, and at routine test dilution (RTD) lyses only *B.abortus*. *B.suis* is lysed at 10,000 RTD, while *B.melitensis* is not lysed at all.

Pathogenicity

All three major species of brucellae are pathogenic to human beings. *B.melitensis* is the most pathogenic, *B.abortus* and *B.suis* being of intermediate pathogenicity.

Brucella is primarily an intracellular pathogen affecting the reticuloendothelial system. This accounts for its refractoriness to chemotherapy and the co-existence of viable bacilli with high levels of circulating antibodies. The lipopolysaccharide component of the *Brucella* cell wall is a virulence factor.

Organisms from the infected animal enter the human body through a wound, the conjunctiva, by

Table 37.1 *Differential characteristics of the* Brucella *species and its biotypes*

Species	Biotypes	Lysis by phage RTD	Lysis by phage RTD × 10⁴	CO₂ requirement	H₂S production	Basic fuchsin 1:50,000	Thionin 1:25,000	Thionin 1:50,000	Mono-specific sera A	Mono-specific sera M	Anti-rough serum	Most common host
B.melitensis	1	−	−	−	−	+	−	+	−	+		Sheep, goats
	2	−	−	−	−	+	−	+	+	−	−	
	3	−	−	−	−	+	−	+	+	+	−	
B.abortus	1	+	+	±	+	+	−	−	+	−	−	Cattle
	2	+	+	+	+	−	−	−	+	−	−	
	3	+	+	±	+	+	+	+	+	−	−	
	4	+	+	±	+	+	−	−	−	+	−	
	5	+	+	−	−	+	−	+	−	+	−	
	6	+	+	−	±	+	−	+	+	−	−	
	9	+	+	±	+	+	−	+	−	+	−	
B.suis	1	−	+	−	+	−	+	+	+	−	−	Pigs
	2	−	+	−	−	−	+	+	+	−	−	Pigs, hare
	3	−	+	−	−	+	+	+	+	−	−	Pigs
	4	−	+	−	−	+	+	+	+	+	−	Reindeer
B.neotomae		−	+	−	+	−	−	−	+	−	−	Wood rats
B.ovis		−	−	+	−	+	+	+	−	−	+	Sheep
B.canis		−	−	−	−	−	+	+	−	−	+	Dogs

inhalation or by ingestion of products from infected animals The incubation period is usually about 10–30 days, but may sometimes be very prolonged. The brucellae spread from the initial site of infection through lymphatic channels to the local lymph glands, in the cells of which they multiply. They then spill over into the bloodstream and are disseminated throughout the body. They have a predilection for the placenta, probably due to the presence in it of erythritol, which has a stimulating effect on brucellae in culture. Fever, sweats and extreme fatigue occur 2–4 weeks after initial infection.

Human infection may be of three **types** (*Case*):
- latent infection with only serological but no clinical evidence;
- acute or subacute brucellosis; and
- chronic brucellosis.

Acute brucellosis is mostly due to *B.melitensis*.
- It is usually known as **undulant fever**, but this is misleading as only some cases show the undulant pattern.
- It is associated with prolonged bacteremia and irregular fever.

- The symptomatology is varied, consisting of muscular and articular pains, asthmatic attacks, nocturnal drenching sweats, exhaustion, anorexia, constipation, nervous irritability and chills.
- The usual complications are articular, osseous, visceral or neurological.

Chronic brucellosis, which may be non-bacteremic, is a low-grade infection with periodic exacerbations.
- The symptoms are generally related to a state of hypersensitivity in the patient.
- Common clinical manifestations are sweating, lassitude and joint pain, with minimal or no pyrexia.
- The illness lasts for years.

Immunity in brucellosis is mainly cell mediated. Activated macrophages can kill the bacteria. The Th1 type of T helper cell response and cell-mediated immunity are required to eliminate brucellae through activated macrophages; tumour necrosis factors alpha and gamma and interleukins 1 and 12 are important mediators of the protective response. This is probably the most important mechanism in recovery and immunity in brucellosis. Tissue reaction to brucella consists of granuloma formation with epithelial cells, giant cells, lymphocytes and plasma cells. Granulomas heal with fibrosis and sometimes become calcified.

Of the laboratory animals, the guinea pig is the most susceptible. The Straus reaction can be elicited in male guinea pigs.

Epidemiology

Human brucellosis is acquired from animals, directly or indirectly. Goats, sheep, cattle, buffaloes and swine are the common sources. In some parts of the world, infection may also be transmitted by dogs, reindeer, caribou, camels and yaks. The modes of infection are ingestion, contact, inhalation or accidental inoculation. Person-to-person spread does not ordinarily occur, but very rarely transmission has been reported through the placenta, breastfeeding and sex.

The most important vehicle of infection is raw milk. Milk products, meat from infected animals and raw vegetables or water supplies contaminated by the feces or urine of infected animals may also be responsible. Contact infection is especially important as an occupational hazard in veterinarians, butchers and animal handlers, and is particularly common during the calving season. Infection is transmitted by inhalation of dried material of animal origin such as dust from wool. Infection by inhalation is a serious risk in veterinary surgeons, and laboratory workers handling brucellae.

Foci of infection with brucellae may also occur in wild animal populations independent of domesticated animals. Infection is transmitted among animals directly or through bloodsucking arthropods, particularly ticks.

Most human infections in various parts of India are due to *B.melitensis* acquired from goats and sheep.

Laboratory diagnosis

The clinical manifestations of human brucellosis are variable, and only if a high index of suspicion is maintained will the disease be identified. Clinical diagnosis is almost impossible and laboratory aid is therefore essential. Laboratory methods for diagnosis include culture, serology and hypersensitivity tests.

1. **Blood culture** is the most definitive method for the diagnosis of brucellosis. Blood is inoculated into a bottle of trypticase soy broth or brucella broth in a biphasic blood culture bottle, also called the **Castaneda method** (Fig. 37.1). It is incubated at 37°C under 5–10% CO_2. As bacteria in blood are

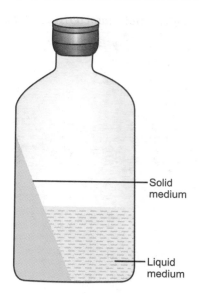

Fig. 37.1 Castaneda's bottle for blood culture

usually scanty, large volumes of blood (5 ml) should be inoculated. Subcultures are made on solid media every 3–5 days, beginning on the fourth day. Growth may often be delayed and cultures should not be declared negative in less than 6–8 weeks. Automated cultures may become positive in 5–6 days.

The Castaneda method of blood culture has several advantages and is recommended. Here, both liquid and solid media are available in the same bottle. Blood is inoculated into the broth and the bottle is incubated in the upright position. For the subculture, it is sufficient if the bottle is tilted so that the broth flows over the surface of the agar slant. It is again incubated in an upright position. Colonies appear on the slant. This method minimises materials and manipulation, reducing the chances of contamination and risk of infection to laboratory workers.

Blood cultures are positive only in about 30–50 per cent of cases, even when repeated samples are tested. *B.melitensis* and *B.suis* are isolated more readily than *B.abortus*. Bone marrow cultures yield a higher rate of isolation and remain positive long after the blood culture has become negative. Cultures may also be obtained from lymph nodes, cerebrospinal fluid, urine and abscesses, if present, and, on occasion, also from sputum, breast milk, vaginal discharges and seminal fluid.

2. As cultures are often unsuccessful, **serological methods** are important in diagnosis. Several serological tests have been developed, including agglutination, complement fixation and ELISA.

- The **standard agglutination test (SAT)** is performed most often. This is a tube agglutination test in which equal volumes of serial dilutions of the patient's serum and the standardised antigen (a killed suspension of a standard strain of *B.abortus*) are mixed and incubated at 37°C for 24 hours or 50°C for 18 hours. A titre of 160 or more is considered significant. Most patients with acute brucellosis develop titres of 640 or more by 3–4 weeks of illness. Titres tend to decline after the acute phase of the illness.

Several sources of error have to be guarded against. Sera often contain **'blocking'** or **'non-agglutinating' antibodies**. The blocking effect may sometimes be removed by prior heating of the serum at 55°C for 30 minutes or by using 4% saline as the diluent for the test. The most reliable method for obviating the blocking effect and detecting 'incomplete' antibodies is the antiglobulin (Coombs) test. As the prozone phenomenon to high titres (up to 1/640) is very frequent in brucellosis, it is essential that several serum dilutions be tested. A positive agglutination test may be produced by cholera, tularemia or yersinia infection, or by immunisation. Cholera-induced agglutinins may be differentiated by the agglutinin absorption test; also, they are removed by treatment with 2-mercaptoethanol. To enable comparison of results from different laboratories, the practice is to express agglutinin titres in International Units. This is done by using a standard reference serum for comparison.

In brucellosis, both IgM and IgG antibodies appear in 7–10 days after the onset of clinical infection. As the disease progresses, IgM antibodies decline, while the IgG antibodies persist or increase in titre. In chronic infections, IgM may often be absent and only IgG can be demonstrated. The agglutination test mainly identifies the IgM antibody, while both IgM and IgG fix the complement. The IgG and IgA antibodies may act as 'blocking' or 'non-agglutinating' antibodies. It is thus evident that the agglutination test is usually positive in acute infection but may be only weakly positive or even negative in chronic cases. The results of the agglutination tests must therefore be evaluated carefully. While a high titre of agglutinins, and especially demonstration of a rise in titre, can be taken as diagnostic, even a negative agglutination test may not exclude the possibility of brucellosis.

- The **complement fixation test** is more useful in chronic cases as it detects the IgG antibody also.
- **ELISA** is sensitive and specific and can detect IgM and IgG antibodies separately. It is therefore useful for differentiation between acute and chronic infection.
- **Rapid methods** such as rapid dipstick test and Rose Bengal card test can be used.

3. **Delayed hypersensitivity-type skin tests** with brucella antigens ('brucellins') are not useful in diagnosing acute brucellosis.

Detection in milk and infected animals: The methods used for the laboratory diagnosis of human brucellosis may also be employed for the diagnosis of animal infections. In addition, brucellae may be demonstrated **microscopically** in pathological specimens by suitable staining or by **immunofluorescence**.

Several **rapid methods** have been employed for the detection of brucellosis in herds of cattle:

- For the detection of infected animals in dairies, pooled milk samples may be tested for bacilli by culture and for antibodies by several techniques. In the **milk ring test**, a sample of whole milk is mixed well with a drop of the stained brucella antigen (a concentrated suspension of killed *B.abortus* stained with hematoxylin) and incubated in a water bath at 70°C for 40–50 minutes. If antibodies are present in the milk, the bacilli are agglutinated and rise with the cream to form a blue ring at the top, leaving the milk unstained. If antibodies are absent, no coloured ring is formed and the milk remains uniformly blue. The whey agglutination test is another useful method for detecting antibodies in milk.
- **Rose Bengal card test and rapid plate agglutination tests** can also be used for screening infected herds.

Prophylaxis

As the majority of human infections are acquired by the consumption of contaminated milk, prevention consists of checking dairy animals for brucellosis. In many developed countries, this is achieved by the detection of infected animals, their elimination by slaughter and the development of certified brucella-free herds. Pasteurisation of milk is an additional safeguard.

An attenuated live vaccine can be administered to individuals with an occupational risk of exposure.

Vaccines have been developed for use in animals. *B.abortus* strain 19 vaccine is protective in cattle. No suitable vaccine is available for human use.

Treatment

The usual regimen for adults is a combination of doxycycline for 45 days with streptomycin IM daily for the first two weeks, and for children, cotrimoxazole with rifampicin or gentamycin.

RECAP

- The genus *Brucella* comprises non-motile, obligatorily aerobic, Gram-negative coccobacilli that grow poorly on ordinary media and have little or no fermentative properties; the bacteria are positive in the oxidase, catalase and urease tests.
- Brucellosis, the disease caused by a species of *Brucella*, is a zoonosis. *Brucella abortus* produces a less severe form of the disease with fewer sequelae than that caused by *Brucella suis* or *Brucella melitensis*.
- Brucellosis is an infection of the reticuloendothelial system. The Th1 cell response and cell-mediated immunity are required to eliminate brucella of the protective response.
- For laboratory diagnosis, blood or biopsy material is obtained for culture. Serological tests are the mainstay of diagnosis.
- An attenuated live vaccine can be administered to individuals with occupational risk of exposure and animals can also be vaccinated.

ESSAY

1. Define zoonosis and enumerate the bacteria causing zoonosis. Explain the laboratory diagnosis of brucellosis.

SHORT ANSWERS

1. Serological tests for the diagnosis of brucellosis
2. Milk ring test
3. Zoonosis (define and give two examples)

SHORT NOTES

1. Castaneda method of blood culture
2. Standard agglutination test
3. Epidemiology of brucellosis

38 Mycobacterium I: M.tuberculosis

INTRODUCTION

Mycobacteria are slender rods that sometimes show branching, filamentous forms resembling fungal mycelium. In liquid cultures, they form a mould-like pellicle (hence, the name *mycobacteria*, meaning fungus-like bacteria). They do not stain readily, but once stained, resist decolourisation with dilute mineral acids, due to the presence of mycolic acid in their cell wall. They are called acid fast bacilli (AFB). Mycobacteria are slow-growing, aerobic, non-motile, non-capsulated and non-sporing.

The genus *Mycobacteria* contains three groups: **obligate parasites**, **opportunistic pathogens** and **saprophytes**.

Obligate parasites

***Mycobacterium tuberculosis* complex**: Koch (1882) isolated the mammalian tubercle bacillus and proved its causative role in tuberculosis by satisfying certain basic principles of infectious agents (known as **Koch's postulates**). Tuberculosis in humans was subsequently shown to be caused by two types of the bacillus: the human and bovine types, designated *Mycobacterium tuberculosis* and *M.bovis,* respectively. *M.tuberculosis* complex includes two other mammalian types: *M.africanum*, causing human tuberculosis in tropical Africa; and *M.microti*, causing disease in voles and other small mammals. Recently, three more species have been added: *M.canetti* (similar to *M.africanum*), *M.caprae* (another cattle pathogen) and *M.pinnipedii* (a pathogen of seals).

Mycobacterium tuberculosis

Clinical Case 1 A 50-year-old man presented with a history of low-grade fever with an evening rise in temperature and productive cough for the previous two months. He sought medical advice, since he had started coughing blood-tinged sputum for the past three days. His history revealed loss of appetite and a weight loss of 10 kgs over the previous four months. A chest x-ray revealed a nodular infiltrate in the apical area of the right upper lobe. The sputum smear was positive for AFB and the culture grew *M.tuberculosis*. He was started on DOTS therapy.

Clinical Case 2 A 12-year-old boy complained of low-grade fever and mild headache for the previous two weeks, which worsened over the last two days. He also had vomiting, confusion and stiffness in the neck, for which his parents sought medical attention. History revealed that his father was a known case of pulmonary TB but had defaulted on treatment. CSF examination showed a mild increase in cell counts with predominant lymphocytes. Proteins were raised and glucose was low. ZN or Gram stain of CSF did not reveal any organisms. PCR assay of the CSF targeting the unique sequence of *M. tuberculosis* was positive. Two weeks later, the culture by automated system was also positive for this organism. A drug sensitivity test showed that the strain was resistant to rifampicin and INH. He was treated with second-line drugs, Ofloxacin, PAS Cycloserine and Ethionamide.

Mycobacterium leprae: The second human pathogenic mycobacterium is the lepra bacillus causing leprosy discovered by Hansen in 1868. Though described first, its properties are poorly understood due to it being non-cultivable in vitro.

Opportunistic pathogens

Non-tuberculous mycobacteria (NTM): This is a mixed group of mycobacteria from diverse sources: birds, cold-blooded and warm-blooded animals, from skin ulcers, and from soil, water and other environmental sources. They are broadly categorised as photochromogens, scotochromogens, non-photochromogens and rapid growers, based on their growth rates and pigmentation in the presence or absence of light. They are opportunistic pathogens and can cause many types of disease especially in immunocompromised individuals.

Saprophytes

Saprophytic mycobacteria: These were isolated from a number of sources and include *M.phlei* from grass and *M.smegmatis* from smegma. *M.smegmatis* (seldom found in smegma, along with other rapidly growing mycobacteria) frequently contaminate urine cultures.

MYCOBACTERIUM TUBERCULOSIS

Morphology

M.tuberculosis is a straight or slightly curved rod, about 3 μm × 0.3 μm in size, occurring singly, in pairs or as small clumps. The size depends on conditions of growth. Long, filamentous, club-shaped and branching forms may sometimes be seen. *M.bovis* is usually straighter, shorter and stouter.

Acid fast staining

They differ in their staining property from other bacteria. When stained with carbol fuchsin by the Ziehl–Neelsen method or by fluorescent dyes (auramine O, rhodamine), they resist decolourisation by 20% sulphuric acid and are therefore called acid fast. Acid fastness has been ascribed to the presence of an unsaponifiable lipid-rich (mycolic acid) wax material in the cell wall or to a semipermeable membrane around the cell.

Staining may be uniform or granular. Beaded or barred forms are frequently seen in *M.tuberculosis*, but *M.bovis* stains more uniformly.

Electron micrographs of thin sections show a thick cell wall composed of three layers enclosing a trilaminar plasma membrane. Spheroplasts and L forms are formed when grown in the presence of lysozymes.

M.tuberculosis is also **alcohol fast** (resists decolourisation with 3% hydrochloric acid in 95% alcohol), which differentiates it from saprophytic mycobacteria which are only acid fast.

Cultural characteristics

The organism is a slow grower with generation time of 14–15 hours. Colonies appear between two weeks to eight weeks. Optimum temperature is 37°C. Temperatures below 25°C or above 40°C do not favour growth. Optimum pH is 6.4–7.0. *M.tuberculosis* is an obligate aerobe (Table 38.1).

Tubercle bacilli are highly susceptible to traces of toxic substances like fatty acids in culture media. The toxicity is neutralised by serum albumin or charcoal.

Several media, both solid and liquid, have been described for the cultivation of tubercle bacilli:

Solid media

Lowenstein–Jensen (LJ) is the most widely employed media for routine culture. This consists of coagulated hen's eggs, mineral salt solution, asparagine and malachite green, the last acting as a selective agent inhibiting other bacteria (Fig. 38.1).

Other solid media used are those containing egg (**Petragnini, Dorset**), blood (**Tarshis**), serum (**Loeffler**) or potato (**Pawlowsky**).

Liquid media

Among the several liquid media described, **Dubos', Middlebrook's, Proskauer and Beck's, Sula's and Sauton's** are more common. Diffuse growth is

Table 38.1 *Some common mycobacteria and their habitats*

Obligate parasites	*M.tuberculosis, M.bovis, M.leprae*	Species always considered pathogens.
Opportunistic pathogens	*M.scrofulaceum, M.kansasii, M.marinum, M.ulcerans, M.avium*-intercelluar complex (MAC)	Uncommon causes of human disease. Infect immunocompromised individuals
Saprophytes	*M.smegmatis, M.gordonae, M.flavescens*	Found in soil and water. Produce environmental contamination.

Fig. 38.1 *M.tuberculosis* on LJ medium (left); LJ medium without growth (right)

obtained in Dubos' medium containing **Tween-80** (sorbitan monooleate). Virulent strains tend to form long serpentine cords in liquid media, while avirulent strains grow in a more dispersed manner. In automated culture systems, liquid media is used.

Newer methods of cultivation

Several **automated culture methods** have been introduced to detect early growth.

- **BACTEC 460**: This method uses radioistopes to detect growth. It is not preferred presently due to the use of radioisotopes.
- **BacT Alert**: This method uses colorimetric method of growth detection, due to production of CO_2 as a result of bacterial metabolism during growth.

BACTEC MGIT: This is an automated **mycobacteria growth indicator tube (MGIT)**. It is a rapid growth detection method, which uses 7H9 Middlebrook medium with fluorometric detection technology via O_2 consumption. An added advantage is that the incorporation of Pyrazinamide (PZA) in the medium detects resistance to this drug.

- **ESP system**: This is a continuous monitoring system for detecting growth of mycobacteria. It detects the pressure changes above the level of the medium either due to gas consumption or gas liberation resulting from bacterial growth. Recently this has been improved to detect drug susceptibility to mycobacteria.

Resistance

Mycobacteria are killed at 60°C in 15–20 minutes. Bacilli in sputum may be viable for 20–30 hours and in droplet nuclei up to 8–10 days under suitable conditions. Cultures remain viable at room temperature for 6–8 months and may be stored for up to two years at –20°C.

> **Susceptibility of mycobacteria to commonly used disinfectants in the hospital**
> Mycobacteria can survive exposure to 5% phenol, 15% sulphuric acid, 3% nitric acid, 5% oxalic acid and 4% sodium hydroxide. They are killed by formaldehyde and glutaraldehyde. They are destroyed by tincture of iodine in five minutes and by 80% ethanol in 2–10 minutes. Ethanol is a suitable disinfectant for skin, gloves and clinical thermometers.

Biochemical reactions

Several biochemical tests have been described for the identification of the mycobacterial species:

Niacin test: Human tubercle bacilli form niacin when grown on an egg medium. When 10% cyanogen bromide and 4% aniline in 96% ethanol are added to a suspension of the culture, a canary-yellow colour indicates a positive reaction. This test differentiates *M.tuberculosis* (positive) from *M.bovis* (negative).

Aryl sulphatase test: This test is positive only with atypical mycobacteria. The bacilli are grown in a medium containing 0.001 M tripotassium phenophthalein disulphate. To the culture, 2 N NaOH is added drop by drop. A pink colour indicates a positive reaction.

Catalase–peroxidase tests: These help in differentiating tubercle bacilli from atypical mycobacteria and indicate sensitivity of the strain to isoniazid. Tubercle bacilli are only weakly positive for catalase and strongly for peroxidase. Catalase and peroxidase activities are lost when the tubercle bacilli become INH-resistant. A mixture of equal volumes of 30 vol. H_2O_2 and 0.2% catechol in distilled water is added to 5 ml of the test culture and allowed to stand for a few minutes. Effervescence indicates catalase production and browning indicates peroxidase activity.

Nitrate reduction test

This is positive with *M.tuberculosis* and negative with *M.bovis*. Addition of sulphanilamide and n-naphthyl-ethylene to the suspension of bacteria in a nitrate medium changes the colour into red; nitrate is interpreted as positive (Fig. 38.2).

Amidase tests
The ability to split amides namely, acetamide, benzamide, carbamide, nicotinamide and pyrazinamide, helps to differentiate mycobacteria.

Pyrazinamidase test
The enzyme pyrazinamidase hydrolyses pyrazinamide to ammonia and pyrazinoic acid which is detected by adding ferric ammonium sulphate. This is positive in *M.tuberculosis* and negative in *M.bovis*.

Inhibition by thiophene-2 carboxylic acid (T2H)
This is also used to differentiate *M.tuberculosis* from *M.bovis*, the former being resistant. The organism is resistant if growth on T2H medium is >1% of the growth in control (Table 38.2).

Neutral red test
Virulent strains of tubercle bacilli can bind neutral red in an alkaline buffer solution, while avirulent strains cannot.

Tween-80 hydrolysis
A positive test is indicated by a change in the colour of the medium, from yellow to red at pH 7. It is useful in differentiating non-tuberculous mycobacteria (NTM).

Antigenic properties
Several antigens have been identified in the mycobacterial cell wall and the cytoplasm. The cell wall contains

Table 38.2 *Characteristics differentiating M.tuberculosis and M.bovis*

Test	M.tuberculosis	M.bovis
Niacin	+	–
Nitrate	+	–
Oxygen preference	Aerobic	Microaerophilic
Growth in T2H	+	–
Host	Human	Bovine
Culture	Eugonic	Dysgonic
0.5% glycerol	Helps growth	No effect
Sodium pyruvate	Helps growth	Helps growth
P-nitrogenic acid	No growth	No effect
Colony character	Dry, rough, raised, irregular, wrinkled surface; Not emulsifiable	Flat, smooth, moist, white; Break up easily
Tween hydrolysis	±	–
Pyrazinamidase 4 days	+	–

three major antigens which are responsible for virulence of the organism:

- **Lipids:** The mycobacterial cell wall is rich in long-chain fatty acids called mycolic acid. Mycolic acids play a role in pathogenesis and, when complexed with peptidoglycan, are responsible for granuloma formation. The pattern of lipids on gas chromatography has been used to classify different species. Another factor called cord factor is also responsible for the virulence of bacteria.
- **Proteins:** These induce delayed type hypersensitivity and elicit tuberculin reaction. There is also some antigenic relationship between lepra and tubercle bacilli.
- **Polysaccharides:** Group specificity is due to polysaccharides. Their role in pathogenesis is not clear but they can induce immediate type of hypersensitivity.

Antibodies against the polysaccharide, protein and phosphatide antigens of tubercle bacilli have been demonstrated in the sera of patients. They have no protective or diagnostic relevance.

Typing methods
They are used to define geographically the routes of transmission and dissemination in the environment and the source of infection in man and animals.

Molecular typing
Most typing methods currently are based on DNA fingerprinting, which is a powerful epidemiological

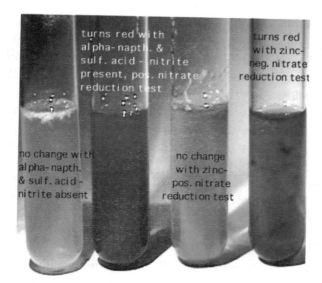

Fig. 38.2   Nitrate test

tool for differentiating between strains of tubercle bacilli.

- **IS6110 Restriction Fragment Length Polymorphism (RFLP) typing:** The IS6110 is a target sequence in several methods currently used for molecular typing of *M. tuberculosis*. Restriction endonuclease treatment yields nucleic acid fragments of varying lengths, the patterns of which are strain-specific and can be used as fingerprinting (IS6110-based PCR Finger printing).
- **Spoligotyping (spacer oligotyping):** This is based on polymorphism in the direct repeat (DR) locus. This is the region present in all MTBC in a unique locus which contains well-conserved sequences. This is more useful in strains that have no or very few copies of IS6110. A great advantage of this method is its ability as a typing tool in non-viable cultures, AFB slides, and paraffin embedded tissues.
- **Insertion-sequence-based typing of non-tubercular mycobacteria (IS-based typing of NTM):** This method is based on differences in the insertion sequences between strains of avium complex. It can also be useful in typing *M.ulcerance, M. gordonae,* etc.

Phenotypic methods

These were used earlier for epidemiological studies in determining strain relatedness. They have low discriminatory power, hence, are no longer used.

- **Bacteriophage typing:** Tubercle bacilli have been classified into four phage types: A, B, C and a type intermediate between A and B, designated I (for 'intermediate').
- **Bacteriocin typing:** *M.tuberculosis* can be typed by means of bacteriocins produced by rapidly growing mycobacteria.

Host range

M.tuberculosis causes natural infection in humans, other primates, dogs and other animals which have close contact with humans. Experimentally, guinea pigs and hamsters are highly susceptible to the infection (mice are only moderately susceptible), and the infection develops progressively following intraperitoneal, intravenous or intracerebral inoculation. Extrapulmonary isolates are less virulent.

  M.bovis produces tuberculosis in cattle, humans, other primates, carnivores including dogs and cats, badgers, swine, parrots and some birds of prey. Experimentally, guinea pigs are highly susceptible to this pathogen while rats are moderately susceptible. BCG, the tuberculous vaccine, is an attenuated strain of *M.bovis*.

TUBERCULOSIS

Tuberculosis is a potentially fatal infection, caused mainly by *M.tuberculosis* complex (MTC), that can affect any part of the body, with lungs being the most common organ involved.

Source: The source of infection is usually an open case of pulmonary tuberculosis. It is estimated that an open case of tuberculosis in India may infect, on an average, 25 contacts before death or cure. The mode of infection is by direct inhalation of aerosolised bacilli contained in the droplet nuclei of expectorated sputum. Coughing, sneezing and speaking release numerous droplets—as many as 3000 infectious nuclei per cough. Dried bacilli in dust are much less infectious. The disease spreads most often among household or close and prolonged contacts of open cases (whose sputum may contain minimum 10,000 bacilli per ml). Infection also occurs infrequently by ingestion, for example, through infected milk, and rarely by inoculation.

  The inhaled bacilli are arrested by the natural defences of the upper respiratory tract. Those that escape reach the lungs and are phagocytosed by the alveolar macrophages. Several factors including the number and virulence of the infecting bacilli, host factors including genetic susceptibility, age, immunocompetence, stress, nutrition and co-existing illness influence the outcome of the infection.

Immunology: Various components of the bacillus have been shown to possess different biological activities which may influence pathogenesis, allergy and immunity in the infection. Humans are evidently able to mount an effective defence against the infection as only about a tenth of those infected develop active tuberculosis. **Cell-mediated immunity** is the specific immune mechanism that plays a major role in tuberculosis. Humoral immunity has little or no role in protection or pathogenesis. The key cell is the activated CD4+ helper T cell which can develop along two different paths: the Th-1 and Th-2 cells, releasing cytokines such as interferon γ (gamma) interleukins 1 and 2, toxic effects of tumor necrosis factor α (TNF α) and others exerting different biological effects. Th-1-dependent cytokines activate macrophages, resulting in protective immunity and containment of the infection.

Th-2 cytokines induce delayed type hypersensitivity (DTH), tissue destruction and progressive disease.

Allergy and immunity: Infection with the tubercle bacillus induces cell-mediated immunity which manifests as delayed hypersensitivity (allergy) and resistance to infection (immunity). The resultant of these two processes determines the course of the infection. Allergy can be induced by infection with virulent as well as avirulent tubercle bacilli.

Koch's phenomenon

This is of historical interest. Robert Koch demonstrated that when virulent tubercle bacilli are injected into a healthy guinea pig, it develops a nodule at the site of inoculation, which develops into an ulcer that persists, with caseation of draining lymph nodes. On the other hand, if the bacilli is injected into an already infected guinea pig (infected 4–6 weeks earlier), the lesion develops rapidly within one or two days, into a shallow ulcer which heals completely without involving the draining lymph nodes.

Tuberculin tests: This was originally prepared by Robert Koch, and is known as **Old Tuberculin (OT)**. Seibert modified it to produce the **purified protein derivative (PPD)**. Subsequently, highly purified preparations of PPD have since been developed which are currently in use.

Pathology: The essential pathology in tuberculosis is the production of a characteristic lesion, the **tubercle,** in infected tissues (Fig. 38.3). This is an avascular **granuloma** composed of a central zone containing giant cells, with or without caseation, and a peripheral zone of lymphocytes and fibroblasts. Tuberculous lesions are primarily of two types: exudative and productive.

- The **exudative type** is an acute inflammatory reaction with accumulation of edema fluid, polymorphonuclear leucocytes, and later of lymphocytes and

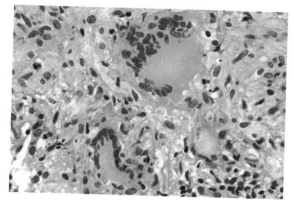

Fig. 38.3   Tubercle or granuloma with caseation

mononuclear cells. This is typically seen when there are plenty of virulent bacilli and the host response is DTH than of protective immunity.
- The **productive type** of lesion is predominantly cellular, associated with protective immunity.

Classification

Depending on the time of infection and the type of response, tuberculosis may be classified as primary and post-primary.

- **Primary tuberculosis** is the initial infection by the mycobacteria in a host. In endemic countries like India, young children usually are more susceptible. Alveolar macrophages engulf the bacilli which multiply intracellularly. They give rise to a subpleural focus of tuberculous pneumonia, commonly located in the lower lobe or the lower part of the upper lobe (**Ghon focus**). The hilar lymph nodes are involved. The Ghon focus together with the enlarged hilar lymph node constitutes the **primary complex**. This occurs about 3–8 weeks from the time of infection and is associated with the development of tuberculin hypersensitivity. In most cases, the lesion heals spontaneously in 2–6 months, leaving behind a calcified nodule. However, a few bacilli may survive in the healed lesion and remain latent. In a few, particularly in children with impaired immunity or other risk factors, the primary lesion may enlarge and cause miliary, meningeal or other forms of disseminated tuberculosis (*Case 2*).
- **Post-primary (secondary or adult) tuberculosis** is due to reactivation of latent infection (post-primary progression, endogenous reactivation) or exogenous re-infection and differs from the primary type in many respects. It affects mainly the upper lobes of the lungs, the lesions undergoing necrosis and tissue destruction, leading to cavitation. Lymph node involvement is unusual. The necrotic materials break out into the airways, leading to expectoration of bacteria-laden sputum, which is the main source of infection to contacts. In the immunodeficient, cavity formation is unusual. Instead, there is widespread dissemination of lesions in the lungs and other organs (*Case 1*).

Epidemiology

Tuberculosis is an ancient disease. It is estimated that a third of the world's population (two billion), is infected with the tubercle bacilli. Every year, between eight and nine million new cases of tuberculosis appear, and three million persons die from the disease. The large majority of the cases and deaths are from the poor nations. India is one of the worst affected countries. More than 40 per cent of the population is infected and around 15 million suffer from tuberculosis. Over three million of these are highly infectious, open cases. Half a million people die from the disease every year in India—one every minute.

Factors of spread:

- **Poverty** and tuberculosis go hand in hand. Tuberculosis has declined rapidly in the affluent nations due to improvement in the standard of living, but continues unabated in the poorer countries.
- Currently, with the AIDS pandemic, tuberculosis has become a problem for developed nations as well, with outbreaks among the HIV-infected individuals. **A close relationship has emerged between tuberculosis and HIV.** Not only does HIV infection reactivate latent tuberculosis but it also makes the disease more serious and renders treatment ineffective. Tuberculosis may, in turn, hasten the development of HIV infection into active disease.
- A third complication that has made the situation more grave is the emergence and spread of **multiple drug resistance** among tubercle bacilli. So serious is the global threat of tuberculosis combined with multidrug resistance and concomitant HIV infection that the World Health Organization in 1993 declared tuberculosis a global emergency.

Human infection with *M.bovis* used to be common in the early part of this century before pasteurisation of milk was widely practised. In many developed countries, such as in the UK, it has been almost eliminated by its control in cattle. The infection spreads to animals through aerosolised bacilli in moist cough sprays. An infected cow sheds the bacilli in milk, which is infectious to humans when consumed raw. The primary infection, mostly in children, would occur in the cervical and mesenteric lymph nodes, from where it could spread to the bone and joints and other extrapulmonary sites. Human infection with *M.bovis* is prevented by drinking only pasteurised or boiled milk. Person-to-person transmission of *M.bovis* is very rare.

Laboratory diagnosis

A person is diagnosed as having tuberculosis by any one or more of the following diagnostic tests:

- Demonstrating the bacilli in the lesion, by microscopy

- Isolating the bacilli in culture
- Using molecular diagnostic methods to detect DNA or RNA of the bacilli from clinical specimen
- Demonstrating hypersensitivity to tuberculoprotein
- Animal experiment: This involves transmitting the infection to experimental animals.

The specimen collected would depend on the site of the lesion, whether pulmonary or extrapulmonary.

Pulmonary tuberculosis

Specimen and collection

- **Sputum**: Bacillary shedding in the sputum is abundant in caseation, but relatively scanty in organised lesions that do not communicate with airways. Sputum is best collected in the morning before any meal. If sputum is scanty, a 24-hour sample may be tested. Sputum sampling on three days increases the chances of detection.
- Where sputum is not available, **laryngeal aspirates** or **bronchial washings** may be collected.
- In small children who tend to swallow the sputum, **gastric lavage** can be examined.

Direct sputum sample smears maybe prepared from the thick part of the sputum in the peripheral laboratories and stained.

Decontamination and concentration of specimens

Specimens from non-sterile sites and sputum need prior treatment so that microorganisms other than mycobacteria may not overgrow during prolonged incubation. Also, the sputum samples contain an organic matrix which may trap mycobacterial cells. Therefore, liquefaction, decontamination and concentration improve the yield. Concentration methods that do not kill the bacilli and that can be used for culture and animal inoculation have been described; these are used for the homogenisation and concentration of sputum and other specimens. All such methods should be done in Class II biosafety cabinets.

- **Petroff's method:** This simple method is widely used. Sputum is incubated with an equal volume of 4% sodium hydroxide solution at 37°C with frequent shaking till it becomes clear, on an average for 20 minutes. It is then centrifuged at 3000 rpm for 20 minutes and the sediment neutralised with N/10 HCl and used for smear, culture and animal inoculation. Excessive exposure to alkali is deleterious and should be avoided.
- **NALC (N acetyl cysteine) combined with 2% NaOH:** This method is considered better than

Petroff's. Here, **N acetyl cysteine** is used for lique-faction of sputum. NaOH kills the contaminating bacteria. The sample is then neutralised with buffer and concentrated by centrifugation. This method is also compatible with culture in automated systems.

Microscopy

Sputum microscopy is the most reliable single method in the diagnosis and control of tuberculosis. Smears should be prepared from the thick purulent part of the sputum.

Staining:

- **Ziehl–Neelsen technique (ZN):** Direct or concentrated smears of sputum are examined for AFB. Thick, purulent sputum needs to be digested and homogenised prior to staining. Two commonly used techniques are Petroff's method using 4% NaOH, or NALC (N-Acetyl Cysteine) with 2% NaOH (Fig. 38.4). Smears are dried, heat-fixed and stained by the Ziehl–Neelsen technique. There are several modified techniques. The smear is covered with strong carbol fuchsin and gently heated to steaming for 5–7 minutes, without letting the stain boil and become dry.
- **Kinyoun's modification of acid fast staining:** This is a modified cold method where heating of the stain is not employed. It requires increasing the concentration of phenol acid and duration of staining. The slide is then washed with water and decolourised with 20% sulphuric acid till slide becomes colourless followed by decolourisation with 95% ethanol for two minutes. The two steps can be combined using acid alcohol (3% HCl in 95% ethanol). After washing, the smear is counterstained with Loeffler's methylene blue, 1% picric acid or 0.2% malachite

green for one minute. Under the oil immersion objective, acid fast bacilli are seen as bright red rods while the background is blue, yellow or green depending on the counterstain used. **At least 10,000 acid fast bacilli should be present per ml of sputum for them to be readily demonstrable in direct smears.** A negative report should not be given till at least 300 fields have been examined, taking about 10 minutes. A positive report can be given only if two or more typical bacilli have been seen. Smears are graded based on Revised National TB Control Program (Table 38.3).

Fluorescent Stains

- **Auramine rhodamine:** When several smears are to be examined daily, it is more convenient to use fluorescent microscopy. Smears are stained with auramine phenol or auramine rhodamine fluorescent dyes and examined under ultraviolet illumination or where source is LED (light emitting diode). Bacilli appear as bright rods against a dark background. Because of the contrast, the bacilli can be seen even under the high dry objective, enabling large areas of the smear to be screened rapidly.

Differences between *M.tuberculosis* and saprophytic mycobacteria on staining: Microscopic demonstration of acid fast bacilli provides only presumptive evidence of tuberculosis, as even saprophytic mycobacteria may present a similar appearance. Saprophytic Mycobacteria stain uniformly without barred or beaded appearance, and are usually only acid fast. Saprophytic mycobacteria may be present in tap water, rubber tubes, cork or bark, and can contaminate clinical materials. Saprophytes may pose problems with gastric aspirates, feces and urogenital specimens.

Culture

Culture is the gold standard for diagnosis of tuberculosis, detecting as few as 10 to 100 bacilli per ml.

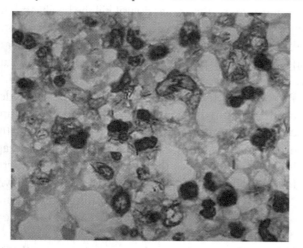

Fig. 38.4 *Mycobacterium tuberculosis* (acid fast bacilli on ZN stain)

Table 38.3 *ZN smear evaluation and AFB report as per RNTCP guidelines*

	RNTCP		
	Result	Grading	No. of fields
>10/field	+ve	3+	20
1–10/field	+ve	2+	50
10–99/100 field	+ve	1+	100
1–9/100 field	+ve	scanty *	100
No. of AFB in 100	-ve		1000

*Record actual no. of bacilli seen in 100 fields.

- **Solid media:** The concentrated material is inoculated into at least two bottles of LJ medium. If the specimen is positive by microscopy, a direct drug sensitivity test may also be set up. Cultures are examined for growth after incubation at 37°C for four days (for rapid growing mycobacteria, fungi and contaminant bacteria) and at least twice weekly thereafter for 8–12 weeks, following which a negative report is given if no growth occurs. A smear is made from any growth, and stained by ZN method. A slow-growing, non-pigmented, niacin-positive, acid fast bacillus is taken as *M.tuberculosis*. When the isolate is niacin-negative, a battery of tests may be needed for identification, including growth at 25°C and 45°C, animal pathogenicity and biochemical tests (Fig. 38.5, Table 38.4).

- **Liquid media:** A liquid medium, Middlebrook 7H9, is available but its use has now become limited due to the increasing use of liquid culture medium (Mycobacteria Growth Indicator Tube (MGIT) for drug susceptibility.

- **Automated systems:** Continuously monitoring systems using BACTEC MGIT, and BacT/ALERT are replacing solid culture methods, because of rapid indication of growth. They use the fluorescence quenching system. Another system uses a colorimetric carbon dioxide sensor in each bottle to detect growth.

All these systems use broth similar to 7H9 supplemented with a variety of growth media and antimicrobial agents.

Anti-tuberculosis drug sensitivity tests: As drug resistance is an important problem in tuberculosis, it is desirable to test the sensitivity of isolates as an aid to treatment. Sensitivity tests for *M.tuberculosis* are carried out using the following methods:

- In the **absolute concentration method**, a number of media containing serial concentrations of the drugs are inoculated and the minimum inhibitory concentrations calculated.

- In the **resistance ratio method**, two sets of media containing graded concentrations of the drugs are

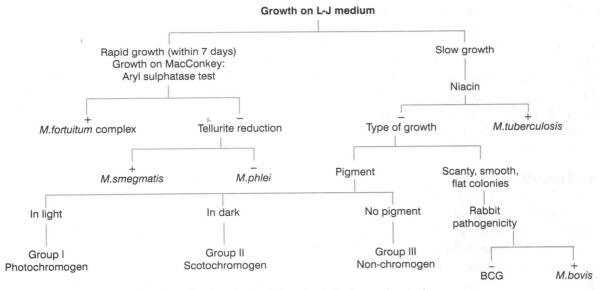

Fig. 38.5   Algorithm for identification of tubercle bacilli and related mycobacteria

Table 38.4   *Tests used for identification*

Type	Niacin	Nitrate reduction	Oxygen preference	Growth in TCH	Phage type
Human (classical)	+	+	Aerobic	+	ABC
Asian type	+	+	Aerobic	–	I
African type	+/–	Variable	Microaerophilic	–	A
Vole	+/–	Variable	Microaerophilic	–	?
Bovine	–	–	Microaerophilic	–	A
*TCH=Thiophene-2-carboxylic acid hydrazide (5 mg/l)					

inoculated, one set with the test strain and the other with a standard strain of known sensitivity.

- In the **proportion method**, the average sensitivity of the strain is indicated, taking into account the fact that any population will contain cells with varying degrees of sensitivity to a drug.
- **Automated systems**, as described above, are used more commonly now as the turnaround time is short.

Molecular methods

- Polymerase chain reaction (**PCR**) and ligase chain reaction (**LCR**) are replacing culture methods especially for extrapulmonary tuberculosis.
- Transcription-mediated amplification (**TMA**) targeting ribosomal RNA has been introduced as an improvement on PCR-based DNA amplification.
- **RFLP and IS fingerprinting** for epidemiological typing of strains has been referred to above. Demonstration of mutations in specific drug sensitivity genes is a useful indicator of drug resistance. Such tests for rifampicin resistance are already available.
- Line probe assay (**LPA**) is used both for identification of MTC and detection of mutations associated with drug resistance genes.
- **GenXPert** is a cartridge-based nucleic acid amplification test which detects the bacilli as well as its resistance to Rifampicin. It is also known as CB NAAT. It has been recommended for the diagnosis of MDR-TB as well as tuberculosis in HIV patients, tuberculous meningitis, tuberculous lymphadentis and paediatric tuberculosis.

Immunodiagnosis

Serological tests are not useful in diagnosis of tuberculosis, especially in endemic areas, and are not recommended. Demonstration of hypersensitivity to tuberculoprotein by **tuberculin testing** is a standard procedure to detect exposure to the bacilli.

Methods:

- **Mantoux test**: This test uses purified protein derivative (PPD) and has been used routinely since 1910. In this test, 0.1 ml of PPD containing 5 TU (tuberculosis unit) is injected intradermally (between layers of skin and not subcutaneously) on the flexor aspect of the forearm with a tuberculin syringe, raising a wheal. The site is examined 48–72 hours later and the induration of 10 mm or more, measured at its widest point transversely to the long axis of the forearm, is taken as positive. Erythema is not taken into account. Induration of 5 mm or less is considered negative and 6–9 mm equivocal. A PPD dose of 1 TU is used when extreme hypersensitivity is suspected. An increased dose of 10 or 100 TU is used when 5 TU test is negative.

- **Heaf test**: Multiple puncture testing is used for screening and surveys, but it is not accurate enough as a diagnostic test.
- **Tine test**: Disposable prongs carrying dried PPD are also available for individual testing.

Interpretation:

- **Positive**: A positive tuberculin test indicates hypersensitivity to tuberculoprotein, denoting infection with the tubercle bacilli or prior immunisation with BCG. The test becomes positive 4–6 weeks after infection or immunisation. Tuberculin allergy wanes gradually and disappears after 4–5 years in the absence of subsequent contact with the mycobacteria. In endemic areas, the allergy is maintained by repeated contacts with the bacilli.
- **Negative**: Persons who have never had contact or been exposed to the tubercle bacilli are tuberculin-negative. False negative tests (anergy) may be seen in miliary tuberculosis, convalescence from some viral infections like measles, lymphoreticular malignancy, sarcoidosis, severe malnutrition, immunosuppressive therapy or impaired cell-mediated immunity.
- **False negative** results may also be due to inactive PPD preparations and improper injection technique.
- **False positive** reactions may be seen in infections with some related mycobacteria ('atypical' mycobacteria).

Repeated tuberculin testing will give a positive reaction in a non-infected person, but may enhance the intensity of response in reactive individuals. This booster effect is useful in persons showing a negative or equivocal test due to waning allergy, in whom re-testing after a week may induce a positive response ('**two-step testing**'). Re-testing is done at a site different from the earlier one.

Uses: Tuberculin testing may be used as an aid in diagnosing active infection in infants and young children. It also helps to determine prevalence of infection in an area, or as an indication of successful vaccination. Tuberculin testing of cattle has helped in the control of bovine tuberculosis.

Interferron gamma release assay: This test uses *Mycobacterium tuberculosis* antigen CFP10 which reacts with T-lymphocytes of the patient to release γ interferon. This test is not very specific for pulmonary TB, hence, is not recommended any longer.

Animal inoculation: The concentrated material is inoculated intramuscularly into the thigh of two healthy guinea pigs about 12 weeks old. Subcutaneous inoculation is not recommended as it leads to a local ulcer which may be infectious. The animals are weighed before inoculation and at intervals thereafter. Progressive loss of weight is an indication of infection. Infected animals show a positive tuberculin skin reaction. One animal is killed after four weeks and autopsied. If it shows no evidence of tuberculosis, the other is autopsied after eight weeks.

Diagnosis of extrapulmonary tuberculosis

The general procedure is as for pulmonary tuberculosis. The **specimen** depends on the site of infection: urine, CSF, joint fluid, biopsy material, blood or any other body fluid. **Microscopy** and **culture (animal inoculation is very rarely done now)** are used for the diagnosis of extrapulmonary tuberculosis, though it is difficult to obtain conclusive results as the bacilli are present in far fewer numbers in these lesions than in pulmonary disease. This has led to the use of molecular techniques for diagnosing extrapulmonary tuberculosis.

- CSF from tuberculous meningitis often develops a spiderweb clot on standing, examination of which may be more successful than of the fluid. The use of PCR and DNA probes may be more efficient in detecting the bacilli.
- Bone marrow and liver biopsy specimens from miliary tuberculosis and blood from those with HIV co-infection are useful for culture. Pus from tuberculous abscess often yields positive results in smear and culture.
- Pleural effusion and other exudates may be collected with citrate to prevent coagulation. They may be directly cultured after centrifugation. If other bacteria are present, prior concentration is necessary.
- Urinary excretion of bacilli in renal tuberculosis is intermittent. Hence, it is advisable to test 3–6 first whole voided morning samples of urine. Each sample is centrifuged at 3000 rpm for 30 minutes and the sediment used for culture after concentration.

Prophylaxis

General measures

For the prevention of tuberculosis, general measures such as adequate nutrition, good housing and health education are as important as specific antibacterial measures.

Immunoprophylaxis

The **BCG (Bacille Calmette–Guerin) vaccine**, administered by intradermal injection of the live attenuated vaccine, was developed by Calmette and Guerin (1921). This is a strain of *M.bovis* attenuated by 239 serial subcultures in a glycerine–bile–potato medium over a period of 13 years. Following BCG vaccination, a tuberculin-negative recipient is converted to a positive reactor. The immunity may last for 10–15 years and is similar to the immunity following natural infection, except that it does not carry any risk of disease due to reactivation, as in the latter case.

> **Safety measures:** The Lubeck disaster, in which several children developed fatal tuberculosis following oral immunisation, faced severe criticism. This was later found to be due to live, virulent tubercle being given instead of BCG by mistake.

Stringent safety measures have been enforced in the manufacture of the BCG vaccine. The recognised complications of this vaccine are as follows:

- **Local:** Abscess, indolent ulcer, keloid, tuberculides, confluent lesions, lupoid lesions, lupus vulgaris
- **Regional:** Enlargement and suppuration of draining lymph nodes
- **General:** Fever, mediastinal adenitis, erythema nodosum, tendency to keloid formation, and, very rarely, non-fatal meningitis. Very few cases of progressive tuberculosis reported are believed to have been in immunodeficient subjects.

Efficacy: The consensus opinion is that BCG may not offer protection from the risk of tuberculosis infection, but gives protection to infants and young children against the more serious types of the disease, such as meningitis and disseminated tuberculosis. The recommendation, therefore, is that in endemic countries such as India, the BCG vaccine be administered to babies by intradermal injection on the deltoid immediately after birth, or as early as possible, before the age of 12 months. The vaccine need not be administered after the age of two years. BCG should not be given to infants and children with active HIV disease, though it may be given with benefit to asymptomatic HIV-positive cases. Babies born to mothers with AFB-positive sputum should not be given BCG at birth, but only after a course of preventive chemotherapy.

Added advantages of BCG vaccine

BCG induces non-specific stimulation of the immune system, providing some protection against leprosy and leukemia. Multiple injections of BCG have been tried as adjunctive therapy in some malignancies. Some workers have reported that BCG is superior to PPD for tuberculin testing.

Restoration of cellular immune capacity by '**transfer factor**' had been shown, many years ago, to help recovery in immunodeficient patients. A vaccine containing heat-killed *M.vaccae*, an environmental mycobacterium from Uganda, is being tested as an immunomodulator for stimulation of Th-1 cells which promote protective immunity.

Chemoprophylaxis or preventive chemotherapy: Administration of anti-TB drugs (usually only isoniazid) to persons with

- Latent tuberculosis (asymptomatic, tuberculin-positive)
- High risk of developing active tuberculosis
- Uninfected, exposed to high risk of infection
- Infants of mothers with active tuberculosis
- Children living with a case of active tuberculosis in the house
- HIV-infected contacts of active tuberculosis

The drug of choice is isoniazid 5 mg/kg daily for 6–12 months as the usual course. Trials have shown that this reduces the risk of developing active disease by 90 per cent.

Treatment

Chemotherapy has revolutionised the management of tuberculosis in such a way that the earlier concept of sanatorium regimens, bed rest, fresh air and rich food, as well as operative interventions, such as artificial pneumothorax and thoracoplasty are no longer essential for cure, if domiciliary treatment with effective anti-tuberculosis drugs are given in optimal dose and duration.

Anti-tuberculosis drugs are of two types:

- **Bactericidal:** Of these, rifampicin (R) and pyrazinamide (Z) are called sterilising drugs because they effectively kill the bacilli in the lesions. On the other hand, bactericidal drugs, isoniazid (H) is effective only against replicating bacilli and streptomycin (S) only against extracellular bacilli and so are not by themselves able to sterilise the lesions.

- **Bacteriostatic:** Ethambutol (E), along with the other bactericidal drugs, constitutes the first-line drug in anti-tuberculosis therapy. The old practice of daily administration of drugs for two years or so has been replaced by short-course regimens of 6–7 months, which are effective and convenient. A typical example of such a schedule for a new smear-positive case is a combination of four drugs (HRZE) given three times a week during an initial intensive phase of two months, followed by 4–5 months of continuing phase with only two drugs (HR) three times a week. The regimen of treatment has undergone modifications over the years and now the treatment provided by the RNTCP follows the **Directly Observed Treatment-short course (DOTS).**

Drug resistance

Drug-resistant tuberculosis has become a problem in high TB burden countries, including India. This is due to mutations, with an approximate rate of 1 in 10^8 cell divisions. This may have been effectively prevented by the strategy of combination drug therapy, which had been introduced for this purpose. Unfortunately, this was improperly implemented. Multiple factors have led to the emergence of MDR-TB. Lapses in prescribing practices, drug delivery and patient compliance have led to build-up of resistance in the bacilli, over the years, reducing the efficacy of treatment.

World Health Organization has described drug resistance as:

- **Resistance in newly treated** (pre-treatment, initial), when the patient is infected with a strain of the tubercle bacilli which is already resistant,
- **Resistance to previously treated** (secondary, post-treatment), when the infecting strain, initially sensitive, becomes resistant, usually as a result of improper or inadequate treatment. This is the more common type of resistance.

When acquired, resistant strains become increasingly common in an area; the chance of new patients presenting with resistance during initial treatment increases.

When an infecting strain acquires resistance to one drug, the chance of it becoming resistant to other drugs increases, unless the treatment schedule contains an adequate number of effective drugs.

Multidrug-resistant tuberculosis (MDR-TB)

A very serious consequence of unchecked drug resistance has been the emergence and spread of **multid-**

rug-resistant tuberculosis (MDR-TB). Though the term multidrug resistance means only resistance to two or more drugs, in the context of tuberculosis, it specifically refers to **resistance to rifampicin and isoniazid**, with or without resistance to one or more other drugs. This is because R and H form the sheet anchor of short-term chemotherapy and any strain resistant to both these drugs is unlikely to respond to treatment.

MDR-TB is a global problem, menacing the poor and rich nations alike. It may be primary or acquired. Its presence in those with concomitant HIV infection makes it more dangerous. When first-line drugs become ineffective, second-line drugs must be tried. Large numbers of old and new drugs are being used: quinolones, aminoglycosides, macrolides, para aminosalicylic acid, thiacetazone, cycloserine, capreomycin and others. They are unsatisfactory, being much less effective, costlier, more toxic and requiring prolonged treatment schedules.

Extensively drug-resistant MTB (**XDR TB**) are extensively resistant strains. It is defined as multidrug-resistant tuberculosis (MDR-TB) that is resistant to isoniazid and rifampicin, plus any fluoroquinolone and at least one of three injectable second-line drugs (i.e., amikacin, kanamycin, or capreomycin).

Revised National Tuberculosis Control Program (RNTCP)

RNTCP was implemented in India in 1992. The aim was to provide standardised treatment and proper diagnosis facilities. This was based on Directly Observed Treatment, Short Course (DOTS) strategy of WHO. The treatment is started following diagnosis made primarily by morning and spot sputum microscopy. This is made available free of cost to patients at designated microscopy centres (DMC). Treatment is provided under direct observation by a DOT Provider at the DOTS centre near the patients' home. This strategy can prevent emergence of drug resistance by ensuring the patient's compliance.

India DOTS is the fastest expanding program in the world. The treatment purposes and regimens are given based on sputum smear positivity and seriousness of the disease as category I, II and III of the treatment. The algorithms for laboratory diagnosis and treatment strategies are standardised. It also identifies accredited laboratories for drug susceptibility testing.

DOTS relies on treatment with first-line drugs rifampicin and INH.

DOTS-Plus refers to DOTS programmes that add components for MDR-TB diagnosis and treatment using quality-assured culture and drug susceptibility testing. Proper triage of patients for Culture and DST testing and management under DOTS-Plus is done in coordination with National and Supra-National Reference Laboratories.

RNTCP—Standardised Treatment Regimen (Cat IV): This regimen is for the treatment of MDR-TB cases (and those with rifampicin resistance) under the RNTCP programme (Table 38.5). Cat IV regimen comprises 6 drugs—kanamycin, ofloxacin (levofloxacin), ethionamide, pyrazinamide, ethambutol and cycloserine during 6–9 months of the Intensive Phase— and 4 drugs—ofloxacin (levofloxacin), ethionamide, ethambutol and cycloserine during the 18 months of the Continuation Phase. *p*-aminosalicylic acid (PAS) is included in the regimen as a substitute drug if any bactericidal drug (K, Ofl, Z and Eto) or 2 bacteriostatic (E and Cs) drugs are not tolerated.

(Ref: Revised National Tuberculosis Control Programme DOTS-Plus Guidelines)

Table 38.5 *Alternative method of grouping anti-TB agents*

Group 1: First-line oral anti-TB agents	Isoniazid (H); Rifampicin (R); Ethambutol (E); Pyrazinamide (Z)
Group 2: Injectable anti-TB agent	Streptomycin (S); Kanamycin (Km); Amikacin (Am); Capreomycin (Cm); Viomycin (Vm).
Group 3: Fluoroquinolones	Ciprofloxacin (Cfx); Ofloxacin (Ofx); Levofloxacin (Lvx); Moxifloxacin (Mfx); Gatifloxacin (Gfx)
Group 4: Oral second-line anti-TB agents	Ethionamide (Eto); Prothionamide (Pto); Cycloserine (Cs); Terizadone (Trd); para-aminosalicylic acid (PAS)
Group 5: Agents with unclear efficacy (not recommended by WHO for routine use in MDR-TB patients)	Clofazimine (Cfz); Linezolid (Lzd); Amoxicillin/Clavulanate (Amx/Clv); Thioacetazone (Thz); Imipenem/Cilastatin (Ipm/Cln); high-dose Isoniazid (high-dose H); Clarithromycin (Clr)

As per Revised National Tuberculosis Control Programme DOTS-Plus guidelines

The Stop TB Strategy of World Health Organization

To reduce the global burden of **TB** and for **a TB-free world**, in line with the Millennium Development Goals and the Stop TB Partnership targets, WHO has laid out the following objectives:

- Achieve universal access to high-quality care for all people with TB.

- Reduce the human suffering and socioeconomic burden associated with TB.
- Protect vulnerable populations from TB, TB/HIV and multidrug-resistant TB.
- Support development of new tools and enable their timely and effective use.
- Protect and promote human rights in TB prevention, care and control.

RECAP

- *Mycobacterium tuberculosis* is an obligatory, aerobic, non-motile, non-sporing, rod-shaped bacterium which stains poorly by the Gram stain because its cell wall contains an abundance of lipids (mycolic acids). It retains strong carbol fuchsin dye during decolourisation with acid and alcohol in the Ziehl–Neelsen (ZN) staining technique (*Mycobacterium tuberculosis* is acid and alcohol fast by this staining technique). It grows very slowly, taking several weeks to form a visible colony on enriched culture media.
- *Mycobacterium tuberculosis* causes tuberculosis (TB) in humans; this is the leading cause of bacteria-related deaths worldwide.
- TB is transmitted by aerosols from an infected individual. Inhaled bacteria penetrate the alveoli and are ingested by alveolar macrophages. Bacteria grow intracellularly and slowly. The general health and robustness of the immune system of the individual determine whether organisms:
  - Are killed and cleared
  - Remain viable but controlled in a granuloma for many years, undergoing 're-activation' when the individual ages or immune status changes
  - Continue to grow, cause damage to the lungs, spread, and destroy other organs
- Cell-mediated immunity is the primary immune response that destroys the organism inside macrophages. Individual susceptibilities to TB reflect differences in the efficacy of an individual's cell-mediated response to infection.
- Early morning sputum is generally collected for diagnosis by:
  - Staining by the ZN method; acid and alcohol fast bacilli appear as long, thin, pink (sometimes beaded) rods.
  - Culture of sputum on Lowenstein–Jensen or Middlebrook medium; this may take up to 6–8 weeks to yield positive results.
- Automated systems have improved the turnaround time of culture and sensitivity:
  - The tuberculin skin test is a sign of exposure to the organism.
  - PCR can be used to detect *Mycobacterium tuberculosis* DNA in sputum and other specimens.
- Individuals suspected to have the disease should be treated with multiple antibiotics. MDR and XDR strains are a cause of concern in treatment.
- DOTS under RNTCP in India ensures proper therapy to patients.

ESSAYS

1. Classify mycobacteria. Describe the laboratory diagnosis of pulmonary tuberculosis.
2. Enumerate the infections caused by *M.tuberculosis* and describe the laboratory diagnosis of extrapulmonary tuberculosis.

SHORT ANSWERS

1. Principle of acid fast staining
2. Kinyoun's method of acid fast staining
3. Role of the BCG vaccine
4. Tuberculin test
5. Methods of anti-tubercular susceptibility tests

SHORT NOTES

1. MDR and XDR-TB
2. DOTS
3. Mantoux test
4. BCG vaccine
5. Automated methods for culture of mycobacteria

39 Mycobacterium II: Non-Tuberculous Mycobacteria (NTM)

INTRODUCTION

Mycobacteria other than mammalian tubercle bacilli, which may occasionally cause human disease resembling tuberculosis, are called **'non-tuberculous mycobacteria (NTM)'** (earlier also called 'atypical', 'anonymous' or 'MOTT' [mycobacteria other than tubercle bacilli], etc.) They cause opportunistic infections in human beings. While human infection with them is common in some areas, disease is rare. They are unable to cause progressive disease when injected into guinea pigs. Over 80 species of NTM are found worldwide in soil and animals.

Saprophytic mycobacteria such as *M.phlei* are incapable of infecting human beings or animals and are distinct from NTM.

Runyoun classification

NTM have been classified into four groups by Runyon (1959) based on pigment production and the rate of growth: Group I photochromogens, Group II scotochromogens, Group III non-photochromogens and Group IV rapid growers. Though other methods of classification have been described, Runyon's has found universal acceptance (Table 39.1).

Species identification depends on several additional characteristics (Table 39.2).

Group I—photochromogens: These strains form colonies that produce no pigment in the dark but when the young culture is exposed to light for one hour in the presence of air, and re-incubated for 24–28 hours, a yellow-orange pigment appears. They are slow growing, though growth is faster than that of the tubercle bacilli. The important species in this group are *M.kansasii*, *M.marinum* and *M.simiae*.

- ***M.kansasii*** causes chronic pulmonary disease resembling tuberculosis, usually affecting the upper lobes, with cavity formation and scarring. It has been isolated from tap water samples around the world and this is believed to be the main reason and source

Table 39.1 Runyoun classification

Group	Nomenclature	Growth characteristics	Members of clinical importance	Diseases
Group I	Photochromogens	No pigment in the dark, become pigmented on exposure to light	M.kansasii, M.marinum	Pulmonary disease resembling tuberculosis; swimming pool granuloma
Group II	Scotochromogens	Pigmented in the dark	M.scrofulaceum, M.gordonae	Cervical lymphadenitis mostly contaminant from tap water
Group III	Non-photochromogens	No pigment even on exposure to light	M.avium, M.intracellulare, M.ulcerans, M.xenopi	Disseminated disease in AIDS patients; Buruli ulcer; chronic lung disease
Group IV	Rapid growers	Growth within seven days	M.fortuitum, M.chelonae, M.smegmatis, M.phlei	Chronic abscess; saprophytes

Table 39.2 *Differentiation between tubercle bacilli and some species of atypical mycobacteria*

Test	M.tuberculosis	M.bovis	M.microti	M.kansasii	M.marinum	M.scrofulaceum	M.avium-intracellulare complex	M.fortuitum	M.chelonei	M.phlei	M.smegmatis
Growth in 7 days	–	–	–	–	–	–	–	+	+	+	+
Growth at 25°C	–	–	–	+	+	+	±	+	+	+	+
Growth at 37°C	+	+	+	+	±	+	+	+	+	+	+
Growth at 45°C	–	–	–	–	–	–	±	–	–	+	+
Pigment in dark	–	–	–	–	–	+	–	–	–	+	–
Pigment in light	–	–	–	+	+	+	+	+	+	+	+
Growth in the presence of p-nitrobenzoic acid 500 µg/ml (PNB)	–	+	+	+	+	+	+	+	+	+	+
Urease	+	+	+	+	+	+	–	+	+	+	+
Niacin	+	–	±	–	–	–	–	+	–	+	+
Nitrate reduction	+	–	–	+	–	–	–	+	–	+	+

of infection. It is the second most common NTM seen in lung disease after the *M.avium complex*.

- *M.marinum* which causes a warty skin lesion (**swimming pool** or **fish tank granuloma**), closely resembles *M.kansasii* but can be differentiated by its poor growth at 37°C, negative nitratase, positive pyrazinamide hydrolase and L-fucosidase activities.
- Several photochromogenic mycobacteria were isolated in 1964 from monkeys exported from India. They have been classified into two species: niacin-positive *M.simiae* and niacin-negative *M.asiaticum*. They have subsequently been associated with pulmonary disease in human beings.

Group II—scotochromogens: These strains form pigmented colonies (yellow-orange-red) even in the dark. They are widely distributed in the environment and sometimes contaminate cultures of tubercle bacilli.

- *M.scrofulaceum* may cause scrofula (cervical adenitis) in children.
- *M.gordonae*, often found in tap water (hence called '**the tap water scotochromogen**'), is a common contaminant in clinical specimens and a rare cause of pulmonary disease. It differs from *M.scrofulaceum* in failing to hydrolyse urea, nicotinamide and pyrazinamide.
- *M.szulgai* is scotochromogenic when grown at 37°C and photochromogenic at 25°C.

Group III—non-photochromogens: These strains do not form pigment even on exposure to light. Colonies may resemble those of the tubercle bacilli. The medically important species are *M.avium*, *M.intracellulare*, *M.xenopi* and the skin pathogen *M.ulcerans*.

- *M.avium*, which causes natural tuberculosis in birds and lymphadenopathy in pigs, is one of the most common opportunist human pathogens.
- *M.intracellulare* and *M.avium* and are so similar that they have been considered as one group, the *M.avium* complex (MAC). They cause lymphadenopathy, pulmonary lesions or disseminated disease, particularly in AIDS patients. *M.intracellulare* is commonly known as the **Battey bacillus** because it was first identified as a human pathogen at the Battey State Hospital for Tuberculosis, Georgia, USA.
- *M.xenopi*, originally isolated from toads, may occasionally cause chronic lung disease in human beings. *M.xenopi* and *M.avium* are thermophiles, capable of growth at 45°C.
- Though usually classified as a non-photochromogen, *M.xenopi* may form scotochromogenic yellow colonies. *M.xenopi* has been isolated from water taps, mostly hot water taps, in hospitals. It has also been isolated from mains water supplies.

Group IV—rapid growers: This is a heterogeneous group of mycobacteria capable of rapid growth, colonies appearing within seven days of incubation at 37°C or 25°C (Fig. 39.1).

Within the group, photochromogenic, scotochromogenic and non-chromogenic species occur.

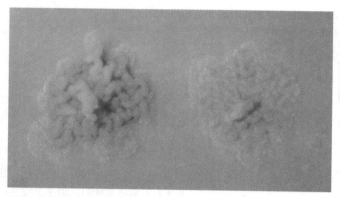

Fig. 39.1   Growth on LJ medium *(M.fortuitum)*

Chromogenic rapid growers are mostly saprophytes (for example, *M.phlei*).

- The medically important species are **M.fortuitum** and **M.chelonae**, both of which can cause **chronic abscesses** in human beings. Outbreaks of abscesses **following injection of vaccines** and other preparations contaminated by these mycobacteria have been reported on a number of occasions. The bacilli are found in the soil, and infection usually follows some injury.

- *M.fortuitum* and *M.chelonei* do not produce any pigment. Pulmonary lesions caused by *M.fortuitum* cannot be distinguished radiologically from typical tuberculosis. No effective chemotherapy is available. **M.smegmatis**, commonly considered as saprophyte in smegma, is seldom seen in that location. It is a frequent isolate from soft tissue lesions following trauma or surgery.

- Some non-cultivable or poorly growing mycobacteria identified from the blood of AIDS patients have been characterised by their 16S RNA base sequences. They grow sparsely in some liquid media. Examples are **M.genevense, M.confluentis** and **M.intermedium**.

- A rapid grower, **M.vaccae**, is reported to be an immunomodulator capable of inhibiting tissue destroying hypersensitivity responses and stimulating protective immune processes in tuberculosis. Clinical trials of the *M.vaccae* vaccine as an adjuvant to chemotherapy in tuberculosis are underway.

SKIN PATHOGENS

Cutaneous lesions may occur in leprosy or tuberculosis, either as localised disease or as part of a generalised infection. In a different class are two species of mycobacteria, *M.ulcerans* (Group III of Runyon) and *M.marinum* (Group I of Runyon), which are exclusively skin pathogens, causing chronic ulcers and granulomatous lesions on the skin (Table 39.3). Systemic invasion does not occur and the regional lymph glands are not involved. Cutaneous localisation is because they multiply optimally at skin temperature. Infection with *M.marinum*, but not *M.ulcerans*, may cause a low-grade tuberculin reaction.

M.ulcerans (Buruli ulcer): This was originally isolated from human skin lesions in Australia (1948) but have subsequently been recovered from similar lesions from Uganda (Buruli ulcer), Congo, Nigeria, Mexico, Malaysia and New Guinea. Ulcers are usually seen on the legs or arms and are believed to follow infection through minor injuries. After an incubation period of a few weeks, indurated nodules appear, which break down, forming indolent ulcers which slowly extend under the skin.

Initially, smears from the edge of the ulcer show large clumps of bacilli which are acid fast and alcohol fast. Later, the immunoreactive phase sets in and the bacilli disappear. The ulcers then heal with disfiguring scars.

A toxin produced by *M.ulcerans* causes inflammation and necrosis when injected into the skin of guinea pigs.

Table 39.3   *Differentiation between* M.ulcerans *and* M.marinum

Character	M.ulcerans	M.marinum
Distribution	Tropics	Temperate zone
Clinical course	Chronic progressive ulcer	Self-limited ulcer
Bacilli in ulcer	Abundant	Scanty
Rate of growth	Slower; 4–8 weeks	Faster, 1–2 weeks
Growth at 25°C	–	+
Growth at 37°C	–	+
Culture film	Bacilli in cords	No cord formation
Pigment in light	–	+
Mouse footpad lesion	Edema, rarely ulcer	Marked inflammation—purulent ulcer

This is the only known instance of a toxin produced by any mycobacterium species.

M.marinum (Swimming pool granuloma): This is a natural pathogen of cold-blooded animals, causing tuberculosis in fish and amphibians. It may also occur as a saprophyte in fresh or salt water. Human infection originates from contaminated swimming pools or fish tanks. The lesion, beginning as a papule and breaking down to form an indolent ulcer, usually follows abrasions and therefore occurs on the prominences—elbows, knees, ankles, nose, fingers or toes.

Its distribution is in temperate areas in contrast to M.ulcerans, which has a tropical prevalence. Human infection may occur in epidemic form. The ulcers are self-limiting and undergo spontaneous healing.

Bacilli are scanty in smears from ulcers. M.haemophilum, first described in 1978, causes skin lesions. It requires hemin for growth. It grows at 32°C in 2–4 weeks but not at 37°C.

Ecology and epidemiology

As environmental bacteria are widely distributed in nature, infection with them is quite common, from soil, water and air. Person-to-person infection does not seem to occur. Infection is mainly asymptomatic, though it may result in sensitisation, causing weakly positive Mantoux reaction, due to cross-reaction with the tubercle bacillus protein. Sensitisation with environmental mycobacteria is believed to influence the protective response to BCG vaccination. This may be one of the reasons for the wide variation in protective effect of the vaccine observed in field trials in different parts of the world.

An inverse relation seems to exist between tuberculosis and disease caused by NTM. Where tuberculosis is endemic, opportunistic mycobacterial disease is rare. Where tuberculosis is rare, NTM disease is more common.

Common laboratory contaminants: Some opportunistic species may colonise tap water (for example, M.avium, M.kansasii, M.xenopi). These may cause problems in the laboratory where they may be mistaken for the tubercle bacilli in acid fast smears, and false positive reports are given.

Treatment

Most environmental mycobacteria are resistant to the usual anti-tuberculous drugs, though pulmonary disease caused by M.avium complex or M.kansasii may respond to prolonged treatment with rifampicin, isoniazid and ethambutol. Various combinations of drugs including rifabutin, clofazimine, quinolones, newer macrolides and others are used in treatment, with a selection of drugs based on sensitivity studies, where feasible.

RECAP

- Over 80 species of non-tuberculous mycobacteria (NTM) are found worldwide in soil and in animals.
- The Runyon classification divides them into:
  - Photochromogens; *Mycobacterium kansasii* and *Mycobacterium marinum*
  - Scotochromogens; *Mycobacterium scrofulaceum* and *Mycobacterium gordonae*
  - Non-chromogens; *Mycobacterium avium, Mycobacterium intracellulare, Mycobacterium xenopi* and *Mycobacterium ulcerans*
  - Rapid growers; *Mycobacterium fortuitum* and *Mycobacterium chelonae* (*M.chelonei*)
- NTM are being increasingly implicated in various human infections including:
  - Lung infections, which manifest as tuberculosis-like disease (with possible dissemination in patients with AIDS)
  - Skin infections (Buruli ulcer, swimming pool granuloma, injection abscess), especially in already diseased tissue or immunocompromised individuals
  - Lymphadenopathy, especially of cervical nodes in children

- Diagnosis of infection due to NTM is established by:
  - Isolation of acid fast (usually non–alcohol fast) bacilli from sputum or skin specimens
  - Characterisation of isolates by growth rate and pigment formation in light (photochromogen), dark (scotochromogen) or no pigment at all (non-photochromogen)
- Infected individuals need to be treated with multiple anti-mycobacterial drugs (they frequently tend to be resistant to the first-line, anti-mycobacterial drugs). Azithromycin or other macrolides need to be given prophylactically to individuals infected with HIV.

ESSAY

1. Describe the classification and epidemiology of NTM.

SHORT ANSWERS

1. Buruli ulcer
2. Swimming pool granuloma

SHORT NOTE

1. Opportunistic infections with NTM

40 Mycobacterium III: M.leprae

INTRODUCTION

Leprosy is a disease of antiquity, having been recognised since Vedic times in India and since Biblical times in the Middle East. It probably originated in the tropics and spread to the rest of the world. Leprosy has always been held in superstitious dread and the person suffering from leprosy considered 'unclean' and a social outcast. The lepra bacillus was first observed by Hansen in 1868. Though this was the first bacterial pathogen of humans to be described, it remains one of the least understood. This is because it has not been possible to grow the bacillus in culture media.

The *M.leprae* genome has been mapped and the genes for its major protein antigens cloned and sequenced.

MYCOBACTERIUM LEPRAE

Morphology

M.leprae is a straight or slightly curved rod, 1–8 × 0.2–0.5 μm in size, showing considerable morphological variation. Polar bodies and other intracellular elements may be present. Clubbed forms, lateral buds or branching may be observed.

It is Gram positive and stains more readily than the tubercle bacillus. It is acid fast, but less so than the tubercle bacillus. Hence 5% sulphuric acid instead of 20% is used for decolourisation after staining with carbol fuchsin. It is the practice to differentiate between live and dead bacilli in stained smears, assuming without conclusive proof that the former appear solid and uniformly stained, while the latter are fragmented and granular. The percentage of uniformly stained bacilli in tissues (morphological index) provides a method of assessing the progress of patients on chemotherapy and is more meaningful than the old criterion of bacteriological index (the number of bacilli in tissues).

The bacilli are seen singly and in groups, intracellularly or lying free outside the cells. They frequently appear as agglomerates, the bacilli being bound together by a lipid-like substance, the glia. These masses are known as '**globi**'. The parallel rows of bacilli in the globi present a '**cigar bundle**' appearance. In tissue sections, the clumps of bacilli resemble cigarette ends. The globi appear in Virchow's '**lepra cells**' or '**foamy cells**' which are large undifferentiated histiocytes (Fig. 40.1).

Cultivation

It has not been possible thus far to cultivate lepra bacilli either in bacteriological media or in tissue culture.

Generation time: In animal experiments, the generation time of the lepra bacillus has been found to be exceptionally long, 12–13 days on the average but may vary from 8 to 42 days, in comparison with about 14 hours in the case of the tubercle bacillus and about 20 minutes in the case of coliform bacilli.

Methods of cultivation:
- **Foot pad of mice**: Shepard (1960) discovered that lepra bacilli could multiply in the footpads of mice

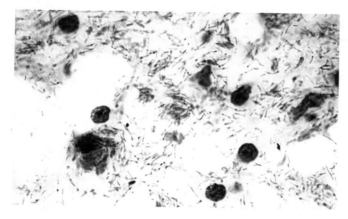

Fig. 40.1 *M.leprae* acid fast pink bacilli with typical 'globi' arrangement

kept at a low temperature (20°C). This has become the standard procedure for experimental work with the bacillus. Following intradermal inoculation into the footpads of mice, a granuloma develops at the site in 1–6 months. If cell-mediated immunity is suppressed by thymectomy or the administration of an antilymphocyte serum, generalised infection is produced, simulating lepromatous leprosy.

- The **nine-banded armadillo** (*Dasypus novemcinctus*) is highly susceptible to infection with the lepra bacilli. Following inoculation into armadillos, generalised infection occurs with extensive multiplication of the bacilli and the production of lesions typical of lepromatous leprosy. Some wild armadilloes in captivity have been observed to be naturally infected with a mycobacterium resembling the lepra bacillus. 'Natural disease' has also been identified in chimpanzees and mangabey monkeys from West Africa but it is not known whether they have any relevance to human infection.

- **Adaptation in artificial culture media:** One of the best known of such reports came from the Indian Cancer Research Centre, Bombay, (1962) where an acid fast bacillus was isolated from leprosy patients using human fetal spinal ganglion cell culture. This ICRC bacillus has been adapted for growth on Lowenstein–Jensen medium. Its relation to the lepra bacillus is uncertain.

Resistance

Lepra bacilli have been found to remain viable in a warm humid environment for 9–16 days and in moist soil for 46 days. They survive exposure to direct sunlight for two hours and ultraviolet light for 30 minutes.

LEPROSY

Leprosy is a chronic granulomatous disease of humans primarily involving the skin, peripheral nerves and nasal mucosa but capable of affecting any tissue or organ. The disease may be classified into four types: **lepromatous, tuberculoid, dimorphous** and **indeterminate** (Madrid classification, 1953). The type of disease is a reflection of the immune status of the host. It is therefore not permanent and varies with chemotherapy and alterations in host resistance. Bacilli isolated from different types of leprosy do not differ in virulence or other properties.

The two extreme or 'polar' forms of the disease are the lepromatous and tuberculoid types.

- The **lepromatous** type is seen where host resistance is low. The bacilli are seen in large numbers or as

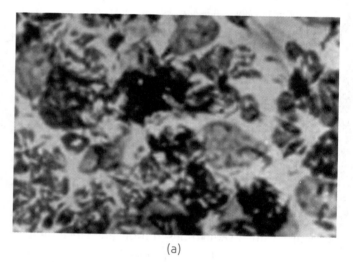

(a)

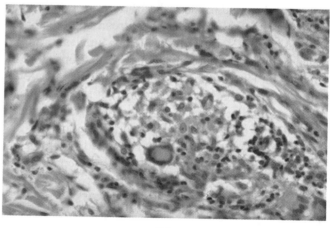

(b)

Fig. 40.2 (a) Lepromatous leprosy (with abundant bacilli); (b) Tuberculoid leprosy (with scanty bacilli)

globi inside lepra cells or extracellularly. This is known as 'multibacillary disease' (Fig. 40.2a). Superficial nodular lesions (lepromata) develop which consist of granulation tissue containing a dense collection of vacuolated cells in different stages of development from mononuclear cells to lepra cells. The nodules ulcerate, become secondarily infected and cause distortion and mutilation. Bacilli invade the mucosa of the nose, mouth and upper respiratory tract and are shed in large numbers in nasal and oral secretions. The reticuloendothelial system, eyes, testes, kidneys and bones are also involved. Bacillemia is common. The lepromatous type is more infective than the other types. Prognosis is poor. Cell-mediated immunity is deficient and the lepromin test is negative in lepromatous leprosy. On the other hand, there is an exaggerated and broad humoral immune response. Antibodies in high titres are seen against mycobacterial as well as several other antigens. Autoantibodies are common. Most cases show biological false positive reaction in standard serological tests for syphilis.

- **Tuberculoid leprosy** is seen in patients with a high degree of resistance. The skin lesions are few and sharply demarcated, consisting of macular anesthetic patches. Neural involvement occurs early and may be pronounced, leading to deformities, particularly in the hands and feet. Bacilli are scanty in the lesions and infectivity is minimal (Fig. 40.2b). This is known as 'paucibacillary disease'. Cell-mediated immunity is adequate and the lepromin test is positive. Anti-mycobacterial and autoimmune antibodies are rare. Prognosis is good.

- The term **borderline** or **dimorphous** type refers to lesions possessing characteristics of both tuberculoid and lepromatous types. It may shift to the lepromatous or tuberculoid part of the spectrum depending on chemotherapy or alterations in host resistance (Table 40.1).

- The **indeterminate** type is the early unstable tissue reaction which is not characteristic of either the lepromatous or the tuberculoid type. In many persons, the indeterminate lesions undergo spontaneous healing. In others, the lesions may progress to the tuberculoid or lepromatous types. The Indian classification of leprosy has an additional type, the **pure neuritic** type, which is bacteriologically negative and shows neural involvement without any skin lesion.

Classification

Ridely and **Jopling** (1966) have introduced a scale for classifying the spectrum of leprosy into five groups: tuberculoid (TT), borderline tuberculoid (BT), borderline (BB), borderline lepromatous (BL) and lepromatous (LL).

Epidemiology

Leprosy is an exclusively human disease and the only source of infection is the patient. The exact mode of infection is not clear. Very large numbers of bacilli are shed in nasal secretions. It is recorded that a patient with untreated lepromatic leprosy may discharge up to 8×10^8 bacilli in one nose blow. The mode of entry may be through the respiratory tract or through the skin. Asymptomatic infection appears to be quite common in endemic areas and these have an important role in transmission.

Leprosy is not highly communicable. The disease develops in only about 5 per cent of spouses living with leprosy patients. However, contacts of patients show a high rate of sensitisation to *M.leprae* by lymphocyte transformation tests. The incubation period is very long and averages 2–5 years. It has been estimated to vary from a few months to as long as 30 years. It is generally held that intimate and prolonged contact is necessary for infection to take place. The disease is more likely if contact occurs during childhood.

Once worldwide in distribution, leprosy is now confined mainly, but not exclusively, to the underdeveloped areas of the tropics and the southern hemisphere. India has the maximum prevalence, with

Table 40.1 *Characterisation of the different types of leprosy*

	Tuberculoid	Borderline	Lepromatous
Lepra bacilli in tissues	±	+	+++
Lepromin test	++	±	−
Mycobacterial antibodies	±	+	+++
Lymphocytic infiltration of lesions	+++	+	−
Plasma cells in lymphoid tissue	+	+	+++

about a third of the global total. Leprosy is present in all states and territories of India, but with marked regional variations—Orissa and Bihar having the highest prevalence (> 5 per 1000 population) and Haryana the least (< 0.1 per 1000).

Immunity

A high degree of **innate immunity** against lepra bacilli seems to exist in human beings so that only a minority of those infected develop clinical disease. Infection with the lepra bacilli induces both humoral and cellular immune response. Humoral antibodies do not have a deleterious effect on the bacilli, while cellular immune mechanisms are capable of destroying them. The type of leprosy in an individual is determined by the status of cell-mediated immunity in that person. When it is adequate, the lesions are of the tuberculoid type.

When **cell-mediated immunity** is deficient, the lepromatous type of disease develops. Delayed hypersensitivity to the lepra bacillus protein is absent.

The deficiency in cell-mediated immunity is specific to the lepra bacillus antigens. Lepromatous patients are not more susceptible to viruses, parasites and other pathogens against which CMI is important. Tuberculin reactivity may be suppressed in untreated lepromatous patients but it becomes positive following treatment, unlike the lepromin response which remains negative—lepromatous patients have large numbers of CD8+ (suppressor) lymphocytes in circulation, which can be specifically activated by the lepra bacillus antigens.

The lymphocytes present in skin granulomas are almost exclusively CD8+ cells, in contrast to tuberculoid lesions which contain predominantly CD4+ cells. In lepromatous leprosy, there is extensive polyclonal B cell activation with large amounts of antibodies being produced, both anti-mycobacterial and autoimmune. The albumin:globulin ratio is reversed. The anti-mycobacterial antibodies are not beneficial. On the other hand, they may have an enhancing effect.

Genetic predisposition: There is evidence of genetic effect in the pattern of response to the lepra bacillus infection. HLA-DR2 is seen preponderantly in persons with the tuberculoid type of reaction, while HLA-MTI and HLA-DQ1are associated with lepromatous disease.

Lepra reactions: Though leprosy is a chronic disease, its course may be interspersed with acute exacerbations which are of an allergic nature. Two types of such reactions occur.

- **Type 1**, the 'reversal reaction' or the **lepra reaction,** is seen mostly in borderline leprosy, occurring spontaneously or more often during chemotherapy. It is a cell-mediated immune reaction, with an influx of lymphocytes into lesions, and a shift to tuberculoid morphology. The lesions develop erythema and swelling, along with pain and tenderness. A similar clinical picture is seen in the 'downgrading reaction' which occurs usually in untreated or pregnant patients. Here, biopsy of the lesions shows a shift to the lepromatous pattern, reflecting a decrease of CMI.
- **Type 2** reaction or **erythema nodosum leprosum** (ENL) occurs in the LL and BL types, usually a few months after institution of chemotherapy. Crops of tender, inflamed subcutaneous nodules appear, with fever, lymphadenopathy and arthralgia. This is an Arthus type response to antigens released from dead lepra cells and is characterised by neutrophil infiltration and IgG and complement deposition in the lesions.

Lepromin test: Till recently, the only method for studying immunity in leprosy was a skin test for delayed hypersensitivity—the lepromin test first described by Mitsuda in 1919. Standard lepromins are prepared from armadillo-derived lepra bacilli (lepromin-A), replacing earlier crude antigens, which are used for this test.

- **Early reaction:** The first is the early reaction of **Fernandez**, which consists of erythema and induration developing in 24–48 hours and usually remaining for 3–5 days. This is analogous to the tuberculin reaction. This is usually poorly defined and carries little significance.
- **Late reaction:** The second and more meaningful is the late reaction of **Mitsuda**, starting in 1–2 weeks, reaching a peak in four weeks and gradually subsiding in the next few weeks. The reaction consists of an indurated skin nodule, which may ulcerate. Histologically, there is infiltration with lymphocytes, epithelioid cells and giant cells. The Mitsuda late reaction does not indicate pre-existing DTH but is a measure of the CMI induced by the injected lepromin itself. It thus distinguishes between persons who can mount a CMI response against the lepra bacillus antigens and those who cannot.

Applied importance: The lepromin test is not used to diagnose leprosy, nor does it indicate prior contact with the lepra bacillus. Healthy persons in non-endemic areas with no chance of contact with the bacillus may give a positive lepromin test. The test is used for the following purposes:

- To **classify** the lesions of leprosy patients. The lepromin test is positive in tuberculoid, negative in lepromatous and variable in dimorphous and indeterminate types of disease.
- To assess the **prognosis** and response to treatment. A positive reaction indicates good prognosis and a negative one bad prognosis. Conversion to lepromin positivity during treatment is evidence of improvement.
- To assess the **resistance** of individuals to leprosy. It is desirable to recruit only lepromin-positive persons for work in leprosaria as lepromin-negative persons are more prone to develop the disease.
- To verify the **identity** of candidate lepra bacilli. Cultivable acid fast bacilli diagnosised to be lepra bacilli should give matching results when tested in parallel with standard lepromin.

Laboratory diagnosis

Bacteriological diagnosis is easy in the lepromatous but may be difficult in the tuberculoid cases. For routine examination, specimens are collected from the nasal mucosa, skin lesions and ear lobules.

1. Specimen:

Nasal smear: A blunt, narrow scalpel is introduced into the nose and the internal septum scraped sufficiently to remove a piece of mucous membrane, which is transferred to a slide and teased out into a uniform smear.

Skin smear: Samples from the skin should be obtained from the edges of the lesion rather than from the centre.

Slit skin smear: The skin over the earlobe is pinched up tight to minimise bleeding and a cut about 5 mm long made with a scalpel, deep enough to get into the infiltrated layers. After wiping off blood or lymph that may have exuded, the scalpel blade is turned transversely to scrape the sides and bottom of the cut so as to obtain a little tissue pulp which is smeared uniformly on a slide. About 5–6 different areas of the skin should be sampled, including the skin over the buttocks, forehead, chin, cheek and ears.

Nerve biopsy: Sample is collected from thickened nerves and submitted for histopathological examination.

2. Microscopy:
Diagnosis consists of demonstration of acid fast bacilli in the lesions. The smears are stained by the **Ziehl–Neelsen technique** using 5% instead of 20% sulphuric acid for decolourisation. Biopsy of the

nodular lesions and thickened nerves, and lymph node puncture may be necessary in some cases.

The smears are graded, based on the number of bacilli as follows:

1–10 bacilli in 100 fields	= 1+
1–10 bacilli in 10 fields	= 2+
1–10 bacilli per field	= 3+
10–100 bacilli per field	= 4+
100–1000 bacilli per field	= 5+
More than 1000 bacilli, clumps and globi in every field	= 6+

The **bacteriological (bacterial) index (BI)** is calculated by totalling the number of pluses (+s) scored in all the smears and divided by the number of smears. Thus, if eight smears examined have a total of sixteen pluses, the BI will be 2. For calculating BI, a minimum of four skin lesions, a nasal swab and both the ear lobes have to be examined.

The **morphological index (MI)** is expressed as the percentage of solid fragmented granular bacilli (SFGB) or uniformly stained bacilli out of the total number of bacilli counted.

Microscopic demonstration of lepra bacilli and histology remain the most useful diagnostic procedures.

3. Culture:

Mouse foot pad inoculation has been reported to be more sensitive than skin slit smears for the detection of lepra bacilli in tissues. But this is unsuitable for routine diagnosis and feasible only for drug potency or resistance testing and research studies.

Armadillo: The nine-banded armadillo (*Dasypus novemcinctus*) is highly susceptible to infection with *M. leprae*.

4. Serology:
Detection of antibody against *M.leprae* phenolic glycolipid antigen has been claimed to be a specific diagnostic test. Their role has not yet been accepted for diagnosis.

5. Molecular methods:
Attempts to develop molecular diagnostic methods are in progress.

Treatment

Dapsone was the first effective chemotherapeutic agent against leprosy. Its use as a monotherapy for several years led to the development of resistant strains of lepra bacilli. In view of this, multiple drug therapy (MDT) is now recommended in leprosy, as in tuberculosis. The current recommendation for patients with paucibacillary lesions (I, TT, BT) is the concurrent administration of rifampicin 600 mg once a month and dapsone 100 mg daily for six months. For multibacillary lesions (BB, BL, LL), the recommendation is rifampicin 600 mg once a month, dapsone 100 mg daily and clofazimine 50 mg daily for two years or until skin smears are negative. Ethionamide or prothionamide may be added to this regimen or substituted for clofazimine. A minimum follow-up of four years for paucibacillary and eight years for multibacillary cases would be necessary to detect any relapse.

An immunotherapeutic **vaccine** (Mycobacterium W) developed at the National Institute of Immunology, New Delhi is claimed to enhance the effect of MDT.

Prophylaxis

- Case finding and adequate therapy have been the methods employed for prophylaxis.
- Long-term chemoprophylaxis has given encouraging results in child contacts of infectious cases in India and the Philippines.

- **BCG vaccine:** No specific vaccine is available. Since there is some degree of antigenic relationship between the lepra and tubercle bacilli, field trials with different leprosy vaccines (BCG + killed lepra bacilli; ICRC bacillus) were conducted but without conclusive evidence.

MYCOBACTERIUM LEPRAE MURIUM

This is the causative agent of rat leprosy. It was first described by Stefansky in 1901 at Odessa. It has been subsequently reported from several countries. Rat leprosy is characterised by subcutaneous indurations, lymphadenopathy, emaciation, ulcerations and loss of hair. Acid fast bacilli resembling lepra bacilli are found in the lesions in large numbers. However, the disease differs from human leprosy in that the nerves are not affected. *M.leprae* and *M.leprae murium* are not closely related by DNA studies.

RECAP

- *Mycobacterium leprae,* an obligate, intracellular organism, causes leprosy. Aerosol droplets, and direct contact with infected skin contribute to transmission.
- Leprosy manifests as a spectrum of diseases. The least severe form is tuberculoid tuberculoid (TT) and the most severe form is lepromatous lepromatous (LL). In between are borderline forms (tuberculoid and lepromatous).
- The severity of leprosy is inversely related to the status of cell-mediated immunity. Delayed type hypersensitivity response to *M.leprae* protein antigens (lepromin) are good in TT but absent in LL.
- Diagnosis can be established by clinical signs and microscopy. Acid fast staining of tissue reveals typical long, thin bacilli or globule clusters. The organism grows in the foot pads of mice (especially for antibiotic sensitivity testing) and the nine-banded armadillo, but not in cell free or tissue culture systems.
- Aggressive multidrug antibiotic therapy has significantly reduced the number of cases worldwide.

SHORT NOTES

1. Lepra reaction
2. Lepromin test
3. Systemic lupus erythematosus (SLE)
4. Methods to culture *Mycobacterium leprae*
5. MDT in leprosy
6. Differences between lepromatous leprosy and tuberculoid

41 Spirochetes

INTRODUCTION

Elongated, motile, flexible bacteria twisted spirally along the long axis are termed **spirochetes** (from *speira*, meaning coil and *chaite*, meaning hair). They are structurally more complex than other bacteria. A characteristic feature is the presence of varying numbers of **endoflagella** (axial filament), which are polar flagella wound along the helical protoplasmic cylinder, and situated between the outer membrane and cell wall.

Spirochetes vary widely in size, some being as long as 500 µm and others as short as 5 µm. They are Gram negative. Many are free-living saprophytes, while some are obligate parasites. They may be aerobic, anaerobic or facultative. Reproduction is by transverse fission.

Spirochetes belong to the order Spirochetales, comprising two families (Fig. 41.1):
- Spirochetaceae containing the genera *Spirochaeta*, *Cristispira*, *Treponema* and *Borrelia*
- Leptospiraceae containing the genus *Leptospira*

Human pathogens are found in the genera *Treponema*, *Borrelia* and *Leptospira*. Members of the genus *Spirochaeta* are saprophytes found in water and sewage, while *Cristispira* are found in molluses.

TREPONEMA

Treponemes *(trepos,* meaning to turn, and *nema,* meaning thread) are relatively short, slender spirochetes with fine spirals and pointed or rounded ends. Some of them are pathogenic, while others occur as commensals in the mouth, intestines and genitalia. Pathogenic treponemes have not been successfully cultivated in cell free media, though commensals may be grown in artificial media.

Treponemes cause the following diseases in humans:
- Venereal syphilis (*T.pallidum*)
- Endemic syphilis (*T.pallidum* [*T.endemicum*])

- Yaws (*T.pertenue*)
- Pinta (*T.carateum*)

They are almost identical in their morphology, antigenic structure and other features, though there are differences in the clinical features and natural history of the diseases they produce. It has been suggested that the pathogenic treponemes represent only evolutionary variations of a single species and that the diseases caused by them, though different clinically and epidemiologically, should be considered as part of a continuous spectrum of **treponematoses**. Accordingly, the species *T.pallidum* is now considered to include three subspecies—*pallidum* causing venereal syphilis, *endemicum* causing endemic syphilis and *pertenue* causing yaws.

TREPONEMA PALLIDUM

> **Clinical Case 1**   A 20-year-old male who works as a truck driver presented to the Skin and Venereal Disease clinic with a genital ulcer which was painless for the previous 10 days. He had had unprotected sexual contact with a commercial sex worker about two weeks previously. On examination, the ulcer was found to be circumscribed, indurated and partially healed. The inguinal lymph nodes were enlarged. A diagnosis of syphilis was made and the serum sent for a VDRL test. This was reactive at 1:64 dilution. The patient was treated with penicillin.

Treponema pallidum, the causative agent of syphilis, was discovered by Schaudinn and Hoffmann (1905) in the chancres and inguinal lymph nodes of syphilitic patients. The name *pallidum* refers to its pale staining.

Morphology

It is a thin, delicate spirochete with tapering ends, about 10 μm long (range 4–14 μm) and 0.1–0.2 μm wide. It has about ten regular spirals, which are sharp and angular, at regular intervals of about 1 μm (Fig. 41.1). It is actively motile, exhibiting rotation around the long axis, backward and forward movements, and flexion of the whole body. During motion, secondary curves appear and disappear in succession but the primary spirals are unchanged.

T.pallidum cannot be seen under the light microscope in wet films but can be discerned by negative staining with Indian ink. Its morphology and motility can be seen under the dark ground or phase contrast microscope. It does not take ordinary bacterial stains but stains a light rose-red with prolonged Giemsa

staining. It can be stained by **silver impregnation** methods. **Fontana's method** is useful for staining films and **Levaditi's method** for tissue sections.

Ultrastructurally, the cytoplasm of *T.pallidum* is surrounded by a trilaminar cytoplasmic membrane, enclosed by a cell wall containing peptidoglycan which gives the cell rigidity and shape. External to this is the lipid-rich outer membrane layer. Originating from each end of the cell, three or four endoflagella wind round the axis of the cell in the space between the cell wall and outer membrane layer, to interdigitate at its centre. Unlike the flagella of other bacteria, these endoflagella do not protrude outside, but remain within the outer membrane layer.

Saprophytic spirochetes are generally coarser in appearance, lack the uniform spirals with regular spacing, and show lashing motility.

Cultivation

Pathogenic treponemes do not grow in artificial culture media.

- The cultivable strains are the non-pathogenic treponemes, showing morphological and antigenic similarities with *T.pallidum*. The best known of these is the **Reiter strain**, which has been widely used as the antigen in group-specific treponemal tests for the diagnosis of syphilis. The Reiter treponeme grows well in thioglycollate medium containing serum. It is now classified as *T.phagedenis*.

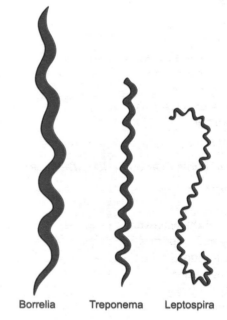

Borrelia   Treponema   Leptospira

Fig. 41.1 Schematic representation of comparative morphology of different spirochetes

- Virulent *T.pallidum* strains cannot be cultivated in artificial media but have been maintained for many decades by serial testicular passage in rabbits. One such strain (**Nichol's strain**), isolated from the brain of a fatal case of general paralysis of the insane in 1912, is still being propagated and used for diagnostic and research purposes.

Resistance

T.pallidum is very delicate, being readily inactivated by drying or by heat (41–42°C in one hour). Hence fomites are of little importance in the transmission of infection. It is killed in 1–3 days at 0–4°C, so transfusion syphilis can be prevented by storing blood for at least four days in the refrigerator before transfusion. Stored frozen at –70°C in 10% glycerol, or in liquid nitrogen (–130°C), it remains viable for 10–15 years. It is inactivated by contact with oxygen, distilled water, soap, arsenicals, mercurials, bismuth, common antiseptic agents and antibiotics.

Antigenic structure

The antigenic structure of *T.pallidum* is complex. Treponemal infection induces at least three types of antibodies:

- The first is the **reagin antibody** that reacts in the standard or non-specific tests for syphilis, such as Wassermann, Kahn and VDRL, in which a hapten extracted from beef heart is used as the antigen. This lipid hapten is known as **cardiolipin** and is chemically a diphosphatidyl glycerol. This lipid has been detected in *T.pallidum* but it is not known whether the reagin antibody is induced by the cardiolipin that is present in the spirochete or that released from damaged host tissues.
- The second is a **group antigen** found in *T.pallidum* as well as in non-pathogenic cultivable treponemes like the Reiter treponeme.
- The third antigen, probably polysaccharide in nature, is **species specific**. The antibody to this antigen is demonstrated by specific *T.pallidum* tests which are positive only with the sera of patients infected with pathogenic treponemes.

Pathogenicity

Natural infection with *T.pallidum* occurs only in human beings. Experimentally, monkeys may be infected. A disease resembling syphilis can be produced experimentally in chimpanzees, with typical lesions of primary and secondary syphilis. Rabbits can be infected by intradermal or intratesticular inoculation, the former giving rise to chancre and the latter to syphilomas. Serial passage in rabbits does not appear to reduce the virulence of the spirochete to human beings, as evidenced by several accidental infections in laboratory workers caused by the Nichol's strain. Hamsters are also susceptible.

SYPHILIS

Syphilis can be acquired by the venereal or non-venereal route or be congenital or acquired.

1. **Venereal syphilis** is acquired by sexual contact. The spirochete enters the body through minute abrasions on the mucosa or skin. Infectivity of a patient to the sexual partner is maximum during the first two years of the disease—the primary, secondary and early latent stages. After five years, the risk is considered minimal. The infective dose is small—as few as 60 treponemes are capable of infecting 50 per cent of human volunteers. It multiplies at the site of entry. Its generation time is 30–33 hours. Clinical disease sets in after an incubation period of about a month (range 10–90 days). The clinical manifestations fall into three stages: primary, secondary and tertiary.

   - The **primary lesion** in syphilis is the **chancre** at the site of entry of the spirochete (Fig. 41.2). In all but a few, the chancre is genital. Other common sites are the mouth and nipples. The chancre is a painless, relatively avascular, circumscribed, indurated, superficially ulcerated lesion. It is known as '**hard chancre**' to distinguish it from the non-indurated lesions of 'soft chancre' caused by *H.ducreyi*, and as Hunterian chancre named after John Hunter who produced the lesion on himself experimentally and described the evolution of the disease. The chancre is covered by a thick, glairy exudate rich in spirochetes. The regional lymph nodes are swollen, discrete, rubbery and non-tender. Even before the chancre appears, the spirochetes spread from the site of entry into the lymph and bloodstream, so the patient may be infectious during the late incubation period. The chancre invariably heals in about 10–40 days, even without treatment, leaving a thin scar. Persistent or multiple chancres may be seen in HIV-infected or other immunodeficient patients (*Case* 1).

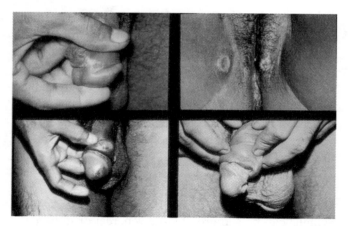

Fig. 41.2 Penile chancre of primary syphilis, yaws and pinta

- **Secondary syphilis** sets in 1–3 months after the primary lesion heals. During this interval, the patient is asymptomatic. The secondary lesions are due to widespread multiplication of the spirochetes and their dissemination through the blood. Roseolar or papular skin rashes, mucous patches in the oropharynx and condylomata at the mucocutaneous junctions are the characteristic lesions. Spirochetes are abundant in the lesions and consequently the patient is most infectious during the secondary stage. There may also be ophthalmic, osseous and meningeal involvement. Secondary lesions are highly variable in distribution, intensity and duration but they usually undergo spontaneous healing, in some instances taking as long as four or five years.
- After the secondary lesions disappear, there is a period of quiescence known as **latent syphilis**. Diagnosis during this period is possible only by serological tests. In many cases, this is followed by natural cure but in others, after several years, manifestations of tertiary syphilis appear. These consist of cardiovascular lesions including aneurysms, chronic granulomata (gummata) and meningovascular manifestations. Tertiary lesions contain few spirochetes and may represent manifestations of delayed hypersensitivity.

2. **Late tertiary** or quanternary syphilis in a few cases, a late tertiary stage may develop, presenting with neurological manifestations such as tabes dorsalis, or general paralysis of the insane may develop several decades after the initial infection.

   In syphilis acquired **non-venereally** (as occupationally in doctors or nurses), the natural evolution is as in venereal syphilis, except that the primary chancre is extragenital, usually on the fingers. In the rare instances where syphilis is transmitted by blood transfusion, the primary chancre does not occur.

3. In **congenital syphilis**, where infection is transmitted from mother to fetus transplacentally, the manifestations and course are different. Transplacental transmission can take place at any stage of pregnancy. A woman with early syphilis can infect her fetus much more commonly (75–95 per cent) than one with syphilis of over two years' duration (35 per cent). The lesions of congenital syphilis usually develop only after the fourth month of gestation, the time when fetal immune competence starts appearing. This suggests that the pathogenesis requires an immune response from the fetus. Congenital syphilis can be prevented if the mother is given adequate treatment before the fourth month of pregnancy. The obstetric history in an untreated syphilitic woman is typically one of abortions and stillbirths followed by live births of infants with stigmata of syphilis and finally of healthy infants.

Laboratory diagnosis

Laboratory diagnosis consists of demonstration of the spirochetes under the microscope and of antibodies in serum or CSF.

1. Specimen: Specimens should be collected with care as the lesions are highly infectious. The lesion is cleaned with gauze soaked in warm saline and the margins gently scraped so that the superficial epithelium is abraded. Gentle pressure is applied to the base of the lesion and the serum that exudes is collected, preventing admixture with blood. Serum is collected for serology. CSF can be collected for neurosyphilis.

2. Microscopy: Diagnosis by microscopy is applicable in the primary and secondary stages and in cases of congenital syphilis with superficial lesions. Wet films are prepared with the exudate and after applying thin coverslips, examined under the dark ground microscope. *T.pallidum* is identified by its slender spiral structure and slow movement. Differentiation from saprophytic spirochetes commonly present in the genital area can be done by morphology and motility.

- **Dark ground examination** is useful and has low sensitivity. A treponemal concentration of 10^4 per ml in the exudates is required for the test to be positive.

- **Direct fluorescent antibody test** for *T.pallidum* (DFA-TP) is a better and safer method for microscopic diagnosis. Smears of the exudate are fixed with acetone and sent to the laboratory, where the DFA-TP test is done using fluorescent tagged anti-*T.pallidum* antiserum. The use of a specific monoclonal antibody has made the test more reliable.
- **Silver impregnation** smears can be stained by methods. Fontana's method is useful for staining films and Levaditi's method for tissue sections.

3. Serological tests: These tests form the mainstay of laboratory diagnosis. A large number of tests have been described, of which only a few are now in use. Serological tests for syphilis may be classified as follows:

Reagin antibody tests: These tests use the lipoidal or cardiolipin antigens and are known as standard tests for syphilis (STS). (The antibody reacting with cardiolipin is known as reagin. This can be misleading, as the IgE antibody in atopy is also called reagin, though there is no connection between the two.)

The antigen is a purified lipid extract of beef heart (called cardiolipin), with added lecithin and cholesterol, as standardised by Pangborn (1945), and the test used is **VDRL (Venereal Disease Research Laboratory**, USPHS, New York, where the test was developed). The VDRL test is rapid and gives quantitative results. In this test, the inactivated serum (serum heated at 56°C for 30 minutes) is mixed with cardiolipin antigen on a special slide and rotated for four minutes. Cardiolipin remains as uniform crystals in normal serum but forms visible clumps on combining with the reagin antibody. The reaction is read under a low power microscope.

Antibody titre interpretation: By testing serial dilutions, the antibody titre can be determined. The results are reported qualitatively as 'reactive', 'weak by reactive' or 'not reactive'. For quantitative reporting, the reciprocal of the end point is given as the titre, for example 'reactive 4 dilution' or 'titre 4'.

The VDRL test can be used for testing CSF also, but not plasma. CSF need not be heated prior to the test.

A number of modifications to the VDRL test have been developed, of which **Rapid Plasma Reagin (RPR)** is the most popular. This test uses the VDRL antigen containing fine carbon particles, which make the result more clear-cut and evident to the naked eye. The RPR test can be done with unheated serum or plasma but is not suitable for testing CSF. Automated RPR test (ART) is available for large-scale testing.

Biological false positive (BFP) reactions: As the cardiolipin antigen is present both in *T.pallidum* and in mammalian tissues, reagin antibodies may be induced by treponemal or host tissue antigens. This accounts for the biological false positive (BFP) reactions, which constitute the major disadvantage of STS. BFP reactions are defined as positive reactions obtained in cardiolipin tests, within specific treponemal tests, in the absence of past or present treponemal infections—and not caused by technical faults. They represent non-treponemal cardiolipin antibody responses.

BFP reactions may occur in about one per cent of normal sera. BFP antibody is usually IgM, while reagin antibody in syphilis is mainly IgG. Clinically, BFP reactions may be classified as acute or chronic. Acute BFP reactions last only for a few weeks or months and are usually associated with acute infections, injuries or inflammatory conditions. Chronic BFP reactions persist for longer than six months and are typically seen in SLE and other collagen diseases. Leprosy, malaria, relapsing fever, infectious mononucleosis, hepatitis and tropical eosinophilia are examples of other conditions associated with BFP reactions.

The reagin antibody becomes detectable 7–10 days after the appearance of primary chancre (or 3–5 weeks after acquiring the infection). Sensitivity in the primary stage is 60–75 per cent, with the titres being low, up to eight. In the secondary stage, sensitivity is 100 per cent and titres range from 16 to 128 or more. The **prozone phenomenon** may be a problem in high titre sera and it is therefore essential to test sera in dilutions.

Another stage of syphilis in which such high titres are seen is congenital syphilis. After the secondary stage, titres diminish and about a third of patients with late syphilis are seronegative. The titres may rise in patients developing cardiovascular, neurological or gummatous lesions. In some cases of neurosyphilis, reagin tests may be negative with serum but positive with CSF. Reagin tests usually become negative 6–18 months after effective treatment of syphilis, depending on the stage at which treatment is given. However, if treatment is started late, the tests may remain positive in low titres.

Group-specific treponemal tests: To avoid BFP reactions, tests using cultivable treponemes as antigens were developed. These used the Reiter treponemes (originally believed to be an adapted strain of *T.pallidum*). The test most commonly employed in this group was the Reiter protein complement fixation (RPCF) test, using a lipopolysaccharide–protein complex antigen derived from the treponeme. Its sensitivity and specificity were lower than those of tests using *T.pallidum*. Though RPCF was generally free from BFP reactions, it still gave some false positive reactions. RPCF and other Reiter treponeme tests are now not in general use.

Specific *T.pallidum* tests: These tests use the virulent Nichol's strain of *T.pallidum* maintained by serial inoculation in rabbit testes.

- ● ***Treponema pallidum* immobilisation (TPI)** the first in this group is the test introduced in 1949. The test serum is incubated with complement and *T.pallidum* maintained in a complex medium anaerobically. If antibodies are present, the treponemes are immobilised, that is, rendered non-motile, when examined under dark ground illumination.

- ● In its time, TPI was the most specific test available for the diagnosis of syphilis and was considered the **gold standard** in syphilis serology. However, because of its extreme complexity, it was available only in a few laboratories. The TPI test has now been supplanted by others such as FTA-ABS and TPHA which are quite as specific and much simpler.

- ● **Fluorescent treponemal antibody (FTA)** test is an indirect immunofluorescence test using as antigen, smears prepared on slides with Nichol's strain of *T.pallidum*. The slides can be stored for several months in deep freeze. The currently used modification of the test is the FTA-absorption (FTA-ABS) test in which the test serum is preabsorbed with a sonicate of the Reiter treponemes (*sorbent*) to eliminate group-specific reactions. FTA-ABS is as specific as the TPI test and is now accepted as a standard reference test. However, as it can be done only in suitably equipped laboratories, it is not available for routine testing.

- ● ***T.pallidum* hemagglutination assay (TPHA)** uses tanned erythrocytes sensitised with a sonicated extract of *T.pallidum* as antigen. The procedure in use is a micro-hemagglutination test (MHA-TP), which is capable of being automated.

- ● The test sera for TPHA are absorbed with a diluent containing components of the Reiter treponeme, rabbit testis and sheep erythrocytes. Sera are screened at an initial dilution of 1:80 but titres of 5120 or more are common in the secondary stage. TPHA is just as specific as FTA-ABS and almost as sensitive, except in the primary stage. It is also much simpler and more economical. No special equipment is needed. Kits are available commercially. These advantages have made TPHA a standard confirmatory test. Table 41.1 shows the relative sensitivities of the serological tests in common use.

- ● **Enzyme immunoassays (EIA)** have been developed using *T.pallidum* antigens and are available commercially (Bio-Enza Bead test; Captia Syphilis-G test). A rapid agglutination test has been developed, using latex particles coated with three immunodominant proteins of *T.pallidum*, obtained by recombinant technology. It is claimed to be as specific as TPHA, and more sensitive.

Diagnostic utility of serological assays: The practice for serological screening for syphilis varies in different countries. In the UK, a combination of VDRL and TPHA tests is used. This is an efficient combination for the detection or exclusion of syphilis at all stages, except the early primary stage. A repeat test 1–3 months later will bring even this to light. In the USA, screening is by VDRL or RPR test alone. This may fail to detect about one per cent of secondary syphilis due to the prozone effect and about 30 per cent of latent or late syphilis.

Response to treatment: Quantitative tests are useful in monitoring the patient's response to treatment, indicating the stage of the disease and in detecting re-infection. **VDRL** or **RPR** is preferred because they usually become negative following treatment. If treatment is given very early, the serum may not become positive at all. Treatment in the primary stage leads to seroreversal in about four months; in the secondary and early latent stages, it takes 12–18 months; in later stages, it may take five years or more. In some cases, low titre reactivity may persist indefinitely in spite of effective treatment. Specific treponemal tests are of little value as indicators of clinical cure as they tend to remain positive in spite of treatment. TPHA titres may

Table 41.1 *Frequency of reactive serological tests in untreated syphilis (percentage)*

Stage	VDRL/RPR	FTA-ABS	TPHA
Primary	70–80	85–100	65–85
Secondary	100	100	100
Latent/late	60–70	95–100	95–100

fall rapidly following treatment in secondary syphilis but remain positive for life in low titres.

4. Diagnosis: TPHA and FTA-ABS are helpful in excluding or confirming the diagnosis of syphilis and for identifying BFP reactions. Though **false positive reactions** were believed to have been eliminated with the introduction of these specific tests, it is not truly so. Both TPHA and FTA-ABS can give false positive results, though very rarely. All serological tests for syphilis may be positive in non-venereal treponematoses, and some in a few other spirochetal infections as well. In Lyme disease, the VDRL test is negative, but FTA-ABS may be positive.

A **negative TPHA** virtually excludes the diagnosis of syphilis, past or present, except in the very early stages. In neurosyphilis, a negative CSF VDRL test may not be conclusive but a negative TPHA test eliminates the possibility of neurosyphilis. Detection of **specific IgM antibody** may be helpful in some situations. Being the initial type of antibody to appear, IgM is detectable by the second week of infection. IgM antibody production ceases soon after elimination of infection by treatment. Persistence of the antibody indicates continuing active disease and the need for treatment.

Diagnosis of congenital syphilis: As IgM does not cross the placenta, its presence in neonatal serum confirms congenital syphilis and helps differentiate it from seropositivity due to passively transferred maternal antibody (syphilotoxemia). Many techniques have been developed for the selective detection of IgM antibodies. These include modifications of the FTA-ABS, TPHA, EIA and VDRL tests, using whole sera or separated IgM fractions. When such tests are not available, parallel tests of maternal and neonatal sera may settle the diagnosis of congenital syphilis, in which the neonatal serum may show a higher titre of antibody than the maternal serum. Serial testing is also useful because the titre of passively transferred antibody decreases rapidly, the VDRL test becoming negative by three months.

Epidemiology

Venereal syphilis is worldwide in distribution. During the five centuries that it has been recorded and studied, the disease has undergone much variation in its natural history and clinical features. As originally described, it was a highly virulent disease with florid cutaneous manifestations. With the discovery of the dramatic therapeutic response to penicillin, it was hoped that it may even be possible to eradicate syphilis, as the disease has no extra human reservoir. However, not only has it not been possible to eliminate the disease but an increase has occurred in its incidence, due to the changing customs, habits and values in society.

HIV and syphilis: The advent of the AIDS pandemic has had an impact on syphilis. In most places, fear of AIDS and safer sex practices led to a fall in the incidence of syphilis and all STDs initially, but this trend did not continue everywhere. Concurrent infection with syphilis and HIV is common and may lead to earlier evolution of neurosyphilis.

Immunity

The immune mechanisms in syphilis are not adequately understood. Humoral immune response against the treponeme does not appear to be effective as the disease progresses even in the presence of a vigorous antibody response. Cell-mediated immunity may be more relevant. T lymphocytes and macrophages are predominant in early syphilitic lesions. Specifically sensitised Th1 cells secrete cytokines favouring the clearance of spirochetes by activated macrophages.

Re-infections do not appear to occur in a person already having active infection. Some degree of immunity to re-infection may occur in persons whose infection has been completely eliminated by treatment.

Prophylaxis

As transmission is by direct contact, it is possible to protect against syphilis by avoiding sexual contact with an infected individual. The use of physical barriers (such as condoms), antiseptics (potassium permanganate) or antibiotics may minimise the risk. The use of prophylactic penicillin carries the danger that it may suppress the primary lesion without eliminating the infection, so that recognition and treatment of the disease may become more difficult. No vaccine is available.

Treatment

Penicillin is uniformly effective in syphilis but it is necessary to give an adequate dose and maintain the drug level for a sufficiently long period to establish cure. A single injection of 2.4 million units of benzathine penicillin G is adequate in early cases. For late syphilis, this amount may be repeated weekly for three weeks. In patients allergic to penicillin, doxycycline may be used. Ceftriaxone is effective, particularly in neurosyphilis.

Penicillin treatment in syphilis sometimes induces the **Jarisch–Herxheimer reaction**, consisting of fever, malaise and exacerbation of symptoms. It is frequent, but harmless, in primary and secondary syphilis, and can be managed with bed rest and aspirin. It is rare in late syphilis but can be dangerous in some cases of gummatous, cardiovascular or neurosyphilis. It is believed to be due to the liberation of toxic products like tumour necrosis factors from the massive destruction of treponemes or due to hypersensitivity.

NON-VENEREAL TREPONEMATOSES

Non-venereal treponemal diseases occur in endemic foci in several parts of the world, in communities with poor standards of hygiene. The diseases have been given different names in different regions and vary somewhat in clinical manifestations, but the treponemes responsible are virtually indistinguishable from *T.pallidum* and are now considered as its subspecies. Infection is usually transmitted by direct body-to-body contact.

Three distinct forms of non-venereal treponematoses are recognised—endemic syphilis, yaws and pinta.

Endemic syphilis

Syphilis, transmitted non-venereally, was endemic in several foci. The causative agent is the *T.pallidum* subspecies *endemicum*.

With recognition of such foci and mass treatment with penicillin under the auspices of the WHO, endemic syphilis has become very rare. It has also been reported from India.

The disease is common in young children. The primary chancre is not usually seen, except sometimes on the nipples of mothers infected by their children. The disease is usually seen with manifestations of secondary syphilis, such as mucous patches and skin eruptions. The disease progresses to tertiary lesions, particularly gummatous lesions. Cardiovascular and neurological involvement is rare. Congenital syphilis is also not found. Laboratory diagnosis and treatment are as for venereal syphilis.

Yaws

Yaws, also known as frambesia, pian, parangi and by many other synonyms, is endemic in the tropical areas of Africa, Asia and America. Yaws eradication campaigns by mass penicillin injection in endemic areas led to the virtual eradication of the disease. However, it

has subsequently reappeared in some areas. In India, cases have been identified in Andhra Pradesh, Orissa and Madhya Pradesh.

The causative agent is *T.pallidum* subspecies *pertenue* (*T.pertenue*) which is morphologically and antigenically indistinguishable from *T.pallidum*. The primary lesion (mother yaw) is an extragenital papule which enlarges and breaks down to form an ulcerating granuloma. As in syphilis, secondary and tertiary manifestations follow, but cardiovascular or neurological involvement is rare. Destructive gummatous lesions of the bones are common.

Infection is by direct contact. Flies may act as mechanical vectors. The small fly, *Hippolates pallippes,* has been found feeding on open sores but its epidemiological importance is not known. Laboratory diagnosis and treatment are as for syphilis. There appears to be some cross-immunity between yaws and syphilis, in that venereal syphilis is rare in communities where yaws is endemic.

Pinta

Pinta (carate, mal del pinto) is endemic in Central and South America and the neighbouring islands. The primary lesion is an extragenital papule, which does not ulcerate but develops into a lichenoid or psoriaform patch. Secondary skin lesions are characterised by hyperpigmentation or hypopigmentation. Tissues other than skin are seldom affected.

The causative agent is *T.carateum*. It is very closely related to *T.pallidum* but is not antigenically identical, so cross-immunity between pinta and syphilis is only partial.

NON-PATHOGENIC TREPONEMES

Several commensal treponemes occur on the buccal and genital mucosa and may cause confusion in the diagnosis of syphilis by dark field examination. They are a heterogeneous group and have not been adequately characterised. Best known among them is the oral spirochete, *T.denticole,* which can be readily cultivated. Treponemes also occur on the surface of gastric and colonic epithelium in human beings and animals.

BORRELIA

Borreliae are large, motile, refractile spirochetes with irregular, wide, open coils. They are usually 5–30 μm long and 0.3–0.7 µm wide. They are readily stained by ordinary methods and are Gram negative. Several species of *Borrelia* occur as commensals on the buccal and genital mucosa. Borreliae of medical importance are *B.recurrentis* causing relapsing fever, *B.vincentii* causing Vincent's angina (Fig. 41.3) and *B.burgdorferi* causing Lyme disease.

RELAPSING FEVER

This has been known since the time of Hippocrates and has occurred in epidemic, endemic or sporadic form throughout the world. RF is an arthropod-borne infection, two types of which occur: louse-borne and tick-borne. The borreliae causing them are indistinguishable in morphology and many other features but differ in their arthropod hosts.

- **Epidemic or louse-borne RF** the causative agent is *B.recurrentis*, first observed by Obermeier (1873) in the blood of patients during an epidemic in Berlin. It is an exclusive human pathogen, being transmitted from person to person through body lice (*Pediculus humanus corporis*). No extra human reservoir is known.
- **Endemic or tick-borne RF** Borreliae causing endemic RF normally live in their natural hosts— rodents or other mammals on which the vector ticks feed. Human infection is only an accidental event. Borrelliae have been assigned to various species based on the ticks that carry them; for example, *B.duttonii*, *B.hermsii*, *B.parkeri*, etc. They are generally confined to certain geographic areas.

DNA homology studies indicate that all of them may belong to a single species, with separate host adaptation. The descriptions that follow apply to all of them, unless stated otherwise.

Morphology

B.recurrentis is an irregular spiral with one or both ends pointed. It is 8–20 µm long and 0.2–0.4 µm wide. It possesses 5–10 loose spiral coils at intervals of about 2 µm. It stains well with Giemsa and bacterial stains and is Gram negative.

Cultural characteristics

Borrelia are microaerophilic. Optimum temperature for growth is 28–30°C. Cultivation is difficult but has been successful in complex media containing serous fluids.

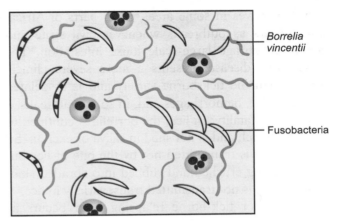

Fig. 41.3 Smear from Vincent's angina

Borrelia vincentii

Fusobacteria

Growth occurs on the chorioallantoic membrane of chick embryos. For primary isolation, the best method is to inoculate mice or rats intraperitoneally. When using experimental animals, great care has to be taken to ensure that the animals are free from pre-existing borreliosis.

Antigenic properties

Borrelia readily undergoes antigenic variations in vivo and this is believed to be the reason for the occurrence of relapses in the disease. Antigenic variations have been shown to be caused by DNA rearrangements in linear plasmids present in borrelia. Ultimate recovery after a number of relapses may be due to the development of immunity to all the antigenic variants.

Pathogenicity

After an incubation period of 2–10 days, relapsing fever sets in as fever of sudden onset. During this period, borreliae are abundant in the patient's blood. The fever subsides in 3–5 days. After an afebrile period of 4–10 days during which borreliae are not demonstrable in blood, another bout of fever sets in. The borreliae reappear in blood during the relapses of fever. The disease ultimately subsides after 3–10 relapses.

Epidemiology

Epidemic or louse-borne relapsing fever tends to occur as epidemics whenever poverty, overcrowding and lack of personal hygiene encourage louse infestation. It used to be very common during wars and in the jails of former days but with improvements in hygiene and the discovery of insecticides, it has now become rare. It survives in some areas, as in parts of Africa, and appears as outbreaks whenever civil strife and famine encourage large-scale louse infestation. The louse-borne disease presents a more severe clinical picture than the tick-borne variety and is associated with jaundice, hemorrhages and, in some outbreaks, a high rate of fatality. In lice, the borrelia is confined to the hemolymph and is not shed in saliva or excreta. So the infection is transmitted not by the bite of lice but by their being crushed and rubbed into abraded skin. *B.recurrentis* is not transmitted transovarially in lice.

Endemic or tick-borne relapsing fever occurs as sporadic cases in endemic areas. It is a 'place disease' and is frequently associated with certain dwellings or other locations inhabited by infected ticks. The disease is milder but relapses are more frequent than in louse-borne fever. The borrelia persists in the body of infected ticks throughout their life and is also transmitted transovarially so that the ticks act as reservoirs as well as vectors. The borrelia invades all parts of the body of the tick and is shed in its saliva and feces. So the infection is transmitted to humans through the bite of ticks or their discharges. Several species of soft ticks belonging to the genus *Ornithodorus* act as vectors, different species being responsible in different regions.

In India, the vector species are *O.tholozoni*, *O.crossi*, *O.lahorensis* and the fowl tick, *Argas persicus*. These soft ticks can live for ten years or more with only an occasional blood meal. They usually feed while the host is sleeping, and painlessly so that the feed goes unnoticed. In some areas, human beings are the only mammals infected but in other areas, rodents and other animals act as the reservoir of infection. Relapsing fever may very rarely be acquired congenitally by transplacental transfer. Laboratory infection may occur through contact with the blood of patients or experimental animals.

Laboratory diagnosis

1. Microscopic examination: Borreliae are found in the blood during the fever but seldom in the apyrexial intervals.

Wet preparation: A drop of blood may be examined as a wet film under the dark ground or phase contrast microscope and borreliae detected by their lashing movement.

Staining: Blood smears may be stained with Giemsa or Leishman stain or with dilute carbol fuchsin and examined for borreliae.

2. Animal inoculation: A more successful method is to inoculate 1–2 ml of blood from the patient intraperitoneally into white mice. The borreliae multiply in the animals and appear in large numbers in peripheral blood within two days. Smears are prepared from blood collected from the tail vein and examined daily for two weeks.

3. Culture: Cultivation of borreliae is not very successful and is not used in diagnosis.

4. Serology: Demonstration of antibodies is too unreliable to be used in diagnosis. Patients with relapsing fever sometimes develop false positive serological tests for syphilis. Agglutinins for *Proteus* OXK are sometimes seen in high titres in louse-borne relapsing fever.

Prophylaxis

Prevention of louse-borne relapsing fever consists of prevention of louse infestation along with the use of insecticides whenever necessary. Prevention of tick-borne disease is less easy and consists of identification of tick-infested places and their avoidance, or eradication of the vectors. No vaccine is available.

Treatment

Tetracyclines, chloramphenicol, penicillin and erythromycin are effective.

BORRELIA VINCENTII

Borrelia vincentii is a motile spirochete, about 5–20 μm long and 0.2–0.6 μm wide, with 3–8 coils of variable size. It is easily stained with dilute carbol fuchsin and is Gram negative. It is a normal mouth commensal but may, under predisposing conditions such as malnutrition or viral infections, give rise to ulcerative gingivostomatitis or oropharyngitis (Vincent's angina). In these cases, *B.vincentii* is always associated with fusiform bacilli (*Fusobacterium fusiforme*). This symbiotic infection is known as *fusospirochetosis*.

Large numbers of spirochetes and fusiform bacilli may also be demonstrated in some cases of lung abscess, phagedenic skin ulcers and gangrenous balanitis. Their significance is uncertain. They are not primary pathogens but may cause opportunistic disease in devitalised tissues.

Diagnosis may be made by demonstrating spirochetes and fusiform bacilli in stained smears of exudates from the lesions (Fig. 41.3). *B.vincentii* may be cultivated with difficulty anaerobically in enriched media. Fusiform bacilli also grow in the culture and it is very difficult to obtain a pure growth. Penicillin and metronidazole are effective in treatment.

LYME DISEASE: *BORRELIA BURGDORFERI*

A new spirochetal disease identified in 1975, while studying a cluster of suspected juvenile rheumatoid arthritis cases, was named **Lyme disease** or **Lyme borreliosis** (originally **Lyme arthritis**), as it was first observed in Lyme, Connecticut, USA. The disease is widespread in the USA, where it is the most common vector-borne infection. It has been reported from other parts of the world also. It is caused by *Borrelia burgdorferi* transmitted by the bite of Ixodid ticks.

Lyme disease occurs in **three stages**. After an incubation period of 3–30 days, the first stage of 'localised infection' appears as an expanding annular skin lesion (**erythema migrans** or EM). A few weeks later, the second stage of 'disseminated infection' develops with fever, headache, myalgia, arthralgia and lymphadenopathy. Some develop meningeal or cardiac involvement. The third stage of 'persistent infection' sets in months or years later with chronic arthritis, polyneuropathy, encephalopathy and acrodermatitis.

B.burgdorferi is a fastidious bacterium which can be grown in a modified Kelley's (BSK) medium, after incubation for two weeks or more, optimally at 33°C. Three species of *Borrelia* have been identified (*B.burgdorferi, garinii* and *afzelii*) each of which is prevalent in different geographical regions, causing regional variations in clinical features.

The natural reservoir hosts are rodents, deer and other mammals. *Ixodes dammini* and related species are the vectors. The borrelia grows mainly in the midgut of the tick. Infection occurs by regurgitation of the gut contents during biting.

Laboratory diagnosis can be made by isolation of the borrelia or by serology. The borrelia has been isolated from ticks as well as from skin lesions, CSF and the blood of patients, but culture is too slow and difficult to be of use in diagnosis. Serological tests such as ELISA and IF have been described and immunoblotting recommended for confirmation. Antibodies take 1–2 months to appear, with initial IgM response followed by IgG. False positive syphilis serology may be seen, with FTA-ABS being positive and the VDRL test negative.

Doxycycline, amoxycillin and cefuroxine are useful for **treatment**.

LEPTOSPIRA

Leptospires are actively motile, delicate spirochetes, possessing a large number of closely wound spirals and characteristic hooked ends. They are too thin to be seen under the light microscope (*leptos*, meaning fine or thin). Several leptospires are saprophytic, while many are parasitic in rodents and other animals.

The first recognised leptospiral disease of human beings was spirochetal jaundice, described by Weil (1886). Stimson (1907) observed slender spirochetes in silver-stained sections of kidneys from a fatal case of jaundice. Several saprophytic leptospires were also isolated from water, sewage and other sources.

— Leptospira —

Clinical Case 2 A 45-year-old woman crossed a flooded street in a slum area in Mumbai during the monsoons. She was not wearing any shoes. Following this episode, she developed fever off and on and did not seek medical advice. After another two weeks, she presented with jaundice and fever. Based on a high degree of suspicion, as an outbreak was reported earlier during the same season in this region, the diagnosis of leptospirosis was made. Her sera tested positive by dipstick test for IgM antibodies to leptospira antigens. For confirmation, her serum sample was sent to the reference laboratory for microscopic agglutination test for leptosira-specific antibodies. This was positive at a titre of 1:10,000. She was treated with doxycyline.

Morphology

Leptospires are delicate, flexible, helical rods about 6–20 μm long and 0.1 μm thick. They possess numerous coils set so close together that they can be distinguished only under dark ground illumination in the living state or by electron microscopy. Their ends are hooked and resemble umbrella handles. They are actively motile. They stain poorly with aniline dyes. They may be stained with Giemsa stain. Better results are obtained by the silver impregnation methods.

Cultural characteristics

Culture media: Leptospires can be grown in media enriched with rabbit serum. Several liquid and semisolid media, such as Korthof's, Stuart's and Fletcher's media, have been described. Semisynthetic media, such as EMJH (Ellinghausen, McCullough, Johnson, Harris), are now commonly used. They are aerobic and microaerophilic. In semisolid media, growth occurs characteristically a few millimetres below the surface. Optimum temperature is 25–30°C and optimum pH 7.2–7.5. The generation time in laboratory media is 12–16 hours and 4–8 hours in inoculated animals.

Embroyonated eggs: Leptospires may be grown on the chorioallantoic membrane of chick embryos. They may be demonstrated in the blood of allantoic vessels 4–5 days after inoculation. Bacterial contamination is a serious problem in isolating and maintaining leptospires in culture. The use of 5-fluorouracil has been recommended for the inhibition of contaminating bacteria in cultures.

Animal inoculation: A simple method for obtaining cultures free of contaminants is to inoculate the material intraperitoneally in guinea pigs and culture the heart blood collected ten minutes later. Leptospires invade the bloodstream more rapidly than other bacteria.

Resistance

Leptospires are very susceptible to heat, being killed in 10 minutes at 50°C and in 10 seconds at 60°C. They are also sensitive to acid and are destroyed by gastric juice and bile. They are also readily destroyed by chlorine and most other antiseptics and disinfectants. Their survival in water or soil depends on the temperature, acidity, salinity and nature and amount of pollution, dying rapidly in acid urine, non-aerated sewage and saltish or brackish water. They can survive for days in moist conditions at pH 6.8–8.

Antigenic properties

Leptospires exhibit considerable antigenic cross-reaction. A genus-specific somatic antigen is present in all members of the genus. Classification into serogroups and serotypes is based on surface antigens. Determination of serotypes is based on agglutination and cross-absorption reactions using immune rabbit sera or more recently with monoclonal antibodies. Genetic methods, such as restriction endonuclease analysis and DNA pairing are used for further classification into serotypes.

Classification

The genus *Leptospira* is now classified into two species, and within each species are serogroups, which are further classified into serotypes (serovars).

- *L.interrogans* containing pathogenic leptospires, with about 22 serogroups having more than 200 serotypes. (Table 41.2). For example, *L.interrogans* is classified into several serogroups (Icterohaemorrhagiae, Canicola, Pyrogenes, Autumnalis, Australis, Pomona, Hebdomadis, Grippotyphosa, etc). Further, serogroup Icterohaemorrhagiae contains serovars *icterohaemorrhagiae, copenhageni, smithi,* etc).
- *L.biflexa* containing saprophytic leptospires found predominantly in surface waters. Over 200 serovars have been identified and assembled into 22 serogroups.

Classification into serogroups and serotypes is based on **surface antigens**. Determination of serotypes is based on agglutination and cross-absorption reactions using immune rabbit sera or, more recently, with monoclonal antibodies. Genetic methods, such as restriction endonuclease analysis and DNA pairing, are used for further classification into serotypes.

Pathogenicity

In natural reservoir hosts, leptospiral infection is asymptomatic. However, when infection is transmitted to other animals, clinical disease may result. It is a zoonotic disease and humans are infected when the leptospires in water contaminated by the urine of carrier animals enter the body through cuts or abrasions on the skin or through the intact mucosa of the mouth, nose or conjunctiva. The incubation period is usually about 10 days (range 2–26 days).

The clinical picture varies from mild, undifferentiated pyrexia to severe or fatal illness with hepatorenal damage (**Weil's disease**). In severe cases, the onset is acute, with rigor, vomiting, headache and intense injection of the eyes. The fever is irregular and usually subsides in about ten days. Jaundice occurs in about 10–20 per cent of cases by the second or third day. Purpuric hemorrhages sometimes occur on the skin and mucosa. Albuminuria is a constant feature (*Case* 2).

This typical presentation is unusual. Leptospirosis is now classified into two clinical types: **icteric** and **non-icteric**. Many cases present as aseptic meningitis and, in some, abdominal symptoms predominate. Clinical diagnosis is impossible in the majority of cases, and unless a high index of suspicion is maintained and laboratory assistance sought, leptospirosis will be missed in all but a few instances.

Leptospires are seen in the blood during the acute phase of the disease but can seldom be demonstrated after 8–10 days. They persist in the internal organs, and most abundantly in the kidneys, so they may be demonstrated in urine in the later stages of the disease.

Serious cases of leptospirosis are caused most often by serotype *icterohemorrhagiae*, though they may also be due to *copenhageni* and less often *bataviae*, *grippotyphosa*, *pyrogenes* and some others. Aseptic meningitis is common in *canicola* infection and abdominal symptoms in *grippotyphosa* infections. However, clinical syndromes are not serotype specific and any type of illness can be produced by any serotype.

Laboratory diagnosis

1. Specimen: Diagnosis may be made by demonstration of the leptospires microscopically in blood or urine, by isolating them in culture or by inoculation of guinea pigs, or by serological tests.

2. Microscopy:

Examination of blood: As leptospires disappear from blood after the first week, blood examination is helpful only in the early stages of the disease, before antibiotics are given. Leptospires may be demonstrated by examination of the blood under the dark field microscope or by immunofluorescence, but this is of little practical value.

Examination of urine: Leptospires appear in urine in the second week of the disease and intermittently thereafter for 4–6 weeks. The urine should be examined immediately after voiding as leptospires readily undergo lysis in acid urine. Centrifuged deposit of the urine may be examined under dark ground illumination. Direct culture of urine is seldom successful because of contamination but isolation is usually possible by inoculation into guinea pigs.

3. Culture: Three or four drops of **blood** are inoculated into each of several bijou bottles containing EMJH or similar medium. The bottles are incubated at 37°C for two days and left thereafter at room temperature in the dark for two weeks. Samples from the cultures are examined every third day for the presence of leptospires under dark ground illumination. Primary isolation may be delayed and may take many weeks to months. Chances of isolation are increased by culturing blood daily at the early stage of the disease. Leptospires may sometimes be isolated from the **CSF** also.

Direct culture of **urine** is seldom successful because of contamination but isolation is usually possible by inoculation into guinea pigs.

Identification of the isolates of leptospires is made by agglutination with type-specific sera. Due to the large number of serotypes and the high degree of antigenic cross-reactions between them, identification of isolates is a complicated procedure and is generally confirmed by one of the WHO/FAO Reference Laboratories.

Table 41.2   *Important leptospiral infections* (L.interrogans)

Serogroup	Disease	Clinical picture	Animal reservoir	Distribution
Icterohemorrhagiae	Weil's disease	Fever, jaundice, hemorrhages	Rat	Worldwide
Canicola	Canicola fever	Influenza-like, aseptic meningitis	Dog	Worldwide
Grippotyphosa	Swamp or marsh fever	Fever, prostration, aseptic-meningitis	Field mice	Europe, Africa, SE Asia, USA
Pomona	Swineherd's	Fever disease	Pig	America, Europe Middle East Indonesia, Australia
Hebdomadis	Seven day fever	Fever, lymphadenopathy	Field mice	Japan, Europe, USA
Fortbragg	Pretibial fever, Fort Bragg fever	Fever, rash over tibia	Not known	Japan, SE Asia, USA
Pyrogenes	Febrile spirochetosis	Fever	Pig	SE Asia, Europe, USA
Bataviae	Indonesian Weil's disease	Fever	Rat	SE Asia, Africa, Europe
Hardjo	Dairy farm fever	Fever	Cattle	UK, USA, New Zealand

4. Animal inoculation: Blood from the patient is also inoculated intraperitoneally into young guinea pigs. With virulent serotypes like *icterohemorrhagiae*, the animals develop fever and die within 8–12 days with jaundice and hemorrhage into the lungs and serous cavities. With other serotypes such as *canicola* and *pomona,* the animal may not become ill and infection will have to be identified by demonstration of the leptospires in the peritoneal fluid, by blood culture or by serology. From the third day after inoculation, the peritoneal fluid is examined daily under dark ground illumination, and when leptospires are detected, the blood withdrawn by cardiac puncture is inoculated into culture media.

5. Serological diagnosis: Antibodies appear in serum towards the end of the first week of the disease and increase till the fourth week, declining thereafter. Agglutinins may, however, be demonstrable years after the infection. Two types of serological tests are available, the broadly reactive screening tests and the serotype-specific tests.

- The **broadly reactive or genus-specific tests** identify leptospiral infection without indicating the exact infecting serovar. The antigens for these tests are prepared from the non-pathogenic *L.biflexa* **Patoc 1 strain.** The tests employed include sensitised erythrocyte lysis (SEL), complement fixation, agglutination and indirect immunofluorescence. ELISA has been used to detect IgM and IgG antibodies separately, in order to indicate the stage of infection. A simple and rapid dipstick assay has been developed for the assay of leptospira-specific IgM antibody in human sera.

- The **type-specific tests** identify the infecting serovar by demonstrating specific antibodies. Macroscopic and microscopic agglutination tests are used for this purpose:
  - **Macroscopic agglutination test:** Here, formalinised suspensions of prevalent leptospira serovars are tested for macroscopic agglutination with serial dilutions of the test serum.
  - **Microscopic agglutination test (MAT):** This uses live cultures of different serotypes, and agglutination is observed under the low power dark field microscope. This test is more specific and is usually done only in reference laboratories. Due to the presence of some degree of cross-reaction between different serovars, agglutinin absorption tests may sometimes become necessary for accurate diagnosis.

6. Diagnosis of leptospirosis in animals: Infection in rodents and other animals may be diagnosed by serological tests or by culturing pieces of kidney.

7. Examination of water for pathogenic leptospires: If a shaved and scarified area of the skin of a young guinea pig is immersed in water for an hour, infection develops through the abrasions.

Epidemiology

Leptospirosis is considered the most widespread of zoonoses, being regularly present in all continents except Antarctica. Pathogenic leptospires survive for long periods in the convoluted tubules of the kidneys in natural hosts, multiply and are shed in the urine. Animal carriers often excrete up to 100 million leptospires per ml of urine. If the infected urine contaminates water or mud that is neutral or slightly alkaline, the leptospires survive for weeks. When people come into contact with such water, the leptospires enter the body through abraded skin or mucosa and initiate infection.

Certain occupational groups such as agricultural workers in rice or cane fields, miners and sewer cleaners are exposed to infection more often, and so leptospirosis is more common in them. Leptospires may be shed in the milk of lactating animals. However, they die rapidly in milk, and human infection through milk is not known. They are not shed in saliva, so animal bites are not infectious. Arthropods are not known to transmit the infection.

Several animals act as carriers. Rats are particularly important as they are ubiquitous and carry the most pathogenic serotype *icterohemorrhagiae*. Field mice carry *grippotyphosa*, pigs *pomona* and dogs *canicola*. However, the same serotype may be carried by different mammals and one mammal may carry different serotypes.

While leptospires are generally non-pathogenic in the reservoir animal, leptospirosis is of veterinary importance as infection of cattle and pigs causes considerable economic loss. Infection among animals is also transmitted by urinary contamination of water and fodder. Human beings are an aberrant or 'end' host. There is no evidence that human patients infect others.

From being predominantly a rural disease of agricultural workers, leptospirosis has in recent times also become an urban problem in the developing countries. This is perhaps due to overcrowding, insanitary conditions, increasing rat population and the habit of walking barefoot.

Prophylaxis

As leptospirosis results from contact of skin or mucosa with contaminated water, general measures of prevention such as rodent control, disinfection of water and the wearing of protective clothing contribute to its prevention. Vaccination has been attempted with some success in dogs, cattle and pigs. Immunity following vaccination or infection is serotype specific. Vaccination has also been tried in persons at high risk such as agricultural workers.

Treatment

Leptospires are sensitive to penicillin and tetracyclines, but treatment should be started early in the course of the disease to be effective. Penicillin is given as IV, 1–2 million units six-hourly for seven days in serious cases. A mild Jarisch–Herxheimer reaction may occur in some. Doxycycline 200 mg orally given once a week is effective in prophylaxis.

RECAP

- Spirochetes, which are helical, slender, relatively long bacteria, are widespread in nature. The principal human diseases are syphilis (*Treponema pallidum*), Lyme disease and relapsing fever (*Borrelia* species) and leptospirosis (*Leptospira* species).
- *T.pallidum* causes syphilis, which can present as primary, secondary and tertiary stages. It can be acquired by venereal or congenital transmission.
- Primary and secondary syphilis can be diagnosed by a combination of microscopic and serological techniques. Material from lesions can be viewed as wet-film preparations by dark ground or phase contrast microscopy to reveal spirochetes with characteristic motility or stained by silver impregnation and viewed under bright field microscopy to demonstrate bacteria with distinctive morphology.
- Serological tests consist of non-specific (screening) tests, such as VDRL (to detect anti-cardiolipin antibody), and specific (confirmatory) tests, such as fluorescent treponemal antibody (FTA) and *T.pallidum* hemagglutination (TPHA) tests, to detect anti-*T.pallidum* antibody.
- *T.pallidum* is closely related to other species of *Treponema*, from which it can be differentiated only by antigenic structure. These species include *T.pertenue*, which causes yaws, *T.carateum*, which causes pinta and *T.pallidum* var *endemicum* which causes endemic syphilis; these species are found in tropical countries, are transmitted by non-sexual means (mainly trauma) and do not affect the central nervous system.
- The genus *Borrelia* comprises spirochetal bacteria that are Gram negative and strictly anaerobic. They are transmitted to humans following the bite of an insect vector (primarily lice or ticks).
- *Borrelia recurrentis* is responsible for the louse-borne or epidemic type of relapsing fever, with humans serving as the reservoir host.
- Lyme disease is a tick-borne illness and is caused by *Borrelia burgdorferi*; the disease occurs in the northern temperate zone, and rodents are the major reservoir (humans are possibly only accidental hosts). The mechanism by which borreliae cause Lyme disease is uncertain.
- Laboratory diagnosis of relapsing fever includes dark field examination of blood during febrile episodes to demonstrate the spirochetes, demonstration of borreliae by inoculation into a mouse and detection of specific antibody to *B.recurrentis* by indirect immunofluorescence assay.
- The genus *Leptospira* comprises very thin, tightly coiled, obligately aerobic spirochetes, which show hooking at the ends and which possess a unique, flexuous type of motility. They can easily be cultivated in vitro. There are pathogenic species and free living species.

- Serotypes of *Leptospira interrogans* cause leptospirosis, a zoonotic disease, while serotypes of *Leptospira biflexa* exist in water and soil as free living organisms.
- Pathogenic leptospires enter the human body through the mucosa and broken skin without any obvious lesion at the site of entry, and then cause a general febrile disease which is biphasic, with an acute leptospiremic phase followed by an immune, leptospiruric phase. The central nervous system, kidneys and liver are the most frequently involved systems.
- For diagnosis, blood, CSF and urine are collected for culture and serum for serological tests (microscopic agglutination test); a fourfold rise in convalescent titres is considered positive. Other tests include dark field examination of blood or urine; recently, rapid commercial tests (enzyme immunoassays) have been developed. Macroscopic slide agglutination test is a refrence test for serological diagnosis.

ESSAYS

1. Enumerate sexually transmitted diseases and describe the laboratory diagnosis of syphilis.
2. Classify spirochetes pathogenic to humans and describe the laboratory diagnosis of syphilis.

SHORT ANSWERS

1. Advantages and disadvantages of the VDRL test
2. Specific *T.pallidum* tests
3. Laboratory diagnosis of syphilis
4. Laboratory diagnosis of leptospirosis

SHORT NOTES

1. Non-venereal treponematoses
2. Vincent's angina
3. Relapsing fever
4. Lyme's disease
5. VDRL test
6. TPHA
7. Wiel's disease

42 Mycoplasma

INTRODUCTION

Mycoplasma are the smallest free-living microorganisms that can be grown in a cell-free medium. The species causing human infections are *M.pneumoniae* causing pneumonia, *Ureaplasma urealyticum* causing non-gonococcal urethritis and *M.hominis* and *M.gentalium* causing genital tract infections.

MYCOPLASMA

Mycoplasmas are a group of bacteria that are devoid of cell walls and so are highly pleomorphic, with no fixed shape or size. They lack even cell wall precursors like muramic acid or diaminopimelic acid. The cells are bounded by a soft trilaminar unit membrane containing sterols. Because of their plasticity, they can pass through bacterial filters and have often been mistaken for viruses.

The first member of the group to be identified was the organism causing bovine pleuropneumonia, isolated by Nocard and Roux (1898). A similar organism was found to cause contagious agalactia in sheep. When many similar isolates were obtained from animals,

human beings, plants and environmental sources, they came to be called '**pleuropneumonia-like organisms**' (**PPLO**). This unsatisfactory name has been replaced by the term *Mycoplasma* (*myco*, from the fungus-like form of the branching filaments; *plasma*, denoting their plasticity of shape).

Morphology

Mycoplasmas, lacking a cell wall, can pass through filters of 450-nm pore size. They occur as granules and filaments of various sizes. The granules may be coccoid, balloon, disc, ring or star forms. The filaments are slender, of varying length and show true branching. Multiplication is by binary fission, but as genomic replication and cell division are often asynchronous, budding forms and chains of beads are produced. A distinctive feature seen in some species is a bulbous enlargement, with a differentiated tip structure, by means of which the organisms attach themselves to suitable host cells carrying neuraminic acid receptors. They may be responsible for the hemadsorption shown by some species.

Mycoplasmas do not possess spores, flagella or fimbria. Some species exhibit gliding motility. Mycoplasmas are Gram negative but are better stained by Giemsa stain.

Culture

Mycoplasma may be cultivated in **fluid** or **solid media**. They are generally facultative anaerobes, growth being better aerobically. They grow within a temperature range of 22–41°C, the parasitic species growing optimally at 35–37°C and the saprophytes at lower temperatures. Media for cultivating mycoplasma are enriched with 20% horse or human serum and yeast extract. Penicillin and thallium acetate are added as selective agents. The high concentration of serum is necessary as a source of cholesterol and other lipids.

Colonies appear after incubation for 2–6 days and are about 10–600 μm in size. The colony is typically biphasic, with a '**fried egg**' **appearance**, consisting of a central opaque granular area of growth extending into the depth of the medium, surrounded by a flat, translucent peripheral zone (Fig. 42.1). Colonies may be seen with a hand lens but are best studied after staining by the **Dienes method**. For this, a block of agar containing the colony is cut and placed on a slide. It is covered with a cover slip on which an alcoholic solution of methylene blue and azure has been dried.

Colonies cannot be picked with loops; instead subculture is carried out by cutting out an agar block with colonies and rubbing it on fresh plates. In a liquid medium, no turbidity is appreciated and pleomorphic forms are found.

Biochemical reactions

Mycoplasmas are chemo-organotrophs, their metabolism being mainly fermentative. Most species utilise glucose or arginine as the major sources of energy. Urea is not hydrolysed, except by ureaplasmas. They are generally not proteolytic.

Unique among prokaryotes is the requirement of most mycoplasmas for cholesterol and related sterols, which are incorporated in their surface membranes. Mycoplasmas also lack the ability to synthesise purines and pyrimidines.

Resistance

Mycoplasmas generally resemble non-sporing bacteria in heat resistance but some strains are more sensitive, being destroyed at 45°C in 15 minutes. They are relatively resistant to lysis by osmotic shock but are very sensitive to lysis by surface active agents and lipolytic

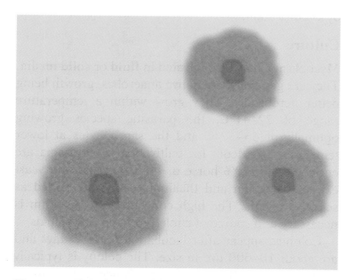

Fig. 42.1   'Fried egg' appearance of colonies

agents such as taurocholate and digitonin. They are resistant to penicillin and cephalosporin as well as to lysozymes that act on bacterial cell walls but are sensitive to tetracycline and many other antibiotics. Susceptibility to erythromycin and some other macrolide antibiotics is useful for species differentiation. Growth is inhibited by gold salts. *M.pneumoniae* can grow in the presence of 0.002% methylene blue in agar, while many other species are inhibited.

Antigenic properties

Serological tests such as complement fixation, agglutination, passive hemagglutination, ELISA and immunofluorescence have been used to detect antibodies in sera and to identify isolates. Mycoplasmal surface antigens are mainly glycolipids and proteins. Glycolipid antigens are identified by complement fixation and protein antigens by ELISA. A particularly useful technique for the identification of isolates is the **growth inhibition test** based on the ability of antisera to specifically inhibit the growth of the homologous species on solid media.

Classification

Mycoplasmas have been placed in the class Mollicutes (literally meaning soft skin), order Mycoplasmatales, which contains the following families and genera:

* Family Mycoplasmataceae, to which belong parasitic mycoplasmas requiring cholesterol or other sterols as an essential growth factor. This contains two genera:
  - Genus *Mycoplasma*, which utilises glucose or arginine but does not split urea
  - Genus *Ureaplasma*, which hydrolyses urea.
* Family Acholeplasmataceae, mostly saprophytic mycoplasmas, which do not require sterols as growth factor.
* Family Spiroplasmataceae, containing the genus *Spiroplasma*, which parasitises arthropods and plants. This is sterol dependent and is helical in shape.
* Family Anaeroplasmataceae, containing the genus *Anaeroplasma*, which comprises strict anaerobes, found in the rumen of cattle and sheep.

Mycoplasmas may be saprophytic, parasitic or pathogenic. More than 100 species of mycoplasma are known to cause disease in a variety of mammalian, insect and plant hosts. About 16 species, belonging to three families are found in human beings (Table 42.1).

Table 42.1 *Mycoplasmas of humans*

A. Parasitic:

1. *Established pathogen:*
   M.pneumoniae causing pneumonia
2. *Presumed pathogens:*
   M.hominis and *U.urealyticum* associated with genital infections
3. *Non-pathogenic:*
   M.orale, M.buccale, M.salivarium, M.faucium in oropharynx
   M.fermentans, M.genitalium, M.penetrans, M.primatum,
   M.spermatophilum in genital tract

B. Saprophytic

   Acholeplasma laidlawii on skin and in mouth

They can grow in the laboratory medium, generate metabolic energy, synthesise their own protein and have both DNA and RNA. They do not have a host cell DNA mechanism responsible for reproduction (like other bacteria and unlike *Chlamydiae*, some *Rickettsiae* and viruses). **They have a specific requirement of sterols for growth and membrane synthesis.**

Pathogenicity

Parasitic mycoplasmas exhibit host specificity. They generally produce surface infections by adhering to the mucosa of the respiratory, gastrointestinal and genitourinary tracts.

Mycoplasma cause two types of disease in humans: pneumonia and genital infections.

Mycoplasmal pneumonia (primary atypical pneumonia) is caused by *M.pneumoniae*. The disease is typically tracheobronchitis. Acute pharyngitis is uncommon and only a third of the patients develop pneumonia. The incubation period is 1–3 weeks.

Onset is gradual, with fever, malaise, headache and sore throat. Paroxysmal cough may occur with blood-tinged sputum. The disease is characterised by paucity of respiratory signs on physical examination but radiological evidence of consolidation, which is usually patchy, involving one of the lower lobes, starting at the hilum and fanning out to the periphery, is seen. The disease is usually self-limiting, recovery occurring in 1–2 weeks, but can be prolonged. Bullous myringitis and otitis are common complications. Rashes, meningitis, encephalitis and hemolytic anemia are other complications.

The disease is found worldwide and at all ages. Transmission is by droplets of nasopharyngeal secretion. Spread is favoured by close contact, as in families and most typically among military recruits. The mycoplasma may remain in the throat for two or more months after recovery from the disease.

Eaton (1944) was the first to isolate the causative agent of the disease in hamsters and cotton rats. He was able to transmit the infection later to chick embryos by amniotic inoculation. Because it was filterable, it was considered to be a virus (**Eaton agent**), but was subsequently shown to be a mycoplasma and named *M.pneumoniae*.

Genital infections are caused by *Mycoplasma hominis*, which has a similar spectrum as *Ureaplasma urealyticum*.

Laboratory diagnosis

1. Specimens: For isolation, throat swabs or respiratory secretions are inoculated into transport media to prevent drying and bacterial overgrowth. The transport medium can be a mycoplasma medium containing glucose and phenol red (PPLO broth) or one containing trypticase soya broth with bovine serum albumin; sputum and blood may be sent as such.

2. Isolation: Growth is slow on primary isolation and may take 1–3 weeks. Culture is made on complex media (such as **PPLO broth**), which include agar, broth and biphasic (combined solid slope–liquid broth) media containing enriching, growth stimulating substances (yeast dialysate, horse serum) and penicillin and thallium to inhibit growth of other bacteria. On solid media incubated aerobically at 37°C, colonies are very small (10–100 µm), slow to appear and grow embedded in the agar (**typical 'fried egg' appearance**). *M.pneumoniae* causes hemolysis in overlaid guinea pig red cells. Growth is indicated by acid production in the medium. *M.pneumoniae* produces beta hemolysis and agglutinates guinea pig erythrocytes. Colonies on agar adsorb erythrocytes. The hemadsorption is enzymatic and occurs optimally at 37°C. Cell receptors are destroyed by neuraminidase. It inhibits ciliary motility in hamster trachea organ cultures. Growth can also be easily screened by **tetrazolium reduction test** in which the mycoplasma colonies reduce the colourless tetrazolium to red-coloured formazan.

M.pneumoniae is unrelated to other human mycoplasmas and may be identified by growth inhibition by specific antisera.

3. Molecular methods: As isolation is difficult and delayed, PCR assay which is rapid and specific is used where feasible.

4. Serology: Serological diagnosis may be made by:
- **Specific tests** using mycoplasmal antigens, which include immunofluorescence, hemagglutination inhibition and growth inhibition as the most sensitive tests. Complement fixation and indirect hemagglutination tests are less sensitive.
- **Non-specific tests** such as Streptococcus MG and cold agglutination tests. The former is carried out by mixing serial dilutions of the patient's unheated serum and a heat-killed suspension of **Streptococcus MG**, and observing agglutination after overnight incubation at 37°C. A titre of 1:20 or over is considered suggestive.

The **cold agglutination test** is based on the appearance in a high proportion of cases with primary atypical pneumonia, of macroglobulin antibodies that agglutinate human group O cells at low temperature. The patient's blood sample should not be refrigerated before separation of the serum, as the agglutinins are readily absorbed by the homologous erythrocytes at low temperatures. For the test, serial dilutions of the patient's serum are mixed with an equal volume of 0.2% washed human O group erythrocytes, and clumping observed after leaving at 4°C overnight. The clumping is dissociated at 37°C. A titre of 1:32 or over is suggestive but demonstration of rise in titre in paired serum samples is more reliable. The indirect Coombs test may also be positive in some cases.

Mycoplasma and HIV infection

Mycoplasmas tend to cause more severe and prolonged infections in HIV-infected and other immunodeficient subjects.

UREAPLASMA UREALYTICUM

Some strains of *Mycoplasma* frequently isolated from the urogenital tract of human beings and animals form very tiny colonies, generally 15–50 µm in size. They are called T strain or T form mycoplasmas (T for tiny). They are peculiar in their ability to hydrolyse urea, which is an essential growth factor in addition to cholesterol. Human T strain mycoplasmas have been reclassified as *Ureaplasma urealyticum.* After *Chlamydia trachomatis,* they are the second most common cause of **non-gonococcal urethritis (NGU).**

Genital infections are caused by *M.hominis* and *U.urealyticum*. They are transmitted by sexual contact, and may cause urethritis, proctitis, balanoposthitis and Reiter's syndrome in men, and acute salpingitis, pelvic inflammatory disease, cervicitis and vaginitis in women. They have also been associated with infertility, abortion, postpartum fever, chorioamnionitis and low birth weight of infants.

Treatment

Tetracycline and doxycycline show some clinical response but ureaplasma can be resistant even to these agents.

Mycoplasmas and L forms of bacteria

Kleineberger (1935) found pleuropneumonia-like forms in a culture of *Streptobacillus moniliformis* and termed them L forms, after Lister Institute, London, where the observation was made. It was subsequently shown that many bacteria, either spontaneously or induced by certain substances like penicillin, lost part or all of their cell wall and develop into L forms. Such L forms may be 'unstable' when they revert to their normal morphology, or 'stable' when they continue in the cell wall–deficient state permanently. Cell wall–deficient forms (L forms, protoplasts, spheroplasts) may not initiate disease but may be important in bacterial persistence during antibiotic therapy and subsequent recurrence of infection. It has been suggested that mycoplasmas may represent stable L forms of bacteria but genetic, antigenic and biochemical evidence is against the possibility.

Mycoplasma as cell culture contaminants

Continuous cell cultures maintained in many laboratories have been found to be contaminated with different species of mycoplasma. The contamination may originate from the worker or from animal sera or trypsin used in cell culture. Contamination generally does not produce cytopathic effects but may interfere with the growth of viruses in such cell cultures and may also produce misleading results in serological tests. Mycoplasmas growing in cell cultures have often been mistaken for viruses. Eradication of mycoplasmas from infected cells is difficult and requires change of cell lines.

RECAP

- Mycoplasma are the smallest known free-living organisms. They have no cell wall but are bounded by a typical three-layered cell membrane. They have pleomorphic morphology and may occur as spheres (0.3–0.5 μm in size) or as filaments. The cells are Gram negative and stain poorly by the Giemsa stain. They grow on cell-free media and require sterols for growth.
- Mycoplasmal (primary atypical) pneumonia is caused by *Mycoplasma pneumoniae*. *M.hominis* and *Ureaplasma urealyticum* may cause non-gonococcal urethritis as well as pelvic inflammatory disease in women.
- Culture is made on complex media. The growth on media resembles a 'fried egg'. In mycoplasmal pneumonia, the diagnosis is usually made by non-specific tests like demonstration of cold agglutinins to human red blood cells. Growth inhibition tests are specific.
- Treatment with erythromycin and tetracycline is usually effective.
- *Ureaplasma urealyticum* causes NGU.

SHORT ANSWERS

1. Laboratory diagnosis of *Mycoplasma pneumoniae*
2. Mycoplasma
3. Primary atypical pneumonia

43 Actinomycetes

INTRODUCTION

Actinomycetes are thin bacteria that possess a cell wall containing muramic acid. They have prokaryotic nuclei and are susceptible to antibacterial antibiotics. They bear a superficial resemblance to fungi as they form branching filaments. Actinomycetes are related to mycobacteria and corynebacteria. They are Gram-positive, non-motile, non-sporing, non-capsulated filaments that break up into bacillary and coccoid elements. Most are free-living, particularly in the soil.

Actinomycetes include many genera of medical interest, such as:

- Anaerobic *Actinomyces*, *Arachnia*, *Bifidobacterium* and *Rothia*. The major pathogenic genus *Actinomyces* is anaerobic or microaerophilic and non–acid fast.
- Aerobic *Nocardia*, *Actinomadura*, *Dermatophilus* and *Streptomyces*. The *Nocardia* species is aerobic and may be acid fast. Some species of *Streptomyces* may cause disease, but their importance is as a major source of antibiotics.

ACTINOMYCES

Bollinger (1877) found a mould-like organism in the lesion of 'lumpy jaw' (actinomycosis) in cattle. The name *Actinomyces* was coined by Harz to refer to the ray-like appearance of the organism in the granules that characterise the lesions (*actinomyces* means ray fungus). Wolff and Israel (1891) isolated an anaerobic bacillus from human lesions and produced experimental infection in rabbits and guinea pigs. This was named *Actinomyces israelii*. It causes human actinomycosis. Actinomycosis in cattle is produced by *A.bovis*.

ACTINOMYCOSIS

> **Clinical Case 1** A 20-year-old woman presented to the Surgery Outpatient department with a soft tissue swelling on the left jaw, which was painless and covered with exudate. On examination, a discharging sinus was found. She had a history of trauma to the area. The pus was sent for a culture test. On macroscopic examination, a sulphur granule was found in the exudate. The Gram stain of the granule showed the presence of branching, Gram-positive bacilli. The patient was diagnosed with cervicofacial actinomycosis and responded to treatment with penicillin.

The disease is a chronic granulomatous infection occurring in human beings and animals. It is characterised by the development of indurated swellings, mainly in the connective tissue, suppuration and the discharge of '**sulphur granules**'. The lesion often points towards the skin, leading to multiple sinuses.

Actinomycosis in human beings is an endogenous infection. The *Actinomyces* species is normally present in the mouth, intestine and vagina as a commensal. Trauma, foreign bodies or poor oral hygiene may favour tissue invasion. *A.israelii* is the most common causative agent. However, other actinomycetes such as *A.naeslundii*, *A.viscosus*, *A.odontolyticum*, *A.meyeri*, *A.gerencsonei* and *Propionibacterium propionicum* may sometimes be responsible. Actinomycosis is usually

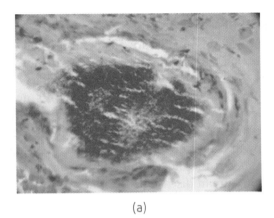

(a)

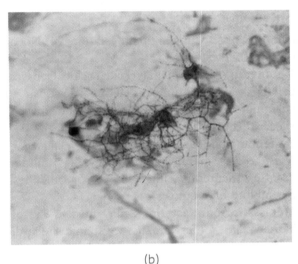

(b)

Fig. 43.1 (a) Sulphur granules in section with H and E stain; (b) Gram-positive filamentous bacilli in pus

a mixed infection, accompanied by other associated bacteria which may enhance the pathogenic effect. These include *Bifidobacterium dentium*, *Actinobacillus actinomycetemcomitans*, *Eikenella corrodens*, *Haemophilus aphrophilus*, bacteroides, fusobacteria, staphylococci and anaerobic streptococci.

Clinical forms: Actinomycosis in human beings occurs in four main clinical forms:

- **Cervicofacial,** with indurated lesions on the cheek and submaxillary regions (*Case 1*).
- **Thoracic,** with lesions in the lung that may involve the pleura and pericardium and spread outwards through the chest wall.
- **Abdominal,** where the lesion is usually around the cecum, and involving the neighbouring tissues and the abdominal wall. Sometimes the infection spreads to the liver via the portal vein.

- **Pelvic,** where many cases of pelvic actinomycosis have been reported in association with the use of intrauterine devices. Generally, abscesses are produced in bone and soft tissue, with chronic draining sinuses to the exterior.

Actinomyces have been incriminated in inflammatory diseases of the gums (gingivitis and periodontitis) and with sublingual plaques leading to root surface caries. Actinomycosis may also present as mycetoma.

Sulphur granules are found in the exudate. The morphology in diseased tissue is of a long, branching mycelium with attached 'sulphur granules'. The *Actinomyces* species requires an anaerobic environment to be isolated from clinical specimens, but can be maintained under microaerophilic conditions. Treatment consists of surgical drainage or excision, together with large doses of penicillin for several weeks or months.

Laboratory diagnosis

1. Clinical specimen: The specimen to be collected is pus or tissue. In pulmonary disease, sputum is collected.

2. Gross examination of granules: Sulphur granules may be demonstrated in pus by shaking it up in a test tube with some saline. On standing, the granules sediment and may be withdrawn with a capillary pipette. Granules may also be obtained by applying gauze pads over the discharging sinuses. The granules are white or yellowish and range in size from minute specks to about 5 mm.

3. Microscopy: This can be used to demonstrate actinomycetes in the lesion or granules. Granules are examined microscopically under a cover slip. They are crushed between slides and stained by Gram stain and examined. The granules are, in fact, bacterial colonies and will be found to consist of a dense network of thin, Gram-positive filaments, surrounded by a peripheral zone of swollen, radiating, club-shaped structures, presenting a sun ray appearance. The 'clubs' are believed to be antigen–antibody complexes (Fig. 43.1).

4. Isolation in culture: Sulphur granules or pus containing actinomycetes are washed and inoculated into thioglycollate liquid medium or streaked on brain–heart infusion agar and incubated anaerobically at 37°C. In thioglycollate, *A. bovis* produces general turbidity whereas *A. israelii* grows as fluffy balls at the bottom of the tube. On solid media, *A. israelii* produces small 'spidery colonies' in 48–72 hours that become heaped up, white and irregular or smooth, large colonies in 10 days. Other species have different types of colonies.

5. Identification of species: The isolate is identified by microscopy, biochemical reactions and fluorescent antibody methods. Gel diffusion and immunofluorescence can differentiate *A.israelii* from other *Actinomycetes* species and from other filamentous anaerobes that may produce granules in tissues.

Epidemiology

The disease occurs throughout the world but its incidence in developed countries has been declining, probably as a result of the widespread use of antibiotics. Actinomycosis is more common in rural areas and among agricultural workers. Young males (10–30 years old) are most commonly affected. The reason for this predisposition is not known. About 60 per cent of the cases are cervicofacial and some 20 per cent are abdominal. Pelvic actinomyces is seen mainly in women using intrauterine devices.

Treatment

The disease responds to prolonged treatment with penicillin or tetracycline. Treatment will have to be continued for several months and supplemented by surgery where necessary.

NOCARDIA

Nocardia resembles *Actinomycetes* morphologically but is aerobic. All species are Gram positive and some such as *N.asteroides* and *N.brasiliensis* are also acid fast. *Nocardia* is frequently found in the soil and infection may be exogenous. Infection causes cutaneous, subcutaneous or systemic lesions in humans (*Case 2*). The species usually responsible are *N.asteroides*, *N.brasiliensis* and *N.caviae*.

Clinical Case 2   A 60-year-old, HIV-positive man developed pneumonia with high-grade fever and productive cough. His T cell (CD4) count was <200/mm³. The initial diagnosis of pulmonary tuberculosis was subsequently ruled out by laboratory tests. Further examination of sputum showed the presence of fine, right-angled branching filaments which were acid fast by modified technique. Culture on blood agar showed the growth of dry, buff-coloured colonies identified as *N.astroides*. The patient responded to treatment with cotrimoxazole and amikacin.

Morphology

Members of this genus are filamentous, rod-shaped bacteria that do not produce spores, do not exhibit motility and are catalase positive; they are Gram-positive and are also positive in **Kinyoun's acid fast staining technique** (weakly acid fast). Aerial hyphae are produced. The organisms are obligate aerobes, and growth can often be enhanced by carbon dioxide. *N.asteroides* is the most commonly involved *Nocardia* species in human disease. It is found worldwide in the soil and can infect animals. Transmission is thought to be through contaminated soil, not from animals or infected humans.

Clinical forms: Clinical manifestation of Nocardia may be as follows:

- **Cutaneous infection** may lead to local abscesses, cellulitis or lymphocutaneous lesions. The subcutaneous lesion is actinomycotic mycetoma (described below).
- **Systemic nocardiosis** usually caused by *N.asteroides* manifests primarily as pulmonary disease, pneumonia, lung abscess or other lesions resembling tuberculosis.
- **Metastatic manifestations** may involve the brain, kidneys and other organs. Systemic nocardiosis occurs more often in immunodeficient persons.

Laboratory diagnosis

1. Direct microscopy: Demonstration of partially acid fast branching, beaded filaments in smears from patient tissue.

2. Isolation in culture: Nocardia are aerobic and grow readily on ordinary media, forming dry, granular, wrinkled colonies, which produce pigments ranging from yellow to red. The species can be identified by biochemical tests.

Treatment

The organisms are resistant to penicillin. The most successful agents have been sulphonamides (particularly sulphamethoxazole and trimethoprim [cotrimoxazole]). Surgery may be required to remove mycetomas. Therapy is most successful with skin and lung infections. Cotrimoxazole or minocycline given for several months may be useful. In immunocompromised patients, amikacin and cefotaxime are advisable in addition.

MYCETOMA (BACTERIAL)

Bacterial mycetomas are usually caused by actinomycetes—*Actinomyces (A.israelii, A.bovis), Nocardia (N.asteroides, N.brasiliensis, N.caviae), Actinomadura (A.madurae, A.pelletierii)* and *Streptomyces (S.somaliensis)*.

Staphylococcus aureus and other pyogenic bacteria may occasionally cause a mycetoma-like lesion (*botryomycosis*).

ACTINOMYCOTIC MYCETOMA

Mycetoma is a localised chronic, granulomatous involvement of the subcutaneous and deeper tissues, commonly affecting the foot and less often the hand and other parts, and presenting as a tumour with multiple discharging sinuses. This clinical syndrome was first described from Madura by Gill (1842) and came to be known as **Maduramycosis**. Mycetomas are usually caused by fungi but may be caused by bacteria as well.

The etiological diagnosis of mycetoma is important in choosing the appropriate treatment. The colour of the granules gives some indication. In actinomycotic mycetoma, the granules are white to yellow, while in eumycotic mycetomas, the granules are generally black. Examination of crushed smears of the granules helps to differentiate actinomycotic from mycotic mycetomas. In the former, the filaments are thin (about 1 μm), while in the latter they are stout (about 4–5 μm). Isolation of the agent in culture establishes the diagnosis.

Actinomycetes and hypersensitivity pneumonitis

Spores of some thermophilic actinomycetes such as the *Faenia* and *Saccharomonosporia* species present in mouldy hay, which when inhaled may induce allergic alveolitis leading to chronic obstructive pulmonary disease (COPD, farmer's lung).

RECAP

- Actinomycetes are bacteria that form a mycelial network of branching filaments. They are thin, possess a cell wall containing muramic acid, have prokaryotic nuclei and are susceptible to antibacterial antibiotics.
- Actinomycetes are Gram-positive, non-motile, non-sporing, non-capsulated filaments. Most are free-living, particularly in the soil.
- The major pathogenic genus, *Actinomyces*, is anaerobic or microaerophilic and non–acid fast, while the *Nocardia* species is aerobic and may be acid fast.

ESSAY

1. Describe the etiology and laboratory diagnosis of actinomycosis.

SHORT ANSWER

1. Mycetoma (definition)

SHORT NOTES

1. Nocardia
2. Sulphur granules

44 Miscellaneous Bacteria

LISTERIA MONOCYTOGENES

Listeria monocytogenes is a short, non-sporing, Gram-positive bacillus. It exhibits a characteristic slow, tumbling motility when grown at 25°C, but is non-motile at 37°C. This is because peritrichous flagella are produced optimally at 20–30°C but not at 37°C. It is aerobic or microaerophilic. Growth is improved when cultures are incubated at reduced oxygen tension and with 5–10% CO_2. It grows best between 30°C and 37°C, but slow growth occurs even at 4°C. Colonies are hemolytic on blood agar. *L.monocytogenes* ferments glucose, maltose, L-rhamnose and alpha methyl D-mannoside, producing acid without gas. It is catalase positive. It grows in the presence of 0.1% potassium tellurite, 10% salt and at pH 9.6.

Epidemiology

L.monocytogenes is widely distributed in nature. It has been isolated from a wide range of mammals, birds, fish, ticks and crustacea. It occurs as a saprophyte in soil, water and sewage. Many serovars have been recognised. Most human infections are caused by serovar 1/2a or 1/2b and 4b. Human infection is believed to result from contact with infected animals, inhalation of contaminated dust or ingestion of contaminated milk or food. Outbreaks of foodborne listeriosis have been known as the bacteria can overcome the food preservation process due to its ability to grow at refrigeration temperature, low pH and high salt concentration.

Experimental inoculation in rabbits causes marked monocytosis (hence the name **monocytogenes**). Monocytosis is a feature of human listeriosis also. Instillation into the eyes of rabbits produces keratoconjunctivitis (**Anton test**).

Pathogenicity

Listeriosis in human beings may present in many forms. Infection of pregnant women may lead to abortion or stillbirth if intrauterine transmission occurs. It may cause **meningitis or sepsis in neonates** due to perinatal transmission, which can be of early or late onset. Infants acquire infection in utero or by inoculation through an infected birth canal. In the immunocompromised and the elderly, it can cause meningoencephalitis. Adults are infected when they ingest **contaminated food**. The bacteria are invasive and produce an important virulence factor, listeriolysin O, which allows the bacterium to escape from cell membranes and contributes to septicemia. Organisms can cross the blood–brain barrier to cause meningitis and encephalitis. Cell-mediated immunity, involving macrophages activated by T lymphocytes, confers protection.

Asymptomatic infection of the female genital tract may cause infertility. Listeriosis may also present as abscess, conjunctivitis, pharyngitis, urethritis, pneumonia, infectious mononucleosis-like syndrome or endocarditis.

Laboratory diagnosis

This is established by the isolation of the bacillus from appropriate clinical material such as cervical and vaginal secretions, lochia, meconium, cord blood, blood and cerebrospinal fluid by incubating under 5% CO_2 environment on blood agar. Identification is by biochemical tests (Table 44.1). Greater success in isolation is achieved if the materials are stored in tryptose phosphate or thioglycollate broth at 4°C and subcultures are done at weekly intervals for 1–6 months (**cold enrichment**). Antibody to listeriolysin O, when detected, aids diagnosis. Isolates are likely to be misdiagnosed as non-pathogenic diphtheroids unless properly investigated.

Treatment

Ampicillin, cotrimoxazole and gentamicin are effective. Cephalosporins are not recommended. Meningitis can be treated with ampicillin.

Prevention

Control is by proper preparation of food by washing of vegetables, pasteurisation of milk and thorough cooking. The condition needs to be recognised early in pregnancy.

ERYSIPELOTHRIX RHUSIOPATHIAE

Erysipelothrix rhusiopathiae is a slender, non-motile, non-sporing, non-capsulated, Gram-positive bacillus with a tendency to form long filaments. It is microaerophilic on primary isolation but on subculture grows as an aerobe or facultative anaerobe. It grows on ordinary media and is catalase negative. Black colonies are developed in tellurite media. It ferments glucose and lactose, producing acid without gas; sucrose and mannitol are not fermented. In the triple sugar iron (TSI) medium, hydrogen sulphide is produced. Different antigenic types have been recognised.

E.rhusiopathiae is a natural parasite of many animals. In humans it causes **erysipeloid**. Human infection usually occurs on the hand or fingers due to direct inoculation at the site of a cut or abrasion, in persons handling animals, fish or animal products. The lesions are painful, edematous and erythematous, usually involving the local lymph nodes and joints. Occasional cases of endocarditis have been reported. The bacillus is sensitive to penicillin, erythromycin and broad-spectrum antibiotics. It is intrinsically resistant to vancomycin.

ALCALIGENES FAECALIS

Alcaligenes faecalis is a Gram-negative, short, non-sporing bacillus. It is a strict aerobe and attacks glucose oxidatively in Hugh and Leifson's OF medium. They are motile by means of peritrichous flagella. They are usually oxidase positive, citrate positive and urease negative. Nitrate reduction is variable.

A.faecalis is a saprophyte found in water and soil contaminated with decaying organic matter. They can also be commensals in human and animal intestines. They can be isolated from the hospital environment in respirators, nebulisers, etc. They have been isolated

Table 44.1   *Differential features of non-sporing Gram-positive bacilli*

	L.monocytogenes	*E.rhusiopathiae*	**Diphtheroids**	*Lactobacilli*
Beta hemolysis	+	−	±	−
Catalase	+	−	±	−
Motility	+ (at 25°C)	−	−	−
H_2S production	−	+	−	−

from a variety of clinical specimens such as urine, pus and blood and have been considered responsible for urinary infections, infantile gastroenteritis and suppuration seen in various parts of the body.

CHROMOBACTERIUM VIOLACEUM

Chromobacterium violaceum is a Gram-negative, non-sporing bacillus, motile by means of polar and lateral flagella, resembling pseudomonads. They are facultative anaerobes, growing on ordinary media and producing violet pigment soluble in ethanol and insoluble in water and chloroform. They are oxidase negative and saprophytic in water and soil. Human infections have been recorded mainly in the tropics and consist of skin lesions with pyemia and multiple abscesses.

FLAVOBACTERIUM MENINGOSEPTICUM

Flavobacterium meningosepticum is a non-motile, Gram-negative bacillus, producing a yellowish pigment. It is oxidase positive, proteolytic and weakly fermentative. It is a ubiquitous saprophyte capable of causing opportunistic infections. It has been responsible for outbreaks of meningitis in newborn infants. Infection in adults leads to a mild febrile illness.

KLEBSIELLA GRANULOMATIS
(FORMERLY *KNOWN AS DONOVANIA GRANULOMATIS* AND *CALYMMATOBACTERIUM GRANULOMATIS*)

Donovan (1905) described the presence of characteristic intracellular bodies in smears from ulcerated lesions of a disease now known as **donovanosis** or **granuloma inguinale** caused by *Klebsiella granulomatis*. He considered the bodies to be parasites. The disease was first described by McLeod in India in 1882 and is seen mainly in the tropics.

Pathogenicity

The incubation period ranges from 1 to 12 weeks. It begins as a painless papule on the genitalia, which leads to a slowly progressive, autoinoculable ulcer and runs a chronic course. Donovanosis is a venereal disease and its pathogenicity is limited to human beings.

Laboratory diagnosis

This can be made by demonstration of **Donovan bodies** in Wright–Giemsa-stained impression smears from the lesions. They appear as rounded coccobacilli, 1–2 µm in size, within cystic spaces in large mononuclear cells. They show bipolar condensation of chromatin, giving a closed safety-pin appearance in stained smears. Capsules are usually seen as dense acidophilic areas around the bacilli. They are non-motile and Gram negative. They can be grown on egg yolk medium and on modified Levinthal's agar.

Treatment

Tetracycline given for at least three weeks is usually curative. Cotrimoxazole, chloramphenicol, gentamicin, quinolones and the newer macrolides are also effective.

ACINETOBACTER

The genus *Acinetobacter* contains strictly aerobic, non-motile, Gram-negative, coccobacillary rods that are oxidase negative, nitrate negative and do not ferment sugars. They are 1–1.5 × 1.5–2.5 µm in size, often appearing in pairs, mimicking neisseriae in appearance. Hence the name *Mimeae* was applied to them for a time. The earliest member of the group was a soil bacterium isolated in 1911 by Beijerinck, who named it *Micrococcus calcoaceticus*.

Clinical Case 1 A 60-year-old man was admitted in the Emergency department with respiratory distress. He was a chronic smoker and a known patient of chronic obstructive airway disease for the previous two years. On examination, he was found to have pneumonia. He was shifted to the ICU, started on empirical antibiotics and was put on the ventilator. Initial culture tests were negative. After seven days, he developed fresh consolidation patches in both lungs and had high-grade fever. A broncho-alveolar lavage was positive for Gram-negative coccobacilli which were non-motile, oxidase-negative and did not ferment sugars; this was identified as *Acinetobacter baumannii*. It was resistant to all antibiotics except carbapenems and colistin.

The classification of *Acinetobacter* has undergone many changes but currently by DNA hybridisation studies, they have been assigned to different DNA homology groups, called **genomo species**, within the genus *Acinetobacter*. Strains commonly isolated in clinical laboratories are called the *Acinetobacter calcoaceticus-baumannii complex* subdivided as follows: glucose oxidising, non-hemolytic clinical strains as *A.baumannii* (corresponding to the former *A.antitratus*); the glucose-negative non-hemolytic strain as *A.lwoffi* (corresponding to the form *Mima polymorpha);* and the hemolytic strain as *A.hemolyticus.*

A.baumannii: These form pinkish colonies on MacConkey medium. Acid without gas is formed in glucose, arabinose, xylose, and occasionally in rhamnose. It can grow at 44°C. A characteristic reaction is the formation of acid in 10%, but not 1%, lactose. Final identification can be done only by DNA hydridisation.

A.lwoffi: This forms yellow colonies on MacConkey medium and does not acidify sugars. Some strains are oxidase positive.

Acinetobacters are opportunistic pathogens and are frequently present on normal skin. They are an important cause of healthcare-associated infections like ventilator-associated pneumonia, meningitis and bacteremia. They can survive for long in the hospital environment and colonise almost all patients on prolonged hospitalisation. The hospital strains are also multidrug resistant, thus posing a great therapeutic challenge (*Case 1*). Prevention of healthcare-associated infections by following standard precautions is the best preventive strategy to control these infections which will indirectly reduce colonisation and antibiotic use.

STREPTOBACILLUS MONILIFORMIS AND SPIRILLUM MINUS

Two different bacteria—*Streptobacillus moniliformis* and *Spirillum minus*—both of which are natural parasites of rodents are responsible for a disease called **rat bite fever (RBF)**. The disease is characterised by relapsing fever, rash and arthralgia occurring days or weeks after a rat bite.

S.moniliformis is a highly pleomorphic, Gram-negative, non-motile bacillus. In cultures, it grows as tangled chains of rods of various lengths, with beaded or fusiform swellings, readily developing into L forms. Growth requires the presence of blood or other body fluids. It is catalase, oxidase, nitrate, urease and indole negative. It ferments glucose and a few other sugars, forming acid but no gas.

Streptobacillary RBF develops 2–10 days after exposure, with abrupt onset of fever, headache and myalgia, followed by petechial rash and arthritis.

Relapses are common in untreated cases. The disease can also occur as outbreaks, in the absence of rat bite. This condition, first observed in Haverhill, USA, is called **Haverhill fever** or **erythema arthriticum epidemicum**. It is believed to be also caused by the consumption of raw milk or water contaminated by rats.

Laboratory diagnosis is by isolation of the bacillus from blood or other body fluids. Smears of joint fluid may show pleomorphic, Gram-negative rods. Agglutination, complement fixation and fluorescent antibody tests have been used for serological diagnosis.

Spirillum minus is a short, actively motile bacterium, $3–5 \times 0.2–0.5$ μm in size, with two or three regular spirals and 1–7 amphitrichous flagella. It is Gram-negative but is better visualised by Giemsa or Fontana stains or by dark field microscopy. It was first observed in a rat by Carter (1888) in India. Japanese workers identified it as the causative agent of one type of RBF, called **sodoku**. It has not been cultivated in laboratory media.

Spirillary RBF has an incubation period of 1–4 weeks. The rat bite wound, which may have healed, suppurates at the onset of fever, with regional lymphadenopathy. The subsequent course is similar to the streptobacillary type. Mortality rates of up to 10 per cent have been reported, mainly due to endocarditis.

Laboratory diagnosis is by **microscopic examination** of blood and exudates from the lesion, by intraperitoneal inoculation into guinea pigs and mice and by demonstration of the spirilla in their blood and peritoneal fluid. Biological false positive reactions for syphilis serology occur in a proportion of RBF patients, more in the spirillary form.

Both types of RBF respond to penicillin and tetracycline. Oral penicillin or doxycycline after a rat bite is effective in prophylaxis.

CAMPYLOBACTER

The genus *Campylobacter* (Greek, meaning *curved rod*) contains slender, spirally curved, Gram-negative rods, 0.2–0.5 μm thick and 0.5–5 μm long. They are typically comma shaped but may occur as 'S' or multispiral chains. Old cultures are coccoid and pleomorphic. They are non-sporing and motile with a single unsheathed polar flagellum at one or both poles. Growth occurs under microaerophilic conditions, 5% oxygen concentration being optimal. Many pathogenic species are thermophilic, growing well at 42°C.

Campylobacters do not attack carbohydrates but are strongly oxidase positive.

Campylobacters first gained prominence in the 1970s as a common cause of human diarrheal disease, affecting children and adults. They can, on occasion, also cause systemic infections. They are important veterinary pathogens. Campylobacters of medical importance are as follows:

- Causing diarrheal disease: *C.jejuni, C.coli, C.lari*
- Causing extraintestinal infection: *C.fetus*
- Causing abscess: *C.sputorum, C.conciscus*

Campylobacter jejuni: Medically, this is the most important campylobacter species as it causes attacks of diarrhea worldwide. The infection is zoonotic, the source being food of animal origin, especially raw milk. It is part of the normal intestinal flora of domestic animals and birds, and is shed in their feces. It can be isolated frequently from surface waters.

Pathogenicity

Infection occurs by ingestion. The jejunum and ileum are the primary sites of colonisation, but it may spread to the colon and rectum. It is an invasive pathogen and may involve mesenteric lymph nodes and cause bacteremia. The incubation period is 1–7 days. Campylobacter is thought to invade the cells of the small intestine, damage them and disrupt fluid absorption.

The illness starts with fever, abdominal pain and watery diarrhea. Stool contains leucocytes and blood. The disease is usually self-limited, though campylobacter shedding may continue for weeks after recovery.

Laboratory diagnosis

Depends on isolation of the campylobacter from feces.

Direct microscopic examination—phase contrast or dark field microscopy to detect the darting or tumbling motility of the spiral rods—or demonstration of the small curved rods in stained smears may be useful for presumptive rapid diagnosis.

For **culture**, feces or rectal swabs are plated on selective media. In case of delay, a transport medium has to be used. Campylobacters survive for 1–2 weeks at 4°C in **Cary–Blair transport medium** but glycerol-saline is not satisfactory. The plating media commonly used are **Skirrow's, Butzler's** or **Campy BAP selective media.**

Resistance: *C.jejuni,* as well as *C.coli* and *C.lari,* are thermophilic and do not grow at 25°C. Inoculated plates are incubated at 42°C in an atmosphere of 5% oxygen, 10% carbon dioxide and 85% nitrogen. Thermophilic campylobacters can grow well at 37°C also but incubation at higher temperatures suppresses normal fecal flora to some extent.

Colonies usually appear in 48 hours. They are non-hemolytic, grey or colourless, moist and flat or convex. Suggestive colonies are screened by Gram staining, motility and oxidase tests. Confirmation is by further biochemical tests, including positive catalase and nitrate reduction tests.

C.coli causes an infection clinically indistinguishable from that due to *C.jejuni. C.coli* is commonly found in healthy pigs. It is differentiated from *C.jejuni* by the hippurate hydrolysis test which is positive only in the case of *C.jejuni.*

C.lari also causes a similar diarrheal disease. It can be distinguished from *C.jejuni* and *C.coli* by its resistance to nalidixic acid. *C.jejuni* and *C.coli* can be serotyped for epidemiological purposes.

C.jejuni is the most common bacterial cause of **diarrheal disease** in many developed countries—more common than salmonellae or shigellae. In the developing countries, *C.jejuni* is endemic, asymptomatic infection being widely prevalent in humans as well as domestic animals and birds. In this situation, clinical disease is infrequent and usually confined to children, while the older age groups are immune due to subclinical infection. For diagnosis, Gram-negative spiral rods with polar flagella can be cultured from stool by microaerophilic growth (5% oxygen, 10% carbon dioxide, 85% nitrogen) and by incubation at 42°C; the bacteria are identified by darting motility on wet mount.

The related genus *Arcobacteria* (*A.butzleri, A.cryaerophila*) also causes diarrheal disease. They are capable of aerobic growth.

Treatment

Fluid and electrolyte replacement is all that is generally required. When needed, erythromycin is the best antibiotic.

Campylobacter fetus: This organism was isolated in 1918 by Theobald Smith from infectious abortions in cattle and was named *Vibrio fetus.* Human infections by *C.fetus* may lead to bacteremia, sepsis and meningitis in immunocompromised hosts. The portal of entry is the gastrointestinal tract.

HELICOBACTER

Spiral, campylobacter-like bacteria were observed in close apposition to the gastric mucosa in several cases of gastritis and peptic ulcer, by Warren and Marshall in Australia in 1983. They were originally named *Campylobacter pylori*. As they differed in many respects from campylobacters, they have been redesignated as *Helicobacter pylori*. It now appears that helicobacters have caused human infection from ancient times. By enzyme immunoassay, helicobacter antigens have been detected in the intestines of pre-Columbian mummies in the USA. Today, helicobacters colonise the stomachs of half the human population of the world!

Clinical Case 2 A 35-year-old man presented to the hospital complaining of pain in the upper abdomen along with nausea, flatulence and bad breath for the previous four weeks. The pain typically increased in the middle of the night. He said that the pain decreased slightly after eating a meal. Initial treatment was with antacids but the episodes of pain continued to occur. On examination, epigastric tenderness was found. An endoscopy was performed and gastric biopsy was taken. It was positive for the urease test and the Gram smear showed the presence of Gram-negative, spiral bacilli. A diagnosis of gastric ulcer with gastritis was made. The patient was relieved of his symptoms after treatment with a combination of amoxicillin, clarithromycin and omeprazole along with other supportive care.

Helicobacters inhabit the stomachs of different animals, each with its own helicobacter species. *H.pylori* is adapted to the human gastric mucosa. The only other animal it infects is the monkey. A larger spiral bacterium of uncertain taxonomy, *H.heilmanii*, can occasionally infect humans and some animals like cats and dogs also. *H.cinaedi* and *H.fennelliae* are associated with proctitis in the HIV infected.

Helicobacter pylori: *H.pylori* is a Gram-negative spiral rod, motile by a unipolar tuft of lophotrichous flagella. It grows on chocolate agar or campylobacter media under microaerophilic conditions, with 5–20% CO_2 and pH 6–7. At 37°C, colonies take 2–7 days to develop. Coccoid forms appear in old cultures. It produces oxidase, catalase, phosphatase and H_2S.

A distinctive feature is the production of abundant urease, and this property has been used as a **rapid urease** test in gastric biopsy samples. It does not metabolise carbohydrates or reduce nitrate.

H.pylori is global, with a prevalence of 30–60 per cent, more in developing than in the developed countries. The sole source of *H.pylori* is the human gastric mucus. The exact mechanism of transmission is not clear, but it is likely to be oral–oral or fecal–oral. Poverty, overcrowding and poor hygiene favour transmission. With improvements in lifestyle, the prevalence of childhood infections has declined in the developed countries.

Pathogenicity

After an **incubation period** of a few days, *H.pylori* causes, in some persons, a mild acute gastritis which may last for about two weeks. The infection may be transient in some, but in most, it persists for years or decades. Such colonisation is usually asymptomatic, though chronic superficial gastritis may be demonstrable histologically. The bacteria are present only in the overlying mucus and do not invade the mucosa. This habitat also protects it from the acidic pH of the stomach. Gastric antrum is the commonest site of colonisation, though any part of the stomach may be involved. The infection is strictly confined to the gastric mucosa, in the stomach as well as in areas of gastric metaplasia and heterotopia in the duodenum. The exact pathogenic mechanisms are not clearly understood. Bacterial protease, toxins or ammonia released by urease activity or autoimmune responses to gastric antigens may all contribute.

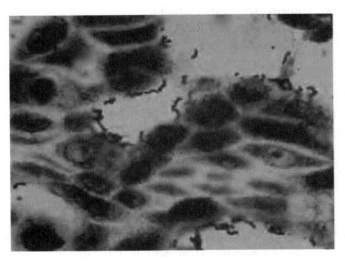

Fig. 44.1 *Helicobacter pylori* gastritis–silver stain

Peptic ulcer disease occurs in a proportion of the infected (*Case 2*). Chronic atrophic gastritis may be seen in the later stages. The infection is recognised as a risk factor for gastric malignancies such as adenocarcinoma and 'mucosa associated lymphoid tissue' (MALT) lymphomas. Such MALTomas appear to be antigen driven and are found to regress after elimination of *H.pylori* by treatment. Infection induces IgM, IgG, IgA and cellular immune response, but they do not seem to be protective.

H.pylori shows considerable **genetic diversity**, as is evident in molecular typing. The complete genome of the bacterium has been mapped. Virulence has been associated with certain alleles in genes, such as *cag* (cytotoxin associated gene) and *vac* (vacuolating cytotoxin gene). Urease production and motility also help in pathogenesis.

Laboratory diagnosis

Diagnostic tests are of two kinds:

- **Invasive tests** involve endoscopic biopsy of gastric mucosa.
  - A piece of the biopsy material put in a urease indicator medium shows a positive result in minutes and is done inside the endoscopy room.
  - Part of the biopsy is sent for examination by microscopy and culture. Microscopy of biopsy sections by silver staining or of Gram-stained smears is a useful method and is positive for spiral bacilli (Fig. 44.1). Culture is more sensitive, requires enriched medium, grows at 37°C in microaerophilic conditions and takes 3–7 days. It is catalase and oxidase positive.
- **Non-invasive tests** include:
  - Serology by ELISA; this is useful for sero epidemiology.
  - The **'urease breath test'**—the subject drinks a carbon labelled urea solution which can be detected in the breath. It is sensitive and reliable, but needs isotope assay facilities.

Treatment

H.pylori is sensitive to several antibiotics and to bismuth salts. The standard treatment is a combination of bismuth subsalicylate, tetracycline (or amoxycillin) and metronidazole for two weeks. An alternative schedule uses a proton pump inhibitor like omeprazole and clarithromycin. Treatment is indicated only for *H.pylori*-related gastric or duodenal ulceration and not for asymptomatic colonisation. Drug resistance and recurrence are frequent.

LEGIONELLA PNEUMOPHILA

The name Legionnaires' disease was given to an apparently new illness which broke out among members of the American Legion who attended a convention in Philadelphia in 1976. The disease was characterised by fever, cough and chest pain, leading on to pneumonia and often ending fatally.

Morphology

Legionellae are thin, non-capsulated bacilli, $2–5 \times 0.1–0.3$ μm in size, coccobacillary in clinical material and assuming longer forms in culture. Most are motile with polar or subpolar flagella. They are Gram negative but stain poorly, particularly in smears from clinical specimens. They stain better by silver impregnation, but are best visualised by direct fluorescent antibody (DFA) staining with monoclonal or polyclonal sera.

Culture characteristics

They have fastidious requirements and grow on complex media such as buffered charcoal, yeast extract (BCYE) agar, with L-cysteine and antibiotic supplements, with 5% CO_2, at pH 6.9, temperature 35°C and 90% humidity. Growth is slow and colonies take 3–6 days to appear.

Epidemiology

Legionellae are widely distributed in natural water sources, such as stagnant waters, mud and hot springs, where the nutritional and growth requirements for these fastidious bacteria are provided by some types of algae. Legionellae survive and multiply inside free-living amebae and other protozoa. They also multiply in some artificial aquatic environments, which serve as amplifiers. Human infection is typically by inhalation of aerosols produced by cooling towers, air conditioners and shower heads which act as disseminators. Aerosolised legionellae can survive for long and can be carried over long distances. No animal reservoir exists, and infection is limited to human beings. No carrier state is established. Human-to-human transmission does not occur.

The outcome of inhalation of legionellae depends on the size of the infecting dose, virulence of the strain and resistance of the host. Known risk factors are smoking, alcohol, advanced age, intercurrent illness, hospitalisation and immunodeficiency. Men are more often affected than women. In the developed countries, legionellosis accounts for 1–3 per cent of community-acquired and 10–30 per cent of hospital-acquired pneumonias. Its prevalence in the developing countries is not adequately known.

The causative agent has been called *Legionella pneumophila*. Subsequent investigations have revealed that the disease is neither new nor localised. Infection with *L.pneumophila* is now known to cause protean manifestations. Two distinct clinical patterns have been identified and designated as Legionnaires' disease and Pontiac fever, together known as **legionellosis**.

Pathogenicity

Following entry into the alveoli through aerosols, legionellae multiply inside the monocytes and macrophages. Dissemination occurs by endobronchial, hematogenous, lymphatic or contiguous spread. Because of their intracellular location, humoral antibodies are ineffective. Cellular immunity is responsible for recovery.

Legionnaires' disease may be either epidemic or sporadic. The incubation period is 2–10 days. The disease presents with fever, non-productive cough and dyspnea, rapidly progressing, if untreated, to pneumonia. Diarrhea and encephalopathy are common. Case fatality may be 15–20 per cent, the cause of death being progressive respiratory failure and shock. All age groups are susceptible, though more cases have occurred in the elderly.

Pontiac fever is a milder, non-fatal, 'influenza-like' illness with fever, chills, myalgia and headache. Outbreaks with high attack rates may occur.

The discovery of *L.pneumophila* led to the isolation of many related bacteria, which have been placed in the genus *Legionella*, under the family Legionellaceae. Some 40 species of legionellae have been recognised, many of them with multiple serogroups. The original isolate in this genus is designated *L.pneumophila* serogroup 1 (SG1), which accounts for nearly all severe infections. Examples of other species that cause human infection less often are *L.micdadei*, *L.bozemanii*, *L.dumoffii* and *L.gormanii*.

Laboratory diagnosis

This is by the demonstration of legionellae in clinical specimens, such as sputum, bronchial aspirate and lung biopsy, by direct fluorescent antibody test and culture, by the identification of legionella antigens in urine by latex agglutination or ELISA, and by the detection of serum antibody by ELISA or indirect immunofluorescent assay. Urinary antigen detection is also useful in conducting community-based studies.

Treatment

For treatment, the newer macrolides, ciprofloxacin and tetracyclines are effective. Rifampicin is used in severe cases. Beta lactamase antibiotics and aminoglycosides are ineffective.

EIKENELLA CORRODENS

This is an oxidase-positive, facultatively anaerobic, capnophilic, Gram-negative bacillus. The name 'corrodens' refers to the characteristic pitting or corroding of blood agar by colonies of the bacterium. It is present in the mouth, upper respiratory tract and gastrointestinal tract of human beings. Infection follows salivary or fecal contamination and usually involves the skin and subcutaneous tissues, though rarely osteomyelitis, pneumonia, endocarditis and meningitis may occur. It is sensitive to penicillin and tetracycline.

CARDIOBACTERIUM HOMINIS

This Gram-negative, pleomorphic bacillus which occurs commonly as a commensal in the human nose and throat may cause endocarditis, particularly in those with pre-existing cardiovascular disease. It grows on blood agar under 3–5% CO_2 and high humidity. It ferments a wide range of sugars, forms indole and is oxidase positive, but catalase and nitrate negative. It is sensitive to many antibiotics, penicillin and streptomycin being the recommended drugs.

CAPNOCYTOPHAGA

The *Capnocytophaga* species are Gram-negative, fusiform gliding bacilli which form part of normal mouth flora. They may occasionally cause systemic infections in the immunodeficient.

GARDNERELLA VAGINALIS

Gardnerella vaginalis is a small, Gram-negative, non-motile, pleomorphic rod which shows metachromatic granules. It was formerly known as *Haemophilus vaginalis* or *Corynebacterium vaginale*. Virulence factors of *G.vaginalis* include pili, production of a hemolytic cytotoxin and phospholipase A2 activity. It grows on blood or chocolate agar aerobically under 5% CO_2. Minute colonies appear in 24–48 hours and are hemolytic on human or rabbit blood agar. It is catalase, oxidase, indole and urease negative.

G.vaginalis is considered responsible for bacterial vaginosis, a mild but common condition characterised by raised vaginal pH > 4.5, foul smelling discharge and the presence of 'clue cells', which are vaginal epithelial cells with their surface studded with numerous small bacteria. Bacterial vaginosis is also associated with anaerobic bacteria, particularly *Mobiluncus* and the diagnosis is made on microscope criteria of a Gram smear of a high vaginal swab using the **Nugent score**. Metronidazole is effective in treatment.

MORAXELLA (BRANHAMELLA) CATARRHALIS

Gram-negative cocci, usually arranged in pairs, growing readily on nutrient agar at 18–42°C, producing non-pigmented colonies and not fermenting sugars were formerly known as *Neisseria catarrhalis*. They have been reclassified as *Branhamella*, and again as *Moraxella catarrhalis*. They form part of the normal pharyngeal flora but can cause respiratory infections, including otitis media, sinusitis, tracheobronchitis and pneumonia. As many strains produce beta lactamases, penicillins are not useful in treatment unless given in combination with clavulanate or sulbactam.

It is the third most common cause of otitis media (after *Streptococcus pneumoniae* and non-typeable *Haemophilus influenzae*). It is a more common cause of pulmonary disease in COPD and in the elderly than previously thought. For diagnosis, sputum from lung disease is used for culture in 5% CO_2, which yields typical colonies on modified Thayer–Martin agar; Gram-negative diplococci can be detected by direct microscopy. The bacteria can also be detected by PCR and by a commercial test kit. *Moraxella* infection is treated with antibiotics that do not induce the production of beta lactamases (amoxycillin-clavulanate).

MORAXELLA LACUNATA

These are short, plump, Gram-negative bacilli usually arranged in pairs. They are non-flagellated but have been reported to be sluggishly motile. Strictly aerobic, they grow on ordinary media. They are oxidase and catalase positive, indole and H_2S negative and non-fermentative.

M.lacunata was first reported as the cause of angular conjunctivitis by Morax and Axenfeld. Hence it is also known as the Morax–Axenfeld bacillus.

KINGELLA

The genus *Kingella*, comprising some species of oxidase-positive, non-motile, Gram-negative rods, with a tendency to occur as coccobacillary and diplococcal forms, was formerly grouped under the genus *Moraxella*. They are part of normal oral flora. *K.kingae* has been associated with endocarditis and infections of the bones, joints and tendons.

RECAP

- *Listeria monocytogenes* is a Gram-positive coccobacillus found in unpasteurised milk and many raw foods. It causes foodborne gastroenteritis, bacteremia in pregnant women and the immunocompromised and early and late onset infections in infants.
- *Erysipelothrix rhusiopathiae* is a rod-shaped bacterium which is non-motile, non-sporing, microaerophilic and Gram positive.
- *Alcaligenes* are aerobic, oxidase-positive, catalase-positive rods exhibiting motility and not producing acid from carbohydrates in conventional culture media.

- *Chromobacterium* are gram-negative bacilli, oxidase and catalase positive.
- *Flavobacterium* spp are Gram-negative bacilli, catalase positive, oxidase positive, and grow on ordinary culture media producing a yellow pigment. *F.meningosepticum* occasionally causes meningitis in infants.
- *Klebsiella granulomatis* is the causative organism of granuloma inguinale (donovanosis). The coccoid, rod-shaped organisms are Gram negative.
- The *Acinetobacter* species are Gram-negative coccobacilli that are non-motile and are strict aerobes. They are an important cause of nosocomial infections and are multidrug resistant.
- Rat bite fever is caused by two different bacilli: *Streptobacillus moniliformis* and *Spirillum minus*:
- Members of *Campylobacter* are curved, Gram-negative, oxidase-positive, motile, rod-shaped microaerophilic organisms. *Campylobacter jejuni* is a common cause of enteritis in humans and animals.
- *Helicobacter pylori* causes duodenal and stomach ulcers and is associated with gastric adenocarcinoma and lymphoma. They produce urease.
- Members of the genus *Legionella* are catalase-positive, weakly oxidase-positive, motile, Gram-negative bacilli whose natural habitat is water.
  - *Legionella pneumophila* causes Legionnaires' disease and Pontiac fever. Infection is acquired by aerosol droplets.
- *Eikenella corrodens* are Gram-negative, non-motile, rod-shaped bacteria which are oxidase positive.
- *Gardnerella vaginalis* is a rod-shaped bacterium which is non-motile, oxidase negative, catalase negative and Gram negative. It is considered to be a cause of vaginosis.
- Members of the genus *Moraxella* are rod-shaped bacteria, which are non-motile, obligate aerobes, both catalase and oxidase positive, asaccharolytic and Gram negative.

SHORT NOTES

1. *Listeria monocytogenes*
2. Donovanosis
3. *Helicobacter pylori*
4. Rate bite fever
5. *Legionella pneumophilia*
6. *Acinetobacter* species
7. *Gardnerella vaginalis*
8. *Campylobacter* species

45 Rickettsiaceae

INTRODUCTION

The family Rickettsiaceae includes a diverse group of organisms that share the common features of intracellular growth and transmission by hemagogous (blood sucking) arthropod vectors (lice, fleas, ticks, mites). It is named after Howard Taylor Ricketts who discovered spotted fever rickettsia (1906) and died of typhus fever contracted during his studies. In vertebrates, including humans, they infect the vascular endothelium and reticuloendothelial cells.

Characteristics

Rickettsiae are small, Gram-negative bacilli. They are virus-like in that they cannot be seen by the ordinary light microscope and are obligate intracellular parasites. They have many features of bacteria:

- A cell wall made of peptidoglycan
- Metabolic enzymes
- Both DNA and RNA
- Reproduction by binary fission
- Susceptibility to antibacterial agents

Classification

The family currently comprises three genera: *Rickettsia*, *Orientia* and *Ehrlichia*, which appear to have descended from a common ancestor. Former members of the family, *Coxiella burnetii*, which causes Q fever, and *Rochalimaea quintana*, causing trench fever, have been excluded because the former is not primarily arthropod-borne and the latter not an obligate intracellular parasite, being capable of growth in cell-free media, besides having different genetic properties.

GENUS *RICKETTSIA*

The genus *Rickettsia* consists of the causative agents of two groups of diseases (Table 45.1):

- Typhus fevers caused by *R.prowazekii*
- Spotted fevers caused by *R.rickettsii*

Table 45.1 *Human diseases caused by the* Rickettsia *and* Orientia *species*

Group	Species	Disease	Vector	Vertebrate reservoir	Distribution
Typhus	*R.prowazekii*	Epidemic typhus	Louse	Human beings	Worldwide
	"	Brill–Zinsser disease	"	Human beings	America, Europe, Australia
	R.typhi	Endemic typhus	Rat flea	Rat	Worldwide
	R.felis	"	Cat flea	Opossum	USA
Spotted fever group	*R.rickettsii*	Rocky Mountain spotted fever	Tick	Rabbit, dog Small rodents	North America
	R.siberica	Siberian tick typhus	"	Wild animals, cattle	Russia, Mongolia
	R.conori	Fever Boutonneuse	"	Dog, rodents	Mediterranean
	"	South African tick typhus	"	"	South Africa
	"	Kenyan tick typhus	"	Rodents	Kenya
	"	Indian tick typhus	"	? Rodents	India
	R.australis	Queensland tick typhus	"	Bush rodents	N Australia
	R.japonica	Oriental spotted fever	"	?	Japan
	R.akari	Rickettsial pox	Gamasid mite	Mouse	USA, Russia
Scrub typhus	*O.tsutsugamushi*	Scrub typhus	Trombiculid mite	Small rodents, birds	East Asia, Pacific Islands, Australia

Morphology

In smears from infected tissues, rickettsiae appear as pleomorphic coccobacilli, 0.3–0.6 × 0.8–2 µm in size. They are non-motile and non-capsulated. They are Gram negative, though they do not take the stain well. They stain bluish-purple with the Giemsa and Castaneda stains and deep red with the Machiavello and Gimenez stains.

Under the electron microscope, rickettsiae are seen to have a three-layered cell wall, a trilaminar plasma membrane and an outer slime layer.

Cultivation

Rickettsiae are unable to grow in cell-free media. Growth generally occurs in the cytoplasm of infected cells, but in the case of spotted fever rickettsiae, growth may take place in the nucleus as well. Rickettsiae grow best in cells that are not metabolising actively. The optimum temperature for growth is 32–35°C.

They are readily cultivated in the yolk sac of developing chick embryos, as first shown by Cox. They also grow on mouse fibroblast, HeLa, HEp-2, Detroit 6 and other continuous cell lines but tissue cultures are not satisfactory for primary isolation. Laboratory animals such as guinea pigs and mice are useful for the isolation of rickettsiae from patients. They may also be propagated in arthropods.

Resistance

Rickettsiae are readily inactivated by physical and chemical agents. They are rapidly destroyed at 56°C and at room temperature when separated from host components, unless preserved in skimmed milk or a suspending medium containing sucrose, potassium phosphate and glutamate (SPG medium).

Antigenic structure

Rickettsiae have species- and group-specific antigens. The immunodominant surface protein antigens (SPA) of *R.prowazekii* and *R.typhi* (typhus group) have both species-specific and cross-reactive epitopes.

Spotted fever rickettsiae have dominant outer membrane proteins (OMP) A and B, the former being a species-specific antigen acting as an adhesin for host cells, and the latter showing limited cross-reaction with SPA of typhus rickettsiae.

The third surface antigen is an alkali stable polysaccharide found in some rickettsiae and in some strains of the *Proteus* bacilli. This sharing of antigens between rickettsiae and proteus is the basis for the **Weil–Felix reaction** used for the diagnosis of rickettsial infections by demonstration of agglutinins to *Proteus* strains OX 19, OX 2 and OX K.

Pathogenesis

Rickettsiae are transmitted to humans by arthropod vectors through their bite or feces. On entry into the human body, the rickettsiae multiply locally and enter the blood. They become localised chiefly in the vascular endothelial cells, which enlarge, degenerate and cause thrombus formation, with partial or complete occlusion of the vascular lumen. The overall pathological features of the rickettsial diseases are similar in that they cause acute febrile illness, characterised by septicemia with maculopapular rash and fever; there may occasionally be hemorrhage and fatalities may occur in about 20 per cent of untreated cases. This can be explained by the damage to the vascular endothelium.

The long survival of rickettsiae in various organs and lymphatic tissues of infected humans and animals is a distinctive feature in its pathogenesis and is of importance in the epidemiology of some rickettsial diseases.

TYPHUS FEVER GROUP

This group of diseases consists of epidemic typhus, recrudescent typhus (Brill–Zinsser disease) and endemic typhus.

Epidemic typhus (louseborne typhus)

R.prowazekii causes epidemic typhus. In recent times, the main foci have been Eastern Europe, Africa, South America and Asia. In India, the endemic spot is Kashmir. Humans are the only natural vertebrate hosts. Several animals—guinea pigs, mice, cotton rats and gerbils—may be infected experimentally. Natural infection in flying squirrels has been reported from southeastern USA. They may possibly act as reservoir hosts, infection being spread by the squirrel louse and flea.

The human body louse *Pediculus humanus corporis* is the vector. The head louse may also transmit the infection but not the pubic louse. The lice become infected by feeding on rickettsiaemic patients. The rickettsiae multiply in the gut of the lice and appear in the feces in 3–5 days. Lice succumb to the infection within 2–4 weeks, remaining infective till they die. They can transmit the infection after about a week of being infected. Lice may be transferred from person to person. Being sensitive to temperature changes in the host, they leave the febrile patient or the cooling carcass and parasitise other persons. Lice defecate while feeding.

Infection is transmitted:
- when the contaminated louse feces is rubbed through the minute abrasions caused by scratching,
- (occasionally) by aerosols of dried louse feces through inhalation or through the conjunctiva.

The incubation period is 5–15 days. The disease starts with fever and chills. A characteristic rash appears on the fourth or fifth day, starting on the trunk and spreading over the limbs but sparing the face,

palms and soles. Towards the second week, the patient becomes stuporous and delirious. Case fatality may reach 40 per cent and increases with age.

Recrudescent typhus (Brill–Zinsser disease)

In some patients who recover from epidemic typhus, the rickettsiae may remain latent in the lymphoid tissues or organs for years. Such latent infection may, at times, be reactivated leading to recrudescent typhus. This explains the manner in which the rickettsia is able to survive without extrahuman reservoirs. In itself, the disease is not important but such cases occurring in louse-ridden communities may initiate epidemics of typhus fever.

Endemic typhus

R.typhi (*R.mooseri*) causes murine (or fleaborne) typhus, which is worldwide in distribution. It mainly affects rats, which are also reservoirs of infection, and is transmitted by the flea *Xenopsylla cheopis*. It is a milder disease than epidemic typhus.

The organism is maintained in nature as a mild infection of rats. The rickettsia multiplies in the gut of the flea and is shed in its feces. The flea is unaffected but remains infectious for the rest of its natural span of life. Humans acquire the disease usually through:
- the bite of infected fleas, when their saliva or feces is rubbed in,
- through aerosols of dried feces or
- by ingesting food recently contaminated with infected rat urine or flea feces
- Human infection is a dead end. Person-to-person transmission does not occur. In Kashmir and China, lice have been known to transmit endemic typhus in humans, producing smouldering outbreaks.

Neil–Mooser reaction: *R.typhi* and *R.prowazekii* are similar but may be differentiated by biological and immunological tests. When male guinea pigs are inoculated intraperitoneally with blood from a case of endemic typhus or with a culture of *R.typhi*, they develop fever and a characteristic scrotal inflammation. The scrotum becomes enlarged and the testes cannot be pushed back into the abdomen because of inflammatory adhesions between the layers of the tunica vaginalis. This is known as the **Neil–Mooser** or **tunica reaction**. This reaction is negative with *R.prowazekii*. Other methods used include IFA, ELISA and PCR-based DNA tests.

Endemic typhus is worldwide in prevalence but is not of much public health importance as the disease is mild and sporadic and can now be easily controlled.

SPOTTED FEVER GROUP

Rickettsiae of this group possess a common soluble antigen and multiply in the nucleus as well as in the cytoplasm of host cells. They are all transmitted by ticks, except *R.akari*, which is mite-borne.

Tick typhus

The rickettsiae are transmitted transovarially in ticks, which therefore act as both vectors and reservoirs. The infection may be transmitted to vertebrate hosts by any of the larval stages or by adult ticks. Ticks are not harmed by the rickettsiae and remain infected for life. The rickettsiae are shed in tick feces but transmission to human beings is primarily by bite, as the rickettsiae also invade the salivary glands of the ticks. All rickettsiae of this group pass through natural cycles in domestic and wild animals or birds.

Rocky Mountain spotted fever is the most serious type of spotted fever and is the first to have been described. It is prevalent in many parts of North and South America and is transmitted by *Dermacentor andersoni* and related species of ticks.

R.conori causes **Indian tick typhus**. The strains isolated from the Mediterranean littoral, Kenya, South Africa and India are indistinguishable. This species is named after Conor, who provided the first description of the Mediterranean disease 'fievre boutonneuse' (1910). The disease was first observed in India by Megaw (1917) in the foothills of the Himalayas. The investigation of Kalra, Rao, Soman, Helig and Naidu established that the disease is found in many parts of India. The tick *Rhipicephalus sanguineus* is the most important vector. *Haemaphysalis leachi*, *Amblyomma* and *Hyalomma* ticks can also transmit the infection.

Rickettsial pox

The mildest rickettsial disease of humans is a self-limited, non-fatal, vesicular exanthem first observed in New York (1946). The name is derived from the resemblance of the disease to chickenpox. It is also called vesicular or varicelliform rickettsiosis. The causative agent is *R.akari* (from *akari*, meaning mite). The reservoir of infection is the domestic mouse, *Mus musculus*, and the vector is the mite, *Liponyssoides* (formerly *Allodermanyssus*) *sanguineus*, in which transovarial transmission occurs. *R.akari* has also been isolated from wild rodents in Korea. The disease has also been reported in Eastern Europe and Korea.

SCRUB TYPHUS (CHIGGER-BORNE TYPHUS)

Scrub typhus is caused by *Orientia tsutsugamushi* (formerly *R.tsutsugamushi*, *R.orientalis*). It occurs all along east Asia, from Korea to Indonesia, and in the Pacific Islands including Australia. It was first observed in Japan where it was found to be transmitted by mites. The disease was therefore called *tsutsugamushi* (from *tsutsuga*, meaning dangerous, and *mushi* meaning insect or mite). It is found only in areas with a suitable climate, plenty of moisture and scrub vegetation.

The vectors are **trombiculid mites** of the genus *Leptotrombidium*—*L.akamushi* in Japan and *L.deliensis* in India. The mites inhabit sharply demarcated areas in the soil where the microecosystem is favourable (**mite islands**). Humans are infected when they trespass onto these mite islands and are bitten by the **mite larvae (chiggers)**. The mites feed on the serum of warm-blooded animals only once during their cycle of development, and adult mites feed only on plants. The microbes are transmitted transovarially in mites. Various rodents and birds act as reservoirs and also help in spreading the orientiae to fresh areas.

Scrub typhus, originally found in scrub jungles, has also been identified in a variety of other habitats, such as sandy beaches, mountain deserts and equatorial rainforests. The term chigger-borne typhus has therefore been suggested as a more apt designation. Four factors are essential for the establishment of a microfocus of infection, namely, co-existence and intimate relationship among *O.tsutsugamushi*, chiggers, rats and secondary or transitional forms of vegetation (known as the **zoonotic tetrad**).

The incubation period is 1–3 weeks. Patients typically develop a characteristic **eschar** at the site of the mite bite, with regional lymphadenopathy and maculopapular rash. The disease sets in with fever, headache and conjunctival injection. Encephalitis and pneumonia may be seen in severe cases.

The disease is not a serious problem in civilian practice but assumes great importance in military medicine, especially during jungle warfare, as was recognised in the Indo-Burmese theatre in the Second World War.

Considerable differences exist among different strains of *O.tsutsugamushi* in antigenic properties and virulence, a factor that complicates serodiagnosis and immunoprophylaxis. Three major antigenic types have been recognised: Karp, Gilliam and Kato.

GENUS *EHRLICHIA*

Ehrlichiae are small, Gram-negative, obligate intracellular bacteria which have an affinity towards blood cells. In the cytoplasm of infected phagocytic cells, they grow within phagosomes as mulberry-like clusters called *morula* (meaning mulberry). They are tick-borne. Similar organisms under the names of *Anaplasma*, *Cowdria* and *Neorickettsia* had long been known to veterinary scientists as causative agents of tick-borne infections of cattle and sheep.

Pathogenicity

Three human infections caused by this group of organisms have been identified:

- The first of these human diseases, reported from Japan in 1954, was a case resembling **glandular fever**; the patient showed serological response against the agent of canine ehrlichiosis. The causative agent has been named *Ehrlichia sennetsu* (from 'sennetsu', the Japanese word for glandular fever). It is endemic in Japan and parts of southeast Asia.It causes lymphoid hyperplasia and atypical lymphocytosis. No arthropod vector has been identified. Human infection is suspected to be caused by ingestion of fish carrying infected flukes.
- The second type of infection is '**human monocytic ehrlichiosis**' caused by *Ehrlichia chaffeensis*. It is transmitted by *Amblyomma* ticks. Deer and rodents are believed to be reservoir hosts. Human disease is associated with leucopenia, thrombocytopenia and elevated liver enzymes. Multisystem involvement and fatality may occur.
- The third is '**human granulocytic ehrlichiosis**' caused by an organism either identical with or closely related to the equine pathogen *Ehrlichia equi* (probably *E.phagocytophila*). It is transmitted by *Ixodes* ticks. Deer, cattle and sheep are the suspected reservoir. Leucopenia and thrombocytopenia are seen in patients. Giemsa-stained blood films may show the morula form of the ehrlichia.

Doxycycline is recommended for the treatment of ehrlichiosis.

Laboratory diagnosis

Rickettsial diseases may be diagnosed in the laboratory either by isolation of the rickettsiae or by serology. As rickettsiae are highly infectious and have caused several serious and fatal infections among laboratory workers, their isolation should be attempted with utmost care and only in laboratories equipped with appropriate safety provisions.

1. Specimens: For diagnosis, blood and tissues samples are collected for culture, and serum for serological tests.

2. Direct microscopy: It is possible to detect aggregations of rickettsial particles (but not individual particles) in cytoplasmic inclusion bodies under the light microscope, when stained by Giemsa (purple-coloured basophilic inclusions) or Machiavello's stain (red-coloured inclusions).

In ehrlichiosis, morula forms are seen in infected phagocytic cells stained by the Giemsa stain.

Skin biopsies from the centre of petechial lesions can be examined (up to 48 hours after anti-rickettsial drugs have been given) by immunofluorescence, immunoenzyme and immunohistochemical methods.

3. Culture: It is not possible to isolate *Rickettsiae* in artificial (cell-free) culture media. However, the species can be grown in:

- The yolk sac of embryonated hens' eggs.
- **Male guinea pigs** or **mice**
  Blood samples are collected from patients in the early phase of the disease. A blood clot ground in skimmed milk or any suitable suspending medium is inoculated intraperitoneally. The animals have to be observed for 3–4 weeks and their temperature recorded daily. Their response to rickettsial infection varies. In Rocky Mountain spotted fever, guinea pigs develop fever, scrotal necrosis and may even die. With *R.typhi*, *R.conori* and *R.akari*, they develop fever and tunica reaction. *R.prowazekii* produces only fever without any testicular inflammation. Smears from the peritoneum, tunica and spleen of infected animals may be stained by the Giemsa or Gimenez methods to demonstrate the rickettsiae.
- In **cell** and **tissue culture**, which is the most widely used method for isolation. *Rickettsiae* grow well in 3–5 days on Vero cell MRC 5 cell cover slip cultures and can be identified by immunofluorescence using group- and strain-specific monoclonal antibodies.

4. Serological tests: These are not used for early diagnosis of rickettsial diseases, from a treatment perspective, but to confirm the diagnosis for epidemiological investigations.

Serological diagnosis may be by the heterophile **Weil–Felix reaction** or by specific tests using rickettsial antigens. The Weil–Felix reaction is an agglutination test in which sera are tested for agglutinins to the O antigens of certain non-motile *Proteus* strains OX 19, OX 2 and OX K. The test was developed from the chance observation of Weil and Felix (1916) that a *Proteus* strain isolated from the urine of a patient of epidemic typhus was agglutinated by the patient's serum as well as by the sera of other typhus patients. The basis of the test is the sharing of an alkali-stable carbohydrate antigen by some rickettsiae and by certain strains of *Proteus*, *Pr.vulgaris* OX 19 and OX 2 and *Pr.mirabilis* OX K. The test is usually done as tube agglutination, though rapid slide agglutination methods have been used for screening.

Sera from epidemic and endemic typhus agglutinate OX 19 and sometimes OX 2 also. The test is negative or only weakly positive in Brill–Zinsser disease. In tick-borne spotted fever, both OX 19 and OX 2 are agglutinated. OX K agglutinins are found only in scrub typhus. The test is negative in rickettsial pox, trench fever, and Q fever (Table 45.2).

The Weil–Felix reaction is a simple and useful test for the diagnosis of some rickettsial diseases. The antibody appears rapidly during the course of the disease, reaches peak titres of up to 1:1000 or 1:5000 by the second week and declines rapidly during convalescence. False positive reaction may occur in some cases of urinary or other infections by *Proteus* and at times in typhoid fever and liver diseases. Hence it is desirable to demonstrate a rise in titre of antibodies for the diagnosis of rickettsial infection.

Complement fixation test: The most frequently used serological method for rickettsial antigens is the complement fixation test. This may be done using the group-specific soluble antigen or the type-specific washed rickettsial antigen. The former test is in routine use but the latter is necessary for differentiation between epidemic and endemic typhus.

Other serological tests include agglutination of rickettsial suspensions, passive hemagglutination of red cells sensitised by ESS (erythrocyte sensitising substance), toxin neutralisation, immunofluorescence and radioisotope precipitation. Currently, more reliable immunofluorescence and enzyme immunoassay diagnostic tests are commercially available.

5. Molecular methods: Rickettsial DNA can be detected by polymerase chain reaction, which permits rapid, specific identification of the infecting agent in skin biopsy, necrotic tissue and blood mononuclear cells.

Treatment

Rickettsiae are susceptible to tetracycline, chloramphenicol and ciprofloxacin. Penicillin and sulphonamides are ineffective but para-aminobenzoic acid has an inhibitory action on rickettsiae. Sulphonamides may actually enhance the growth of rickettsiae and worsen the condition if administered to patients.

Immunoprophylaxis

Rickettsial diseases may be prevented by general measures such as control of vectors and animal reservoirs. Immunisation is useful in special situations. Killed and live vaccines have been prepared against epidemic typhus. The earliest of these was phenolised intestinal contents of lice infected per rectum with *R.prowazekii* (Weigl's vaccine). This was too complicated for mass production. Castaneda developed a formalinised mouse lung vaccine. Effective vaccination became possible only after Cox developed the inactivated yolk sac vaccine. A live vaccine using the attenuated *strain E* has been found to be highly immunogenic but a proportion

Table 45.2 *Weil–Felix reaction in rickettsial diseases*

Disease	Agglutination pattern with		
	OX 19	OX 2	OX K
Epidemic typhus	+++	+	−
Brill–Zinsser disease	Usually negative or weakly positive		−
Endemic typhus	+++	±	−
Tickborne spotted fever	++	++	−
Scrub typhus	−	−	+++

of vaccines develop mild disease. The Cox type vaccine has also been prepared against Rocky Mountain spotted fever. However, there is no satisfactory vaccine available against any of the rickettsial diseases.

Control

Eradication of rickettsial diseases appears to be virtually impossible because of the cycles maintained in rodents, wild animals and vectors. Measures to reduce rodent or ectoparasite populations may help. Infested persons should be deloused, and their clothing and bedding decontaminated. Persons entering endemic areas should wear protective clothing to avoid infestation by vectors. There is currently no safe, effective vaccine for any of the rickettsial diseases.

GENUS *COXIELLA*: Q FEVER

Derrick (1935) investigating an outbreak of typhoid-like fever in abattoir workers in Brisbane, Australia, transmitted the infection to guinea pigs by inoculation of blood from patients. As the causative agent of the disease was unknown, it was referred to as 'Query' or Q fever.

Morphology

Coxiella burnetii is a pleomorphic coccobacillary bacterium, with a Gram-negative cell wall and an ill-defined developmental cycle. It is an obligate intracellular pathogen, primarily infecting monocyte-macrophage cells. It occurs as rods 0.2–0.4 × 0.4–1.0 μm in size or as spheres 0.3–0.4 μm in diameter. It is filterable. Generally regarded as Gram negative, it is better stained with Gimenez and other rickettsiae strains.

It shares many features with the Rickettsiae (exhibits obligate intracellular parasitism, has a cell wall composed of peptidoglycan, possesses both DNA and RNA, is susceptible to antibacterial agents), but differs in being more heat resistant and in not having a vector for transmission. The Weil–Felix test cannot be used for the diagnosis of *Coxiella* infection. The organisms show small and large forms at various stages, the significance of which is uncertain. Infection is endemic and largely subclinical in cattle, sheep and goats, from where most human infection is acquired.

In humans, Q fever manifests in acute (severe influenza-like illness) and chronic (endocarditis) forms.

Complications (hepatitis, chronic infection, endocarditis, cirrhosis) may occur in untreated or poorly responsive patients.

Epidemiology

Q fever is distributed worldwide as a **zoonosis** solidly established in domestic livestock. Wild animals such as the bandicoot may be the primary reservoir. It is transmitted among them and to cattle, sheep and poultry by *Ixodid* ticks. Transovarial transmission occurs in ticks. *Coxiella* are abundant in tick feces and survive in dried feces for long periods. They are shed in the milk of infected animals. They are particularly abundant in their products of conception and contaminate the environment at parturition.

Pathogenicity

Human infection may occur occupationally through handling wool or hides, meat or other animal products contaminated with the organism. Drinking infected milk can transmit the infection. *Coxiella* may enter through abraded skin, mucosa, lungs or the intestinal tract. Person-to-person transmission is rare. Ticks do not seem to be important in human infection.

C.burnetii is widely prevalent in birds and animals in India, as shown by serological surveys, but human disease has been identified only rarely.

- The human disease is an acute systemic infection characterised by interstitial pneumonia. The clinical picture is very variable and asymptomatic infections very common.
- In chronic Q fever, the organism spreads through almost all organs and may cause hepatitis, meningoencephalitis or endocarditis. Spontaneous recovery is usual.
- The coxiella may remain latent in the tissues of patients for 2–3 years.

In dried feces or wool it survives for a year or more at 4°C and in meat at least for one month. It is not completely inactivated at 60°C or by 1% phenol in one hour. In milk it may survive pasteurisation by the holding method, but the flash method is effective. It grows well in the yolk sac of chick embryos and in various cell cultures.

Phase variation: *C.burnetii* shows phase variation. Fresh isolates are in Phase I. It becomes Phase II on repeated passage in the yolk sac, but reverts to Phase I by passaging in guinea pigs. Phase I cells are autoagglutinable and are phagocytosed in the absence of antibody. Phase I activity is due to a periodate-sensitive trichloracetic acid–soluble surface carbohydrate. Phase I is a more powerful immunogen than Phase II and elicits good antibody response to both I and II antigens. Phase II antigen is more suitable for complement fixation tests. Q fever sera do not cross-react with rickettsial or proteus bacillus antigens.

Laboratory diagnosis

This is by serology, complement fixation or indirect immunofluorescence assay. Isolation of the coxiella from blood, sputum or other clinical specimens is possible but not recommended due to the hazard of laboratory infection.

For diagnosis, the specimens to be collected include **blood** for microscopy and **culture** and **serum** for serological tests. Blood or vegetation from heart valves is used to prepare a smear, which is stained by Macchiavello's stain (coxiellae appear as very minute red coccobacilli). **Culture** is not possible on artificial (cell-free) culture media but only in animals (guinea pigs), yolk sac of embryonated eggs or tissue culture. The diagnosis of Q fever is based mainly on **serological tests**, such as microagglutination, complement fixation, immunofluorescence and enzyme-linked immunosorbent assay using Phase I and II antigens. PCR has been found to improve the early diagnosis of acute Q fever in the first four weeks of the disease, and a real-time PCR assay can also assess antibiotic susceptibilities.

Treatment

The treatment of choice is tetracycline; the response may be slow. Erythromycin, ciprofloxacin, rifampicin and the newer macrolides (clarithromycin) are also active. Treatment of endocarditis requires prolonged therapy, preferably with a combination of antibiotics (including tetracycline) for the first 14 days.

Immunoprophylaxis

Vaccines have been prepared from formalin-killed whole cells, trichloracetic acid extracts and attenuated strains, but they are not for general use.

GENUS BARTONELLA

Bartonellae are tiny Gram-negative bacilli, usually transmitted by arthropods, which invade mammalian endothelial cells and blood cells. Human pathogenic strains are *B.bacilliformis*, *B.quintana* and *B.henselae*. The genus contains species causing a number of tick-borne fevers of animals. Identification and classification of members of bartonellae, rickettsiae, chlamydiae and related bacteria often depend on sophisticated molecular methods like 16S RNA analysis.

BARTONELLA BACILLIFORMIS

Oroya fever presents as fever and progressive anemia due to bacterial invasion of erythrocytes. Mortality is high in untreated cases. A late sequel in survivors or in those with asymptomatic infection is **verruga peruana**. The common origin of these two conditions was established tragically in 1885 by the Peruvian medical student Daniel Carrion. He inoculated himself with material from verruga and developed Oroya fever from which he died. Oroya fever is therefore also known as **Carrion's disease**. *B.bacilliformis* is seen inside erythrocytes and in the skin lesions. It is a pleomorphic, Gram-negative rod, which is motile by a tuft of polar flagella. It can be cultivated in semisolid agar with rabbit or human blood.

BARTONELLA (ROCHALIMAEA) QUINTANA

During the First World War, over a million cases of a disease known as **trench fever** or **five-day fever** occurred among soldiers fighting in the trenches in Europe.

Trench fever is an exclusively human disease and no animal reservoir is known. It is transmitted by the body louse. The feces of lice become infectious 5–10 days after an infectious meal. The lice are unharmed and remain infective throughout their lives. Vertical transmission does not occur in lice. The causative agent was identified as a rickettsia and named *R.quintana* (from *quintana*, meaning fifth, referring to 'five-day fever', a synonym for trench fever). As it was found to differ from rickettsiae in a number of respects, including its ability to grow in cell-free culture media such as blood agar, it was separated into a new genus *Rochalimaea* (after da Rocha Lima, an early investigator of rickettsial diseases). In a subsequent taxonomical shift, it has been reclassified as *Bartonella* and named *B.quintana*.

The disease frequently leads to chronic or latent infection. Recrudescence may occur as in

Brill–Zinsser disease and relapses have been reported as long as 20 years after the primary disease. The chronic infection and late relapses help to maintain the bartonella in the absence of animal reservoirs.

Trench fever was thought to have vanished with the World Wars. But the recent isolation of *B.quintana* from Tunisia and Mexico suggests that the disease may be more widely distributed than realised. Trench fever cases have been identified in some homeless persons living in unsanitary conditions in the USA.

BARTONELLA HENSELAE

A febrile illness with lymphadenopathy following a cat scratch had been known for long under the name **'cat scratch disease'**, but its origin remained elusive. *B.henselae* has been isolated from the blood of patients, in blood media after prolonged incubation and is now considered as its causative agent. It can be demonstrated in lymph node biopsy smears and sections by Warthin–Starry staining.

B.henselae has been also linked with two other conditions, seen more commonly in HIV-infected and other immunodeficient persons. These are *bacillary angiomatosis*, in which vascular nodules or tumours appear on the skin, mucosa and other locations, and *bacillary peliosis* involving the liver and spleen.

Angiomatosis may also be due to *B.quintana* in some cases. Another organism, *Afipia felis,* had also been proposed as a cause of cat scratch disease.

RECAP

- The family Rickettsiaceae includes three genera: *Rickettsia, Orientia* and *Ehrlichia.* They share the common features of intracellular growth and transmission by hemagogous (blood sucking) arthropod vectors (lice, fleas, ticks, mites).
- *Rickettsiae* are bacteria that cannot be seen by the ordinary light microscope and are obligate intracellular parasites. The important species in the family include *Rickettsia prowazekii, Rickettsia typhi, Rickettsia rickettsii, Orientia* (formerly *Rickettsia) tsutsugamushi* and the *Ehrlichia species.*
- In rickettsial infections, there is no direct human-to-human spread. Spread is from humans or an animal reservoir to an arthropod vector (lice, fleas, ticks, mites).
- For diagnosis, blood and tissues samples are collected for culture, and serum for serological tests.
    ⬦ Direct microscopy: Cytoplasmic inclusion bodies
    ⬦ Culture: Yolk sac of embryonated hens' eggs, in mice, guinea pigs or in cell and tissue culture
    ⬦ Skin biopsies: By immunofluorescence, immunoenzyme and immunohistochemical methods
    ⬦ The Weil–Felix test where certain antigens (OX19, OX 2, OXK) of *Proteus* are used
    ⬦ Other older serological tests include complement fixation and neutralisation
    ⬦ Rickettsial DNA can be detected by polymerase chain reaction
- For treatment, tetracycline and chloramphenicol can be administered.
- Scrub typhus is caused by *Orientia tsutsugamushi,* transmitted by the bite of mite larvae (chiggers).
- Ehrlichiae are small, Gram-negative, obligate intracellular bacteria which have an affinity towards blood cells.
- The causative agent of glandular fever is *Ehrlichia sennetsu.* It causes lymphoid hyperplasia and atypical lymphocytosis. No arthropod vector has been identified.
- 'Human monocytic ehrlichiosis' is caused by *E.chaffeensis,* transmitted by ticks.
- 'Human granulocytic ehrlichiosis' is caused by an organism closely related to *E.equi* (probably *E.phagocytophila*). This is transmitted by ticks.
- Doxycycline is recommended for the treatment of ehrlichiosis.

- *Coxiella burnetii* is a pleomorphic coccobacillary bacterium, Gram-negative obligate intracellular parasite. There is no vector for transmission. The Weil–Felix test cannot be used for the diagnosis of *Coxiella* infection.
- For diagnosis, culture is not possible on artificial (cell-free) culture media. Serological tests such as microagglutination, complement fixation, immunofluorescence and enzyme-linked immunosorbent assay using Phase 1 and 2 antigens are employed.
- The treatment of choice is tetracycline.
- Q fever is a worldwide zoonosis. Humans acquire the infection from animals among whom the disease is endemic and by inhalation of infectious aerosols.
- Bartonella are transmitted by arthropods and invade mammalian endothelial cells and blood cells.
- *B.bacilliformis* causes Oroya fever and verruga peruana, *B.quintana* causes trench fever, *B.henselae* causes 'cat scratch disease'.

ESSAY

1. Describe the laboratory diagnosis of rickettsial infections.

SHORT ANSWER

1. Neil–Mooser reaction

SHORT NOTES

1. Q fever
2. Weil–Felix reaction
3. Scrub typhus
4. Trench fever

46 Chlamydiae

INTRODUCTION

Chlamydiae are obligate intracellular bacterial parasites of humans, animals and birds, with tropism for squamous epithelial cells and macrophages of the respiratory and gastrointestinal tracts. They are classified as bacteria belonging to the genus *Chlamydia,* in the family Chlamydiaceae, under the order Chlamydiales.

They were considered to be viruses on account of their filterability and failure to grow in cell-free media. Based on the human diseases they were then known to cause, they were called psittacosis-lymphogranuloma-trachoma (PLT) viruses, or non-committally as PLT agents. However, they are now recognised as bacteria as they have many of their attributes, including:

- Presence of both DNA and RNA
- Presence of cell wall and ribosomes
- Replication by binary fission without an 'eclipse phase'
- Susceptibility to antibiotics

The chlamydial **cell wall** resembles that of Gram-negative bacteria; this is divided into an outer layer, an outer membrane complex (which possibly confers rigidity and stability) and an inner layer. Although lipopolysaccharide is present in the outer membrane complex, only small amounts of peptidoglycan are present.

Unlike bacteria, however, they do not have peptidoglycan cell walls. They lack enzymes of the electron transport chain and so require ATP and nutrient resources from host cells. They have therefore been called **energy parasites**.

Classification

The genus *Chlamydia* contains four species: *Chlamydia trachomatis, Chlamydophila psittaci* and *Chlamydophila pneumoniae,* which can affect humans (Table 46.1), and the fourth species, *C.pecorum,* created recently to include some strains affecting ruminants. Species differentiation is based on growth characters, nucleic acid profile, antigens, plasmids and the nature of the inclusion body.

C.trachomatis strains form compact inclusions with the glycogen matrix, are sensitive to sulphonamides and are natural parasites of humans, usually causing localised infections of the eyes and genitals. *C.psittaci* strains form diffuse vacuolated inclusions without the glycogen matrix, are resistant to sulphonamides and are natural parasites of birds and animals, capable of causing pneumonia and generalised infection in humans. *C.pneumoniae* is an exclusive human pathogen with no animal or avian host. It is a common cause of acute respiratory disease worldwide.

Table 46.1 *Human diseases caused by Chlamydiae*

Species	Serotype*	Disease
C.trachomatis	A, B, Ba, C	Endemic blinding trachoma
C.trachomatis	D, E, F, G, H, I, J, K	Inclusion conjunctivitis (neonatal and adult)
		Genital chlamydiasis
		Infant pneumonia
C.trachomatis	L1, L2, L3	Lymphogranuloma venereum
C.psittaci	Many serotypes	Psittacosis
C.pneumoniae	Only one serotype	Acute respiratory disease

* Predominamt types associated with the disease

Morphology

Chlamydiae occur in two forms:

- The **elementary body** is the extracellular, infective form. It is a spherical particle, 200–300 nm in diameter, with a rigid trilaminar cell wall similar to the cell walls of Gram-negative bacteria, and an electron-dense nucleoid.
- The **reticulate body** (formerly called the 'initial body') is the intracellular growing and replicative form, 500–1000 nm in size. Its cell wall is fragile and pliable, leading to pleomorphism.

Growth cycle

Infection is initiated by the attachment of the elementary body to the surface of a susceptible epithelial cell, followed by its endocytosis (Fig. 46.1). Inside the host cell, the elementary body lies within the endosome, being separated from the host cell cytoplasm by the endosomal membrane throughout its active growth cycle. By about eight hours, the **elementary body** within the endosome undergoes spheroplast-like transformation to the **large reticulate body**, which begins to divide by binary fission in 12 hours. Within 20–24 hours, the pleomorphic progeny show central condensation and are converted to elementary bodies. Binary fission continues till about 40 hours. The developing chlamydial microcolony within the host cell is called the **inclusion body**. The mature inclusion body contains 100–500 elementary bodies which are ultimately released from the host cell.

In the developmental cycle of *Chlamydia*, the elementary body alternates with the reticulate body. Chlamydiae enter the host cells by phagocytosis as infectious elementary bodies in a cytoplasmic vacuole.

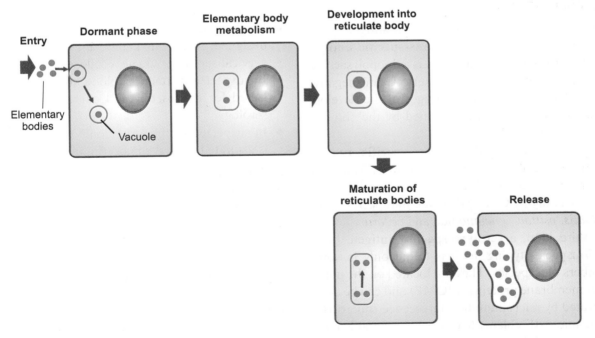

Fig. 46.1 Reproductive cycle of *Chlamydia*

- *C.trachomatis* forms compact, glycogen containing, cytoplasmic inclusions in the cells and is susceptible to sulphadiazine and cycloserine. With *C.trachomatis*, the mature inclusion appears to be exocytosed in 72–96 hours, the host cell being left with a scar.
- *C.psittaci* forms diffuse cytoplasmic inclusions which do not have a glycogen matrix, and is susceptible to cycloserine but not sulphadiazine. In *C.psittaci* infections, the host cell is severely damaged and release of the elementary bodies occurs within 48 hours by host cell lysis.

During active intracellular growth, the chlamydia-specific lipopolysaccharides accumulate on the host cell surface. This highly antigenic material induces inflammatory and immunological responses which contribute to the pathogenesis of chlamydial diseases.

Chlamydiae can be propagated in the mouse or chick embryo or in cell culture though they show individual variations in susceptibility.

Resistance

Chlamydiae are heat labile, being inactivated within minutes at 56°C. They are susceptible to ethanol, ether and low concentrations of phenol and formalin. Infectivity is maintained for several days at 4°C. They can be preserved frozen at −70°C or lyophilised.

Antigenic properties

Chlamydiae possess three main kinds of antigens:
- The first is the heat stable, **genus-specific antigen** common to all chlamydiae. This is a lipopolysaccharide resembling the LPS of enteric Gram-negative bacilli. This is present in all stages of the developmental cycle and can be identified by the complement fixation test.
- The second type is the **species-specific protein antigen** present at the envelope surface. These are present in all strains of a chlamydial species. They help in classifying Chlamydiae into the species—*trachomatis, psittaci, pneumoniae* and *pecorum*.
- The third kind, a **serotype-specific antigen**, helps in intraspecies typing, as it is found only in some members of a species. They are located on the major outer membrane proteins (MOMP) and can be demonstrated by microimmunofluorescence (micro-IF). Using micro-IF, chlamydiae have been classified into many serological variants (serovars, serotypes).

Type-specific antigens are used to classify all *C.trachomatis* strains into two broad biovars (biological variants): one which causes trachoma inclusion conjunctivitis (TRIC) and another which causes lymphogranuloma venereum (LGV). The TRIC biovar has been classified into 12 serovars—A, B, Ba and C causing blinding trachoma in endemic areas, and serovars D to K associated with the less serious ocular infection, inclusion conjunctivitis and various genital infections. Serovars L1, L2 and L3 cause LGV and hemorrhagic proctitis.

The serological classification of *C.psittaci* is complex, many serotypes having been identified. *C.pneumoniae* has not been subclassified as only one serotype is known.

Laboratory diagnosis

Four approaches are available for the laboratory diagnosis of chlamydial infections:
- Microscopic demonstration of inclusion or elementary bodies
- Isolation of chlamydia
- Demonstration of chlamydial antigen
- Demonstration of antibodies or hypersensitivity.

1. Clinical specimen: For the diagnosis of suspected chlamydial infection, specimens collected will depend on the type of the infection:
- Conjunctival material is collected with a metal or special plastic impression spatula in ocular infections
- Urethral scrapings are collected using a specially designed curette in genital infections; in women, cervical scrapings are also collected
- In suspected psittacosis, blood and sputum are collected for microscopy and culture, and serum for serology
- In suspected lymphogranuloma venereum, material is aspirated from the bubo (inguinal lymphadenitis)

2. Microscopy: Chlamydial elementary bodies and inclusions are large enough to be seen under the light microscope. Chlamydiae are Gram negative but are stained better by the **Giemsa, Castaneda, Macchiavello** and **Gimenez** stains. Microscopic examination of Giemsa-stained conjunctival scrapings for the inclusion bodies is useful in the diagnosis of ocular infections, particularly in neonatal inclusion conjunctivitis. Because of the glycogen matrix of *C.trachomatis* inclusions, they can be stained with Lugol's iodine. Iodine staining of conjunctival scrapings has been used as a rapid and simple screening method for trachoma and inclusion conjunctivitis. However, its sensitivity is poor as iodine staining occurs only in certain stages of development of the inclusions. It is, however, useful in rapid screening for chlamydial inclusions in cell cultures inoculated with clinical samples. Iodine staining is not applicable in *C.psittaci* because its inclusions do not contain glycogen.

- **Immunoflourescence (IF):** A more sensitive and specific method of microscopic examination is immunofluorescence using monoclonal antibodies. IF can identify not only inclusions but also extracellular elementary bodies. Besides ocular infections, IF is also useful in the examination of cervical or urethral specimens, which may contain elementary bodies but few intact intracellular inclusions. It is more sensitive than iodine staining for the detection of inclusions in infected cell cultures.

3. Isolation: This can be done by inoculation into embryonated eggs. Chlamydia can grow in the yolk sac of 6–8-day-old chick embryos. The group-specific CF antigen as well as the elementary and inclusion bodies can be demonstrated in the yolk sac. However, as isolation by egg inoculation is tedious and relatively insensitive, it has been replaced by tissue culture.

- **Experimental animals (mice):** Chlamydiae differ in their infectivity to mice. *C.psittaci* strains infect mice by the intracerebral, intranasal, intraperitoneal and subcutaneous routes. Among *C.trachomatis* strains, only the LGV serovars (L1, L2, L3) infect mice when injected intracerebrally. The TRIC serovars do not infect mice by any route, though they can kill mice infected intravenously due to a toxic effect. Mice can be protected against infection and toxic effect by prior injection of type-specific antisera. Mouse inoculation is no longer in use for isolation of chlamydia.

- **Tissue culture:** Today, cell culture is the preferred mode of isolation. Many cell lines are susceptible but the McCoy and HeLa cells are commonly used. *C.trachomatis* strains vary in their infectivity to cell cultures. LGV strains grow well, while TRIC strains are less infective. Cell cultures used for isolation are pretreated by irradiation or chemicals such as 5-iodo-2-deoxyuridine or cycloheximide to enhance chlamydial replication and facilitate detection of inclusion bodies. Pretreatment of cells with DEAE dextran or centrifugation after inoculation promotes contact between chlamydial particles and the cell monolayer, thereby increasing the chances of isolation. *C.psittaci* strains grow well on cell culture, but because of the risk of laboratory infection, their isolation should be attempted only where appropriate containment facilities are available.

4. Antigen detection: For diagnosis by demonstration of chlamydial antigens, the method commonly used is micro-IF. The infected ocular or genital samples are smeared on a slide, stained with fluorescent conjugated antibody and examined under the UV microscope. This test approaches cultures in sensitivity. The ELISA method is preferred for screening as it enables rapid testing for the LPS antigen in a large number of specimens. Molecular methods like DNA probes and amplification techniques (PCR, ligase chain reaction) have greatly increased the sensitivity and specificity of antigen detection. Another advantage of molecular techniques is that non-invasive samples like urine can be used, thus simplifying specimen collection and transport.

5. Antibody detection: Diagnosis by demonstration of antibody in serum may be done by the group-specific CF test or type-specific micro-IF. During chlamydial infection, specific antibodies are produced, first IgM antibodies (signifying primary infection), which persist for approximately two months, then IgG antibodies are formed. The antibody titre varies according to the species responsible, and the site and severity of the infection.

The **CF test** is used mainly in invasive chlamydial infections, such as psittacosis and LGV. A fourfold rise in titres is diagnostic. As low-titre, group-specific antibody may be present in the sera of many persons due to exposure to other chlamydiae, a single CF antibody test is not diagnostic of psittacosis or LGV unless the titre is high—1:64 or greater. CF test is of little value in TRIC infections, in which micro-IF is more useful. **Micro-IF** can test IgG and IgM antibodies separately. Titres of 1:8 or greater are usual in infected persons. Enzyme immunoassays are also available. The initial antibody response is IgM, which is replaced by IgG after about a month. Recurrent infection with the same serotype induces only IgG response. As low titre antibodies are frequently seen in healthy individuals, the diagnostic criteria for serology are seroconversion, fourfold rise in IgG titre or presence of IgM antibody. High titre antibodies are usually seen only in infant pneumonia, salpingitis and LGV.

Demonstration of hypersensitivity by skin testing (**Frei's test**) was widely used earlier for the diagnosis of LGV but has been given up because false positive results were very frequent.

CHLAMYDIA TRACHOMATIS

C.trachomatis is a leading cause of ocular and genital infections worldwide.

TRACHOMA

Trachoma is a chronic keratoconjunctivitis characterised by follicular hypertrophy, papillary hyperplasia, pannus formation and in the late stages, cicatrisation. The name trachoma is derived from the Greek *trakhus* (rough) referring to the roughness of the conjunctiva in the disease. Though Halberstaedter and Prowazek in 1907 transmitted the infection to orangutans and demonstrated in conjunctival smears the characteristic inclusion body that bears their names, cultivation of the chlamydia became possible only half a century later, when Tang and colleagues (1957) grew it in the yolk sac of eggs.

Pathogenicity

Infection is transmitted from eye to eye by fingers or fomites. Flies may transmit the infection mechanically. It may also be carried by dust, in which case infection may be facilitated by minor abrasions caused by dust particles. The incubation period is variable and influenced by the severity of infection. Onset is insidious.

Trachoma has been classified into several stages. The earliest is **trachoma dubium**, where the disease is just a suspicion. **Protrachoma** is the stage of conjunctival lesion before follicles become visible. The inclusion bodies are not usually demonstrable in these early stages. **Established trachoma** progresses through stages I–IV. Infectivity is maximum in the early cases. Stage IV is non-infectious.

Laboratory diagnosis

1. Staining: The characteristic inclusions (**Halberstaedter–Prowazek** or **HP bodies**) may be demonstrated in conjunctival scrapings, after staining by Giemsa, Castaneda or Macchiavello methods. Because they possess a glycogen matrix, they may be stained with iodine which enhances the sensitivity of smear diagnosis.

2. Culture: The chlamydia may be grown in the **yolk sac** of 6–8-day-old eggs. The material is treated with streptomycin or polymyxin B before inoculation. The eggs are incubated at 35°C in a humid atmosphere. Blind passages may be necessary for isolation. This method is seldom used now as it is time-consuming, cumbersome and relatively insensitive.

Tissue culture using stationary phase cells (non-replicating cells) is the method of choice for isolation. McCoy cells rendered non-replicating by irradiation or antimetabolites are used. HeLa or HL cells treated with DEAE dextran may also be used. The inoculum has to be driven into the cells by centrifugation up to 15,000 g to obtain good growth.

Treatment

Local application and oral administration of erythromycin and tetracycline or other suitable antibiotics should be continued for several weeks. A single-dose azithromycin treatment has been used with good results.

Chlamydia trachomatis

Clinical Case 1   The mother of a five-day-old neonate complained of a thick, yellowish discharge in both the eyes of her child. The child was afebrile and able to feed properly. Gram staining of the exudate did not reveal any bacteria. A Giemsa-stained smear of the exudates was positive for a large cytoplasmic inclusion. A diagnosis of inclusion conjunctivitis was made and the child responded to a course of erythromycin.

Clinical Case 2   A 20-year-old was treated in an STD clinic for urethral discharge with a single dose of ceftriaxone. However, his symptoms of discharge and dysuria reappeared in two weeks, even though there was no history of any sexual contact in this time. The patient was subjected to laboratory investigations and a Gram smear of the discharge showed plenty of pus cells but no bacteria. Culture was negative. The chlamydial antigen detection test was positive. A diagnosis of non-gonococcal urethritis was made and treatment with tetracycline was given for seven days.

Epidemiology and control

Trachoma is worldwide in distribution and about 500 million people are estimated to be affected. It is particularly prevalent in the developing nations because of overcrowding and unhygienic conditions. It is endemic in the Middle East, Africa, India and the Far East. Control of the disease involves mass education and chemotherapy. Vaccination has not proved to be an effective or practicable method of control.

INCLUSION CONJUNCTIVITIS

The epidemiology of this condition, first recognised by Halberstaedter and Prowazek in 1910, had to be re-established in recent years. The natural habitat of *C.trachomatis* types D to K is the genital tract in both sexes.

Inclusion blenorrhea, the neonatal form of inclusion conjunctivitis, develops when the infant is infected in the birth passage. It usually becomes apparent between 5 and 12 days after birth. It was considered to be benign and self-limiting but has a high incidence of micropannus, conjunctival scars and late recurrences. These can be prevented by local application of antibiotics (*Case 1*).

In the adult form of the disease, there is follicular hypertrophy with scanty non-purulent discharge. It was known as 'swimming pool conjunctivitis' as the infection was associated with bathing in community swimming pools which presumably become contaminated with chlamydia from the genital secretions of bathers. Contamination of the eye with the patient's own genital secretion may more often be the cause.

INFANT PNEUMONIA

C.trachomatis can cause pneumonia in infants, usually around 4–16 weeks of age. Characteristically, they develop prominent respiratory symptoms with cough and wheezing but fever and toxicity are minimal. Conjunctivitis often precedes pneumonia. They show eosinophilia and high titre IgM antibodies to the infecting serovar. Immune response is believed to play a role in the pathogenesis of this condition.

GENITAL INFECTIONS

C.trachomatis causes two types of genital infections: miscellaneous urogenital syndromes caused by the oculogenital serotypes D to K, collectively referred to as genital chlamydiasis, and LGV caused by serotypes L1, L2 and L3.

Genital chlamydiasis: Chlamydial infections have become the most common sexually transmitted disease worldwide. Their clinical spectrum parallels that of gonococcal infections. Indeed, the two infections may often co-exist (*Case 2*).

In men, they cause urethritis (**non-gonococcal urethritis** or **NGU**), epididymitis, proctitis, conjunctivitis and **Reiter's syndrome**. (Reiter's is a triad of recurrent conjunctivitis, polyarthritis and urethritis or cervicitis, associated with many infections but most commonly with *C.trachomatis*). Women develop acute urethral syndrome, bartholinitis, mucopurulent cervicitis, endometritis, salpingitis, pelvic inflammatory disease, conjunctivitis, perihepatitis (Fitz-Hugh–Curtis syndrome) and Reiter's syndrome. Genital chlamydiasis may cause infertility, ectopic pregnancy, premature deliveries, perinatal morbidity and postpartum fever.

The true prevalence of genital chlamydiasis is not known in the developing countries as laboratory diagnosis is not widely available. In India, chlamydial infection has been reported in 20–30 per cent of women with mucopurulent cervicitis and 30–60 per cent of those with salpingitis and pelvic inflammatory disease.

In the laboratory, chlamydial infection is to be suspected if Gram-stained smears of urogenital exudates show a significant number of neutrophils (more than 4 per oil immersion field in urethritis, more than 30 in cervicitis), in the absence of gonococcal infection. Confirmatory tests are chlamydial cultivation and antigen detection by micro-IF. Antigen detection by ELISA and by molecular techniques is also useful.

LYMPHOGRANULOMA VENEREUM

This sexually transmitted disease, characterised by suppurative inguinal adenitis, has been known in the tropics for a long time under various names: lymphogranuloma inguinale, poradenitis, climatic or tropical bubo. It is caused by the LGV serovars of *C.trachomatis*, L1, L2 and L3—most commonly L2. LGV serovars are more invasive than the other immunotypes. Their preferred site of multiplication is the regional lymph nodes, in contrast to TRIC serovars which grow in epithelial cells.

Pathogenicity

1. The **primary lesion** is a small, painless, papulovesicular lesion appearing on the external genitalia

(or rarely extragenital sites) after an incubation period of three days to five weeks.

2. The **secondary stage**, developing about two weeks later, results from lymphatic spread to the draining lymph nodes. In men, the inguinal lymph nodes are involved most often, and in women, the intrapelvic and pararectal nodes. Women and homosexual men may develop hemorrhagic proctitis with regional lymphadenitis. The nodes enlarge, suppurate, become adherent to the skin and break down to form sinuses discharging pus. Metastatic complications may sometimes occur, with involvement of the joints, eyes and meninges.

3. The **tertiary stage** is chronic, lasting for several years, representing the sequelae of scarring and lymphatic blockage. Late sequelae are more distressing in women, leading to rectal strictures and elephantiasis of the vulva (esthiomene).

Laboratory diagnosis

The primary lesion usually goes unnoticed and the disease is usually first seen at the stage of inguinal adenitis (bubo). Smears of material aspirated from the bubos may show the elementary bodies (Miyagawa's granulocorpuscles). The sensitivity of microscopic diagnosis is very low. Isolation of the chlamydia by intracerebral inoculation into mice and into the yolk sac of eggs has been replaced by cell cultures. LGV patients develop high titres of circulating antibodies, with titres of 1:64 or more in CF test and 1:512 or more in micro-IF. Serological diagnosis is therefore feasible.

An intradermal test orginally described by Frei used crude chlamydial antigen obtained from bubo pus. **Frei's test** is now not in use.

Treatment is with tetracycline, which should be given for at least three weeks.

CHLAMYDIA (CHLAMYDOPHILA) PSITTACI

PSITTACOSIS

Psittacosis is a disease of parrots (*psittacos* means parrot) and other psittacine birds, transmissible to human beings. A similar disease acquired by non-psittacine birds was called ornithosis (*ornithos* meaning birds) but the distinction is now no longer employed, both conditions being called psittacosis.

Infection in birds is usually subclinical leading to a carrier state. Overt disease may be precipitated by caging or overcrowding and is manifested as diarrhea, mucopurulent respiratory discharge and emaciation. Chlamydia are shed in the droppings or nasal discharge and aerosols are liberated. Human infections are mostly occupational, as in poultry workers, pigeon farmers, pet shop owners, bird fanciers and veterinarians. Infection is by inhalation. Rare cases of infection by parrot bite have been reported. Consumption of poultry products does not lead to infection. Case-to-case transmission in humans is rare but has been recorded. The high infectivity of psittacosis is indicated by the frequency of laboratory infections. Strains from parrots and turkeys are more virulent than those from other avian sources.

Pathogenicity

The incubation period is about 10 days. Clinical disease varies from a mild influenza-like syndrome to a fatal pneumonia. Though pneumonia is the usual clinical manifestation, psittacosis is a septicemia and may lead to meningoencephalitis, endocarditis, pericarditis, arthritis or a typhoid-like syndrome.

Laboratory diagnosis

The chlamydia can be isolated from blood during the early stages of the disease and from sputum later on. Infected cells, including alveolar macrophages from patients, and mouse brain, yolk sac and cell cultures show inclusion bodies (**Levinthal–Cole–Lillie** or **LCL bodies**). These differ from *C.trachomatis* inclusions in being more diffuse and irregular, not stained by iodine and not inhibited by sulphadiazine or cycloserine. It is generally difficult to recover the chlamydia from patients treated with antibiotics. Isolation should be attempted only in laboratories where special containment facilities are available as laboratory infection is a serious hazard. Serological diagnosis may be made by the group-specific CF test or type-specific micro-IF.

CHLAMYDIA (CHLAMYDOPHILA) PNEUMONIAE

Grayston and colleagues (1986) isolated a chlamydial strain from acute respiratory disease in adults in Taiwan and designated it as *C.psittaci* strain TWAR (from Taiwan Acute Respiratory). It possessed the group-specific antigen in common with *C.psittaci* and *C.trachomatis* but could be distinguished from both by species-specific antigens, DNA hybridisation and restriction endonuclease analysis. This appears to be an exclusively human chlamydia transmitted from human to human without any avian or animal host. It grows poorly in cell cultures. Because of these properties, it has been classified as a separate species called *C.pneumoniae*.

It appears to be a common cause of respiratory disease in older children and adults worldwide. Antibodies have been demonstrated in the sera of about 50 per cent of adults from different parts of the world. Its clinical spectrum includes pharyngitis, sinusitis, bronchitis and pneumonia, which resembles *Mycoplasma* pneumonia. It has also been associated with adult onset asthma. The incubation period is 1–3 weeks. Outbreaks have been reported in closed communities. Primary infections occur in young children. Re-infections are common. Serum antibodies do not appear to be protective.

Considerable interest has been aroused by recent reports linking *C.pneumoniae* with atherosclerosis and its clinical effects like coronary, carotid and cerebral arterial disease.

Diagnosis is by antigen detection by EIA, direct immunofluorescence or molecular methods, as isolation of the organism is very difficult. Serodiagnosis is by CF, ELISA or micro-IF.

Treatment is by one of the new macrolide antibiotics like clarithromycin or azithromycin.

RECAP

- The *Chlamydia* species is now recognised as bacteria as they have many of the attributes of one, including a cell wall that resembles that of Gram-negative bacteria.
- Since Chlamydiae lack cytochromes, they are obligate intracellular bacteria.
- The elementary body is the metabolically inert, extracellular infectious form of *Chlamydia*, and the reticulate body is the metabolically active, dividing, intracellular form.
- Four species of *Chlamydia* are recognised: *C.trachomatis*, *C.psittaci*, *C.pneumoniae* and *C.pecorum*.
  - There are three biovars of *C.trachomatis*, of which the trachoma biovar and the lymphogranuloma venereum (LGV) biovar preferentially infect humans.
- Chlamydiae possess antigens that are present in all stages of the developmental cycle and are used in the indirect fluorescent antibody serological test:
  - Group-specific polysaccharide antigen (common to both *C.psittaci* and *C.trachomatis*) is useful for the diagnosis of psittacosis and LGV
  - Species-specific proteinaceous antigens, which can be used to differentiate *C.psittaci* from *C.trachomatis*
  - Type-specific antigens, which can be used to classify all *C.trachomatis* serotypes
- Type-specific antigens are used to classify *C.trachomatis* into two broad biovars (biological variants) which cause trachoma inclusion conjunctivitis (TRIC) and LGV, respectively.
- Cell-mediated immunity is very important for protection against *Chlamydia*.
- Clinical features of chlamydial infection include:
  - Ocular infection with *C.trachomatis*.
  - Sexually transmitted disease, manifesting in women as urethritis or cervicitis; complications include acute or chronic salpingitis, pelvic inflammatory disease and perihepatitis. In men, infections manifest as urethritis; complications include acute unilateral epididymitis, with sterility as the end result.
  - In the neonate, chlamydial infections may manifest as conjunctivitis and, later, interstitial pneumonia.
  - Reiter's syndrome
  - *C.pneumoniae* causes pneumonia.

- For diagnosis:
  - Direct microscopy, using smears stained by Lugol's iodine, Giemsa stain or microimmunofluorescence
  - Isolation in the yolk sac of embryonated hens' eggs or in McCoy cells lines.
  - Serological tests based on group-specific, species-specific and type-specific chlamydial antigens in indirect fluorescent antibody technique or ELISA.
- Treatment with antibiotics of patient and partner is important.

SHORT ANSWERS

1. Reticulate body of *Chlamydia* (definition)
2. Elementary body of *Chlamydia* (definition)
3. Chlamydial infections that occur in humans
4. Causes of NGU

SHORT NOTES

1. LGV
2. Inclusion conjunctivitis
3. TRIC agents
4. Psittacosis
5. Trachoma

47 General Properties of Viruses

INTRODUCTION

Unicellular microorganisms may be classified in descending order of complexity as **eukaryotes**, such as protozoa and fungi, and **prokaryotes**, such as bacteria, mycoplasmas, rickettsiae and chlamydiae. Viruses do not fall strictly into the category of unicellular microorganisms as they do not possess cellular organisation. Even the simplest of microorganisms are cells enclosed within a cell wall, containing both types of nucleic acid (DNA and RNA), synthesising their own macromolecular constituents and multiplying by binary fission.

Viruses occupy the twilight zone that separates the 'living' from the 'non-living'. The demonstration by Stanley (1935) that viruses could be crystallised like chemicals, and the extraction by Geirer and Schramm (1956) of 'infectious nucleic acid' from a virus that could infect host cells and yield complete virus progeny made it appear that viruses were only 'living chemicals'.

Defining characteristics

- Viruses do not have cellular organisation.
- They contain only one type of nucleic acid, either DNA or RNA, but never both.
- They are obligate intracellular parasites.
- They lack the enzymes necessary for protein and nucleic acid synthesis and are dependent for replication on the synthetic machinery of host cells.
- They multiply by a complex process and not by binary fission.
- They are unaffected by antibacterial antibiotics.

The main differences between viruses and other microorganisms are shown in Table 47.1

The medical importance of viruses lies in their ability to cause a very large number of human diseases. Viral diseases range from minor ailments such as the common cold to terrifying diseases such as rabies or AIDS. They may be sporadic like mumps, endemic like infectious hepatitis, epidemic like dengue fever or pandemic like influenza. They may be localised to circumscribed areas (like some arbovirus diseases) or occur worldwide (like herpes simplex). The control of bacterial infection with antibiotics has enhanced the role of viral infections in human disease. Viruses can cause cancer in animals and birds, as well as in humans.

MORPHOLOGY

Size

The extracellular infectious virus particle is called the **virion**. Viruses are much smaller than bacteria. It was their small size and 'filterability' (ability to pass through filters that can hold back bacteria) that led

Table 47.1   *Properties of prokaryotes and viruses*

	Cellular organisation	Growth on inanimate media	Binary fission	Both DNA and RNA	Ribosomes	Sensitivity to antibacterial antibiotics	Sensitivity to interferon
Bacteria	+	+	+	+	+	+	−
Mycoplasmas	+	+	+	+	+	+	−
Rickettsiae	+	+	+	+	+	+	−
Chlamydiae	+	−	+	+	+	+	+
Viruses	−	−	−	−	−	−	+

to their recognition as a separate class of infectious agents. Hence, they were for a time known as 'filterable viruses'. Viruses are too small to be seen under the light microscope and can only be seen under the electron microscope. Some of the larger viruses, such as poxviruses, can be seen under the light microscope when suitably stained (Fig. 47.1).

Viruses vary widely in size. The largest among them (for example, poxviruses) measuring about 300 nm, are as large as the smallest bacteria (mycoplasma). The smallest viruses (for example, parvovirus) measuring about 20 nm are nearly as small as the largest protein molecules such as hemocyanin.

Electron microscopy is used now to estimate the size of virus particles. Purified preparations of virions may be examined under the electron microscope unstained or stained. By this method, both the shape and the size of virions can be studied.

Structure and shape

Capsid: The virion consists essentially of a nucleic acid surrounded by a protein coat, the capsid. The capsid with the enclosed nucleic acid is known as the nucleocapsid. The function of the capsid is to protect the nucleic acid from inactivation by nucleases and other deleterious agents in the environment.

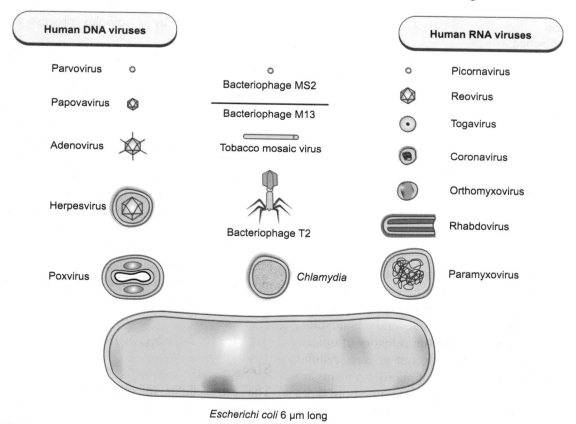

Fig. 47.1   Relative sizes of representative viruses, bacteriophages (bacterial viruses) and bacteria, inlcuding chlamydia

The capsid is composed of a large number of capsomers which form its morphological units. The chemical units of the capsid are polypeptide molecules arranged symmetrically to form an impenetrable shell around the nucleic acid core. One of the main functions of the capsid is to introduce the viral genome into host cells by adsorbing readily to cell surfaces.

Three kinds of **symmetry** are encountered in the capsid:

- **Icosahedral (cubical):** An icosahedron is a polygon with 12 vertices or corners and 20 facets or sides. Each facet is in the shape of an equilateral triangle. Two types of capsomers constitute the icosahedral capsid. They are the pentagonal capsomers at the vertices (pentons) and the hexagonal capsomers making up the facets (hexons). There are always 12 pentons but the number of hexons varies with the virus group.
- **Helical:** In nucleocapsids with helical symmetry, the capsomers and nucleic acid are wound together to form a helical or spiral tube. The tube may be rigid, as in the tobacco mosaic virus, but in the case of animal viruses, the tubular nucleocapsid is pliable and may be coiled on itself. Not all viruses show the typical icosahedral or helical symmetry.
- **Complex:** Some, like the poxviruses, exhibit complex symmetry.

Envelope: Virions may be enveloped or non-enveloped (naked). The envelope or outer covering is derived from the host cell membrane when the progeny virus is released by budding. The envelope is made of lipoprotein (Fig. 47.2). The lipid is largely of host cell origin while the protein is virus coded. Protein subunits may be seen as projecting spikes on the surface of the envelope. These structures are called **peplomers** (from *peplos*, meaning envelope). A virus may have more than one type of peplomer. The influenza virus carries two kinds of peplomers: the **hemagglutinin** which is a triangular spike and the **neuraminidase** which is a mushroom-shaped structure.

Envelopes confer chemical, antigenic and biological properties on viruses. Enveloped viruses are susceptible to the action of lipid solvents like ether, chloroform and bile salts. Specific neutralisation of virus infectivity depends on antibodies to the surface antigens. Biological properties such as attachment to host cell surface or hemagglutination depend on the envelope. Some viruses possess additional structural

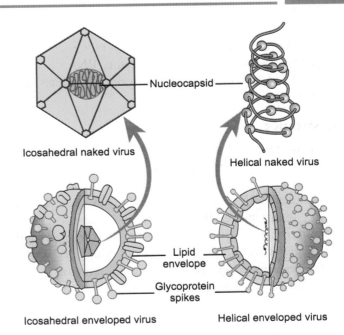

Fig. 47.2   Illustration of viral particle

features. For example, fibrils protrude from the vertices of adenovirus particles.

Shape: Overall, this varies among different groups of viruses. Most animal viruses are roughly **spherical**. Some are **irregular** and **pleomorphic**. The rabies virus is **bullet shaped**, ebolavirus **filamentous** and poxviruses **brick shaped**; the tobacco mosaic virus is **rod shaped**. Bacterial viruses have complex morphology.

Chemical properties

- **Nucleic acid:** Viruses contain only one type of nucleic acid, either single or double-stranded DNA or RNA. In this respect, viruses are unique, for nowhere else in nature is genetic information solely carried by RNA. Viral nucleic acids may be extracted by treatment with detergents or phenol and, in the case of some viruses (for example, picornavirus, papovavirus), the extracted nucleic acid is capable of initiating infection when introduced into host cells.
- **Proteins:** Viruses also contain proteins which make up the capsid. Viral protein, besides protecting the nucleic acid, also determines the antigenic specificity of the virus.
- **Lipids:** Enveloped viruses contain lipids derived from the host cell membrane.
- **Others:** Some viruses also contain small amounts of carbohydrate. Most viruses do not possess any enzymes for the synthesis of viral components or for

energy production, but some have other **enzymes,** for example, neuraminidase in the influenza virus. Retroviruses have a unique enzyme, RNA dependent DNA polymerase or 'transcriptase' which can transcribe RNA into DNA.

Resistance

- **Temperature:** With few exceptions, viruses are very heat labile. There are individual variations but in general, they are inactivated within seconds at 56°C, minutes at 37°C and days at 4°C. They are stable at low temperatures. For long-term storage, they are kept frozen at −70°C. A better method for prolonged storage is lyophilisation or freeze drying (drying the frozen virus under vacuum). Lyophilised viruses can be stored for years and reconstituted when required by adding water. Some viruses (such as the poliovirus) do not stand freeze drying.
- **pH:** Viruses vary greatly in their resistance to acidity. For example, enteroviruses are very resistant to acid pH while rhinoviruses are very susceptible. All viruses are disrupted under alkaline conditions.
- **Radiations:** Viruses are inactivated by sunlight, UV rays and ionising radiation.
- **Disinfectants:** They are, in general, more resistant than bacteria to chemical disinfectants, probably because they lack enzymes. Phenolic disinfectants are only weakly virucidal. Bacteria are killed in 50% glycerol saline but this acts as a preservative for many viruses (for example, vaccinia, rabies). Molar concentrations of certain salts ($MgCl_2$, Na_2SO_4) also protect some viruses (for example, poliovirus) against heat inactivation. The most active antiviral disinfectants are oxidising agents such as hydrogen peroxide, potassium permanganate and hypochlorites. Organic iodine compounds are actively virucidal. Chlorination of drinking water kills most viruses but its efficacy is greatly influenced by the presence of organic matter. Some viruses (such as hepatitis virus, polioviruses) are relatively resistant to chlorination. Formaldehyde and beta propiolactone are actively virucidal and are commonly employed for the preparation of killed viral vaccines. Overall, non-enveloped viruses are more resistant to disinfectants.
- **Lipid solvents:** The action of lipid solvents such as ether, chloroform and bile salts is selective, the enveloped viruses being sensitive and the naked viruses resistant to them. This selective action is useful in the identification and classification of viruses.

- **Antibiotics:** Antibiotics active against bacteria are completely ineffective against viruses. This property is made use of in eliminating bacteria from clinical specimens by antibiotic treatment before virus isolation.

VIRAL HEMAGGLUTINATION

Viral hemagglutination was originally observed with the influenza virus by Hirst (1941). A large number of viruses have since been shown to agglutinate erythrocytes from different species. Hemagglutination by the influenza virus is due to the presence of hemagglutinin spikes on the surface of the virus. The influenza virus also carries on its surface another peplomer, the enzyme neuraminidase which acts on the receptor and destroys it. Neuraminidase is, therefore, called the **receptor destroying enzyme (RDE).** RDE is produced by many microbes including cholera vibrios, and is also present in many vertebrate cells. Destruction of the receptor leads to reversal of hemagglutination and the release of the virus from the red cell surface. This is known as **elution.**

Hemagglutination is a convenient method of detection and assay of the influenza virus. When red cells are added to serial dilutions of a viral suspension, the highest dilution that produces hemagglutination provides the hemagglutination titre. The hemagglutination test can be carried out in test tubes or special plastic trays. Red cells which are not agglutinated settle at the bottom in the form of a 'button', while the agglutinated cells are seen spread into a shield-like pattern (Fig. 47.3). As the inactivated virus can also hemagglutinate, the test serves to titrate killed influenza vaccines. As hemagglutination is specifically inhibited (HAI) by the antibody to the virus, hemagglutination inhibition provides a convenient test for the antiviral antibody. Hemagglutination and elution also help in purifying and concentrating the virus.

Elution is found only in myxoviruses that possess neuraminidase. With other viruses, hemagglutination is stable. In arboviruses, hemagglutination appears to be a reversible state of equilibrium between the virus and erythrocytes, being influenced by slight variations in pH and temperature. Poxviruses agglutinate red cells from only some fowls. The hemagglutinin of the poxvirus is distinct from the virion and can be separated by centrifugation. Table 47.2 shows the characteristics of hemagglutination by different viruses.

Fig. 47.3 Viral hemagglutination. Virus-containing fluid is diluted in doubling dilutions and 0.5% suspension of chick red cells is added. Where no virus is present, the cells settle down to a button-like aggregate with sharp edges. Where the virus is present, there is a diffuse widespread shield-like pattern on the bottom of the wells in the plastic plate.

VIRAL MULTIPLICATION

The genetic information necessary for viral replication is contained in the viral nucleic acid, but lacking biosynthetic enzymes, the virus depends on the synthetic machinery of the host cell for replication. Early studies on viral replication employed the bacteriophage as the model. While there are general similarities in the pattern of multiplication of bacterial and animal viruses, there are also important differences. The viral multiplication cycle can be divided into six sequential phases (Fig. 47.4), though the phases may sometimes overlap.

1. Adsorption: Virions may come into contact with cells by random collision but adsorption takes place only if there is affinity between the two. The cell surface should contain specific receptor sites to which the virus can gain attachment.

In influenza viruses, the hemagglutinin on the virus surface gets attached to glycoprotein receptor sites on the surface of the respiratory epithelium. Destruction of the receptor sites by RDE prevents viral adsorption. With HIV, attachment is between the CD4 receptor on host cells and the viral surface glycoprotein gp 120. In the case of polioviruses, the receptor is the lipoprotein present on the surface of primate but not rodent cells. The poliovirus can, therefore, attach itself to primate cells but not to rodent cells. Differences in susceptibility to viral infection are to a large extent based on the presence or absence of receptors on cells. If the phase of adsorption can be bypassed, cells normally insusceptible to viruses may be rendered susceptible to them. Thus, infectious nucleic acid extracted from picornaviruses can infect rodent cells, which are resistant to infection by the whole virus.

2. Penetration: Bacteria possess rigid cell walls. Bacterial viruses cannot, therefore, penetrate into bacterial cells, and only the nucleic acid is introduced intracellularly by a complex mechanism. Animal cells do not have rigid cell walls and the whole virus can enter into them. Virus particles may be engulfed by a mechanism resembling phagocytosis, a process known as 'viropexis'. Alternatively, in enveloped viruses, the viral envelope may fuse with the plasma membrane of the host cell and release the nucleocapsid into the cytoplasm.

3. Uncoating: This is the process of stripping the virus of its outer layers and capsid so that the nucleic acid is released into the cell. With most viruses, uncoating is effected by the action of lysosomal enzymes of the host cell. In poxviruses, uncoating is a two-step process. In the first step, the outer coat is removed by lysosomal enzymes in the phagocytic vacuole. The inner core of the virus, containing the internal protein and nucleic

Table 47.2 *Characteristics of hemagglutination by viruses*

Virus	*Erythrocyte species and other conditions*
Influenza virus	Fowl, human, guinea pig, others; elution at 37°C
Parainfluenza, mumps, NDV	Fowl, human, guinea pig, others; elution at 37°C; hemolysin present
Measles	Monkey, 37°C
Togavirus—several groups of Arbovirus	Goose, pigeon, one-day-old chick; pH and temperature critical
Rubella	Goose, pigeon, one-day-old chick; 4°C
Enterovirus, some Coxsackie and ECHO	Human; 4°C and 37°C
Rhinovirus, some serotypes	Sheep; 4°C
Rabies	Goose; 4°C, pH 6.2
Reovirus	Human; 37°C

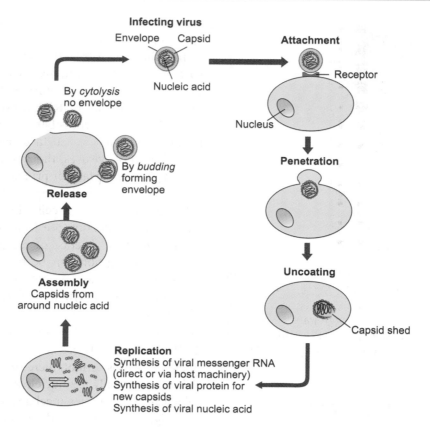

Fig. 47.4   Stages in the infection of a host's cell and replication of a virus

acid, is released into the cytoplasm where the second step of uncoating is effected by a viral uncoating enzyme and the DNA is liberated.

4. Biosynthesis: This phase includes the synthesis not merely of the viral nucleic acid and capsid protein but also of enzymes necessary in the various stages of viral synthesis, assembly and release. In addition, certain 'regulator proteins' are also synthesised which serve to shut down normal cellular metabolism and direct the sequential production of viral components. The site of viral synthesis depends on the type of virus. In general, most DNA viruses synthesise their nucleic acid in the host cell nucleus. The exceptions are the poxviruses, which synthesise all their components in the host cell cytoplasm. Most RNA viruses synthesise all their components in the cytoplasm. Exceptions are orthomyxoviruses, some paramyxoviruses and retroviruses which are synthesised partly in the nucleus. Viral protein is synthesised only in the cytoplasm.

Steps in biosynthesis:
- Transcription of messenger RNA (mRNA) from the viral nucleic acid.

- Translation of the mRNA into 'early proteins'. These 'early or non-structural proteins' are enzymes which initiate and maintain the synthesis of virus components. They may also induce shutdown of host protein and nucleic acid synthesis.
- Replication of viral nucleic acid.
- Synthesis of 'late' or structural proteins, which are the components of daughter virion capsids.

The critical step in viral biosynthesis is the transcription of mRNA from the viral nucleic acid. Once this is achieved, the host cell resources can be utilised for translating mRNA into viral components. Depending on the structure of their genome, viruses use different strategies for the transcription of mRNA.

Replication mechanisms: Viruses have been categorised into six classes by Baltimore (1970) based on their replication mechanisms.
- **Class 1:** In the case of fully double-stranded DNA viruses (such as adeno, herpes, papovaviruses), the DNA enters the host cell nucleus and uses the host cell enzymes for transcription. The extracted DNA from these viruses is infectious. With hepadnavi-

ruses which have a partially double-stranded DNA, the duplex is completed by a viral DNA polymerase, inside the host cytoplasm. The mature DNA then moves into the nucleus, to be transcribed by host transcriptases. Extracted hepadnavirus DNA is not infectious. Poxviruses which replicate in the cytoplasm form mRNA using polymerases contained in the virion itself. Poxvirus DNA is not infectious.

- **Class 2:** With single-stranded DNA viruses (for example, parvovirus), the DNA molecule moves into the host cell nucleus and is converted into the duplex form. Transcription is achieved by host enzymes.
- **Class 3:** In reoviruses, the double-stranded RNA is transcribed to mRNA by viral polymerases.
- **Class 4:** Depending on the method of mRNA transcription, single-stranded RNA viruses are classified into two categories. In the positive strand (plus strand, positive sense) RNA viruses, the viral RNA itself act as the mRNA. Viral RNA is infectious by itself and is translated directly into viral proteins in the host cell cytoplasm (for example, picorna, togaviruses).
- **Class 5:** In the negative strand (minus sense) RNA viruses (for example, rhabdo, orthomyxo, paramyxoviridae), the RNA is 'antisense', with polarity opposite to mRNA. They possess their own RNA polymerases for mRNA transcription. Extracted nucleic acids from these viruses are not infectious.
- **Class 6:** Retroviridae exhibit a unique replicative strategy. Their single-stranded RNA genome is converted into an RNA:DNA hybrid by the viral reverse transcriptase (RNA directed DNA polymerase) enzyme. Double-stranded DNA is then synthesised from the RNA:DNA hybrid. The double-stranded DNA form of the virus (provirus) is integrated into the host cell chromosome. This integration may lead to transformation of the cell and development of neoplasia.

5. Maturation: Assembly of daughter virions follows the synthesis of viral nucleic acid and proteins. Virion assembly may take place in the host cell nucleus or cytoplasm. Herpes and adenoviruses are assembled in the nucleus, while picorna and poxviruses are assembled in the cytoplasm. At this stage, the non-enveloped viruses are present intracellularly as fully developed virions, but in the case of enveloped viruses, only the nucleocapsid is complete. Envelopes are derived from the host cell membrane during the process of budding. The host cell membrane which becomes the envelope is modi-

fied by incorporation of virus-specific antigens. Herpes viruses assembled in the nucleus acquire their envelope from the nuclear membrane as they are released into the cytoplasm enclosed in a vesicle. Myxoviruses bud from the cell surface and their envelope is formed by the modified cytoplasmic membrane of the host cell. The incorporation of viral antigen (hemagglutinin) on the cell membrane endows the cell with the property of hemadsorption.

6. Release: In bacterial viruses, the release of progeny virions takes place by lysis of the infected bacterium. However, in animal viruses, release usually occurs without cell lysis. Myxoviruses are released by a process of budding from the cell membrane over a period of time. The host cell is unaffected and may even divide, the daughter cells, continuing to release virions. Progeny virions are released into the surrounding medium and may infect other cells. In some viruses (for example, varicella), transmission occurs directly from cell to cell, very little free virus being demonstrable extracellularly in the medium. Not all animal viruses spare the host cell. The poliovirus causes profound damage to the host cell and may be released by cell lysis.

Eclipse phase: From the stage of penetration till the appearance of mature daughter virions, the virus cannot be demonstrated inside the host cell. This period during which the virus seems to disappear or go 'underground' is known as the 'eclipse phase'. The time taken for a single cycle of replication is about 15–30 minutes for bacteriophages and about 15–30 hours for animal viruses. A single infected cell may release a large number of progeny virions. While this can be determined readily in bacteriophages (burst size), it is difficult to assess in animal viruses that are released over a prolonged period.

Abnormal replicative cycles:

- A proportion of daughter virions produced may not be infective. This is due to defective assembly. Such **'incomplete viruses'** are seen in large proportions when cells are infected with a high dose of the influenza virus. The virus yield will have a high hemagglutinin titre but low infectivity. This is known as the **von Magnus phenomenon**.
- Virus infection in some cells does not lead to production of infectious progeny. In such cells **(non-permissive cells)**, the viral components may be synthesised but maturation or assembly is defective, and either no release occurs or the progeny is

non-infectious. This is known as **abortive infection**. Here, the defect is in the type of cell and not in the parental viruses.

- Some viruses are **genetically defective** in that when they infect cells, they are unable to give rise to fully formed progeny. Yield of progeny virions occurs only if the cells are simultaneously infected with a helper virus, which can supplement the genetic deficiency. For example, some strains of the Rous sarcoma virus (RSV) cannot code for the synthesis of the viral envelope. When RSV infects a cell that harbours a helper virus (for example, avian leukosis virus), infectious progeny result, the helper virus contributing to the synthesis of the envelope. The envelope antigen of progeny RSV will therefore be determined by the type of helper virus. Other examples of defective viruses are the **hepatitis D virus** and **adeno-associated satellite viruses** which replicate only in the presence of their helper viruses—hepatitis B and adenoviruses, respectively. Viruses which are genetically deficient and therefore incapable of producing infectious daughter virions without the helper activity of another virus are known as 'defective viruses'.

CULTIVATION OF VIRUSES

As viruses are obligate intracellular parasites, they cannot be grown on any inanimate culture medium. Three methods are employed for the cultivation of viruses: inoculation into animals, embryonated eggs or tissue cultures.

Animal inoculation

The earliest method for the cultivation of viruses causing human diseases was inoculation into human volunteers. Reed and colleagues (1900) used human volunteers for their pioneering work on yellow fever. The use of white mice, pioneered by Theiler (1903) extended the scope of animal inoculation, and mice are still the most widely used animals in virology. Infant (suckling) mice are very susceptible to coxsackie and arboviruses, many of which do not grow in any other system. Mice may be inoculated by several routes: intracerebral, subcutaneous, intraperitoneal or intranasal. Other animals such as guinea pigs, rabbits and ferrets are used in some situations.

The growth of the virus in inoculated animals may be indicated by death, disease or visible lesions. Serial blind passages may sometimes be necessary before evidence of virus growth can be obtained. The disadvantages of animal inoculation are that immunity may interfere with viral growth and that animals often harbour latent viruses. Animal inoculation is also used for the study of pathogenesis, immune response, epidemiology and oncogenesis.

Embryonated eggs

Embryonated hen's egg was first used for the cultivation of viruses by Goodpasture (1931) and the method was further developed by Burnet. The embryonated egg offers several sites for the cultivation of viruses (Fig. 47.5).

- Inoculation on the **chorioallantoic membrane (CAM)** produces visible lesions (pocks). Different viruses have different pock morphology. Under optimal conditions, each infectious virus particle can form one pock. Pock counting, therefore, can be used for the assay of pock-forming viruses such as variola or vaccinia.
- Inoculation into the **allantoic cavity** provides a rich yield of influenza and some paramyxoviruses.
- Inoculation into the **amniotic sac** is employed for the primary isolation of the influenza virus.
- **Yolk sac inoculation** is used for the cultivation of some viruses, chlamydiae and rickettsiae.

Allantoic inoculation is employed for growing the influenza virus for vaccine production. Other chick embryo vaccines in routine use are the yellow fever **(17D strain)** and rabies **(Flury strain)** vaccines. Duck eggs are bigger and have a longer incubation period than hen's eggs. They therefore provide a better yield of rabies virus and were used for the preparation of the inactivated non-neural rabies vaccine.

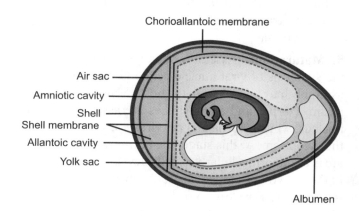

Fig. 47.5 10-day-old embryonated hen's egg

Tissue culture

The main obstacle to the development of tissue culture was the presence of bacterial contamination. It was only when antibiotics became available for the prevention of bacterial contamination that tissue culture became a routine laboratory method. The turning point which made tissue culture the most important method for the cultivation of viruses was the demonstration by Enders, Weller and Robbins (1949) that the poliovirus, till then considered a strictly neurotropic virus, could be grown in tissue culture of non-neural origin. Since then, almost every human virus has been grown in tissue culture (Fig. 47.6).

Types of tissue cultures:

Organ culture: Small bits of organs can be maintained in vitro for days and weeks, preserving their original architecture and function. Organ cultures are useful for the isolation of some viruses which appear to be highly specialised parasites of certain organs. For example, the tracheal ring organ culture is employed for the isolation of coronavirus, a respiratory pathogen.

Explant culture: Fragments of minced tissue can be grown as 'explants' embedded in plasma clots. They may also be cultivated in suspension. This was what was originally known as 'tissue culture'. This method is now seldom employed in virology. Adenoid tissue explant cultures were used for the isolation of adenoviruses.

Cell culture: This is the type of culture routinely employed for growing viruses. Tissues are dissociated into component cells by the action of proteolytic enzymes such as trypsin and mechanical shaking. The cells are washed, counted and suspended in a growth medium. The essential constituents of the growth medium are physiologic amounts of essential amino acids and vitamins, salts, glucose, and a buffering system generally consisting of bicarbonate in equilibrium with atmosphere containing about 5% carbon dioxide. This is supplemented with up to 5% calf or fetal calf serum. Antibiotics are added to prevent bacterial contaminants and phenol red is used as indicator. Such media will enable most cell types to multiply with a division time of 24–48 hours. The cell suspension is dispensed in bottles, tubes or petri dishes. The cells adhere to the glass surface and on incubation, divide to form a confluent monolayer sheet of cells covering the surface within about a week.

Cell culture tubes may be incubated in a sloped horizontal position, either as 'stationary culture' or may be rolled in special 'roller drums' to provide better aeration. Some fastidious viruses grow only in such roller cultures.

Based on their origin, chromosomal characters and the number of generations through which they can be maintained, cell cultures are classified into three types (Table 47.3):

1. **Primary cell cultures:** These are normal cells freshly taken from the body and cultured. They are capable of only limited growth in culture and cannot be maintained in serial culture. Common examples of primary cell cultures are monkey kidney, human embryonic kidney, human amnion and chick embryo cell cultures. Primary cell cultures are useful for the isolation of viruses and their cultivation for vaccine production.

2. **Diploid cell strains:** These are cells of a single type that retain the original diploid chromosome number and karyotype during serial subcultivation for a limited number of times. After about fifty serial passages, they undergo 'senescence'. Diploid strains developed from human fibroblasts are susceptible to a wide range of human viruses and are very useful for the isolation of some fastidious pathogens. They are also used for the production of viral vaccines.

3. **Continuous cell lines:** These are cells of a single type, usually derived from cancer cells that are capable of continuous serial cultivation indefinitely. Standard cell lines derived from human cancers, such as HeLa, HEp-2 and KB cell lines have been used in laboratories throughout the world for many years. These cell lines may be maintained by serial subcultivation or stored in the cold (–70°C) for use

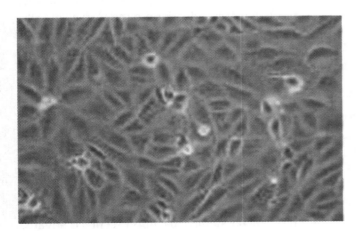

Fig. 47.6   Normal Vero cell monolayer

Table 47.3   *Some cell cultures in common use*

a. Primary cell cultures	
1. Rhesus monkey kidney cell culture	
2. Human amnion cell culture	
3. Chick embryo fibroblast cell culture	
b. Diploid cell strains	
1. WI-38	Human embryonic lung cell strain
2. HL-8	Rhesus embryo cell strain
c. Continuous cell lines	
1. HeLa	Human carcinoma of cervix cell line
2. HEp-2	Human epithelioma of larynx cell line
3. KB	Human carcinoma of nasopharynx cell line
4. McCoy	Human synovial carcinoma cell line
5. Detroit 6	Sternal marrow cell line
6. Chang C/I/L/K	Human conjunctiva (C)
	Intestine (I), Liver (L) and Kidney (K) cell lines
7. Vero	Vervet monkey kidney cell line
8. BHK-21	Baby hamster kidney cell line

when necessary. Some cell lines are now permitted to be used for vaccine manufacture, for example, vero cell for rabies vaccine.

Detection of viral growth in infected tissues is seen as inclusions.

Detection of virus growth in cell cultures: In cell cultures growth can be detected by the following methods:

- **Cytopathic effect:** Many viruses cause morphological changes in cultured cells in which they grow. These changes can be readily observed by microscopic examination of the cultures. These changes are known as 'cytopathic effects' (CPE) and the viruses causing CPE are called 'cytopathogenic viruses'. The CPE produced by different groups of viruses are characteristic and help in the presumptive identification of virus isolates (Fig. 47.7). For example, enteroviruses produce rapid CPE with crenation of cells and degeneration of the entire cell sheet; the measles virus produces syncytium formation; the herpes virus causes discrete focal degeneration; the adenovirus produces large granular clumps resembling bunches of grapes; and SV40 produces prominent cytoplasmic vacuolation.
- **Metabolic inhibition:** In normal cell cultures, the medium turns acid due to cellular metabolism. When viruses grow in cell cultures, cell metabolism is inhibited and there is no acid production. This can be made out by the colour of the indicator (phenol red) incorporated in the medium.
- **Hemadsorption:** When hemagglutinating viruses (such as influenza and parainfluenza viruses) grow

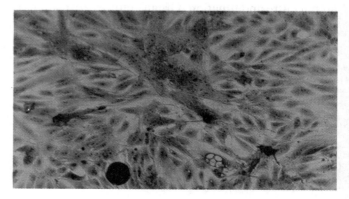

Fig. 47.7   Vervet monkey kidney cells (Vero cell line) infected with measles virus. Note syncytium formation, crystal violet stained, X 100

in cell cultures, their presence can be indicated by the addition of guinea pig erythrocytes to the cultures. If the viruses are multiplying in the culture, the erythrocytes will adsorb onto the surface of cells. This is known as 'hemadsorption'.
- **Interference:** The growth of a non-cytopathogenic virus in cell culture can be tested by the subsequent challenge with a known cytopathogenic virus. The growth of the first will inhibit infection by the second virus by interference.
- **Transformation:** Tumour forming (oncogenic) viruses induce cell 'transformation' and loss of contact inhibition, so that growth appears in a piled-up fashion producing 'microtumours'.
- **Immunofluorescence:** Cells from virus-infected cultures can be stained by fluorescent conjugated antiserum and examined under the UV microscope

for the presence of virus antigen. This gives positive results earlier than other methods and, therefore, finds wide application in diagnostic virology.

VIRAL ASSAY

The virus content of a specimen can be assayed in two ways—either with reference to the total virus particles or with reference to the infectious virions only. Two methods are used for total particle enumeration:

- By simple negative staining, the virus particles in a suspension can be counted directly under the **electron microscope**. The virus suspension can be mixed with a known concentration of latex particles. The ratio between the virus and latex particles under the electron microscope gives an indication of the virus count.
- With hemagglutinating viruses, a convenient method of quantitation is the determination of **hemagglutination titres**. Hemagglutination is not a very sensitive indicator of the presence of small amounts of virus particles. Thus, approximately 10^7 influenza virions are required to produce macroscopic agglutination of a convenient quantity of chicken erythrocytes (0.5 ml of 0.5% suspension). However, because of its simplicity, hemagglutination is a very convenient method of virus assay.

ASSAY OF INFECTIVITY

Two types of infectivity assays can be carried out: quantitative and quantal. Quantitative assays measure the actual number of infectious particles in the inoculum, while quantal assays only indicate the presence or absence of infectious viruses.

Quantitative assays: The quantitative infectivity assay of viruses is similar to the estimation of bacterial viable counts by colony counting. Two methods are available:

- **Plaque assay** was introduced in animal virology by Dulbecco (1952) as a modification of the bacteriophage plaque assay. A viral suspension is added to a monolayer of cultured cells in a bottle or Petri dish, and after allowing time for absorption, the medium is removed and replaced with a solid agar gel, to ensure that the spread of progeny virions is confined to the immediate vicinity of infected cells. In this system, each infectious viral particle gives rise to a localised focus of infected cells that can be seen with the unaided eye. Such foci are known as 'plaques' and each plaque indicates an infectious virus. Some viruses which are transmitted directly from cell to cell (for example, herpesvirus) may form plaques even without an agar overlay. Oncogenic viruses produce cell transformation which can be seen as micro-tumours. Hence, they can be enumerated by the transformation assay.

- **Pock assay** is where viruses that form pocks on CAM (for example, vaccinia) can be assayed by counting the number of pocks formed on CAM by the appropriate inocula of virus.

Quantal assays: Using serial dilutions of virus suspensions and with the aid of statistical methods, reasonably accurate estimates of infectivity can be obtained in quantal assays. Quantal assays of infectivity can be carried out in animals, eggs or tissue culture. Examples of endpoints used for infectivity titration are the death of the animal, production of hemagglutinin in allantoic fluid or the appearance of CPE in cell cultures. The titre is usually expressed as the '50 per cent infectious dose' (ID_{50}) per ml, which indicates the highest dilution of the inoculum that would produce an effect in 50 per cent of animals, eggs or cell cultures inoculated. ID_{50} is calculated by the application of statistical methods, such as that of Reed and Muench.

VIRAL GENETICS

Like all other 'living beings', viruses obey the laws of genetics. Several properties of viruses, such as virulence and antigenicity, that are of great concern to human beings in the context of infections at the level of the cell, individual and community, are under genetic control. Genetic studies, therefore, have contributed to a better understanding of virus–host interactions and the development of better viral vaccines. Genetic mechanisms such as mutation and selection were utilised in the past without recognising the biological mechanisms involved. The development of the 'fixed' rabies virus by Pasteur (1885) is a case in point.

The two main mechanisms for genetic modification in viruses are mutation and recombination. In addition, viruses may exhibit many non-heritable variations due to gene product interactions.

Mutation

The frequency of mutation in viruses is about 10^{-4} to 10^{-8}, approximately the same as in bacteria. Mutations, therefore, occur during every viral infection. Most mutations are lethal. A mutant becomes evident only if the mutation confers some readily observable property or survival advantage. Mutation may occur spontaneously or may be induced by mutagens, physical agents such as irradiation or chemical agents such as 5-fluorouracil.

Types of mutants: Some mutations of clinical and laboratory interest are those affecting virulence, host range, antigenicity and pock or plaque morphology:

Conditional lethal mutant: This class of mutants is of great importance in laboratory studies. These mutants can grow under certain conditions (called **permissive conditions**), but are lethal, that is, they cannot grow under certain other specified conditions (called **non-permissive** or **restrictive conditions**). There are different types of conditional lethal mutants.

Ts mutant: Ts or temperature sensitive mutant is most widely employed in genetic studies. These can grow at a low (permissive) temperature (28–31°C), but not at a higher (restrictive) temperature (37°C). The advantage here is that by using a single selective test (temperature sensitivity), a large numbers of mutants with lesions in different genes may be obtained. The Ts mutants have not only contributed largely to fundamental studies on viral genetics but they also, because of their low virulence, offer prospects of better live viral vaccines.

Host dependent mutants: These can grow in permissive cells but they cause abortive infection in non-permissive cells.

Recombination

Genetic recombination may occur when two different, but related, viruses infect a cell simultaneously. The two viruses exchange segments of nucleic acid so that a hybrid results, possessing genes from both parents. Such recombinants breed true thereafter. Recombinants may occur between:

- two active (infectious) viruses;
- one active and one inactive virus; and
- two inactive viruses.

When two different strains of the same virus (such as vaccinia or influenza), possessing distinctive markers (such as pock morphology or antigenic properties) are grown together, recombinants or reassortant viruses may be derived that possess the distinctive properties of both parents. Thus, if a human and an avian strain of influenza virus (whose hemagglutinin and neuraminidase antigens are different and easily identifiable) are grown together, a hybrid may be obtained with the

hemagglutinin of one parent and the neuraminidase of the other. This has been demonstrated experimentally in vitro and in vivo. This may be one of the ways by which the pandemic strains of the influenza virus originate in nature.

When a cell is 'infected' with an active virus and a different but related inactivated virus, progeny possessing one or more genetic traits of the inactivated virus may be produced. This phenomenon is called **cross-reactivation** or **marker rescue.** New antigenic variants of the influenza virus causing epidemics often do not grow well in eggs as compared to established laboratory strains. When such an epidemic strain (for example, strain A_2) is grown in eggs along with a standard strain (for example, strain A_1) inactivated by UV irradiation, a progeny may be obtained which has the antigenic characters of A_2 but the growth characteristics of A_1. This finds application in the manufacture of the influenza virus vaccines.

When a cell is 'infected' with a large dose (high multiplicity of infection [high MOI]) of a single virus inactivated by UV irradiation, a live virus may be produced. The different virions that cause multiple infections of a cell may have caused damage to different genes. Thus, from the total genetic pool it may be possible to obtain a full complement of undamaged genes. This explains how infectious progeny can be produced. This phenomenon is called **multiplicity reactivation.** There is the potential danger of multiplicity reactivation taking place following the administration of UV irradiated vaccines. UV irradiation is therefore not acceptable as a method of producing inactivated virus vaccines.

Recombination may take place between the virus genome and host chromosome. No viral progeny is produced but genetic recombination leads to changes in the host cell, such as malignant transformation.

As a general rule, virus capsids enclose viral nucleic acids. Sometimes, segments of host nucleic acid become encapsidated instead. For example, in a papovavirus capsid, a linear piece of host DNA roughly the same size as the papovavirus genome may be found. This is known as pseudovirion. As far as is known, each pseudovirion contains a different piece of host DNA. Generally, pseudovirions make up only a small fraction of the yield. When cells are infected with many virus particles (as in papovavirus), these progeny contain DNA molecules that consist of partly viral and partly host sequences.

Viral particles containing host DNA sequences are important because of their potential ability to transduce host genes from one cell to another. This could be exploited for correcting inborn errors of metabolism.

NON-GENETIC INTERACTIONS

Phenotypic mixing: When two different viruses multiply in a cell, some 'mix up' may take place during assembly, so that the genome of one virus may be surrounded by a capsid belonging partly or entirely to the other virus. This is known as phenotypic mixing. This is not a stable variation. On subsequent passage, the capsid will be found to be of the original type only. In phenotypic mixing, when the nucleic acid of one virus is surrounded by the entire capsid of the other virus, it is known as **transcapsidation**. When phenotypic mixing occurs between two enveloped viruses, resulting in the sharing of peplomers, mosaic envelopes result.

Genotypic mixing: This heterozygosis results from the incorporation of more than one complete genome into a single virus particle. There is no recombination between the different genomes so that the two kinds of viral progeny are formed on passage.

Complementation: Complementation is a functional interaction between the gene products (proteins specified by genes) of two viruses, one or both of which may be defective, resulting in the multiplication of one or both under conditions in which replication would not ordinarily occur. There is no genetic interaction and the progeny are like parental viruses. A number of different types of complementation may occur. When a rabbit is injected with a mixture of heat inactivated virulent myxomavirus and active avirulent fibroma virus, it develops fatal myxomatosis. Both myxoma and fibroma are poxviruses. Heat inactivated myxoma virus cannot initiate infection because a heat labile enzyme (DNA dependent RNA polymerase) is destroyed. When co-infected with active fibroma virus, it provides the necessary enzyme so that the myxoma virus can cause infection.

Tests for complementation between different mutants of a virus provide information about the functional organisation of the viral genome. Such tests using Ts mutants have been very useful in the genetic mapping of viruses.

Interference: The usual result of mixed or multiple infections of cells is interference in which infection of a cell by one virus inhibits the simultaneous or subsequent infection by another virus. The most important mediator of interference is interferon, a soluble cellular product. Interference may also be produced by the destruction of cell receptors by an active or inactive virus, so that subsequent viral attachment is not possible. Such viral attachment interference is seen with myxoviruses and enteroviruses for which cell receptors are important for the initiation of infection. Another type of interference is 'autointerference', in which a high multiplicity of infection inhibits the production of infectious progeny.

Viral interference has been applied in the field in controlling poliomyelitis outbreaks by introducing into the population, the live attenuated poliovirus vaccine. The vaccine virus interferes with the spread of wild poliovirus and halts the outbreak. On the other hand, interference by pre-existing enteric viruses may pose a problem in live poliovirus vaccination.

Enhancement: Mixed infection of cells may sometimes lead to increased virus yield or greater CPE. This is known as 'enhancement'.

CLASSIFICATION AND NOMENCLATURE OF VIRUSES

Viruses are classified into two main divisions depending on the type of nucleic acid they possess: riboviruses are those containing RNA and deoxyriboviruses are those containing DNA. Further classification is based on other properties such as the strandedness of nucleic acid, symmetry of the nucleocapsid, presence of an envelope, size and shape of the virion and the number of capsomers. Short descriptions of the major groups of viruses are given below (Table 47. 4).

DNA viruses

Poxviridae family: These are large, brick-shaped or ovoid viruses (300 × 240 × 100 nm), with complex structure, having a lipid containing an outer coat, one or two lateral bodies and a core carrying a single linear molecule of double-stranded DNA. Multiplication and maturation take place in the cytoplasm. The family is divided into several genera.

Herpesviridae family: These are medium-sized viruses containing linear double-stranded DNA. The icosahedral nucleocapsid (100 nm) has 162 capsomers and is surrounded by a lipid-containing envelope. Multiplication takes place in the nucleus and maturation by budding through the nuclear membrane. Only one genus, *Herpesvirus*, has been characterised, but several members of the family await classification.

Table 47.4   *Classification of viruses*

Family	Nature	Envelope	Members causing human disease
DNA Viruses			
1. Poxviridae	ds	±	Variola virus, vaccinia virus, cowpox, monkeypox
2. Herpersviridae	ds	Yes	Herpes simplex 1 and 2, EBV, CMV, varicella zoster, HSV 6,7,8
3. Adenovirus	ds	No	Human adenoviruses A-F
4. Papovaviridae	ds	No	Papilloma virus, polyomavirus
5. Hepadenoviridae	ds	Yes	Hepatitis B virus
6. Parvoviridae	ss	No	Parvovirus
RNA Viruses			
1. Picornaviridae	ss	No	Enteroviruses – poliovirus, coxsackie, echo viruses
2. Orthomyxoviridae	ss	Yes	Influenza virus A–C
3. Paramyxoviridae	ss	Yes	Paramyxovirues – mumps and parainfluenza viruses Morbillivirus – measles virus, Pneumoviruses – RSV
4. Togaviridae	ss	Yes	Alpha (group A) – Chikungunya virus Rubiviruses – rubella virus
5. Flaviviruridae	ss	Yes	Flaviviruses – yellow fever, dengue viruses Japanese encephalitis virus, Hepatitis C virus
6. Bunyaviridae	ss	Yes	Sandfly fever, hantaviruses
7. Arenaviruses	ss	Yes	LCM, Lassa fever
8. Rhabdoviridae	ss	Yes	Vesiculovirus – Chandipura virus, Lyssavirus – Rabies virus
9. Reoviridae	ds	No	Human rotavirus
10. Coronaviridae	ss	Yes	Human coronaviruses, SARS virus
11. Retroviridae	ss	Yes	HIV 1 -2, HTLV1-2
12. Calciviridae	ss	No	Norwalk virus, hepatitis E virus
13. Filoviridae	ss	Yes	Marburg, Ebola viruses
14. Astroviridae	ss	No	Human astroviruses
15. Deltaviruses	ss	Yes	Hepatitis deltavirus
16. Prions	NA	NA	CJD, Kuru, GSSS

Adenoviridae family: These are medium-sized (70–90 nm) non-enveloped, icosahedral viruses with 252 capsomers. Members have been classified into two genera: *Mastadenovirus* (mammalian adenoviruses) and *Aviadenovirus* (adenoviruses of birds)

Papovaviridae family: These are small (40–55 nm) non-enveloped, double-stranded DNA viruses with 72 capsomers. Two genera have been identified: *Papillomavirus* and *Polyomavirus*.

Parvoviridae family: These are very small (18–26 nm) non-enveloped viruses with 31 capsomers. The genome consists of single-stranded DNA. Three genera have been described: *Parvovirus*, *Adenosatellovirus* and *Densovirus*.

Hepadnaviridae family: This consists of the human hepatitis type B virus and related viruses of animals and birds. (The name comes from *hepa* = liver, and *dna* for DNA core.) The virion is spherical, 42 nm in diameter, consisting of a 27-nm core surrounded by an envelope having virus-specific antigens.

RNA viruses

Picornaviridae family: These are small (20–30 nm), non-enveloped, icosahedral viruses with a single-stranded RNA genome. Three genera are of medical importance:

- *Enterovirus*, including polio, coxsackie, echo and several other related viruses.
- *Rhinovirus*, including human, bovine and equine rhinoviruses.
- *Hepatovirus*: Hepatitis A virus.

Orthomyxoviridae family: These are medium-sized (80–120 nm) spherical or elongated enveloped viruses carrying hemagglutinin and neuraminidase peplomers. The genome consists of single-stranded RNA in several (eight) pieces. Only one genus *Influenzavirus* has been recognised. *Influenzavirus* type C possesses several distinctive features and may have to be separated into a new genus.

Paramyxoviridae family: These are pleomorphic virions (150 nm) with lipid envelope, having surface projections. The genome is an unsegmented single-stranded linear RNA. Three genera have been recognised:

- *Paramyxovirus*, which consists of the Newcastle disease virus, mumps virus and parainfluenza viruses of humans, other mammals and birds
- *Morbillivirus*, containing measles, canine distemper, rinderpest and related viruses
- *Pneumovirus*, containing respiratory syncytial virus of humans and related viruses

Togaviridae family: These are spherical viruses, 40–70 nm in size, with a lipoprotein envelope and single-stranded RNA genome. Most members multiply in arthropods as well as in vertebrates. Three genera have been described:

- *Alpha virus*, consisting of viruses formerly classified as Group A arboviruses
- *Rubivirus*, consisting of the rubella virus
- *Pestivirus*, consisting of the mucosal disease virus, hog cholera virus and related viruses

Flaviviridae family: Flaviviruses, formerly grouped under togaviridae, as Group B arboviruses, have been classified as a separate family because of differences in their molecular structure and replication strategy.

Bunyaviridae family: Spherical, enveloped virions, 90–100 nm in size. All are arthropod-borne viruses. Five genera are established: the large genus Bunyavirus containing about 150 species, and four other genera—*Hantavirus, Nairovirus, Phlebovirus, Ukuvirus*—and many unassigned viruses.

Arenaviridae family: Spherical or pleomorphic viruses, 50–300 nm in size, containing a number of electron-dense ribosome-like particles giving a sandy appearance (hence the name; *arena*, meaning sand in Latin). Members are generally rodent parasites causing persistent infection in the natural host but capable of infecting human beings rarely, leading to severe hemorrhagic illness. Only one genus, *Arenavirus*, has been recognised. Species include lymphocytic choriomeningitis virus, Lassa and members of the Tacaribe complex.

Rhabdoviridae family: Bullet-shaped viruses, 130–300 nm long and 70 nm wide, with a lipoprotein envelope carrying peplomers. Two genera have been recognised:

- *Vesiculovirus*, containing vesicular stomatitis virus, Chandipura virus (isolated from humans in India) and related species

- *Lyssavirus*, containing the rabies virus and related viruses such as Lagos bat, Mokola, Duvenhage and others

Other genera have been suggested to include rhabdoviruses of insects and plants.

Reoviridae family: Icosahedral, non-enveloped viruses, 60–80 nm in size with double-layered capsids. Genome consists of double-stranded RNA in 10–12 pieces. Three genera have been recognised:

- *Reovirus*, containing reoviruses from humans, other mammals and birds
- *Orbivirus*, containing several species of arboviruses such as blue tongue virus, African horse sickness virus and Colorado tick fever virus
- *Rotavirus*, including human rotaviruses, calf diarrhea virus and related agents.

Other genera may have to be defined to include plant and insect viruses belonging to this family.

Coronaviridae family: Pleomorphic enveloped viruses around 100 nm in size, with unique club-shaped peplomers projecting as a fringe from the surface, resembling the solar corona (hence the name). Only one genus, Coronavirus, has been recognised. Members include human corona viruses causing upper respiratory disease, SARS avian infectious bronchitis virus, calf neonatal diarrhea corona virus, murine hepatitis virus and related viruses.

Retroviridae (re = reverse, tr = transcriptase) family: These are RNA tumour viruses and related agents. Virions are icosahedral, about 100 nm in size, with lipoprotein envelopes. The characteristic biochemical feature is the presence of RNA dependent DNA polymerase (reverse transcriptase) within the virus. Three subfamilies are recognised:

- Oncovirinae, the RNA tumour virus group
- Spumivirinae, the foamy virus group (*spuma* = foam)
- Lentivirinae (*lenti* = slow), visna and maedi viruses of sheep belonging to the slow virus group

Caliciviridae family: These are naked spherical particles (35–39 nm) with 32 cup-shaped depressions arranged in symmetry.

Filoviridae family: These are long, filamentous, enveloped viruses (80 nm diameter and up to 14,000 nm long) with helical nucleocapsid and the ss RNA genome. This contains the *Marburg* and *Ebola* viruses causing human hemorrhagic fevers.

VIROIDS

The term 'viroid' was introduced by Diener (1971) to describe a new class of subviral agents characterised by the apparent absence of an extracellular dormant phase (virion) and by a genome much smaller than those of known viruses. The infective agent is a protein-free, low-molecular-weight RNA resistant to heat and organic solvents but sensitive to nucleases. First identified in the potato spindle tuber disease, viroids have been shown to cause some plant diseases also. It is possible that the causative agents of some animal and human diseases may turn out to belong to the class of viroids.

PRION

Yet another unconventional, virus-like agent has been named prion (1982). The causative agent of scrapie Kuru and Creutzfeldt–Jakob disease has been shown to be a small particle (MW 50,000 and probably 4–6 nm in diameter), without any detectable nucleic acid, resistant to heat (90°C for three minutes), UV rays and nucleases, and sensitive to proteases. Prions are proteinaceous infectious particles. It has been suggested that they are may also be responsible for some other chronic neurological degenerative disease of humans.

RECAP

- Viruses are obligate intracellular parasites because they are dependent on the synthetic machinery of the host cell for replication. They are considered to be the smallest 'living units not affected by antibacterial antibiotics'.
- The extracellular infectious virus particle is the virion. Viruses are much smaller than bacteria and can be visualised directly by electron microscopy.
- Viruses are either DNA or RNA and never both together.
- Virions may be enveloped or non-enveloped. The envelope helps in attachment to the host cell surface or erythrocytes.
- Protein subunits (peplomers) may occur as projecting spikes on the envelope surface (hemagglutinin and neuraminidase of the influenza virus).
- The viral multiplication (replication) cycle consists of six sequential phases (overlaps may occur):
  - adsorption (attachment)
  - penetration into the cell
  - uncoating
  - biosynthesis
  - maturation, and
  - release of progeny.
- The virus cannot be demonstrated within the host cell from the stage of penetration till the stage of release—the 'eclipse phase'.
- Cultivation of viruses can be done by inoculation into animals, embryonated hens' eggs or tissue culture, but may vary. Viruses can be cultivated in suckling mice (24–48 hours old), guinea pigs and rabbits.
- For cell culture, primary cell cultures, secondary and continuous cell lines—for example, HeLa, HEp-2, Vero, BHK-21—can be used.
- The growth of a virus in such cell cultures can be detected by tests that demonstrate cytopathic effect (CPE), metabolic inhibition, hemadsorption (HEA) and transformation and by immunofluorescence.
- The virus content of a specimen can be assayed either with reference to the total virus particles or to the infectious virions alone. Two types of infectivity assays can be performed: quantitative, which measures

the actual number of infectious particles in the inoculum, and quantal, which only indicates the presence or absence of infectious viruses.

- There are two main mechanisms for genetic modification in viruses, namely, mutation (which occurs during every viral infection) and recombination (which occurs when two different but related viruses simultaneously infect a cell).
- Non-genetic interactions between viruses may occur when two different viruses simultaneously infect a single cell.
- DNA viruses comprise the following families: Poxviridae, Herpesviridae, Adenoviridae, Papovaviridae, Parvoviridae and Hepadnaviridae.
- RNA viruses comprise the following families: Picornaviridae, Orthomyxoviridae, Paramyxoviridae, Togaviridae, Flaviviridae, Bunyaviridae, Arenaviridae, Rhabdoviridae, Reoviridae, Coronaviridae, Retroviridae, Caliciviridae and Filoviridae.
- A viroid is a subviral agent that does not have an extracellular dormant (virion) phase and has a genome that is much smaller than those of known viruses.
- Prions are proteinaceous infectious particles which appear to lack nucleic acid.

SHORT ANSWERS

1. General characters of viruses
2. Properties of viruses
3. Viral multiplication
4. Methods of cultivation of viruses
5. Inclusion bodies
6. Hemagglutination in viruses
7. Draw a diagram of the structure of a virus.
8. Five RNA viruses and the diseases caused by them
9. Five DNA viruses and the diseases caused by them

SHORT NOTES

1. Cell cultures for virus isolation
2. Use of embryonated eggs in virology
3. Interference in viruses
4. Prions
5. Cytopathic effects of viruses
6. Interferons
7. Temperature-sensitive mutants (definition)

48 Virus–Host Interactions: Viral Infections

INTRODUCTION

Virus–host interactions may be considered at different levels: the cell, the individual and the community.

At the **cellular level**, viral infection may cause a broad spectrum of effects, ranging from no apparent cellular damage to rapid cell destruction. Some viruses, like the poliovirus, cause **cell death** (**cytocidal effect**) or even **lysis** (**cytolysis**). Others may cause **cellular proliferation** (as molluscum contagiosum) or **malignant transformation** (as oncogenic viruses).

In some instances, the virus and host cells enter into peaceful co-existence, both replicating independently without any cellular injury, a condition known as **steady state infection**. In tissue culture, viral infection may lead to readily observable cellular changes (**cytopathic effects**). These may not parallel the changes produced in the infected animal, as in the latter situation, infection is influenced by the various defence mechanisms of the body.

Causes of cellular injury:
- **Early** or **non-structural viral proteins** often cause shutdown of host protein and DNA synthesis.
- Large amounts of **viral macromolecules** that accumulate in the infected cell may distort the cellular architecture and exert a toxic effect.
- The **permeability of plasma membranes** may be altered, releasing lysosomal enzymes and leading to autolysis.
- Many viruses produce alterations in the **cytoplasmic membrane** of infected cells.
- Some (such as the respiratory syncytial virus) cause fusion of adjacent cell membranes, leading to polykaryocytosis or **syncytium** formation.
- Virus-coded antigens may appear on the surface of infected cells. These antigens may confer new properties on the cells. For example, viral **hemagglutinin** appears on the surface of cells infected with the influenza virus and causes adsorption of erythrocytes to the cell surface (hemadsorption). **Virus-coded antigens** also appear on the surface of cells transformed by oncogenic viruses.

Certain viruses such as measles, mumps, adenoviruses, cytomegalovirus and varicella virus cause damage to the chromosomes of host cells. Chromatid gaps and breaks in chromosome 17 occur frequently in cultured cells infected with adenovirus types 12 and 31.

Inclusion bodies: The most characteristic histological feature in virus infected cells is the appearance of inclusion bodies. Inclusion bodies are structures with distinct size, shape, location and staining properties that can be demonstrated in virus infected cells under the light microscope.

They may be situated in the cytoplasm (as with poxviruses), nucleus (herpesviruses) or both (measles virus). They are generally acidophilic and can be seen as pink structures when stained by the Giemsa method or with eosin methylene blue. Some viruses (for example, adenovirus) form basophilic inclusions.

Demonstration of inclusion bodies helps in the diagnosis of some viral infections. The presence of intracytoplasmic eosinophilic inclusions (**Negri bodies**) in the brain cells of animals justifies the presumptive diagnosis of rabies. Vaccinia infected cells show rather smaller multiple inclusions known as **Guarnieri bodies**. Large inclusions (**Bollinger bodies**) are seen in fowlpox. Inclusion bodies in molluscum contagiosum

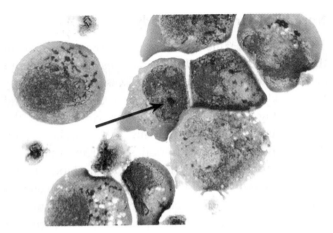

Fig. 48.1   Inclusion bodies in herpesvirus (Giemsa stain)

(**molluscum bodies**) are very large (20–30 µm) and can be readily seen under the low power microscope. Intranuclear inclusion bodies were classified into two types by Cowdry (1934): **Cowdry type A inclusions** are of variable size and have a granular appearance (as with herpesvirus, yellow fever virus), while **type B inclusions** are more circumscribed and often multiple (as with adenovirus, poliovirus).

Inclusion bodies may be crystalline aggregates of virions or made up of virus antigens present at the site of virus synthesis. Some inclusions represent degenerative changes produced by viral infection which confer altered staining properties on the cell (Fig. 48.1).

PATHOGENESIS OF VIRAL INFECTION

Depending on the clinical outcome, viral infections can be classified as follows:

- Inapparent (**subclinical**) infections
- Apparent (**clinical** or overt) infections which may be acute, subacute or chronic
- **Latent** infections:
    - **Recurrent** herpes simplex and herpes zoster are examples of latent infections in which clinical manifestations appear after prolonged periods of quiescence during which the viruses remain hidden in the nerve root ganglia
    - **Persistent** tolerant infection occurs when the virus is readily demonstrable in the tissues of the host but neither disease nor immune response develops. The host is immunologically tolerant to the virus as a result of congenital or neonatal infection. Disease sets in when the tolerance is interrupted. The classical example of persistent

tolerant infection is lymphocytic choriomeningitis of mice.

- Slowly progressive or **slow infection** (incubation period is unusually long) is seen in neurological diseases such as scrapie in sheep and *kuru* in human beings.
- Infection by **oncogenic** viruses
- The **HIV virus** leads to a special type of latency, with an initial asymptomatic period followed by progressive immune damage causing secondary diseases, ending fatally after many years.

Routes of entry

Viruses enter the body through the respiratory and alimentary tracts, skin, conjunctiva and the genital tract. Many viruses are transmitted vertically from mother to child.

The **respiratory tract** offers the most important portal of entry for viruses. A large number of viruses can infect the cells of this tract. Some of them multiply locally to initiate a silent local infection which is followed by lymphatic or hematogenous transport to other situations where more extensive multiplication takes place before systemic illness is manifested. Smallpox and chickenpox are examples of such systemic diseases in which the portal of entry is the respiratory tract. Other viruses such as influenza and rhinoviruses are restricted to the respiratory tract, where they multiply and produce local disease. These are known as respiratory viruses.

The **alimentary tract** is the next most important route of entry for viruses. However, only some viruses can establish infection in the intestines. All enveloped viruses are destroyed by bile. Rhinoviruses are inactivated by gastric acidity. Only enteroviruses, adenoviruses, reoviruses, hepatitis viruses and the viruses causing gastroenteritis can set up intestinal infection. Some of these such as rotavirus remain confined to the gut, causing local disease. Others such as poliovirus, after initial multiplication locally, are transported to other sites for further multiplication and subsequent spread to the target organs.

Of the viruses that enter through the **skin**, only a few produce local lesions. Papilloma, vaccinia, cowpox, molluscum contagiosum and orf are viruses that produce dermal lesions at the site of entry. Skin lesions of exanthematous viral diseases are secondary to systemic infection. Viruses enter the skin through abrasions (papillomavirus), insect bites (arboviruses), animal bites (rabies) or injections (type B hepatitis).

Systemic spread occurs through lymphatics or blood. The rabies virus travels along the nerves to the spinal cord or brain.

The **conjunctiva** also may act as a portal of entry for viruses. This may lead to local disease (adenovirus) or to systemic spread (measles). Some viruses may enter through the genital tract or other sites of sexual contact (HIV).

Congenital infection may occur at any stage, from the development of the ovum up to birth. In acute systemic infections, congenital infection usually leads to fetal death and abortion. Rubella and cytomegalovirus produce maldevelopment or severe neonatal disease. Vertical transmission is the natural mode of spread of many tumour viruses. The avian leukosis virus is transmitted in ovo and murine mammary tumour virus through breast milk.

Spread of virus in the body

The manner in which the infecting virus spreads from the point of entry, multiplies in sites of election and causes lesions in target tissues was first studied by Fenner (1948) using mousepox as the experimental model (Fig. 48.2). The mousepox virus enters the skin, where it multiplies initially and proceeds along the lymphatics to the local nodes. After multiplication in the lymph nodes, the virus enters the bloodstream (**primary viremia**) and is transported to the spleen and liver which act as the 'central foci' for viral multiplication. After extensive multiplication in the central foci, there occurs a massive spillover of the virus into the bloodstream (**secondary viremia**). This heralds the onset of clinical symptoms (the prodromal phase in eruptive fevers). The virus reaches the target organ

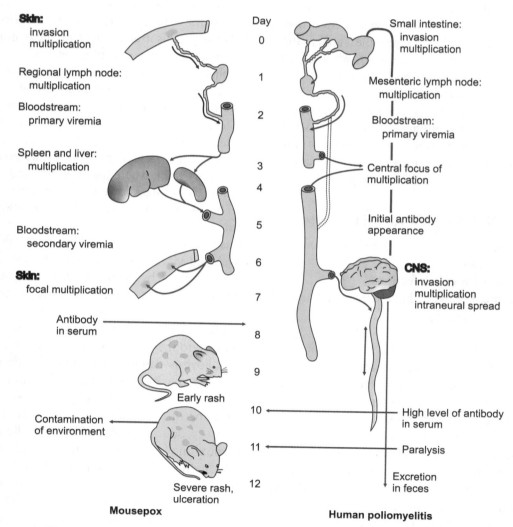

Fig. 48.2   Schematic illustrations of the pathogenesis of mousepox and poliomyelitis

(skin in eruptive fevers) through the bloodstream. Multiplication in the target sites produces the distinctive lesions. With minor modifications, this model holds good for most systemic virus diseases. The reasons for the difference in the foci of multiplication and target organs in the case of different viruses are obscure.

Significance of the incubation period

The incubation period represents the time taken for the virus to spread from the site of entry to the organs of viral multiplication and thence to the target organs for the production of lesions. Its duration is therefore influenced by the relation between the sites of entry, multiplication and lesion. Where the site of entry and site of lesion are the same, the incubation period is short—one to three days, as in respiratory viral infections and in gastroenteritis. In systemic diseases where the virus enters through the respiratory or alimentary tract and produces lesions in remote target sites, the incubation period is longer—10–20 days, as in chickenpox or poliomyelitis. There are, however, exceptions to this rule. In arbovirus diseases, as in yellow fever or dengue, the incubation period may be shorter (5–6 days), probably because the virus is introduced directly into the bloodstream by the insect vectors. The incubation period in type B hepatitis may be 2–6 months and in slow viral infections, many years. Papillomas and molluscum contagiosum have long incubation periods, probably because the viruses multiply slowly.

HOST RESPONSE TO VIRUS INFECTIONS

The outcome of a virus infection is influenced by the virulence of the infecting strain and the resistance offered by the host. Mechanisms of host resistance may be immunological or non-specific. The latter includes various genetic and physiological factors such as interferon production, body temperature, nutrition and hormones.

Immunological response

Virions in general are good antigens and induce both humoral and cellular immune response. The multiplication of a virus in the body during infection induces not only a quantitatively greater immune response but also liberates and makes available to the immune system the whole range of virus antigens, including surface and internal antigens as well as non-structural antigens such as early proteins.

Humoral: In mediating humoral antiviral immunity, the important classes of antibodies are IgG, IgM and IgA. IgG and IgM play a major role in blood and tissue spaces, while IgA is more important on mucosal surfaces. Antibodies effect virus neutralisation by several mechanisms. They may prevent adsorption of the virus to cell receptors, cause enhanced virus degradation or prevent the release of the progeny virus from infected cells. Complement acts in conjunction with antibodies in causing surface damage to enveloped virions and in producing cytolysis of virus infected cells.

Not all antibodies can neutralise viral infectivity. Antibodies to internal antigens are non-neutralising. Antibodies to surface antigens vary in their neutralising ability. For instance, two types of surface antibodies appear following influenza infection: antihemagglutinin and antineuraminidase. The former can neutralise infectivity but the latter cannot. The antineuraminidase antibody can, however, inhibit the release of progenal virions from infected cells. Some antibodies can paradoxically enhance viral infectivity. Humoral antibodies may sometimes actually contribute to pathogenesis. Antibodies may cause complement dependent injury to cells or induce an immune complex type of tissue injury. The enhanced severity of respiratory syncytial viral infection in early infancy is believed to be due to the presence of passively acquired maternal antibodies. In older children who have no antibody, the virus causes a milder disease. The pathogenesis of some viral hemorrhagic fevers is immune thrombocytopenia. Most extrahepatic lesions in type B hepatitis are due to damage caused by immune complexes.

Cell mediated: Cell-mediated immunity is of critical importance in viral infections. The earliest indication of cell-mediated immunity in viral infections was the demonstration of delayed hypersensitivity following vaccination in immune individuals. Similar skin reactivity is also seen in mumps. The normal resistance to virus infections shown by agammaglobulinemics is ascribed to their cell-mediated immunity, though it may also be due to interferon or other non-immune mechanisms. Individuals with deficient cellular immunity show heightened susceptibility to infection by the herpes, pox and measles viruses. The administration of antilymphocyte serum induces fatal infection in mice injected with a sublethal dose of the ectromelia virus. Cell-mediated immunity is considered to play a major role in recovery from viral infections in which viremia is not important and in which infected cells have viral specific antigens on their surface. In some virus infections, cell-mediated immunity may contribute to tissue damage, as in lymphocytic choriomeningitis in mice.

Suppression: Some viral infections cause suppression of the immune response. Measles infection induces a temporary depression of delayed hypersensitivity to tuberculin. Infection of adult mice with lymphocytic choriomeningitis or leukemia viruses inhibits antibody response to other antigens. HIV strikes at the centre of the immune system by infecting the CD4+ helper T cell.

In general, viral infections are followed by solid immunity to re-infection, which may often be lifelong. Apparent exceptions like the common cold and influenza are not due to lack of immunity but to re-infection being caused by antigenically different viruses. Live virus vaccines also induce more durable protection than bacterial vaccines.

Non-immunological responses

Phagocytosis: Polymorphonuclear leucocytes do not play any significant role in the defence against viral infections. In fact, more viral diseases are characterised by polymorphonuclear leucopenia. On the other hand, macrophages phagocytose viruses and are important in clearing viruses from the bloodstream.

Body temperature: Fever may act as a natural defence mechanism against viral infections as most viruses are inhibited by temperatures above 39°C. An exception is herpes simplex which is usually reactivated by fever to produce 'fever blisters'. *Herpes febrilis* is a frequent accompaniment of fevers caused by pneumococci, streptococci, influenza virus and malaria parasites, but for some unknown reason, is very rare in other fevers (typhoid, tuberculosis).

Hormones: Corticosteroid administration enhances most viral infections. Coxsackie virus B1 does not normally cause disease in adult mice but will induce a fatal infection in mice treated with cortisone. Normally mild infections such as varicella and vaccinia may be lethal in patients on cortisone. Injudicious use of steroids in the treatment of herpetic keratoconjunctivitis may cause blindness. The particularly severe course of many viral infections in pregnancy may be related to the associated hormonal changes. The deleterious effect of cortisone may be due to its depression of the immune response and inhibition of interferon synthesis.

Malnutrition: Some viral infections, such as measles, produce a much higher incidence of complications and a higher case fatality rate in malnourished children than in well-fed patients.

Age: Most viral infections are commoner and more dangerous at the two extremes of age. A notable exception was the influenza pandemic of 1918–19 which caused the highest fatality in young adults.

Interferon: Isaacs and Lindenmann (1957) observed that chick chorioallantoic membrane fragments treated with live or inactivated influenza virus produced a diffusible antiviral substance which rendered the cells resistant to viral infection. They gave the name interferon to this antiviral substance. It was subsequently found that interferon production is a natural defence mechanism possessed by vertebrate cells against viral infection.

Interferons are a family of host-coded proteins produced by cells on induction by viral or non-viral inducers. Interferon by itself has no direct action on viruses but acts on other cells of the same species, rendering them refractory to viral infection. On exposure to interferon, cells produce a protein (translation inhibiting protein, TIP) which selectively inhibits translation of viral mRNA, without affecting cellular mRNA. What has been called TIP is actually a mixture of at least three different enzymes (a protein kinase, an oligonucletide synthetase and an RNAase) which together block translation of viral mRNA into viral proteins. It has also been suggested that inhibition of viral transcription may also be responsible for the antiviral activity of interferon.

Interferons are species specific, in that the interferon produced by one species can protect only cells of the same or related species against viral infections but not cells of unrelated species. Thus, the antiviral effect on human cells is shown by human interferon, and to some extent by monkey interferon but not by chick or mouse interferon. The activity is not virus specific. The interferon induced by one virus (or even by non-viral inducers) can confer protection against infection by the same or unrelated viruses. However, viruses vary in their susceptibility to interferon. Viruses also vary in their capacity to induce interferon, cytocidal and virulent viruses being poor inducers and avirulent viruses being good inducers. RNA viruses are better inducers than DNA viruses. Examples of potent inducers are togaviruses, vesicular stomatitis virus, Sendai virus and NDV. Nucleic acids (for example, double-stranded RNA and some synthetic polymers (for example, Poly I:C) are particularly efficient inducers.

Interferon production is increased by increasing the temperature to about 40°C and is inhibited by steroids and increased oxygen tension. Interferon synthesis begins within about an hour of induction and reaches high levels in 6–12 hours. The promptness of interferon induction—much quicker than the antibody response—suggests that interferons may play a primary role in host defence against viral infections. Cellular transcription and protein synthesis are necessary for interferon production.

Types: Based on antigenic character, cell of origin and other properties, interferons have been classified into three types: **alpha, beta** and **gamma**. The abbreviation IFN designates interferon and species of origin is indicated as a prefix—for example, human interferon alpha is usually abbreviated as HuIFN-α.

- **Alpha interferon (IFN-α)**, formerly known as leucocyte interferon, is produced by leucocytes following induction by suitable viruses. It is a non-glycosylated protein. At least 16 antigenic subtypes have been identified.
- **Beta interferon (IFN-β)**, formerly known as 'fibroblast interferon, is produced by fibroblasts and epithelial cells following stimulation by viruses or polynucleotides. It is a glycoprotein.
- **Gamma interferon (IFN-γ)**, formerly known as immune interferon, is produced by T lymphocytes on stimulation by antigens or mitogens. It is a glycoprotein. It is more concerned with immunomodulatory and anti-proliferative functions than with antiviral defence. It also differs from alpha and beta interferons in having a separate cell receptor.

Interferons are inactivated by proteolytic enzymes but not by nucleases or lipases. They resist heating at 56–60°C for 30–60 minutes and are stable over a wide range of pH (2–10), except gamma IFN, which is labile at pH 2. They have a molecular weight of about 17,000, are non-dialysable and non-sedimentable (100,000 g). They are poorly antigenic, so no routine serological tests are available for their detection and estimation. Interferon assay is based on its biological activity, such as the ability to inhibit plaque formation by a sensitive virus. The potency of IFN is expressed as International Units (IU) per ml.

Clinical uses: Many properties of interferon make it an ideal candidate for use in the prophylaxis and treatment of viral infections; it is non-toxic, non-antigenic, diffuses freely in the body and has a wide spectrum of antiviral activity. The major drawback initially was its species specificity—interferon produced by non-human cells was not clinically useful. This was overcome to some extent by producing interferon from buffy coat leucocytes from blood banks, with NDV or the Sendai virus as the inducer. Now, human interferon is available in unlimited quantities following its commercial production by cloning in bacteria and yeast. Even so, its initial promise as an antiviral agent has not been fulfilled. Local application of high doses has shown some benefit against upper respiratory infections, herpetic keratitis and genital warts. Limited success has also been reported against generalised herpes infection in immunocompromised hosts, and against hepatitis B and C infections. Some encouraging results have been reported in the use of interferon as an anticancer agent, particularly in lymphomas but there have been reports of toxic effects in cancer patients given high doses of interferon.

Although interferon was first recognised as an antiviral agent; it is now known to be a more general regulatory peptide belonging to the class of **cytokines**.

The main biological effects of interferons are as follows:
- **Antiviral effects**: Induction of resistance to infection
- **Antimicrobial effects**: Resistance to intracellular infections, for example toxoplasma, chlamydia, malaria
- **Cellular effects**: Inhibition of cell growth and proliferation; and of DNA and protein synthesis; increased expression of MHC antigens on cell surfaces
- **Immunoregulatory effects**: Enhanced cytotoxic activity of NK, K and T cells; activation of macrophage cytocidal activity; modulation of antibody formation; activation of suppressor T cells; suppression of DTH

LABORATORY DIAGNOSIS OF VIRAL DISEASES

Technical difficulties in virus isolation and identification, the length of time required for these procedures and the lack of specific therapy for viral infections have contributed to the sparse use of diagnostic virology till recently. With the development of rapid techniques for the diagnosis of many virus infections and the availability of specific drugs against at least a few viruses, diagnostic virology is fast becoming a routine procedure.

The demonstration of viral infection in selected groups of persons (**screening**) is an important procedure in the prevention of some diseases (such as screening for HBV and HIV in blood donors). Etiological diagnosis of viral infections is useful in many ways. It is of vital important in some cases, as in rubella in pregnant women. It helps institution of early specific therapy as in herpetic encephalitis and lesions of the eye. It serves to define the cause of vague syndromes such as upper respiratory infection or aseptic meningitis. It is essential for the detection and prediction of epidemics and the identification of anti-genic variation in viruses. It is invaluable in the prompt control of outbreaks. It may lead to the discovery of new viral infections.

Specimen: Successful diagnosis of viral infections depends as much on the awareness of the physician as on the capability of the virus laboratory. The appropriate specimens should be collected from patients, preserved and transported to the laboratory in the proper manner along with pertinent clinical and epidemiological information (Table 48.1).

Microscopy: The demonstration of virus elementary bodies by examination of stained smears by light microscopy can be done but is now seldom employed with the availability of better diagnostic modalities. Detection of the virus by **electron microscopy** is being used increasingly. In some diseases, it used to be the only diagnostic method (for example, viral diarrhea). In Nipah viruses, **immunoelectron microscopy** has been used—a specific antibody is added to react with viral antigens and then visualised by electron microscope. Demonstration of the inclusion body (Negri bodies) on Seller's stain is a routine diagnostic method for rabies in dogs.

A fluorescent microscope can be used for the microscopic diagnosis of rabies by **fluorescent antibody** techniques. The use of direct and indirect fluorescent antibody techniques for the examination of material from lesions, as well as for the early demonstration of viral antigen in tissue cultures inoculated with

Table 48.1 *Types of specimens to be sent for virus diagnosis*

System	Specimens required[1]		
	For isolation	**For direct examination[2]**	**For serology**
Respiratory system; nasopharyngeal	Throat swab, throat washings (EM) aspirates	Nasopharyngeal aspirate (IF)	Paired sera
Central nervous system	Feces, blood (for arbovirus isolation) CSF (brain biopsy, throat swab, rectal swab)	Brain biopsy (IF & EM); CSF (EM & IF)	Paired sera
Cardiovascular system	Feces	Nil	Paired sera
Skin	Macular/papular scrapings, vesicular/pustular fluid, ulcer scrapings, crust, feces, throat swab	Vesicular/pustular fluid (EM&ID) Ulcer scrapings (EM), crusts, (EM & ID)	Paired sera
Eye	Conjunctival scrapings or swabs	Conjunctival scrapings, as smears on microscope slides (LM & IF)[3]	Paired sera
Liver	Blood (for yellow fever)	Serum (feces)	Serum
General; congenital infections	Throat swab (products of conception)	Nil	Single sera (mother & baby)
General; PUO	Heparinised blood (arbovirus and arenavirus infections) throat swabs, feces (fresh urine)	Nil	Paired sera

[1]Specimens within brackets are not appropriate for routine diagnosis but may be indicated in particular circumstances
[2]IF = Immunofluorescence; EM = Electron Microscopy; ID = Immunodiffusion; LM = Light Microscopy
[3]For diagnosis of rabies only.
(*Adapted from WHO*)

specimens, has enlarged the scope and greatly increased the speed of virus diagnosis.

Demonstration of virus antigen: In cases where the virus antigen is abundant in the lesions, its demonstration by serological methods such as precipitation in gel or immunofluorescence offers a rapid method of diagnosis. Highly sensitive serological tests such as counterimmunoelectrophoresis, radioimmunoassay and enzyme-linked immunosorbent assay have found wide application in diagnostic virology for the detection of viral antigens in clinical samples.

Isolation of virus: For virus isolation it is imperative that the specimen be collected properly and transported with least delay to the laboratory. As most viruses are heat labile, refrigeration is essential during transport. The methods used for isolation depend on the virus sought. In general, they consist of inoculation into animals, eggs or tissue culture, after the specimen is processed to remove bacterial contaminants. The isolates are identified by neutralisation or other suitable serological procedures. It has to be emphasised that the mere recovery of a virus from a patient does not justify the assumption that it is the causative agent of the patient's illness. Many viruses (for example, adenoviruses, enteroviruses) are frequently found in normal individuals. The results of isolation should always be interpreted in light of the clinical data. Demonstration of an immunological response to the virus isolate in the patient during the course of the disease reinforces the significance of the isolation.

Serological diagnosis: The demonstration of a rise in titre of antibodies to a virus during the course of a disease is strong evidence that it is the causative agent. For this, it is essential to examine paired sera, the 'acute' sample collected early in the course of the disease and the '**convalescent**' sample collected 10–14 days later. Examination of a single sample of serum for antibodies may not be meaningful except when IgM-specific tests are done. The serological techniques employed would depend on the virus but those in general use are neutralisation, complement fixation, ELISA and hemagglutination inhibition tests.

Molecular diagnosis: The availability of molecular methods has transformed the diagnosis of viral diseases, enlarging the scope, sensitivity and specificity of such tests. In situ hybridisation using nucleic acid probes have been used to diagnose human papillomaviruses. Nucleic acid amplification techniques like PCR, reverse transcriptase PCR and real time PCR have increased the sensitivity of the diagnostic assays. Following PCR, DNA or RNA sequencing of the product can be done.

IMMUNOPROPHYLAXIS OF VIRAL DISEASES

Prolonged and effective immunity is characteristic of most viral infections. Viral vaccines also confer solid protection and are, in general, more effective than bacterial vaccines. Viral vaccines may be live or killed (Table 48.2).

Live vaccines are more effective than killed vaccines. The smallpox vaccine has been used as the sole tool for the global eradication of the disease. The early live vaccines were developed empirically from natural viruses (as Jenner's cowpox vaccine) or by attenuation by serial passage (as yellow fever vaccines). The basis of the latter technique was an unconscious selection of avirulent mutants. With the development of more precise genetic techniques, live vaccines have been developed by plaque selection (Sabin vaccine for poliomyelitis) or from *ts* mutants or by recombination (as in influenza).

Live vaccines have the following **advantages**: A single dose is usually sufficient. They can be administered by the route of natural infection so that local immunity is induced. They induce a wide spectrum of immunoglobulins to the whole range of viral antigens. They also induce cell-mediated immunity. They provide more effective and more lasting immunity than killed vaccines. They can, in general, be prepared more economically and administered more conveniently, especially for mass immunisation. Some of them can be given as combined vaccines (measles–mumps–rubella vaccine).

They have the following **disadvantages**: There is a risk, however remote, of reversion to virulence. The vaccine may be contaminated with potentially dangerous viruses or other infectious agents. The virus may spread from the vaccines to contacts. While this is a serious danger in some situations, as when spread occurs to immunodeficient or other high risk contacts, in other cases, it may even be an advantage (as in poliomyelitis where the range of vaccination is extended by the natural spread of the vaccine virus among children and adults). Interference by pre-existing viruses may sometimes prevent a good immune response following live vaccination. Live vaccines are heat labile and have to be kept under refrigeration.

Table 48.2   *Viral vaccines in common use*

Disease	Type of vaccine	Mode of preparation
Poliomyelitis	Live	Avirulent strains grown in monkey kidney cell culture
	Killed	Virulent strains grown in monkey kidney cell culture, formalin-killed
Rabies	Killed (Semple type)	Fixed virus grown in sheep brain and inactivated by phenol or beta propiolactone
	Killed	Virus grown in cell culture and inactivated with beta propiolactone
Yellow fever	Live (17D)	Attenuated virus grown in chick embryos and lyophilised
Japanese encephalitis	Killed	Virus grown in mouse brain and inactivated by formalin
Varicella	Live	Attenuated virus grown in chick embryo fibroblast culture
Mumps	Live	Attenuated virus grown in human diploid cell culture
Influenza	Killed (subunit)	Virus disintegrated with sodium deoxycholate
	Live (attenuated)	Virus attenuated by serial passage in eggs
	Live (mutant)	*ts* mutants which are avirulent
	Live (recombinant)	Recombinants with surface antigens of new strains and growth characters of established strains
Measles	Live	Attenuated virus grown in tissue culture
Rubella	Live	Attenuated virus grown in tissue culture
Hepatitis B	Cloned subunit	HBsAg cloned in yeast

Some live vaccines may cause local and remote complications (as with smallpox vaccine).

Killed vaccines have been prepared by inactivating viruses with heat, phenol, formalin or beta propiolactone. Ultraviolet irradiation is not satisfactory because of the risk of multiplicity reactivation. Reduction of the reactogenicity of killed vaccines has been attempted by purification of the viruses. Adverse reactions may also be reduced by the use of '**subunit vaccines**' in which the virus is split by detergents or other chemicals and only the relevant antigens incorporated in the vaccine. Vaccine production by cloning the desired antigen in bacteria or yeast is becoming increasingly common, as in hepatitis B.

Killed vaccines have the **advantage** of stability and safety. They can be given in combination as polyvalent vaccines. There is also no danger of spread of the virus from the vaccine. The **disadvantages** are that multiple injections are required and that local immunity and cell-mediated immunity are not induced.

Passive immunisation with human gammaglobulin, convalescent serum or specific immune globulin gives temporary protection against many viral diseases such as measles, mumps and infectious hepatitis. These are indicated only when non-immune individuals who are at special risk are exposed to infection. Combined active and passive immunisation is an established method for the prevention of rabies.

CHEMOPROPHYLAXIS AND CHEMOTHERAPY OF VIRUS DISEASES

As viruses are strict intracellular parasites that use the biosynthetic mechanisms of the host cell for replication, it was feared that it may not be possible to inhibit viral replication without damaging the host cell. However, there are several areas available for attack on viruses selectively.

Viral infection may be checked at the level of:
- attachment
- transcription of viral nucleic acid
- translation of viral mRNA
- replication of viral nucleic acid and
- assembly and release of viral progeny.

It may even be possible to target cell-free virions. A number of virus-specific enzymes have been identified which can be inhibited selectively, thereby preventing viral multiplication without affecting the host cells.

The first clinically useful antiviral drug was developed in 1960 when *N*-methylisatin-β-thiosemicarbazone (Methisazone, Marboran) was found to be effective against poxviruses. It was used successfully against eczema vaccinatum and for the prevention and treatment of smallpox. Shortly thereafter smallpox was eradicated and the drug went out of use.

In 1962, the antineoplastic drug idoxyuridine was found to be effective for herpetic eye infection. At about the same time, **amantadine**, a molecule with an unusual structure, was found to be active against the influenza A virus. A landmark event was the discovery in the 1970s of **acyclovir** which was effective against herpesviruses and safe enough for parenteral administration. Serendipity as well as planned pursuit has led to the development of many antiviral agents, the need for which became urgent with the advent of the AIDS pandemic (Table 48.3).

Available **antiviral agents** can be considered under the following categories:

Nucleoside analogues:
- **Deoxyuridines**: These analogues of thymidine block thymidine kinase and are effective against the herpes simplex virus. The first of these was 5-iodo-2-deoxyuridine (idoxuridine, IDU) used topically in herpetic keratitis. The related 5-trifluoromethyl-2-deoxyuridine (trifluridine, *TFT*) is more soluble and less toxic and has replaced IDU. Bromovinyl deoxyuridine (BVDU) is non-toxic and even more active, particularly against the varicella zoster virus.
- **Adenine arabinoside (Vidarabine, ara-A)** has ribose substituted by arabinose in adenine. It was used topically in herpetic keratitis and parenterally against herpes simplex and varicella zoster infections. However, it has been replaced by acyclovir

for the treatment of systemic infections. The related cytosine arabinoside (cytarabine, ara-C) is cytotoxic and immunosuppressive, and not used systemically.
- **Acyclovir (acylguanosine)** is an analogue of guanine, acting against herpesviruses through thymdine kinase. Herpes viruses that code for their own thymidine kinase (HSV-VZV) are far more susceptible than those which do not (CMV-EBV). The related drug Ganciclovir is more active against CMV.
- **Azidothymidine (Zidovudine, AZT)** used against HIV infection is a thymidine analogue which blocks the synthesis of proviral DNA by inhibiting viral reverse transcriptase. AZT is used widely in HIV infection, but is toxic and costly.
- A series of **dideoxynucleosides** (Didanosine, Zalcitabine, Stavudine, Lamivudine) have been synthesised and found to possess anti-HIV activity by blocking reverse transcriptase. The second group of drugs used in HIV infection is protease inhibitors (Saquinavir, Ritonavir, Indinavir).
- **Ribavirin (Virazole)** is a synthetic nucleoside related to guanosine. It shows activity against many DNA and RNA viruses. Administered as an aerosol, it has been effective in the treatment of respiratory syncytial viral infection and also in influenza. Intrave-

Table 48.3   Antiviral agents

Class of drugs	Antiviral agents	Target	Antiviral spectrum
Nucleoside analogues:			
	Acyclovir	Viral polymerase inhibition	VZV
	Trifluridine		HSV
	Vidarabine		
	Ganciclovir	Viral polymerase inhibition	CMV
	Lamivudine	Reverse transcriptase inhibition	HIV-1, HIV-2, HBV
	Didanosine		
	Stavudine		
	Zidovudine (AZT)	Reverse transcriptase inhibition	HIV-1, HIV-2
			HTLV-1
	Ribavirin	Blocks capping of viral mRNA	RSV, Influenza A and B
Nucleoside analogue	Cidofovir	Viral polymerase inhibition	CMV, HSV
Protease inhibitors	Indinavir	HIV protease inhibition	HIV-1, HIV-2
	Retonovir		
	Saquinavir		
RT inhibitor	Nevirapine	Reverse transcriptase inhibition	HIV-1
Neuraminidase inhibitor	Oseltamivir	Viral neuraminidase inhibition	Influenza A and B
Host cell penetration/uncoating	Amantidine	Blocks viral uncoating	Influenza A
DNA polymerase inhibitor	Foscarnet	Viral polymerase inhibition	HSV, HBV,
			HIV-1
Integrase inhibitor	Raltigravir	HIV integrase inhibitor	HIV-1

nous ribavirin has been reported to be effective against Lassa fever and other hemorrhagic fevers.

- **Amantadine (Adamantanamine hydrochloride, Symmetrol)** blocks host cell penetration by the influenza A virus but not by B or C. A derivative rimantadine is less toxic and equally effective. A second line of drugs against influenza employs neuraminidase inhibition.
- **Enviroxine** and related chemicals have shown activity against rhinoviruses.
- **Foscarnet (Trisodium phosphonoformate)** specifically inhibits DNA polymerase of the herpes simplex virus and has some effect against hepatitis B and HIV also.
- **Suramin** developed as an antiparasitic drug in 1916 was found to inhibit reverse transcriptase activity and so was one of the first drugs used against AIDS.

Because of toxicity and inadequate efficacy its use was discontinued.

Despite intensive efforts, progress in the field of antiviral chemotherapy has not been satisfactory. Various factors contribute to this. Many compounds show antiviral activity in tissue culture but most of them are ineffective or toxic in animal tests. The available drugs have a narrow range of activity. They are seldom able to eradicate the virus from the host, so recurrence is common. Viruses develop resistance to the drugs and breakthrough infection takes place even during treatment. The AIDS pandemic has been a catalyst in the development of antiretroviral drugs. It is hoped that better understanding of the molecular and cellular biology of viruses and of virus–host interactions may lead to the development of more effective antiviral agents.

RECAP

- Virus–host interactions can take place at the level of the cell, individual and community. At the cellular level, viral infection may cause a broad spectrum of effects, ranging from no apparent effects to rapid cell destruction.
- Many viruses produce alterations in the cytoplasmic membrane of infected cells and cause fusion of adjacent cell membranes or the appearance of hemagglutinins on the surface of infected cells.
- The most characteristic histological feature in virus-infected cells is the appearance of inclusion bodies; these can be seen by light microscopy and may be acidophilic or basophilic and intracytoplasmic or intranuclear. The Negri body is an acidophilic, intracytoplasmic inclusion body in rabies virus.
- Depending on the clinical outcome, viral infections can be classified as inapparent (subclinical), apparent (clinical or overt) or latent infections which remain quiescent for long periods while kuru is another latent infection that is slowly progressive.
- Viruses enter the body through the respiratory tract, alimentary tract, skin, conjunctiva and the genital tract.
- The infecting virus usually spreads from the point of entry, multiplies in sites of election. In systemic virus infections, there is entry, spread to the local lymph nodes, multiplication, entry into the bloodstream (primary viremia), spread to central liver and spleen and cauisng secondary viremia and finally spread to the target organs.
- The incubation period is the time taken for the virus to spread from the site of entry to the organs of viral replication.
- Viruses are intracellular parasites and a cell infected by a virus may undergo immediate degeneration or destruction, proliferate and then undergo necrosis or not change at all, but may cause latent virus infections.
- Interferon is a protein that may be produced by a virus-infected cell or a sensitised lymphocyte encountering such a cell. Interferon alters cellular metabolism so that further assembly of viral particles is prevented.
- Specific humoral and cell-mediated immune responses may be observed in viral infections. Cell-mediated immune responses confer protection against viral diseases.

- Vaccination (active immunisation) against various viral diseases augments cell-mediated immunity. Overreaction of cell-mediated immune responses to viral infections may result in tissue damage (delayed hypersensitivity reactions).
- Several methods are used in the laboratory for the diagnosis of viral infections:
    - Viruses in infected specimens may be detected by electron microscopy. Light microscopy can be used to detect viral inclusion bodies in Giemsa-stained smears.
    - Specific viral antigens in the blood or body fluids of an infected individual can sometimes be detected.
    - Viruses can be cultivated in animals, embryonated eggs or tissue cultures.
- The growth of a virus in such cell cultures can be detected by tests that demonstrate cytopathic effect, metabolic inhibition, hemadsorption and transformation and by immunofluorescence.
    - Serological diagnosis using neutralisation, complement fixation, hemadsorption inhibition, immunofluorescence, enzyme immunoassays and radioimmunoassay is useful. IgM antibody or four-fold rise in IgG antibody levels in paired serum against a specific virus denotes an active infection.
    - Diagnosis of viral infections by polymerase chain reaction (PCR) is a very sensitive technique that can detect a single molecule of viral DNA in a clinical specimen.
- Amantadine and rimantadine block viral penetration into the cell or uncoating of virus in the cell; idoxuridine, trifluorothymidine and bromovinyldeoxyuridine are thymidine analogues that interfere with viral DNA synthesis; acyclovir and ganciclovir are nucleoside (guanine) analogues; antiretroviral drugs are available for HIV infections.

SHORT ANSWER

1. Antiviral vaccines

SHORT NOTE

1. Anti-retroviral agents

49 Bacteriophages

INTRODUCTION

Bacteriophages (commonly abbreviated as phages) are viruses that infect bacteria. Twort (1915) described a degenerative change in staphylococcal colonies isolated from the calf lymph, which could be transmitted serially by application of culture filtrates from the original growth. d'Herelle (1917) observed that filtrates of feces cultures from dysentery patients induced transmissible lysis of a broth culture of a dysentery bacillus. He suggested that the lytic agent was a virus and gave it the name bacteriophage.

Phages occur widely in nature in close association with bacteria. They can be readily isolated from feces, sewage and other natural sources of mixed bacterial growth. Early hopes that phages could be used in the treatment of bacterial infections have not been fulfilled, but these viruses have contributed much to microbiology. As phages could be grown easily on bacterial cultures, they provided the only convenient model for the study of virus–host interactions at the cellular and molecular levels before the development of cell culture techniques made similar studies with animal viruses possible.

Phages play an important role in the transmission of genetic information between bacteria by the process of **transduction**. The presence of phage genome integrated with bacterial chromosomes confers on bacteria certain properties by a process known as **phage conversion**. Phages have been used as cloning vectors in genetic manipulations. The presence of high concentrations of phage particles, up to 10^8 per ml in some natural waters, suggests that they may have a role in the control of bacterial populations in such environ-ments. The specificity of the host range of phages is the basis of phage typing methods, by which bacteria can be identified and typed.

Morphology

Certain bacteriophages that infect *E.coli,* called the T even phages (T2, T4, T6), have been studied in great detail and have traditionally served as the prototypes in describing the properties of bacteriophages. T even phages have a complex and characteristic morphology. They are tadpole shaped, with a hexagonal head and a cylindrical tail.

- The **head** consists of a tightly packed core of nucleic acid (double-stranded DNA) surrounded by a protein coat or capsid. The size of the head varies in different phages, from 28 nm to 100 nm.
- The **tail** is composed of a hollow core, a contractile sheath surrounding the core and a terminal base plate which has prongs, tail fibres or both attached to it (Figs 49.1 and 49.2).

Though most bacteriophages have the morphology and structure described above, phages that are spherical or filamentous and possess single-stranded DNA or RNA have also been identified.

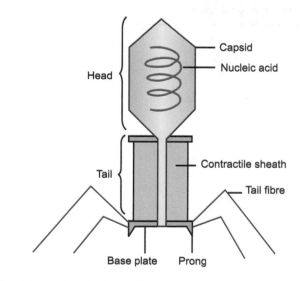

Fig. 49.1   Morphology of bacteriophage

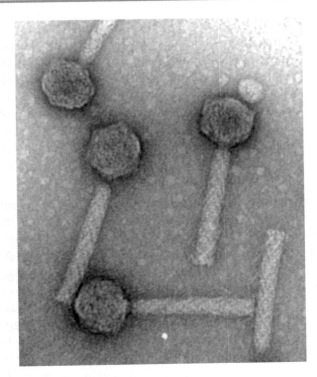

Fig. 49.2 Bacteriophages

Life cycle

Phages exhibit two different types of life cycles. In the virulent or lytic cycle, intracellular multiplication of the phage culminates in lysis of the host bacterium and the release of progeny virions. In the temperate or lysogenic cycle, the phage DNA becomes integrated with the bacterial genome, replicating synchronously with it, causing no harm to the host cell (Fig. 49.3).

Lytic cycle: Replication of a virulent phage can be considered in the following stages: adsorption, penetration, synthesis of phage components, assembly, maturation and release of progeny phage particles.

1. **Adsorption**: Phage particles come into contact with bacterial cells by random collision. A phage attaches to the surface of a susceptible bacterium by its tail. Adsorption is a specific process and depends on the presence of complementary chemical groups on the receptor sites of the bacterial surface and on the terminal base plate of the phage. Under optimal conditions, adsorption is a very rapid process, completed within minutes. Certain co-factors, such as cations, are necessary for adsorption. The bacterial receptor sites may be situated in different layers of the cell wall or on surface structures (such as the Vi antigen of the typhoid bacillus) or appendages (such as flagella

or sex pili). Bacterial protoplasts, which are devoid of cell wall components, cannot adsorb phages and will therefore not be infected. Host specificity of phages is determined at the level of adsorption. Experimental infection by direct injection of phage DNA can be achieved even in bacterial strains that are insusceptible to infection by the whole phage. The infection of a bacterium by the naked phage nucleic acid is known as **transfection**.

2. **Penetration**: Adsorption is followed by the penetration of the phage nucleic acid into the bacterial cell. The process of penetration resembles injection through a syringe. The base plate and tail fibres are held firmly against the cell, causing the hollow core to pierce through the cell wall. The contractile tail sheath acts like a muscle and derives its energy from a small amount of adenosine triphosphate present on the tail of the phage. The phage DNA is injected into the bacterial body through the hollow core. Penetration may be facilitated by the presence on the phage tail of lysozyme, which produces a hole on the bacterial wall for the entry of the phage

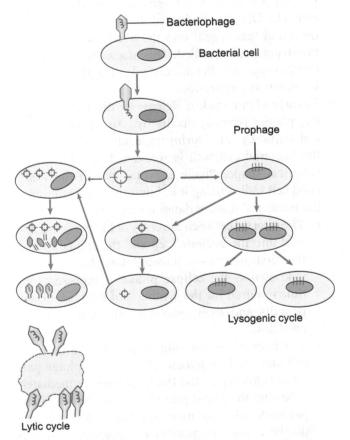

Fig. 49.3 Lytic and lysogenic cycles of bacteriophage

core. The complex structure of the phage particle is required only for injection of the nucleic acid into the host cell. The phage DNA alone is necessary for initiation of the synthesis of daughter phages. After penetration, the empty head and tail of the phage remain outside the bacterium as the shell or 'ghost'.

When bacteria are mixed with phage particles at high multiplicity (that is very large number of phages per bacterial cell), multiple holes are produced on the cell, with the consequent leakage of cell contents. Bacterial lysis occurs without viral multiplication. This is known as 'lysis from without'.

3. **Synthesis**: Immediately after penetration of the phage nucleic acid, synthesis of the phage components is initiated. The first products to be synthesised (called **early proteins**) are the enzymes necessary for the building of the complex molecules peculiar to the phage. Subsequently, **late proteins** appear, which include the protein subunits of the phage head and tail. During this period, the synthesis of bacterial protein, DNA and RNA ceases.

4. **Maturation**: The phage DNA, head protein and tail protein are synthesised separately in the bacterial cell. The DNA is condensed into a compact polyhedron and '**packaged**' into the head and, finally, the tail structures are added. This assembly of the phage components into the mature infective phage particle is known as maturation.

5. **Release (Lytic cycle)**: Release of the mature progeny phages typically occurs by lysis of the bacterial cell (Lytic cycle). During replication of the phage, the bacterial cell wall is weakened and assumes a spherical shape. Phage enzymes act on the weakened cell wall causing it to burst or lyse, resulting in the release of mature daughter phages.

- The interval between the entry of the phage nucleic acid into the bacterial cell and the appearance of the first infectious intracellular phage particle is known as the **eclipse phase**. It represents the time required for the synthesis of the phage components and their assembly into mature phage particles.

- The interval between the infection of a bacterial cell and the first release of infectious phage particles is known as the **latent period**. Immediately following the latent period, the number of phage particles released increases for a few minutes till the maximum number of daughter phages is attained.

- This period, during which the number of infectious phages released rises, is known as the **rise period**. The average yield of progeny phages per infected bacterial cell is known as the **burst size**. This is estimated by experiments in which infection is established with one phage per bacterium and the release of infected phage particles is estimated serially over a period of time. The results of such an experiment plotted on a graph are known as the **one-step growth curve** (Fig. 49.4).

Lysogenic cycle (Temperate cycle): Unlike virulent phages which produce lysis of the host cell, temperate phages enter into a symbiotic relationship with their host cells without destroying them (Temperate cycle). Following entry into the host cell, the temperate phage nucleic acid becomes integrated with the bacterial chromosome. The integrated phage nucleic acid is known as the prophage. The prophage behaves like a segment of the host chromosome and replicates synchronously with it. This phenomenon is called lysogeny and a bacterium that carries a prophage within its genome is called a lysogenic bacterium. Lysogenisation does not upset the bacterial metabolism.

The prophage confers certain new properties on the lysogenic bacterium. This is known as lysogenic conversion or phage conversion. This is due to the synthesis of new proteins coded for by prophage DNA. An example is toxin production by the diphtheria bacillus, which is determined by the presence in it of the prophage **beta**. Elimination of the prophage abolishes the toxigenicity of the bacillus.

During the multiplication of lysogenic bacteria, the prophage may become 'excised' from occasional cells. The excised prophage initiates lytic replica-

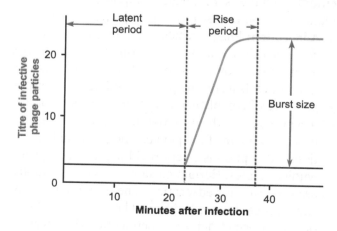

Fig. 49.4   One-step growth curve of bacteriophage

tion and the daughter phage particles are released, which infect other bacterial cells and render them lysogenic. This is known as **spontaneous induction of prophage**. While this is a rare event, all lysogenic bacteria in a population can be induced to shift to the lytic cycle by exposure to certain physical and chemical agents. Such inducing agents include UV rays, hydrogen peroxide and nitrogen mustard. A lysogenic bacterium is resistant to re-infection by the same or related phages. This is known as superinfection immunity.

Transmission of genetic information

Bacteriophages may act as carriers of genes from one bacterium to another. This is known as **transduction**. Two types of transduction are recognised. In **restricted transduction**, only bacterial genes contiguous to the prophage are transmitted. For example, transduction by the prophage lambda in *E.coli* K12 transfers only the gal$^+$ gene (determining fermentation of galactose), which is the bacterial gene contiguous to the prophage. On the other hand, any bacterial gene may be transferred in **generalised transduction**. Transduction has been demonstrated in many genera of bacteria and constitutes one of the most important mechanisms of genetic exchange among bacteria in nature. Plasmid-mediated drug resistance in staphylococci is an example of a medically important property that is transmitted by transduction.

Phage particles exhibit general stability of type and a low rate of heritable variation.

If a bacterium simultaneously adsorbs two related but slightly different DNA phage particles, both can infect and reproduce. On lysis, both types are released. When this occurs many of the progeny are observed to be recombinants.

Significance of phages

Phage assay: When a phage is applied on the lawn culture of a susceptible bacterium, areas of clearing occur after incubation. These zones of lysis are called **plaques**. The size, shape and nature of plaques are characteristic for different phages. Under optimum conditions, a single phage particle is capable of producing one plaque, plaque assay can be employed for titrating the number of viable phages in a preparation. As plaques are analogous to bacterial colonies, plaquing is also useful for the purification of phages.

Phage typing: The specificity of phage–bacterium interaction is made use of in the identification and typing of bacteria. Phages exhibit different degrees of host specificity. Some phages possess wide host ranges, covering many bacterial genera, while others have a narrow range limited to certain strains of bacteria only. With some phages, serial passage in a strain of bacterium makes them specific for that strain and related strains (adaptation of host range).

Phages that lyse all the members of a bacterial genus (for example, genus-specific bacteriophage for *Salmonella*), all the members of a species (for example, specific bacteriophage for *B.anthracis*) and all the members of a biotype or subspecies (for example, Mukerjee's phage IV which lyses all strains of classical *V.cholerae* but not *V.cholerae* biotype El Tor) are available. The most important application of phage typing is for intraspecies typing of bacteria, as in the phage typing of *S.*Typhi and staphylococci. Adapted phages, active only against fresh isolates possessing the Vi antigen, are used for phage typing of the typhoid bacilli. Staphylococcal phage typing is a pattern method using a set of standard phages. A strain of *Staphylococcus* may be lysed by a number of phages and the phage type of a strain is designated by the numbers of the different phages that lyse it.

As lysis is influenced by the dose of infection, phage preparations used for typing should be standardised by titration. Titration is carried out by applying serial dilutions of the phage preparation on a lawn culture of a susceptible strain and observing the lysis after incubation. The highest dilution of the phage preparation that produces confluent lysis is known as the **routine test dose (RTD)**.

RECAP

- The bacteriophage is a type of virus that specifically infects bacteria and fungi.
- Bacteriophages exhibit two different types of life cycles:
  - ❖ In the lytic (virulent) cycle, intracellular multiplication of the phage ends in lysis of the host bacterium and release of progeny virions.
  - ❖ In the lysogenic (temperate) cycle, phage DNA becomes incorporated within the bacterial genome and then replicates synchronously with it, causing no harm to the host cell.
- The replication of a virulent bacteriophage proceeds through the stages of adsorption (attachment to the host cell), penetration of the nucleic acid into the cell, synthesis of phage components, assembly of phage components and maturation and release of progeny phage particles from the cell.
- Phages play an important role in the transmission of genetic information between bacteria by the process of transduction. They can carry antibiotic resistance genes or virulence genes. Bacteria can be typed by phage typing methods for epidemiological purposes.

ESSAY

1. Describe the types of bacteriophages and explain their life cycle.

SHORT ANSWERS

1. Eclipse phase of bacteriophages
2. Phage typing (definition)
3. Lysogeny (definition)

SHORT NOTES

1. Labelled diagram of a bacteriophage
2. Use of bacteriophages
3. Lysogenic phages
4. Lytic phages

50 Poxviruses

INTRODUCTION

Poxviruses are the largest viruses that infect vertebrates. They are large enough to be seen under the light microscope. This group contains several viruses belonging to the family Poxviridae that infect humans, animals, birds and insects. Based on genetic, antigenic and ecological criteria, it has been classified into two subfamilies.

Family Poxviridae

Subfamily Chordopoxvirinae:

These are the poxviruses of vertebrates. They are classified into six genera or subgroups:

Orthopoxvirus: Mammalian poxviruses that tend to cause generalised infection with rash—variola, vaccinia, cowpox, monkeypox, rabbitpox, buffalopox, camelpox, mousepox

Parapoxvirus: Viruses of ungulates that may occasionally infect humans—orf (contagious pustular dermatitis), paravaccinia (milker's nodes, bovine papular stomatitis)

Capripoxvirus: Viruses of goats and sheep—sheep-pox, goatpox, lumpy skin disease

Leporipox virus: Viruses of leporids (rabbits, hares, squirrels)—myxoma and fibromas

Avipoxvirus: Viruses of birds—fowlpox, turkeypox, pigeonpox, canarypox

Suipoxvirus: Swinepox

Subfamily Entomopoxvirinae:

These are the poxviruses of insects which do not infect vertebrates.

Unclassified

Poxviruses that have not been officially assigned to any genus include the virus of **molluscum contagiosum**, **tanapox** and the **yaba monkey tumour**.

Human infections: Poxvirus diseases are characterised by skin lesions which may be localised or generalised. The most important of these was smallpox caused by the variola virus. Other poxviruses which can infect humans are vaccinia, cowpox, monkeypox, tanapox, molluscum contagiosum, paravaccinia and orf. Buffalopox and camelpox may occasionally infect humans, causing lesions resembling vaccination.

VARIOLA AND VACCINIA

The variola virus is the causative agent of smallpox. For thousands of years, smallpox raged as a scourge of humans, causing death and disfigurement. The global eradication of smallpox, achieved after 10 years of concerted campaigns under the auspices of the WHO, has been a most impressive medical achievement. Naturally occurring smallpox came to an end in 1977. On 8 May, 1980, the WHO formally announced the **global eradication of smallpox**.

Variola virus: The virus causing classical smallpox was called **variola major** and that causing alastrim **variola minor**. Variola major and minor were antigenically identical but they differed in certain biological characteristics. They were stable variants as the disease produced by each always bred true; alastrim did not lead to smallpox and vice versa.

Vaccinia and the small pox vaccine: The vaccinia virus was used as the smallpox vaccine. Jenner originally used the cowpox virus for vaccination against smallpox, but during the several years in which the original vaccine virus was maintained by arm-to-arm passage in humans, it underwent some permanent changes so that it could be readily differentiated from fresh isolates of cowpox and smallpox viruses. The vaccinia virus is unique in that it is an 'artificial virus' and does not occur in nature as such. It has been studied in greater detail than variola, as it is safer to work with. The vaccinia virus is being used as a vector for the development of recombinant vaccines. The vaccinia genome can accommodate about 25,000 foreign base pairs, sufficient for introducing several genes. Many genes have been inserted, including those coding for the antigens of the hepatitis B virus, HIV, rabies, and for pharmacologically important products such as neuropeptides. However, the vaccinia virus is not suitable as a vector for human use due to its pathogenic effects.

The vaccinia and variola viruses are so similar in their properties that they can be considered together.

Morphology

The virion is brick shaped. In vertical section, it consists of a double-layered membrane which surrounds a biconcave 'nucleoid' containing the DNA core. On either side of the nucleoid is a lens-shaped structure called the lateral body (Fig. 50.1). The virion measures about 300 × 200 × 100 nm and so can be seen under the light microscope. The variola virus was first demonstrated microscopically by Buist in 1887. Paschen in 1906 developed a staining technique for the virus particles and demonstrated the elementary bodies (Paschen bodies) in smears from smallpox lesions.

Physical and chemical properties

Poxviruses are stable and if protected from sunlight may remain viable for months at room temperature. In the cold or when freeze dried, they survive for years. They are susceptible to ultraviolet light and other irradiations. They are resistant to 50% glycerol and 1% phenol but are readily inactivated by formalin and oxidising disinfectants. The virion consists essentially of DNA, protein and lipid. Though enveloped, the virus is not inactivated by ether. The virion contains a multiplicity of enzymes. The entire multiplication of the virus takes place in the cytoplasm of the infected cell.

Antigenic structure

All poxviruses share a common nucleoprotein (NP) antigen. By immunodiffusion, some twenty different antigens have been identified. These include the LS antigen (a complex of two antigens, the heat labile L and the heat stable S antigens), agglutinogen, and hemagglutinin, which is responsible for the agglutination of erythrocytes of those fowls, which are also agglutinated non-specifically by tissue lipids.

Cultivation and host range

The variola and vaccinia viruses can be differentiated by their growth characteristics and host range.

Chick embryo: Both viruses grow on the CAM of 11–13-day-old chick embryo, producing pocks in 48–72 hours. Variola pocks are small, shiny, white, convex, non-necrotic, non-hemorrhagic lesions. Vaccinia pocks are larger, irregular, flat, greyish, necrotic lesions, some of which are hemorrhagic (Fig. 50.2). The viruses may also be differentiated by their 'ceiling temperatures', the highest temperature above which pocks are not produced. The ceiling temperatures are 41°C for vaccinia, 38°C for variola major and 37.5°C for variola minor.

Tissue culture: Variola and vaccinia viruses can be grown in tissue cultures of monkey kidney, HeLa and chick embryo cells. Cytopathic effects are produced by vaccinia in 24–48 hours and more slowly by variola. Eosinophilic inclusion bodies—Guarnieri bodies—can

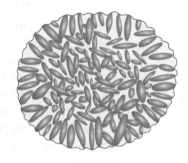

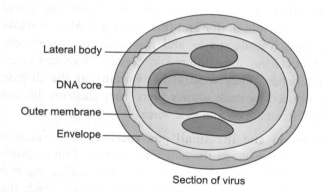

Lateral body
DNA core
Outer membrane
Envelope

Section of virus

Fig. 50.1 The structure of vaccinia virus; top: surface structure; bottom: section view

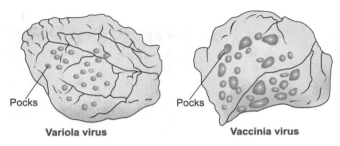

Pocks

Variola virus

Pocks

Vaccinia virus

Fig. 50.2   Variola and vaccinia pocks on CAM

be demonstrated in stained preparations. The inclusion bodies consist of aggregations of virus particles in a matrix. Vaccinia, but not variola, produces plaques in chick embryo tissue cultures.

Animals: The vaccinia virus can infect a wide range of animals experimentally. Monkeys, calves, sheep and rabbits can be infected by scarification, leading to vesicular lesions. The variola virus produces similar lesions only in monkeys. Scarification of rabbit cornea with variola virus leads to keratitis, and sections of the cornea will show typical Guarnieri bodies. Intranasal instillation of the variola virus in the monkey produces a self-limited attack of smallpox with generalised skin lesions.

SMALLPOX

Smallpox has been eradicated. The last natural case of variola major detected was Saiban Bibi, a Bangladeshi woman found with smallpox on the Karimganj railway platform in Assam on 24 May, 1975. The last case of variola minor occurred in Merca, Somalia, in October 1977. The coming generations are unlikely to witness the disease but its disappearance has been too recent for it to be ignored altogether. A brief account of smallpox is therefore being presented.

Smallpox was an exclusively human infection, with no animal reservoir. There were no carriers as the virus was eliminated completely from the patient on recovery. The source of infection was a patient in the early phase of the disease, though infectivity extended from the appearance of buccal mucosal lesions (enanthems) to the disappearance of all the skin lesion (exanthems). Infection usually occurred only in close contacts. Virus entered the body by inhalation. After initial multiplication in the local lymphoid tissues, the virus reached the reticuloendothelial cells, where further multiplication took place, leading to

severe viremia with seeding of the mucosa and skin heralding the clinical disease. The incubation period was around 12 days.

The single crop of centrifugal exanthems passed through macular, papular, vesicular and pustular stages, before scabbing and healing by scar formation in 2–4 weeks. The exanthems varied in severity from the hemorrhagic, flat, ordinary or modified form, in descending order.

Smallpox could be diagnosed in the laboratory by detection of virus antigen or by isolation of the virus from the blood in the early phase (in severe cases only) or from the eruptive lesion (in all cases). On account of the distinctive morphology of the virion, rapid diagnosis was possible by electron microscopy, where the facility was available.

Two factors which contributed to the success of the small pox eradication programme were the use of freeze dried vaccine (in place of the unreliable liquid vaccine used earlier) and the technique of vaccination by multiple puncture with the bifurcated needle, which was simple, effective and economical.

Though natural smallpox ceased in 1977, a small outbreak of variola major occurred in August 1978, in Birmingham, following the accidental spread of the virus from the virus laboratory in the medical school. It was promptly identified and controlled but the incident showed the hazard of keeping variola stocks in laboratories. Following a directive by the WHO, all such laboratory stocks of the virus have been destroyed. The last stocks of smallpox virus were held under high security in the Centers for Disease Control and Prevention, Atlanta, Georgia (USA) and the Centre for Research on Virology and Biotechnology, Koltsova (Russia). They were to have been destroyed by June 30, 1999. As a measure of protection against the remote danger of smallpox re-emerging or posing a bioterrorism threat, large stocks of smallpox vaccine are maintained by the WHO for rapid deployment, if needed.

OTHER POXVIRUS DISEASES

With the elimination of smallpox, it has become important to identify and characterise other orthopoxviruses which can infect human beings and cause disease resembling smallpox (Table 50.1).

Monkeypox: This virus was first isolated in 1958 from an outbreak of pox disease in a captive monkey colony in Copenhagen. Monkeys are only incidental,

Table 50.1   *Comparison of properties of some orthopoxviruses*

	Variola	Monkeypox	Vaccinia	Cowpox	Camelpox
Isolated from	Humans	Humans, monkey, anteater	Origin unknown	Humans, cow, large felines	Camel
Pocks on CAM	Small, white	Small, pink	Large, white	Hemorrhagic	Small, white
Ceiling temperature on CAM (°C)	37.5–38.5	39	41	39.5	38.5
Growth on rabbit skin	–	++	+ or ++	+	+
Thymidine kinase sensitivity	+	–	–	–	–
Pathogenicity for baby mice	Low	High	High	High	Low
Antigens specific for { vaccinia	–	–	+	+	+
variola	+	–	+	?	+
monkeypox	–	+	–	?	–
Polypeptide pattern	Character of variola	Character of monkeypox	Character of vaccinia	Character of cowpox	?

rodents being the hosts. The first human case was reported in 1970 from Zaire. Human infection is common in Central and West Africa, with a fatality rate of 5–10 per cent. The outbreak in America occurred in 2003, in Wisconsin, USA, affecting 11 local persons and many prairie dogs. The source of infection is said to be an imported African rodent, which had infected local human contacts and prairie dogs.

The cases clinically resembled smallpox. However, person-to-person transmission appears to be rare. Serological studies have shown evidence of widespread natural infection in monkeys in Africa. The virus can be distinguished from variola.

Buffalopox was identified in cattle in India in 1934 and was considered as an outbreak of vaccinia. Epizootics had occurred in buffaloes and lesions had been observed on the hands of persons in contact with infected animals. Two decades after the eradication of smallpox and cessation of vaccination, buffalopox still occurs, proving it to be distinct from variola and vaccinia. Though it resembles them closely, it is possible to distinguish between them in the laboratory. The smallpox vaccine does not seem to protect persons against occupational buffalopox.

Cowpox and milker's nodes: Both these infections are obtained from cows. Cowpox lesions are seen on the udder and teats of cows and may be transmitted to humans during milking. The lesions in humans usually appear on the hands or fingers and resemble primary vaccinia. The disease is associated with some fever and constitutional symptoms. The cowpox virus resembles variola and vaccinia antigenically but can be differentiated by the hemorrhagic lesions it produces on CAM and rabbit skin. Restriction endonuclease maps of vaccinia and cowpox genomes show distinct differences.

Cowpox infection has been observed only in Britain and Europe. There have been outbreaks of fatal cowpox infection in wild animals kept in zoos, including cheetahs and elephants. Natural infection has been observed in domestic cats. It has been suggested that the primary host of cowpox may not be cows but more likely wild rodents or cats.

Milker's node (paravaccinia) is a trivial occupational disease that humans contract by milking infected cows. The lesions are small ulcerating nodules. The virus is unrelated to cowpox and does not grow in eggs. It can be grown in bovine kidney cultures. It resembles the orf virus morphologically.

Orf (Contagious pustular dermatitis):   Orf is a disease of sheep and goats transmitted to humans by contact. In humans, the disease occurs as a single papulovesicular lesion with a central ulcer, usually on the hand, forearm or face. The virus is unrelated to the variola–vaccinia group and resembles the paravaccinia virus morphologically.

Tanapox: This virus was isolated from epidemics of a febrile illness along the Tana river in Kenya in 1957–19. The patients had a single pock-like lesion on the upper part of the body. The virus is antigenically unrelated to other poxviruses and does not grow in eggs. It can be grown in human and monkey tissue cultures. Monkeys are the only animals susceptible. The virus is now active in Africa, particularly in Zaire. A similar virus has been isolated from outbreaks of disease in primate colonies in America.

Molluscum contagiosum: This disease, seen usually in children and young adults, is characterised by pink or pearly white wart-like nodules on the skin. Sections of the lesions show large (20–30 μm) eosinophilic hyaline inclusion bodies which displace the nuclei to the margin. These **molluscum bodies** are composed of large num-

bers of virus particles, embedded in a protein matrix. Humans are the only susceptible hosts. The virus cannot be grown in eggs, tissue cultures or animals.

The incidence of molluscum contagiosum as a sexually transmitted disease in young adults is increasing. When it occurs in the genital area, it may become inflamed and ulcerated and may simulate HSV infections.

Yabapox: This is a monkey tumour virus which is related to poxviruses.

RECAP

- The poxviruses are large, being 250–300 nm by 300–350 nm in size, and just visible under a light microscope. The genus *Orthopoxvirus* includes the viruses causing cowpox, vaccinia and variola.
- Cowpox is an orthopoxvirus of cattle of the type thought to have been used by Jenner as a vaccine against smallpox.
- The vaccinia virus is an orthopoxvirus and is closely related to the variola virus. It was used as a vaccine for the control and final eradication of smallpox.
- The variola virus causes smallpox. It has been eradicated as a naturally occurring pathogen and most of the stocks of the virus have also been destroyed.
- The monkeypox virus is an orthopoxvirus of monkeys, closely resembling the variola virus. It is zoonotic in humans, causing a relatively mild, smallpox-like illness.
- The virus causing molluscum contagiosum is a poxvirus. It causes pink or pearly white warty lesions of the skin in children and young adults. The incidence of this disease as a sexually transmitted disease is increasing; lesions on the genitalia may become secondarily infected by HIV.
- The orf virus is a parapoxvirus of sheep and goats that causes zoonotic infection in humans.
- Milker's node (paravaccinia) is an occupational disease acquired by milking infected cows.

SHORT ANSWERS

1. Important orthopoxviruses and the diseases caused by them

SHORT NOTES

1. Smallpox – present status
2. Monkeypox
3. Molluscum contagiosum
4. Vaccinia virus

51 Herpesviruses

INTRODUCTION

The herpesvirus family contains over a hundred species of **enveloped DNA viruses** that affect humans and animals. They are characterised by their ability to establish **latent infections**, enabling the virus to persist indefinitely within infected hosts and to undergo **periodic reactivation.**

Morphology

The herpesvirus capsid is icosahedral, composed of 162 capsomers, and enclosing the core containing the linear double-stranded DNA genome. The nucleocapsid is surrounded by the lipid envelope derived from the modified host cell nuclear membrane through which the naked virions bud during replication. The envelope carries surface spikes, about 8 nm long (Fig. 51.1). Between the envelope and the capsid is an amorphous structure called the tegument, containing several proteins. The enveloped virion measures about 200 nm and the naked virion about 100 nm in diameter.

Replication

Herpesviruses replicate in the host cell nucleus. They form Cowdry type A intranuclear (Lipschutz) inclusion bodies.

Resistance

Like other enveloped viruses, herpesviruses are susceptible to fat solvents like alcohol, ether, chloroform and bile salts. They are heat labile and must be stored at −70°C.

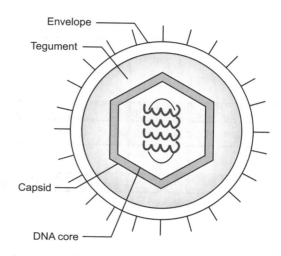

Envelope

Tegument

Capsid

DNA core

Fig. 51.1   Herpes simplex virus

Table 51.1 *Classification of human herpesviruses*

Species		Subfamily	Cytopathology	Site of latent infection
Official name	Common name			
Human herpesvirus type 1	Herpes simplex virus type 1	alpha	Cytolytic	Neurons
Human herpesvirus type 2	Herpes simplex virus type 2	alpha	Cytolytic	Neurons
Human herpesvirus type 3	Varicella zoster virus	alpha	Cytolytic	Neurons
Human herpesvirus type 4	Epstein–Barr virus	gamma	Lymphoproliferative	Lymphoid tissues
Human herpesvirus type 5	Cytomegalovirus	beta	Cytomegalic	Secretory glands, kidneys, other organs and tissues
Human herpesvirus type 6	Human B cell lymphotropic virus*	beta	Lymphoproliferative	Lymphoid tissues
Human herpesvirus type 7	R K virus*	beta	Lymphoproliferative	Lymphoid tissues
Human herpesvirus type 8		gamma		

* These names are no longer in use

Classification

Eight different types of herpesviruses are known whose primary hosts are humans. They have been officially designated 'human herpesvirus types 1–8' but their common names continue to be in general use, except for types 6,7 and 8 (Table 51.1).

The family Herpesviridae is divided into three subfamilies based on biological, physical and genetic properties:

- *Alphaherpesviruses,* with a relatively short replicative cycle (12–18 hours), variable host range and a tendency to cause latent infection in sensory ganglia. In culture, they are rapidly cytopathic and infectious viruses may be released from cells, for example, **herpes simplex virus, varicella zoster virus.**

- *Betaherpesviruses,* which replicate slowly (>24 hours), have a narrow host range, grow best in fibroblasts with a tendency to cause enlargement of infected cells (cytomegaly) and latent infection of salivary glands and other organs. In culture, the cytopathic effect is slow and the virus remains cell associated, for example, **cytomegalovirus.**

- *Gammaherpesviruses,* which have a narrow host range, replicate in lymphoblastoid cells, are specific for either B or T lymphocytes and frequently cause latent infection in lymphoid tissue, for example, the **Epstein–Barr virus.**

The herpesvirus family has no common group antigen and the different species do not show any significant antigenic cross-reaction, except between herpes simplex types 1 and 2.

HERPES SIMPLEX VIRUS

Clinical Case 1 A 25-year-old woman presented with complaints of genital blisters for the previous seven days and fever, headache and vomiting for the previous two days. On examination, she was found to have neck rigidity, and a lumbar puncture was performed for CSF examination. The CSF was clear, with a cell count of 100 cells/mm³; lymphocytes were predominant. CSF glucose was normal and the proteins slightly elevated. The CSF was inoculated into Vero cell lines in the laboratory and the PCR test was positive for herpesvirus type 2 DNA. The patient was started on treatment with gancyclovir; supportive treatment was also provided and the patient responded. She was advised to recount this history to her doctor at any future pregnancy.

The herpes simplex virus (HSV) occurs naturally only in humans, but it can produce experimental infection in many laboratory animals. The virus is of two types. HSV type 1 (human herpes virus type 1 or HHV type 1) is usually isolated from lesions in and around the mouth and is transmitted by direct contact or droplet spread from cases or carriers. HSV type 2 (HHV type 2) is responsible for the majority of genital herpes infections and is commonly transmitted venereally. Intracerebral inoculation in rabbits and mice leads to encephalitis, and corneal scarification produces keratoconjunctivitis in rabbits.

The virus grows in a variety of primary and continuous cell cultures (monkey or rabbit kidney, human amnion, HeLa Fig. 51.2a) producing cytopathic changes, well-defined foci with heaped up cells and

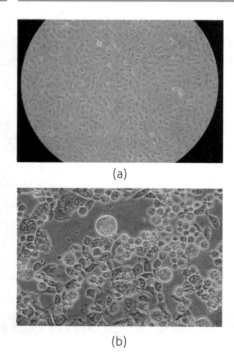

(a)

(b)

Fig. 51.2 (a) Vervet monkey kidney cells (Vero cell line), uninfected, X 100; (b) Vervet monkey kidney cells (Vero cell line) infected with herpes simplex virus: note rounded cells and giant cell formation, X 200

syncytial or giant cell formation (Fig. 51.2b). On chick embryo CAM, small (diameter less than 0.5 mm), white, shiny, non-necrotic pocks are produced. The two types of the virus cross-react serologically.

Differentiating features:

- Antigenic differences can be made out using type-specific monoclonal antibodies.
- On chick embryo, CAM type 2 strains form larger pocks resembling variola.
- Types 2 strains replicate well in chick embryo fibroblast cells, while type 1 strains do so poorly.
- The infectivity of type 2 is more temperature sensitive than that of type 1.
- Type 2 strains are more neurovirulent in laboratory animals than type 1.
- Type 2 strains are more resistant to antiviral agents like IUDR and cytarabine in culture.
- Restriction endonuclease analysis of viral DNA enables differentiation between the two types as well as between strains within the same type.

Pathogenicity

Herpes simplex is one of the most common viral infections in humans, about 60–90 per cent of adults showing detectable antibody. Primary infection is usually acquired in early childhood, between two and five years of age. Humans are the only natural hosts and the sources of infection are saliva, skin lesions or respiratory secretions. Asymptomatic carriers form the more important source of infection, especially in genital infection with type 2 strains.

Route of infection: Transmission occurs by close contact and may be venereal in genital herpes. The virus enters through defects in the skin or mucous membranes and multiplies locally, with cell-to-cell spread. The virus enters cutaneous nerve fibres and is transported intra-axonally to the ganglia where it replicates. Centrifugal migration of the virus can take place from the ganglia to the skin and mucosa to cause cutaneous and mucosal lesions. The virus remains latent in the ganglia, particularly of the trigeminal (HSV type 1) and sacral (HSV type 2) nerves, to be reactivated periodically in some individuals causing recurrent oral and genital lesions.

Antibodies may not prevent recurrences, but can reduce the severity of the clinical disease. Cell-mediated immunity is more important in resistance to and recovery from herpes simplex infections. Herpesvirus diseases are more frequent and severe in the HIV-infected and other immunodeficient subjects.

The typical herpes lesions are thin-walled, umbilicated vesicles, the roof of which breaks down, leaving tiny superficial ulcers. They heal without scarring. In general, primary infections, though self-limited, are more severe and widespread and associated with systemic manifestations. Recurrent infections are more localised.

As a general rule, HSV 1 produces 'above the waist' and HSV 2 'below the waist' lesions but the rule is not absolute. HSV 2 infection confers some protection against HSV 1, but not vice versa.

Clinical features

The clinical manifestations and course depend on the site of infection, age and immune status of the host, and the antigenic type of the virus.

Cutaneous infections: The most common site is the face—on the cheeks, chin, around the mouth or on the forehead. Lesions may also appear on the buttocks in infants as napkin rash. The typical lesion is the '**fever blister**' or **herpes febrilis**, caused by viral reactivation in febrile patients (Fig. 51.3). In some sensitive persons, very minor stimuli, like the common cold, exposure to sun or even mental strain or menses, may bring on such reactivation.

An occupational variety of cutaneous herpes is the herpetic whitlow seen in doctors, dentists and nurses. **Eczema herpeticum** is a generalised eruption caused by herpes infection in children suffering from eczema. Crops of vesicles appear on the affected area with widespread ulceration. A clinically indistinguishable picture is also produced by vaccinia virus infection, both designated **Kaposi's varicelliform eruption**.

Mucosal: The buccal mucosa is the most commonly affected site. Gingivostomatitis and pharyngitis are the most frequent conditions in primary infection and recurrent herpes labialis in recurrent infection. The vesicles may ulcerate and become secondarily infected.

Ophthalmic: HSV infection is the most common cause of corneal blindness in some developed countries. Acute keratoconjunctivitis may occur by itself or by extension from facial herpes. Follicular conjunctivitis with vesicle formation on the lids is another manifestation. The cornea may be involved, with typical branching dendritic ulcers. Debridement, topical antiviral drugs and interferon help in healing. Steroids are con-

traindicated as they lead to deep stromal involvement and healing may be delayed, with scarring and corneal blindness. Chorioretinitis and acute necrotising retinitis are uncommon but serious manifestations.

Nervous system: HSV encephalitis, though rare, is the most common sporadic acute viral encephalitis in most parts of the world. HSV encephalitis has an acute onset, with fever and focal neurological symptoms. Brain biopsy was used for diagnosis to institute early specific therapy. This is now replaced by a demonstration of HSV DNA in CSF by PCR, which is a very sensitive test in the acute stage (*Case 1*). HSV meningitis is a self-limiting disease, usually resolving in about a week, without sequelae. The CSF shows lymphocytic pleocytosis and may yield the virus in culture.

HSV can cause sacral autonomic dysfunction and also rarely transverse myelitis or the Guillian–Barré syndrome. HSV has been implicated in the causation of Bell's palsy.

Visceral: HSV esophagitis may cause dysphagia, substernal pain and weight loss. It may involve the respiratory tract, causing tracheobronchitis and pneumonitis. HSV is an uncommon cause of hepatitis. Erythema multiforme may be seen in association with HSV infection. Disseminated HSV infection may occur in patients with immunodeficiency, malnutrition or burns.

Genital: In the 1970s, genital herpes became the most rapidly increasing venereal disease, particularly in the USA. In men, the lesions occur mainly on the penis or in the urethra causing urethritis. In women, the cervix, vagina, vulva and perineum are affected. When only the cervix is involved, the infection may be asymptomatic. The primary infection is usually more serious, accompanied by systemic features like fever and malaise. It is followed by several recurrent episodes which are milder. The vesiculo-ulcerative lesions may be very painful. Rectal and perineal lesions occur in homosexuals. Both types of HSV may cause genital lesions, though HSV 2 is responsible more frequently and causes many more recurrences.

There have been several reports of an association between HSV 2 and carcinoma of the cervix uteri but a causal relationship has not been established.

Congenital: Transplacental infection with HSV 1 or 2 can lead to congenital malformations, but this is rare. Infection may occur during birth, particularly if the mother has genital lesions due to HSV 2. In such cases, cesarean section may prevent infection.

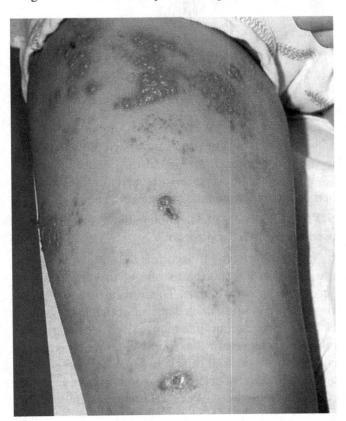

Fig. 51.3 Fever blister

Postnatal infection is more commonly due to HSV 1. Neonatal herpes may be confined to the eyes, mouth or skin, but is more commonly a disseminated disease involving multiple organs, with or without encephalitis. The mortality rate is very high and survivors may have neurological impairment.

Laboratory diagnosis

1. Specimens: Vesicle fluid, skin swabs, saliva, corneal scrapings, CSF or brain biopsy on autopsy.

The diagnosis of herpes virus infection may be made by microscopy, antigen or DNA detection, virus isolation or serology.

2. Microscopy:

- The **Tzanck smear** is a rapid, fairly sensitive and inexpensive diagnostic method. Smears are prepared from the lesions, preferably from the base of vesicles and stained with 1% aqueous solution of toluidine blue '0' for 15 seconds. Multinucleated giant cells with faceted nuclei and homogeneously stained **'ground glass'** chromatin (Tzanck cells) constitute a positive smear (Fig. 51.4).
- Intranuclear type A inclusion bodies may be seen in **Giemsa-stained smears**.
- The virus particle may also be demonstrated under the **electron microscope**. It is not possible to differentiate between herpes simplex and varicella zoster by microscopy.
- The herpesvirus antigen may be demonstrated in smears or sections from lesions by the **fluorescent antibody technique**. The fluorescent antibody test on brain biopsy specimens provides reliable and speedy diagnosis in encephalitis.

3. Virus isolation: Inoculation in mice and on chick embryo CAM is not sensitive and has been replaced by tissue culture for virus isolation. Primary human embryonic kidney, human amnion and many other cells are susceptible, but human diploid fibroblasts are preferred. Typical cytopathic changes may appear as early as in 24–48 hours, but cultures should be observed for two weeks before being declared negative. Drug susceptibility too can be tested in cell cultures.

Differentiation between HSV types 1 and 2 may be made by a variety of serological techniques, by nucleic acid hybridisation or by restriction endonuclease cleavage and electrophoretic analysis of viral DNA or viral proteins.

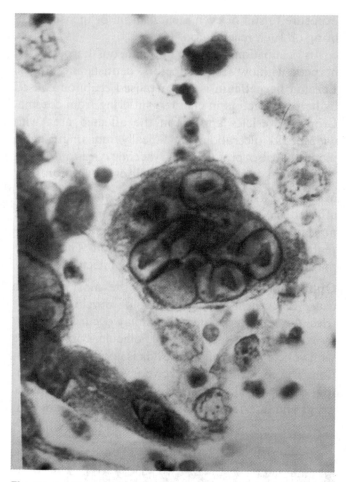

Fig. 51.4   Herpesvirus in Tzanck smear

4. Serology: Serological methods are useful in the diagnosis of primary infections. Antibodies develop within a few days of infection and rise in titre of antibodies may be demonstrated by ELISA, neutralisation or complement fixation tests. In recurrent or re-infection herpes, there may be little change in the antibody titre.

5. PCR: PCR-based detection methods are now being used more often for diagnosis.

6. Chemotherapy: Idoxyuridine used topically in eye and skin infections was one of the first clinically successful antiviral agents. The introduction of acyclovir and vidarabine enabled the effective management of deep and systemic infections. Early treatment with intravenous acyclovir has improved the outcome of encephalitis. Oral and topical use may help in less serious conditions. Valaciclovir and famciclovir are more effective oral agents. When resistance to these drugs develop, drugs like foscarnet which are independent of viral thymidine kinase action may be useful.

VARICELLA ZOSTER VIRUS

Clinical Case 2 A 50-year-old, HIV-positive man developed vesicular eruptions on the right side of the spine in the lumbar region which were very painful. Scrapings from the base of the lesions were positive for the VZ antigen by direct fluorescent antibody test. A culture from the fluid was inoculated on cell lines and the PCR test was positive for varicella zoster virus. The patient was treated with acyclovir. On further enquiry, the patient revealed to the doctor that he had had chickenpox in childhood.

As early as 1889, Von Bokay had suggested that varicella (chickenpox) and herpes zoster are different manifestations of the same virus infection. Virological and epidemiological observations have proved this concept. The virus is therefore called the varicella zoster virus (VZV).

Chickenpox follows primary infection in a non-immune individual, while herpes zoster is a reactivation of the latent virus when immunity has fallen to ineffective levels. Thus, chickenpox is 'caught' but not zoster. Contact with either zoster or chickenpox may lead only to chickenpox but not zoster.

VZV is similar to the herpes simplex virus in its morphology. It does not grow in experimental animals or chick embryos. The virus was first isolated by Weller in human embryonic tissue culture. It can be grown in cultures of human fibroblasts, human amnion or HeLa cells. The cytopathic effects are similar to, but less marked than, those produced by the herpes simplex virus. In cultures, the virus remains cell associated and does not appear free in the medium. By using highly specific antisera, it is possible to distinguish between herpes virus types 1, 2 and varicella zoster viruses. Only one antigenic type of VZV is known.

VARICELLA (CHICKENPOX)

Chickenpox is one of the mildest and most common of childhood infections. The disease may, however, occur at any age. Adult chickenpox, which is more serious, is rather common in some tropical areas.

The source of infection is a chickenpox or herpes zoster patient. Infectivity is maximum during the initial stages of the disease, when the virus is present abundantly in the upper respiratory tract. The buccal lesions which appear in the early stage of the disease and the vesicular fluid are rich in virus content. Infectivity wanes as the disease progresses and the scabs are virtually non-infectious. There are no animal reservoirs of varicella.

Pathogenicity

The portal of entry of the virus is the respiratory tract or conjunctiva. After an incubation period of about two weeks (7–23 days), the lesions begin to appear. The patient is considered to be infectious during two days before and five days after the onset of the lesions. In children, there is little prodromal illness and the disease is first noticed when skin lesions appear. Buccal lesions may not be noticed. The rash appears usually on the trunk. **The evolution of the rash is so rapid that the various stages—macule, papule, vesicle, pustule and scab—cannot be readily followed in individual lesions.** The rash is **centripetal** in distribution, affecting mainly the trunk and sparing the distal parts of the limbs, and is very superficial without involving the deeper layers of the skin, resembling a dew-drop lying on the skin. The rash appears in crops during the first three or four days of the disease, so that lesions of varying age can be noticed on the same patient. It matures very quickly, beginning to crust within 48 hours.

When varicella occurs in adults, systemic symptoms may be severe, the rash very profuse and the entire disease much more intense than in children. The rash may become hemorrhagic and occasionally bullous lesions appear. Pitted scars on the skin may remain after recovery. Varicella pneumonia is more common in adults, and often fatal in the elderly. Other complications like myocarditis, nephritis, acute cerebellar ataxia, meningitis and encephalitis may ensue. Secondary bacterial infections, usually due to staphylococci or streptococci, may occur. **Reye's syndrome** may follow varicella in some cases with a history of administration of salicylates. But in most cases, chickenpox is an uneventful disease and recovery is the rule. One attack confers lasting immunity.

Chicken pox in pregnancy: Chickenpox in pregnancy can be dangerous for both the mother and the baby. The disease tends to be more severe in pregnant women, with enhanced risk of complications like pneumonia. The baby may develop two types of complications, depending on the period of gestation when the woman develops chickenpox. If maternal varicella occurs during the first half of pregnancy, the fetal infection may usually be asymptomatic. Some infants may develop **fetal varicella syndrome**, manifesting as cicatrising skin lesions, hypoplasia of the limbs, chorioretinitis and CNS defects. Some babies may not exhibit any defects, but may carry latent VZV infection.

When maternal varicella occurs near delivery, babies may develop **congenital (neonatal) varicella**, within two weeks of birth. If the mother's rash began a week or more before delivery, she would have developed antibodies which would have been passed, along with the virus, to the fetus transplacentally. Such a baby, though infected, usually escapes clinical disease. If the mother develops chickenpox less than a week (or within two days) of delivery, the baby would have received from the mother only the virus and not the antibody, so that it develops neonatal varicella. This is usually a serious disseminated disease, with a high risk of pneumonia and encephalitis. As treatment for such conditions will have to be started early to be of any use, the babies are given VZV antiserum and chemotherapy immediately after birth.

Laboratory diagnosis

Diagnosis is usually clinical.

1. Microscopy: Multinucleated giant cells and type A intranuclear inclusion bodies may be seen in smears prepared by scraping the base of the early vesicles (Tzanck smears) and stained with toluidine blue, Giemsa or Papanicolou stain. Electron microscopy of vesicle fluid may demonstrate the virus with typical herpes morphology.

2. Virus isolation: This may be attempted from the buccal or cutaneous lesions in the early stages by inoculating human amnion, human fibroblast, HeLa or Vero cells.

3. Serology: The virus antigen can be detected in scrapings from skin lesions by immunofluorescence, and in vesicle fluid by counterimmunoelectrophoresis with zoster immune serum. The ELISA and PCR techniques are also in use.

Prophylaxis and treatment

Vaccine: A live varicella vaccine was developed by Takahashi in Japan in 1974 by attenuating a strain of varicella virus (Oka strain, so named after the patient) by serial passage in tissue culture. Given subcutaneously, it induced good antibody response but was very labile and had to be stored frozen. A modified lyophilised form of the vaccine is now available, which can be stored between 2°C and 8°C. All children should routinely receive the first dose of varicella vaccine (live-attenuated Oka strain of VZV) at 12 to 15 months of age. The second dose of the vaccine is recommended at 4 to 6 years of age. It is safe and effective. Occasionally, children may develop a few vesicles which resolve quickly. It is not considered safe in pregnancy.

Passive protection: Varicella zoster immunoglobulin (VZIG) prepared from patients convalescing from herpes zoster provides passive protection in immunocompromised children exposed to infection, but its availability is limited. It is not useful in treatment.

Specific treatment is indicated mainly in immunodeficient and elderly subjects and those with complications such as varicella pneumonia, encephalitis and disseminated zoster. Acyclovir and famciclovir are effective. Corticosteroids are contraindicated in varicella as they enhance the risk of pneumonia and disseminated disease.

HERPES ZOSTER (SHINGLES, ZONA)

While varicella is typically a disease of childhood, herpes zoster (from *herpein*, meaning to creep; *zoster*, meaning girdle) is one of old age, being common after the age of fifty years. The disease may, however, occur at any age and zoster has been reported very rarely even in the newborn.

Herpes zoster usually occurs in persons who had chickenpox several years earlier. The virus remaining latent in the sensory ganglia may leak out at times but is usually held in check by the residual immunity. Years after the initial infection, when the immunity has waned, the virus may be reactivated, and triggered by some precipitating stimulus, travel along the sensory nerve to produce zoster lesions on the area of the skin or mucosa supplied by it. This reactivation is associated with inflammation of the nerve, which accounts for the neuritic pain that often precedes the skin lesions.

Pathogenicity

The rash is typically unilateral and confined to the area supplied by a single sensory ganglion (*Case 2*). The most common sites are the areas innervated by spinal cord segments D3 to L2 and the trigeminal nerve, particularly, its ophthalmic branch. The lesions are identical in nature to varicella lesions, except for their limited distribution. The rash heals in about two weeks. Pain and paresthesia at the affected area may persist for weeks or months. Other complications are lower motor neuron paralysis which sometimes ensues, meningoencephalitis and generalised zoster where the lesions are scattered widely, perhaps due to hematogenous dissemination of the virus. Herpes zoster ophthalmicus is a common and troublesome presentation. The **Ramsay Hunt syndrome** is a rare form of zoster affecting the facial nerve, with eruption on the tympanic membrane and the external auditory canal, and often a facial palsy. Chronic or recurrent zoster is often seen in the HIV infected.

Laboratory diagnosis

Diagnosis is easily made clinically. Laboratory diagnosis and treatment are as for chickenpox. Herpes zoster represents a mode of evolutionary adaptation by the VZ virus which is an obligate human parasite. The ability of the virus to remain latent and reappear as zoster years later confers on it a great survival advantage.

CYTOMEGALOVIRUSES

Clinical Case 3 A 25-year-old man diagnosed with HIV and AIDS presented with a complaint of diminishing vision, which has been slowly progressive, for the previous three months. His CD4 counts at the time of presentation were <100 cells/mm³. On fundus examination, retinal infilterates which were fluffy in nature were found, along with the presence of multiple hemorrhages. Serological tests were positive for CMV IgG antibodies and PCR on blood was positive for CMV DNA. The patient was diagnosed with CMV retinitis and treatment with gancyclovir was started. Further investigation revealed that the patient had not been taking his anti-HIV treatment regularly; so he was advised to do so again. Subsequently, there was no further deterioration in the symptoms.

Cytomegaloviruses (CMV), formerly known as **salivary gland viruses**, are a group of ubiquitous herpesviruses of humans and animals. They are characterised by enlargement of infected cells and prominent intranuclear inclusions. Like other herpesviruses, they lead to prolonged latency in infected hosts. In the neonate and the immunodeficient, they cause severe disseminated disease, while in normal children and adults the infection is usually asymptomatic or self-limited.

CMV are the largest viruses in the herpesvirus family, being 150–200 nm in size. The virus exhibits strict host specificity and infection—both in vivo and in vitro can be established only in the homologous species. Cytomegaloviruses have been identified in human beings, monkeys, guinea pigs and some other species. Human cytomegaloviruses can be grown in human fibroblast cultures. Epithelial cell cultures are not susceptible though epithelial cells are affected in vivo. Cultures have to be incubated for prolonged periods, up to 50 days, as the cytopathic effects are slow in appearance.

Human CMV is unrelated antigenically to other herpesviruses, and even to CMV of other species, except for simian CMV with which some antigenic cross-reaction exists. Minor genetic and antigenic differences exist among human CMV isolates but they are of no clinical significance.

Clinical features

Cytomegalovirus disease is rare but infection with the virus is extremely common. As with herpes simplex, the large majority of infections are inapparent, leading to prolonged latency, with occasional reactivation. Clinical disease may be caused by either intrauterine or postnatal infections.

Congenital infections: Intrauterine infection leads to fetal death or cytomegalic inclusion disease of the newborn which is often fatal. This is a generalised infection associated with hepatosplenomegaly, jaundice, thrombocytopenic purpura and hemolytic anemia. The cytomegalic inclusion disease is probably the most important cause of microcephaly. Other manifestations include chorioretinitis and cerebral calcification resembling congenital toxoplasmosis. Survivors may show mental retardation.

Infection in infants: Cytomegalic inclusion disease is seen almost exclusively in infants born to mothers who develop primary CMV infection during pregnancy. Infants of mothers who have CMV reactivation during pregnancy tend to have chronic subclinical infection. Perinatal infection may be acquired from the infected mother through genital secretions or breast milk.

Infection in children: Primary infections in older children and adults are usually asymptomatic. However, a heterophile, antibody-negative, infectious mononucleosis may be seen. This is more common following transfusion of CMV-infected blood (**post-transfusion mononucleosis**).

In the immunocompromised host, CMV can cause severe and even fatal infections (*Case* 3). This occurs in transplant recipients, cancer patients on chemotherapy and, more particularly, in the HIV infected. CMV is an important pathogen in AIDS. In AIDS patients, the already weakened immune response is further damaged by the non-specific CMI-inhibiting effect of CMV. One of the glycoproteins on the surface of CMV acts as a receptor for the *Fc* portion of immunoglobulin molecules. This leads to masking of the virus by attachment of irrelevant immunoglobulin molecules, thereby preventing access to specific anti-CMV antibody.

Epidemiology

CMV spreads slowly and probably requires close contact for transmission. It may spread through salivary or other secretions or by sexual contact. A special method of transmission is by blood transfusion or organ transplants. The virus has been detected in saliva, urine, cervical secretions, semen, blood and milk. Congenitally infected infants have viruria for up to 4–5 years. They are highly infectious in early infancy. About 1 per cent of neonates in the USA are infected with CMV. In the developing countries, the rate may be much higher. Up to 80 per cent of adults show CMV antibodies, indicating the high prevalence of infection. Once infected, the person carries the virus for life.

Laboratory diagnosis

1. Specimens: The virus can be isolated from urine, saliva, semen and cervical secretions.

2. Isolation: Diagnosis may be established by recovery of the virus from urine, saliva or other body fluids by inoculating human fibroblast cultures. Growth in cultures can be detected early by using shell vial cultures and by staining the cells with fluorescent tagged antibody to early antigens of CMV.

A simpler but less reliable technique is the demonstration of cytomegalic cells in centrifuged deposits from urine or saliva in which inclusion bodies are seen which are described as '**owl's eye**' (Fig. 51.5).

3. Serology: Demonstration of antibody is useful in the diagnosis of primary infection but not in reactivation. Serological techniques in use include CF, IHA, IF and ELISA. Antibody detection may be necessary for screening blood or organ donors. IgM antibody detection helps in the diagnosis of congenital infections.

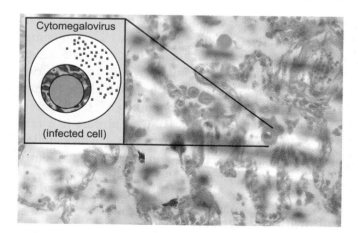

Fig. 51.5   H & E stained lung tissue showing 'owl's eye'-like inclusion bodies of cytomegalovirus, X 1000

Prevention and treatment

Prevention is indicated only in high-risk cases such as organ transplants, immunodeficient persons and in premature infants. Screening of blood and organ donors and administration of CMV immunoglobulins have been employed in prevention. Acyclovir is useful in prophylaxis but not in treatment. Ganciclovir and foscarnet have been found to be effective and are used for the treatment of CMV disease in patients with AIDS.

No vaccine is available. Experimentally, live attenuated vaccines (Towne 125 and AD 169 strains) and a purified CMV polypeptide vaccine have been found to be immunogenic but not effective in protecting immunodeficient subjects from CMV infection.

EPSTEIN–BARR VIRUS

Clinical Case 4 A 16-year-old girl presented with a complaint of malaise and loss of appetite for the previous month, and sore throat and fever of 40°C with a rise in temperature, especially in the afternoon, for the previous five days. On examination, cervical lymphadenopathy and mild hepatosplenomegaly were detected. In the complete blood counts, she was found to have absolute mononuclear lymphocytosis, with most of the lymphocytes being atypical. Her serum tested positive for the Paul–Bunnell test. Her IgM was also positive for EBNA. The patient improved on supportive care.

In 1958, Burkitt described an unusual lymphoma among children in certain parts of Africa and suggested, on epidemiological grounds, that the tumour may be caused by a mosquito-borne virus. This led to several attempts at isolating viruses from such tumours. A number of different viruses, apparently 'passenger viruses', were isolated from cultured lymphoma cells. One virus observed in the cultured lymphoma cells by Epstein, Barr and Achong in 1964 was a new type of herpesvirus, named the EB virus, specifically affecting cells of the B lymphocyte lineage. Only human and some subhuman primate B cells have receptors (CD 21 molecules) for the virus. EBV-infected B cells are transformed so they become capable of continuous growth in vitro.

Epidemiology

The Epstein–Barr (EB) virus is ubiquitous in all human populations. As with other herpesviruses, infection with the EB virus leads to latency, periodic reactivation and lifelong persistence. EB virus antibodies are present in about 95 per cent of adults. In the overcrowded developing world, EB virus infection occurs in infancy and childhood, when it is usually asymptomatic. In affluent countries, primary infection is often delayed till adolescence and early adulthood, when it may lead to infectious mononucleosis.

The **source** of the infection is usually the saliva of infected persons who shed the virus in oropharyngeal secretions for months following primary infection and intermittently thereafter. The EB virus is not highly contagious, and droplets and aerosols are not efficient in transmitting infection. Intimate oral contact, as in kissing, appears to be the predominant mode of transmission. This accounts for infectious mononucleosis being called the '**kissing disease**'. Infection may also follow blood or marrow transfusion but these are rare events.

EB virus infection may lead to the following clinical conditions:
- Infectious mononucleosis
- EBV associated malignancies:
  - Burkitt's lymphoma
  - Lymphomas in immunodeficient persons such as those with AIDS and transplant recipients
  - Nasopharyngeal carcinoma in persons of Chinese origin

Pathogenicity

The virus enters the pharyngeal epithelial cells through CR 2 (or CD 21) receptors, which are the same as for the C3d component of complement. It multiplies locally, invades the bloodstream and infects B lymphocytes in which two types of changes are produced. In most cases, the virus becomes latent inside the lymphocytes, which become transformed or '**immortalised**' so that they become capable of indefinite growth in vitro. They are polyclonally activated to produce many kinds of immunoglobulins. The heterophile sheep erythrocyte agglutinin seen characteristically in infectious mononucleosis is an example of such polyclonal activation. A second type of effect, shown by a few infected B cells, is lytic infection with cell death and release of mature progeny virions.

Mononucleosis represents a polyclonal transformation of infected B lymphocytes. EB virus antigens are expressed on the surface of infected B cells. The atypical lymphocytes seen in blood smears in infectious mononucleosis are T lymphocytes undergoing blast transformation in response to such neoantigens.

Intermittent reactivation of the latent EB virus leads to clonal proliferation of infected B cells. In immunocompetent subjects, this is kept in check by activated T cells. In the immunodeficient, B cell clones may replicate unchecked, resulting in lymphomas. Hyperendemic malaria prevalent in Africa is believed to be responsible for the immune impairment in children with Burkitt's lymphoma. The frequency of lymphomas seen in many types of immunodeficiencies, most typically in AIDS, may have a similar pathogenesis. Nearly half the lymphomas seen in immunodeficient subjects contain EB virus DNA sequences.

Genetic and environmental factors are said to be important in the nasopharyngeal carcinoma seen in men of Chinese origin. EB virus DNA is regularly found in the tumour cells. These patients have high levels of EB virus antibodies. Genetic influence is best illustrated in the X-linked lymphoproliferative (XLP or Duncan) syndrome associated with extreme susceptibility to EB virus infection.

INFECTIOUS MONONUCLEOSIS (GLANDULAR FEVER)

This is an acute self-limited illness, usually seen in non-immune young adults following primary infection with the EB virus (Fig. 51.6). The incubation period is 4–8 weeks. The disease is characterised by fever, sore throat, lymphadenopathy and the presence of abnormal lymphocytes in peripheral blood smears (*Case 4*). A mild transient rash may be present. Some patients treated with ampicillin may develop a maculopapular rash due to immune complex reaction to the drug. There is often associated hepatitis, which is usually subclinical and demonstrable only by liver function tests. A number of other complications have been recorded, including hematological, neurological, cardiac and pulmonary conditions and splenic rupture. In most cases, spontaneous resolution of the disease occurs in 2–4 weeks. In some, it may be more prolonged and lead to a state of mental and physical fatigue in convalescence.

Laboratory diagnosis

Blood examination during the initial phase may show leucopenia due to a drop in the number of polymorphs. Later there is prominent leucocytosis, with the appearance of **abnormal mononuclear cells** characterised by deeply basophilic vacuolated cytoplasm and kidney-shaped nuclei showing a lattice of fenestrated chromatin. These atypical mononuclear cells are not virus-infected B lymphocytes but lymphoblasts derived from

T cells reactive to the virus infection. The blood picture may sometimes resemble lymphocytic leukemia.

Serology:

Paul–Bunnell test: The standard diagnostic procedure is the Paul–Bunnell test. In infectious mononucleosis, **heterophile antibodies** agglutinate sheep erythrocytes. However, such antibodies may also occur after injections of sera and sometimes even in normal individuals. Infectious mononucleosis antibodies may be differentiated by absorption tests. Inactivated serum (56°C for 30 minutes) in doubling dilutions is mixed with equal volumes of a 1% suspension of sheep erythrocytes. After incubation at 37°C for four hours the tubes are examined for agglutination. An agglutination titre of 100 or above is suggestive of infectious mononucleosis.

Differential agglutination test: For confirmation, differential absorption of agglutinins with guinea pig kidney and ox red cells is necessary. The Forssman antibody induced by injection of horse serum is removed by treatment with guinea pig kidney and ox red cells. Normally occurring agglutinins are removed by guinea

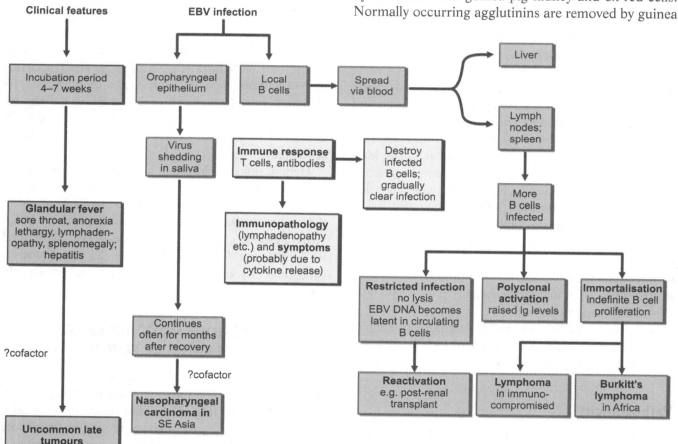

Fig. 51.6   Clinical and immunovirological events in Epstein–Barr virus infection

pig kidney, but not by ox red cells.Infectious mononucleosis antibody is removed by ox red cells but not guinea pig kidney. This differential agglutination test has largely been replaced by a simple slide agglutination test employing sensitised horse erythrocytes, with the same sensitivity and specificity. The Paul–Bunnell antibody develops early during the course of infectious mononucleosis and disappears within about two months (Table 51.2).

Tests are also available for the demonstration of specific EB virus antibodies. **Immunofluorescence** and **ELISA** are commonly employed. **The IgM antibody to VCA** (virus capsid antigen) appears soon after primary infection and disappears in 1–2 weeks. It is a reliable indication of primary infection. The IgG anti-VCA antibody persists throughout life and indicates past or recent infection. The new appearance of **antibody to the EB nuclear antigen** (EBNA) is also a useful marker for primary infection.

Antibodies to early antigens (EA) are present in high titres in EB-associated lymphomas. However, these specific tests are of limited availability.

The infectious mononucleosis syndrome can follow infection by other agents such as cytomegalovirus and toxoplasmosis or occur as a reaction to non-infectious stimuli. However, the heterophile Paul–Bunnell test is positive only in disease caused by the EB virus.

HUMAN HERPESVIRUS TYPES 6, 7, 8

A herpesvirus, first isolated in 1986 from the peripheral blood of patients with lymphoproliferative disease, was called the **human B lymphotropic virus**. It has since been renamed **HHV 6**. This is ubiquitous and spreads apparently through saliva in early infancy. Two variants have been recognised: A and B.

Variant B is the cause of mild but common childhood illness 'exanthem subitum' (roseola infantum or 'sixth disease'). In older age groups, it has been associated with infectious mononucleosis syndrome, focal encephalitis and, in the immunodeficient, with pneumonia and disseminated disease.

HHV 7 was isolated in 1990 from peripheral CD4 cells of a healthy person. Like HHV 6, HHV 7 also appears to be widely distributed and transmitted through saliva. It shares with HIV the same CD4 receptor on T cells and could therefore contribute to a further depletion of CD4 T cells in HIV-infected persons. It has been said to cause some cases of exanthem subitum.

In 1994, DNA sequences presumed to represent a new herpesvirus were identified from tissues of Kaposi's sarcoma from AIDS patients. This has been named **HHV 8**. This has subsequently been identified also in Kaposi's sarcoma in persons not infected with HIV. It has been therefore referred to sometimes as **Kaposi's sarcoma-associated herpesvirus (KSHV)**, but an causative relationship is yet to be proved. The incidence is higher in men who have sex with men.

HERPESVIRUS SIMIAE: B VIRUS

This virus was isolated by Sabin and Wright (1934) from the brain of a laboratory worker who developed fatal ascending myelitis after being bitten by an apparently healthy monkey. It came to be known as the 'B' virus, from the initials of this patient. Many similar cases have been reported since then. Herpesvirus simiae infects old world monkeys in the same manner that herpes simplex infects humans, the infection usually being asymptomatic. The typical lesions produced are vesicles on the buccal mucosa which ulcerate, shedding the virus and infecting contacts. Though most human cases have followed monkey bites, in some the infection was acquired through the handling of monkey tissues.

Herpesvirus simiae is similar to herpes simplex virus in its properties. The two are antigenically related but the herpes simplex virus antibody does not protect against herpesvirus simiae infection. A formolised vaccine has been tried experimentally in laboratory workers at risk.

The disease in humans is usually fatal. The rare patients who survive have serious neurological sequelae. The official name for the B virus is **Cercopithecine herpesvirus 1**.

Table 51.2 *Differential absorption test for Paul–Bunnell antibody*

	Result of absorption by	
	Guinea pig kidney	Ox red cells
Normal serum	Absorbed	Not absorbed
Antibody after serum therapy	Absorbed	Absorbed
Infectious mononucleosis	Not absorbed	Absorbed

RECAP

- All the major herpesviruses are found worldwide. Most adults have antibodies to these viruses, suggesting that exposure is common. However, serious disease is relatively infrequent. Age and immune status affect how infection manifests as disease.
- Herpes simplex virus 1 and 2 (HSV-1 and HSV-2) cause mucocutaneous vesicular and ulcerative lesions, As a general rule, HSV 1 produces 'above the waist' and HSV 2 'below the waist' lesions but the rule is not absolute.
  - ❖ Infection is transmitted following intimate contact between the infected and the non-infected host: oral or genital (or both). Replication occurs in local epithelial cells until eruption occurs on the surface as vesicles. Both humoral and cell-mediated immune response are important.
  - ❖ The infection is prevented by avoiding intimate contact with individuals with lesions. Antiviral drugs (acyclovir) may need to be given in serious infection. There is no vaccine.
- The varicella zoster virus (VZV) is the cause of chickenpox (varicella), a vesicular rash mainly seen in children that starts at the head and trunk and moves to the extremities. Vesicles may become pustular, crusted and scabbed prior to healing. In adults, VZV infection usually manifests as zoster or 'shingles', characterised by painful vesicular lesions along the distribution of a single nerve.
  - ❖ Infection is transmitted by the spread of aerosols from an infected individual. Initial infection of epithelial cells of the nasopharynx in a susceptible individual is followed by viral replication, viremia, skin rash and latency in the dorsal root ganglia. Later in life, VZV may emerge to cause zoster. Humoral and cell-mediated immunity are important in determining the outcome of infection.
  - ❖ A live, attenuated vaccine is available for childhood immunisation. High-titre human immunoglobulin may need to be given for immunocompromised individuals exposed to VZV infection. In individuals who are seriously ill due to VZV infection (encephalitis), antiviral therapy with acyclovir or related drugs may be needed.
- Cytomegalovirus (CMV) causes congenital infection of the liver, retina and central nervous system (CNS) with rash; a mononucleosis syndrome in some older children and adults; a life-threatening disseminated infection in patients with acquired immunodeficiency syndrome and transplant patients which affects the lungs, CNS, liver, retina and gastrointestinal tract.
  - ❖ The infection is transmitted by intimate contact with secretions (breast milk, saliva and urine) of an infected individual. CMV replicates in salivary glands and kidney cells, often causing cells to fuse into large, multinucleated giant cells; the virus tends to persist in these tissues, with chronic shedding. As with other herpesviruses, humoral and cell-mediated immunity are important.
  - ❖ Transmission of infection can be prevented by screening blood and organs before transplants. Specific immunoglobulin against CMV and the antiviral drug ganciclovir have together been found to reduce mortality of CMV pneumonia in bone transplant patients.
- The Epstein–Barr virus (EBV) is definitely known to cause infectious mononucleosis and Burkitt's lymphoma. It has also been implicated in the pathogenesis of nasopharyngeal carcinoma, but not with certainty.
  - ❖ EBV is transmitted by intimate contact; it grows in B lymphocytes and other lymphatic tissues. Both antibody and cell-mediated immunity are important in determining the outcome of infection.
  - ❖ In addition to the other diagnostic techniques mentioned above, infectious mononucleosis can be diagnosed using the Paul–Bunnell test, where heterophile antibodies are sought in the serum of an infected individual which recognise antigens found on sheep and horse RBCs.
- In 1994, a new herpesvirus was identified from tissues of Kaposi's sarcoma from AIDS patients. This has been named HHV 8. It has also been identified in Kaposi's sarcoma in persons not infected with HIV. It has been therefore referred to sometimes as Kaposi's sarcoma-associated herpesvirus (KSHV).

- Herpes simian B virus causes cold sores in monkeys and severe CNS disease in humans. It is a Risk Group 4 pathogen. The unexpected appearance of herpes-like cytopathic effects in primary monkey kidney cells should be investigated with abundant caution in a biological safety cabinet.

ESSAYS

1. Classify herpes viruses. Mention their general characteristics. Add a brief note on Herpes simplex virus.
2. Describe the pathogenesis and laboratory diagnosis of Herpes simplex virus infections.
3. Describe the pathogenesis and laboratory diagnosis of the Varicella virus.
4. Describe the pathogenesis and laboratory diagnosis of Herpes zoster.
5. Describe the pathogenesis and laboratory diagnosis of Cytomegalovirus.
6. Describe the pathogenesis and laboratory diagnosis of the Epstein–Barr virus.

SHORT ANSWERS

1. Diseases caused by HHV-6, 7, 8
2. Infectious mononucleosis
3. Cancers associated with EBV

SHORT NOTES

1. Congenital CMV infections
2. Paul–Bunnell test
3. Tzank smear

52 Adenoviruses

INTRODUCTION

In 1953, Rowe and associates grew surgically removed human adenoid tissue in plasma clot cultures and noticed that the epithelial outgrowths underwent spontaneous degeneration resembling viral cytopathic change. This was neutralised by human sera. A viral agent was shown to be responsible for this degeneration. This was the prototype of the group of viruses subsequently designated as adenoviruses because they were originally isolated from the adenoids.

ADENOVIRUSES

Clinical Case During the monsoon period, 10 students from a boarding school presented with irritation and redness in the eyes along with mild fever and sore throat. Three of them had severe pain in the eye with excessive watering, and corneal ulcers. Conjunctival swabs were collected for viral examination. Direct smear examination by indirect immunofluorescent assay was positive for Adenovirus type 8 antibody. PCR was also positive for Adenovirus type 8 in all the students. Supportive therapy was given for corneal ulcers and the students of the conjunctivitis group responded in eight days while the corneal ulcers took three weeks to heal. The children were advised precautionary isolation and further spread was controlled.

Adenoviruses are a group of medium-sized, non-enveloped, double-stranded DNA viruses that share a **common complement fixing antigen**. They infect humans, animals and birds, showing **strict host specificity.** Adenovirus infections are common worldwide mostly in children. Many infections are asymptomatic. The virus may persist in the host for many months. They cause infections of the respiratory tract and eyes, and less often of the intestine and urinary tract.

Morphology

Adenoviruses are 70–75 nm in size. They have a characteristic morphology. The capsid is composed of 252 capsomers arranged as an icosahedron with 20 triangular facets and 12 vertices (Fig. 52.1). Of the 252 capsomers, 240 have six neighbours and are called hexons, while the 12 capsomers at the vertices have five neighbours and are called pentons. Each penton unit consists of a penton base anchored in the capsid and a projection or fibre consisting of a rod-like portion with a knob attached at the distal end. Thus, the virion has the appearance of a space vehicle (Fig. 52.2)

Resistance

Adenoviruses are relatively stable, remaining viable for about a week at 37°C. They are readily inactivated at 50°C. They resist ether and bile salts.

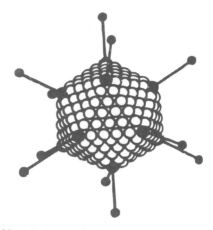

Fig. 52.1 Morphology of adenovirus

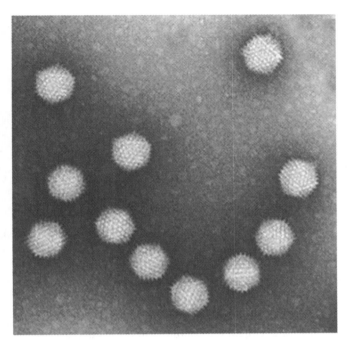

Fig. 52.2 Adenovirus

Growth and host range

Adenoviruses are host specific and so laboratory animals are not susceptible to adenoviruses infecting humans. Human adenoviruses grow only in tissue cultures of human origin, such as human embryonic kidney, HeLa or HEp-2. Cytopathic changes may take several days to develop and consist of cell rounding and aggregation into grape-like clusters. Intranuclear inclusions may be seen in stained preparations.

Classification

The family Adenoviridae contains two genera: *Mastadenovirus*, the adenovirus of mammals, and *Aviadenovirus*, that of birds. Over 50 serotypes of adenoviruses have been isolated from human sources and are divided into groups A–F (Table 52.1). Most of the recent serotypes were recovered from AIDS patients. They infect only the homologous species, with the exception of oncogenic human adenoviruses (for example, types, 12, 18, 31) that cause sarcomas when injected into newborn hamsters.

All mammalian adenoviruses share a common complement fixing antigen. The group antigens are present mainly on hexons and can be detected by immunofluorescence or ELISA. Type-specific antigens are located on pentons and fibres. Serotypes are identified by the neutralisation test. Human adenoviruses are classified into six groups (also called subgroups or subgenera) based on properties such as hemagglutination, fibre length, DNA fragment analysis and oncogenic potential.

Pathogenicity

Adenoviruses cause infections of the respiratory tract, eye, bladder and intestine. More than one type of virus may produce the same clinical syndrome and one type of virus may cause clinically different diseases (Table 52.2).

Table 52.2 *Common syndromes associated with adenovirus infection*

Syndrome	Principal serotypes
Respiratory disease in children	1, 2, 5, 6
Sore throat, febrile cold, pneumonia	3, 4, 7, 14, 21
ARD in military recruits	4, 7, 21
Follicular (swimming pool) conjunctivitis	3, 7
Epidemic keratoconjunctivitis (shipyard eye)	8, 19, 37
Diarrhea	40, 41

Table 52.1 *Classification of human adenoviruses*

Group (Subgenus)	Serotype (Species)	Hemagglutination		Oncogenic potential	
		Red cells	Pattern	Tumourogenicity	Transformation of in vivo cultured cells
A	12, 18, 31	Rat	±	High	+
B	3, 7, 11, 14, 16, 21, 34, 35	Monkey	+	Weak	+
C	1, 2, 5, 6	Rat	±	Nil	+
D	8–10, 13, 15, 17, 19, 20, 22–30, 32, 33, 36–39, 42–47		+	Nil	+
E	4	Rat	±	Nil	+
F	40, 41	Rat	±	NK	+

Note: + complete hemagglutination and ± partial; NK = not known

The following syndromes have been recognised:

Pharyngitis: Adenoviruses are the main cause of non-bacterial pharyngitis and tonsillitis, presenting as febrile common cold. Types 1–7 are commonly responsible.

Pneumonia: Adenovirus types 3 and 7 are associated with pneumonia in adults resembling primary atypical pneumonia. In infants and young children, type 7 may lead to more serious and even fatal pneumonia.

Acute respiratory diseases (ARD): This occurs usually as outbreaks in military recruits. Serotypes 4, 7 and 21 are the agents commonly isolated.

Pharyngoconjunctival fever: This syndrome of febrile pharyngitis and conjunctivitis seen in the civilian population is usually associated with serotypes 3, 7 and 14.

Epidemic keratoconjunctivitis (EKC): This is a serious condition which may appear as an epidemic, usually caused by type 8 and less often by types 19 and 37 (*Case*).

Acute follicular conjunctivitis: This is a non-purulent inflammation of the conjunctiva with enlargement of the submucous lymphoid follicles and of the pre-auricular lymph nodes. Types 3, 4 and 11 are commonly responsible. Adenoviral and chlamydial conjunctivitis are clinically similar.

Diarrhea: Adenoviruses can often be isolated from feces but their connection to intestinal disease has not been conclusively established. However, some fastidious adenoviruses, which can be demonstrated abundantly in feces by electron microscopy but fail to grow in conventional tissue cultures, can cause diarrheal disease in children (for example, types 40, 41). They have been designated as enteric type adenoviruses. They are not grown in a routine cell culture and special techniques of tissue culture (use of trypsinised monkey kidney cells or transformed human embryonic kidney cells) have been developed for their cultivation. They can also be identified by stool ELISA.

Acute hemorrhagic cystitis in children and **generalised exanthem** are two other syndromes which have been reported. Adenoviruses types 11 and 21 are responsible for the former.

Adenoviruses have been isolated from mesenteric lymph nodes in cases of **mesenteric adenitis** and **intussusception** in children.

Laboratory diagnosis

Diagnosis can be established by:

1. **Tissue culture:** Isolation of the virus from the throat, eye, urine or feces. The materials are inoculated in tissue cultures. Preliminary identification is possible by:
   - Noting the cytopathic effects
   - Complement fixation tests with adenovirus antiserum
   - Subgrouping by hemagglutination with rat and monkey erythrocytes
   - Typing by neutralisation tests

2. **Serodiagnosis:** For serological diagnosis, rise in titre of antibodies should be demonstrated in paired sera. Examination of a single sample of serum is inconclusive as adenovirus antibodies are so common in the population.

3. **Electron microscopy** is used for fecal virus detection.

4. **Immunofluorescence** for viral antigen detection in nasopharyngeal and ocular infections are useful.

5. **PCR-based tests** have been used for the detection of viral DNA.

Prophylaxis

Specific prevention is required only for the control of outbreaks in closed communities, as in military recruits. Killed and live vaccines have been used for prevention of ARD, with some success. No vaccine is available for general use.

Transformation of cells: In 1962 Huebner reported that adenovirus types 12 and 18 produced sarcoma when inoculated into baby hamsters. Types 12, 18 and 31 have been shown to induce tumours in animals while all types have been shown to transform cells in culture. However they have no role in human cancers.

Gene therapy: Adenoviruses appear to have a spare capacity to carry DNA inserts of up to 7 kb and are being investigated as potential vectors in gene therapy

ADENO-ASSOCIATED VIRUSES (AAV)

Electron microscopy of adenovirus preparations have revealed small icosahedral viral particles, 20–25 nm in diameter They are unable to replicate independently and are called defective viruses or viruses dependent on helper viruses. They can multiply only in cells simultaneously infected with adenoviruses and are called adeno-associated viruses (AAV) or adenosatellite viruses. They have been classified as the genus *dependovirus* (referring to their dependence on adenoviruses) under the family Parvoviridae. They can be detected by electron microscopy and complement fixation or immunofluorescence with specific antisera. Types 1, 2 and 3 are of human origin and cause natural infection, while type 4 is of simian origin. Their pathogenic role is uncertain.

RECAP

- Adenoviruses are icosahedral, non-enveloped, DNA viruses. Human adenoviruses are divided into six groups, A to F, based on their physical, chemical and biological properties, with many serotypes in each group.
- Human adenoviruses exhibit a narrow host range.
- Adenoviruses infect epithelial cells of the pharynx, conjunctiva, small intestine and, occasionally, other organ systems.
- A more serious disease is epidemic keratoconjunctivitis, which is highly contagious.
- Adenovirus serotypes 40 and 41 have been causatively associated with infantile gastroenteritis. These enteric adenoviruses are very difficult to cultivate.
- Adeno-associated viruses are dependent on adenoviruses for replication and belong to the family Parvoviridae.

SHORT ANSWER

1. Diseases caused by adenoviruses.

SHORT NOTES

1. Eye infections caused by adenoviruses
2. Laboratory diagnosis of adenovirus infections
3. Adeno-associated viruses (definition)

53 Picornaviruses

INTRODUCTION

The family Picornaviridae comprises a large number of very small (*pico*, meaning small) RNA viruses. They are non-enveloped viruses, 27–30 nm in size, resistant to ether and other lipid solvents. Two main groups *Enterovirus* and *Rhinovirus* may be found transiently in the alimentary tract or the nasopharynx respectively.

Classification

Four genera of picornaviruses are of medical importance:
- *Enterovirus,* that infects the intestinal tract
- *Rhinovirus,* that infects the nasopharynx
- *Hepatovirus*
- *Parechovirus*

Two other picornavirus genera of veterinary importance are
- *Aphthovirus,* which causes foot-and-mouth disease in cattle
- *Cardiovirus* causing encephalomyocarditis of mice

ENTEROVIRUSES

Paralytic disease of children has been recognised from very early times. Experimental transmission of the disease to monkeys was demonstrated by Landsteiner and Popper. **Enders, Weller** and **Robbins** (1949) demonstrated that polioviruses could grow in cultures of non-neural cells from human embryos, producing cytopathic effects, a discovery for which they got the **Nobel Prize**.

Dalldorf and Sickles (1948) demonstrated the Coxsackie virus from the feces of children with paralytic poliomyelitis, which caused paralysis on inoculation into suckling mice. These patients came from the village of Coxsackie in New York, hence, the name.

The introduction of tissue culture techniques in diagnostic virology led to the isolation of several cytopathogenic viruses from the feces of sick as well as healthy persons. They were called orphan viruses as they could not be associated with any particular clinical disease. They came to be known by the descriptive term 'enteric cytopathogenic human orphan (**ECHO**) viruses'. Most enteroviruses are host-specific, infecting only one or a few related species. There is no common group antigen for enteroviruses, though some of them show antigenic cross-reactions.

Classification

Enteroviruses of medical importance include
- Poliovirus types   1–3
- Coxsackievirus A types   1–24 (types not included: 15, 18 or 23)
- Coxsackievirus B types   1–6
- Echovirus types   1–34 (types not included: 8, 10, 22, 23, 28 and 34)
- Enterovirus types   68–116 (type not included: 72)

Retaining the enterovirus nomenclature, subsequently, Coxsackie A virus now falls into human enterovirus species A (HEV-A) and HEV-C, while Coxsackie B virus falls into HEV-B which also includes ECHO virus. Newer enteroviruses after 1969 have been assigned enterovirus (EV) type numbers, starting with 68. Enterovirus 72, causing infectious hepatitis (Hepatitis type A), has been reclassified as a separate genus Hepatovirus. Rhinoviruses were considered a separate genus earlier, but are now included in the genus *Enterovirus*. They have 100 antigenic types and are classified into 3 species of Human Rhinovirus (HRV) A, B, and C.

POLIOVIRUS

Clinical Case A 10-year-old boy from a labour colony presented to the emergency department with a history of mild fever, headache and sore throat for the previous eight days. This was accompanied by vomiting for the previous two days. There was a brief asymptomatic period of two days. On the morning of presentation, he experienced pain in the right lower limbs; followed by weakness, and inability to walk at the time of presentation. His mother gave no history of vaccination during the first five years of the boy's life. Throat swab, rectal swab and cerebrospinal fluid (CSF) were sent for viral studies. The throat and rectal swabs showed cytopathic effect in tissue culture which was confirmed as poliovirus type 1 by the neutralisation test. Reverse transcriptase PCR in CSF was positive for poliovirus. General condition of the child improved on supportive treatment.

Morphology

The virion is a spherical particle, about 27 nm in diameter, composed of 60 subunits, each consisting of four **viral proteins** (VP1–VP4), arranged in icosahedral symmetry. VP1, which faces outside, carries the major antigenic site for combination with type-specific neutralising antibodies. The genome is a single strand of positive-sense RNA of 7.4 kb. It can be directly translated by host ribosomes to form a polyprotein which is cleaved into 11 different proteins. The positive-sense genome RNA is infectious.

The virus can be crystallised, and arrays of virus crystals can be seen in the cytoplasm of infected cells (Fig. 53.1).

Resistance

- Poliovirus is resistant to ether, chloroform, bile, proteolytic enzymes of the intestinal contents and detergents. It is stable at a pH of 3. In feces, it can survive for months at 4°C and years at −20°C. Depending on conditions like temperature, moisture, pH and the amount of virus, its survival in feces at room temperature may vary from one day to several weeks.
- It is readily inactivated by heat (55°C for 30 minutes). Molar $MgCl_2$ protects the virus against heat inactivation. Milk or ice cream also provides such protection.
- Formaldehyde and oxidising disinfectants destroy the virus. Chlorine at 0.1 ppm can destroy purified polio. However, higher concentrations are required to destroy the virus in sewage water, with organic matter and in feces. Phenolic disinfectants are not effective.
- Poliovirus does not survive lyophilisation as well.

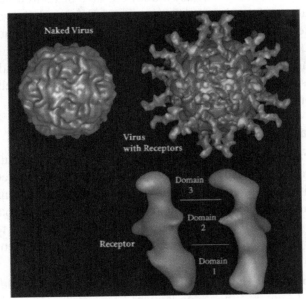

Fig. 53.1 Poliovirus

Antigenic Types: There are three antigenic types: 1, 2 and 3. The prototype strains are Brunhilde and Mahoney strains for type 1, Lansing and MEFI for type 2 and Leon and Saukett for type 3.

- **Type 1** is the most common and causes most epidemics.
- **Type 2** usually causes endemic infections.
- **Type 3** strains have caused epidemics. Immunity is type-specific.

Two antigens C and D (C—coreless or capsid, D—dense) can be recognised based on **complement fixation, ELISA or precipitation tests**.

- The **D antigen**, also called the **native or N antigen**, is associated with the whole virion and is type-specific.
- The **C antigen**, also called the **heated or H antigen**, is associated with the 'empty' non-infectious virus. Anti-C antibody does not neutralise virus infectivity and is not protective.
- The D antigen is converted into the C antigen by heating the virus at 56°C. Anti-D antibody is protective. Potency of the injectable polio vaccine can be measured in terms of D antigen units.

Host range and cultivation

Natural infection occurs only in humans. Experimentally, chimpanzees and cynomolgus monkeys may be infected by intracerebral, intraspinal or by oral route.

The virus grows readily in tissue cultures of primate origin. Primary monkey kidney cultures or continuous cultures from human tissues are used for isolation of the virus from clinical material and vaccine production. The infected cells round up, become refractile and pyknotic. Eosinophilic intranuclear inclusion bodies may be demonstrated in stained preparations. Well-formed plaques develop in infected monolayers.

Pathogenicity

Transmission: The virus enters by the oral route through ingestion of food and water contaminated with human feces. The virus colonises the nasopharynx and multiplies initially. It may be found in the throat or feces in the initial phases. Then it passes down to Peyer's patches and the epithelial cells of the alimentary canal lymphatic tissues.

Spread: It then spreads to the regional lymph nodes and enters the bloodstream (**primary viremia**). After further multiplication in the reticuloendothelial system, the virus enters the bloodstream again (**secondary viremia)** and is carried to the spinal cord and brain. The virus can pass along the axon of peripheral nerves to the central nervous system (CNS). Direct neural transmission to the central nervous system may also occur under special circumstances, as in poliomyelitis following tonsillectomy.

In the **central nervous system**, the virus multiplies selectively in the neurons and destroys them. The earliest change is the degeneration of Nissl bodies (**chromatolysis**). Nuclear changes follow. When degeneration becomes irreversible, the necrotic cell lyses or is phagocytosed by leucocytes or macrophages. Lesions are mostly in the **anterior horns of the spinal cord**, causing **flaccid paralysis**, but the posterior horns and intermediate columns may also be involved to some extent. Pathological changes are usually more extensive compared to the extent of paralysis. In some cases, encephalitis may occur involving the brainstem but extending up to the motor and premotor areas of the cerebral cortex.

Clinical features

- **Inapparent infection:** Following exposure to the poliovirus, 90–95 per cent of susceptible individuals develop only inapparent infection, which causes seroconversion alone. It is only in 5–10 per cent that any sort of clinical illness results. The incubation period is about 10 days on an average, but may range from four days to four weeks.

- **Abortive poliomyelitis or minor illness:** The earliest manifestations are associated with the phase of primary viremia consisting of fever, headache, sore throat and malaise lasting 1–5 days.

- **Paralytic poliomyelitis or major illness:** If the infection progresses, the minor illness is followed 3–4 days later by the major illness. The fever returns (**biphasic fever),** along with headache, stiff neck and other features of meningitis. This marks the stage of viral invasion of the central nervous system (*see clinical case*).

- **Non-paralytic poliomyelitis:** Sometimes, the disease does not progress beyond the stage of aseptic meningitis.

In those proceeding to paralytic poliomyelitis, flaccid paralysis develops. Paralysis is focal in distribution initially but spreads over the next 3–4 days. Depending on the distribution of paralysis, cases are classified as spinal, **bulbar** or **bulbospinal**. The mortality range is 5–10 per cent and is mainly due to respiratory failure. Recovery of the paralysed muscles takes place in the next 4–8 weeks and is usually complete after six months, leaving behind varying degrees of residual paralysis. Rarely, myocarditis or lymphatic hyperplasia may occur.

Laboratory diagnosis

1. **Specimen:** Throat swab and feces (rectal swabs), including blood and CSF.
2. **Viral isolation:** Isolation of the virus in tissue culture is the best method for specific diagnosis.
   - The virus can be isolated from **blood** during primary viremia, 3–5 days after infection, before neutralising antibodies appear. But this is of little practical importance.
   - The virus can be isolated from the **throat** in the early stages of the disease.
   - Virus isolation from **feces** is usually possible in over 80 per cent of patients in the first week, 50 per cent till the third week and 25 per cent till the sixth week. As fecal excretion may be intermittent, the best results are obtained by testing fecal samples collected on two separate days, as early in the illness as possible. Prolonged fecal excretion may be seen in the immunodeficient. Carrier stages do not occur.
   - Unlike other enteroviruses, the poliovirus can seldom be isolated from cerebrospinal fluid (CSF) but can be obtained from the **spinal cord and brain**, postmortem.

   After appropriate processing to destroy bacteria (centrifugation, treatment with ether, addition of antibiotics), specimens are inoculated into primary monkey kidney cells or tissue culture (human or simian cell culture may be used). Virus growth is indicated by typical cytopathic effects in 2–3 days. Identification is made by neutralisation tests with pooled and specific antisera. It must be remembered that the mere isolation of the poliovirus from feces does not constitute a diagnosis of poliomyelitis as symptomless infections are common. Virus isolation must be interpreted along with clinical and serological evidence.

3. **Serodiagnosis:** Antibody rise can be demonstrated in paired sera by **neutralisation** or **complement fixation** tests. Antibodies appear soon after the onset of paralysis. Neutralising antibodies appear early and persist for life. In the CF test, antibodies to the C antigen appear first and disappear early, while anti-D antibodies take some weeks to appear after infection but last for about five years. The CF test is useful to identify exposure to the poliovirus but not for type-specific diagnosis.

4. **Molecular diagnosis:**
   - **Reverse transcriptase PCR:** PCR-based tests have improved the demonstration of viral RNA in CSF.
   - **Sequencing:** In a population, three types of strains may be in circulation: wild virus, oral polio vaccine (OPV) virus strain and vaccine-derived polioviruses (**VDPVs**). These can be differentiated by sequencing.

Immunity

Immunity in poliomyelitis is **type-specific and permanent**. Humoral immunity provided by circulating and secretory antibodies is responsible for protection against poliomyelitis. The IgM antibody appears within a week of infection and lasts for about six months. The IgG antibody persists for life. Neutralising antibodies in blood generally protect against disease by a virus of the same serotype, but may not prevent infection of intestinal epithelial cells and virus shedding in feces. Antibodies cannot protect once the infection spreads to the CNS. **Hence, vaccination must be prior to onset of CNS symptoms.** Secretory IgA in the gastrointestinal tract provides mucosal immunity, preventing intestinal infection and virus shedding. Breast milk containing IgA antibody protects infants from infection. Poliomyelitis tends to be more severe with prolonged virus shedding in those with impaired humoral immune response. The virus also induces cell-mediated immunity (CMI), but its effect is doubtful. Response to poliovirus infection is normal in persons with defective CMI.

Immunoprophylaxis

Passive immunisation by the administration of human gammaglobulin is of little value.

Active immunisation

Salk's killed vaccine: This is formalin-inactivated types 1–3 poliovirus, grown in monkey kidney tissue culture. Inactivation with formalin (1:4000) is done at 37°C for 12–15 days. Stringent tests are carried out to ensure complete inactivation and freedom from extraneous agents. Tests for safety and potency are done prior to issue for use.

A setback to Salk candidate vaccine occurred in 1955, when over 100 cases of paralytic poliomyelitis occurred in the vaccinated persons and their contacts. The '**Cutter incident**' (so called after the manufacturer of the particular vaccine) occurred due to incomplete inactivation of viruses. This led to the introduction of further safeguards. The vaccine, after these modifications, has been completely safe.

Vaccination schedule: The killed vaccine is given by injection, hence called **inactivated** or **injectable polio vaccine** (IPV). Three doses are given 4–6 weeks apart, which is followed by a booster six months later.

- The **first dose** should be given to babies beyond six months of age to ensure that maternal antibodies do not interfere.
- **Second dose:** An enhanced potency IPV produced in human diploid cell induces better seroconversion following two subcutaneous doses 4–8 weeks apart.
- **A third dose** may be given 6–12 months later.

Immunity can be sustained by booster doses every 3–5 years thereafter.

Sabin's live attenuated vaccine: Live polio vaccines were developed independently by Koprowsky, Cox and Sabin. All three were used initially, but currently Sabin's attenuated strains are employed. The attenuated virus immunises by active multiplication. It stimulates systemic production of IgM, IgG and secretory IgA in the intestine producing local immunity.

Criteria for attenuation of strains:
- ❖ Should not be neurovirulent as tested by intraspinal inoculation in monkeys
- ❖ Should be able to set up intestinal infection following feeding and should induce an immune response
- ❖ Should be stable and should not acquire neurovirulence after serial enteric passage
- ❖ Should possess stable genetic characteristics (markers) by which they can be differentiated from the wild virulent strains

Markers to differentiate wild from attenuated strains:
- ❖ **d marker**: Wild strains grow well at low levels of bicarbonate but avirulent strains will not
- ❖ **rct 40**: Wild strains grow well at 40°C, while avirulent strains grow poorly
- ❖ **MS**: Wild strains grow well in a stable cell line of monkey kidney, while avirulent strains grow poorly
- ❖ **McBride's intratypic antigenic marker** shown by the rate of inactivation by specific antiserum

The above markers have **not** been found to be discriminative. Molecular epidemiological methods give better results. These methods include the use of monoclonal antibodies specific for vaccine strains, oligonucleotide fingerprinting and nucleic acid sequencing.

Vaccination schedule: Live polio vaccine is administered orally and is therefore known as the **oral polio vaccine (OPV)**. It is prepared by growing attenuated strains in monkey kidney cells. Very stringent precautions are taken to ensure freedom from extraneous agents like SV 40 and the B virus. **Monovalent or trivalent forms** in pleasantly flavoured syrup is prepared. $MgCl_2$ or sucrose stabilises the vaccine against heat inactivation, particularly in tropical conditions. The vaccine is usually given in the trivalent form.

The **bivalent vaccine containing type 1 and 3**, are to replace the trivalent Oral Polio Vaccine (OPV), by removing the type 2 component (OPV2) from immunisation programmes.

Dosage: Theoretically, a single dose should be sufficient to establish infection and immunity, but in practice, three doses are given at 4–8-week intervals, to ensure that all three types of the vaccine virus multiply in the intestine, overcoming interference among themselves and with other enteric viruses. It has been recommended that, in the tropics, the number of doses of vaccine be increased to five to enhance seroconversion in the vaccinated.

OPV used in India is stated to contain type 1 virus 10 lakhs, type 2 virus 2 lakh and type 3 virus 3 lakh TC ID50 per dose (0.5 ml). The liquid vaccine is thermostabilised with $MgCl_2$ which acts only at a pH below 7.0. To maintain the pH, the vaccine is kept in airtight containers. The shelf life of the vaccine at 4–8°C is four months and at −20°C is two years. Improper storage conditions and failure of 'cold chain' may be partly responsible for the apparent failure of OPV to control poliomyelitis in developing countries.

There has been much controversy about the relative merits of killed and live vaccines.

Safety: Both vaccines are safe. It has been suggested that the attenuated strains tend to acquire neurovirulence on serial enteric passage, as may happen following vaccination. A few cases of vaccine-induced poliomyelitis have been reported but the incidence is so low that the risk is negligible. However, it assumes importance where the disease has been eradicated by immunisation. About 5–10 cases of paralytic poliomyelitis are seen each year in the USA, all of which are caused by the vaccine strains, in vaccinated people or their contacts. OPV is not safe

Differences between IPV and OPV

Sl.No.	Features	IPV (Salk type)	OPV (Sabin Type)
1	Type of virus	Killed formolised	Live attentuated
2	Route of administration	Subcutaneous or intramuscular	Oral
3	Immunity	Systemic immunity good, mucosal is slight to moderate	Systemic immunity good, mucosal is excellent
4	Mutations leading to reversal of virulence	Not known	Possible
5	Interference of vaccine efficiency by enteric viruses	No interference	Interference is possible
6	Vaccine-associated disease complication?	No	Possible
7	Administration to immunocompromised host	Is allowed	Not allowed/recommended
8	Storage	Stringent conditions for storage and transport not required. Longer shelf life	Needs to be stored and transported at sub-zero temperatures, unless stabilised
9	Cost of manufacture	High	Low

in immunodeficient or immunosuppressed subjects but the killed vaccine is harmless.

On very rare occasions, OPV can lead to vaccine-associated paralytic polio or vaccine-derived poliovirus (VDPV). It is caused by a strain of poliovirus that has genetically changed in the intestine from the original attenuated vaccine strain contained in OPV.

A **VDPV** is a very rare strain of poliovirus, genetically changed from the original strain contained in OPV. On very rare occasions, under certain conditions, a strain of poliovirus in OPV may change and revert to a form that may be able to cause paralysis (VDPV) in humans and develop the capacity for sustained circulation. The latter is known as a **circulating VDPV (cVDPV).**

Efficiency: A full course of killed vaccine induces a satisfactory immune response (Fig. 53.2).

One or two doses of OPV have produced 90–100 per cent seroconversion in children in the developed countries. However, in the developing countries in the tropics, the response has not been satisfactory. This is seen with polio type 1, with more than half the vaccines in some series failing to show seroconversion after two or three doses. The reason for this disparity is not certain, though several possibilities have been suggested.

Issues related to vaccine failure in the tropics:

- Interference by other enteroviruses common in the tropics (experimentally, it has been shown that coxsackie B viruses may interfere with the poliovirus, while coxsackie A may be synergistic)
- Frequent diarrheal diseases preventing colonisation by the vaccine virus

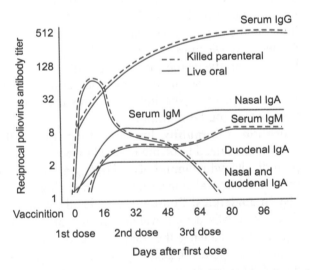

Fig. 53.2 Serum and secretory antibody response to 3 doses of OPV or 3 doses of IPV

Source: WHO (1993), *The Immunological Basis of Immunisation Series, Module 6: Polimyelitis*, Global Programme for Vaccines and Immunisation EPI, WHO.

- Breastfeeding immediately before or after the vaccine. The virus may be neutralised by antibodies in breast milk or by other inhibitory agents in the intestinal secretions.
- An inhibitor of poliovirus has been identified in saliva. This can be countered by horse antiserum to human gamma globulin. Because of the poor rate of seroconversion after oral immunisation in India and other tropical areas, primary immunisation with killed vaccines (given along with the triple antigen) has been proposed. This may be fol-

lowed by live oral vaccines for achieving intestinal immunity.

Key advantages of OPV:

- **Ease of administration**: OPV is obviously preferable to killed vaccines given by injection. However, an advantage of the killed vaccine is that it can be administered along with the DPT vaccine as a quadruple vaccine.
- **Economy:** The live vaccine is much more economical. This is an important aspect in mass vaccination campaigns in the developing countries.
- **Nature of immunity:** This is perhaps the most important difference between the two. Killed vaccine induces only systemic antibody response. There is no **intestinal immunity**; even in the vaccinated, infection with a wild strain may lead to intestinal multiplication and dissemination of the virus. The individual alone is protected by the circulating antibodies. Live vaccines, on the other hand, also induce local immunity in the gut so that wild viruses are unable to multiply in the intestines and be shed. Hence, it protects the individual and the community, producing herd immunity.
- **Duration of immunity:** Immunity following a killed vaccine may need to be maintained by booster doses periodically, while immunity following a live vaccine resembles natural active immunity in lasting longer.
- **Use in epidemics:** Community-wide administration of OPV, ideally a monovalent vaccine of the same type as that causing the epidemic, early during an epidemic of paralytic poliomyelitis can stop the epidemic. This has been successfully practised in different parts of the world.
- **Spread of vaccine virus in the community:** The tendency of the vaccine virus to spread naturally in the community, especially among children, is a disadvantage in developed countries.

Vaccine virus may even be beneficial and may help extend the vaccine coverage in countries where the wild virus is endemic. Ideally, however, it is desirable to vaccinate the whole community at one time so that natural dissemination is prevented. The strategy of administering the vaccine to all children in a region on the same day (**pulse immunisation**) has been found to be useful in developing countries.

Eradication of poliomyelitis: By global immunisation with OPV, it was considered possible to eradicate the disease. The World Health Organization Assembly in 1988 had proposed the global eradication of poliomyelitis by the year 2000. Successful polio immunisation program relied on effective planning with measurable outcomes including vaccine procurement and supply, cold chain and logistics, health worker training, communications, and social mobilisation. The end game strategic plan of the **Global Polio Eradication Initiative** is to deliver a sustained, polio-free world by detection and interruption of poliovirus transmission, immunisation strengthening and withdrawal of OPV, containment and certification, and legacy planning.

> **Pulse Polio Immunisation Programme (PPI):** Government of India has used this program to achieve a goal of eradicating poliomyelitis. It includes mass administration of OPV on a single day to all children aged 0–5 years in the community, irrespective of whether they have been vaccinated or not, through national universal immunisation program (UIP). It does not replace the UIP. The strategy was to give two rounds of doses at an interval of 4–6 weeks during the low polio transmission period in winter (November to February).

Epidemiology

Poliomyelitis is an exclusively human disease. The only source of the virus is humans, the patient or, much more commonly, the symptomless carrier. Patients shed the virus in feces for varying periods, about 50 per cent for three weeks, and a small proportion for 3–4 months. No permanent carriage occurs. However, the virus may persist in the environment (sewage) for up to six months. Virus shed in throat secretions during the early part of the disease may also be a source of infection.

Infection is, mostly, asymptomatic. The ratio of subclinical to clinical infections has been stated to be 100 or 1000 to 1. The outcome of infection is influenced by the virulence of the infecting strain, the infective dose and the age of the individual (adults being more susceptible than children). The following factors may influence the incidence of paralysis:

- Pregnancy carries an increased risk of paralysis, perhaps due to the associated hormonal changes.
- Tonsillectomy during the incubation period may predispose the affected person to bulbar poliomyelitis.
- Injections such as triple vaccine, especially alum-containing preparations, may lead to paralysis involving the inoculated limb in an asymptomatic or mild case. The mechanism is uncertain. The trauma may lead to virus entry into local nerve fibres, or the segment of spinal cord corresponding to the

site may be more susceptible to viral damage due to reactive hyperemia.

- Severe muscular exertion or trauma during the pre-paralytic stage increases the risk of paralysis.

Poliovirus type 1 is responsible for most epidemics of paralytic poliomyelitis. Type 3 also causes epidemics to a lesser extent. Type 2 usually causes inapparent infections in western countries but, in India, paralysis due to type 2 is common. Immunity is type-specific but there is a significant amount of cross-protection between types 1 and 2, and types 2 and 3 and little or none between types 1 and 3.

COXSACKIEVIRUSES

The characteristic feature of this group is its ability to infect suckling but not adult mice. Also, only few types can grow in cell cultures. Based on the pathological changes produced in suckling mice, coxsackieviruses are classified into two groups: A and B.

Properties

Coxsackieviruses are typical enteroviruses. Two groups, A and B, are known. By neutralisation tests, group A viruses are classified into 24 types and group B into 6 types. Their properties are as follows:

Group A viruses (24 serotypes):

- Following inoculation in suckling mice, group A viruses produce generalised myositis and flaccid paralysis, leading to death within a week.
- Coxsackie A23 is the same as echovirus 9, and coxsackie A24 the same as echovirus 34. Some coxsackieviruses (A 7, 20, 21, 24 and B 1, 3, 5, 6) agglutinate human or monkey erythrocytes.

Group B viruses (6 serotypes):

- Following inoculation in suckling mice, they produce patchy focal myositis, spastic paralysis, necrosis of brown fat and, often, pancreatitis, hepatitis, myocarditis and encephalitis.
- All types in group B share a common complement-fixing antigen.

Host range and cultivation

Coxsackievirus can be isolated by inoculation of suckling mice. Inoculation is usually made by the intracerebral, subcutaneous and intraperitoneal routes. Adult mice are not susceptible. Suckling hamsters can also be infected experimentally.

All coxsackie B viruses grow well in monkey kidney tissue cultures, while only types 7 and 9 of group A, grow well in this. The A 21 virus grows in HeLa cells.

Clinical features

Coxsackieviruses produce a variety of clinical syndromes in humans, ranging from trivial to fatal infections. The following types have been recognised (Table 53.1).

Group A:

- **Herpangina** (vesicular pharyngitis) is a common clinical manifestation of coxsackie group A infection in children. It is a severe febrile pharyngitis, with headache, vomiting and pain in the abdomen. The characteristic lesions are small vesicles, on the fauces and posterior pharyngeal wall, that break down to form ulcers.
- **Aseptic meningitis** may be caused by most group A and all group B viruses. A maculopapular rash may be present. The disease may sometimes occur as epidemics. Type A7 had caused outbreaks of paralytic disease in Russia, Scotland and elsewhere, the virus for a time having been erroneously referred to as poliovirus type 4.
- **Hand, foot and mouth disease (HFMD)** is an exanthematous fever affecting mainly young children, characterised by clusters of papulovesicular lesions on the skin and oral mucosa. It occurs as sporadic cases and as outbreaks. Coxsackie A16, A9 and B 1–3 were common causative agents initially. It was a benign illness resolving in 1–2 weeks. In the 1970s, enterovirus 71 caused extensive epidemics with serious complications like aseptic meningitis, encephalitis, flaccid paralysis, pulmonary hemorrhage, with many fatalities, particularly in East Asia, from Taiwan to Singapore. HFMD in now an important emerging disease.
- **Minor respiratory infections** resembling common cold may be caused by A10, A21, A24 and B3.

Group B:

- Epidemic myalgia or **pleurodynia,** also known as **Bornholm disease** (first described on the Danish island of Bornholm), is a febrile disease with a sharp piercing pain in the chest and abdomen, caused by group B viruses. The disease may occur sporadically or as epidemics.

Table 53.1   *Clinical syndromes commonly caused by enteroviruses*

Syndrome	Poliovirus	Coxsackie A	Coxsackie B	ECHO	New entero-virus types
Paralysis	1, 2, 3	7	–	–	–
Aseptic meningitis	1, 2, 3	7, 9, 23	1–6	Several (2, 3, 4, 6, 7, 9, 11, 14, 16, 17, 18, 19, 25, 33)	71
Encephalitis	1, 2, 3	9	3–6	6, 9, 17, 19	71
Fever with rash	–	9, 16, 23	–	4, 6, 9, 16	–
Hand, foot and mouth disease	–	5, 10, 16	–	–	71
Herpangina	–	1–6, 8, 10	–	–	–
Upper respiratory infection	–	21	–	11, 20	–
Pneumonitis, bronchiolitis	–	–	–	–	68
Bornholm disease	–	–	1.5	–	–
Myocarditis, pericarditis	–	–	1.5	–	–
Acute hemorrhagic conjunctivitis	–	24	–	–	70

- **Myocarditis** and **pericarditis** in the newborn, associated with high fatality, may be caused by group B viruses. The disease may sometimes occur in older children and adults as well.
- **Juvenile diabetes** has been claimed to be associated with coxsackie B4 infection but a causal role for this virus has not been established.
- **Orchitis** due to coxsackievirus has also been reported.
- **Transplacental and neonatal transmission** has been demonstrated with coxsackie B viruses resulting in a serious disseminated disease that may include hepatitis, meningoencephalitis and adrenocortical involvement.
- Type B viruses have been associated with a condition called **post-viral fatigue syndrome**, but neither the condition nor the association has been clearly defined.

Laboratory diagnosis

- **Animal inoculation:** Virus isolation from lesions or feces may be made by inoculation into suckling mice. Identification is by studying the histopathology in infected mice and by neutralisation tests.
- **Tissue culture** is not useful as all serotypes do not grow well in cell lines.
- Due to the existence of several antigenic types, **serodiagnosis** has not been of much use.

Epidemiology

Like other enteroviruses, the coxsackievirus primarily inhabits the alimentary canal and spreads by the fecal–oral route. Coxsackie B virus epidemics tend to occur every 2–5 years. Young infants are most commonly affected. Vaccination is not practicable as there are several serotypes and immunity is type-specific. Many enteroviruses share similarity with coxsackieviruses. They may occur together in the environment, sewage or gut of the same human host.

ECHOVIRUSES

These viruses were not pathogenic for laboratory animals and were recognised after tissue cultures came into use in diagnostic virology. As they could not be associated with any particular clinical disease then, they were called orphans. They have since been given the descriptive designation '**enteric cytopathogenic human orphan viruses**' and are generally known by the term 'echoviruses'. Similar 'orphan' viruses have also been isolated from many animals.

Properties

Echoviruses resemble other enteroviruses in their properties. By neutralisation tests, they have been classified into 34 serotypes. Types 10 and 28 have been removed from the group, the former becoming a reovirus and the latter a rhinovirus.

Some echoviruses (types 3, 6, 7, 11, 12, 13, 19, 20, 21, 24, 29, 30 and 33) agglutinate human erythrocytes. Hemagglutination is followed by elution, rendering the cells inagglutinable by echo or coxsackieviruses but not by myxoviruses.

Host range and cultivation

All echoviruses grow well in human and simian kidney cultures, producing cytopathic effects. Echoviruses infect only human beings naturally. They are not pathogenic to laboratory animals, though occasional strains may produce paresis on inoculation into monkeys and newborn mice.

Clinical features

Though echoviruses were originally considered orphans, they have since been shown to produce a variety of disease patterns. Most infections are asymptomatic. In general, the clinical features resemble those produced by coxsackieviruses. Fever with rash and aseptic meningitis, sometimes as epidemics, can be produced by several serotypes, predominantly by types 4, 6, 9, 16, 20, 28 and 30. Echoviruses constitute perhaps the most common cause of aseptic meningitis. They have frequently been isolated from respiratory disease in children (types 1, 11, 19, 20 and 22) and gastroenteritis (type 18), but their causative role has not been proved. Occasional cases of paralysis and hepatic necrosis have also been reported.

Laboratory diagnosis

Feces, throat swabs or CSF may be inoculated into monkey kidney tissue cultures and virus growth detected by cytopathic changes. The large number of serotypes makes identification by neutralisation tests laborious. This may be simplified by hemagglutination and the use of serum pools for neutralisation. Serological diagnosis is not practicable except in case of epidemics where the causative serotype has been identified.

Epidemiology

Like other enteroviruses, echoviruses primarily inhabit the alimentary tract and are spread by the fecal–oral route. Epidemics may occur, especially in summer. Vaccination has not been attempted.

NEW ENTEROVIRUS TYPES

New enteroviruses include types 68–71. Type 68 was isolated from pharyngeal secretions of children with pneumonia and bronchitis. Type 69 is not associated with any human disease. Type 70 causes acute hemorrhagic conjunctivitis. EV-71, originally isolated from cases of meningitis and encephalitis, causes many other syndromes,

including HFMD (Table 53.1). Additional new enteroviruses include EV 79–88, EV 97 and EV 100–116.

Acute hemorrhagic conjunctivitis

A pandemic of acute hemorrhagic conjunctivitis, apparently arising in West Africa in 1969, spread widely, involving several parts of Africa, the Middle East, India, South East Asia, Japan, England and Europe. The incubation period for this virus is about 24 hours and the symptoms are sudden swelling, congestion, watering and pain in the eyes. Subconjunctival hemorrhage is a characteristic feature. There is transient corneal involvement but recovery is usually complete in 3–7 days. Radiculomyelopathy has been reported from India, as a complication. Sometimes it leads to paralysis resembling poliomyelitis.

The causative agent was identified as enterovirus type 70 (**EV-70**). It grows only on human embryonic kidney or HeLa cell lines for primary isolation, but can be adapted to grow on monkey kidney cells. Coxsackievirus type A24 also produces the same disease. Both these viruses show intratypic antigenic differences. Over the years, the condition has recurred in different parts of the world. Enterovirus 71 has been associated with fatal meningitis, encephalitis and paralysis.

RHINOVIRUSES

Common cold is probably the most common infectious disease of humans. The **common cold virus** was isolated by Tyrrell and his colleagues (1960). Thereafter, several similar viruses from common cold cases were reported by other workers. They were called *rhinovirus* ('rhino' referring to 'nose', the organ primarily affected). Currently, more than 100 serotypes are known, classified through neutralisation tests.

Properties

Rhinoviruses resemble other picornaviruses in size and structure. They differ from enteroviruses in being more acid-labile, but more heat-stable. They are inactivated below pH 6, inactivation being complete at pH 3. They are relatively stable at 20–37°C and may remain viable on fomites for days. Some serotypes survive for one hour at 50°C.

Host range and cultivation

Apart from humans, rhinoviruses can produce experimental infection only in chimpanzees. Related rhinoviruses have been isolated from cattle and horses but their significance in human infection is not known.

Rhinoviruses can be grown in tissue cultures of human or simian origin with cytopathic changes, if good oxygenation (achieved by rolling), low pH (around 7) and low temperature (33°C) are provided. Depending upon growth in tissue culture, rhinoviruses were classified into three groups, H, M and O. H strains grew only in human cells, while M strains grew equally well in human and monkey cells. O strains could be grown only in nasal or tracheal ciliated epithelium. This classification is no longer in use as the growth characteristics are not stable and can be changed by adaptation. Immunity is type-specific.

Pathogenicity

The virus attaches to receptors on nasal ciliated epithelial cells, enters and replicates within them, spreading to other cells. The cilia and cells are damaged and the epithelium is subjected to secondary bacterial infection. Local inflammation and cytokines may be responsible for the symptoms of common cold. Interferon production occurs early and specific antibody appears in nasal secretions. Both these may help in recovery. The antibody response, both nasal and systemic, varies in intensity and duration with different strains.

Laboratory diagnosis

Isolation of the virus may be obtained from nasal or throat swabs collected early in the infection, in human cell cultures, preferably MRC5 or W138 strains. Growth as evidenced by cytopathic Effect (CPE) may take two weeks to appear. Due to the large number of serotypes, serology is not feasible for diagnosis.

Epidemiology

The common cold is an infectious disease seen across the globe. It is transmitted by droplets. Hand-to-hand contact, followed by self-inoculation of conjunctival or nasal mucosa, appears to be an important mode of transmission. The incubation period is about two days, but may go up to seven days. The duration of virus shedding is not known, though it is unlikely to be prolonged. Contrary to popular belief, there appears to be no direct relationship between inclement weather and the common cold. The multiplicity of serotypes makes vaccination impossible. Moreover, the common cold is a syndrome produced not only by rhinoviruses but also by a variety of other groups such as respiratory syncytial, corona, coxsackie, echo, adeno, influenza and parainfluenza viruses. Hopes of specific control, therefore, lie in the development of antiviral chemotherapy.

RECAP

- Picornaviridae is a family of non-enveloped viruses, 25–30 nm in diameter (among the smallest of viruses), with icosahedral symmetry and a single-stranded RNA genome. The enteroviruses and rhinoviruses are important human pathogens.
- *Enterovirus* is a genus of the family Picornaviridae, comprising 3 polioviruses, 21 coxsackie A and six coxsackie B viruses, 29 echoviruses and enteroviruses types 68–71.
- Poliomyelitis is caused by three types of polioviruses, with type I producing the most severe disease. Only humans are naturally infected.
- Polioviruses can be isolated in tissue culture. Viral RNA can be detected by RT-PCR in throat swabs or samples of feces.
- Poliomyelitis is prevented by an inactivated (killed) injectable vaccine (Salk vaccine) or an attenuated live, orally administered vaccine (Sabin vaccine), which confers immunity by raising neutralising antibodies.
- Pulse Polio Immunisation Programme (PPI) helps increase herd immunity.
- Coxsackie A viruses are associated with hand, foot and mouth disease and meningitis; Coxsackie B viruses are associated with Bornholm disease, meningitis, pericarditis and myocarditis. For both, only a few serotypes grow in cell culture, and suckling mice are the most susceptible laboratory animals.

- Echoviruses are commonly found in the feces of healthy children. They are now known to cause meningitis, exanthema and severe neonatal diseases. They grow readily in cell culture, but rarely cause any lesions in suckling mice.
- Rhinoviruses have worldwide distribution and cause the common cold. There are over 100 antigenic types and cross-protection among them is limited, allowing repeated infections to occur.
- There are no specific antiviral agents against *Enterovirus* unlike some other viral agents causing human infection.

ESSAY

1. Describe the etiology, modes of transmission, pathogenesis and laboratory diagnosis of polio.

SHORT ANSWERS

1. Prophylaxis against polio
2. Pulse polio immunisation programme
3. Enteroviruses of public health importance and the diseases caused by them

SHORT NOTES

1. Oral polio vaccine and criteria for its attenuation
2. Inactivated polio vaccine
3. Coxsackie virus
4. Acute hemorrhagic viral conjunctivitis
5. Rhinoviruses
6. Types of polio virus and their epidemiology
7. Eradication of polio

54 Orthomyxoviruses

INTRODUCTION

The name Myxovirus was used originally for a group of enveloped RNA viruses characterised by their ability to adsorb onto mucoprotein receptors on erythrocytes, causing hemagglutination. The name referred to the affinity of the viruses to mucins (from *myxa*, meaning mucus). They are now classified into two separate families: Orthomyxoviridae, consisting of the influenza viruses, and Paramyxoviridae, consisting of the Newcastle disease virus, mumps virus, parainfluenzaviruses, measles and respiratory syncytial viruses. Table 54.1 lists the important differences between orthomyxovirus and paramyxovirus.

INFLUENZA

History

Influenza is an acute infectious disease of the respiratory tract which occurs in sporadic, epidemic and pandemic forms. The modern history of the disease may be considered to date from the pandemic of 1889–90, during which Pfeiffer isolated *Haemophilus influenzae* and claimed that it was the causative agent. The most severe pandemic occurred in 1918–19, when it was shown that Pfeiffer's bacillus was not the primary cause of the disease, though it might act as a secondary invader. The influenza virus was isolated in 1933 by Smith, Andrewes and Laidlaw—a milestone in the development of medical virology. They reproduced the disease in ferrets by intranasal inoculation with bacteria-free filtrates of nasopharyngeal secretions from patients. Burnet (1935) developed chick embryo techniques for the propagation of the virus.

A notable advance was the independent discovery by Hirst, and by McClelland and Hare (1941), that influenza viruses agglutinate fowl erythrocytes. The property of hemagglutination was found to be a common feature of many other viruses.

Influenza also occurs in animals and birds in nature. Indeed, the avian influenza virus was demonstrated as early as in 1901, but the association between the two remained unknown till 1955, when Schaefer demonstrated that the fowl plague virus was antigenically related to type A influenza virus. Shope (1931) isolated the swine influenza virus. Not only did the swine disease resemble human influenza clinically but there was also epidemiological association between the two. It was widely held that the virus spread to swine from humans at the time of the 1918 pandemic. Influenza viruses have also been isolated from horses, whales and seals.

Birds, particularly aquatic, appear to be the primary reservoir of influenza viruses and natural infection has been identified in several avian species. In birds it is usually an asymptomatic intestinal infection. The cloaca of healthy wild birds is the best source for isolation of avian influenza viruses. All isolates from non-human hosts belong to type A. Influenza virus types B and C appear to be exclusively human viruses and natural infection with them has not been identified in animals or birds. Ordinarily, non-human influenza viruses do not cause human infection. However, they play an important role in the emergence of pandemic influenza.

Table 54.1 *Distinguishing features of orthomyxovirus and paramyxovirus*

Property	Orthomyxovirus	Paramyxovirus
Size of virion	80–120 nm	100–300 nm
Shape	Spherical; filaments in fresh isolates	Pleomorphic
Genome	Segmented; eight pieces of RNA	Single linear molecule of RNA
Diameter of nucleocapsid	9 nm	18 nm
Site of synthesis of ribonucleoprotein	Nucleus	Cytoplasm
Genetic reassortment	Common	Absent
Dependent RNA synthesis	Required for multiplication	Not required
Effect of Actinomycin D	Inhibits multiplication	Does not inhibit
Antigenic stability	Variable	Stable
Hemolysin	Absent	Present

Clinical Case A 60-year-old woman from an old age home complained of headache, myalgia and pain in the eyes during winters. She had a history of chronic obstructive airway disease and had never been vaccinated for influenza. She also complained of severe pain in the throat and runny nose. After 3–4 days of these symptoms, she developed cough and fever of 39°C. Her fever and cough showed rapid progression and later she had dyspnea. The blood gas analysis was consistent with hypoxia and her chest x-ray showed bilateral signs diagnostic of adult respiratory distress symptoms. Her sputum and nasopharyngeal aspirate tested negative for bacterial cultures, and PCR was positive for influenza virus H1N1. She died despite supportive care and antiviral therapy with oseltamivir.

INFLUENZA VIRUS

Morphology

The influenza virus is typically spherical, with a diameter of 80–120 nm but pleomorphism is common. Filamentous forms, up to several micrometres in length and readily visible under the dark ground microscope, are frequent in freshly isolated strains. The virus core consists of ribonucleoprotein in helical symmetry. The negative sense single-stranded **RNA genome** is segmented and exists as eight pieces. Also present is a viral RNA-dependent RNA polymerase which is essential for transcription of the viral RNA in infected host cells.

The nucleocapsid is surrounded by an **envelope**, which has an inner membrane protein layer and an outer lipid layer. The membrane protein is also known as the matrix or 'M protein' composed of two components, M1 and M2. The protein part of the envelope is virus coded but the lipid layer is derived from the modified host cell membrane, during the process of replication by budding.

Projecting from the envelope are two types of spikes (**peplomers**): **hemagglutinin** spikes which are triangular in cross-section and the mushroom-shaped **neuraminidase** peplomers which are less numerous (Fig. 54.1).

Resistance

The virus is inactivated by heating at 50°C for 30 minutes. It remains viable at 0–4°C for about a week. It can be preserved for years at −70°C or by freeze drying. The virus survives slow drying and may remain viable on fomites such as blankets for about two weeks. Ether, formaldehyde, phenol, salts of heavy metals and many other chemical disinfectants destroy infectivity. Iodine is particularly effective.

Hemagglutinating, enzymic and complement-fixing activities of the virus are more stable than infectivity.

Antigen classification

The antigens of the influenza virus can be classified into two types:

Internal antigen:

- The internal antigen is the ribonucleoprotein and is hence called the **RNP antigen**. Because it is found

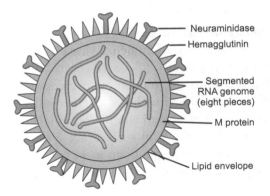

Fig. 54.1 Influenza virus

free in infected tissues and occurs in the supernatant when the virus-containing fluid is centrifuged, it was also called the 'soluble' (S) antigen. The RNP antigen can be demonstrated by complement fixation and immunoprecipitation tests. It is type specific and based on its nature, influenza viruses are classified into types A, B and C. The RNP antigens of types A, B and C are distinct but all strains of any one type possess the same antigen. The RNP antigen is stable and does not exhibit any significant antigenic variation. Anti-RNP antibody develops after infection but not following killed vaccines.

- **M protein antigen,** like the RNP antigen, is also type specific and distinct for A, B and C types of influenza viruses. The envelope lipid antigen is host specific and is determined by the species in which virus replication takes place.

Surface antigen: The term 'viral' or **V antigen** was formerly used to describe the surface antigen of the influenza virus. Antibodies to the V antigen were estimated by complement fixation. The V antigen is actually composed of at least two virus-coded proteins, hemagglutinin and neuraminidase. The two proteins have been isolated and purified.

- **Hemagglutinin** is a glycoprotein composed of two polypeptides, HA 1 and HA 2. It is responsible for hemagglutination and hemadsorption. It enables the virus to adsorb to mucoprotein receptors on red cells as well as on respiratory epithelial cells. Anti-hemagglutinin antibodies are produced following infection and immunisation. This antibody is protective by preventing adsorption of the virus to cells. Hemagglutinin is a strain-specific antigen and is capable of great variation. Fifteen distinct HA subtypes, H1–H15, have been identified in avian influenza viruses, but only four of them have been found in human isolates so far.

Hemagglutination: Hemagglutination is an important characteristic of influenza viruses. When mixed with a suspension of fowl erythrocytes, the virus is adsorbed onto the mucoprotein receptors on the cell surface. The virus links together adjacent cells producing hemagglutination. The hemagglutinin peplomers on the viral surface are responsible for this activity. Hemagglutination is followed after a time by detachment of the virus from the cell surface, reversing the hemagglutination. This process is known as **elution** and is caused by neuraminidase

(sialidase) present on the viral surface. The enzyme acts on the cell receptor, destroying it by splitting off N-acetylneuraminic acid from it.

Virus particles which have eluted from red cells are still capable of agglutinating fresh red cells, but red cells that have been acted on by the virus are not susceptible to agglutination by the same strain of the virus. Such red cells may, however, be agglutinated by other myxoviruses. The inability of these red cells to be re-agglutinated by the same virus is due to destruction of the specific cell receptors by initial treatment with the virus. Myxoviruses can be arranged in a series in which the treatment of red cells with any one virus removes the receptors for that virus and the preceding viruses but not for the viruses later in the series. This is called the 'receptor gradient'. For myxoviruses in general, the gradient is mumps, Newcastle disease virus and influenza, in that order.

Hemagglutination takes place within a wide temperature range (0–37°C). Influenza viruses vary in their ability to agglutinate red cells of different species. In general, types A and B agglutinate erythrocytes of fowls, humans, guinea pigs and other species. Influenza virus type C agglutinates the red cells of fowls only, at 4°C.

Hemagglutination provides a convenient method for the detection and titration of the influenza virus in egg and other culture fluids. The highest dilution of the virus suspension that produces agglutination of a fixed quantity of cells is known as its **hemagglutination (HA) titre**. Hemagglutinin is more resistant to physical and chemical agents than infectivity. Therefore, hemagglutination can be used for the titration of the inactivated influenza virus also, as, for example, in the standardisation of killed influenza virus vaccines.

- **Neuraminidase** is a glycoprotein enzyme which destroys cell receptors by hydrolytic cleavage. The anti-neuraminidase antibody is formed following infection and immunisation. It is not as effective in protection as the anti-hemagglutinin antibody. It does not prevent the adsorption of virus onto cells but can inhibit the release and spread of progeny virions and may thus contribute to limiting the infection. It is a strain-specific antigen and exhibits variation. Nine different subtypes have been identified (N1–N9).

Neuraminidase is an isoenzyme and different serotypes of influenza virus possess enzymes that vary in their characteristics such as antigenic structure, temperature optima and heat stability. Neuraminidases are also present in bacteria and in the cells of higher organisms. Culture filtrates of *V.cholerae* are rich in neuraminidase activity and red cells pretreated with them are resistant to hemagglutination by influenza viruses. The culture filtrate was therefore called the receptor destroying enzyme (RDE) of *V.cholerae*

Influenza virus classification

The classification of influenza viruses into the three serotypes A, B and C is based on the antigenic nature of the 'internal' or ribonucleoprotein (RNP) and the matrix (M) protein antigens. These antigens are not cross-reactive amongst the three types.

Influenza virus type A is further divided into subtypes based on the HA and NA glycoprotiens. Till now 15 HA subtypes (H1–H15) and 9 NA subtypes (N1–N9) are known, of which human isolates belong to H1–H3, H5 and N1, N2 subtypes.

Nomenclature systems

The standard nomenclature systems include the following information: serotype, host of origin (except for human isolates), geographic origin, strain number and year of isolation, followed by HA and NA subtypes in parenthesis. For a human isolate, it is as follows: A/ Hong Kong/01/68 (H3N2) and for other host origin: A/swine/Iowa/15/30(H1N1) (Table 54.2).

Antigenic variation

A unique feature of the influenza virus is its ability to undergo antigenic variation. This is of great importance in the epidemiology of the disease. Antigenic variability is highest in influenza virus type A and less in type B, while it has not been demonstrated in type C.

The internal RNP antigen and M protein antigen are stable but both surface antigens undergo independent antigenic variations, which may be of two types:

- **Antigenic drift** the gradual sequential change in antigenic structure occurring regularly at frequent intervals is known as **antigenic drift**. Here, the new antigens, though different from the previous antigens, are still related to them, so they react with antisera to the predecessor virus strains to varying degrees. Antigenic drift is due to mutation and selection, the process being influenced by the presence of antibodies to the predecessor strains in the host population. Antigenic drift accounts for the periodic epidemics of influenza.

- **Antigenic shift**, on the other hand, is an abrupt, drastic, discontinuous variation in the antigenic structure, resulting in a novel virus strain unrelated antigenically to predecessor strains. Such changes may involve hemagglutinin, neuraminidase or both. Antibodies to predecessor viruses do not neutralise the new variants and can, therefore, spread widely in the population causing major epidemics or pandemics. The changes involved in antigenic shift are too extensive to be accounted for by mutation.

Host range

The human influenza virus can cause experimental infection in a number of animal species. In most, the infection is asymptomatic, though virus shedding occurs from the respiratory tract for a few days. Intranasal inoculation in ferrets produces an acute respiratory disease. This was the manner in which the influenza virus was first isolated. Strains vary considerably in virulence to ferrets, some producing severe febrile disease and others only asymptomatic infection. The virus can be 'adapted' by serial intranasal passage in mice to produce fatal pulmonary infection. Neurotropic mutants have been isolated which regularly produce fatal encephalitis after intracerebral inoculation in mice.

The virus grows well in the amniotic cavity of chick embryos. After a few egg passages, the virus grows well in the allantoic cavity also, except for the type C virus which does not generally grow in the allantoic

Table 54.2 *Classification and nomenclature of influenza virus A subtypes*

Old designation	Current classification	1971 classification	Reference strains
A swine ⎫		HSWN1	A/Swine/Wisconsin/15/30
AO ⎬	H1N1	HON1	A/PR/8/34
A1 ⎭		H1N1	A/FM/1/4
A2	H2N2	H2N2	A/Singapore/1/57
A2 (Hong Kong)	H3N2	H3N2	A/Hong Kong/1/68

cavity. The influenza virus does not damage chick embryos, which may hatch out normally. Virus growth is detected by the appearance of hemagglutinin in the allantoic and amniotic fluids.

The virus grows in primary monkey kidney cell cultures, as well as in some continuous cell lines. Cytopathic effects are not prominent and virus growth is detected by hemadsorption or demonstration of hemagglutinin in the culture fluid.

When passaged serially in eggs, using as inocula undiluted infected allantoic fluid, the progeny virus will show high hemagglutinin titres, but low infectivity. This has been called the **Von Magnus phenomenon** and is due to the formation of incomplete virus particles lacking nucleic acid.

Pathogenicity

The route of entry is the respiratory tract. In experimental infection in volunteers, very small doses (approximately three viable particles) can initiate infection when given as aerosols. Larger doses are required when infection is by intranasal instillation. The viral neuraminidase facilitates infection by reducing the viscosity of the mucus film lining the respiratory tract and exposing the cell surface receptors for virus adsorption. The ciliated cells of the respiratory tract are the main sites of viral infection. These cells are damaged and shed, laying bare the basal cells in the trachea and bronchi. This renders the respiratory tract highly vulnerable to bacterial invasion. Viral pneumonia, seen only in the more severe cases, is associated with hyperemia and thickening of the alveolar walls, interstitial infiltration with leucocytes, capillary thrombosis and leucocytic exudation. In some cases, a hyaline membrane is formed, occupying the alveolar ducts and alveoli. In the late stages, there is infiltration with macrophages which engulf and remove desquamated alveolar cells.

The disease is ordinarily confined to the respiratory tract. Very rarely was the virus isolated from the spleen, liver, kidneys and other organs during the 1957 pandemic.

Clinical features

The incubation period is 1–3 days. The disease varies in severity from a mild coryza to fulminating and rapidly fatal pneumonia. Most infections are subclinical.

In the typical clinical disease, onset is abrupt, with fever, headache and generalised myalgia. Respiratory symptoms are prominent and severe prostration is com-

mon. Abdominal pain and vomiting may occur, especially in type B infection in children, which may even present as an acute abdominal emergency. The uncomplicated disease resolves within about seven days.

The most important complication is pneumonia, which is mainly due to bacterial superinfection or, rarely, caused by the virus itself (*Case*). Cardiac complications, such as congestive failure or myocarditis and neurological involvement, such as encephalitis, may occur rarely.

Influenza, particularly infection with type B, has been associated with Reye syndrome. It especially affects young children and is characterised by acute degenerative changes in the brain, liver and kidneys. Type B infections may sometimes cause gastrointestinal symptoms (gastric flu).

Laboratory diagnosis

1. **Demonstration of the virus antigen:** Rapid diagnosis of influenza may be made by demonstration of the virus antigen on the surface of the nasopharyngeal cells by immunofluorescence.

2. **Isolation of the virus:** Virus isolation is obtained readily during the first two or three days of the illness but less often in the later stages. Throat garglings are collected using broth saline or other suitable buffered salt solution. If the specimen is not processed immediately, it should be stored at 4°C, or if the delay is long, at −70°C. The specimen should be treated with antibiotics to destroy bacteria. Isolation may be made in eggs or in monkey kidney cell culture.

Procedure: The material is inoculated into the amniotic cavity of 11–13-day-old eggs, using at least six eggs per specimen. After incubation at 35°C for three days, the eggs are chilled and the amniotic and allantoic fluids harvested separately. The fluids are tested for hemagglutination using guinea pig and fowl cells in parallel, at room temperature and at 4°C. Some strains of the influenza virus type A agglutinate only guinea pig cells on initial isolation. The type B virus agglutinates both cells, while type C strains agglutinate only fowl cells with antisera to types A, B and C.

Subtype identification is made by hemagglutination inhibition test. Some of the recent type A strains can be isolated by direct allantoic inoculation of the clinical specimen into 9–11-day-old eggs. However, type B and C viruses will be missed if only allantoic inoculation is used.

Inoculation into monkey kidney or other suitable continuous cell cultures, such as baboon kidney, is the preferred method where the facility is available. Inoculated cell cultures are incubated without serum, and in the presence of trypsin, which increases sensitivity of isolation. Incubation at 33°C in roller drums is recommended.

Rapid results can be obtained by demonstrating virus antigen in infected cell cultures by **immunofluorescence**.

Hemagglutination and elution can be used for purifying and concentrating influenza viruses along with subtype identification.

Virus growth can be identified by hemadsorption with human O group, fowl or guinea pig erythrocytes. The plasma membranes of tissue culture cells in which the virus is multiplying contain the hemagglutinin. Therefore, red cells are adsorbed onto the surface of such cells and is the basis of **hemadsorption**.

3. Serology: Complement fixation and hemagglutination inhibition tests are used for the serological diagnosis of influenza. It is essential to examine paired sera in parallel, to demonstrate rise in titre of antibodies.

- **Hemagglutination inhibition** (HI) offers a convenient method for the detection and quantitation of the antibody to the virus. A disadvantage of this technique is the frequent presence in sera of certain substances that cause non-specific inhibition of hemagglutination. Different kinds of non-specific inhibitors have been identified in sera and have been given names such as **alpha** (Francis), **beta** (Chu) and **gamma** (Shimojo) inhibitors. They are mostly glycoproteins. A variety of techniques has been introduced for inactivating them without affecting the antibody content of sera. These include treatment with RDE, trypsin, potassium periodate, kaolin and CO_2. No single method has been found effective in completely destroying inhibitors to all types of viruses from all kinds of sera. Virus strains vary in their susceptibility to non-specific inhibitors. When available, the use of a strain insusceptible to such inhibitors would enhance the value of hemagglutination inhibition tests.

  Hemagglutination inhibition is a convenient and sensitive test for the serological diagnosis of influenza. However, it has some disadvantages. As the anti-hemagglutinin antibodies are subtype specific, it is necessary to use as antigen the strain currently causing infection. The sera, suitably treated for the removal of non-specific inhibitors, are diluted serially in hemagglutination plates and the influenza virus suspension containing 4 HA units added to each cup. Fowl red cells are then added. The highest dilution of serum that inhibits hemagglutination is its HI titre.

- **Complement fixation tests** with the RNP antigen of influenza virus types A, B and C are very useful as the antibodies are formed during infection only, and not following immunisation with inactivated vaccines. Complement fixation can also be done using V antigens for the demonstration of strain-specific antibodies. Because of its complexity, CF tests are now used only rarely.

- **Radial immunodiffusion** tests in agarose gel have been described for the identification of antibodies to the RNP antigen, hemagglutinin and neuraminidase. However, these are more useful as screening tests than for routine diagnosis.

4. PCR-based diagnosis: With specific primers to the subtypes, this can be used in a multiplex PCR assay to identify the virus in a clinical specimen.

Immunity

An attack of influenza confers effective protection for one or two years. The apparent short duration of immunity is due to the antigenic variation that the virus undergoes frequently. Following infection and immunisation, circulating antibodies are formed against the various antigens of the virus. However, it is the local concentration of anti-hemagglutinin and, to a smaller extent, of anti-neuraminidase antibodies (mainly IgA) in the respiratory tract that is more relevant in protection.

When an individual experiences repeated infections with different antigenic variants of influenza virus type A, he responds by forming antibodies not only against each infecting strain but also against the strain that he first came into contact with. The dominant antibody response will be against the strain that caused the earliest infection. This phenomenon has been called the doctrine of 'original antigenic sin'.

Influenza virus infection induces cell-mediated immunity also but its role in protection has not been clarified.

Epidemiology

Influenza occurs sporadically as epidemics or in pandemic form. The source of infection is an infected individual. The virus is shed in respiratory secretions shortly before the onset of illness and for 3–4 days thereafter. Subclinical infections are common. Influenza virus type C is **endemic** throughout the world and causes very mild or unapparent infections. Type B strains cause sporadic as well as epidemic influenza, while type A strains can cause pandemics as well (Table 54.2). **Sporadic** influenza is of little public health importance as it is a mild self-limiting condition. **Epidemic influenza** is important in temperate regions where it strikes during the winter months, causing considerable mortality in the aged and in those with cardiopulmonary diseases. In the tropics, epidemic influenza does not exhibit winter prevalence, though it tends to occur frequently in the monsoon season.

What makes influenza an important and challenging disease is its propensity for causing **pandemics**. It is for this reason that worldwide surveillance is maintained on influenza, under the auspices of the WHO. Influenza pandemics have been recorded at irregular intervals from 1173. Pandemics of modern times date from 1889. The most severe pandemic in recorded history occurred in 1918–19 ('**Spanish flu**'), during which over 200 million people were affected and more than 20 million perished. India suffered the most, with some 10 million deaths. An unusual feature of this pandemic was the very high rate of mortality among young adults. The next pandemic occurred in 1957 when the '**Asian strain**' H2N2 originated in China and spread throughout the world within a short period. However, the mortality rate was low though it caused widespread morbidity. The Hong Kong H3N2 strain appearing in 1968 also caused a pandemic but it was much less severe.

In 1977, epidemic influenza appeared in China and then in Russia (hence called the 'red flu' facetiously). The disease was mainly confined to the under-20 age group. The isolate was identified as the H1N1 virus, antigenically very close to the strains prevalent from 1946 to 1957. This H1N1 virus has spread through most of the world, and with the H3N2 virus, currently causes human influenza.

Ability to cause epidemics and pandemics: The reason the virus is able to cause epidemics and pandemics lies in its ability to undergo antigenic variation. Antigenic drift, resulting from mutation and selection, is responsible for the epidemics. It has been shown experimentally that passaging the virus in the presence of antiserum leads to the appearance of such mutants. Pandemics are caused by a virus strain that has under-

gone antigenic shift. The variation in such instances is so marked and involves different polypeptides simultaneously that mutation cannot explain it. It is now held that pandemic strains originate from some animal or avian reservoir, either spreading to humans directly by host range mutation, or as a result of recombination between human and non-human strains. Hybrids can be produced by growing human and non-human strains together in eggs. Recombinants can also be obtained from experimental animals exposed to mixed infection. It has been shown by genetic studies that both the 1957 Asian virus and the 1968 Hong Kong virus were such recombinant hybrids.

Avian influenza: The mere appearance of a new or hybrid strain may not lead to a pandemic. For this, the new strain should be capable of spreading rapidly among people. In fact there have been several instances when new hybrids have been detected, which failed to spread. The swine flu virus H1N1 caused a localised outbreak in a military camp in New Jersey, USA in 1976, leading to much anxiety and panic vaccination, but it did not spread. Though a few similar incidents have occurred since then, what raised a real threat of a new pandemic was the outbreak in Hong Kong of chicken flu in 1997 with a new strain of the H5N1 influenza virus, which caused 18 confirmed human cases with six deaths. However, all human cases were shown to have spread directly from chickens, without any transmission from person to person. Immediate containment measures and the slaughter of all (over 1.6 million) chickens in Hong Kong stopped the danger before the strain developed person-to-person transmissibility, which could have initiated a pandemic. This incident indicated the value of influenza surveillance and the potential danger from avian strains.

It is now known that wild aquatic birds carry the full repertoire of genes of all influenza strains, including old human pandemic strains, and that the viruses do not cause any disease in them or undergo any mutational changes. Birds shed the viruses abundantly in feces, which contaminate lakes and ponds. In cold climates as in Canada, the viruses persist in such waters for long periods and can readily be isolated from them. Domestic birds like ducks can get infected from wild birds and carry the infection to pigs, which may be an important link in the chain, as they are susceptible to infection by both human and avian influenza strains. Recombination may take place in pigs and such hybrid strains may lead to human infection with potential pandemic spread. The postulated role of ducks and pigs in the development of new hybrids explains why pandemic strains tend to originate in China where millions of birds, pigs and people live closely together. The reappearance of old strains, like the H1N1 in 1977 may have been from an avian reservoir of strains. Similarly, it is possible that an old pandemic strain present in wild birds may suddenly reappear. If this hypothesis is true, it would be prudent to keep wild and domestic birds separate, and also to keep pigs away from them. The practice of keeping several species of birds along with chickens in live bird markets is potentially dangerous.

A unique feature of influenza epidemiology was that once an antigenic variant emerged, it completely displaced the pre-existing strain. Thus when A1 (H1N1) strains arose in 1946–47, they became the only viruses causing human disease, and the previous A0 (H0N1) strains disappeared completely. The A1 strains were displaced by Asian (H2N2) strains in 1957 and they, in turn, by the A2 Hong Kong (H3N2) strains in 1968. However, this rule has not been observed in recent years. Even after the re-emergence and wide dissemination of the H1N1 strain in 1977, the A2 Hong Kong H3N2 strains continue to be prevalent. The reason for this co-existence is not known.

There is considerable evidence to suggest that there occurs an orderly recycling of the virus subtypes at least with regard to their hemagglutinin (H) antigen. Seroepidemiological (seroarcheological) studies indicate that the severe pandemic of 1889 was caused by a virus with the antigenic structure H2N8 and that this was followed in 1900 by the subtype H3N8 which led to a moderate pandemic. In 1918 came the most severe of all pandemics, caused by the 'Swine type' H1N1

(formerly HSW NI) virus. Mild epidemics occurred around 1933 and 1946 associated with minor variations in the H antigen (from HSW to HO in 1933, HO to H1 in 1946). The next severe pandemic came in 1957 with the H2N2 (Asian) subtype. This was followed in 1968 by the H3N2 (Hong Kong) virus leading to a moderate pandemic. The year 1977 saw the reappearance of the H1N1 virus. Thus the sequence of variation in the H antigen has been H2 → H3 → H1 → H2 → H3 → H1 from 1889 to the present time. From 1977, both H3N2 and H1N1 viruses have been circulating together. Table 54.3 lists the sequence of appearance of these various subtypes.

Swine influenza: In March 2009 a new H1N1 virus was detected which was a reassortant between previously circulating swine virus and a Eurasian swine virus and was also called swine origin influenza (S-OIV). It spread from person to person and caused a pandemic.

Immunoprophylaxis

Influenza vaccines have been in use for many decades and are the mainstay in the prevention of influenza.

The main difficulty in the immunoprophylaxis of influenza is the frequent change in the antigenic make up of the virus. Vaccines cannot be made in bulk and stockpiled, as the appearance of a new variant will make the old vaccine obsolete. In cold countries, where it is necessary to protect old persons and other high-risk individuals, the practice is to immunise them with a vaccine containing the latest strains of type A and B viruses.

The most important indication for immunoprophylaxis is when a pandemic is threatened by a new virus.

Table 54.3 *Calendar of appearance of influenza A virus subtypes (from 1889) (Data before 1933 based on 'Seroarcheology')*

Date	Antigenic subtype	Remarks
1889–1900	H2N8?	Pandemic and epidemics
1900–1910	H3N8	Extensive epidemics
1918–1933	H1N1 (former Hsw N1)	'Spanish flu'. The most severe pandemic recorded; heavy mortality
1933–1946	H1N1 (former HON1)	Discovery of influenza virus (WS strain–1933); epidemics of 'AO' strains
1946–1957	H1N1	Epidemics of ' A1' strains
1957–1968	H2N2	Extensive pandemics of 'Asian flu' formerly clled A2 (Asian) strain, low mortality
1968 to the present	H3N2	Moderate pandemic of 'Hong Kong flu' formerly called A2 time (Hong Kong) strains, very low mortality
1977 to the present	H1N1	Re-emergence of former A1 strains. First appeared in Russia and China ('Red flu'); Mild pandemic, very low mortality

Here, the time taken for the manufacture of the vaccine with the new variant is crucial, as the virus is likely to spread fast and infect whole populations before the vaccine becomes available.

The vaccines are of **two types:**

Inactivated vaccines: The original vaccines consisted of the virus grown in the allantoic cavity of eggs, partially purified, and inactivated with formalin. Due to the presence of egg protein in it, this vaccine may cause reactions in allergic individuals. The whole virus vaccine induces fever and local pain. **'Subunit' vaccines** have been introduced to minimise toxic reactions. The purified virus is disrupted by treatment with detergents so that the vaccine contains the immunogenic hemagglutinin and neuraminidase subunits. The **recombinant vaccine** has been introduced to manufacture a vaccine with antigens from a new variant. A recombinant possesses the growth characters of old established strains and carries the surface antigens of the new variant. Moreover, most fresh isolates do not grow well in eggs till they are passaged serially. The recombinant will grow well in eggs, facilitating vaccine manufacture.

While killed vaccines induce the formation of circulating antibodies, they do not lead to any local protection in the respiratory tract. The level of antibodies on the respiratory mucosa is only a fraction of the serum level.

- **Live attenuated (cold adapted) vaccine:** To enable specific local immunisation, live vaccines have been used. The earliest live vaccine was the virus attenuated by repeated egg passage. It was administered by intranasal instillation. However, it sometimes gave rise to clinical disease, especially in children.

Another approach to live vaccines is the use of temperature sensitive mutants. Mutants can be readily isolated which are able to grow at the lower temperature of the nasopharyngeal mucosa (32–34°C) but not in the lungs at 37°C. Such ts mutants are avirulent. Recombinant live vaccines may be obtained by hybridisation between the ts mutants of established strains and a new antigenic variant.

Chemoprophylaxis has been reported to be successful with the antiviral drugs amantadine and rimantadine which block the viral M2 protein which functions as an ion channel. These act only with the type A virus and not with the type B, which lacks the M2 components.

Treatment

Amantadine and rimantadine are useful in the treatment of influenza. They reduce the average duration of the disease and cause symptomatic improvement, though virus shedding and antibody response are not affected. Resistance to these drugs develops rapidly.

Zanamivir and oseltamivir, new drugs designed to block viral neuraminidase, have been found effective in the treatment and prevention of influenza, when administered as a nasal spray.

RECAP

- The Orthomyxoviridae family comprises enveloped, helical, RNA viruses, 80–120 nm in diameter.
- The single-stranded RNA genome is segmented into eight pieces, each piece representing a gene. Genetic reassortment of the various genes of influenza A is a common natural event.
- The virus envelope consists hemagglutinins and neuraminidase, HA and NA
- The influenza A virus is the major cause of epidemic and pandemic forms of influenza.
- Major antigenic changes (antigenic shift) and continuous minor variations (antigenic drift) are features of this virus. Genes for 15 hemagglutinins and 9 neuraminidases are known. The virus may be isolated in fertile hens' eggs and in monkey kidney primary cells.
- The influenza B and C types do not have subtypes.
- Influenza is an acute upper respiratory disease characterised by fever, headache, chills, malaise, myalgia, anorexia, sore throat, respiratory symptoms of non-productive cough, rhinorrhea, sneezing and nasal obstruction. Droplets containing the virus are transmitted by aerosol from person to person.

- Antibody is protective when directed to the hemagglutinin (the adhesin of influenza viruses) by neutralising virus binding to host cells.
- For diagnosis the virus can be grown in tissue culture cells or chick embryos; fluorescent antibody can be used to detect viral antigens in nasopharyngeal cells; serology by HAI or CFT can be used if done in a paired serum sample.
- Inactivated vaccines are developed every year in developed countries to keep pace with the yearly strains of influenza viruses A and B. Rimantadine or amantadine can be given to treat or prevent type A infection only. Neuraminidase inhibitors are new agents effective against both influenza A and B.

ESSAY

1. Describe the classification and nomenclature system of the influenza virus.

SHORT ANSWERS

1. Antigenic shift
2. Influenza pandemics
3. Antiviral agents for influenza
4. Four differences between the influenza and parainfluenza viruses

SHORT NOTES

1. Swine influenza
2. Avian influenza
3. Hemagglutinin of influenza virus
4. Neuraminidase of influenza virus
5. Culture of influenza virus
6. Influenza vaccines
7. HAI test for influenza diagnosis
8. Structure of influenza virus
9. Recombinant influenza vaccine

55 Paramyxoviruses

INTRODUCTION

The family Paramyxoviridae contains important pathogens of infants and children, responsible for a major part of acute respiratory infections (respiratory syncytial virus and parainfluenza viruses) and also for two of the most contagious diseases of childhood (measles and mumps). Though much less common, infections may also occur in adults.

Paramyxoviruses resemble orthomyxoviruses in morphology but are larger and more pleomorphic (Table 54.1). They are roughly spherical in shape and range in size from 100 nm to 300 nm, sometimes with long filaments and giant forms of up to 800 nm. The helical nucleocapsid is much wider than in orthomyxoviruses, with a diameter of 18 nm (except in the pneumovirus, where it is 13 nm). The genome is a molecule of linear single-stranded RNA.

Unlike orthomyxoviruses, in which the segmented nature of the genome facilitates genomic reassortment and antigenic variation so typical of influenza viruses, the paramyxoviruses with their unsegmented genome do not undergo genetic recombination or antigenic variation. Hence all paramyxoviruses are antigenically stable.

Antigenic structure

- The **nucleocapsid** (Fig. 55.1) is surrounded by a **lipid envelope** which has the **matrix (M)** protein

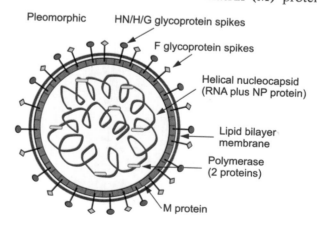

Fig. 55.1 Mumps virus

Table 55.1   *Properties of genera in the family Paramyxoviridae*

Property	Genus			
	Parainfluenzavirus	*Mumps*	*Morbillivirus*	*Pneumovirus*
Human viruses	*Parainfluenza 1–4*	*Mumps*	*Measles*	*Respiratory syncytial virus*
Diameter of nucleocapsid (nm)	18	18	18	13
Fusion (F) protein	+	+	+	+
Hemolysin	+	+	+	–
Hemagglutinin/Hemadsorption	+	+	+	–
Neuraminidase	+	+	–	–
Intracellular inclusions in cytoplasm (C)/nucleus (N)	C	C	N, C	C

at its base and two types of transmembrane glycoprotein spikes at the surface. The longer spike is **hemagglutinin (H)**, which may also possess neuraminidase (N) activity and is hence known as the H or **HN protein.** It is responsible for adsorption of the virus to the host cell surface.

- The second spike is the **F (fusion) protein**, responsible for fusion of the viral envelope with the plasma membrane of the host cell, which is the essential early step for infection. It also brings about cell-to-cell fusion, causing large giant cells or syncytia, which are characteristic of paramyxovirus infections. The F protein also mediates the hemolytic activity of paramyxoviruses.

Classification

The family Paramyxoviridae is divided into four genera (Table 55.1):

- Rubulavirus – mumps virus
- Parainfluenzavirus – parainfluenza types 1–4
- Pneumovirus – respiratory syncytial virus
- Morbillivirus – measles virus

RUBULAVIRUS

MUMPS VIRUS

The mumps virus causes mumps, an acute infectious disease commonly affecting children and characterised by non-suppurative enlargement of the parotid glands. As epidemic parotitis, it had been described by Hippocrates in the fifth century BC. The viral origin of mumps was demonstrated by Johnson and Goodpasture (1934) by its experimental transmission to monkeys. Habel in 1945 cultivated the virus

in embryonated eggs. In 1955, Henle and Deinhardt grew it in tissue culture.

Properties

The mumps virus is a typical paramyxovirus possessing both HN and F proteins. It agglutinates the erythrocytes of fowls, guinea pigs, humans and many other species. Hemagglutination is followed by hemolysis and elution at 37°C. The virus can be grown in chick embryos—in the amniotic cavity for primary isolation and the allantoic cavity after adaptation. Eggs are inoculated at 6–8 days and incubated at 35°C for five days before harvesting.

Cell cultures are better suited for isolation—primary monkey kidney being the preferred cell. The cytopathic effect is slow and consists of syncytium formation and the presence of acidophilic cytoplasmic inclusions. Growth is best identified by hemadsorption.

The mumps virus is labile, being rapidly inactivated at room temperature or by exposure to formaldehyde, ether or ultraviolet light. It can be preserved at −70°C or by lyophilisation. The mumps virus is antigenically stable and only one serotype exists. Two complement fixing antigens can be recognised, as in influenza viruses—the soluble (S) antigen and the 'viral' (V) antigen.

Clinical features

Infection is acquired by inhalation, and probably also through the conjunctiva. The virus replicates in the upper respiratory tract and cervical lymph nodes and is disseminated through the bloodstream to various organs. The incubation period is about 12–25 days.

Parotid swelling is usually the first sign of illness, though it may sometimes be preceded by prodromal malaise. Parotid swelling is unilateral to start with but may become bilateral. It is accompanied by fever, local pain and tenderness but the skin over the gland is not warm or erythematous. Parotitis is non-suppurative and usually resolves within a week. However, involvement of extraparotid sites may be more serious and may sometimes occur even in the absence of parotitis.

Complications

Epididymo-orchitis is a complication seen in about a third of postpubertal male patients. The testis becomes swollen and acutely painful, with accompanying fever and chills. **Orchitis** is usually unilateral but when it is bilateral and followed by testicular atrophy, sterility or low sperm counts may result.

The central nervous system is involved in about 60 per cent of cases, as indicated by pleocytosis in the CSF, but only about 10 per cent show symptoms of **meningitis.** Mumps has been reported to cause about 10–15 per cent of cases of 'aseptic meningitis'. Mumps meningitis and **meningoencephalitis** usually resolve without sequelae but deafness may sometimes result. Mumps meningitis may occasionally occur in the absence of parotitis, when diagnosis rests solely on laboratory evidence. The virus can be grown readily from the CSF in the early phase of meningitis.

Other less common complications are arthritis, oophoritis, nephritis, pancreatitis, thyroiditis and myocarditis.

Epidemiology

Mumps is endemic worldwide but has become less common in the developed nations due to immunisation. It often occurs as epidemics in children 5–15 years of age, and also in young people living in groups such as in army camps. Household spread is common. Humans are the only natural hosts. The source of infection is a patient in the late incubation or early clinical stage of the illness. No human carriers or animal reservoirs exist.

Infection is transmitted by direct contact, airborne droplets or fomites contaminated with saliva, and also possibly urine. The virus is detectable in saliva for about a week before and a week or two after onset of parotitis. However, peak infectivity is about a day or two before parotitis becomes evident, and subsides rapidly thereafter. The virus is also shed in urine for up to two weeks after the clinical symptoms begin, though its role in the transmission of infection is not clear.

One attack of mumps confers lasting immunity so that second attacks do not occur.

Immunity

Infection leads to antibody response against both the internal (S) and surface (V) antigens. Antibodies to the S antigen appear early, within 3–7 days of the onset of symptoms, but disappear after about six months. Demonstration of the antibody to the S antigen indicates current or recent infection. Antibodies to the V antigen take about a month to appear but persist for years. The anti-hemagglutinin antibody correlates well with immunity to infection. Even subclinical infections lead to HI antibody and resistance to infection. As antibodies are widespread in the population, passive immunity protects newborns. Mumps is therefore very rare before six months of age.

Cell-mediated immunity develops following infection, but its significance is not known. Interferon also appears early in mumps infection.

Laboratory diagnosis

A typical case of mumps needs no laboratory confirmation but it may be essential in atypical infection and where meningitis or other systemic involvement is the sole manifestation. Diagnosis may be established by virus isolation and serological tests.

1. Specimen: The virus may be isolated from saliva (within 4–5 days), urine (up to two weeks) or CSF (8–9 days after onset of illness).

2. Virus isolation: The specimens must be inoculated soon after collection as the virus is labile. The prepared specimen is inoculated into monkey kidney cell cultures. Human amnion or HeLa cells are also suitable. Virus growth can be detected by hemadsorption and identified by hemadsorption inhibition using specific antiserum. Cytopathic changes are not reliable. Isolation may take 1–2 weeks. More rapid results can be obtained by immunofluorescence testing of infected cell cultures. This may become positive as early as 2–3 days after inoculation.

Isolation can also be made by inoculation into six-to-eight-day-old chick embryos by the amniotic route and testing the amniotic fluid after 5–6 days for hemagglutinins. The virus can be identified by hemagglutination inhibition using specific antisera. Egg inoculation is less sensitive than cell cultures for isolation.

Direct antigen detection by IFA is helpful in early diagnosis

3. Serology: Serological diagnosis depends on demonstration of a rise in the titre of antibodies in paired serum samples. The CF and HI tests are commonly used but cross-reactions with parainfluenza viruses cause problems. IgM-ELISA is useful in this respect because cross-reacting antibodies are IgG and do not interfere with IgM-ELISA.

A positive CF test for antibody to the S antigen in the acute phase serum is presumptive evidence of current infection.

4. PCR: Molecular diagnosis using **reverse transcriptase PCR** is more rapid and sensitive.

Prophylaxis

Vaccination: An effective live virus vaccine is available against mumps. The **Jeryl–Lynn strain** of the mumps virus, attenuated by passage in eggs and grown in chick embryo fibroblast culture, is used as the vaccine. It is recommended for use only after one year of age as maternal antibodies may interfere with the multiplication of the vaccine virus if given earlier. Contraindications are pregnancy, immunodeficiency and hypersensitivity to neomycin or egg protein. The vaccine is given as a single subcutaneous injection, alone or in combination with the measles and rubella vaccines (**MMR vaccine**). It provides effective protection for at least ten years. The vaccine may not prevent the disease if given after exposure to the infection but there are no contraindications for its use in this situation.

PARAINFLUENZA VIRUSES

Four types of parainfluenza viruses (1–4) have been identified (Table 55.2):

- The first to be discovered was the **Sendai virus** in Japan in 1952. This has since been identified as a widespread natural parasite of mice, causing inapparent infections. Sendai virus antibodies were prevalent in human sera throughout the world. This observation was explained when an antigenically identical virus was isolated in 1958 from children with acute respiratory infections, by the technique of hemadsorption in cell cultures. As a similar hemadsorption virus named HA-1 had been discovered earlier, this was designated HA-2. The Sendai and HA-2 viruses are now classified as **parainfluenza virus type 1**—the Sendai virus representing the murine and HA-2 the human variety.

    The Sendai virus is different from other parainfluenza viruses in growing readily in eggs, with the infected allantoic fluid showing high titres of hemagglutinin, resembling the influenza virus. So, for a time, it was called the 'hemagglutinating virus of Japan' (HVJ) and 'influenza virus type D'.

- **Parainfluenza virus type 2** was originally isolated in 1955 from children with acute laryngotracheobronchitis or **croup**. It was therefore known as the 'croup associated' or **CA virus**. It grows in monkey kidney cell cultures, producing a syncytial cytopathic effect. Antigenically similar viruses (simian viruses 5 and 41) cause natural infection in monkeys.

- **Parainfluenza virus type 3** was first detected in 1958 from children with respiratory infection, by hemadsorption in cell cultures and was named hemadsorption virus type 1 (HA-1). A related virus (SF-4) causes a respiratory illness in cattle known as '**shipping fever**'.

- **Parainfluenza virus type 4** was isolated in 1960 from children with mild respiratory infection. Two antigenic subtypes, A and B, have been recognised.

Clinical features

Parainfluenza viruses are responsible for about 10 per cent of respiratory infections in children needing hospitalisation. The most serious clinical disease caused is croup, which is most frequently due to types 1 and 2. Type 3 causes lower respiratory disease, including

Table 55.2 *Parainfluenza virus types*

Nomenclature of human types		Related animal viruses
Current	**Former**	
Parainfluenza type 1	Hemadsorption type 2(HA-2)	Sendai (mouse)
Parainfluenza type 2	Croup associated (CA)	Simian viruses 5, 41 (monkey)
Parainfluenza type 3	Hemadsorption type 1 (HA-1)	Shipping fever (cattle)
Parainfluenza type 4 (4A 4B)		

bronchitis, bronchiolitis and pneumonia. Type 4 causes minor respiratory illnesses. In adults, parainfluenza viruses cause milder respiratory infection in which sore throat and hoarseness of the voice are common. Rarely, they cause parotitis.

Parainfluenza viral infection is confined to the respiratory tract, unlike mumps which is a systemic disease, with the virus disseminating through blood and multiplying in various organs and tissues.

Epidemiology

These are ubiquitous viruses. Parainfluenza virus type 3 infection is often experienced in the first year of life with about 50 per cent of infants being seropositive by 12 months of age. Types 1 and 2 cause disease mainly in preschool children. Type 3 infection is more endemic than types 1 and 2 which tend to occur as epidemics.

First infections are more serious than re-infections, which are not infrequent. With the type 4 virus, even first infections are very mild. Infected children shed the virus in respiratory secretions for about a week. Spread is by air or through fingers. Nosocomial spread is not uncommon. No vaccine is available.

Laboratory diagnosis

1. Specimen: Throat and nasal swabs

2. Virus isolation: Throat and nasal swabs are inoculated in primary monkey kidney cell cultures, or continuous monkey kidney cell lines (LLC–MK2) with trypsin. Cytopathic changes are not readily apparent, except with the type 2 virus. Isolation may take ten days or more. Virus growth is detected by hemadsorption. Typing is by immunofluorescence, hemadsorption inhibition or hemagglutination inhibition.

3. Serology: Serological diagnosis is hampered by wide antigenic cross-reactions. Paired sera can be tested by neutralisation, ELISA, HI or CF for rise in the titre of antibodies.

4. PCR: Molecular diagnosis using reverse transcriptase PCR is gaining more acceptance.

NEWCASTLE DISEASE VIRUS (NDV)

The Newcastle disease virus (avian paramyxovirus type 1) is a natural pathogen of poultry in which it causes explosive outbreaks of pneumoencephalitis or 'influenza' with high mortality. In India it is known as the Ranikhet virus. Control measures consist of vaccination, and slaughter of infected birds.

Human infection with NDV is confined to self-limited conjunctivitis in poultry workers and others in contact with infected birds.

Other types of avian paramyxoviruses cause inapparent infection in many species of birds.

PNEUMOVIRUS

RESPIRATORY SYNCYTIAL VIRUS (RSV)

RSV was first isolated in 1956 from chimpanzees with coryza and was called the 'chimpanzee coryza agent' (CCA). A year later, the virus was obtained from children with lower respiratory tract infection. Because it caused cell fusion and the formation of multinucleated syncytia in cell cultures, it was named respiratory syncytial virus (RSV). It is now recognised as the most important cause of lower respiratory tract infection in infants, particularly in the first few months of life.

RSV is pleomorphic and has a size range of 150–300 nm. The viral envelope has two glycoproteins—the G protein by which the virus attaches to cell surfaces, and the fusion (F) protein which brings about fusion between viral and host cell membranes. The F protein is also responsible for cell-to-cell fusion, which leads to the characteristic syncytial cytopathic changes in RSV infection.

RSV differs from other paramyxoviruses in not possessing hemagglutinin activity. It also does not have neuraminidase or hemolytic properties. Another difference is that its nucleocapsid diameter (13 nm) is less than that of other paramyxoviruses (18 nm).

RSV does not grow in eggs but can be propagated on heteroploid human cell cultures, such as HeLa and HEp-2. It is highly labile and is inactivated rapidly at room temperature. It can be preserved by lyophilisation. It is antigenically stable and only one antigenic type exists. However, studies using monoclonal antibodies have identified two subtypes, A and B.

Clinical features

Most RSV infections are symptomatic. The virus is hardly ever found in healthy persons. Infection causes a broad range of respiratory illnesses. In infants, the disease may begin as febrile rhinorrhea, with cough and wheezing, progressing in 25–40 per cent to lower respiratory involvement, including tracheobronchitis, bronchiolitis and pneumonia. In about one per cent, the illness is serious enough to require hospitalisation.

RSV is considered responsible for about half the cases of bronchiolitis, and a quarter of all pneumonias occurring in the first few months of life. Most patients recover in 1–2 weeks but those with immunodeficiency or cardiac defects may have protracted illness and high death rates.

RSV is an important cause of otitis media in young children. A relation between RSV and the sudden death syndrome in infants has been proposed but not proven. In adults RSV infection may present as a febrile common cold. It can cause pneumonia in the elderly.

Epidemiology

RSV is global in distribution. It causes annual epidemics in the temperate regions during winter and in the tropics during the rainy season. Outbreaks are common in children's wards, nurseries and day care centres. Infection is most common in children six weeks to six months of age, with the peak at 2–3 months. Newborns are believed to be protected by high levels of maternal antibody.

The virus is transmitted by close contact, and through contaminated fingers and fomites. Coarse droplets of respiratory secretions discharged during coughing and sneezing are more efficient in spreading the virus than fine aerosols. The incubation period is 4–6 days. Virus shedding may persist for 1–3 weeks, though children with defective cell-mediated immunity may continue to shed the virus for months.

Re-infection with the virus is not uncommon but the disease so produced is milder than in primary infection. The role of the antibody in protection against the infection is not clear. Secretory IgA is considered more important than circulating IgG in protection. Cell-mediated immunity appears more important than humoral antibodies in recovery from infection. RSV does not induce high levels of interferon production.

Laboratory diagnosis

1. Specimen: Nasopharyngeal swabs or nasal washings

2. Virus isolation: Samples should be inoculated in cell cultures (HeLa or HEp-2) immediately after collection. Freezing of clinical samples may destroy the virus. In cultured cells, RSV causes characteristic giant cell and syncytial formation but cytopathic effects take about 10 days to appear. Earlier detection of viral growth in cells is possible by immunofluorescence tests. Rapid diagnosis of RSV infection can be made by the immunofluorescence test on smears of nasopharyngeal swabs.

3. Serology: Serological diagnosis is by demonstration of rising antibody titres in paired serum samples by ELISA, CF, neutralisation or immunofluorescence tests.

4. PCR: Molecular diagnosis by reverse transcriptase PCR is sensitive and rapid.

Prophylaxis

No effective vaccine is available. Attempts at immunisation by formalinised vaccines had to be given up as the vaccinees developed more serious illness than the control group on subsequent exposure to the infection.

Treatment

Management is primarily by supportive care. Administration of ribavirin by continuous aerosol has been found beneficial in hospitalised patients, decreasing the duration of illness and of virus shedding.

MORBILLIVIRUS

MEASLES (RUBEOLA)

Measles is an ancient disease but for a long time no clear distinction was made between measles and other exanthematous diseases, including smallpox. It was only in 1629 that measles came to be considered a separate entity. Thomas Sydenham in 1690 gave the first clear and accurate description of measles in the English language.

In 1846 an outbreak of measles occurred in the remote Faroe Islands, affecting 75 per cent of the islanders. The classic study of this epidemic by Peter Panum, a Danish medical student, laid the basis of our scientific knowledge about measles.

---- *Measles* ----

Clinical Case A 10-year-old boy was brought to a primary health centre with the complaint of fever, cough, running nose and conjunctivitis. His mother was unable to recall neither the vaccines administered nor the schedule. On examination, the physician noticed white lesions inside the patient's mouth (adjacent to the molar teeth). The patient was given aspirin and asked to return for follow up after two days. The patient returned the next day with maculopapular rash on the face, chest and back. The serum measles virus IgM antibody ELISA tested positive. The patient improved with supportive care and aspirin.

The viral origin of measles was established by Goldberger and Anderson in 1911 when they transmitted the disease to monkeys by inoculation of filtrates of blood and nasopharyngeal secretions from patients. The virus was isolated in monkey and human kidney cells by Enders and Peebles in 1954.

Measles virus

The virus has the general morphology of paramyxoviruses. It is a roughly spherical but often pleomorphic particle, 120–250 nm in diameter. The tightly coiled helical nucleocapsid is surrounded by the lipoprotein envelope carrying on its surface hemagglutinin (H) spikes. The envelope also has the F protein which mediates cell fusion and hemolytic activities. The measles virus agglutinates monkey erythrocytes but there is no elution, as the virus does not possess neuraminidase activity.

The measles virus grows well on human or monkey kidney and human amnion cultures which are the preferred cells for primary isolation. Isolates can be adapted for growth on continuous cell lines (HeLa, Vero) and in the amniotic sac of hen's eggs. Cytopathic effects consist of multinucleate syncytium formation, with numerous acidophilic nuclear and cytoplasmic inclusions. Multinucleate giant cells (**Warthin–Finkeldey cells**) are also found in the lymphoid tissues of patients.

The virus is labile and readily inactivated by heat, ultraviolet light, ether and formaldehyde. It can be stabilised by molar $MgSO_4$, so that it resists heating at 50°C for one hour. The measles virus is antigenically uniform. It shares antigens with the viruses of canine distemper and bovine rinderpest.

Epidemiology

Measles is endemic throughout the world and produces epidemics every 2–3 years. Epidemics are usually seen in late winter and early spring, with a peak in April. The disease has maximum incidence in children 1–5 years of age. It is uncommon in the first six months of life due to the presence of maternal antibody. One attack confers solid immunity.

Humans are the only natural hosts of measles. Monkeys are often infected but they seem to acquire the infection from humans. Patients are infectious from three days before the onset of symptoms until the rash desquamates. Infectivity is maximum at the prodrome and diminishes rapidly with onset of the rash. Spread is by direct contact with respiratory secretions and aerosols created by coughing and sneezing. The virus enters the body through the respiratory tract and conjunctiva. In the non-immune, infection almost always results in clinical disease.

In remote islands, the population may be highly susceptible to measles. When the virus is introduced into such communities, it may induce epidemics with high mortality. A classical example was observed in the Faroe Islands where measles appeared in 1846 after an absence of some 60 years. The epidemic spared only the very old who had been alive during the previous epidemic. When Greenland had its first exposure to the measles virus in 1951, the epidemic affected nearly all of the indigenous population.

Clinical features

It takes about 9–11 days from the time of exposure to infection for the first signs of clinical disease to appear. These consist of prodromal malaise, fever, conjunctival injection, cough and nasal discharge. After 3–4 days of prodromal illness, a rash appears. A day or two before the rash begins, **Koplik's spots** develop on the buccal mucosa and occasionally on the conjunctiva and intestinal mucosa. The prodromal illness subsides within a day or two of appearance of the rash. The red maculopapular rash of measles typically appears on the forehead first and spreads downwards, to disappear in the same sequence 3–6 days later, leaving behind a brownish discolouration and finely granular desquamation (*Case*).

Complications

Most patients recover uneventfully but quite a few develop complications which may be due to the virus (croup, bronchitis) or to secondary bacterial infection (pneumonia, otitis media). Rarely, the virus may cause fatal giant cell pneumonia, particularly in children with immunodeficiencies or severe malnutrition. Complications are more common and serious in the developing countries.

The most serious complication is meningoencephalitis. Many survivors have neurological sequelae. A rare late complication is subacute sclerosing panencephalitis (**SSPE**). Protracted diarrhea is often seen as a complication in children in the less developed nations. The virus may be recovered from the stools of patients with measles enteritis.

There occurs a suppression of delayed hypersensitivity after measles infection, which may last for weeks or a few months. Mantoux and other allergic skin tests may be negative during this period. Underlying tuberculosis may become worse following an attack of measles. Recovery from measles may also be associated with an improvement of allergic eczema or asthma, Hodgkin's disease or lipoid nephrosis.

Measles induces labour in some pregnant women, resulting in spontaneous abortion or premature delivery. The virus may cross the placenta and infect the fetus in maternal measles but there is no evidence of teratogeny. Thrombocytopenia may develop, leading to purpura and bleeding from the mouth, intestines and genitourinary tract.

Pathogenicity

The virus enters the body through the respiratory tract or the conjunctiva and multiplies locally and in the adjoining lymph nodes. The virus spreads to the reticuloendothelial system through blood. After multiplication there, a secondary viremia transports the virus to the epithelial surfaces including the skin, mouth, respiratory tract and conjunctiva.

The pathognomonic **Koplik's spots**, which are small bluish-white ulcerations on the buccal mucosa opposite the lower molars, contain giant cells, cytoplasmic and intranuclear inclusions and virion components, indicating local viral replication. Evidence of viral replication can also be seen in the vascular endothelial cells at the sites of the skin rash. The rash represents an immune reaction between T lymphocytes and cells in which viral replication is taking place.

During the prodromal phase, which lasts for 2–4 days, the virus can be isolated from blood, washed leucocytes, tears and respiratory secretions. It can be recovered from urine up to four days after the appearance of the skin rash.

Laboratory diagnosis

In a typical case of measles, diagnosis is self-evident. In atypical cases, and for differentiation from rubella, laboratory tests are useful.

1. Specimen: Nasal secretions, throat, conjunctiva and blood can be used. CSF is collected in SSPE.

2. Direct microscopy: A simple diagnostic test, which can be used even before the rash appears, is the demonstration of multinucleated giant cells in Giemsa-stained smears of nasal secretions.

3. IFA: The measles virus antigen can be detected in cells of nasal secretions by immunofluorescence.

4. Virus isolation: The virus can be isolated from the nose, throat, conjunctiva and blood during the prodromal phase and up to about two days after the appearance of the rash. The virus may be obtained from urine for a few more days. Primary human or monkey kidney and amnion cells are most useful. Cytopathic changes may take up to a week to develop, but earlier diagnosis of viral growth is possible by immunofluorescence.

5. Serological diagnosis: Specific neutralisation, hemagglutination inhibition (HAI) and complement fixing antibodies (in CFT) develop early. A fourfold rise in titre is looked for using paired sera collected during the acute phase and 10–21 days after. Demonstration of measles-specific IgM in a single specimen of serum drawn between one and two weeks after the onset of the rash is confirmatory. False negatives may occur if the serum is taken earlier than one week before or later than two weeks after onset of the rash.

Demonstration of high titre measles antibody in the CSF is diagnostic of SSPE.

6. PCR: Reverse transcriptase PCR is a sensitive and specific method of diagnosis.

Prophylaxis

Passive protection: Normal human gammaglobulin given within six days of exposure can prevent or modify the disease, depending on the dose. This is useful in children with immunodeficiency, pregnant women and others at special risk.

Active immunisation: A safe and effective live attenuated measles vaccine is available. The original live vaccines used the **Edmonston strain** developed by multiple passage through human kidney, amnion and chick embryo cultures. Due to its high risk of causing febrile rash (vaccination measles), further attenuation became necessary. The **Schwartz** and **Moraten strains** so developed were safe but effective only in children older than 15 months. In the tropics, measles is common and serious in children below 12 months. Therefore the **Edmonston–Zagreb strain**, attenuated by passage in human diploid cells, is preferred because it is able to produce seroconversion even in infants 4–6 months old. The recommended age for measles vaccination in developing countries is now nine months, while in the advanced nations it remains 15 months.

The vaccine is given either by itself, or in combination, as the MMR vaccine. A single subcutaneous injection of the measles vaccine provides protection beginning in about 12 days and lasting for over 20 years. Contraindications are immunodeficiency, untreated tuberculosis and pregnancy.

A live attenuated vaccine has been developed which can be given by intranasal aerosol to young babies and gives good protection irrespective of the presence of maternal antibodies. Efforts are being made to eradicate measles by vaccination. Considerable progress has been achieved in the USA and some other countries.

NIPAH AND HENDRA VIRUSES

In the 1990s a new genus, *Henipavirus*, was identified in an outbreak in Australia and Malaysia. Two zoonotic paramyxoviruses were found to be associated with zoonotic outbreaks. Fruit bats are their natural hosts.

- **Nipah virus**: In Malaysia, severe encephalitis was caused by this virus, with direct transmission from pigs to humans. Mortality was high.
- **Hendra virus**: This caused the death of many horses in Australia. Some human cases were also reported.

As the mortality is high with these infections, they have been classified as Biosafety level 4 agents.

HUMAN METAPNEUMOVIRUS

This is a respiratory pathogen first described in 2001 by using molecular methods to identify unknown causative agents in children suffering from respiratory illness, which otherwise resembled RSV infection. Besides children, this virus can cause disease in adults with lymphomas or leukemias and also in the elderly.

RECAP

- Paramyxoviridae is a family of enveloped, helical, RNA viruses which are 100–300 nm in diameter. There are four genera: *Rubulavirus, Paramyxovirus, Morbillivirus* and *Pneumovirus*.
- Paramyxovirus is a genus of the family Paramyxoviridae, characterised by the presence of both hemagglutinin and neuraminidase.
- Parainfluenza viruses types 1–4 cause upper respiratory infections.
- Newcastle disease virus is of great economic importance.
- The mumps virus belongs to *Rubulavirus* and causes mumps and aseptic meningitis. This virus may also be the most common cause of aseptic meningitis. Vaccination in childhood with a live attenuated virus (Jeryl–Lynn strain) gives longlasting immunity.
- The respiratory syncitial virus (RSV) differs from other members of the family in lacking both hemagglutinin and neuraminidase. It commonly infects children, causing a common cold-like illness. Infection during the first year of life may induce a severe, life-threatening bronchiolitis, Two types of RSV, A and B, can be detected.
- Antibodies to RSV can be demonstrated in serum; the presence of rising antibody titres or high IgM titres in a single serum sample is diagnostic. Aerosolised ribavirin can be used to treat RSV infections, if indicated.
- Morbillivirus includes the measles virus, which causes measles. Diagnosis is by virus isolation in cell culture, by serological methods which demonstrate a rise in serum antibody titres or PCR. Vaccination in childhood with a live attenuated virus gives immunity that should be boosted at 4–6 years of age.

- A new genus Henipavirus has been recently identified with the Nipah and Henda viruses causing zoonotic outbreaks.
- Human Metapnuemovirus causes respiratory illness in children and diseases in adults with lymphoma and leukemia.

ESSAYS

1. Explain the pathogenesis and complications of mumps virus infections.

SHORT NOTES

1. RSV
2. Immunisation against mumps and measles
3. Nipah and Hendra viruses
4. Metapneumovirus
5. SSPE

56 Arthropod- and Rodent-borne Viral Infections

INTRODUCTION

Arboviruses (**arthropod-borne viruses**) are a varied group of RNA viruses which have common ecological and epidemiological attributes. They multiply in and are transmitted by hematophagous insect vectors to vertebrates, including humans. Insect viruses and viruses of vertebrates that are sometimes mechanically transmitted by insects do not come into this category.

Arboviruses are classified according to their physical and chemical features into taxonomical families named Togaviridae, Flaviviridae, Bunyaviridae, Reoviridae, Arenaviridae and Filoviridae (Table 56.1). Within each family, they are classified into genera and antigenic groups, based on serological relationships. Some viruses are ungrouped.

Arboviruses are worldwide in distribution but are far more numerous in the tropical than in the temperate zones. Over 500 viruses have been listed; most cause silent infections in rodents and other wild mammals but about 100 of them can infect humans. In India, over 40 arboviruses have been detected, of which more than 10 are known to produce human disease. Natural cycles of the virus involve infected non-human vertebrate host including many species of animals and birds. The virus is transmitted by an arthropod.

Arthropod vectors: The ability to multiply in arthropods is a special characteristic of the viruses. The most common arbovirus vectors are mosquitoes, followed by ticks. *Phlebotomus, Culicoides* and *Cimicidae* are less common vectors.

Cultivation

In the laboratory, mice are commonly used for growing arboviruses, intracerebral inoculation in suckling mice being the most sensitive method for their isolation. They can be grown in the yolk sac or chorioallantoic membrane of chick embryo, in tissue cultures of primary cells like chick embryo fibroblasts or continuous cell lines like Vero or HeLa, and in cultures of appropriate insect tissues.

Resistance

In general, arboviruses are labile, being readily inactivated at room temperature and by bile salts, ether

Table 56.1 *Taxonomy of some important arboviruses*

Family	Genus	Important species
Togaviridae	*Alphavirus*	Chikungunya, O'nyong-nyong, Mayaro, Semliki forest, Sindbis, Ross River, Eastern, Western and Venezuelan equine encephalitis viruses
Flaviviridae	*Flavivirus*	Japanese encephalitis, Murray Valley encephalitis, West Nile, Ilheus, St. Louis encephalitis, yellow fever, dengue types 1, 2, 3, 4, Russian spring summer encephalitis complex, Louping ill, Powassan, Zika virus, Kyasanur Forest disease, Omsk hemorrhagic fever
Bunyaviridae	*Bunyavirus* *Phlebovirus* *Nairovirus* *Hantavirus*	California encephalitis, Oropouche, Turlock Sandfly fever viruses, Rift valley fever virus Crimean Congo hemorrhagic fever viruses, Nairobi sheep disease virus, Ganjam virus Hantan, Seoul, Puumala, Prospect Hill, Sin Nombre viruses
Reoviridae	*Orbivirus*	Colorado tick fever, African horse sickness, Blue tongue viruses
Arenaviridae	*Arenavirus*	Junin, Machupo, Lymphocytic choriomeningitis and Lassa fever
Filoviridae	*Marburgvirus*	African hemorrhagic fevers Ebola virus

and other lipid solvents. Infectivity may be retained at −70°C or by lyophilisation.

Antigenic structure

Three antigens are important in serological studies: **hemagglutinins, complement fixing and neutralising antigens**—all integral parts of the virus particle. Considerable antigenic cross-reactions occur among arboviruses. The plaque reduction neutralisation test (PRNT) shows the greatest specificity for the identification of the viruses.

Hemagglutination: Most arboviruses agglutinate the red cells of day-old chicks or geese. Hemagglutination is influenced by pH and temperature, the optimal requirements varying with different viruses. Spontaneous elution does not occur. Hemagglutination is inhibited specifically by antibody which can be used in a diagnostic assay and non-specifically by lipoprotein inhibitors in serum, brain and other tissues.

Pathogenicity

Arboviruses produce three main clinical entities:
- Fevers with or without rashes
- Hemorrhagic fevers
- Encephalitis

Sometimes, they may be associated with more than one syndrome. The virus enters the body through the bite of the insect vector. After multiplication in the reticuloendothelial system, viremia of varying duration ensues and, in some cases, the virus is transported to the target organs, such as the central nervous system in encephalitis, the liver in yellow fever and the capillary endothelium in hemorrhagic fevers.

Case fatality in hemorrhagic fevers and encephalitis is often high (Table 56.2). All infections occur with varying degrees of severity, subclinical infections being common. Arboviruses also cause a number of veterinary diseases such as Eastern, Western and Venezuelan equine encephalitis in horses in America, Rift Valley fever in sheep and cattle in Africa, blue tongue in donkeys in India, Africa and America, Ganjam disease of sheep in India and African horse sickness in horses and mules in Africa and Asia.

Laboratory diagnosis

Diagnosis may be established by virus isolation or serology. Strict biosafety measures are required to carry out virus isolation.

1. Specimen: As all arbovirus infections are viremic, blood collected during the early phase of the disease may yield the virus. Isolation may also be made from the cerebrospinal fluid (CSF), in some encephalitic cases and tissues.

2. Virus isolation: Specimens are inoculated intracerebrally into suckling mice. The animals develop fatal encephalitis, though serial blind passages may be necessary in some cases. Some viruses, mainly alpha and flavivirus, may also be isolated in cell cultures namely, HeLa, BHK, MRC-5 and Vero. Mosquito cell lines have been used for isolation. Isolates are identified by hemagglutination inhibition, complement fixation, immunofluorescence, immunochromatography, ELISA or neutralisation with appropriate antisera. Isolation of

Table 56.2 *Reservoir hosts, geographic distribution and vectors of arboviruses and rodent-borne virus associated with different clinical syndromes*

Virus	Genus	Reservoir/hosts	Geographic distribution	Vector
FEVER WITH OR WITHOUT RASH AND ARTHRALGIA				
Chikungunya	Alphavirus	Not known (suspected to be monkeys)	Africa, Asia	Mosquito
O' nyong-nyong	Alphavirus	Not known	Africa	Mosquito
Ross River	Alphavirus	Small animals	Australia	Mosquito
Sindbis	Alphavirus	Birds, mammals	Africa, Asia	Mosquito
Mayaro	Alphavirus	Monkeys, marsupials	South America	Mosquito
Dengue, types 1–4	Flavivirus	Not known	Widespread, especially Asia and the Caribbean	Mosquito
West Nile	Flavivirus	Birds	Asia, Africa, USA	Mosquito
Sandfly fever	Bunyavirus	Not known	The Mediterranean, Asia, Tropical America	Sandfly
Rift Valley fever	Bunyavirus	Sheep, cattle	Africa	Mosquito
Oropouche	Bunyavirus	Not known	South America	Mosquito
Colorado tick fever	Orbivirus	Rodents	USA	Tick
ENCEPHALITIS				
Eastern equine encephalitis	Alphavirus	Birds	Americas	Mosquito
Western equine encephalitis	Alphavirus	Reptiles	Americas	Mosquito
Venezuelan equine encephalitis	Alphavirus	Rodents	Americas	Mosquito
St. Louis encephalitis	Flavivirus	Birds	Americas	Mosquito
West Nile	Flavivirus	Birds	Africa, Europe, USA, West Asia	Mosquito
Japanese encephalitis	Flavivirus	Birds	East and Southeast Asia	Mosquito
Murray Valley encephalitis	Flavivirus	Birds	Australia	Mosquito
RSSE complex	Flavivirus	Rodents, other mammals, birds mammals, birds, ticks	East Europe, the (former) USSR	Tick
Louping ill	Flavivirus	Sheep	Britain	Tick
Powassan	Flavivirus	Rodents	North America	Tick
California	Bunyavirus	Rodents	North America	Mosquito
HEMORRHAGIC FEVER				
Chikungunya	Alphavirus	Not known	Africa, Asia	Mosquito
Dengue types1–4	Flavivirus	Not known	Tropics	Mosquito
Yellow fever	Flavivirus	Monkeys, man	Africa, South America	Mosquito
Kyasanur Forest disease	Flavivirus	Rodents, shrews, monkeys and ticks	India	Tick
Omsk hemorrhagic fever	Flavivirus	Small mammals	The (former) USSR	Tick
Crimean Congo	Nairovirus	Small mammals	The (former) USSR, Central Asia	Tick
RODENT-BORNE HAEMORRHAGIC FEVERS				
Hanta virus pulmonary syndrome	Hantavirus	Deer mouse	South America and United States	Deer mice
Hemorrhagic fever with Renal Syndrome (HFRS)	Hantavirus	Rodents	China, Russia and Korea	Rodents
Lassa fever	Lassavirus	Rodents	Western Africa	Rodents

the virus from insect vectors, birds or animals in reservoir areas indicates arbovirus activity in the area.

3. Serology: Diagnosis may also be made by demonstrating IgM antibodies in acute phase by ELISA or rise in IgG titres in paired serum samples by hemagglutination inhibition (HAI), complement fixation (CFT) or neutralisation tests. These tests are time-consuming and laborious.

Serological diagnosis is often complicated due to the antigenic cross-reaction between related viruses.

Detection of viral proteins and antigens, or RNA by molecular methods (conventional or real-time PCR) are more specific and rapid. They have replaced conventional CFT, HAI and neutralisation tests.

Epidemiology

Arbovirus infections are zoonoses, maintained in nature by animals in a vector cycle, with a few possible exceptions such as dengue and O'nyong-nyong. In some areas, the arbovirus infection appears to be seasonal, and outbreaks are known to occur periodically. The reason for this could be an increase in the vector population or reintroduction of the virus to the area through migratory birds or other reservoirs.

The epidemiology of arbovirus infections has **two patterns**:

- It is linked with the ecology of the arthropod vectors and vertebrate hosts. Most arboviruses exist in nature in animal or avian species in which infection is asymptomatic. The vector arthropod gets infected by biting a viremic vertebrate. The vector becomes infective only after the incubation period (extrinsic incubation period). Human disease results when the virus is accidentally transmitted to humans, either directly by the vector or through the intermediary of animal reservoirs.
- A second epidemiological pattern is seen in diseases like dengue where no non-human vertebrate host has been identified. Here, the virus is maintained in a cycle composed of humans and the domestic mosquito. Transovarial transmission in ticks maintains the virus in the vector.

Control

Control measures are indicated only in those infections that lead to epidemics or epizootics. These consist essentially of vector control.

Vaccine against yellow fever has been successful, but not in the control of other arbovirus diseases. Vaccines have been used against Japanese encephalitis in Asia and the US.

TOGAVIRIDAE

Morphology

Togaviruses are spherical, enveloped viruses with a diameter of 50–70 nm. The genome is a molecule of single-stranded RNA. The virus replicates in the host cell cytoplasm and is released by budding through host cell membranes. The name Togavirus is derived from 'toga', meaning the Roman mantle or cloak, and refers to the viral envelope.

Classification

The family Togaviridae contains, besides the arboviruses belonging to the genus *Alphavirus*, the rubella virus (genus *Rubivirus*) and others, which are not arthropod-borne and differ in their epidemiology and other features, which are described elsewhere.

ALPHAVIRUS

The genus *Alphavirus* contains 32 species, of which at least 13 are known to infect humans. **All of them are mosquito-borne.** They exhibit cross-reaction in HAI and CFT, but not by neutralisation tests.

They produce epidemics of encephalitis in America and dengue-like fever in the tropics.

Encephalitis viruses

Three members of this group—Eastern, Western and Venezuelan equine encephalitis viruses—cause encephalitis in horses and humans. Eastern equine encephalitis (EEE) occurs along eastern Canada, USA and the Caribbean, causing sporadic cases and small epidemics. Western equine encephalitis (WEE) is more widely distributed in America and causes large epidemics. Venezuelan equine encephalitis (VEE), prevalent in Central and South America, usually causes an influenza-like illness, with encephalitis in a small proportion of cases. Several species of *Culex* and *Anopheles* mosquitoes are the vectors, and wild birds the reservoirs. Formalinised vaccines have been developed for EEE and WEE and a live attenuated vaccine for VEE available for horses but not humans.

Viruses causing febrile illness

Chikungunya virus: This virus was first isolated from human patients in Tanzania in 1952. The vector is *Aedes aegypti*. No animal reservoir has been identified. The name 'chikungunya' is derived from the native word for the disease in which the patient lies 'doubled up' due to severe joint pain. Epidemics of chikungunya have occurred in many African countries. The virus first appeared in India in 1963, when along with dengue, it caused very extensive epidemics in Kolkata, Chennai and other areas. Chikungunya outbreaks occurred at irregular intervals along the east coast of India and in Maharashtra till 1973. Since then, the virus had been quiescent till it reappeared in 2006. There was a large outbreak that began in Andhra Pradesh and Tamil Nadu, which spread to Kerala, Karnataka and Delhi, affecting nearly a million people.

Genotypes: There are three major Chikungunya virus genotypes:

● West African
● East/Central/South African (ECSA)
● Asian genotypes

They are generally restricted to these geographic areas. However, spread of ECSA to Asian regions has been reported.

Reasons for re-emergence: The disease appears in epidemics after a gap of a decade or two. The reason for this is unknown. During interepidemic periods, the virus is thought to be maintained in the sylvatic cycle in non-human primates.

Symptoms: The disease presents with a sudden onset of fever, crippling joint pain, lymphadenopathy and conjunctivitis. A maculopapular rash is common, although hemorrhagic manifestations are rare. The fever is typically biphasic with a period of remission after 1–6 days.

Clinically, chikungunya cannot be differentiated from uncomplicated dengue. Laboratory tests based on IgM detection can help in confirming.

Diagnosis: Detection of IgM or IgG in a paired serum sample by ELISA is the mainstay of diagnosis. Reverse transcriptase PCR can be used to detect viral RNA.

Treatment: No vaccine is available.

O'nyong-nyong virus, Semliki Forest virus and Sindbis virus: They are the other alphaviridae which are mosquito-borne and produce febrile illness in humans. They are localised to Uganda, Africa. Sindbis virus has been recovered from Philippines and Australia and antibodies have been detected in some human sera in India.

The family Flaviviridae contains only one genus, *Flavivirus*. They are smaller than alphaviruses, being 40 nm in diameter. The name *Flavivirus* refers to the yellow fever virus (*flavus* in Latin means yellow).

There are over 60 arthropod-borne flaviviruses. Representative members of this group are distributed in all parts of the world, covering all the zoogeographic regions. They may be considered under two sections: **mosquito-borne** and **tick-borne viruses.**

MOSQUITO-BORNE GROUP

Encephalitis viruses

Five members of this group cause encephalitis, each of them limited to a geographic zone:

St. Louis encephalitis virus: This is prevalent in North and Central America and is the most important mosquito-borne disease in the USA. Wild birds act as the reservoir and *Culex tarsalis* as the vector.

Ilheus virus: This occurs in South and Central America, and is maintained in forests by a cycle of mosquitoes, wild birds and monkeys. Human infection is largely subclinical. Encephalitis is rare.

West Nile virus: This virus was originally isolated in 1937 from the West Nile province of Uganda. It has since been reported from African countries, Israel, Cyprus, France and India. It causes a dengue-like illness in humans and encephalitis in horses. The virus is maintained in nature in wild birds. In India, the virus has been isolated from *Culex* mosquitoes and from febrile as well as encephalitic patients, from Rajasthan to Karnataka.

In 1999, West Nile fever appeared in New York, and since then the virus has spread over much of the USA, becoming a major public health problem.

Murray Valley encephalitis virus: This is confined to Australia and New Guinea. The virus is believed to occur normally in an enzootic cycle involving wild birds and mosquitoes, and to break out only occasionally into epidemics. *Culex annulirostris* is the vector.

Japanese encephalitis (JE):

Geographical distribution: This virus occurs from East Asia to South Asia, from Korea and Japan in the north to India and Malaysia in the south. The disease has been recognised in Japan since 1871 and was named Japanese 'B' encephalitis to distinguish it from 'encephalitis A' (encephalitis lethargica, von Economo's disease). The virus was first isolated in Japan during an epidemic in 1935. Several large epidemics have occurred since then. Epidemics show seasonal incidence (summer–autumn) in the temperate regions, though this is not evident in the tropical areas. *Culex tritaeniorhynchus*, a rural mosquito that breeds in rice fields, is the principal vector.

Clinical features: Japanese encephalitis virus causes the most serious clinical disease in this group. The disease has an abrupt onset with fever, headache and vomiting. After 1–6 days, signs of encephalitis set in with nuchal rigidity, convulsions, altered sensorium and coma. The fever is high and continuous. There is presence of neutrophil leucocytosis in peripheral blood and pleocytosis with normal or raised sugar levels and slightly raised protein levels in the CSF. The mortality rate in some epidemics has been up to 50 per cent. Convalescence may take several weeks. Up to 50 per cent of survivors may have neurological or psychiatric sequelae. Infection in pregnant women during first and second trimester has led to fetal death. The large majority of infections are, however, asymptomatic and it has been estimated that 500–1000 inapparent infections occur for every case of clinical disease.

JE in the Indian setting: In India, Japanese encephalitis was first recognised in 1955 when the virus was isolated from mosquitoes of the *Culex vishnui* complex from Vellore during an outbreak of encephalitis in Tamil Nadu. The virus continues to be active in Tamil Nadu and Andhra, causing illness mainly in children, indicating the endemic nature of the virus. Most of the cases occur between October and November.

Since 1976, the highest rates of human disease have been reported from the states of Andhra Pradesh, Assam, Bihar, Haryana, Goa, Karnataka, Kerala, Tamil Nadu, Pondicherry, Uttar Pradesh, and West Bengal. In addition, sporadic cases have been reported from different parts of the country, excepting Dadra, Daman, Diu, Gujarat, Himachal Pradesh, Jammu and Kashmir, Lakshadweep, Meghalaya, Nagar Haveli, Punjab, Rajasthan, and Sikkim. Japanese encephalitis has become a major public health problem of national importance in India.

Epidemiology:

Hosts: Herons act as reservoir hosts and pigs as amplifier hosts (Fig. 56.1). Human infection is a 'dead end' event and occurs when the infected mosquitoes reach high density. The natural cycle in India also may be similar. Cases occur throughout the year in India,

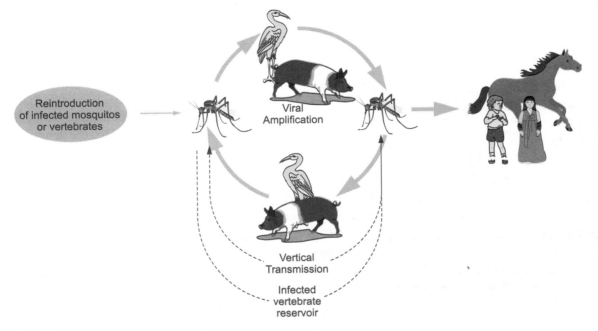

Fig. 56.1 Transmission cycle of Japanese encephalitis virus

more during the rainy season. Natural infection has been demonstrated in *Ardeid* birds (herons and egrets); bird-to-bird transmission also takes place through *Culex tritaeniorhynchus*. Other birds such as ducks, pigeons and sparrows may also be involved. Vertebrate hosts may include cattle and buffaloes, besides pigs.

The mosquito *Culex tritaeniorhynchus* has a predilection for cattle and bites them in preference to humans or pigs, but cattle do not develop viremia, hence, do not spread the virus. Pigs are the amplifier hosts. The high cattle–pig ratio in India has been suggested to be a factor limiting human infection.

Control measures: Preventive measures include mosquito control and locating piggeries away from human dwellings.

Vaccine:

- A **formalin-inactivated mouse brain vaccine** using the **Nakayama strain** has been used successfully for immunisation in Japan and, on a small scale, in India as well. Two doses at two weeks' interval followed by a booster 6–12 months later constitute a full course. Immunity produced by the vaccine is short-lived.
- A **live attenuated vaccine** has been developed in China from **JE strain SA 14-14-2**, passed through weanling mice. It is administered in two doses, one year apart. The vaccine has reportedly been effective in preventing clinical disease.

Vaccines licensed in India
- Inactivated vero cell culture-derived SA-14-14-2
- Inactivated vero cell culture-derived Kolar strain, 821564XY, JE vaccine

These are recommended for children living in endemic areas.

The vaccination of pigs has been proposed in view of their importance as amplifier hosts.

Yellow fever

Yellow fever was recognised as a clinical entity as early as the seventeenth century but since the early twentieth century, the disease has largely been confined to certain areas of Africa and South and Central America.

Clinical features: After an incubation period of 3–6 days, the disease starts as a fever of acute onset with chills, headache, nausea and vomiting. The pulse is usually slow despite a high temperature. Jaundice, albuminuria and hemorrhagic manifestations develop and the patient may die of hepatic or renal failure. Most cases are less severe, especially in the endemic areas,

and may present as undifferentiated fever without jaundice.

Epidemiology: The disease occurs in two distinct patterns.

- In the **urban cycle,** humans act as the natural reservoir, the virus being transmitted by the domestic *Aedes aegypti* mosquito.
- In the forest or **sylvatic cycle,** wild monkeys act as the reservoirs and forest mosquitoes (*Haemagogus spegazzinii* in South America and *Aedes africanus* and *A.simpsoni* in Africa) as the vectors. Human cases occur only when humans trespass into the forest or when the monkeys raid villages near the forest.

Control: Control of urban yellow fever could be achieved by eradicating the vector mosquito, but this is obviously impracticable with the concomitant existence of sylvatic disease.

A safe and effective vaccine, the non-neurotropic **17D vaccine,** is administered by subcutaneous inoculation. Vaccination is mandatory for travel to or from endemic areas. It is valid for 10 years, beginning 10 days after vaccination. In India, the 17D vaccine is manufactured at the Central Research Institute, Kasauli.

Geographical distribution: Yellow fever is largely confined to Central and South America and Africa. India is a yellow fever 'receptive' area but the disease **does not exist in India.** Hence, it is important to prevent establishment of the disease. India offers a receptive area with a large population of *Aedes aegypti* and non-immune humans. Strict vigilance is enforced on vaccination and quarantine for travel from endemic areas. This has checked the entry of the virus into India through legitimate passengers. It is likely that any stray virus introduced may have been kept out by the prevalence in the local *Aedes aegypti* of the dengue virus, and of antibodies to a wide range of arboviruses in the local population.

Another reason could have been that in Africa, yellow fever was mainly in the west, and in India, *Aedes* mosquitoes were common along the east coast, so that even stray importations of the virus by sea may not have found suitable vectors. This is no longer valid as yellow fever has in recent years caused epidemics in East Africa, and *Aedes* mosquitoes have spread all along the west coast of India. If yellow fever gets established in India, the consequences could be catastrophic due to the large vulnerable non-immune population.

Dengue virus

> ## Dengue
>
> **Clinical Case**   A 40-year-old man presented to the medical OPD with high fever, severe headache and pain around the eyes for the past five days. On examination, petechial lesions were noted on the forearm. The tourniquet test (to detect the fragility of the capillaries) and Dengue NS1 antigen capture ELISA were positive. Platelet count was 30,000/mm³. The patient recovered with supportive management. The case was notified to the District Health Department.

The dengue virus is widely distributed throughout the tropics and subtropics (in Swahili, *Ki denga pepo* means a sudden seizure by a demon). The term **'break-bone fever'** was coined during the Philadelphia epidemic in 1780. Dengue fever is clinically similar to the illness caused by the chikungunya and O'nyong-nyong viruses. Four types of dengue virus exist: DEN 1 first isolated from Hawaii in 1944, DEN 2 from New Guinea in 1944 and DEN 3 and 4 from the Philippines in 1956. Dengue has been increasing worldwide over the last few decades and today ranks as the most important vector-borne disease, with about 2.5 billion people in 200 countries at risk.

Clinical findings: Dengue manifests after an incubation period of 3–14 days.

Febrile phase: Patients typically develop a high-grade fever of sudden onset with headache, retrobulbar pain, photophobia, accompanied by facial flushing, skin erythema and pain in the back and limbs (break-bone fever), lymphadenopathy and maculopapular rash. The fever is typically biphasic (saddle back) (*see clinical case*). This acute febrile phase usually lasts 2–7 days and is often characterised by generalised body ache, myalgia, arthralgia, rubeliform exanthema and headache.

Critical phase: These patients become worse around the time of defervescence, when the temperature drops to 37.5–38°C or less and remains below this level, usually on days 3–8 of illness. Progressive leukopenia followed by a rapid decrease in platelet count usually precedes plasma leakage. An increasing haematocrit above the baseline may be one of the earliest additional signs.

Complications with hemorrhagic manifestations (**dengue hemorrhagic fever**) or with shock (**dengue shock syndrome**) can occur in persons who have non-neutralising heterologous antibodies from a previous infection, or in infants with maternal antibodies. These complications, first recognised in Thailand, have since occurred in many countries in Western Pacific, Southeast Asia including India. They are also common in previously healthy children in the indigenous populations of endemic areas.

Dengue virus is transmitted from person to person by *Aedes aegypti* mosquitoes. The extrinsic incubation period is 8–10 days. No vertebrate hosts other than humans have been identified.

> **Clinical criteria for dengue fever/dengue hemorrhagic fever/dengue shock syndrome**
>
> **Dengue fever (DF):** An acute febrile illness with two or more of the following manifestations: Headache, retro-orbital pain, myalgia, arthralgia, rash, hemorrhagic manifestations.
>
> **Dengue hemorrhagic fever (DHF):**   Clinical criteria of dengue fever plus hemorrhagic tendencies evidenced by one or more of the following:
> * Positive tourniquet test
> * Petechiae, ecchymoses or purpura
> * Bleeding from mucosa, gastrointestinal tract, injection sites or other sites
> * Thrombocytopenia, a more than 20% drop in haematocrit following volume replacement treatment compared to baseline
> * Signs of plasma leakage (pleural effusion, ascites, hypoproteinemia)
>
> **Dengue shock syndrome (DSS):** All the above criteria for DHF with evidence of circulatory failure manifested by rapid and weak pulse and narrow pulse pressure (mm Hg) or hypotension for age, cold and clammy skin and restlessness.

Distribution: Dengue was initially confined to the east coast of India and has caused epidemics (sometimes along with the chikungunya virus). Subsequently, it spread westwards and, in the 1990s, Surat and Delhi had major epidemics with deaths due to DHF and DSS. All four types of dengue virus are present in this country. Occasionally, more than one type has been isolated from the same patient.

Laboratory diagnosis: The virus can be isolated in the first week of illness. But this is rarely done. Mainstay of diagnosis is the detection of a non-structural viral protein antigen (NS1). This can be detected in the blood up to 7–10 days. Demonstration of circulating IgM antibody provides early diagnosis as it appears within two to five days of onset of illness and persists for one to three months. The IgM ELISA test offers reliable diagnosis. A strip immunochromatographic test for IgM is available for rapid diagnosis. However, the test has to be confirmed by ELISA. The IgG antibodies are detected in a paired serum sample to show rising titres.

Control of dengue is limited to vector control. WHO has approved a vaccine which has been licensed and launched in some South American countries. In India, the vaccine is yet to be launched.

Treatment: There is no specific treatment for dengue. Supportive management, with cold tepid sponging, paracetamol for fever (Aspirin/NSAIDS like Ibuprofen, etc., should be avoided since it may cause gastritis, vomiting, acidosis, platelet dysfunction and severe bleeding); fluid and electrolyte replacement and platelet infusion when counts are 10,000 and less, should be done. Dengue shock is treated with whole blood transfusion and management of shock.

Zika virus

Zika virus has recently been recognised as a global threat. The virus belongs to the Flaviviridae group and is transmitted by Aedes mosquito.

It was first isolated in 1947 from a rhesus monkey in Zika forest in Uganda. Zika is a sylvatic disease being maintained in mosquito and non-human primates. Outbreaks have occurred in French Polynesia and South Pacific islands. It is associated with neurological complications and Guillain-Barre syndrome. Diagnosis is by demonstrating the viral RNA by RT-PCR.

TICK-BORNE GROUP

These viruses produce two clinical syndromes: **encephalitis** and **hemorrhagic fevers**.

Tick-borne encephalitis viruses

A number of viruses belonging to the Russian Spring Summer Encephalitis (RSSE) complex cause encephalitis along a wide area of the northern landmass, from Scotland to Siberia. The names given to the disease vary from one area to another depending on variations in the prominent clinical features. RSSE is the most serious form, with high rates of fatality and permanent paralytic sequelae in some survivors. Infection is transmitted by the bite of *Ixodid* ticks. The virus is transmitted transovarially in ticks so that they can act as vectors as well as reservoir hosts. Wild rodents and migrating birds are other reservoirs. Biphasic meningoencephalitis may be transmitted to human beings when they drink the milk

of infected goats. Control of infection by the RSSE complex depends on avoiding tick bites. A formalin-inactivated RSSE vaccine has been found useful.

Tick-borne hemorrhagic fevers

Kyasanur Forest disease (KFD): This is a hemorrhagic fever found in Karnataka state (India). In 1957, several dead monkeys were found in Kyasanur Forest in Shimoga district of Karnataka and a severe prostrating illness was noticed in some of the villagers in the area. A new arbovirus antigenically related to the RSSE complex was isolated by investigators from the National Institute of Virology (then Virus Research Centre), Pune, from the patients and dead monkeys. It was named the KFD virus after the place where the first isolations were made. An outbreak of KFD has been reported in 2015 from Wayanad and Malappuram districts of Kerala.

Forest birds and small mammals are believed to be the reservoir hosts. Infection is transmitted by the bite of ticks, the principal vector being *Haemaphysalis spinigera*. As infection in monkeys leads to fatal disease, they are not the primary reservoirs but only amplifier hosts. *Haemaphysalis* ticks may act as the reservoir to some extent as transovarial transmission of the virus has been demonstrated in them.

Clinical features: KFD has an abrupt onset of fever, headache, conjunctivitis, myalgia and severe prostration. Some cases develop hemorrhages in the skin, mucosa and viscera. The case fatality rate is about 5 per cent. A killed KFD virus vaccine was used in a small field trial and appeared to provide some degree of protection.

History

For many years after its discovery in 1957, the epizootic and epidemic activity of KFD remained confined to the areas contiguous to its original focus in the Sagar, Sorab and Shikarpur taluks of Shimoga district.

Following felling of a part of an evergreen reserve forest in the area in September 1982, an epizootic and epidemic of KFD occurred in south Kanara. The outbreak, known locally as '**monkey fever**', started with dead monkeys being observed followed by 1142 human cases with 104 deaths. The ecological disturbance caused by felling of the virgin forest is believed to have activated a silent enzootic focus of the virus.

KFD has spread to neighboring Kerala, as a few cases were reported in 2015 in Wayanad and Malappuram districts.

Omsk hemorrhagic fever: This occurs in Russia and Romania. It is clinically similar to KFD and is caused by a related virus. *Dermacentor* ticks are the vectors.

BUNYAVIRIDAE

This family contains over 300 species and is the largest group of arboviruses. The virus is about 100 nm in diameter and has a complex structure, with a triple segmented genome of single-stranded RNA.

Most bunyaviruses are **mosquito-borne**. Some are transmitted by **sandflies** (for example, Phlebotomus fever) or **ticks** (Crimean Congo hemorrhagic fever). Some are established causes of natural disease, including epidemics and epizootics, while others have been isolated only from insect vectors, not associated with any human or animal disease. Bunyaviruses are so named from the type species *Bunyamwera* virus isolated from mosquitoes in Uganda in 1946.

The family Bunyaviridae contains four genera of medical importance: *Bunyavirus*, *Phlebovirus*, *Nairovirus* and *Hantavirus* (Hantaviruses are not arthropod-borne and so are discussed under rodent-borne infections). A number of viruses are as yet ungrouped.

Genus *Bunyavirus*

The genus contains over 150 species, of which only a few cause human infections. The clinical disease caused is encephalitis, aseptic meningitis and fever. The California encephalitis group of viruses are endemic in the USA. Large epidemics of fever with aseptic meningitis have been caused by the Oropouche virus (member of the Simbu group) in Brazil. The midge *Culicoides paraensia* is the main vector for the Oropouche virus.

Genus *Phlebovirus*

The main members of this genus are the sandfly fever and Rift Valley fever viruses.

Phlebotomus or **sandfly fever**, also known as Pappataci fever and three-day fever, is a self-limiting, non-fatal fever transmitted by the bite of the sandfly *Phlebotomus papatasii*. It occurs along the Mediterranean coast and Central Asia, extending as far east as Pakistan and North West India. The virus has been isolated from sandflies and patients in India. No vertebrate host other than humans have been identified.

Rift Valley fever is a mosquito-borne virus causing enzootic hepatitis in sheep and other domestic animals in Africa. It is named after the Rift Valley, Kenya. Human infections resemble influenza. It has been reported from Egypt, Kenya, Yemen and Saudi Arabia, causing epidemics and deaths.

Genus *Nairovirus*

The genus is named after the type species Nairobi sheep disease virus. Members of the Crimean Congo hemorrhagic group are the main human pathogens in this genus. The Crimean hemorrhagic fever virus, first isolated in Crimea in 1945, was subsequently found to be identical with the Congo fever virus isolated in 1956 in Congo (Zaire), hence the name Crimean Congo hemorrhagic fever (CCHF). The disease is endemic in eastern Europe, Central Asia and many parts of Africa. Cattle, sheep, goats and other domesticated animals act as natural reservoirs. It is transmitted by *Hyalomma* ticks. During the acute phase of the disease, the blood of the patient is highly infectious and direct transmission may occur through contact. A related virus, *Hazara*, has been isolated in Pakistan. It is also widespread in Iran, Iraq and the UAE. Small outbreaks and antibodies to the CCHF viruses have been detected in human and animal sera from India.

The **Ganjam virus**, isolated from ticks collected from sheep and goats in Orissa, India, is closely related to the Nairobi sheep disease virus. This virus has also been isolated from humans.

REOVIRIDAE

The genus *Orbivirus* of the family Reoviridae contains arthropod-borne viruses which infect animals and humans that differ from other arboviruses in having double-stranded RNA genomes.

The Colorado tick fever virus, an orbivirus, causes a self-limited mild fever without rash. It is spread by the wood tick *Dermacentor andersoni*.

The Palyam, Kasba and Vellore viruses belonging to the *Orbivirus* group have been isolated from mosquitoes in India but their pathogenic significance is not known.

UNGROUPED ARBOVIRUSES

A number of arboviruses isolated from insects, animals, birds and human beings have not yet been assigned to any taxonomic group. Examples of ungrouped arboviruses isolated from India are as follows:

Wanowri virus: This was isolated from *Hyalomma* ticks in India and from the brain of a young girl who died after a two-day fever in Sri Lanka. The virus is also present in Iran and Egypt.

Bhanja virus: This was isolated from *Haemophysalis* ticks from goats in Ganjam. Human infections with disease and death have been reported from Yugoslavia.

RODENT-BORNE VIRUSES

A similar ecological group is that of the rodent-borne (robo) viruses maintained in nature and transmitted by rodents, and sometimes infecting other species, including humans. Roboviruses, like arboviruses, belong to different taxonomical families, some of them in common with arboviruses.

Genus *Hantavirus*

This virus causes hemorrhagic fever with renal syndrome (HFRS), also known as endemic or epidemic nephrosonephritis.

The disease occurs in two forms: the milder epidemic nephritis (EN) common in Scandinavia and the more serious epidemic hemorrhagic fever (EHF) in the Far East. The clinical picture resembles typhoid, leptospirosis and scrub typhus.

The genus contains at least four species:

I.   **Hantaan virus** causing the severe HFRS in the Far East, North Asia and Russia

II. **Seoul virus** causing a milder type of disease and probably present worldwide

III. **Puumala virus** responsible for nephropathia epidemica in northern and eastern Europe

IV. **Prospect Hill virus** isolated from voles in the USA, which has not been associated with human illness

Hantavirus species are natural pathogens of rodents—field mice (*Apodemus agrarius*) and rats (*Rattus rattus and R.norvegicus*) in Seoul, and voles in Puumala and Prospect Hill viruses. Viremia is present in infected rodents and shed in urine, feces and saliva in high titres. Transmission from rodent to rodent and rodent to humans is primarily by inhalation of the virus contained in dried excreta. Domestic rats appear to be the source of infection in urban cases of HFRS. Demonstration of IgM antibody by ELISA or of rising titres of immune adherence hemagglutinating antibodies in paired sera confirms the diagnosis.

A new syndrome, the **Hantavirus pulmonary syndrome,** was identified in southwestern USA in 1993. After a prodrome of fever, malaise, myalgia and gastrointestinal symptoms lasting for 3–4 days, patients develop pulmonary involvement with pulmonary edema. In severe cases, tachypnea, tachycardia, hypotension and hypoxia lead to death. The disease is caused by a newly identified Hantavirus, the *Sin Nombre* (meaning nameless) virus, which is associated with the deer mouse and other rodents. No arthropod has been linked with transmission of the virus. Infection appears to be caused by inhalation of virus aerosols in dried rodent feces.

RECAP

- Arboviruses (arthropod-borne viruses) are transmitted by hematophagous insect vectors. They multiply in bloodsucking insects (mosquitoes and ticks) and are transmitted by bite to vertebrate hosts.
- They can be cultivated by intracerebral inoculation of suckling mice (optimal method), primary cell cultures (chick embryo fibroblasts) and continuous cell lines (HeLa, Vero embryonated hen eggs (yolk sac, chorioallantoic membrane)).
- Most arboviruses agglutinate chick erythrocytes by hemagglutinin antigens; inhibition of this by specific antibody is used for diagnosis.
- Complement fixing and neutralising antibodies have also been detected in serological studies.
- Arboviruses are generally labile, being inactivated at room temperature and by bile salts, ether and other lipid solvents.
- Arboviruses cause the following syndromes with varying degrees of severity (sometimes, subclinical infections):

- ❖ Fever with or without rash and arthralgia (Dengue types 1–4, Chikungunya, O'nyong-nyong, Ross River, West Nile, sandfly fever, Rift Valley fever, Colorado tick fever)
  - ❖ Encephalitis (Equine encephalitis, Japanese B encephalitis, West Nile fever)
  - ❖ Hemorrhagic fevers (Chikungunya, Dengue types 1–4, Kyasanur Forest disease, Crimean Congo hemorrhagic fever)
  - ❖ Yellow fever affecting the liver
- Japanese encephalitis is a serious illness, and there have been several outbreaks in India. It is transmitted by *Culex* mosquitoes and amplifier hosts include birds, cattle, buffaloes and pigs.
- Yellow fever is a hemorrhagic fever of humans and primates caused by the yellow fever virus—a member of Flaviviridae. It is confined to certain areas of the world (Central Africa, parts of South and Central America). Active immunisation with the 17D strain of live, attenuated yellow fever vaccine is required by travellers visiting endemic regions.
- Dengue fever is an acute febrile disease caused by the dengue fever virus (Types 1–4). The virus is transmitted by the *Aedes* mosquito. Primary infection results in moderately severe febrile illness. Subsequent infection with a different serotype may induce severe hemorrhagic fever and dengue shock syndrome. Laboratory diagnosis is usually by demonstrating antibodies, detection of viral RNA, rarely isolation of the virus.
- The Chikungunya virus caused epidemics in India. Humans are the host, and *Aedes aegypti* mosquitoes the vectors.
- Kyasanur Forest disease is a hemorrhagic fever from Shimoga district in Karnataka which has now spread to other areas within and adjoining the state. The tick *Haemaphysalis spinigera* is the vector.
- Rodent-borne viruses: The genus *Hantavirus* consists of at least four serogroups. Wild rodents (species of mice, rats, voles) are the hosts. Transmission to humans is through inhalation of infectious aerosols from rodent excreta. Acute Hantavirus infections are characterised either by acute renal failure (nephritis) and hemorrhage or a syndrome of acute non-cardiogenic pulmonary edema.

ESSAYS

1. How are arboviruses classified? List the diseases caused by them in India. Describe the laboratory diagnosis of any one virus.
2. Define arboviruses. Discuss mosquito-borne arboviral infections in India.
3. Describe the epidemiology and diagnosis of dengue fever.
4. Describe the epidemiology, laboratory diagnosis and prevention of Japanese encephalitis.

SHORT ANSWERS

1. Name the tick-borne arboviruses. Describe the epidemiology of tick-borne diseases seen in India.
2. Draw a flowchart for the transmission of Japanese encephalitis.
3. Name the vectors and the viral infections transmitted by them.

SHORT NOTES

1. Dengue hemorrhagic fever
2. Yellow fever
3. Serological tests for the diagnosis of arboviral infections
4. Kyasanur forest disease
5. List of rodent-borne viruses and epidemiology of Hantaviruses

57 Rhabdoviruses

exposure) as the dog died two days later. Its brain was sent to the veterinary lab and tested positive for Negri bodies on histopathology.

Clinical Case 2 A 30-year-old woman was brought to a referral hospital from a rural area where she was admitted with fever, anorexia and vomiting for the previous four days. However, she became delirious and developed hallucinations and was started on supportive therapy in the hospital pending laboratory results. On enquiry, her relatives informed the doctor that she used to go out to collect firewood and that she had been bitten by a stray dog about three months previously. No medical help was sought at that time and only some local treatment given for wound care. However, the next day she developed severe spasms in the pharyngeal muscles in an attempt to drink fluids. This spasm increased in intensity and distribution leading to generalised convulsions. She died during one of these attacks due to respiratory failure. Post-mortem was conducted and the brain tissue was found positive for rabies virus antigen by direct fluorescent antibody test.

INTRODUCTION

Bullet-shaped, enveloped viruses with a single-stranded RNA genome are classified as rhabdoviruses (from *rhabdos*, meaning rod). The family Rhabdoviridae contains viruses that infect mammals, reptiles, birds, fish, insects and plants. Some members multiply in vertebrates and arthropods.

Rhabdoviruses infecting mammals belong to **two genera**: *Vesiculovirus* containing vesicular stomatitis virus and related viruses, and *Lyssavirus* (*lyssa*, meaning rage, a synonym for rabies) containing rabies virus and related viruses.

Clinical Case 1 A five-year-old boy was bitten by a rabid dog and presented to the Emergency department with multiple scratches on the upper arms and the neck. The parents stated that dog was a stray present most of the time in their area (so it could be observed). The child was given local wound toileting, followed by application of povidone iodine. The wound was left open. He was given tetanus toxoid (as his booster was due) and Vero cell culture vaccine was started. He completed the course (0, 3, 7, 14 and 28 days post-

RABIES VIRUS

Morphology

The rabies virus is bullet shaped, 180×75 nm in size, with one end rounded or conical and the other planar or concave. The lipoprotein envelope carries knob-like spikes, composed of glycoprotein G. Spikes do not cover the planar end of the virion. Spikes may be released from the envelope by treatment with lipid solvents or detergents. Beneath the envelope is the membrane or matrix (M) protein layer which may be invaginated at the planar end. The membrane may project outwards from the planar end of some virions, forming a bleb. The core of the virion consists of helically arranged ribonucleoprotein (**Fig. 57.1**). The genome is an unsegmented, linear, negative sense RNA. Also present in the nucleocapsid are RNA-dependent RNA transcriptase and some structural proteins.

Resistance

The virus is sensitive to ethanol, iodine preparations, quaternary ammonium compounds, soap, detergents

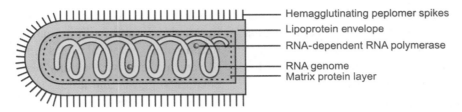

Hemagglutinating peplomer spikes
Lipoprotein envelope
RNA-dependent RNA polymerase
RNA genome
Matrix protein layer

Fig. 57.1   Rabies virus

and lipid solvents such as ether, chloroform and acetone. It is inactivated by phenol, formalin, beta propiolactone, ultraviolet irradiation and sunlight. Thermal inactivation occurs in one hour at 50°C and five minutes at 60°C. It dies at room temperature but can survive for weeks when stabilised by 50% glycerol. It survives at 4°C for weeks. It can be preserved at −70°C or by lyophilisation. For storage in dry ice, the virus has to be sealed in vials as it is inactivated on exposure to CO_2.

Antigenic properties

Glycoprotein: The surface spikes are composed of glycoprotein G, which is important in pathogenesis, virulence and immunity. The important properties are as follows:

- It mediates the binding of the virus to acetylcholine receptors in neural tissues
- It induces hemagglutination inhibiting (HI) antibodies. Rabiesvirus possesses hemagglutinating activity, optimally seen with goose erythrocytes at 0–4°C and a pH of 6.2. It is inactivated by heat (56°C for 30–60 minutes), ether, trypsin, pronase, deoxycholate or Tween-80 but not by beta propiolactone. HI antibodies develop following infection or immunisation and parallel neutralising antibodies. The hemagglutinin antigen is species specific and distinct from the antigens on rabies-related viruses.
- It induces neutralising antibodies (protective antibodies)
- It stimulates cytotoxic T cell immunity.
- It is a serotype-specific antigen.
- Purified glycoprotein may act as a safe and effective subunit vaccine.

Nucleoprotein: This is a nucleocapsid protein, with the following properties:

- It induces complement fixing antibodies.
- The antibodies are not protective.
- The antigen is group specific and cross-reactions are seen with some rabies-related viruses.

- The antiserum prepared against the nucleocapsid antigen is used in diagnostic immunofluorescence tests.

Other antigens identified include two membrane proteins, glycolipid and RNA-dependent RNA polymerase.

Host range and cultivation

Animals: All mammals are susceptible to rabies infection, though differences in susceptibility exist between species. Cattle, cats and foxes are highly susceptible, whereas skunks, opossums and fowl are relatively resistant. Humans and dogs occupy an intermediate position. Pups are more susceptible than adult dogs. Experimental infection can be produced in any laboratory animal but mice are the animals of choice. They can be infected by any route. After intracerebral inoculation, they develop encephalitis and die within 5–30 days.

Street virus: The rabies virus isolated from natural human or animal infection is termed the street virus. Following inoculation by any route, it can cause fatal encephalitis in laboratory animals after a **long and variable incubation period** of about 1–12 weeks. Intracytoplasmic inclusion bodies (**Negri bodies**) can be demonstrated in the brain of animals dying of street virus infection. Negri bodies are composed of a finely fibrillar matrix and rabies virus particles and are most abundant in the cerebellum and hippocampus.

Fixed virus: After several serial intracerebral passages in rabbits, the virus undergoes certain changes and becomes what is called the fixed virus. The fixed virus is more neurotropic, though it is much less infective by other routes. After intracerebral inoculation, it produces fatal encephalitis after a **short and fixed incubation period** of 6–7 days. Negri bodies are usually not demonstrable in the brain of animals dying of fixed virus infection. The fixed virus is used for **vaccine production**.

Chick embryos: The rabies virus can be grown in chick embryos. The usual mode of inoculation is into the yolk sac. Serial propagation in chick embryos has led to the development of attenuated vaccine strains like Flury and Kelev. Strains adapted to duck eggs which give high yields of the virus have been used for the preparation of inactivated vaccines.

Tissue culture: The rabies virus can grow in several primary and continuous cell cultures such as chick embryo fibroblast, and porcine or hamster kidney but cytopathic effects are not apparent and the yield of virus is low. The fixed virus strains adapted for growth in human diploid cell, chick embryo and Vero cell cultures are used for the production of vaccines.

RABIES

Rabies has been recognised since ancient times as a disease transmitted to humans and animals by the bite of 'mad dogs'. The name 'rabies' comes from the Latin word *rabidus*, meaning mad, derived from the Sanskrit root *rabhas*, for frenzy. The disease in human beings is called **hydrophobia** because the patient exhibits fear of water, being incapable of drinking though subject to intolerable thirst. Rabies in animals is not called hydrophobia because they do not have this peculiar feature.

The causative agent of rabies had, for centuries, been associated with the saliva of rabid dogs. In a series of studies dating from 1881, Pasteur established that the rabies virus was present in the brain of infected animals. By serial intracerebral passage in rabbits, he obtained the fixed virus and demonstrated that dogs could be rendered immune by a series of injections of fixed virus of graded infectivity. This vaccine was prepared by drying, for various periods, pieces of spinal cord from rabbits infected with the fixed virus. In July 1885, **Joseph Meister**, a nine-year-old boy, severely bitten by a rabid dog and in grave risk of developing rabies, was given a course of 13 inoculations of the infected cord vaccine by Pasteur. The boy survived. This dramatic event was a milestone in the development of medicine.

Pathogenicity

Human infection is usually caused by the bite of rabid dogs or other animals. The virus present in the saliva of the animal is deposited in the wound. If untreated, about half of such cases may develop rabies (Fig. 57.2). Rarely, infection may also occur following non-bite exposures such as licks or aerosols or transplantation of cornea or other virus infected tissues. Humans appear to possess a high degree of natural resistance

to rabies. The extent of inapparent or abortive infection with rabies virus in humans is not known but the finding, in a survey, of rabies antibodies in six per cent of veterinarians without any history of antirabic vaccination suggests that it does occur.

The virus appears to multiply in the muscles, connective tissue or nerves at the site of deposition for 48–72 hours. It penetrates the nerve endings and **travels in the axoplasm** towards the spinal cord and brain. The movement of the virus in the axons is passive, at a speed of about **3 mm per hour**. The infection spreads **centripetally from the axon to the neuronal bodies**, and progressively up the spinal cord through the synapses of the neurons. The virus ascends rapidly to the brain where it multiplies and spreads centrifugally along the nerve trunks to various parts of the body including the salivary glands. **It multiplies in the salivary glands**

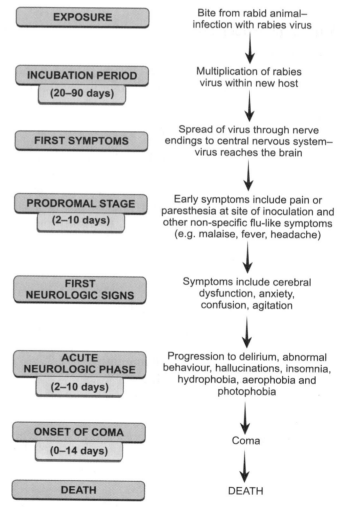

Fig. 57.2 Pathogenesis of rabies

and is shed in saliva. The presence of the virus in saliva and the irritability and aggression brought on by the encephalitis ensure the transmission and survival of the virus in nature. The virus ultimately reaches virtually every tissue in the body, though centrifugal dissemination may be interrupted at any stage by death. The virus is almost invariably present in the cornea and facial skin of patients because of their proximity to the brain. This provides a method for the antemortem diagnosis of human rabies.

In humans the incubation period is usually 1–3 months, though it may be as short as seven days or as long as three years. The incubation period is usually short in persons bitten on the face or head, and long in those bitten on the legs. This may be related to the distance the virus has to travel to reach the brain. The incubation period is generally shorter in children than in adults (*Cases 1* and *2*).

Clinical stages

The course of the disease in humans can be classified into four stages:

1. **Prodrome**: Onset is marked by prodromal symptoms such as fever, headache, malaise, fatigue and anorexia. An early symptom is often a neuritic type of pain or paresthesia and fasciculation at the site of virus entry. Apprehension, anxiety, agitation, irritability, nervousness, insomnia and depression characterise the prodromal phase, which usually lasts 2–4 days. Excessive libido, priapism and spontaneous ejaculation may occur rarely.

2. **Acute encephalitic phase**: The acute neurological phase usually begins with hyperactivity, which is characteristically intermittent, with bouts of bizarre behaviour, agitation or seizures appearing between apparently normal periods. Such hyperactivity may be spontaneous or precipitated by external stimuli. The pathognomonic feature is difficulty in drinking, together with intense thirst. Patients may be able to swallow dry solids but not liquids. Attempts to drink bring on such painful spasms of the pharynx and larynx, producing choking or gagging, that patients develop a dread of even the sight or sound of water (**hydrophobia**). Generalised convulsions follow.

3. **Coma**: Some patients may enter into a comatose state.

4. **Death** usually occurs within 1–6 days due to respiratory arrest during convulsions.

In dogs, the incubation period is usually 3–6 weeks but it may range from 10 days to a year. The initial signs are an alert, troubled air and a change in disposition with restlessness, snapping at imaginary objects, licking or gnawing at the site of the bite. After 2–3 days of this prodromal stage, the disease develops into either the furious or dumb type of rabies.

- In **furious rabies,** which is much more common, the dog runs amok, biting without provocation and indiscriminately. The lower jaw droops and saliva drools from the mouth. Paralysis, convulsions and death follow.

- The second type, **dumb rabies**, is the paralytic form in which the animal lies huddled, unable to feed. The dog may not bite but attempts to feed it are dangerous. The dumb form is as infectious as the furious type. About 60 per cent of rabid dogs shed the virus in saliva. Rabid dogs usually die in 3–5 days.

Laboratory diagnosis

Laboratory diagnosis of **human rabies** till recently was of little practical importance as death was considered inevitable and no serious attempt at treatment was made, other than heavy sedation. If a patient survived, he was considered not to have had rabies! But now that survival from established rabies has been demonstrated in rare instances, it is necessary to be able to make a laboratory distinction between rabies and other forms of encephalitis, particularly that following antirabic vaccination.

1. Specimen: The specimens tested are corneal smears and skin biopsy (from face or neck) or saliva antemortem, and brain postmortem.

2. Direct microscopy:
- **Antemortem**: The method most commonly used for diagnosis is the demonstration of rabies virus antigens by immunofluorescence. **Direct immunofluorescence** is done using monioclonal antibodies tagged with fluorescein isothiocyanate. Immunoperoxidase staining can be used in to antigen in tissues.

- **Postmortem**: Diagnosis may be made postmortem by demonstration of **Negri bodies** in the brain, but they may be absent in about 20 per cent of cases.

3. Isolation:
- **Animal inoculation**: Isolation of the virus by intracerebral inoculation in mice can be attempted from the brain, CSF, saliva and urine (biological test). Chances of isolation are greater early in the disease.

A few days after onset, neutralising antibodies appear and the virus can then be isolated only occasionally. The inoculated mice are examined for signs of illness, and their brains are examined at death or at 28 days post-inoculation for Negri bodies, or by immunofluorescence.

- **Tissue culture**: A more rapid and sensitive method is isolation of the virus in tissue culture cell lines (WI 38, BHK 21, CER). CPE is minimal and so virus isolation is identified by immunofluorescence. A positive IF test can be obtained as early as 2–4 days after inoculation. The identity of the isolate can be established by the neutralisation test with specific antirabies antibody.

- **Antibody demonstration**: High titre antibodies are present in the CSF in rabies but not after immunisation. Their demonstration can therefore be used for diagnosis. Demonstration of antibodies by ELISA has been used for determining the antibody response in laboratory personnel who are exposed to the rabies virus before deciding booster doses. Their diagnostic role is limited in antemortem diagnosis as the disease is largely fatal.

- **Molecular methods**: Detection of rabies virus RNA by reverse transcription PCR is a sensitive method, if facilities are available.

Laboratory diagnosis of rabies in **dogs and other biting animals** is of great importance in assessing the risk of infection and deciding post-exposure treatment. The whole carcass or the severed head of the animal suspected to have died of rabies may be sent to the laboratory. Alternatively, the brain may be removed carefully and two portions—one in 50% glycerol saline and the other in Zenker's fixative—sent for biological test and microscopy, respectively. The portion of brain sent should include the hippocampus and cerebellum as **Negri bodies** are most abundant there. The following tests are done in the laboratory:

Demonstration of inclusion bodies (Negri bodies): This is still the most commonly used method as facilities for immunofluorescence and biological tests are not available in many laboratories. Impression smears of the brain are stained by **Seller's technique** (basic fuchsin and methylene blue in methanol), which has the advantage that fixation and staining are done simultaneously. Negri bodies are seen as intracytoplasmic, round or oval, purplish pink structures with characteristic basophilic inner granules. Negri bod-

ies vary in size, 3–27 µm (Fig. 57.3). Other types of inclusion bodies may sometimes be seen in the brain in diseases such as canine distemper but the presence of inner structures in the Negri bodies makes differentiation easy. If impression smears are negative, the tissue should be sectioned and stained by Giemsa or Mann's method. Failure to find Negri bodies does not exclude the diagnosis of rabies.

Demonstration of rabies virus antigen by immunofluorescence: In experienced hands, this is more sensitive than the visualisation of Negri bodies, and quite as sensitive as the 'biological' (mouse inoculation) test, with the advantage of immediate results. Examination of salivary glands by immunofluorescence is useful. It may indicate whether the animal was shedding the virus in saliva.

Isolation of the rabies virus (animal inoculation): This is done as described above, for human rabies diagnosis.

Prophylaxis

Pre-exposure: Specific prophylaxis is ideally given before exposure to infection. In animals, this is imperative but human pre-exposure immunisation was only used in persons at high risk, such as veterinarians and dog handlers because neural vaccines carry some risk of serious complications. The introduction of cell culture vaccines, which are free from serious complications, has made pre-exposure immunisation in humans safe and feasible.

Post-exposure: Specific prophylaxis is generally used after exposure to infection and is therefore called antirabic treatment. This consists of local treatment, active immunisation with antirabic vaccines and passive immunisation with antirabies serum.

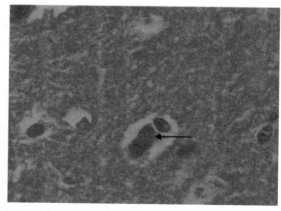

Fig. 57.3   Seller's stain showing intracytoplasmic negri bodies

Local treatment: Animal bites deposit the virus in the wound. Prompt cauterisation of the wound therefore helps destroy the virus. The wound should be scrubbed well immediately with soap and water. This is a very important step in the prevention of rabies as soap destroys the virus effectively. After washing the soap away completely, the wound is treated with quaternary ammonium compounds (such as cetavlon), tincture or aqueous solution of iodine, or alcohol (40–70%). In severe wounds, antirabic serum may be applied topically and infiltrated around the wound. It is advisable to postpone suturing the wound. Anti-tetanus measures and antibiotics to prevent sepsis may be used as necessary.

Antirabic vaccines: These fall into two main categories: neural and non-neural. The neural vaccines are associated with serious risk of neurological complications and are no longer used.

- **Neural vaccines**: These are suspensions of nervous tissues of animals infected with the fixed rabies virus. The earliest was Pasteur's cord vaccine prepared by drying over caustic potash, for varying periods, pieces of infected rabbit spinal cord. This was replaced by infected brain vaccines, of which there have been several preparations. Neural vaccines are unsatisfactory for many reasons. They are poor immunogens as they contain mostly nucleocapsid antigen, with only small quantities of glycoprotein G, which is the sole protective antigen. They may contain infectious agents which may not be inactivated during vaccine preparation and storage. They are encephalitogenic. Neural vaccines have been abandoned now in most parts of the world as tissue culture vaccines are available at an affordable cost.
  - **Semple vaccine**: This vaccine developed by Semple (1911) at the Central Research Institute, Kasauli (India), was the most widely used vaccine for over half a century. It is a 5% suspension of sheep brain infected with fixed virus and inactivated with phenol at 37°C, leaving no residual live virus.
  - **Beta propiolactone (BPL) vaccine**: This is a modification of the Semple vaccine, in which beta propiolactone is used as the inactivating agent instead of phenol. It is believed to be more antigenic, so smaller doses are considered adequate. The major antirabic vaccine producing laboratories in India manufacture BPL vaccine.

  - **Suckling mouse brain vaccines**: The encephalitogenic factor in brain tissue is a basic protein associated with myelin. It is scanty or absent in the non-myelinated neural tissue of newborn animals. So vaccines were developed using infant mouse, rat or rabbit brain. Occasional cases of neurological reactions have occurred following infant brain vaccines also. Infant brain vaccine is impractical in India due to the very large quantities required.

- **Non-neural vaccines**:
  - **Egg vaccines**:
    Duck egg vaccine prepared from a fixed virus adapted for growth in duck eggs and inactivated with beta propiolactone was used, but was discontinued because of its poor immunogenicity. A purified, more potent duck egg vaccine was developed, but was supplanted by tissue culture vaccines which became available then.

    Live attenuated chick embryo vaccines: Two types of vaccines were developed with the Flury strain: the Low Egg Passage (LEP) vaccine at 40–50 egg passage level for immunisation of dogs and the High Egg Passage (HEP) vaccine at 180 passage level for cattle and cats. These are not in use now.
  - **Tissue culture vaccines**: The first cell culture vaccine was the human diploid cell (HDC) vaccine developed by Koprowsky, Wiktor and Plotkin. It is a purified and concentrated preparation of fixed rabies virus (Pitman–Moore strain) grown on human diploid cells (WI 38 or MRC 5) and inactivated with beta propiolactone or tri-n-butyl phosphate. It is highly antigenic and free from serious side effects. Its only disadvantage is its high cost.

    Other equally effective and more economical vaccines have been developed. These include primary cell culture vaccines grown on chick embryo, and continuous cell culture vaccines grown on the Vero cell line derived from the monkey kidneys. In India the following cell culture vaccines are available: human diploid cell **(HDC) vaccine**, purified chick embryo cell **(PCEC) vaccine** and purified Vero cell **(PVC) vaccine**. All three of them are equally safe and effective. These are currently used for immunisation.

    Subunit vaccine: The glycoprotein subunit on the virus surface, which is the protective antigen, has been cloned and recombinant vaccines produced. They are still in the experimental stage.

Vaccination schedules

Antirabic vaccine should be administered when a person has been bitten, scratched or licked by an animal which is rabid or cannot be apprehended. When the biting animal can be observed, it should not be destroyed but should be kept for 10 days. This observation period is recommended because the virus may be present in saliva 3–4 days before onset of symptoms and the animal usually dies within 5–6 days of developing the disease. If the animal remains healthy after this period, there is no risk of rabies and vaccination, if already started, may be discontinued. This, of course, does not take into account the rare possibility of the carrier state in dogs.

In cases where the vaccine is started with the biting animal kept under observation, an alternative recommendation is to stop treatment after five days. The animal is observed for a further five days, the vaccine being started again if the animal becomes ill or dies during the period. The WHO guidelines on **post-exposure prophylaxis** depends on the risk category to which the patient is belongs (Table 57.1). All three cell culture vaccines available in India (HDC, PCEC and PVC) have the same dosage schedule, which is the same for both adults and children.

Post-exposure prophylaxis requires five or six doses, on days 0, 3, 7, 14, 30 and optionally 90. This course is expected to give protection for at least five years, during which period any further exposure may need only one or two booster doses (on days 0, 3) depending on the degree of risk. After five years, it is advisable to give a full five-injection course on exposure to infection.

The vaccine is to be given IM or SC in the deltoid region, or in children on the anterolateral aspect of the thigh. Gluteal injections are to be avoided as they have been found to be less immunogenic.

It has been shown that a dose of 0.1 ml administered intradermally is as effective as a 0.5–1.0 ml dose SC or IM and that immunisation may thus be made more economical. However, this is not recommended as routine practice, as intradermal injection is technically difficult, and it will be ineffective if this dose is given subcutaneously by mistake.

Pre-exposure prophylaxis requires three doses of the vaccine injected on days 0, 7, 21 or 0, 28 and 56. A booster dose is recommended after one year and then once every five years.

Passive immunisation

This can be provided by:

- **Equine rabies immune globulin (ERIG):** Antirabic serum is manufactured by hyper immunisation of

Table 57.1   *Type of contact, exposure and recommended post-exposure prophylaxis*

Category	Type of contact with a suspect or confirmed rabid domestic or wild[a] animal, or animal un-available for testing	Type of exposure	Recommended post-exposure prophylaxis
I	Touching or feeding of animals Licks on intact skin	None	None, if reliable case history is abailable
II	Nibbling of uncovered skin Minor scratches or abrasions without bleeding	Minor	Administer vaccine immediately[b] Stop treatment if animal remains healthy throughout an observation period of 10 days[c] or fi animal is proven to be negative for rabies by a reliable laboratory, using appropriate diagnostic techniques
III	Single or multiple transdermal bites or scratches, licks on broken skin Contamination of mucous membrane with saliva (i.e. licks) Exposures to bats[d]	Severe	Administer rabies immunolobulin and vaccine immediately. Stop treatment if animal remains healthy throughout an observation period of 10 days, of if animal is found to be negative for rabies by a reliable laboratory using appropriate diagnostic techniques

a   Exposure to rodents, rabbits and hares seldom, if ever, requires specific anti-rabies post-exposure prophylaxis.

b   If an apparently healthy dog or cat in/or from a low-risk area is placed under observation, the situation may warrant delaying initiation of treatment.

c   This observation period applies only to dogs and cats. Except in the case of threatened or endangered species, other domestic and wild animals suspected as rabid should be humanely killed and their tissues examined for the presence of rabies antigen using appropriate laboratory techniques.

d   Post-exposure prophylaxis should be considered when contact between a human and a bat has occurred, unless the exposed person can rule out a bite or scratch, or exposure to a mucous membrane.

horses. Crude equine antirabies serum is not to be used as it is liable to induce anaphylactic reactions. Purified ERIG is much safer, though not completely free from risk.

- **Human rabies immune globulin (HRIG)**: Though limited in availability and more costly, HRIG is preferred over ERIG. It is free from the danger of sensitisation but should also be free from HIV and hepatitis viruses.

Passive immunisation is an important adjunct to vaccination and should be invariably employed whenever the exposure is considered of high risk. The recommended dose of HRIG is 20 IU/kg body weight, half the volume infiltrated at the site of the wound and the other half injected in the gluteal region. Passive immunisation should be given before or simultaneously with the first injection of the vaccine, but not after it. In persons receiving the serum and vaccine, a booster dose of cell culture vaccine on day 90 may be given.

'Vaccine failures' (persons developing rabies even after a full course of immunisation) are not uncommon with neural vaccines, while they are extremely rare when immediate local treatment has been followed by rabies immunoglobulin and a full course of a cell culture vaccine. In view of the safety of the cell culture vaccine, it would be advisable to recommend the vaccine even when there is the slightest risk of exposure to rabies.

Vaccine for animals: Antirabies immunisation in animals is to be done as pre-exposure prophylaxis. Post-exposure treatment is not generally of much use. Neural vaccines are not satisfactory as they are not adequately immunogenic, need multiple doses and have to be repeated every six months. Concentrated cell culture vaccines containing inactivated virus are now available, which give good protection after a single IM injection. Injections are given at 12 weeks of age and repeated at 1–3-year intervals. Rabies vaccines may be given separately or as a combined vaccine for immunisation against other common veterinary infections also.

Vaccine baits (chicken head or other meat containing live attenuated rabies virus) have been used to immunise the red fox in an attempt to check the epizootic in the forests of Europe.

Treatment

Until recently, rabies was considered to be invariably fatal and no serious attempt at treatment was made, apart from sedation. It has now been demonstrated that complete recovery can occur from established rabies, with intensive supportive care and management of complications. No specific antirabies agent is available.

Epidemiology

Human rabies is a dead end. Direct person-to-person transmission of rabies has not been recorded, though the virus is present in the saliva of patients. Therefore, there is no danger in examining or nursing hydrophobia patients provided suitable precautions are taken. An unusual mode of transmission of rabies has occurred in some recipients of corneal grafts. The donors had died of unsuspected rabies and the infection was transmitted through the cornea.

The rabies virus is present in terrestrial animals in all parts of the world except Australasia and Antartica, and some islands like Britain. Two epidemiological types of rabies exist: **urban,** transmitted by domestic animals like dogs and cats; and **sylvatic,** involving animals in the wild, such as jackals, wolves, foxes, mongooses, skunks and bats. Most cases of human rabies follow dog bites but in endemic areas almost any animal can transmit rabies. In India, antirabic treatment is to be considered following the bite of any animal except rats. Where urban or domestic rabies has been controlled, as in the USA, the majority of infections are due to bites by wild animals.

The **primary source** of the rabies virus in nature seems to be in the mustelids and viverrids. The virus survives in this reservoir population by achieving a state of latency. From here foxes, wolves and jackals acquire the infection and the disease spreads to dogs and other domestic animals.

Another natural cycle of rabies concerns bats. A fatal paralytic disease of cattle and humans was noticed in Central and South America and the West Indies early in the twentieth century and was shown to be transmitted by vampire bats that sweep down on their prey at night. **Vampire bats** may shed the rabies virus as symptomless carriers over a period of several months.

Rabies also occurs in **insectivorous and frugivorous bats.** Infection in insectivorous bats is symptomatic, while frugivorous bats become asymptomatic carriers. While in canines rabies is neurotropic, in bats the virus is primarily adapted to the respiratory tract. Humans may be infected by aerosols if they enter caves colonised by infected bats. Pneumotropic rabies virus strains have been obtained from bats. Bat rabies is largely confined to the Americas. A few strains of the rabies virus have been isolated from bats in Europe but their epidemiological significance is not known.

Rabies is endemic in India. It has been estimated that more than 30,000 people die of rabies in India every year and more than 700,000 receive antirabies vaccine. Human rabies can be checked by control of rabies in domestic animals, by registration, licensing and vaccination of pets and destruction of stray animals. With the dog population in India estimated to be over 16 million, the problem is immense. However, rabies can be eliminated only if the wild vectors such as jackals and foxes, and the reservoir mustelids and viverrids are controlled. Rabies has been eliminated from islands like Britain and Japan by rigid quarantine. Australia which has no native mustelid or viverrid population has no rabies.

RABIES-RELATED VIRUSES

The genus *Lyssavirus* consists of the rabies virus and other serologically related viruses (Table 57.2). Lyssaviruses have been classified into seven serotypes:

- **Rabies** virus is classified as *Lyssavirus* serotype 1.
- The **Lagos bat** virus, classified as *Lyssavirus* serotype 2, was isolated in 1956 from the pooled brains of frugivorous bats from Lagos Island, Nigeria. It causes a rabies-like illness following intracerebral inoculation. Negri bodies are found in infected monkey brain but not in mice or dogs.
- The **Mokola** virus, first isolated in 1968 from shrews captured near Ibadan, Nigeria, has later been found in many wild and domestic animals in Africa. It was also recovered from two children with central nervous system disease, one of whom died. A case of laboratory infection with the virus occurred in a person possessing high titres of antibody to the rabies virus. It is classified as *Lyssavirus* serotype 3.
- The **Duvenhage** virus was reported in 1971 from the brain of a man who died in South Africa of clinical rabies after being bitten by a bat. It is classified as *Lyssavirus* serotype 4.
- Rabies-like viruses isolated from European bats have been classified into two groups: **European bat Lyssavirus types 1 and 2**. They can infect humans, as was found in the UK in 2002, when a wildlife worker fell ill with 'rabies' and died. This was the first 'rabies' death in the UK in a century.
- Australia was considered free of rabies and related viruses till 1996, when a lyssavirus was isolated from a frugivorous bat. Since then a number of similar isolates have been obtained from different types of bats in Australia. Fatal infections have occurred in persons having contact with bats. The virus antibody is widely prevalent among Australian bats which appear to be carriers. The virus, named **Australian bat lyssavirus** is closely related to, but distinct from the rabies virus. Antirabic vaccine and serum appear to protect against experimental infection.

The relevance of rabies related viruses in human disease is not clear, though some of them have caused illness and death in humans. They are considered to represent a biological bridge between the rabies virus and other rhabdoviruses.

Table 57.2   Lyssavirus *sero/genotypes*

Genotype/ Serotype	Virus	Isolated from	Distribution
1	Rabies	Warm-blooded animals	Worldwide with few exceptions
2	Lagos bat/Natal bat	Bat/cat	Nigeria/Central and SouthAfrica
3	Mokola	Shrew/cat/dog/human	Nigeria/other African countries
4	Duvenhage	Human/bat	South Africa
5	European bat *Lyssavirus*: Type I	Bat/human	Europe
6	European bat *Lyssavirus*: Type II	Bat/human	Europe
7	Australian bat *Lyssavirus*	Bat/human	Australia

RECAP

- Rhabdoviruses are enveloped, helical, RNA viruses, which are bullet shaped. Two genera infect humans and economically important animals: *Lyssavirus* and *Vesiculovirus*. Lyssavirus includes the rabies virus.
- The rabies virus causes rabies in humans and a wide variety of animals:
  - The main reservoir of infection is in carnivores (foxes, skunks, raccoons, jackals, certain types of bats). The virus is spread to humans by the bite injury inflicted by an infected animal.
  - Rabies, an almost invariably fatal disease of the central nervous system, has a greatly variable incubation period.
  - Laboratory diagnosis of rabies is often made post-mortem by demonstration of Negri bodies in brain cells, or by using immunofluorescence to detect the viral antigens. The virus may also be isolated from the brain and saliva; this is the most definitive means of diagnosis for which tissue culture lines, such as W-138 or BHK-21, are used.
  - Prevention is achieved by active immunisation with vaccines and passive immunisation with the rabies immunoglobulin. The vaccines available for use in humans at present are inactivated tissue culture vaccines which are safe and effective. Passive immunisation is provided by antirabies sera.

ESSAYS

1. Describe the pathogenesis and laboratory diagnosis of rabies.
2. Describe immunisation against rabies.

SHORT ANSWERS

1. Tissue culture vaccines for rabies.
2. Pre-exposure prophylaxis against rabies.

SHORT NOTES

1. Fixed and street rabies virus
2. Negri bodies
3. Rabies-related viruses
4. Urban and sylvatic rabies

58 Hepatitis Viruses

Types of viral hepatitis

TYPE A HEPATITIS
  Hepatitis A virus (HAV)

TYPE B HEPATITIS
  Hepatitis B virus (HBV)

TYPE C HEPATITIS
  Hepatitis C virus (HCV)

TYPE D (DELTA) HEPATITIS

TYPE E HEPATITIS

HEPATITIS G VIRUS

(B — DNA) (A, C, D, E & G — RNA)

INTRODUCTION

The term 'viral hepatitis' refers to a primary infection of the liver by any one of a heterogeneous group of 'hepatitis viruses', which currently consists of types A, B, C, D, E and G. (The designation 'type F' had been proposed for a putative virus believed to cause transfusion-associated hepatitis, distinct from types A to E. But it proved to be a mutant [HBx] of the type B virus and not a separate entity. Type F was therefore deleted from the list of hepatitis viruses.)

Hepatitis viruses are taxonomically unrelated. Except for type B, which is a DNA virus, all the others are RNA viruses. The features common to them are their hepatotropism and ability to cause a similar icteric illness, ranging in severity from the unapparent to the fulminant fatal forms.

As all types of hepatitis viruses cause a clinically indistinguishable acute illness, their differentiation is based on their serological and molecular markers. Hepatitis may occur incidentally during many other viral infections, such as yellow fever, Lassa fever, Marburg, EB, cytomegalovirus, herpes simplex, varicella zoster, measles, rubella or coxsackie viruses. These are not included in the category of viral hepatitis.

Types of viral hepatitis

By epidemiological and clinical criteria, two types of viral hepatitis had been recognised for long:

- One type occurred sporadically or as epidemics, affecting mainly children and young adults, and transmitted by the fecal–oral route. This was called **infective** or **infectious hepatitis**, later termed **type A hepatitis.**

- A second type of viral hepatitis, transmitted mainly by inoculation, was originally observed in persons receiving serum inoculation or blood transfusion. This had been given various names such as **homologous serum jaundice, serum hepatitis** (because of its association with human or homologous antisera so commonly used for prophylaxis or therapy early in the twentieth century) and **transfusion hepatitis.** It was later called **type B hepatitis.**

Non-A non-B hepatitis (NANB): For a time it was believed that all viral hepatitis was caused by either of the two hepatitis viruses, type A accounting for all infectious hepatitis and type B for all post-transfusion or serum hepatitis. However, with the development of techniques for identifying type A and type B viruses, it became apparent that in many cases of infectious and post-transfusion hepatitis no evidence could be found of infection with either type A or B viruses. It therefore became evident that the clinical syndrome of type A or B hepatitis could also be caused by one or more other uncharacterised viruses. The term **non-A non-B hepatitis** was applied to this group but is no longer used now as it is now possible to diagnose specific infections. These non-A non-B viruses include the following types:

- **Type C virus** was later identified as causing many non-A non-B transfusion-associated hepatitis cases.
- A defective virus which depends on the helper functions of type B virus was called **delta** or **type D viruses.**
- Type E virus is yet another type of non-A non-B hepatitis transmitted by the fecal–oral route, prevalent mostly in the developing nations was found to be caused by the **type E virus.**

- **Type G hepatitis** can also cause hepatitis virus, can also cause hepatitis, but its role has not yet been adequately understood.

TYPE A HEPATITIS

Type A hepatitis (infectious hepatitis) is a subacute disease of global distribution, affecting mainly children and young adults.

Clinical features: The large majority of infections are asymptomatic. Overt illness is seen in only about 5 per cent of those infected. The incubation period is 2–6 weeks. The clinical disease consists of two stages: the prodromal or preicteric and the icteric stages. Onset may be acute or insidious, with fever, malaise, anorexia, nausea, vomiting and liver tenderness. These usually subside with onset of jaundice. Recovery is slow, over a period of 4–6 weeks. Very rarely a rapidly fatal fulminant hepatitis may occur. The disease is milder in children, in whom many infections may be anicteric. Mortality is low (0.1–1 per cent), with most of the deaths occurring in adults.

Hepatitis A virus (HAV)

In 1973, Feinstone and co-workers, using immuno-electron microscopy (IEM), demonstrated this virus in the feces of experimentally infected human volunteers. Chimpanzees and marmosets can be infected experimentally. HAV can be grown in some human and simian cell cultures and is the only human hepatitis virus which can be cultivated in vitro. It has also been cloned.

Morphology: HAV is a 27-nm, non-enveloped RNA virus belonging to the picornavirus family. It was originally designated as 'enterovirus 72' (Fig. 58.1). Because of its unique features, HAV is now recognised as the prototype of a new genus *Hepatovirus*. Only one serotype of the virus is known.

Resistance: HAV is resistant to inactivation by heat at 60°C for one hour, ether and acid at pH 3, but is inactivated by boiling for one minute, 1:4000 formaldehyde at 37°C for 72 hours, and chlorine 1 ppm for 30 minutes. It is not affected by anionic detergents. It survives prolonged storage at a temperature of 4°C or below.

Epidemiology: Natural infection with HAV is seen only in humans. Though primates such as chimpanzees have been shown to acquire the infection from humans

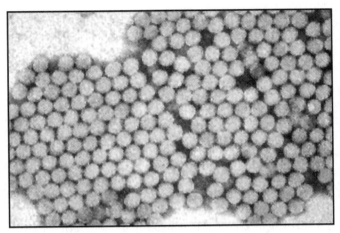

Fig. 58.1 Electron micrograph of 27-nm hepatitis A virus aggregated with antibody

and transmit it to human contacts, there is no evidence of any extrahuman source of the virus in nature.

HAV transmission is by the fecal–oral route. Infection is by ingestion. The virus multiplies in the intestinal epithelium and reaches the liver by hematogenous spread. It is shed in feces during the late incubation period and prodromal phase of the illness. Once jaundice develops, it is rarely detectable in feces. Chronic carriers are not seen. Virus persistence in nature depends on continuing inapparent infections.

A brief viremia occurs during the preicteric phase, but ceases with the onset of jaundice. Chronic viremia does not occur. Parenteral transmission is therefore very rare. Infection has been reported in recipients of some clotting factor concentrates. Transplacental infection has not been documented. HAV may be present occasionally in the saliva and urine of patients, but this is not considered relevant in its spread.

Type A hepatitis occurs sporadically or as outbreaks, which may be caused by contaminated food, water or milk. Shellfish have been known to be responsible for outbreaks. Domestic or institutional spread of infection among children is common. Overcrowding and poor sanitation favour its spread.

The epidemiology of type A hepatitis resembles that of poliomyelitis. In the developing countries, infection is acquired in childhood and by the age of 10, 90 per cent of the population possess the antibody to the virus and are immune. In India, type A hepatitis is the most common cause of acute hepatitis in children, but is much less frequent in adults. In affluent countries, and even in those developing countries with improved personal hygiene and sanitation, its incidence has been declining, with an upward shift in the age group affected. In the temperate regions, the disease shows an autumn–winter predilection, but in the tropics no seasonal distribution is evident. In India, the disease tends to be associated with heavy rainfall.

Laboratory diagnosis:

1. **Specimen:** Feces or serum may be collected for demonstration of the virus or its antibody.

2. **Direct demonstration:** The virus can be visualised by IEM in fecal extracts during the late incubation period and the preicteric phase, but seldom later. This is not commonly used for diagnosis.

3. **Serology:** Diagnosis is usually by detection of antibody. IgM anti-HAV antibody appears during the late incubation period, reaches peak levels in 2–3 weeks and disappears after 3–4 months. The IgG antibody appears at about the same time, peaks in 3–4 months and persists much longer, perhaps for life. Demonstration of IgM antibody in serum indicates current or recent infection, while the IgG antibody denotes recent or remote infection and immunity. ELISA kits for detection of IgM and IgG antibodies are available (Fig. 58.2).

Prophylaxis:

General prophylaxis consists of improved sanitary practices and prevention of fecal contamination of food and water. A safe and effective formalin inactivated, alum conjugaged vaccine containing HAV grown in human diploid cell culture is available. A full course consists of two intramuscular injections of the vaccine.

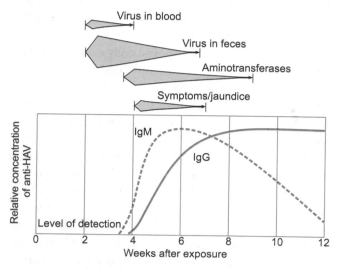

Fig. 58.2 Immunologic and biologic events associated with human infection with hepatitis A virus

Protection begins 4 weeks after injection and lasts for 10–20 years.

Specific passive prophylaxis by pooled normal human immunoglobulin (16% solution in a dose of 0.2–0.12 ml/kg body weight) IM, before exposure or in the early incubation period, can prevent or attenuate clinical illness, while not necessarily preventing infection and virus excretion.

Natural infection with HAV, clinical or subclinical, leads to lifelong immunity. There is no cross-immunity between HAV and any of the other hepatitis viruses.

Treatment: This is symptomatic. No specific antiviral drug is available.

TYPE B HEPATITIS

Type B hepatitis is the most widespread and the most important type of viral hepatitis. More than a third of the world's population is estimated to be have been infected by HBV. About a quarter of them become HBV carriers. A quarter of these develop serious liver disease, including chronic hepatitis, cirrhosis and primary hepatic cancer. As there is an effective vaccine against HBV, hepatocellular carcinoma has become the only human cancer which is vaccine-preventable. The WHO estimates that HBV infection causes more than a million deaths a year worldwide.

Clinical features: The incubation period is long, about 1–6 months. The clinical picture of hepatitis B is similar to that of type A, but it tends to be more severe and protracted. Onset is insidious and fever is not prominent. Extrahepatic complications like arthralgia, urticaria and rarely polyarteritis or glomerulonephritis may occur. These are ascribed to circulating immune complexes containing the viral surface antigen.

About 90–95 per cent of adults with acute hepatitis B infection recover within 1–2 months of onset and eliminate the virus from the body within about six months, remaining immune thereafter. Mortality is about 0.5–2.0 per cent, but may be more in post-transfusion cases. About 1 per cent of patients, particularly those having simultaneous delta virus infection develop fatal fluminant hepatitis.

A proportion of cases (1–10 per cent) remain chronically infected. They may be asymptomatic carriers or may progress to recurrent or chronic liver disease or cirrhosis. A few of them may develop hepatocellular carcinoma after many decades.

The pathogenesis of hepatitis appears to be immune mediated. Hepatocytes carry viral antigens and are subject to antibody-dependent NK cell and cytotoxic T cell attack. In the absence of adequate immune response, HBV infection may not cause hepatitis, but may lead to carrier state. Therefore infants and immunodeficient persons are more likely to become asymptomatic carriers following infection.

Hepatitis B virus (HBV)

Hepatitis

Clinical Case A 40-year-old woman who had received multiple blood transfusions over the previous six months presented with persistent fatigue, loss of appetite, nausea, vomiting and abdominal pain for a duration of 10 days. She had a history of passing high-coloured urine. Her liver function tests showed elevated serum bilirubin and liver enzymes. A viral hepatitis panel was advised and showed HBsAg positive, anti-HBc IgM positive, anti-HAV IgM negative and anti-HCV IgM negative. She was diagnosed with acute HBV infection, placed on supportive therapy and the liver enzymes and viral markers monitored every month to check for seroconversion from HBsAg to anti-HBsAg positivity (indicative of resolution of the disease).

Morphology: HBV is a 42-nm DNA virus with an outer envelope and an inner core, 27 nm in diameter, enclosing the viral genome and a DNA polymerase. Because of its unique features, HBV is assigned to a separate family Hepadnaviridae (hepatotropic DNA viruses), which consists of two genera: *Orthohepadnavirus* containing HBV as well as the woodchuck and ground squirrel hepatitis viruses, and *Avihepadnavirus*, containing the Pekin duck and grey heron hepatitis viruses. HBV is Hepadnavirus type 1.

The discovery of HBV was serendipitous. In 1965, Blumberg, studying human serum lipoprotein allotypes, observed in the serum of an Australian aborigine, a new antigen which gave a clearly defined line of precipitation with sera from two hemophiliacs who had received multiple blood transfusions. This was named the **Australia antigen**. By 1968 it was found to be associated with serum hepatitis. It was subsequently shown to be the surface component of HBV. Therefore the name Australia antigen was changed to **hepatitis B surface antigen (HBsAg)**.

Under the electron microscope, sera from type B hepatitis patients show three types of particles (Fig. 58.3):

- The most abundant form is a spherical particle, 22 nm in diameter.
- The second type of particle is filamentous or tubular with a diameter of 22 nm and of varying length. These two particles are antigenically identical and are surface components of HBV (HBsAg) which are produced in great excess.
- The third type of particle, far fewer in number, is a double-walled spherical structure, 42 nm in diameter. This particle is the complete hepatitis B virus. It was first described by Dane in 1970 and so is known as the Dane particle.

The envelope proteins expressed on the surface of the virion and the surplus 22-nm-diameter spherical and filamentous particles constitute the hepatitis B surface antigen. HBsAg consists of two major polypeptides, one of which is glycosylated.

Antigenic diversity:

HBsAg exhibits antigenic diversity. It contains two different antigenic components: the common group reactive antigen a, and two pairs of type specific antigens d-y and w-r, only one member of each pair being present at a time. HBsAg can thus be divided into four major antigenic subtypes: **adw, adr, ayw and ayr**. The subtypes do not seem to be important in immunity because of the dominant antigen a shared by all. The subtypes

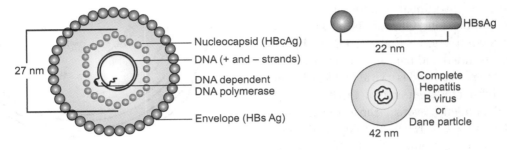

Fig. 58.3 Structure of hepatitis B virus

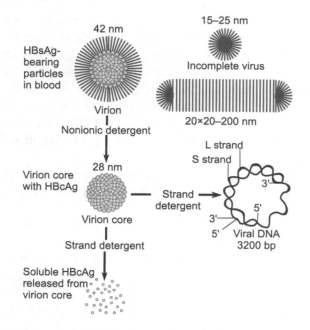

Fig. 58.4 Hepatitis B virus

breed true, and the index case and contacts in an outbreak have the same subtype. They show a distinct geographical distribution. Subtype ayw is common from West Asia through the Middle East, to Western and Northern India; adw is common in Europe, Australia and the Americas; adr is prevalent in South and East India and the Far East; ayr is very rare. A number of other surface antigenic reactivities (a, x, f, t, j, n, g) have been reported, but not been adequately studied.

HBcAg: Mild detergent treatment disrupts the viral envelope and exposes the core or nucleocapsid. The antigen expressed on the core is called the hepatitis B core antigen (HBcAg) (Fig. 58.4).

HBeAg: A third antigen called the hepatitis B antigen (HBeAg) is a soluble non-particulate nucleocapsid protein. HBcAg and HBeAg, though immunologically distinct, are coded for by the same gene.

Viral genome: The nucleocapsid encloses the viral genome consisting of two linear strands of DNA held in a circular configuration. One of the strands (the plus strand) is incomplete, so that the DNA appears partially double-stranded and partially single-stranded. Associated with the **plus strand** is a viral **DNA polymerase**, which has both DNA dependent DNA polymerase and RNA dependent reverse transcriptase functions. This polymerase can repair the gap in the plus strand and render the genome fully double-stranded (Fig. 58.5).

The genome has a compact structure with four overlapping genes:

● The **S gene** codes for the surface antigen. It consists of the S region and two Pre-S regions: Pre-S2 and Pre-S1. The protein coded for by the S region is called the S or major protein. When translation begins from the Pre-S2 region, the M or middle protein is formed. When the entire gene from Pre-S1 is translated, the L or large protein results. The L protein is present only in the virion, while the M and S proteins are found in the circulating HBsAg particles also.

● The **C gene** has two regions, C and Pre-C. When the C region alone is translated, the core antigen (HBcAg) is formed. HBcAg is assembled as the nucleocapsid core particles. It is not secreted and does not circulate in blood, but can be demonstrated in hepatocytes by immunofluorescence. Antibodies to HBc, both IgM and IgG, appear in blood. The IgG antibody to HBcAg persists in blood long after all other serological markers have disappeared and so provides a useful marker of prior infection with HBV. If translation begins from the Pre-C region, the resulting protein is HBeAg, a non-particulate soluble antigen possessing a signal protein which enables it to be secreted. It is therefore present in circulation. The presence of HBeAg in blood provides a convenient and readily detectable marker of HBV replication and high infectivity.

● The **P gene** is the largest and codes for the DNA polymerase enzyme.

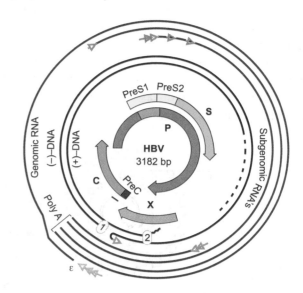

Fig. 58.5 Genetic organisation of the HBV genome

- The **X gene** codes for a small non-particulate protein (HBxAg), which has transactivating effects on both viral and some cellular genes. This leads to enhanced replication of HBV, as well as of some other viruses, such as the human immunodeficiency virus. HBxAg and its antibody are present in patients with severe chronic hepatitis and hepatocellular carcinoma.

Mutations: A few cases of infection by mutant viruses have been identified. Two types of mutations have been studied:

- One type, initially identified in Mediterranean countries, presents as severe chronic hepatitis, caused by pre-core mutants unable to synthesise HBeAg. Those infected with **precore mutants** may be positive for anti-HBe and anti-HBc.
- The second group of so-called **'escape mutants'** have been seen in some infants born to HBeAg-positive mothers, and in liver transplant recipients who had received combined immunisation with anti-HBV immunoglobulin and vaccine. They show mutation in the common a determinant of HBsAg, preventing them from being neutralised by the anti-HBsAg antibody. If such mutants become more common, they may pose problems in hepatitis B prophylaxis.

HBV replicates within hepatocytes. Viral DNA exists in the hepatocyte nucleus in the free extrachromosomal state or integrated with the cell chromosome. Replication resembles that seen in retroviruses, in that DNA is synthesised from an RNA template by reverse transcription.

HBV DNA and protein have also been identified in extrahepatic sites such as the bone marrow, spleen, lymph nodes and circulating lymphocytes, but apparently no damage is produced in these locations. The significance of this extrahepatic presence is not understood.

HBV does not grow in any conventional culture system. However, limited production of the virus and its proteins can be obtained from several cell lines transfected with HBV DNA. HBV proteins have been cloned in bacteria and yeast. The chimpanzee is susceptible to experimental infection and can be used as a laboratory model.

Resistance: HBV is a relatively heat stable virus. It remains viable at room temperature for long periods. Heat at 60°C for 10 hours reduces infectivity by 100- to 1000-fold. It is susceptible to chemical agents. Exposure to hypochlorite (10,000 ppm available chlorine) or 2% glutaraldehyde inactivates infectivity, though HBsAg may not be destroyed by such treatment.

Epidemiology: Hepatitis B occurs throughout the world. Natural infection occurs only in humans. There is no animal reservoir. The virus is maintained in the large pool of carriers whose blood contains circulating viruses for long periods, in some even lifelong. There is no seasonal distribution. The infection is usually sporadic, though occasional outbreaks have occurred in hospitals, orphanages and institutions for the mentally handicapped.

The prevalence of hepatitis carriers varies widely in different countries, in relation to their living standards. India falls in the intermediate group: carrier rate 2–7 per cent, with higher carrier rates in the southern part of the country and lower rates in the northern part.

A carrier is a person with detectable HBsAg in blood for more than six months. Following infection, about 5–10 per cent of adults, 30 per cent of children and 90 per cent of neonates become carriers. The carrier state is more common among males. There are over 350 million carriers now worldwide. Of them, about 45 million are in India, which has the second largest carrier pool, next only to China.

Carriers: Carriers are of two categories:

- **Super carriers:** These are highly infectious, having high titre HBsAg, along with HBeAg, DNA polymerase and HBV in circulation, and generally elevated transaminases. Some of them have enormous antigenemia and viremia, up to 10^{13} HBsAg particles equal to 500 µg of protein, and 10^8 HBV per ml of blood. About a quarter of the carriers in India are HBeAg positive.
- **Simple carriers** have low infectivity and low titre HBsAg in blood, with negative HbeAg, HBV and DNA polymerase. Many super carriers in time become simple carriers.

Transmission: HBV is a bloodborne virus and the infection is transmitted by parenteral, sexual and perinatal modes.

- **Parenteral transfusion:** Blood of carriers, and less often of patients, is the most important source of infection. The virus may also be present in other body fluids and excretions, such as saliva, breast milk, semen, vaginal secretions, urine, bile and feces. Of these, semen and saliva are known to transmit the infection; others may also do so, though much less efficiently than blood. Feces is not known to be infectious.

Transfusion of carrier blood, once the most widely known mode of infection has largely been eliminated wherever donor screening is strictly enforced. Therapeutic and prophylactic preparations from pooled human blood and serum have led to hepatitis, but this risk is now minimal, with screening of donors and production techniques ensuring virus inactivation. However, HBsAg screening is not a totally fail safe method as infection has occurred even with HBsAg-negative, anti-HBc–positive blood, which may have had undetectable amounts of virus.

Many other therapeutic, diagnostic, prophylactic and even non-medical procedures are now the main modes of infection. HBV is very highly infectious, far more that HIV. Any object or procedure than can convey minute traces of infected blood or other material, as little as 0.00001 ml, can be infectious. These include shared syringes, needles and other sharp items or endoscopes, personal articles such as razors, nail clippers or combs, and practices such as acupuncture, tattooing, ritual circumcision, ear or nose piercing, and field camps for surgery or disease detection by blood testing where separate sterile articles may not be available. Professionals using sharp articles like barbers, dentists and doctors may unwittingly transmit the virus if great care is not taken.

Infection by direct contact with open skin lesions such as pyoderma, eczema, cuts and scratches is very common among young children in developing countries, as also through household transmission where opportunities exist for contact with blood or saliva among members.

HBV has been said to survive in mosquitoes and bed bugs for about two weeks after blood meal, but no virus multiplication occurs. They do not appear to transmit the infection.

- **Perinatal transmission**: Congenital or vertical transmission is quite common from carrier mothers. The risk to babies is high if the mother is HBeAg positive (60–90 per cent) and low if negative (5–15 per cent). True congenital infection (in utero, transplacental) is rare. Infection is usually acquired during birth by contact of maternal blood with the skin and mucosa of the fetus, or in the immediate postnatal period. Infection by ingestion has been reported, but its efficiency is very low. However it is safer if carrier mothers do not breastfeed when proper nutrition of their babies can be otherwise ensured. HBV-infected neonates generally do not suffer from any clinical illness, but remain carriers for life and some of them may develop hepatocellular carcinoma after many decades.

- **Sexual transmission** of HBV occurs everywhere, but is more important in the developed countries, particularly in the promiscuous homosexual. The risk of transmission by heterosexual and homosexual contact increases with the number of partners and the duration of such relationships. HBV infection has occurred after artificial insemination. Semen donor screening is therefore obligatory.

Occupational risk: Certain groups and occupations carry a high risk of infection. These include medical and paramedical personnel, staff of blood banks, dialysis units, medical laboratories and mental health institutions, barbers and sex workers. Dentists and doctors have been responsible for small outbreaks. In non-endemic countries like Britain, HBV carriers are barred from invasive medical practice. Carriers are also not permitted to be medical students.

Laboratory diagnosis: Detection of viral markers: Specific diagnosis of hepatitis B rests on serological demonstration of the viral markers. It is therefore necessary to understand the sequence of their appearance in blood (Fig. 58.6).

1. **HBsAg** is the first marker to appear in blood after infection, being detectable even before elevation of transaminases and onset of clinical illness. It remains in circulation throughout the icteric or symptomatic course of the disease. In the typical case, it disappears within about two months of the start of clinical disease, but may sometimes last for six months and even beyond. When it is no longer detectable, its antibody, anti-HBs, appears and remains for very long periods. Anti-HBs is the protective antibody.

2. **HBcAg** is not demonstrable in circulation because it is enclosed within the HBsAg coat, but its antibody, anti-HBc, appears in serum a week or two after the appearance of HBsAg. It is therefore the earliest antibody marker to be seen in blood, long before anti-HBe or anti-HBs. As anti-HBc remains lifelong, it serves as a useful indicator of prior infection with

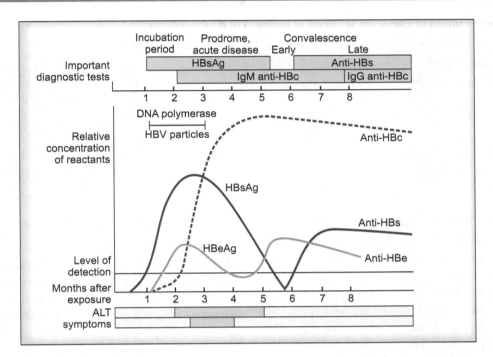

Fig. 58.6 Clinical and serologic events occurring in a patient with acute hepatitis B virus infection

HBV, even after all the other viral markers become undetectable. Initially, anti-HBc is predominantly IgM, but after about six months, it is mainly IgG. Selective tests for IgM or IgG anti-HBc therefore enable distinction between recent or remote infection respectively.

3. **HBeAg** appears in blood concurrently with HBsAg, or soon afterwards. Circulating HBeAg is an indicator of active intrahepatic viral replication, and the presence in blood of DNA polymerase, HBV DNA and virions, reflecting high infectivity. The disappearance of HBeAg coincides with the fall of transminase levels in blood. It is followed by the appearance of anti-HBe.

For the diagnosis of HBV infection, detection of HBsAg in blood is all that ordinarily necessary. The simultaneous presence of IgM anti-HBc indicates recent infection and the presence of IgG anti-HBc remote infection. Occasionally, when the level of HBsAg is too low to be detectable, diagnosis has to be made by testing for IgM anti-HBc (*Case*).

HBeAg provides information about relative infectivity. Its presence denotes high infectivity and its absence, along with the presence of anti-HBe, indicates low infectivity. As it is invariably present during acute hepatitis, its testing is indicated only in chronic infection and carriers.

The presence of anti-HBs without any other serological virus marker indicates immunity following vaccination. Table 58.1 shows the interpretation of various serological patterns in hepatitis B.

Like HBeAg, HBV DNA is also an indicator of viral replication and infectivity. Molecular methods such as DNA:DNA hybridisation and PCR, at present used for HBV DNA testing are highly sensitive and quantitative. HBV DNA level in serum reflects the degree of viral replication in the liver and so helps to assess the progress of patients with chronic hepatitis under antiviral chemotherapy.

Prophylaxis: General prophylaxis consists in avoiding risky practices like promiscuous sex, injectable drug abuse and direct or indirect contact with blood, semen or other body fluids of patients and carriers. Health education, use of the disposable syringes and needles, screening of blood, semen and organ donors, have all helped to an extent, but these alone cannot eliminate the risk altogether, particularly in the developing countries.

Immunisation: The only certain method appears to be universal immunisation. Both passive and active methods of immunisation are available.

● **Passive immunisation:** Hyperimmune hepatitis B immune globulin (HBIG) prepared from human volunteers with high titre anti-HBs, administered

Table 58.1   *Interpretation of commom serological patterns in HBV infection*

Virus/Antibody markers					Interpretation
HBsAg	HBeAg	Anti-HBc	Anti-HBs	Anti-HBe	
+	+	IgM	–	–	Acute HBV infection; highly infectious
+	+	IgG	–	–	Late/chronic HBV infection or carrier state; highly infectious
+	–	IgG	–	+/–	Late/chronic HBV infection or carrier state; low infectivity
–	+/–	IgM	–	+/–	Seen rarely in early acute HBV infection; infectious
–	–	IgG	+/–	+/–	Remote HBV infection; infectivity nil or very low
–	–	–	+	–	Immunity following HBV vaccine

IM in a dose of 300–500 i.u. soon after exposure to infection constitutes passive immunisation. It may not prevent infection, but protects against illness and the carrier state.

- **Active immunisation:** This is more effective. The first vaccine introduced in 1982, was prepared from pooled plasma of healthy human carriers with high level antigenemia. This was immunogenic, but became unacceptable because its source was human plasma, limited in availability and not totally free from possible risk of unknown pathogens.

The vaccine currently preferred is genetically engineered by cloning the S gene of HBV in baker's yeast. It consists of non-glycosylated HBsAg particles alone. It is given with alum adjuvant, IM into the deltoid or, in infants into the anterolateral aspect of the thigh. Gluteal injection is not recommended as it may result in poor immune response. Three doses given at 0, 1 and 6 months constitute the full course. Seroconversion occurs in about 90 per cent of the vaccinees. A special vaccine containing all antigenic components of HBsAg (Pre-S1, Pre-S2 and S) has been developed, which gives greater seroconversion. Seroconversion can be checked by testing for anti-HBs which is usually detectable for about five years. Clinical protection is believed to last much longer. Booster doses are needed only for those at high risk.

Now that the vaccine is manufactured in India, and is available at lower cost, it should be possible to include this in the national immunisation schedule.

- **Combined immunisation:** For non-immune persons exposed to HBV, combined immunisation is recommended. For babies born to carrier mothers, a single injection of 0.5 ml of HBIG given IM immediately after birth, is followed by the full course of vaccine at a different anatomical site, the first dose being given within 12 hours of birth. When HBIG is not available, the vaccine given alone has been reported to provide protection.

Treatment: No specific antiviral treatment is available for acute HBV infection. Interferon alpha, alone or in combination with other antiviral agents such as lamivudine and famcyclovir, has been beneficial in some cases of chronic hepatitis. There is no effective treatment for the carrier state, though spontaneous resolution takes place in some of them.

TYPE C HEPATITIS

Attempts to identify the group of 'non-A non-B' viruses by experimental infection in chimpanzees led to the discovery of hepatitis C virus (HCV). It is now the most common cause of post-transfusion hepatitis in the developed countries.

Clinical features: The incubation period is long, 15–160 days, with a mean of 50 days. The acute illness is usually mild or anicteric. Overt jaundice is seen in about 5 per cent of patients only. The important part in type C hepatitis is the chronic illness. About 50–80 per cent of patients progress to chronic hepatitis, with some developing cirrhosis and hepatocellular carcinoma.

Epidemiology: HCV infection is seen only in humans. The source of infection is the large number of carriers, estimated to be about 200 million worldwide. In general the epidemiology resembles that of hepatitis B.

Infection is mainly by blood transfusion and other modes of contact with infected blood or blood products. Injectable drug abusers, transplant recipients and immunocompromised persons are at high risk. Sexual transmission is probably less important. Vertical transmission from mother to baby may take place.

The infection occurs throughout the world, with carrier rates of 1–20 per cent. HCV infection is prevalent in India too, with an estimated 12.5 million cases.

A quarter of all chronic hepatitis cases in India are believed to be due to HCV infection.

Hepatitis C virus (HCV)

The virus has not been grown in culture, but has been cloned in *Escherichia coli*. HCV is a 50–60 nm virus with a linear, single-stranded RNA genome, enclosed within a core and surrounded by an envelope, carrying glycoprotein spikes (Fig. 58.7). HCV resembles flaviviruses in structure and organisation, and has been classified as a new genus *Hepacivirus* in the family Flaviviridae.

The virus shows considerable genetic and antigenic diversity. At least six different genotypes and many subtypes have been identified, indicating high mutability. Some genotypes are seen worldwide, while others are localised. Because of this diversity there is little heterologous or even homologous postinfection immunity in hepatitis C.

Laboratory diagnosis: The standard method of diagnosis is antibody detection by ELISA. The antigens used are various structural and non-structural proteins cloned in *E.coli*. Three successive generations of such antigens have been introduced to improve sensitivity and specificity of serological diagnosis. Even the third-generation ELISA currently in use, employing NS-5 region protein and synthetic peptides, becomes positive only months after the infection and shows non-specific reactions. Confirmation by immunoblot assay is therefore recommended. In HCV infection, antibodies appear irregularly and late, limiting their diagnostic utility. Culture is not yet established.

Identification of HCV RNA in blood provides more sensitive and specific results within a few days of exposure to HCV. Molecular methods like PCR and branched DNA assay are employed for the purpose.

Prophylaxis: Only general prophylaxis, such as blood screening, is possible. No specific active or passive immunising agent is available.

Treatment: Prolonged treatment with interferon alpha, either alone or in combination with antiviral agents like ribavirin has been reported to be useful in some cases.

TYPE D (DELTA) HEPATITIS

In 1977, Rizzetto and colleagues in Italy identified a new viral antigen in the liver cell nuclei of patients infected with hepatitis B virus. This has been shown to be due to the hepatotropic virus delta or Hepatitis D Virus (HDV). Delta is a defective RNA virus dependent on the helper function of HBV for its replication and expression. Therefore, it has no independent existence and can survive and replicate only as long as HBV infection persists in the host.

Morphology: HDV is a spherical, 36-nm particle with an outer coat composed of the hepatitis B surface antigen surrounding the circular single-stranded RNA genome. Though it resembles some plant viruses, such as viroids or satellite viruses, it has been proposed to be classified in a new genus *Deltavirus*, because of its special features.

Clinical features: Its mode of transmission is the same as for HBV. Two types of infection are recognised:

- **Co-infection:** Here delta and HBV are transmitted together at the same time. Co-infection clinically presents as acute hepatitis B, ranging from mild to fulminant disease.
- **Superinfection:** Here delta infection occurs in a person already harbouring HBV. It usually leads to more serious and chronic illness, with deterioration of the underlying HBV infection. No association has been noted between HDV and hepatocellular carcinoma.

Laboratory diagnosis: The delta antigen is primarily expressed in liver cell nuclei, where it can be demonstrated by immunofluorescence. It is only occasionally present in serum. Anti-delta antibodies appear in serum and can be identified by ELISA. The IgM antibody appears 2–3 weeks after infection and is soon replaced by the IgG antibody in acute delta infection. However, in chronic infection, the IgM antibody per-

Fig. 58.7 HCV virus

sists for years. Delta RNA sequences have been cloned and DNA probes have been developed for the rapid identification of delta particles in circulation. The woodchuck has been found to be a suitable experimental model for the study of HDV infection.

Epidemiology: HDV is distributed worldwide but is more common in certain endemic areas. In the Mediterranean countries, where it is endemic, infection is spread commonly by non-percutaneous routes, especially by close personal contact. In the non-endemic areas, such as northern Europe and North America, infection is more often through blood and blood products and is commonly seen in drug addicts and hemophiliacs. Introduction of HDV into non-endemic areas where HBV infection is common may lead to outbreaks of severe hepatitis with high mortality.

Prophylaxis: No specific prophylaxis exists, but immunisation with the HBV vaccine is effective as HDV cannot infect persons immune to HBV. Screening of blood donors for HBsAg automatically limits blood-borne HDV infection.

TYPE E HEPATITIS
(ENTERICALLY TRANSMITTED NANB OR EPIDEMIC NANB HEPATITIS)

Hepatitis viruses A and B account for less than half the cases of acute hepatitis in many developing countries. The bulk of NANB hepatitis in these areas is transmitted enterically through fecal pollution of drinking water (hence the name **enterically transmitted NANB or E-NANB**). It often appears as epidemics (hence also called **epidemic NANB**). The largest such epidemic occurred in Delhi during the winter of 1955–56, affecting over 30,000 persons within six weeks. Several outbreaks and sporadic infections have been reported from many parts of the Indian subcontinent, Central and South Asia, North Africa and Central America. This hepatitis was not seen in Western countries except when imported from endemic areas, but recently occasional cases have been reported from Europe. The disease is now called type E hepatitis and its causative agent hepatitis E virus (HEV). In India, HEV is responsible for the majority of epidemic and sporadic hepatitis in adults.

Type E hepatitis was previously mistaken for hepatitis A because of clinical and epidemiological similarities. It was recognised as a separate entity because of the absence of serological and virological evidence of HAV infection in these cases. The source of infection is fecal contamination of drinking water and the environment. Secondary attack rate among household contacts is very low in type E hepatitis, 2–3 per cent as against 10–20 per cent in HAV infection.

Clinical features: The incubation period ranges 2–9 weeks with an average of six weeks. Most cases occur in the young to middle aged adults (15–40 years old). The disease is generally mild and self-limited, with a low case fatality of about 1 per cent. A unique feature is the clinical severity and high case fatality rate of 20–40 per cent in pregnant women, especially in the last trimester of pregnancy.

Morphology: HEV is a spherical non-enveloped virus, 32–34 nm in diameter, with a single-stranded RNA genome. The surface of the virion shows indentation and spikes. The virus is very labile. In morphology and physical characteristics, it resembles Caliciviruses such as the Norwalk virus. It has been provisionally classified in *Hepeviridae*.

Laboratory diagnosis: HEV can be demonstrated by immuno-electron microscopy (IEM) in the bile and feces of patients in the incubation period or acute phase of illness. The carrier state has not been observed. Experimental infection can be transmitted to many species of primates. It has been reported to be prevalent in animal reservoirs such as pigs. In vitro cultivation has not been successful so far. The viral genome has been cloned. Comparison of virus strains from different areas indicates that only one serotype of the virus exists. ELISA kits are available for IgG and IgM antibodies, using recombinant and synthetic peptide antigens.

Table 58.2 lists out the comparative features of the various viral hepatitis types.

HEPATITIS G VIRUS

Two flavivirus-like isolates were obtained in 1995 from Tamarin monkeys inoculated with blood from a young surgeon (GB) with acute hepatitis. A similar virus was isolated from another human specimen the same year. These isolates were called GB viruses A, B and C, respectively.

In 1996, an isolate closely resembling GBV-C was obtained from a patient with chronic hepatitis. This has been called the hepatitis G virus (HGV). It has not been grown, but its RNA genome has been cloned. HGV RNA has been found in patients with acute, chronic

Table 58.2 *Viral hepatitis types: comparative features*

	A	B	C	D	E
Virus	HAV, 27 nm RNA, Picornavirus (Hepatovirus)	HBV, 42 nm DNA (Hepadnavirus)	HCV, 50–60 nm RNA, Flavivirus (Hepacivirus)	HDV, 35–37 nm Defective RNA Deltavirus	HEV, 32–34 nm RNA Hepevirus
Modes of infection	Fecal–oral	Percutaneous, Vertical, Sexual	Percutaneous	Percutaneous	Fecal–oral
Age affected	Children	Any age	Adults	Any age	Young adults
Incubation period (days)	15–45	30–180	15–160	30–180	15–60
Onset	Acute	Insidious	Insidious	Insidious	Acute
Illness	Mild	Occasionally severe	Moderate	Occasionally severe	Mild, except in pregnancy
Carrier state	Nil	Common	Present	Nil (only with HBV)	Nil
Oncogenicity	Nil	Present specially after neonatal infection	Present	Nil	Nil
Prevalence	Worldwide	Worldwide	Probably worldwide	Endemic areas (Mediterranean, N Europe, Central and N America)	Only developing countries (India, Asia, Africa, Central, America)
Specific prophylaxis	Ig and vaccine	Ig and vaccine	Nil	HBV vaccine	Nil

and fulminant hepatitis, hemophiliacs, patients who had undergone multiple transfusions and hemodialysis, intravenous drug addicts and blood donors. HGV appears to be a bloodborne virus resembling HCV and its prevalence is higher in patients infected with HIV and HCV. Its role in hepatitis is yet to be clarified.

HGV RNA can be detected in the blood samples of infected patients using RT PCR. The presence of virus-specific antibodies in the serum of patients has been associated with viral clearance and protective immunity. However, these are not widely used for the diagnosis of viral hepatitis as the role of HGV in causing hepatitis is still not clear.

RECAP

- The hepatitis viruses include a range of unrelated human pathogens that specifically infect the liver.
- All the hepatitis viruses are RNA viruses, except the hepatitis B virus (HBV), which is a DNA virus belonging to the family Hepadnaviridae.
- The hepatitis A virus (HAV) is an enterovirus (type 72). It is worldwide in distribution and infection is by the feco–oral route.
  - Antibody to HAV is protective whereas cell-mediated immunity may contribute to pathology.
  - Diagnosis is done by demonstration of specific antibodies.
  - Infection by HAV can be prevented by good personal hygiene and prevention of fecal contamination of drinking water and food.
- HBV is an enveloped, 42-nm spherical particle with a partially double-stranded DNA genome.
  - Infection due to HBV is acquired through sexual intercourse, shared needles in drug use, perinatally from infected mothers to newborn infants or by transfusion of blood and blood products,
  - HBV causes hepatitis B; it has also been implicated in hepatocellular carcinoma.

- For lab diagnosis, tests include detection in the serum of the surface antigen (HBsAg) and of IgM antibody to core antigen (anti-HBc); detection of envelope antigen itself (HBeAg) or antibody to HBeAg (anti-HBe) helps in assessment of infectivity of the individual.
- Amplification of HBV DNA by PCR and isolation of the virus from blood or tissue are other diagnostic means.
- Screening of donated blood has greatly reduced the spread of HBV.
- Vaccination with cloned HBsAg has further reduced disease in some populations in developed countries. Antiviral therapies can help treat chronic infections.

- The hepatitis C virus (HCV) is an enveloped virus 50–60 nm in diameter, with a genome of single-stranded RNA. Hepatitis C infection is one of the most common of all liver diseases, the infection being transmitted by contaminated blood products and by shared injections during drug use:
  - HCV typically causes a chronic form of hepatitis. It has also been implicated in hepatocellular carcinoma.
  - For diagnosis, antibody to HCV antigen can be detected by enzyme immunoassay. The HCV RNA can be amplified by RT-PCR. Routine culture of HCV has not been established.
  - The disease can be prevented by screening of blood and blood products prior to transfusion for the presence of anti-HCV antibody or HCV RNA.
- The hepatitis D virus (HDV) is an unusual, single-stranded, circular RNA virus that requires hepadnavirus helper functions for propagation in hepatocytes.
- The hepatitis E virus (HEV) causes enterically transmitted, non-A, non-B hepatitis. It is a non-enveloped, single-stranded RNA virus.
  - HEV is an important cause of large epidemics of acute hepatitis in the Indian subcontinent and elsewhere.
  - Specific diagnostic tests for infection due to HEV include PCR to detect HEV RNA, and detection of both IgG and IgM anti-HEV antibodies.
  - General measures for preventing HEV infection are similar to those for prevention of HAV infection.
- HGV RNA has been found in patients with acute, chronic and fulminant hepatitis, hemophiliacs, patients who had undergone multiple transfusions and hemodialysis, intravenous drug addicts and blood donors.

ESSAY

1. Enumerate the viruses affecting the liver. Discuss the pathogenesis and laboratory diagnosis of Hepatitis B.

SHORT ANSWERS

1. Viral markers of HBV
2. Laboratory diagnosis of HBV

SHORT NOTES

1. Hepatitis B prophylaxis
2. Labelled diagram of HBV
3. Mutants of HBV
4. Hepatitis C virus
5. HBsAg (definition)
6. HBeAg (definition)
7. HBcAg (definition)
8. Hepatitis B carriers (definition)

59 Miscellaneous Viruses

PAPOVAVIRUSES

The term 'papova' is coined from the names of viruses included in this group: the *papilloma* and the *polyoma* viruses. The family **Papovaviridae** has two genera:

- *Polyomavirus* which contains the simian vacuolating virus (SV 40) and human polyomaviruses JC and BK
- *Papillomavirus* which contains several genera, five of which cause human infections

They are small, non-enveloped, icosahedral **DNA tumour viruses**. SV 40 produces malignant tumours when inoculated into newborn mice or hamsters—hence, the name *polyoma*. These viruses have been widely used in the study of viral oncogenesis.

Cell lines used for vaccine preparation have to be screened for SV40 infection, to avoid vaccine contamination with this virus.

Human papillomaviruses

Papillomaviruses are species-specific and infect squamous epithelia and mucous membranes, inducing different types of warts or papillomata in their hosts. The **human papillomavirus (HPV)** infects only humans and grows only in organ cultures of human skin. Over 82 types of HPV have been recognised based on genetic homology. There is correlation between the virus type and the type of lesion produced.

> **Association of HPV with some clinical conditions**
> - Common warts (verruca vulgaris, plantar warts), usually found on the hands and feet of children and adolescents, are mostly caused by types 1, 2, 3 and 4.
> - **Condyloma acuminatum** or genital wart, which is a more moist, soft, pedunculated wart found on the external genitalia, is usually due to types 6 and 11, 42–44. This may be transmitted venereally and may occasionally turn malignant.
> - **Intraepithelial neoplasia** is due to HPV types **6 and 11**. There is a close association between specific HPV types and genital malignancies in both sexes.
> - **Cervical cancer** is caused by HPV types **16 and 18**. Co-factors appear to be important in the induction of HPV-associated malignancies.
> - **Laryngeal and oesophageal carcinomas**: It is associated with HPV types 16, 18, 30, 31, 33 51–53.

HPV vaccine: Two recombinant vaccines are now available: one containing antigens from **HPV 6, 11, 16** and **18,** and a second containing only particles from types **16** and **18**. Both are indicated in preventing persistent and precancerous genital lesions, in adolescent and young adult women but is contraindicated in pregnancy.

Human polyomaviruses

Human polyomaviruses (formerly papovavirus group) have been isolated from a number of patients with impaired immunity. They contain the JC and BK viruses. Antibodies to these viruses are present widely in human sera, in about 75 per cent of adults. In an impaired immune system following disease or transplantation, the virus may be reactivated, leading to progressive multifocal leukoencephalopathy (PML) or renal disease.

The **JC virus** was isolated in 1971 from the brain of a patient with Hodgkin's disease and PML. This virus **grows only in human fetal glial cell cultures**. It is oncogenic, producing malignant gliomas following intracerebral inoculation in newborn hamsters.

The **BK virus** was isolated in 1971 from the urine of a patient who had undergone a kidney transplant. Several similar isolates have been reported from other kidney transplant patients. The BK virus can **grow in a wide range of primary and continuous cell cultures**.

PARVOVIRUSES

Parvoviruses are small, 20 nm viruses with a single-stranded DNA genome. They are dependent on the host cell DNA for replication. There is only one medically important human parvovirus, *Parvovirus B19*. It was discovered in the blood of symptomless blood donors.

Parvovirus B19

It is present worldwide. Infection is commonly acquired in childhood and is often asymptomatic.

- **Erythema infectiosum:** It usually presents as a respiratory infection, with an erythematous maculopapular rash and arthralgia. It begins as a prominent erythema of the cheeks (slapped cheek disease), spreading to the trunk and limbs, followed by lymphadenopathy and arthralgia. It occurs usually in children 5–10 years old and has been called the fifth disease, as it was the fifth in the old list of six exanthematous fevers of children.
- **Aplastic crisis:** It occurs in children with chronic hemolytic anemias, as in sickle cell disease. In the immunodeficient, it may cause persistent anemia.
- **Fetal hydrops**: Parvovirus B19 infection during the second or third trimester of pregnancy leads to this condition.

Transmission appears to be respiratory, though it may also be through blood. Infection leads to viremia and virus replication in the throat, followed by antibody response. Diagnosis may be made by detection of the virus in blood in early cases, and of the antibody later.

Bocavirus

A new parvovirus called bocavirus has been isolated from the respiratory tract of children presenting with acute respiratory disease.

RUBELLA VIRUS

Rubella or German measles is a mild exanthematous fever characterised by transient macular rash and lymphadenopathy. In itself, the disease is trivial but rubella in pregnant women may lead to **congenital malformations** in the baby.

> The teratogenic property of rubella virus was discovered by an Australian ophthalmologist Gregg, who in 1941 observed a sudden increase in congenital cataract in infants and related it to maternal rubella. Observations from different countries soon confirmed that maternal rubella induces congenital malformations of different kinds, the commonest being the triad of cataract, deafness and cardiac defects. Further progress had to wait till the rubella virus was isolated in tissue culture in 1962.

Properties

The rubella virus is a pleomorphic, roughly spherical particle, 50–70 nm in diameter, with a single-stranded RNA genome and surrounded by an envelope carrying hemagglutinin peplomers (Fig. 59.1). It agglutinates goose, pigeon, one-day-old chick and human erythrocytes at 4°C. Structurally and in many other features, it resembles togaviruses. The rubella virus has been classified in the family Togaviridae as the only member of the genus ***Rubivirus***.

> **Inactivation of rubella**
> The virus is inactivated by ether, chloroform, formaldehyde, beta propiolactone and desoxycholate. It is destroyed by heating at 56°C, but survives for several years at –60°C.

Fig. 59.1   Rubella virus

Cultivation and host range

The virus can be grown in many primary cell cultures and continuous cell lines, such as rabbit kidney (RK 13), baby hamster kidney (BHK 21) and Vero. Cytopathic changes develop only in a few cell lines such as RK 13. In others, virus growth can be identified by interference, using a challenge virus such as ECHO 11.

Experimental model for the teratogenic effects of rubella is the pregnant rabbit, in which the virus infects the fetus transplacentally, leading to congenital malformations.

Clinical features

Infection is acquired by inhalation. After an incubation period of 2–3 weeks, generalised rash develops on the face, spreading to the neck, trunk and extremities sparing the palms and soles. The rash is generally discrete and disappears by the third day. There is non-tender enlargement of posterior cervical glands. Koplik spots, seen in measles, are absent. The disease occurs principally in children but may affect all ages. The common complications are arthralgia and arthritis, commoner in women and with increasing age. Based on the results of in vitro studies, rubella infection is presumed to cause chromosomal breakages and inhibition of mitoses in infected embryonic cells.

The virus can be recovered from the throat up to seven days before the rash. Viremia has been demonstrated as early as the seventh day before the rash and ceases shortly after the appearance of the rash. The virus can also be demonstrated in feces and urine. Some patients develop subclinical infection and are infectious to others. Infection of the fetus is through the maternal bloodstream.

Congenital rubella: Fetal damage caused by maternal rubella is related to the stage of pregnancy.

- Very early pregnancy: Infection at this stage ends in abortion.
- First trimester: There is a reported risk of up to 90 per cent of occurrence of congenital malformations.
- Later on in pregnancy: The damage caused may be more subtle, in the form of communication defects or developmental retardation and may not be apparent till the child grows older.

Congenital rubella syndrome: The commonest malformations caused by rubella are cardiac defects, cataract and deafness. Several other features have been recognised in babies with congenital rubella, including hepatosplenomegaly, thrombocytopenic purpura, myocarditis and bone lesions, constituting the **'expanded rubella syndrome'**.

The rubella virus is present in all excretions of congenitally infected infants. About a third of them continue to shed the virus for six months, and a few for a year or more. The virus may persist in tissues such as cataractous lenses for several years. Infected babies constitute an important source of infection to the staff in nurseries.

Laboratory diagnosis

Routine diagnosis of rubella is not called for but laboratory confirmation becomes important when rubella is suspected in pregnant women.

In pregnancy: Diagnosis can be established by serology or virus isolation.
- **Serology:** Serological diagnosis is mainstay of diagnosis. ELISA to detect IgM and IgG antibodies gives valuable information. A finding of IgM antibody alone, without IgG, means current acute infection. IgG antibody alone, without IgM, means past infection or vaccination and denotes immunity. Paired serum sample is tested 10 days apart to demonstrate a significant rise or fall in antibody titre. A screening test for pregnant women by TORCH panel (Toxoplasmosis, Rubella, Cytomegalovirus and Herpes) is done to rule out the possibility of congenital confections including rubella.
- **Isolation:** Rubella virus isolation is not commonly used for diagnosis because of the difficulties and delay involved. The virus may be isolated from blood during the early stage or more successfully from throat swabs in rabbit kidney or Vero cells. The virus grows better if cultures are incubated at a lower temperature, such as 33–35°C.

In congenital rubella:
- **Serology**: IgM antibodies in the newborn indicate intrauterine infection. IgM does not cross the placenta and thus indicates response of the fetus to the infection. If diagnosis is needed at a later time, paired serum from the mother and child can be used to demonstrate IgG antibodies. In congenital infection, the IgG antibodies will be present in the newborn beyond six months. If they are passively transferred from the mother, levels will decline in the newborn while remaining same in the mother.
- **Isolation:** In congenital rubella, the virus may be isolated from a variety of sources such as urine,

throat swabs, leucocytes, bone marrow or cerebrospinal fluid.

Prophylaxis

Rubella infection confers lasting immunity as the virus has only one antigenic type. Re-infections have, however, been reported.

Live attenuated vaccines have been developed by serial passage of the virus in tissue culture. The vaccine in use today is the RA 27/3 strain grown in human diploid cell culture and administered by subcutaneous injection, alone or in combination with measles and mumps components as the **MMR vaccine**. The vaccine is generally well tolerated, though minor reactions like lymphadenopathy, rash and arthralgia may sometimes occur. It should not be given to immunodeficient subjects. Pregnancy is an absolute contraindication and should be avoided for three months after vaccination. The vaccine virus is apparently not teratogenic. Inadvertent administration of the vaccine to pregnant women may not therefore lead to congenital defects in the baby.

Epidemiology

Rubella is worldwide in distribution. Serological surveys in different countries have shown that 80–90 per cent are immune by the age of 15 years. About 10–20 per cent of mothers are non-immune and therefore vulnerable.

SLOW VIRUS DISEASES

The term 'slow virus disease' is applied to a group of infections in animals and human beings, characterised by a very long incubation period and a slow but relentless course, terminating fatally. The concept of 'slow infection' was originally proposed by Sigurdsson (1954), a veterinary pathologist for slowly progressing infections of sheep, such as scrapie, visna and maedi. The recognition in recent years that some chronic degenerative neurological diseases of human beings may have a similar pathogenesis has led to considerable interest in this concept.

> **Characteristics of slow virus infections:**
> ❖ Incubation periods ranging from months to years
> ❖ Course of illness lasting for months or years, with remissions and exacerbations
> ❖ Predilection for involvement of the central nervous system
> ❖ Absence of immune response or an immune response that does not arrest the disease, but may actually contribute to pathogenesis

> ❖ Genetic predisposition
> ❖ Invariable fatal termination

Slow virus diseases may be classified into three groups:

* **Group A** consisting of slowly progressive infections of sheep, caused by serologically related, non-oncogenic retroviruses called **lentiviruses** (from the Latin *lentus*, meaning slow); the human immunodeficiency virus, the causative agent of AIDS, also belongs to this group of lentiviruses; AIDS shows many features of a slow virus disease.
* **Group B** comprising prion diseases of the central nervous system (CNS), scrapie, mink encephalopathy, Kuru and Creutzfeldt–Jakob disease, collectively known as the subacute spongiform viral encephalopathies.
* **Group C** consisting of two unrelated CNS diseases of human beings: subacute sclerosing panencephalitis (SSPE) and progressive multifocal leucoencephalopathy (PML).

Group A

Visna is a demyelinating disease of sheep. The disease has an incubation period of about two years. It has an insidious onset with pareses, progressing to total paralysis and death.

Maedi (progressive pneumonia) is a slowly progressive, fatal hemorrhagic pneumonia of sheep, with an incubation period of 2–3 years. It is classified as one of the lentivirus groups.

Group B (prion diseases)

The transmissible spongiform encephalopathies. **(subacute spongiform viral encephalopathies)** are chronic progressive degenerative diseases of the CNS. The pathology consists of progressive vacuolation in the dendritic and axonal processes of the neurons and extensive astroglial hypertrophy and proliferation, culminating in spongiform degeneration in grey matter. There is no sign of any inflammatory or immune response.

The infectious agents are proteinaceous in nature, devoid of DNA and RNA. They are unusually resistant to physical and chemical agents such as heat, irradiation and formalin. They can be transmitted to experimental animals by parenteral and oral challenge. Stanley B Prusiner gave the name **prion** to these **proteinaceous** infectious agents. He was awarded the Nobel Prize for Medicine in 1997 for his pioneering work on prions.

The pathogenic mechanism appears to be proliferation of an **abnormal prion protein (PrP^{sc})** which is derived from the normal cellular prion protein PrP^c. The accumulation of PrP^{sc} in the central nervous system as diffuse deposits and in the form of plaques disrupts the architecture and function of the brain, causing disease.

Human prion diseases:

- **Creutzfeldt–Jakob disease (CJD)**: This is subacute, presenile encephalopathy, with progressive incoordination and dementia, ending fatally in about a year. Both sporadic and inherited forms of the disease have been seen. Iatrogenic CJD has occurred after corneal transplantation and injection of the pituitary growth hormone, presumably from donors who had the infection.

  Variant CJD: The appearance of a new variant of CJD affecting younger persons (below 45 years) in Britain in 1996 raised fears of infection through eating bovine spongiform encephalopathy (BSE)-infected beef. This aroused a panic reaction about the export of British beef, and many thousands of British cattle had to be slaughtered before the anxiety was allayed.

- **Gerstmann–Straussler–Scheinker (GSS) syndrome and fatal familial insomnia**: These are two variants of CJD. The familial form of CJD is rare. It is due to inheritance of mutation of the PrP gene.

- **Kuru**: Identified in 1957, Kuru (meaning tremor) was a mysterious disease seen only in the Fore tribe inhabiting the eastern highlands of New Guinea. The disease had an incubation period of 5–10 years and led to progressive cerebellar ataxia and tremors, ending fatally in 3–6 months. The infection is believed to have been introduced through cannibalism and maintained by the tribal custom of eating the dead bodies of relatives after death as a part of a ritual. The disease has disappeared following the abolition of cannibalism in New Guinea. **Carlton Gajdusek** was awarded the Nobel Prize for Medicine in 1976 for his important contributions on Kuru.

Prion diseases of animals: **Scrapie** is the prototype prion disease. It has been known as a natural disease of sheep for two centuries. Transmission occurs vertically, from ewe to lamb, and less often by contact. **Mink encephalopathy** is a scrapie-like disease of mink. It is believed to have spread to mink when they fed on scrapie-infected sheep meat. **Bovine spongiform encephalopathy (BSE, 'mad cow disease')** has been enzootic in Britain since 1986. The infection is presumed to have spread to cattle by the practice of feeding them with scrapie-infected meat.

Group C

Subacute sclerosing panencephalitis (SSPE) is seen in young adolescents. It is a very rare delayed **sequel to infection with the measles virus**. The disease sets in many years after the initial infection and is characterised by progressive deterioration of mental and motor functions. Death occurs 1–3 years after the onset of symptoms. Brain cells from patients show serological and electron microscopic evidence of measles virus infection. The virus cannot be isolated in routine cultures, but only by co-cultivation of infected brain cells with susceptible cells of non-neural origin. Measles virus strains isolated from SSPE are defective. Patients show very high levels of measles virus antibody in serum. The antibody is regularly found in CSF and is pathognomonic. Cellular immune response to measles virus is absent in SSPE.

Progressive multifocal leucoencephalopathy (PML) is a rare subacute demyelinating disease seen in elderly persons whose immune process is impaired as a result of malignancy or immunosuppression. There is progressive deterioration of motor function, vision and speech. Death occurs in 3–4 months. Human polyomavirus has been demonstrated by electron microscopy and cultured from brain biopsies of patients.

VIRAL HEMORRHAGIC FEVERS

Hemorrhagic manifestations are sometimes seen in many viral fevers. However, the term hemorrhagic viral fever is not applied to them, but only to a group of diseases, apparently **zoonotic** in nature, with features of hemorrhage caused by viruses belonging to two families: **Arenavirus** and **Filovirus**. Their distribution is geographically restricted to **South America** and **Africa**. They usually cause asymptomatic infection in the local population but at times they erupt in sudden outbreaks killing large populations and causing panic.

Arenaviruses

A group of enveloped viruses with a negative sense, single-stranded RNA genome, causing chronic inapparent infection in rodents has been classified as arenaviruses. Electron microscopy of thin sections shows characteristic electron-dense granules resembling grains of sand within virus particles. Hence, they have been named *arena* (Latin), meaning sand. These particles are cellular ribosomes picked up by the virus, presumably during maturation by budding from host cells. Arenaviruses are spherical or pleomorphic particles, ranging in size from 80 to 300 nm.

Arenaviruses have assumed considerable medical importance after the recognition that some members of the family cause hemorrhagic fevers in humans (Argentinian and Bolivian hemorrhagic fevers and Lassa fever).

Lymphocytic choriomeningitis (LCM): The prototype is the **lymphocytic choriomeningitis (LCM)** virus which is a natural parasite of mice. Humans probably acquire the infection from the excreta of rodents. Most human infections are asymptomatic but some may develop an influenza-like illness or meningitis. LCM has been reported to account for 5–10 per cent of sporadic viral meningitis in human beings.

South American hemorrhagic fevers: Two related viruses, the Junin and Machupo viruses, cause the Argentinian and Bolivian hemorrhagic fevers, respectively. They belong to the Tacaribe group of arenaviruses. Rodents act as reservoirs and transmission is believed to occur through rodent excreta.

Lassa fever: This is the most highly publicised of viral hemorrhagic fevers and is caused by another arenavirus. It was first noticed in 1969 in an American Mission station in Lassa, Nigeria. Many outbreaks have subsequently occurred in widely separated foci in West Africa. The case fatality rate has been 35–70 per cent in hospitalised patients. The natural reservoir is the multimammate rat. Rodent excreta probably act as the source of infection. The incubation period is 3–16 days. The virus is present in the throat, urine and blood of patients. Person-to-person transmission may occur by droplet infection. Nosocomial infection has occurred frequently. Ribavirin has proved useful in treatment.

Filoviruses

These are long, thread-like viruses, hence the name (*filum* means thread). They range in size from 80 to 800–1000 nm. Ebolaviruses and Marburg viruses causing hemorrhagic fever belong to the genus *Filovirus*.

Ebola virus: In 1976, several cases of a similar hemorrhagic fever occurred in the equatorial provinces of Sudan and Zaire, with high fatality. The causative virus was morphologically identical to the Marburg virus but antigenically distinct. It has been called Ebola virus after the Ebola river, beside which the first cases were noticed (Fig. 59.2). In 1979, Ebola re-emerged in Sudan, with serial person-to-person spread. In 1995, a large outbreak with heavy fatality was seen in Kikwit, Zaire. Three distinct strains of Ebola virus have been recognised: the Zaire strain (EBO-Z) with a case fatality rate of up to 90 per cent, the Sudan strain (EBO-S) with a case fatality rate of up to 50 per cent, and the mild Reston strain (EBO-R) isolated from quarantined monkeys, imported from the Philippines and held at Reston, Virginia, USA. Recent outbreak between 2013 and 2016 in West Africa (Guinea, Liberia, Sierra Leone) has resulted in more

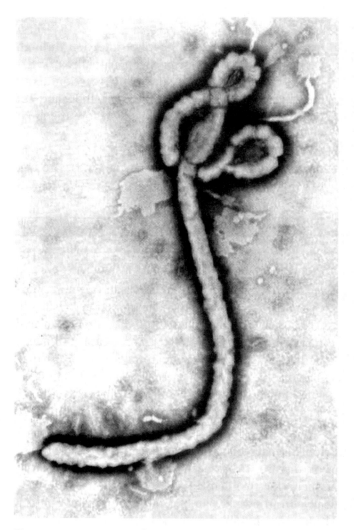

Fig. 59.2 Ebola virus (long thin filamentous form)

than 11,000 deaths. Trials of a **vaccine rVSV-ZEBOV** have met with some success.

The reservoir of Ebola virus and its natural history still remain unclear, despite frequent outbreaks with high fatality.

Marburg virus: Marburg disease is a hemorrhagic fever that occurred simultaneously in laboratory workers in Marburg, Frankfurt (Germany) and Belgrade (Yugoslavia) in 1967. The infection arose from tissues of African green monkeys to which the laboratory workers had been exposed. The monkeys had been imported from Uganda. Person-to-person transmission occurred. The primary cases had a fatality rate of 30 per cent but the secondary cases were non-fatal.

The Marburg virus was isolated in guinea pigs and tissue culture from the blood and tissues of these patients. The virus appears to persist in the body and has been isolated after 80 days of onset of illness from semen and the anterior chamber of the eye. A case of sexual transmission has been recorded.

No further Marburg virus infection was seen except for three cases identified in South Africa in 1975 and two in Kenya in 1980.

CORONAVIRUSES

A group of spherical or pleomorphic enveloped RNA viruses, carrying petal- or club-shaped peplomers on their surface has been classified as coronaviruses. The name refers to the fringe of surface projections surrounding the virus, resembling the solar corona (Fig. 59.3). There are two groups: **acid-labile viruses** (associated with common cold-like illnesses) and **acid-stable viruses** (associated with human and animal gastroenteritis). There are many serotypes, which are mostly fastidious and difficult to grow in cell culture systems.

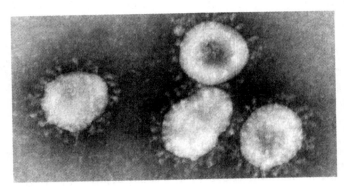

Fig. 59.3   Coronavirus

Coronavirus types
- Human coronavirus 229E.
- Human coronavirus OC43.
- SARS-CoV.
- Human coronavirus NL63 (HCoV-NL63, New Haven coronavirus).
- Human coronavirus HKU1.
- Middle East respiratory syndrome coronavirus (MERS-CoV), previously known as Novel coronavirus 2012 and HCoV-EMC.

Human coronaviruses were first isolated from cases of common cold by inoculating organ cultures of human embryonic trachea with nasopharyngeal washings. Inhibition of ciliary motility indicates virus growth. Inoculation in human volunteers induces common cold after an incubation period of 2–5 days. The resulting immunity is poor and re-infections can occur even with the same serotype. They appear to be the second most common cause of the common cold, particularly in winter, next only to rhinoviruses.

Severe acute respiratory syndrome (SARS): In November 2002, Guangdong province in South China experienced an outbreak of an unusual respiratory infection, with many deaths. The world outside knew about it only in February 2003, when a physician from Guangdong visited Hong Kong, fell ill and died there, after infecting 12 persons who had stayed in the same hotel. They, in turn, went to their countries to fall ill and initiate outbreaks there. By July, when the pandemic was controlled, it had affected over 30 countries, with many thousands of cases and over 800 deaths. India escaped the SARS epidemic; however, a few suspect cases were detected and quarantined.

The coronavirus responsible for SARS appears to be a new virus distinct from other coronaviruses, which had been classified into three types: **mammalian viruses in types 1 and 2** and **avian viruses in type 3**. The new SARS virus is **coronavirus type 4**.

The fact that it is a new virus is indicated by the absence of an antibody to it in human and animal sera collected from previous years. It may be a recombinant of some animal and human viruses. The virus has been isolated from Chinese wild civets and raccoon dogs, but not from pigs, dogs, cattle or poultry (Fig. 59.4).

Spread: SARS spreads by inhalation of the virus present in droplets or aerosols of respiratory secretions of patients. Fecal aerosols also may be infectious. The incubation period is under 10 days. The disease starts as a fever with cough or other respiratory symptoms.

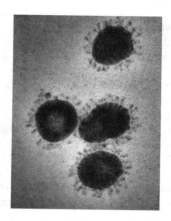

Fig. 59.4 Transmission electron microscopic (TEM) image (digitally-colorized) of members of the genus Coronavirus. Image credit: CDC / Dr Fred Murphy; Sylvia Whitfield."

Diarrhea is sometimes seen. The chest radiograph shows pneumonic changes. Death is due to respiratory failure.

Laboratory diagnosis: The virus was identified by electron microscopy, and confirmed by growth in Vero cell culture, animal inoculation, cloning, sequencing and histology. Molecular and serological tests for rapid diagnosis have been developed. Reverse transcription PCR has been used for early diagnosis, while demonstration of rise in titre of antibodies by ELISA or indirect immunofluorescent test in paired serum samples is useful later.

No specific therapy or prophylaxis has been identified. The virus is highly mutable and so vaccine prophylaxis may not be easy. Control has been achieved by strict isolation and quarantine.

MERS-CoV: Middle East Respiratory Syndrome (MERS) is a viral respiratory illness that has recently been reported. It was first detected in Saudi Arabia in 2012. The virus that causes MERS is called Middle East Respiratory Syndrome Coronavirus (MERS-CoV). Coronaviruses are common viruses that infect most people at least some time in their lives. Human coronaviruses usually cause mild to moderate upper-respiratory tract illnesses. However, MERS-CoV is different from any other coronavirus previously found in people. This virus is thought to have come from animals including camels. Infection spreads though respiratory secretions.

Symptoms: Persons infected with MERS-CoV develop severe respiratory illness. They have fever, cough and shortness of breath. Severe cases may have acute renal failure.

Treatment: Currently there is no vaccine to prevent the infection. Strict isolation and barrier nursing is the only way to prevent spread.

REOVIRIDAE

The family Reoviridae derives its name from the prototype virus which was known as the respiratory enteric orphan (REO) virus, because it could be isolated frequently from the respiratory and enteric tracts, but was not associated with any disease. Members of this family are double-shelled icosahedral viruses, 55–57 nm in diameter. The genome consists of **double-stranded RNA** in 10–12 pieces, a feature unique among animal viruses. They are non-enveloped and resistant to lipid solvents. The family contains three genera: *Reovirus*, *Orbivirus* and *Rotavirus*.

Reovirus

The genus *Reovirus* contains three mammalian serotypes (1, 2 and 3). Reoviruses have not been proved to cause any human disease.

Orbivirus

These have a double shell in which the outer layer is fuzzy and indistinct. The inner layer has 32 ring-shaped capsomers. The name *Orbivirus* is derived from *orbi* in Latin, meaning ring. Orbiviruses multiply in insects and vertebrates, thus qualifying as **arboviruses**. They are responsible for veterinary diseases such as African horse sickness and blue tongue. The only known orbivirus infection of human beings is **Colorado tick fever**.

Rotavirus

Rotaviruses resemble cart wheels with short spokes radiating from a wide hub to a clearly defined outer rim. The name is derived from *rota*, in Latin, meaning wheel. The complete or **'double-shelled'** virus measures about 70 nm in diameter and has a smooth surface. The incomplete or **'single-shelled'** virus is smaller, about 60 nm, with a rough surface that has lost the outer shell (Fig. 59.5). 'Empty' particles without the RNA core are also seen.

Identified by Bishop and colleagues (1973) in Melbourne, rotaviruses are now recognised as the **most common cause of diarrheal disease in infants and children**.

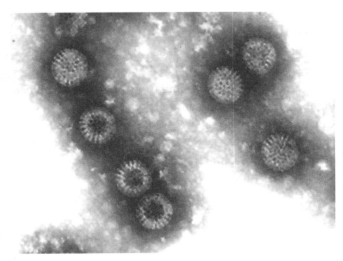

Fig. 59.5 Electron micrographic appearance of Rotavirus—double-shelled' virus and 'single-shelled' virus

Outbreaks of rotavirus diarrhea in older children and adults have been reported from different parts of China. This rotavirus is called 'adult diarrhea rotavirus' (ADRV).

Classification: Rotaviruses have been classified into antigenic groups (A to G). Group A strains, which cause the majority of human infections, have been classified into **subgroups (I and II)** by ELISA, CF or immune adherence agglutination, and into many **serotypes (1, 2, 3, etc.)** by neutralisation tests. ADRV strains belong to Group B. By polyacrylamide gel electrophoresis, rotavirus strains can be classified into several electrophoretypes, based on the patterns of migration of the viral RNA.

Serological techniques: IgM and IgG antibodies can be demonstrated in the blood of infected children. Rotaviruses share a common group antigen situated in the inner capsid layer.

Human rotavirus does not grow readily in cell cultures but some strains have been adapted for serial growth in tissue cultures. Rotavirus growth is facilitated by trypsin treatment and rolling of tissue cultures. As calf and simian viruses grow readily in cell cultures, they have been used as antigens for serological studies.

Rotaviruses are a class of viruses causing diarrhea in the young of many animals and some birds. The human rotavirus is related to the viruses of epidemic diarrhea of infant mice (EDIM), Nebraska calf diarrhea and the simian virus SA11. All rotaviruses share common antigens. Though the viruses are in general species-specific, interspecies infection can be induced experimentally. Human rotavirus infection has been transferred to piglets, calves and monkeys. It is not known whether human infection can be caused by animal rotaviruses.

Epidemiology: Rotaviruses are the commonest cause of diarrhea in infants and children the world over and account for about half the cases of children hospitalised for diarrhea. It occurs throughout the year but is predominant in the winter months, when the virus may be detected in most of the patients. It sometimes produces large epidemics of diarrhea in winter. Rotavirus diarrhea is usually seen in children below the age of five years, but is most frequent between 6 and 24 months of age. Infection is not infrequent in neonates but they seldom develop diarrhea because of maternal passive immunity. By the age of five years, most children have had clinical or subclinical infection, so rotavirus diarrhea is very uncommon in older children and adults.

Infection is by the fecal–oral route. The incubation period is 2–3 days. Vomiting and diarrhea occur with little or no fever. Stools are usually greenish yellow or pale, with no blood or mucus. The disease is self-limited and recovery occurs within 5–10 days. Mortality is low. Rehydration is all the treatment needed.

Treatment: Rotavirus vaccines are in use in 23 countries. Commonly the RotaTeq (RV5) vaccine is used. India has also recently introduced an indigenously developed rotavirus vaccine Rotarix (RV1). Both vaccines are given orally.

OTHER VIRUSES CAUSING DIARRHEA

Besides rotaviruses, the following viruses are known or suspected to cause diarrheal disease:

Norwalk virus: A 27 nm virus was shown to be responsible for an epidemic of gastroenteritis affecting school children and teachers in Norwalk, Ohio, in 1972. Serological surveys have shown that infection with Norwalk virus is widespread in many countries. Epidemics of Norwalk virus diarrhea associated with consumption of raw oysters have been reported from Australia and America.

The virus can be demonstrated in feces by electron microscopy. Antibody to the virus can be detected by immune electron microscopy and radioimmunoassay. It has been included in the family Caliciviridae which consists of small round RNA viruses, 22–30 nm in size, many of which have been reported from diarrheal feces. The name is derived from the presence of 32 cup-shaped depressions on the virus surface (from *calyx*, meaning cup).

Adenovirus: Several outbreaks of diarrhea in children have been associated with the presence of large numbers of adenoviruses in feces. These can be grown only with difficulty in tissue culture. They have been designated types 40 and 41. Adenovirus-associated diarrhea has been seen more often in the summer months.

Astrovirus: These star-shaped, 28 nm isometric particles have been associated with some epidemics of diarrhea in children. Similar viruses have also been identified in lamb and calf diarrhea.

Coronavirus: These are well-established causes of acute diarrhea in calves, piglets and dogs. They have been observed in human feces also, but their relation to diarrhea is uncertain.

RECAP

- The family Papovaviridae has two genera: polyomavirus, containing SV40 and human polyomaviruses, and papillomavirus, containing human and animal papillomaviruses.
- Papillomaviruses are species-specific and infect squamous epithelia and mucous membranes.
  - HPV types 1, 2, 3 and 4 cause common warts (verruca vulgaris).
  - HPV types 6 and 11 cause condyloma acuminatum (genital warts) and are also associated with intraepithelial neoplasia.
  - HPV 16 and 18 are causatively related to severe cervical cancer.
- Parvovirus B19 is clinically important, causing erythema infectiosum (also aplastic crisis in children with chronic hemolytic anemia).
- Rubella (German measles) is a mild erythematous fever, characterised by transient macular rash and lymphadenopathy (sometimes arthralgia). Rubella in pregnant women may cause congenital malformations in the baby.
  - Rubella virus (family Togaviridae) has a single-stranded RNA genome and an envelope with hemagglutinin peplomers.
  - Infection is acquired by inhalation. The incubation period is 2–3 weeks.
  - The virus may spread to the fetus through the bloodstream, causing death or congenital malformations.
  - In classical congenital rubella syndrome, cardiac defects, cataract and deafness are seen; hepatosplenomegaly, thrombocytopenic purpura, myocarditis and bone lesions can occur.
  - Diagnosis of rubella infection can be established by IgM antibody showing current, acute infection, or IgG antibody alone means past infection or vaccination and denotes immunity.
  - Virus may be isolated from urine, throat swabs, WBCs, bone marrow or CSF in congenital rubella; Serological diagnosis is by demonstrating IgM antibodies.
  - Rubella infection usually confers lasting immunity. Currently, the live attenuated vaccine (RA 27/3 strain grown in human diploid cell culture) is administered by subcutaneous injection as such or in combination (MMR).
- Slow virus diseases are classified into:
  - Group A; slowly progressive infections of sheep such as visna and maedi.
  - Group B; prion diseases of the CNS (subacute spongiform viral encephalopathies). Prions are proteinaceous in nature and devoid of DNA and RNA. Human prion diseases include Creutzfeldt–Jakob disease and Kuru.
  - Group C diseases; include subacute sclerosing panencephalitis and progressive multifocal leucoencephalopathy.

- Hemorrhagic viral fevers are a group of zoonotic infections with typical hemorrhagic features, caused by viruses belonging to the Arenaviridae and Filoviridae families; the infections (usually asymptomatic) are localised to South America and Africa and may occur as sudden outbreaks.
- Coronaviridae is a family of markedly pleomorphic, enveloped, spherical RNA viruses which have a helical nucleocapsid. Severe acute respiratory syndrome (SARS) refers to a severe atypical pneumonia that assumed pandemic proportions in 2003. Since then, there has been no major outbreak.
- Reoviridae is a family of non-enveloped RNA viruses with a double layer of capsomeres arranged in concentric spheres around the nucleoprotein. There are three genera: *Reovirus*, *Orbivirus* and *Rotavirus*. Rotavirus is a common cause of human and animal gastroenteritis.
- Viruses that are important causes of diarrhea include rotaviruses, the Norwalk virus, certain adenoviruses and coronaviruses, and astroviruses.

SHORT NOTES

1. Important papillomaviruses of medical importance and associated diseases
2. Parvoviruses
3. Prions
4. Congenital rubella syndrome and diagnosis
5. Diagnosis of rubella in pregnant women
6. Epidemiology and laboratory diagnosis of rotavirus
7. Viruses causing diarrhea
8. Viral hemorrhagic fevers
9. Slow virus disease
10. Prion disease

60 Oncogenic Viruses

INTRODUCTION

Viruses that produce tumours in their natural hosts or in experimental animals, or which induce malignant transformation of cells on culture, are known as oncogenic viruses.

History

The association of viruses with malignancy was described by **Rous** in 1911 when he showed that a solid malignant tumour, fowl sarcoma, was caused by a virus, a discovery for which he was awarded the **Nobel Prize** belatedly in 1966.

Viruses causing tumours in animals were first demonstrated by Shope, who isolated the rabbit fibroma virus in 1932 and the **papilloma virus** in 1933. Considerable interest was aroused by the discovery by Stewart and Eddy (1957) of the **polyoma virus** which could produce a wide variety of neoplasms when injected into newborn rodents. Injection of certain types of human **adenovirus** into newborn hamsters was shown by Trentin (1962) to cause sarcomas. Burkitt (1963) identified a peculiar geographical distribution of lymphoma in African children. The **Epstein–Barr virus** isolated from Burkitt's lymphoma has been identified as the causative agent.

However, it is now acknowledged that virus infections account for 10–20 per cent of human malignancies. These include **hepatocellular carcinoma** caused by Hepatitis B and C viruses, **cervical cancer** by certain types of papilloma viruses, anaplastic **nasopharyngeal carcinomas** by the EB virus and adult cutaneous **T cell lymphoma/leukemia** by HTLV-1.

Transformation

This represents the various changes that accompany the conversion of a normal cell into a malignant cell (by oncogenic viruses) (Table 60.1). This is a multistep process and may be partial or complete. For example, some viral agents can '**immortalise**' infected cells, so that they become capable of continuous multiplication in culture, without possessing other features of malignancy. Transformation is recognised primarily by a change in the morphology of cultured cells. Transformed cells are altered in shape and lose the property of 'contact inhibition' so that, instead of growing as monolayer, they grow piled up, one over another, forming 'microtumours'. Foci of transformation can be discerned easily and are used in the assay of oncogenic viruses, such as the Rous sarcoma virus.

About a quarter of the 600 or so animal viruses possess oncogenic potential (Table 60.2). The viruses associated with cancers in human beings are shown in Table 60.3. Both RNA and DNA viruses are oncogenic.

All oncogenic **RNA viruses** belong to a single family: Retrovirus. Retroviruses are responsible for naturally occurring leukemia and sarcoma in several species of animals. Among **DNA viruses**, some herpesviruses and hepadnaviruses cause malignant tumours in their natural hosts.

ONCOGENIC DNA VIRUSES

Papovaviruses

HPV: The association between human papilloma virus (HPV) infection and cancer of cervix uteri, particularly

Table 60.1   *Properties of cells transformed by viruses*

I	**Altered cell morphology:** Fibroblasts become shorter, parallel orientation is lost, chromosomal aberrations appear
II	**Altered cell metabolism:** Increased growth rate, increased production of organic acids and acid mucopolysaccharides
III	**Altered growth characteristics:** Loss of contact inhibition, formation of heaped-up growth (microtumours), capacity to divide indefinitely in serial culture, capacity to grow in suspension or in semisolid agar
IV	**Antigenic alterations:** Appearance of new virus specified antigens (T antigen–TSTA), loss of surface antigens, cells become agglutinable by lectins
V	**Capacity to induce tumours** in susceptible animals

Table 60.2   *List of oncogenic viruses*

RNA Viruses

I. Retroviruses	1. Avian leukosis viruses
	2. Murine leukosis viruses
	3. Murine mammary tumour virus
	4. Leukosis-sarcoma virus of various animals
	5. Human T cell leukemia viruses

DNA Viruses

I. Papovavirus	1. Papillomaviruses of human beings, rabbits and other animals
	2. Polyomavirus
	3. Simian virus 40
	4. BK and JC viruses
II. Poxvirus	1. Molluscum contagiosum
	2. Yaba virus
	3. Shope fibroma
III. Adenovirus	Many human and non-human types.
IV. Herpesvirus	1. Marek's disease virus
	2. Lucke's frog tumourvirus
	3. Herpes virus pan, papio, ateles and saimiri
	4. Epstein–Barr virus
	5. Herpes simplex virus types 1 and 2
	6. Cytomegalovirus
V. Hepatitis B and C viruses	

HPV types 16 and 18, has been established. A vaccine for this is now available.

The continuous cell line HeLa, derived many decades ago from a cervical carcinoma and used widely in various laboratories, has been found to contain HPV-18 DNA.

Polyoma virus: The BK and JC viruses, which cause widespread asymptomatic human infection, can induce tumours in immunodeficient subjects.

Simian virus 40 (SV 40): Transformation is induced in cultured cells from several species, including human cells.

Poxvirus

Three members of the poxvirus group induce benign tumours: rabbit fibroma, molluscum contagiosum and Yaba virus. Similar tumours can be induced experimentally in many species of primates, including human beings. The tumours regress spontaneously in a few weeks.

Adenovirus

Though some types (12, 19, 21) may produce sarcomas in newborn rodents after experimental inoculation, they do not appear to have any association with human cancer.

Herpesvirus

Many herpesviruses have been associated with natural cancers in animals and humans.

Marek's disease: This is a fatal contagious neurolymphomatosis of chickens. No infectious virus particle can be isolated from the lesions or seen under the electron microscope. Marek's disease can be prevented by a live avirulent vaccine. This is the first instance of a malignant disease being controlled by a viral vaccine.

Lucke's tumour of frogs: A herpesvirus is considered to be the causative agent of a renal adenocarcinoma in frogs.

Table 60.3   *Viruses associated with human cancer*

Virus Family	Virus	Types of cancer
Papovaviridae	Human papilloma virus	Cervical, vulvar, penile cancers Squamous cell carcinoma
Herpesviridae	EB Virus	Nasopharyngeal carcinoma African Burkitt's lymphoma
	HSV type 2	B cell lymphoma, cervical carcinoma
Hepadnaviridae	Hepatitis B virus	Hepatocellular carcinoma
Flaviviridae	Hepatitis C virus	
Retroviridaee	HTL virus	Adult T cell leukemia

Herpesvirus saimiri: This virus was isolated from a culture of squirrel monkey kidney cells. It causes fatal lymphoma or reticulum cell sarcoma when injected into owls, monkeys or rabbits.

Epstein–Barr virus: This is regularly found in cultured lymphocytes from **Burkitt's lymphoma** patients. In the body, the tumour cells contain no virus. but cell lines established from them contain 5–20 per cent of cells that produce the virus. The virus multiplies only in human lymphoid cell lines. Serological surveys show that infection with the virus is worldwide. Infection is usually asymptomatic. In young adults without pre-existing antibodies, EB virus infection induces **infectious mononucleosis.** Lymphoma is believed to occur when the infection takes place in children whose immune systems are compromised, as for instance, by chronic malaria. EB virus–associated lymphomas have been reported in transplant recipients. EBV has also been linked to nasopharyngeal carcinoma in the Chinese male population in southeast Asia and East Africa.

Herpes simplex virus: An association has been proposed (though not proved) between herpes simplex type 2 infection and cancer of the uterine cervix. It has also been suggested that herpes simplex type 1 infection may be associated with cancer of the lip. Herpesvirus type 8 has been linked to Kaposi's sarcoma.

Cytomegalovirus infection: This has been associated with carcinoma of the prostate and Kaposi's sarcoma.

Hepatitis B virus

HBV has been claimed to be directly or indirectly involved in the causation of **hepatocellular carcinoma.** Studies in many countries have demonstrated an excess prevalence of markers of HBV infection in patients with primary hepatocellular carcinoma as compared with matched controls or with the general population. Hepatitis C virus infection has also been reported to lead to hepatocellular carcinoma.

ONCOGENIC RNA VIRUSES

Retrovirus

Retroviruses are enveloped, spherical viruses that are released by budding through the host cell membrane. They are approximately 100 nm in size. The genome consists of two identical, linear, single-stranded RNA molecules. The icosahedral nucleocapsid core encloses the helical ribonucleoprotein and is surrounded by an envelope composed of glycoprotein and lipid.

The characteristic feature of retroviruses is the presence within the virion of the unusual enzyme **RNA dependent DNA polymerase** or **reverse transcriptase** (hence the name *retro*, meaning reverse). Unlike the classical transcription of genetic information from DNA to RNA, the reverse transcriptase enzyme prepares a DNA copy of the retroviral RNA genome—initially an RNA:DNA hybrid and then its double-stranded DNA form, called the **provirus**, which is integrated into the DNA of the infected host cell. It is from the provirus that all retrovirus proteins are translated. Infection with oncogenic retroviruses does not lead to cytolysis or death of infected cells but the provirus remains integrated with host cell DNA for the rest of the life of the cell.

Classification: While all oncogenic RNA viruses belong to the family Retroviridae, all retroviruses are not oncogenic. The family Retroviridae is classified into three subfamilies:

- Oncovirinae, comprising all oncogenic RNA viruses (formerly called oncornavirus)
- Spumavirinae, containing the non-oncogenic 'foamy viruses' (*spuma* = foam) causing asymptomatic infection in several animal species
- Lentivirinae, including the viruses causing 'slow infections' (*lentus* = slow) in animals, as well as the human and related animal immunodeficiency viruses.

Types based on host range: Retroviruses are widely distributed, being found in nearly all vertebrates, including animals, birds and reptiles. Based on the host range and types of disease caused, oncogenic retroviruses can be considered under the following groups:

- **Avian leukosis complex:** A group of antigenically related viruses which induce avian leukosis (lymphomatosis, myeloblastosis and erythroblastosis viruses) or sarcoma in fowls (Rous sarcoma virus [RSV])
- **Murine leukosis viruses:** This group consists of several strains of murine leukemia and sarcoma viruses, named after the investigators who first described them (for example, Gross, Friend, Moloney, Rauscher)
- **Mammary tumour virus of mice:** This virus occurs in certain strains of mice having a high natural incidence of breast cancer
- **Leukosis-sarcoma viruses of other animals:** A number of viruses have been isolated from

leukosis and sarcomas in various species of animals: cat, hamster, rat, guinea pig and monkey

- **Human T cell leukemia (lymphotropic) viruses (HTLV):** These were isolated in 1980 from cell cultures from adult patients with cutaneous T cell lymphoma (mycosis fungoides) and leukemia (Sezwary syndrome) in the USA. Similar viruses have been isolated from patients with adult T cell leukemia in Japan and the Caribbean. HTLV type I is present worldwide but the disease is limited to endemic areas. Besides adult T cell leukemia, HTLV-I has also been associated with tropical spastic paraparesis, a demyelinating disease. The virus preferentially infects T4 (CD4) cells. Infected T cells express large quantities of interleukin-2 receptors. The closely related HTLV-II is also associated with T cell malignancy. HTLV infection is known to be spread through blood transfusions and other methods of transfer of leucocytes.

Host specificity: Retroviruses usually infect only one host species, the specificity being conditioned mainly by the presence of viral receptors on the host cell surface. Depending on their ability to grow in cells from different species, retroviruses have been classified as:

1. **Ecotropic** (multiplying in cells of native host species only);
2. **Amphotropic** (multiplying in cells of native and foreign species); and
3. **Xenotropic** (multiplying only in cells of foreign species but not of native host species).

Virus transmission: Two types of retrovirus transmission occur:

- **Exogenous retroviruses** are spread horizontally. Most oncogenic retroviruses are exogenous.
- **Endogenous retroviruses** are transmitted vertically from parent to offspring, by the provirus integrated with the germline cell genome. The endogenous retrovirus provirus behaves like a cellular gene and is subject to regulatory control by the host cell. Endogenous retroviruses are usually silent and do not transform cells or cause any disease. They can be detected either by 'activation' after exposure to radiation or chemicals, or by nucleic acid hybridisation techniques.

Resistance: Retroviruses are labile, being inactivated at 56°C in 30 minutes, by mild acids, ether and formalin. They are stable at −30°C.

Antigens: Two types of antigens are present:

1. Type-specific glycoprotein antigens on the envelope
2. Group-specific nucleoprotein antigens in the virion core

Cross-reactions do not occur between surface antigens of retroviruses from different host species.

Genomic structure: Retroviruses have a relatively simple genomic structure (Fig. 60.1).

The provirus of a standard retrovirus (such as a non-defective avian or murine leukemia virus) consists of three genes required for viral replication: **gag, pol,** and **env** in that order from the 5' to the 3' end.

- The gag gene codes for the nucleocapsid core proteins which are group-specific antigens (hence the name).
- The pol gene encodes the RNA dependent DNA polymerase.
- The env gene encodes the envelope glycoproteins. Long terminal repeat (LTR) sequences are present at either end of the provirus and linked directly to the host DNA.
- LTRs exert regulatory control on provirus gene functions.

Some retroviruses (transregulating viruses) such as HTLV and HIV carry a fourth gene, **tex** or **tat,** after the env gene. This is a transactivating gene that regulates the function of viral genes.

Virus transformation:

Slow transforming viruses: The standard oncogenic retroviruses, such as chronic leukemia viruses, are slow transforming viruses, that is they have low oncogenic

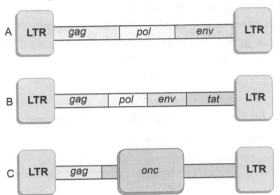

Fig. 60.1 Provirus genomic structure of different types of retroviruses; A. Basic retrovirus genome. Avian leukemia viruses, slow transforming viruses; B. Transregulating retroviruses HTLV, HIV; C. Acute transforming retrovirus; oncogene replacing part of basic genome. Replication defective.

potential and induce malignant change, generally only of blood cells, after a long latent period. They do not transform cultured cells. They are capable of replicating normally.

Acute transforming viruses: The acute transforming viruses are highly oncogenic and cause malignancy after a short latent period of weeks or months. They can cause different types of malignancies—sarcoma, carcinoma, leukemia—and also transform cells in culture. They can be:

- **Replication defective:** Most acute transforming viruses are unable to replicate normally because they carry on their genome an additional gene, the viral oncogene (**V-onc gene**), which replaces some of the genes essential for viral replication. Such V-onc viruses can replicate only if co-infected with a standard helper retrovirus.
- **Replication competent:** The Rous sarcoma virus which carries the oncogenic *src* (pronounced 'sark') is the best known among acute transforming viruses and it can replicate normally because it possesses the full complement of *gag, pol* and *env* genomes.

ONCOGENES

Viral oncogenes (V-onc), commonly known as 'cancer genes' are genes which encode proteins triggering the transformation of normal cells into cancer cells (Table 60.4). Oncogenes are not essential for the replication of the virus and mutants lacking them occur, which replicate normally without being oncogenic.

Genes closely resembling viral oncogenes are found in normal as well as cancer cells. Oncogenes isolated from cancer cells are called **cellular oncogenes (C-onc)**. Similar genes found in normal cells are called **proto-oncogenes**. They are not of viral origin. On the contrary, viral oncogenes appear to be of host cell origin.

Cellular oncogenes contain introns characteristic of eukaryotic genes, whereas viral oncogenes do not. Apparently viral oncogenes originated at some distant past from the proto-oncogenes by recombination between retroviral and cellular genes.

Proto-oncogenes are widespread in vertebrates and metazoa—from human beings to fruitflies. They are well conserved in their genomes, suggesting that they serve some essential functions in normal cells. They have been found to code for proteins involved in regulating cell growth and differentiation. The presumed functions of many oncogenes have been identified. For example, the oncogene *src* is related to tryrosine-specific protein kinases, *sis* to a platelet-derived growth factor and **myc** to DNA-binding proteins, all concerned with the regulation of normal cell growth.

Transfection: This is a useful method for the study of oncogenes. Certain mouse fibroblast cell lines, such as NIH 3T3, can take up foreign DNA, incorporate them into their genome and express transfection. By this technique, DNA extracted from human tumour cells has been shown to transform 3T3 cells, and such transforming genes have been shown to be identical with cellular oncogenes.

ANTI-ONCOGENES

A class of genes has been identified in the normal retinoblastoma (Rb) gene, the loss of which is associated with the development of retinoblastoma in children. The **p53 gene** appears to be a **tumour suppressor gene** with a wide range of effects. Specific chromosomal deletions, recognised in association with certain types of human cancers may reflect the loss of tumour suppressor genes.

Table 60.4 *Some oncogenes* and their chromosomal location in humans*

Viral oncogene	Origin	Natural	Human gene tumour	Chromosomal location in human beings
V-src	Chicken	Sarcoma	C-src	20
V-ras	Rat	Sarcoma	C-ras	11
V-myc	Chicken	Leukemia	C-myc	8
V-fes	Cat	Sarcoma	C-fes	15
V-sis	Monkey	Sarcoma	C-sis	22
V-mos	Mouse	Sarcoma	C-mos	8

* Oncogenes are given three-letter codes from the animal or tumour from which they are derived, preceded by either V- or C-, for viral or cellular genes respectively;
src = sarcoma of chicken, ras = rat sarcoma, sis = simian sarcoma, myc = myelomatosis of chicken, fes = feline sarcoma, mos = mouse sarcoma

MECHANISMS OF VIRAL ONCOGENESIS

While it is known that oncogenic viruses can transform cells in culture and induce tumours in animals, under natural or experimental conditions, the exact mechanisms of viral oncogenesis are not well understood. Malignancy is a stable heritable change and, as such, should be the result of a modification of the host cell genome.

Oncogenic DNA viruses: Here the viral DNA (or a portion of it) is **integrated with the host cell** genome. The viral DNA being incomplete or 'defective', no infectious virus is produced. However, under its influence, the host cell undergoes malignant transformation. A virus transformed cancer cell is in many ways analogous to a bacterium lysogenised by a defective phage. In both cases, the cell is not destroyed and no virus is produced. Acquisition of new characteristics by the transformed cell resembles lysogenic conversion in bacteria.

Oncogenic RNA viruses: In general, retroviruses induce tumours by one of two mechanisms:
- By introducing into the cellular genome a new transforming gene (**oncogene**)
- By **inducing or altering the expression** of a preexisting cellular gene. Several molecular mechanisms have been suggested for the conversion of benign proto-oncogenes to cancer genes. The genes may get overexpressed and the overproduced gene product may lead to abnormal growth. Recombination between retroviral and cellular genes, promoter insertion, chromosomal translocation, gene amplification and mutation are some of the genetic processes relevant in this connection.

RECAP

- Viruses that produce tumours in their natural hosts or in experimental animals, or which induce malignant transformation of cells on culture, are known as oncogenic viruses.
- Examples of oncogenic viruses in humans:
    - Epstein–Barr Virus (EBV), which causes Burkitt's lymphoma, common in Central Africa
    - Human papillomaviruses (HPV), associated with cervical cancer
    - HTLV-1 retrovirus, linked to leukemia
    - Chronic infection due to the hepatitis B virus, which may lead to hepatocellular carcinoma

SHORT NOTES

1. Oncogenic viruses of humans

61 Human Immunodeficiency Virus: AIDS

INTRODUCTION

The emergence and pandemic spread of the acquired immunodeficiency syndrome (AIDS) has posed the greatest challenge to public health in modern times. After the sudden appearance of syphilis in Europe five hundred years ago, rarely has any new disease had as great an impact on medicine, science and society and caused as much panic among the public and governments globally as has AIDS. The full consequences of this phenomenon may not be evident for several years because of the silent spread and slow evolution of this infection.

History

The first indication of this new syndrome came in the summer of 1981, with reports from New York and Los Angeles (USA), of a sudden unexplained outbreak of two very rare diseases, Kaposi's sarcoma and *Pneumocystis carinii* (jirovecii) pneumonia in young adults who were homosexuals or addicted to injected narcotics. This condition was given the name **acquired immune deficiency syndrome (AIDS)**.

In **1983, Luc Montagnier** and colleagues from the Pasteur Institute, Paris, isolated a retrovirus from a West African patient with persistent generalised lymphadenopathy, and called it **lymphadenopathy-associated virus (LAV)**. It produced lytic infection in fresh peripheral blood lymphocytes. In **1984, Robert Gallo** and colleagues from the National Institutes of Health, USA, reported the isolation of a retrovirus from AIDS patients and called it **human T cell lymphotropic virus III or HTLV III**. Retroviruses HLTV I and II had already been described in association with human T cell leukemia. International Committee on Virus Nomenclature in 1986 decided on the generic name **human immunodeficiency virus (HIV)** for these viruses.

In 1985, serological tests (ELISA) became available for the detection of anti-HIV antibodies. Serological screening of high-risk groups, blood donors and others revealed a very large and expanding reservoir of HIV in patients and carriers in different parts of the world.

HUMAN IMMUNODEFICIENCY VIRUS (HIV)

HIV, the causative agent of AIDS, belongs to the **lentivirus** subgroup of the family **Retroviridae**. Besides HIV, related animal immunodeficiency viruses are also assigned to this group

Members of the Lentivirus group causing immunodeficiency
I. In primates
  1. Human immunodeficiency viruses (HIV) types 1, 2
  2. Simian immunodeficiency viruses (SIV) causing Simian AIDS (SAIDS):
     a) isolated from sooty mangabeys (SIV-SM) and from rhesus macaque (SIV-MAC) closely related to HIV type 2
     b) isolated from chimpanzee (cpz)—closely related to HIV type 1
II. In non-primates
  1. Feline T lymphotropic virus (FTLV) causing feline AIDS (FAIDS)

Structure

Envelope: HIV is a spherical, enveloped virus, about 90–120 nm in size (Fig. 61.1). The nucleocapsid has

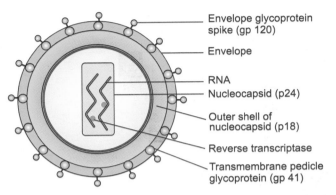

Fig. 61.1 Structure of HIV (diagrammatic representation)

an outer icosahedral shell and an inner cone-shaped core, enclosing the ribonucleoproteins.

Genome: The genome is composed of two identical single-stranded, positive-sense RNA copies, with the reverse transcriptase enzyme, (a characteristic feature of retroviruses). When the virus infects a cell, the viral RNA is transcribed by the enzyme, first into single-stranded DNA and then to double-stranded DNA (provirus) which is integrated into the host cell chromosome. The provirus can remain latent for long periods, influencing host cell function. In response to viral promoters, the provirus initiates viral replication by directing the synthesis of viral RNA and other components.

Lipoprotein envelope: When the naked virus buds out through the host cell surface during viral replication, it acquires a lipoprotein envelope, which consists of lipid derived from the host cell membrane and glycoproteins coded by the virus. The major virus-coded envelope proteins are the projecting knob-like spikes on the surface and the anchoring transmembrane pedicles. The spikes constitute the main surface component of the virus, which binds to the CD4 receptors (along with co-receptors CXCR4 and CCR5) on susceptible host cells. Transmembrane pedicles cause cell fusion.

Viral genes and antigens

The HIV genome contains the three structural genes (*gag, pol* and *env*) as well as other non-structural and regulatory genes specific to the virus (Fig. 61.2). The products of these genes, both structural and non-structural, act as antigens. Detection of these antigens and their antibodies is useful for diagnosis and prognosis of HIV infection.

Major antigens of HIV
A. Envelope antigens
  1. Spike antigen—gp120 (Principal envelope antigen)
    2. Transmembrane pedicle protein—gp 41
B. Shell antigen
  1. Nucleocapsid protein—p18
C. Core antigens
  1. Principal core antigen—p24
  2. Other core antigens—p15, p55
D. Polymerase antigens—p31, p51, p66

Genes coding for structural proteins:

● The *gag* gene determines the core and shell of the virus. It is expressed as a precursor protein, p55. This precursor protein is cleaved into three proteins, p15, p18 and p24, which make up the viral core and shell. The major core antigen is p24 which can be detected in serum during the early stages of HIV infection before antibodies appear. Decline of free anti-p24 antibody and reappearance of p24 antigen in circulation indicates exacerbation of the illness.

● The *env* gene determines the synthesis of the envelope glycoprotein gp160, which is cleaved into the two envelope components: gp120, which forms the surface spikes, and gp41, which is the transmembrane anchoring protein. Antibodies to gp120 are present in circulation till the terminal stage of the infection.

● The *pol* gene codes for polymerase reverse transcriptase and other viral enzymes, such as protease and endonuclease. It is expressed as a precursor protein, which is cleaved into proteins p31, p51 and p66. They do not have much diagnostic or prognostic significance.

Non-structural and regulatory genes
❖ *tat* **(trans activating gene)** enhances the expression of all viral genes
❖ *nef* **(negative factor gene)** down–regulates viral replication
❖ *rev* (regulator of virus gene) enhances the expression of structural proteins
❖ *vif* **(viral infectivity factor gene)** influences the infectivity of viral particles
❖ *vpu* **(only in HIV-1) and vpx** (only in HIV-2) enhance the maturation and release of progeny virus from cells **(detection of the type-specific sequences vpu and vpx is useful in distinguishing between infection by HIV-1 and 2)**
❖ *vpr* stimulates the promoter region of the virus
❖ **LTR (long terminal repeat) sequences**, one at either end, contain the sequences that give the promoter, enhancer and integration signals.

Antigenic variation and diversity of HIV

HIV is a highly mutable virus, unlike HTLV. It exhibits frequent antigenic variation as well as differences in

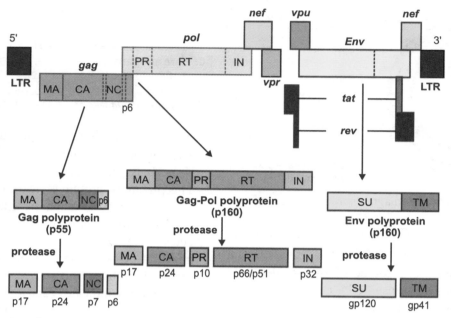

Fig. 61.2 HIV genome—diagrammatic representation

other features such as nucleotide sequences, cell tropism, growth characteristics and cytopathology. Antigenic variation exists in isolates of HIV from different places or persons and also between sequential isolates from the same person. This variability of HIV is believed to be due to the error-prone nature of reverse transcription.

HIV 1 and HIV 2: Based on molecular and antigenic differences, two types of HIV have been recognised. The original isolates of HIV and the related strains prevalent all over the world belong to HIV type 1. HIV strains, first isolated from West Africa in 1986, which react with HIV type 1 antiserum very weakly or not at all have been termed HIV type 2. HIV 2 has only 40 per cent genetic identity with HIV 1. It is more closely related to simian immunodeficiency virus than to HIV 1. It is much less virulent than HIV 1. It is largely confined to West Africa with a few reports from other areas, including western and southern India.

HIV 1 subtypes show geographical distribution, though this is often blurred by viral trafficking. All known HIV virus groups and subtypes are present in Cameroon, West Africa. Subtype A is the most prevalent, worldwide, while B is the most common in the Americas and Europe. The common subtypes in Africa are A, C and D, while in Asia the common subtypes are E, C and B. Type E is presently considered a recombination of A and E called the AE type (also known as CRFs or circulating recombinant forms). **In India and China, subtype C is the most prevalent.**

Antigenic differences between HIV strains may be important in serodiagnosis. Infection by HIV 1 or 2 may not be identified unless the corresponding type is represented in the test antigen.

Transmissibility of subtypes: The subtypes seem to vary in frequency of transmissibility by different routes. The subtypes common in Asia and Africa (C and E) are more readily transmitted by heterosexual contact than the American strains (subtype B) which are preferentially spread through blood—by injection and homosexual contact.

Growth characteristics: Differences in growth characteristics are sometimes observed between HIV isolates from asymptomatic carriers (grow slowly) and from AIDS patients (grow faster). Variations may account for differences in the clinical course of HIV-infected persons.

HIV 1 subtypes

HIV 1 strains have been classified into at least ten subtypes based on sequence analyses of their *gag* and *env* genes. These subtypes are designated A to J.

- All the subtypes constitute Group M (for 'major'), which cause most of the HIV 1 infections worldwide.
- A few HIV 1 strains isolated from West Africa (Cameroon, Gabon) do not fall within Group M and have been designated Group O (for 'outlier').
- Some later isolates of HIV 1 from Cameroon, distinct from the M and O groups have been called Group N (for new).

Resistance

HIV is thermolabile, being inactivated in 10 minutes at 60°C and in seconds at 100°C. At room temperature (20–25°C) in dried blood, it may survive for up to seven days. At autopsy, HIV has been isolated from various tissues up to 16 days after death. It withstands lyophilisation. The virus in lyophilised blood products can be inactivated by heating at 68°C for 72 hours and in liquid plasma at 60°C for 10 hours.

HIV is inactivated in 10 minutes by treatment with 50% ethanol, 35% isopropanol, 0.5% lysol, 0.5% paraformaldehyde, 0.3% hydrogen peroxide, 1% nonidet p40 or 10% household bleach. It is also inactivated at the extremes of pH (pH 1 and 13). Bleaching powder and household bleach are effective for surface decontamination. The standard recommendation is a hypochlorite solution at a concentration of 0.5% available chlorine (5 g/l; 5000 ppm). For the treatment of contaminated medical instruments, a 2% solution of glutaraldehyde is useful.

Pathogenicity

Infection is acquired when the virus enters the blood or tissues of a person and comes into contact with a suitable host cell, principally the CD4 lymphocyte.

Cell receptors for virus attachment: The receptor for the virus is any cell bearing **CD4 antigen,** primarily the CD4+ (helper/inducer) T lymphocyte. About 5–10 per cent of B lymphocytes and 10–20 per cent of monocytes and macrophages, including alveolar macrophages in the lungs and Langerhans cells in the dermis are susceptible. Glial cells and microglia in the central nervous system are also susceptible. **Follicular dendritic cells from tonsils can be infected by HIV without the involvement of CD4.**

Specific binding of the virus to the CD4 receptor is by the envelope glycoprotein gp120. Cell fusion is essential for infection to take place. This is brought about by transmembrane gp41. Binding to the CD4 receptor requires the participation of a co-receptor molecule, which has been identified as CXCR 4 for T cell-tropic HIV strains and CCR 5 for macrophage-tropic strains.

Replication: After fusion of the virus with the host cell membrane, the HIV genome is uncoated and internalised into the cell. Viral reverse transcriptase mediates the transcription of its RNA into double-stranded DNA, which is integrated into the genome of the infected cell through the action of the viral enzyme integrase, caus-

ing a latent infection. The long and variable incubation period of HIV infection is because of the latency. In an infected individual, HIV can be isolated from the blood, lymphocytes, cell-free plasma, semen, cervical secretions, saliva, tears, urine and breast milk.

The **primary pathogenic mechanism** in HIV infection is the damage to the CD4+ T lymphocyte. The T4 cells decrease in number with reversal of T4:T8 (helper:suppressor) cell ratio. Infected T4 cells do not release normal amounts of interleukin-2, gamma interferon and other lymphokines, suppressing cell-mediated immune response.

Though the main damage is to cellular immunity, humoral mechanisms are also affected. Helper T cell activity is essential for optimal B cell function. AIDS patients are unable to respond to new antigens. An important feature in HIV infection is the polyclonal activation of B lymphocytes leading to hypergammaglobulinemia of all classes of immunoglobulins, particularly IgG and IgA. In infants and children, IgM levels are also elevated. The hypergammaglobulinemia may also be responsible for allergic reactions due to immune complexes (type 3 hypersensitivity).

Monocyte–macrophage function is also affected, apparently due to lack of secretion of activating factors by the T4 lymphocytes. As a result, chemotaxis, antigen presentation and intracellular killing by monocytes/macrophages are diminished. The activity of NK cells and cytotoxic T lymphocytes is also affected.

The principal immunological abnormalities seen in HIV infection are listed in the box below.

Immunological abnormalities in HIV infection

I. **Features that characterise AIDS**
1. Lymphopenia
2. Selective T cell deficiency—Reduction in number of T4 (CD4) cells, inversion of T4:T8 ratio
3. Decreased delayed hypersensitivity on skin testing
4. Hypergammaglobulinemia—predominantly IgG and IgA; IgM also in children
5. Polyclonal activation of B cells and increased spontaneous secretion of Ig

II. **Other consistently observed features:**
1. Decreased in vitro lymphocyte proliferative response to mitogens and antigens
2. Decreased cytotoxic response by T cells and NK cells
3. Decreased antibody response to new antigens
4. Altered monocyte/macrophage function
5. Elevated levels of immune complexes in serum

Clinical manifestations in HIV infections are due not primarily to viral cytopathology but secondary to the failure of immune response. This renders the patient susceptible to opportunistic infections and malignancies. Dementia and other degenerative neurological lesions are due to the action of the virus on central nervous system (CNS) cells.

ACQUIRED IMMUNE DEFICIENCY SYNDROME (AIDS)

> **Clinical Case:** A 35-year-old commercial sex worker presented to the medical OPD with history of weight loss, decreased appetite and cough with expectoration for a duration of one month. Total WBC count was low, sputum AFB was positive and graded 2+; HIV serology was reactive with three test strategy of National Aids Control Organisation (NACO). CD4 count was 350 cells/µL. The patient was referred to the ART centre for antiretroviral and antitubercular chemotherapy. She was advised to return for a follow-up after two weeks and to use a condom during sexual contact.

Clinical features of HIV infection

AIDS is the last stage in the wide spectrum of clinical features in HIV infection. The Centers for Disease Control and Prevention, USA, have classified the clinical course of HIV infection under various groups (see box below).

The natural course of HIV infection passes through the following stages:

Group I—Acute HIV infection: Within 3–6 weeks of infection with HIV, about 50 per cent of persons experience low-grade fever, malaise, headache, lymphadenopathy, sometimes with rash and arthropathy resembling glandular fever. Rarely, there may be acute encephalopathy. Spontaneous resolution occurs within weeks.

- Seroconversion illness: Tests for HIV antibodies are usually negative at the onset of the illness but become positive during its course, though in many of those infected there may not be any apparent clinical illness.
- Acute retroviral syndrome: Patients with this syndrome may have fever, fatigue, rash, pharyngitis or other symptoms. HIV antigenemia (p24 antigen) can be demonstrated at the beginning of this phase.

Group II—asymptomatic or latent infection: All persons infected with HIV, whether or not they experience seroconversion illness, pass through a phase of symptomless infection (clinical latency) which may last up to several years. They are positive for HIV antibody and are infectious.

The infection progresses in course of time through various stages, CD4 lymphocytopenia, minor opportunistic infections, persistent generalised lymphadenopathy (PGL), AIDS-related complex (ARC), ultimately terminating in full-blown AIDS. The median time between primary HIV infection and the development of AIDS has been stated as approximately 10 years.

> About 5–10 per cent of the infected appear to escape clinical AIDS for 15 years or more. They have been termed 'long-term survivors' or 'long-term non-progressors'. The mechanisms for such prolonged survival are not clear, though many viral and host determinants may be responsible.

This period of clinical latency, however, does not mean latency as virus multiplication goes on throughout.

Classification system for HIV infection (Centers for Disease Control and Prevention, USA)		
Group I		Acute HIV syndrome
Group II		Asymptomatic infection
Group III		Persistent generalised lymphadenopathy
Group IV		Other diseases
	Subgroup A	Constitutional disease—AIDS-related complex (ARC)
	Subgroup B	Neurologic diseases
	Subgroup C	Secondary infectious diseases
	Subgroup C1	Specified infectious diseases listed in the CDC surveillance definition for AIDS, such as *P.carinii* pneumonia, cryptosporidiosis, toxoplasmosis, generalised strongyloidiasis, cryptococcosis CMV or herpes infections
	Category C2	Other specified secondary diseases, such as oral hairy leukoplakia, salmonella bacteremia, nocardiosis, tuberculosis, thrush
	Subgroup D	Secondary cancers, such as Kaposi's sarcoma, lymphomas
	Subgroup E	Other conditions

The virus load in the plasma is of prognostic value. Viral killing of cells goes on throughout the illness. The steady state of virus (**virus set point**) in a patient varies with individuals. High set point correlates with rapid disease progression.

The host mounts an immune response against the virus, both humoral and cellular, which can only limit the virus load, but not clear it completely. A chronic persistent infection with varying degrees of viral multiplication is the result. The CD4+ T cell count decreases steadily, from over 1000 per microlitre to about 500 or less in the stage of acute infection. When the count falls to < 200, clinical AIDS usually sets in. Hence, case definition by CDC includes all HIV-infected cases with CD4+ T cell counts of 200 or less, irrespective of their clinical condition (*Case*).

Group III—persistent generalised lymphadenopathy (PGL): This has been defined as the presence of enlarged lymph nodes, in two or more non-contiguous extrainguinal sites, that persist for at least three months. This is in the absence of any current illness or medication that may cause lymphadenopathy. The cases may progress to ARC or AIDS.

Group IV—AIDS-related complex (ARC): The typical constitutional symptoms are fatigue, unexplained fever, persistent diarrhea and marked weight loss ('diarrhea and dwindling') of more than 10 per cent of body weight. The common opportunistic infections are oral and esophageal candidosis, herpes zoster, hairy cell leucoplakia, salmonellosis or tuberculosis. Generalised lymphadenopathy and splenomegaly are usually present. ARC patients are usually severely ill and many of them progress to AIDS in a few months.

AIDS: This is the **end-stage disease**, representing the irreversible breakdown of immune defence mechanisms, leaving the patient open to progressive opportunistic infections and malignancies (see box below).

The clinical severity of AIDS varies with the type of infection or malignancy present. In early AIDS, many patients are ill only during episodes of infection, which may respond to treatment. Between episodes, they may be relatively well and able to resume normal life. Patients with Kaposi's sarcoma are less ill than those with other malignancies. The illness progresses inexorably and death ensues in months or years.

- **Respiratory symptoms:** The commonest presentation is **dry cough, dyspnea and fever**. In developing countries including India, the most important pathogen is *M.tuberculosis,* with increasing incidence of multidrug-resistant strains. A double epidemic of HIV and drug-resistant tuberculosis is the current challenge in developing countries. Pneumonia may be viral (CMV) or fungal (cryptosporidium, Cryptococcus or histoplasma).

- **Gastrointestinal system:** Oral thrush, herpetic stomatitis, gingivitis, hairy leukoplakia or Kaposi's sarcoma are common oral manifestations. Dysphagia may be due to esophageal candidosis. Cryptosporidium, salmonellae, mycobacteria, isospora, CMV or adenoviruses frequently cause intestinal infections. Disseminated strongyloidosis may also occur.

'Gay bowel syndrome' is chronic colitis commonly seen in male homosexuals. Amoeba, giardia and a host of diarrheagenic bacteria have been reported to be responsible for this condition.

- **Central nervous system:** The typical CNS opportunistic infections are toxoplasmosis and cryptococcosis. Infections are also seen with CMV, herpes simplex, papovaviruses, mycobacteria, aspergillus and candida. Lymphomas of the central nervous system are common.

- **Malignancies:** Kaposi's sarcoma, Hodgkin's lymphoma and other non-Hodgkin's lymphomas are associated with AIDS.

Major opportunistic infections and malignancies commonly associated with untreated AIDS patients	
Parasitic	1. Toxoplasmosis
	2. Cryptosporidiosis
	3. Isosporiasis
	4. Generalised strongyloidiasis
Mycotic	1. *Pneumocystis jirovecii*
	2. Candidosis
	3. Cryptococcosis
	4. Aspergillosis
	5. Histoplasmosis
Bacterial	1. Mycobacterial infections—tuberculosis and non-tuberculous infections
	2. Salmonellosis
	3. Campylobacter infection
	4. Nocardia and actinomycetes
	5. Legionellosis
Viral	1. CMV
	2. Herpes simplex
Malignancies	1. Kaposi sarcoma
	2. Lymphomas—Hodgkin and non-Hodgkin types

• **Cutaneous:** Herpes lesions, candidosis, xeroderma, seborrheic dermatitis, prurigo, folliculitis, impetigo and molluscum contagiosum are the common cutaneous lesions besides Kaposi's sarcoma.

Dementia: HIV may cause direct cytopathogenic damage in the central nervous system. It can cross the blood–brain barrier and cause encephalopathy leading to loss of higher functions, progressing to dementia.

Pediatric AIDS: About a third to half the number of babies born to infected mothers are infected with HIV. Virus transmission to the fetus may occur as early as the first trimester, but infection is more common perinatally. Many of the infected children may not survive the first year of life. Children may also acquire the infection from blood transfusion or blood products.

Differences between adult and pediatric AIDS:
• Children develop humoral immunodeficiency early, leading to recurrent bacterial infections.
• They fail to thrive.
• Chronic diarrhea is more common.
• Lymphadenopathy is more pronounced.
• Tuberculosis and opportunistic bacterial infections are common manifestations in pediatric AIDS.
• Lymphocytic interstital pneumonia is seen mostly in children.
• Kaposi's sarcoma, toxoplasmosis and cryptococcosis are less common than in adults.

Laboratory Confirmation of HIV AIDS

Laboratory tests are done for
• Diagnosis of clinically suspected cases
• Monitoring of treatment
• Screening of blood
• Antenatal screening of mothers
• Screening high-risk groups

Methods: Tests depend on the stage of the disease. Principally, three methods can be employed
• Viral isolation
• Detection of antibody to various antigens of the virus
• Detection of viral DNA, RNA or antigens

Policy of National Aids Control Organisation (NACO), Government of India
To bring about a reliable set of standardised tests in India, the **National AIDS Control Organisation (NACO),** Government of India, is credited for implementing a strategy for testing different categories of suspected individuals exposed to HIV. To ensure quality and uniformity in reporting the incidence and prevalence of the disease, a set of guidelines have been provided for conducting serological tests and their interpretation. It has been made mandatory for all testing laboratories to follow these guidelines. A **pre-** and **post-test counselling** must be conducted to educate the patient. And no test can be carried out without the prior consent of the patient.

Specific tests for detection of HIV infection:

Antigen detection: Following a single massive infection, as by blood transfusion, the viral antigens may be detectable in blood after about two weeks. The major core antigen, p24, is the earliest virus marker to appear in blood, hence, is tested for early diagnosis. IgM antibodies appear in about 4–6 weeks, to be followed by IgG antibodies (Fig. 61.3).

Seroconversion: This refers to the appearance of IgM antibody in the patient's serum, following the initial period of p24 antigenemia and viremia. Later, free p24 antigen disappears from circulation and remains absent during the long asymptomatic phase, to reappear only when severe clinical disease sets in.

p24 capture assay
Antibody-bound p24 antigen may be demonstrable after dissociation. The p24 antigen capture assay (ELISA) which uses anti-p24 antibody as the solid phase can be used for this. The test is positive in about 30 per cent of HIV-infected persons. With prior dissociation of the antigen–antibody complex, the positive rate increases to about 50 per cent. The test is most useful in persons recently exposed to risk of infection, in whom the antibody test is negative in the first few weeks of infection and in the terminal phase of illness.

Virus isolation: Once infected with HIV, a person remains infected for life. The virus is present in circulation in body fluids, within lymphocytes or is cell-free. Virus titres parallel p24 titres.

The virus isolation is done in containment laboratories. HIV is isolated from infected persons from the peripheral lymphocytes, by **co-cultivation.** The patient's lymphocytes are cultivated with uninfected healthy lymphocytes, in the presence of interleukin-2. Viral replication can be detected by the demonstration of reverse transcriptase activity as well as antigens, in the culture supernatant. However, viral isolation is not routinely done for diagnosis. The test is positive only in a proportion of persons infected with HIV.

Detection of viral nucleic acids: Amplification of viral DNA and RNA are the most sensitive and specific tests. They can be detected by DNA PCR, RNA PCR (RT-PCR) and bDNA assay.

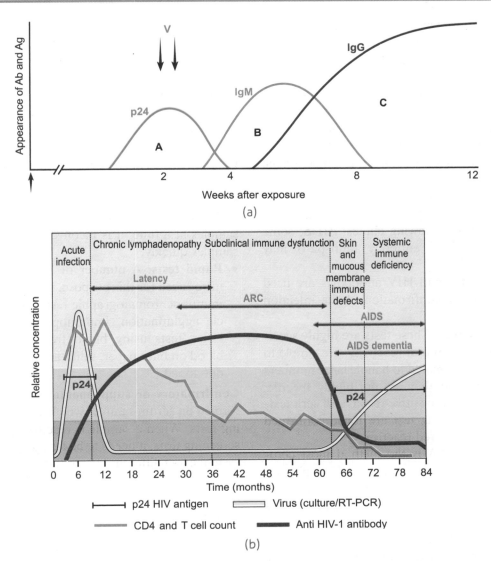

Fig. 61.3 (a) Sequence of appearance of p24 antigen and antibodies after a massive HIV infection; (b) Illustration of the usual time-course of immune response, viremia, and disease resulting from untreated HIV-1 infection.

- **DNA PCR**: Peripheral lymphocytes from the subject are lysed and the proviral DNA is amplified using primer pairs from relatively constant regions of the HIV genome (from the gag and LTR regions). The amplified DNA is detected by probes based on nucleic acid hybridisation. The test is highly sensitive and specific when done with proper controls and can detect HIV proviral DNA at a frequency of one copy per 10,000 cells.
- **RT-PCR**: This method uses an enzymatic method to amplify HIV RNA. This is a useful test to detect the disease progression and monitor response to therapy.
- **bDNA assay**: Sequential oligonucleotide hybridisation steps are used to amplify the viral RNA.

Dried blood spots on filter paper may be used as an alternate to plasma. This is adopted to transport specimens to molecular testing facilities from remote places in developing countries.

The PCR tests are complex and costly and are indicated for confirming, monitoring and as tools for early infant diagnosis.

Antibody detection: Demonstration of antibodies is the simplest and most widely employed technique for the diagnosis of HIV infection. However, it may take 2–8 weeks to months for antibodies to appear after infection. During this period, the individual may be highly infectious. **This seronegative infective stage is**

known as the window period. Hence, antibody testing is not totally dependable for detecting infectious persons, e.g., from among blood donors. Infection can be detected during the window period by p24 antigen assay. Following sexual exposure, if infection has been acquired, antibodies to HIV may take two months to appear. Therefore, testing for antibodies needs to be done only after 2–6 months to ascertain whether infection has occurred or not, after a single sexual exposure.

IgM antibodies disappear in 8–10 weeks while IgG antibodies remain throughout. When immunodeficiency becomes severe following clinical AIDS, some components of anti-HIV antibody (anti-p24) may disappear.

Serological tests for anti-HIV antibodies are used for either screening or confirmation of the infection (Table 61.1).

Tests used for screening: These tests are highly sensitive, have a broad spectrum of reactivity, are simple to perform and can be automated to handle large numbers of samples at a time. As they are not highly specific, they may give a few false positive results. All sera testing positive on a screening test are to be confirmed before the sample is declared reactive.

- **ELISA:** Indirect ELISA is the method most commonly used. HIV grown in continuous T lymphocyte cell line or obtained by recombinant techniques is the source of the antigen. It includes groups and subtypes of HIV 1 and HIV 2. The antigen is coated on microtitre wells or other suitable solid phase. The test serum is added, and if the antibody is present, it binds to the antigen. After washing the excess unbound antibodies, antihuman immunoglobulin linked to a suitable enzyme is added, followed by a colour-forming substrate. If the test serum contains anti-HIV antibody, a photometrically detectable colour is formed, which can be read by the ELISA reader.

ELISA is simple and relatively inexpensive but false positive reactions are not uncommon, particularly with sera containing rheumatoid factor, anti-lymphocyte or other autoantibodies and in hepatic disease.

Modifications of ELISA in which the antibody in the test serum either competes with enzyme-conjugated anti-HIV antibody or is captured by antihuman immunoglobulin onto a solid phase are more specific. Capture ELISA specific for IgM antibody is also available. Immunometric assays are highly sensitive and specific.

While ELISA is ideal for screening several serum samples at a time, it is inconvenient for testing single samples quickly.

- **Rapid tests:** A number of 'rapid tests' have been introduced for this purpose, such as cassette ELISA, immunochromatographic tests (ICT), coated particle agglutination, immunoperoxidase or dip-stick tests. Tests using blood from finger-prick, dried blood on filter paper, saliva and urine have also been developed.

Confirmatory or supplemental tests: These are performed on serum samples which are reactive in screening tests. When a sample is reactive by any one of the screening tests, it needs to be tested again by a different system using different HIV antigens or a different principle of test to confirm the diagnosis. If a specimen is reactive by two different systems, it has to be tested again using one of the supplemental tests which may be a third ELISA/rapid/simple test, in individuals who are not at high risk to have acquired the infection.

The confirmatory tests may also be needed to resolve discordant results of two or more rapid or ELISA tests.

Western blot test: This is the most commonly used confirmatory test (Fig. 61.4).

Procedure: HIV proteins, separated according to their electrophoretic mobility (and molecular weight)

Table 61.1 *Serological markers detected during various phases of HIV infection*

State of infection	Antigens/Antibodies	Anti-HIV IgM	Anti-HIV IgG	Western blot pattern
Early infection	+ (P24 antigen)	–	–	–
Acute (seroconversion)	+ → –	– → +	– → +	+
Partial illness	gp120, gp41, gp160 antibodies gp120	+ → –	+	+
Carriers and asymptomatic individuals	P24 ag – gp120, gp41, gp160 antibodies +	–	+	+
PGL	P24 antibodies → –	–	+	+
AIDS	P24, P17 and P55 antibodies → decline	–	+	+

Negative WB
- No bands corresponding to the molecular wts of known viral Ags
- Bands at other locations
  - Cross reacting Ags
  - Not specific to HIV

Positive WB
- CDC Atlanta, USA (Associate of state and territorial public health lab directors)
- HIV –1 ⟶ 2 of 3 bands
  - p24, gp41 or gp160/120
- HIV –2 ⟶ gp36

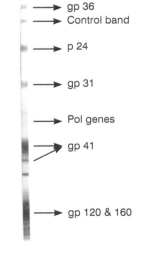

gp 36
Control band
p 24
gp 31
Pol genes
gp 41
gp 120 & 160

Fig. 61.4   Western blot test for HIV antibody

by polyacrylamide gel electrophoresis, are blotted onto strips of nitrocellulose paper. Patient's sera are reacted with these proteins on the strips followed by an enzyme-conjugated antihuman globulin. A suitable substrate is then added, which produces a distinct colour band where the specific antibody has reacted with the blotted viral protein.

Results: The position of the band on the strip indicates the antigen with which the antibody has reacted. In a positive serum, multiple proteins' bands are seen, Mainly, p24 (*gag* gene, core protein), p31 (*pol* gene, reverse transcriptase) and gp41, gp120 or gp160 (*env* gene, surface antigens) bands are noted. A positive reaction with proteins representing three genes is conclusive. The test may be considered positive if it also shows bands against at least two of the following gene products: p24, gp41, gp120/160. However, interpretation becomes difficult when bands other than those specified above appear. This may happen in early infection or may be non-specific. Western blot is a useful confirmatory test but the interpretation remains subjective and demands considerable experience. In indeterminate cases, the Western blot may be repeated after a specified period of time. It may be necessary to do a p24 assay in indeterminate results.

Apart from diagnosing HIV infection, the laboratory needs to identify the opportunistic infections that are a feature of AIDS. Routine microbiological methods would suffice for this. Serological diagnosis markers of infection may not be reliable in AIDS as

antibody formation may be affected by the immune deficiency.

Line immunoassays (LIAs): These are based on the application of recombinant and synthetic peptide antigens on a plastic support strip in a manner similar to the immunoblot assay. LIAs are second- or third-generation assays and have the potential to be used as supplemental tests. Combination assays and differentiating infection by HIV 1 and HIV 2 can also be done in LIA.

> HIV screening or testing is required for the following reasons:
> ❖ Epidemiological surveillance using unlinked anonymous HIV testing
> ❖ Transfusion and transplant safety
> ❖ Diagnosis of HIV infection in symptomatic and asymptomatic individuals
> ❖ Prevention of parent-to-child transmission
> ❖ For post-exposure prophylaxis (PEP)
> ❖ Research

Strategies for HIV testing

In India, the National Aids Control Organisation (NACO) of the Ministry of Health, Government of India, has laid out guidelines and strategies for screening, testing and monitoring HIV infected/suspected individuals.

- ELISA/Rapid tests/Supplemental tests (E/R/S) used in strategies I, II and III
- Supplemental test in cases of indeterminate/discordant result of E/R/S

NACO strategies for testing different categories of samples:

Strategy I: This strategy is used to screen blood/blood products organ, tissues, sperms, etc. The sample is subjected once to E/R for HIV (Fig. 61.5).

NACO recommends the use of ELISA kits with a sensitivity of ≥99.5 percent and specificity of ≥98 percent and rapid kits with a sensitivity of ≥99.5 percent and specificity of ≥98 percent.

Strategy II: This strategy is used for surveillance (2A) and for diagnosis (2B), if some AIDS indicator disease is present (Figs 61.6 and 61.7) . If a serum sample is positive in the first ELISA, it is subjected to a second ELISA which utilises a system different from the first one. By second ELISA, if the test is positive, then it is reported as positive. If it is negative (by the second test) the result is considered negative.

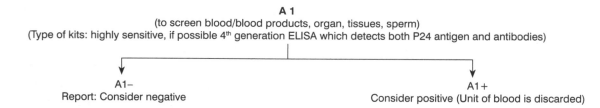

Fig. 61.5   Interpretation of tests A1– and A1+

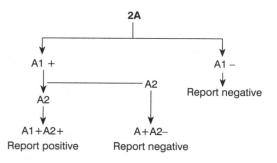

Fig. 61.6   2A (for surveillance- anonymous unlinked)

Strategy 2B: This strategy is used to determine the HIV status of clinically symptomatic suspected AIDS cases in which blood/serum/plasma is tested with highly sensitive screening and confirmatory tests based on different principles and/or antigens as compared to the first test.

Strategy III: This is used in asymptomatic individuals. It is similar to strategy II, with the added third positive ELISA test being required for a sample to be reported HIV-reactive. In this, the first ELISA is the one with the highest sensitivity and the second and third ELISAs have the highest specificity (Fig. 61.8).

Applications of serological tests

Serological tests for HIV infection are used in the following situations:

Screening: Screening is done of populations or selected target groups for epidemiological purposes. Screening of entire populations is neither feasible nor practicable. However, screening of a target population is useful. It is mandatory for all donors of blood, blood products, semen, cells, tissues and organs to be screened. Screening for the p24 antigen can detect those in the window period also. Hence, tests to detect both P24 antigen and HIV antibodies are recommended in blood banks. HIV-positive individuals must not donate blood tissue or organs. As the infection can be transmitted from mother to baby before, during or

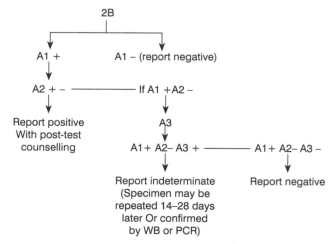

Fig. 61.7   2B (for diagnosis of symptomatic or high-risk individuals)

after birth, antenatal screening of all antenatal women has been made mandatory.

Seroepidemiology: Antibody surveys have been most useful in identifying the geographical extent of HIV infection and in other epidemiological studies such as spread of the infection from identified sources.

Diagnosis: Serology is almost always positive in persons with clinical features of AIDS. It may, however, be negative in acute illness and sometimes in the very late cases where the immune system is non-reactive. Routine serology may also be negative when the infection is with a different AIDS virus. For example, HIV 2 infections are likely to be missed if antibody testing is done with the HIV 1 antigen alone. Test antigens should be updated when new virus types or subtypes are identified, and should be able to detect antibody against all prevalent types of HIV.

Although HIV-1 and HIV-2 are related, there are important structural differences between them. Accurate diagnosis and differentiation of HIV-1 and HIV-2 is crucial for treatment, as HIV-2 is intrinsically resistant to NNRTI, the pillar of national first-line ART regimen.

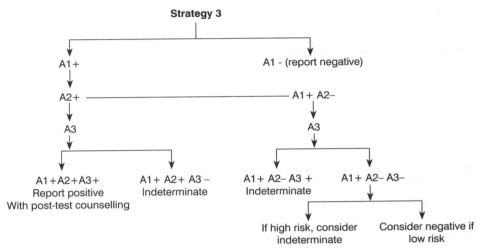

Fig. 61.8 Strategy 3 (for diagnosis of asymptomatic individuals)

Antibody testing may also help to check whether infection has taken place following an exposure, such as sexual contact, blood transfusion or needle-stick injury. Serology after two months and, if negative, after six months, would be sufficient. If serology is negative six months after exposure, infection is unlikely to have occurred.

Prognosis: In a person infected with HIV, loss of detectable anti-p24 antibody indicates clinical deterioration. This is also associated with HIV antigenemia and increased virus titre in circulation.

Non-specific or immunological tests: The following parameters indicate immunodeficiency in HIV infection:
- Total leucocyte and lymphocyte count to demonstrate leucopenia (count usually below 2000/mm³)
- T cell subset assays. Absolute CD4+ T cell count is usually less than 200/mm³. T4:T8 cell ratio is reversed
- Thrombocytopenia (low platelet count)
- Raised IgG and IgA levels
- Diminished CMI as indicated by skin tests
- Lymph node biopsy shows abnormalities

Laboratory monitoring of HIV infection: Some laboratory tests are important in monitoring the course of HIV infection. CD4+ T cell count which reflects the current immunological competence of the patient is most often used to monitor the course. A count below 500 indicates disease progression and the need for antiretroviral therapy. Counts below 200 denote risk of serious infection.

It is necessary to monitor measurement of HIV RNA during the course of treatment. This is usually done by two methods, RT-PCR and bDNA assay.

Beta-2-microglobulin and neopterin are two substances that have a predictive value on the progression of HIV disease as they rise with advancing disease.

Epidemiology and prevention

Progenitor of HIV 1 entered the human population from chimpanzees of the subspecies *Pan troglodytes troglodytes* living in equatorial West Africa (Cameroon, Gabon, equatorial Guinea). HIVs are believed to have been present in monkeys for over 100,000 years. Simian Immunodeficiency virus may have taken root in humans by converting to HIV through mutation or recombination.

HIV 1 M, O, N types may represent independent transmissions from chimpanzees to humans. The source of HIV 2 has been established as SIV from the Sooty Mangabey monkey *Cercocebus atys*.

Transmission: The virus has spread globally, with geographically different prevalence rates. HIV is spread only by three modes (Table 61.2):
- Sexual contact with infected persons (heterosexual or homosexual)
- By blood and blood products
- Infected mother to babies (intrapartum, perinatal, postnatal)

There is no evidence of HIV transmission by other means including casual contact or through insects.
- HIV is primarily a **sexually transmitted infection**, initially predominant in male homosexuals. In the affluent countries, homosexual and bisexual men are infected

Table 61.2 *Common modes of transmission of HIV and their relative risk*

Types of exposure	Approximate chance of infection per exposure
I Sexual intercourse: anal, vaginal, oral	0.1–1.0%
II Blood and blood products, Factor VII, etc., blood transfusion	>90%
III Tissue and organ donation: semen, cornea, bone marrow, kidney, etc.	50–90%
IV Injections and injuries: shared needles by drug addicts Injections with unsterile syringes and needles Needle-stick and other injuries in health staff Surgical wounds	0.5–1.0%
V Mother to baby: Transplacental At birth After birth Breast milk	30%

far more often than heterosexuals. Hence, it is found predominantly in men and only occasionally in women. However, the situation in Africa and Asia shows men and women are equally affected. Transmission in the developing countries is almost always heterosexual and can take place in both partners.

The best method of checking sexual transmission and other high-risk activities for infection is through counselling and health education.

- The second mode of transmission is **through blood and blood products**. Screening of blood donors is now mandatory, which must include p24 antigen screening.

- **Contaminated needles** can transmit the infection. This is particularly relevant in drug addicts who share syringes and needles. Higher incidence has been detected in northeastern states of India besides some other parts of the country. The use of **unsterile syringes and needles** by health workers makes iatrogenic infection likely. The use of disposable syringes, needles and other equipment has reduced the incidence.

The risk of **needle-stick injury** is present for health-care personnel, though the chances of infection are much less than with the hepatitis B virus. Transmission of infection from **mother to child** can take place before,

during or after birth. As infection occurs in about half such infants, a mandatory testing in the antenatal period is carried out and infected women are informed. Early infant diagnosis has now been introduced by NACO to detect HIV infection in newborns. This is done by testing for pro-viral DNA by PCR on blood collected from the newborn by heel prick. This is absorbed on dry filter paper. This dried blood spot is sent to a referral laboratory for testing, and the baby is treated. HIV may be present in breast milk and may be transmitted through breastfeeding.

HIV is not transmitted by: social and domestic contact, shaking hands, hugging, putting cheeks together or dry kissing. There has been no confirmed case of transmission through saliva, though the virus may be present in the saliva of infected persons. A salivary protein called secretory leucocyte protease inhibitor has anti-HIV activity. There is no evidence of mosquitoes, bed bugs or other blood-sucking insects transmitting the virus.

HIV infection was detected rather late in India, the first cases having been found in female sex workers in Madras (Chennai) in 1986 and the first AIDS patient the same year in Bombay (Mumbai). Since then, the rate of infection has been increasing among high-risk group in certain states and target populations. With several intervention programmes of the NACO, it is hoped to control the infection.

Prophylaxis

Prevention of AIDS depends on general measures such as health education, identification of sources and decrease in high-risk behaviour. No specific vaccine is available. The high mutability, diverse antigenic types and subtypes, long latency and persistence as provirus in infected cells pose several problems in the development of vaccines.

Vaccine research
Several possible strategies have been explored for vaccine production. These include **immunisation** of experimental animals like chimpanzees and monkeys with:
- Modified whole virus
- Subunits, based on envelope glycoproteins expressed in animal cells, bacteria, viruses—or as synthetic epitopes on adjuvant carriers
- Target cell protection by anti-CD4 antibody or genetically engineered CD4. A number of candidate vaccines are being tested in clinical trials in humans
- Post-exposure prophylaxis

This refers to the comprehensive management given to minimise the risk of infection following potential exposure to bloodborne pathogens, such as HIV.

'**Exposure**' for risk of developing bloodborne infections is defined as:

- Percutaneous injury (needle-stick injury)
- Contact with mucous membrane of eye or mouth
- Contact with non-intact skin
- Contact with intact skin when the duration of contact is prolonged with blood or other potentially infectious body fluids

It is expressed as exposure code (EC).

Although the risk of HIV transmission by these routes is less than 1%, PEP is recommended within 72 hours of exposure, depending on the exposure category of HCP and the HIV status code of the patient (Figs 61.9 and 61.10).

Management of AIDS

Approaches to the treatment of AIDS include:

- The treatment and prophylaxis of infections and tumours
- General management
- Immunorestorative measures
- Specific anti-HIV agents

Prompt diagnosis, counselling and appropriate treatment of opportunistic infections and tumours in the early stage of AIDS can be very useful and the patient may be able to resume normal life in between episodes of illness. General management of the patient requires the understanding and cooperation of the health staff in the hospital and of relatives at home. Fears about imaginary risks have to be allayed and reassurance given that the patient can be kept at home or treated in the hospital without danger to contacts, if proper precautions are taken.

Antiretroviral treatment: Highly Active Anti-Retroviral Treatment (HAART) is the mainstay of treatment. It leads to complete suppression of plasma viremia, opportunistic infection rates are decreased and the quality of life for people living with HIV and AIDS (PLHA) is improved. Adherence to treatment can delay the development of drug resistance and the need for second-line treatment. Specific treatment with antiretroviral drugs is the mainstay in the management of HIV infection. A number of effective drugs have become available in

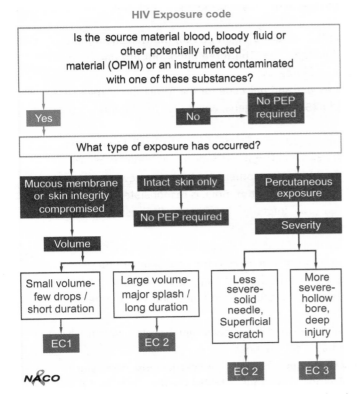

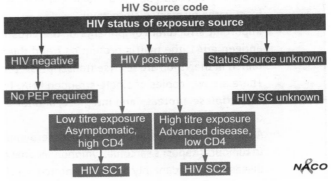

Effectiveness of PEP depends on...

- Efficacy of PEP is best, if administered within two hours of exposure
- PEP needs to be given within 72 hours of exposure
- Do not delay PEP while waiting for result of HIV testing
- Informed consent must be obtained before testing a source as per National guidelines
- Base line rapid HIV testing before PEP
- Negative result doesn't exclude HIV infection
- Positive HIV result helps in stopping the PEP

Fig. 61.9 Guidelines of National AIDS Control Organisation (NACO)

Determining PEP recommendation

EC	HIV SC	PEP recommendation
1	1	May not be warranted
1	2	Consider basic regimen (Two drugs)
2	1	Recommend basic regimen (Two drugs)
2	2	Recommend expanded regimen (Three drugs)
3	1 or 2	Recommend expanded regimen (Three drugs)
2/3	Unknown	Consider basic regimen if HIV prevalence is high in the given population

NACO

Fig. 61.10   Recommendations for post-exposure prophylaxis (PEP)

recent years. These include nucleoside analogues like zidovudine (azidothmidine, AZT), didanosine, zalcitabine, lamivudine and protease inhibitors like saquinavir, ritonavir, indinavir, which have been used as monotherapy or in various combinations. Adverse reactions and high cost restrict their wide use in resource-poor countries.

The National AIDS Control Organisation (NACO) provides free anti-retroviral treatment through several ART centres across India.

Steps at immunorestorative therapy such as administration of interleukin-2, thymic factors, leucocyte transfusion and bone marrow transplantation have not been very helpful.

RECAP

- Human immunodeficiency virus types 1 and 2 (HIV 1 and HIV 2) are the causative agents of acquired immunodeficiency syndrome (AIDS) worldwide. The HIV viruses are about 90–120 nm in size, spherical in shape, icosahedral in symmetry and enveloped.
- There are ten subtypes, A through J, which fall into group M, other groups being O and N. It is easily inactivated by many disinfectants.
- Important structural components of the virus include the surface antigen gp120, the transmembrane antigen gp41, the matrix protein p17 and the capsid antigen p24. The three important enzymes contained in the virion are reverse transcriptase, protease and integrase.
- There are two copies of single-stranded RNA. Two genes, *gag* and *pol*, code for the formation of reverse transcriptase, protease and integrase, and for p17 and p25. Another gene, *env*, codes for the formation of gp120 and gp41.
- AIDS is a late manifestation of HIV disease. Symptoms are varied, from asymptomatic to flu-like symptoms to tumours (Kaposi's sarcoma, lymphomas, anal and cervical carcinoma) and opportunistic infections. The disease is spread mainly by sexual intercourse, blood and from the mother to the fetus or newborn.
- In India, the National AIDS Control Organisation (NACO), Government of India, is responsible for implementing government policy on the control of AIDS and HIV infection. Laboratory diagnosis includes antigen detection, virus isolation, PCR and antibody detection.
- The mainstay of diagnosis of HIV infection is serological tests: ELISA is the most frequently used method for screening blood samples for anti-HIV antibody. The Western blot assay is the gold standard for diagnosis, and seropositivity is diagnosed when antibodies against the *Env* and *Gag* proteins are detected.
  - HIV antigen can be detected as early as at three weeks in the course of HIV infection, and before the appearance of antibody.
  - Isolation of the virus is accomplished by co-cultivation of the patient's lymphocytes with fresh peripheral blood cells of healthy donors or with suitable culture lines.
- HIV RNA can be demonstrated by probes or by RT-PCR techniques. The latter are particularly useful since the viral RNA can be detected as early as 72 hours after infection, thus establishing diagnosis, and the response to therapy can be assessed.

- There are three strategies for HIV testing as per NACO, which are based on the type of setting where the testing is done. Screening tests like ELISA/simple/rapid tests (E/R/S) are used in strategies I, II and III. Supplemental or confirmatory tests are done in cases of indeterminate/discordant results of E/R.
- Prevention of AIDS depends on changes in human behaviour. Treatment of AIDS depends on antiviral medication and prevention and treatment of opportunistic infections and tumours.

ESSAY

1. Enumerate the sexually transmitted infections and write the laboratory diagnosis of HIV.

SHORT ANSWERS

1. HIV viral genes and antigens
2. Antigenic variations of HIV
3. Pathogenesis of AIDS
4. Laboratory diagnosis of HIV infection
5. Significance of viral markers in HIV infection

SHORT NOTES

1. Western blot test and interpretation for diagnosis of HIV infection
2. NACO strategies for HIV testing in India
3. Prevention of HIV
4. Opportunistic infections in AIDS patients
5. Rapid tests for HIV
6. Role of PCR in the diagnosis of HIV
7. Monitoring of patient on ART

62 General Aspects

CHARACTERISTICS OF FUNGI
  Classification
  Laboratory diagnosis
  Treatment

INTRODUCTION

Mycology (from the Greek *mykos*, meaning fungus) is the branch of microbiology that deals with the study of fungi (yeasts and moulds).

Fungi were recognised earlier than bacteria as causative agents of human disease. Fungi causing favus (*Trichophyton schonleinii*) and thrush (*Candida albicans*) were described as early as in 1839. Unfortunately, despite these early beginnings, the study of pathogenic fungi received only scant attention in comparison with the study of other microbial pathogens. This is probably due to the relatively benign nature of the common mycotic (fungal) diseases and because the techniques used in the field of mycology are more those used by botanists than by bacteriologists.

Fungal infections, however, are extremely common and some of them are serious and even fatal. As developed countries have managed to control most bacterial infections, fungal infections have assumed greater importance. For instance, in the USA, fungal infections reportedly cause as many fatalities today as do whooping cough, diphtheria, scarlet fever, typhoid, dysentery and malaria put together. Most fungi are saprophytes in the soil and human mycotic infections are mainly opportunistic. The widespread use of modern advances in treatment, such as antibiotics, steroids and immunosuppressive agents, has reportedly led to an increase in opportunistic fungal infections.

CHARACTERISTICS OF FUNGI

Fungi are eukaryotic protista that differ from bacteria and other prokaryotes in many ways. They possess rigid cell walls containing chitin, mannan and other polysaccharides. The cytoplasmic membrane contains sterols. They possess true nuclei with nuclear membrane and paired chromosomes. They divide asexually, sexually or by both processes. They may be unicellular or multicellular. The cells show various degrees of specialisation.

Classification

Fungi are classified as follows:

Morphological classification: From a diagnostic point of view, fungi may be classified depending on cell morphology into four groups (Figs 62.1 and 62.2):

- Yeast
- Yeast-like fungi
- Moulds
- Dimorphic fungi

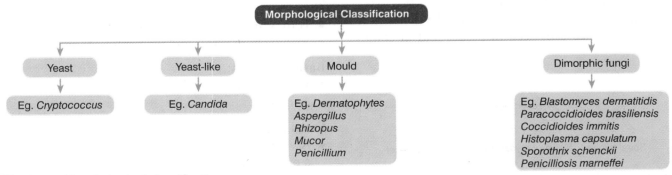

Fig. 62.1 Morphological classification

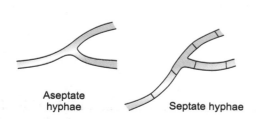

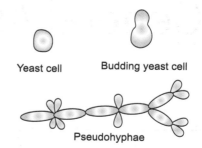

Fig. 62.2   Vegetative forms of fungi

Yeasts (for example, *Cryptococcus neoformans*)
- Unicellular fungi
- Reproduce by budding (bud = blastospore [blastoconidium])
- Macroscopic appearance—pasty colonies (resembling bacterial colonies) in culture
- Microscopic appearance—oval to round (3–15 μm in diameter); occur as spherical or oval forms in tissues and in culture; filamentous (hyphae-like) structures are not seen in tissues or in culture.

Yeast-like fungi (for example, *Candida albicans*)
- Unicellular fungi
- Reproduce by budding and by fission
- Macroscopic appearance—pasty colonies (resembling bacterial colonies) in culture
- Microscopic appearance—spherical or oval forms in tissues and in culture; filamentous structures (**pseudohyphae**) may be seen.

Filamentous fungi or moulds (for example, *Aspergillus fumigatus*)
- Composed of hyphae which may have cross-walls or septa (multicellular) or may be devoid of septa (coenocytic).
- Reproduce by asexual means (spore formation); some exhibit sexual reproduction
- Macroscopic appearance—surface texture may be cottony/woolly/velvety/granular; pigmentation may be observed from the reverse
- Microscopic appearance—thread-like filamentous hyphae (2–10 μm) seen in tissues and in culture.

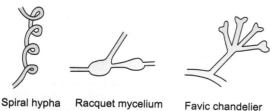

Fig. 62.3   Different forms of hypha

These may be aseptate (without cross-walls; for example, *Zygomycetes*) or septate (with cross-walls; for example, *Aspergillus fumigatus*). Mycelium may be vegetative or aerial. Hyphae may take any of the following shapes: racquet, nodular, pectinate, spiral, root-like (rhizoid), chandelier-like (a repeatedly branched cluster of hyphal apices that resembles a chandelier) (Fig. 62.3).

Thermally dimorphic fungi (for example, *Histoplasma capsulatum*)
- Grow as filamentous forms in culture at 22–25°C and in the environment
- Grow as yeast forms in culture at 37°C and in tissues

Systemic classification: The systematic classification of fungi, based on their sexual spore formation, recognises four classes (Figs 62.4 and 62.5):

Phycomycetes:
- Lower fungi that have non-septate hyphae and form endogenous asexual spores, called sporangiospores, contained within swollen sac-like structures called **sporangia**.
- Also produce sexual spores known as **oospores** in some fungi and **zygospores** in others.
- The other three classes (the higher fungi) have septate hyphae and form exogenous asexual spores called **conidia**.

Ascomycetes:
- Form sexual spores (**ascospores**) within a sac or ascus.
- Include both yeasts and filamentous fungi.

Basidiomycetes:
- Form sexual spores (**basidiospores**) on a 'basidium' or base.

Fungi imperfecti:
- Also called deuteromycetes or hyphomycetes, this is a provisional group consisting of fungi whose sexual phases have not been identified.

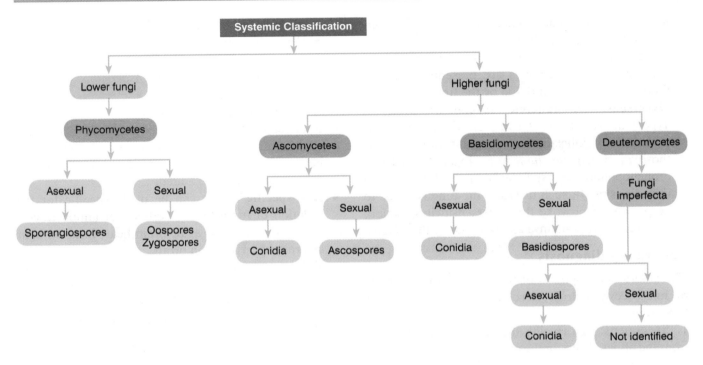

Fig. 62.4 Systemic classification

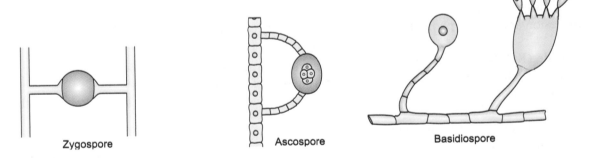

Fig. 62.5 Sexual spores

- Most fungi of medical importance belong to this group.

Pathogenic classification: Based on their pathogenic potential, fungi may be considered as:

- **Primarily pathogenic**—able to cause infections in healthy individuals; for example, thermally dimorphic fungi
- **Opportunistic pathogens**—able to cause infections by various mechanisms in patients who have pre-existing defects in their immune mechanisms (for example, individuals receiving immunosuppressive drugs or individuals suffering from diabetes mellitus or debilitating conditions and individuals infected with HIV)

Pathogenic fungi may cause:

- **Actual infection of tissues (mycoses)**
  - superficial mycoses
  - cutaneous mycoses
  - subcutaneous mycoses
  - deep or visceral mycoses

  Here, the fungus needs to be present in the tissue to cause its pathogenic effects (in many instances, there is actual invasion of the tissue by the fungus.

- **Mycotoxicoses:** These are diseases due to toxic metabolic products released by fungi. Examples: aflatoxicosis due to consumption of grains containing aflatoxins secreted by *Aspergillus flavus* contaminating the groundnuts, corn and peas; ergotism after ingestion of rye contaminated with *Claviceps purpurea*. Here, the fungus does not necessarily have to be present in the tissues to exert its pathogenic effect, since its toxic metabolites are present; moreover, there is no invasion of tissue by the fungus.

- **Hypersensitivity (allergic reactions):** Here, a Type I and/or Type III hypersensitivity reaction is provoked by inhalation of fungal spores, notably those of *Aspergillus fumigatus*. Examples: allergic bronchopulmonary aspergillosis and allergic fungal rhinosinusitis. In such diseases, the fungus needs to be present to provoke the hypersensitivity reaction; however, there is no invasion of tissue by the fungus.

Laboratory diagnosis

The laboratory diagnosis of fungal infections is made by microscopy, culture, serology and skin tests (for hypersensitivity).

1. Specimens: Normally, the specimen is collected from the affected site. In the case of suspected disseminated (spreading) infections, samples of blood need to be collected as well.

2. Microscopy: Fungal structures can be detected in clinical specimens by direct microscopic examination of material from the lesion and by morphological study of fungal isolates:

- **Potassium hydroxide (KOH) preparation**
  - Tissue specimens, such as skin scrapings, are generally examined as wet mounts after treatment with 10% potassium hydroxide.
  - The alkali digests cells and other tissue materials, enabling the fungal elements to be seen clearly.
- **Calcoflour white (CFW)** is a sensitive staining procedure that provides good visualisation of the morphology of the fungus.
- **Gram stain** is useful in identifying yeast and yeast-like fungi.
- **India ink preparation** is used for negative staining of capsulated yeast; for example, Cryptococcus.
- **Methenamine silver stain** and **periodic acid–Schiff (PAS)** are valuable methods used for demonstrating fungi in tissues.
- **Lactophenol cotton blue (LCB)** is used for the microscopic study of fungus colonies that are teased on to a slide and mounted.

3. Culture: The following points must be considered when attempting to culture fungi in the laboratory:

- Most fungi are grown in media similar to those used for bacteria, although usually at a lower pH.

- All fungi are basically aerobic.
- Fungi grow better at a temperature of 25–30°C (exceptions are those causing deep mycoses [grow well at 37°C] and *Aspergillus fumigatus* [can grow even at 50°C]).

Media: The media can be classified as:

- **Specific media** such as Sabouraud dextrose agar (Sabouraud glucose neopeptone agar), which may have an acid (pH 5.4) or neutral pH, and to which antibacterials may be added.
- **Non-specific media** can be made specific for the isolation of fungi by the addition of antibacterials. Examples are blood agar, brain heart infusion agar or brain heart infusion broth.

The most common culture media used in mycology are Sabouraud dextrose agar (pH 5.4), Czapek–Dox medium, bird seed agar and corn meal agar. The addition of antibiotics prevents bacterial contamination. Cycloheximide (Actidione) incorporated in the medium inhibits many contaminant moulds. Cultures are routinely incubated in parallel at room temperature (22°C) for weeks and at 37°C for days. Identification is based on the morphology of the fungus and of its colony. Diagnostic mycology rests largely on a detailed study of the morphological evolution of the isolate.

Growth characteristics useful for identification are:

- Rapidity of growth
- Colour and morphology of the colony on the obverse
- Pigmentation on the reverse
- Morphology of hyphae (diameter, septa), conidia (spores) and other special structures

Teased mount: These morphological features can be studied in teased mounts, slide cultures and cellophane tape preparations. The teased mount is the easiest to prepare, as a bit of the fungal colony is '**teased out**' from the culture plate, placed in a drop of lactophenol cotton blue, covered by a coverslip and then viewed under the microscope; however, the 'in situ' microscopic appearance of the fungus is difficult to view in a teased mount.

Slide culture: This is technically the most difficult, but has the major advantage of preserving the 'in situ' appearance of the fungal structures for viewing under the microscope.

A sterile microscopic slide is placed on a bent glass rod in a petri dish. A 1-cm square block of SDA is placed on the slide. The fungal strain to be identified is inoculated at the four sides of the agar block. The inoculated block is covered with a sterile cover slip and incubate at 25°C. After 48 hours, growth appears; then a drop of LCB is placed on a fresh slide and the cover slip is transferred from the block of SDA onto this slide. The preparation is viewed under the microscope. The undisturbed morphology of the fungus is observed.

Cellophane tape mount: This is a compromise, being technically easier to perform while at the same time allowing the 'in situ' appearance to be viewed under the microscope; however, the fungal culture may subsequently become contaminated due to contact with the unsterile cellophane tape.

4. Serology: Tests are done to demonstrate either antigen or antibody in serum or body fluids:

Antibody detection
- Agglutination
- Compliment fixation
- Immunodiffusion
- Counter immunoelectrophoresis
- ELISA

- Indirect fluorescent antibody

Antigen detection
- Latex agglutination for cryptococcal capsular antigen, *Candida* and *Aspergillus*

Immunohistochemistry
- Useful for a number of important pathogens

Skin test: This is used to detect delayed-type hypersensitivity (DTH) for pathogens like *Histoplasma* or *Coccidioides*.

Newer rapid diagnostic tests for fungal infections are:
- Nucleic acid hybridisation
- Polymerase chain reaction

Treatment

Antifungal agents: Medical therapy of mycotic infections involves the use of compounds belonging to different groups: polyenes, pyrimidines, azoles, grisans and echinocandins (Table 62.1). Some medications are used only topically for application on the skin or mucous membranes (pimaricin for eye or skin infections), some only orally (griseofulvin) while others (amphotericin B, some azoles) can be administered by a variety of routes.

Table 62.1 *Antifungal antibiotics*

Class	Compounds	Mechanism	Uses
Polyene	Amphotericin B Nystatin Pimaricin	Binds to sterols causing perturbations in cell membrane	Systemic disease Skin infection Eye infection
Imidazole and Triazole	Itraconazole, Voriconazole Ketoconazole	Inhibits ergosterol biosynthesis	Topical disease (ringworm) Systemic disease
Pyrimidine	5-fluorocytosine (5FC)	Inhibits DNA and RNA synthesis	Used in association with amphotericin B
Grisans	Griseofulvin	Inhibits microtubule assembly	Dermatophytoses
Echinocandins	Caspofungin Micafungin	Inhibits beta glucan synthesis in cell wall	Systemic diseases due to *Candida* and *Cryptococcus*

RECAP

- Fungi are eukaryotic protista that posses a rigid cell wall containing chitin, mannan and other polysaccharides. They have true nuclei with nuclear membrane and paired chromosomes.
- Medically important fungi are classified based on their morphology as yeasts, yeast-like fungi, moulds (filamentous fungi) and thermally dimorphic fungi while from the standpoint of disease-causing potential in humans, fungi are regarded as primary pathogens and opportunist pathogens.
- Fungi are classified based on the method of sexual reproduction into Zygomycetes (asexual spores in sporangium), Ascomycetes (sexual spores within ascus), Basidiomycetes (sexual spores borne on basidium) and Deuteromycetes ('fungi imperfecti', no known sexual form).
- Pathogenic fungi cause true infections or mycoses, mycotoxicoses and allergic diseases (Type I and Type III hypersensitivity reactions).
- Specimens for diagnosis are usually collected from the affected site (also from blood in disseminated infections). Specimens are examined by direct microscopy or used for culture (Sabouraud agar). New diagnostic methods are increasingly being used.
- Antifungal agents include polyenes, azoles, pyrimidines, grisans and echinocandins.

ESSAY

1. Describe the laboratory diagnosis of fungal infections.

SHORT NOTES

1. SDA
2. Culture media used in mycology
3. Slide culture

63 Superficial and Subcutaneous Mycoses

SUPERFICIAL MYCOSES

    Pityriasis versicolor (Tinea versicolor)

    Tinea nigra

    Piedra

    Dermatophytoses

SUBCUTANEOUS MYCOSES

    Mycetoma

    Chromomycosis

    Sporotrichosis

    Rhinosporidiosis

    Subcutaneous zygomycosis
    (Entomophthoromycoses)

Table 63.1 *Major mycoses and the diseases*

Category	*Fungal diseases*
Superficial (localised to the stratum corneum)	Pytriasis versicolor, Tinea nigra, white piedra, black piedra (produce concretions in the hair due to fungal growth)
Cutaneous	Dermatophytosis, Candidosis of skin, nail and mucosa
Subcutaneous	Mycetoma, Chromomycosis Sporothicosis, Phaeohyphomycosis
Deep or systemic (often endemic)	Histoplasmosis, Coccidiodomycosis Blastomycosis, Paracoccidiodomycosis
Opportunistic	Candidosis, Cryptococcosis Aspergillosis, Penicilliosis, Zygomycosis, Pneumocystis pneumonia

INTRODUCTION

Fungal infections in humans are broadly classified into these types (Table 63.1 and Fig. 63.1), depending on the tissue affected

- Superficial mycoses
- Cutaneous mycoses
- Subcutaneous mycoses
- Systemic infections
- Opportunistic mycoses

This chapter will discuss superficial and subcutaneous mycoses.

SUPERFICIAL MYCOSES

Superficial mycoses is a group of infections caused by fungi that live exclusively on the dead layers of the skin and its appendages. They have no contact with living tissue and, hence, elicit no inflammatory response; the only changes produced are cosmetic effects. Examples: *Tinea (Pityriasis) versicolor, Tinea nigra* and *T.piedra*.

Cutaneous infections: The most important cutaneous infection is **dermatophytosis** caused by a group of related fungi called the dermatophytes. Infection is generally confined to the cornified layer of the skin and its appendages. Various inflammatory and allergic responses are induced in the host by the presence of the fungi and by their metabolic products. *Candida albicans* may also cause infections of the skin and mucosa as well as systemic disease (rare). *Candida* infection, therefore, represents a bridge connecting superficial and deep mycoses.

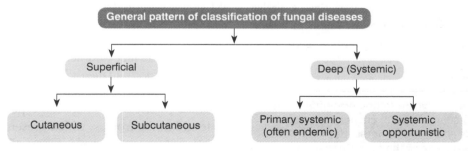

Fig. 63.1 Classification of mycoses

Pityriasis versicolor (Tinea versicolor)

This is a chronic, usually asymptomatic, involvement of the stratum corneum.

Distribution: The disease is worldwide in distribution but is particularly prevalent in the tropics. It occurs mainly in young adults.

Causative agent: The lipophilic, yeast-like fungus *Malassezia furfur* (formerly *Pityrosporum orbiculare*)

Clinical features: Characteristic discrete or confluent macular areas of discolouration or depigmentation occur on the skin of the chest, abdomen, upper limbs and back. The fungus may be demonstrated on normal skin also and the disease may be considered an opportunistic infection.

Diagnosis: Examination of skin scrapings shows an abundance of yeast-like cells and short, branched filaments. The fungus can be grown on Sabouraud agar, covered with a layer of olive oil.

Tinea nigra

This is a localised infection of the stratum corneum, particularly of the palms, producing black or brownish macular lesions.

Distribution: This disease mainly occurs in the tropics.

Causative agent: *Exophiala werneckii* (formerly *Cladosporium wernickii, Hortaea wernickii*) and *Exophiala castellanii*.

Diagnosis: Skin scrapings show brownish, branched, septate hyphae and budding cells. Colonies on Sabouraud agar are grey or black in colour.

Piedra

This fungal infection of the hair is characterised by the presence of firm, irregular nodules along the hair shaft; these nodules are composed of fungal elements cemented together on the hair. Two varieties of piedra are recognised: black piedra caused by *Piedraia hortae* and white piedra caused by *Trichosporon beigelii*.

Dermatophytoses

Clinical Case 1 A nine-year-old boy presented at the Dermatology OPD complaining of change in the colour of his toenails for about four months. He had no history of trauma or eczema of the foot. On examination, onycholysis (separation of the nail plate from the nail bed) of multiple toenails was observed. The nails were clipped and a 20% potassium hydroxide preparation on microscopy revealed the presence of thin septate hyphae. Culture on Sabouraud dextrose agar containing cycloheximide showed the growth of mycelial fungi, which on lactophenol cotton blue (LCB) mount revealed the presence of slender septate hyphae with a few pencil-shaped macroconidia and many oval microconidia. This was identified as *Trichophyton rubrum* (the most common pathogen in onychomycosis). The patient was treated with oral griseofulvin and recovered.

Dermatophytosis (commonly called *tinea* or ringworm) refers to infection of keratinised structures (the skin, hair and nails) caused by a group of keratinophilic fungi called the **dermatophytes**. The infections caused may be acute or chronic (persistent dermatophytosis that runs a chronic course with episodes of remission and exacerbation). The term dermatophytosis should not be confused with **dermatomycosis,** which refers to skin lesions produced by other fungi such as *Candida albicans* and also the cutaneous manifestations of systemic mycoses.

Characteristics of dermatophytes: Dermatophytic fungi are hyaline filamentous fungi that digest keratin by enzymatic means but are unable to invade living tissue. Dermatophytes digest keratin by keratinases and are resistant to cycloheximide. They are classified into three genera.

- *Microsporum*
- *Trichophyton*
- *Epidermophyton*

Microsporum contains several species (e.g., *M.gypseum, M.canis, M.nanum*), as does *Trichophyton* (e.g., *T.rubrum, T.mentagrophytes, T.verrucosum*). *E.floccosum* is the only species in the genus *Epidermophyton*. About 40 species of dermatophytes are known to cause infection in humans and animals.

Clinical aspects of dermatophytosis: Dermatophytosis is twice as common in males as in females. Clinical classification is according to the anatomic site involved:

- *Tinea barbae* (barber's itch) involves the bearded areas of the face and neck.
- *Tinea corporis* (*Tinea glabrosa*) is ringworm of the smooth or non-hairy skin of the body.
- *Tinea imbricata* is a special type of *Tinea corporis* found in the tropics, which presents with characteristic extensive concentric rings of papulosquamous scaly patches.

- *Tinea capitis* is ringworm of the scalp; favus and kerion are variants.
- *Tinea cruris* (jock itch) involves the groin and perineum.
- *Tinea pedis* (athlete's foot) is ringworm of the foot.
- *Tinea manuum* involves the hand.
- *Tinea unguium* involves the nails.

Table 63.2 lists the clinical types of dermatophytoses and their common causative agents.

Clinical features: Lesions in the skin tend to be circular, dry, erythematous, scaly and itchy. Lesions of the hair include kerion, scarring and alopecia.

Favus: A chronic type of ringworm in which dense crusts (scutula) develop in the hair follicles, leading to alopecia and scarring

Kerion: Severe boggy lesions with marked inflammatory reaction that sometimes develops in scalp infection due to dermatophytes. Nails infected by dermatophytes are deformed, friable and discoloured, and there is accumulation of debris under the nails. In lesions, dermatophytes appear as hyphae and arthrospores.

Pathogenicity: Mechanisms of pathogenesis are unclear. Fungal products may be responsible for inciting local inflammation. Hypersensitivity to fungal antigens result in sterile vesicular lesions sometimes seen in sites distant from the ringworm. The reaction may follow oral antifungal therapy and can be confused with an allergic drug reaction. These lesions are called **dermatophytids** (or the 'id' reaction).

Diagnosis: Diagnosis is established by clinical features, use of Wood's lamp where applicable and by laboratory investigations.

Table 63.2 *Clinical types of dermatophytoses and their common causative agents*

Disease	Common causative agents
Tinea capitis	*Microsporum* any species *Trichophyton* most species
Favus	*T.schoenleinii, T.violaceum, M.gypseum*
Tinea barbae	*T.rubrum, T.mentagrophytes, T.verrucosum*
Tinea imbricata	*T.concentricum*
Tinea corporis	*T.rubrum* and any other dermatophyte
T cruris	*E.floccosum, T.rubrum*
T pedis	*T.rubrum, E.floccosum*
Ectothrix hair infection	*Microsporum* species, *T.rubrum, T.mentagrophytes*
Endothrix hair infection	*T.schoenleinii, T.tonsurans, T.violaceum*

Wood's lamp examination for detecting superficial fungal infections

This test is performed in a dark room by shining an ultraviolet light on the area of interest. A Wood's lamp emits ultraviolet light and can be a diagnostic aid in determining if someone has a fungal infection of the skin or scalp. Normally, the skin does not fluoresce or shine under ultraviolet light. However, if the region of the skin on which the Wood's lamp light is focussed is infected, that area of the skin will fluoresce. In particular, if the skin or hair is infected by the **Microsporum** species, the infected area will fluoresce a bright greenish-yellow. **Malassezia** infections (*Pityriasis versicolor*) will show golden-yellow fluorescence.

Laboratory investigations:

1. **Specimens:** Scrapings of the skin (from the edges of ringworm lesions) and nail, hair clippings (hair plucked from the scalp).

2. **Microscopic examination:** A wet preparation of the specimen is made by placing the scrapings in a drop of 10–20% potassium hydroxide (KOH) on a slide, which is then covered by a coverslip and left for 10–20 minutes to digest the keratin. Additional time may be required to digest nails. Digestion of keratin ('clearing') is helped by gently warming the slide. A positive finding by direct microscopic examination of the specimen establishes the diagnosis of ringworm, irrespective of whether culture is performed. The presence of **branching hyaline (non-pigmented) septate hyphae** is considered positive for fungi; spores may sometimes be seen (Fig. 63.2).

In suspected *Tinea capitis*, fungal elements are looked for in plucked hair. Selection of infected hair for examination is facilitated by exposure to UV light (**Wood's lamp**). Infected hair will be fluorescent. Two types of hair infection may be distinguished in wet mounts (**Fig. 63.3**): **ectothrix**, in which arthrospores are seen as a sheath surrounding the hair, and **endothrix**, in which the spores are inside the hair shaft.

Hair perforation test: This test is done to differentiate Trichophyton rubrum from Trichophyton mentagrophytes. A few strands of human hair are placed in a petri dish with 20 ml of distilled water and autoclaved. A few drops of sterile 10% yeast extract and a few fragments of test fungus are added to the hair strands. These are incubated at 25°C for 2–3 weeks. The hair is removed and examined microscopically in a lactophenol cotton blue-stained wet preparation. T.mentagrophytes causes surface erosion of the hair shaft, resulting in a wedge-shaped appearance of the shaft.

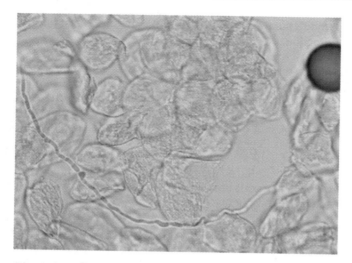

Fig. 63.2 Dermatophyte hyphae in skin scraping, KOH mount

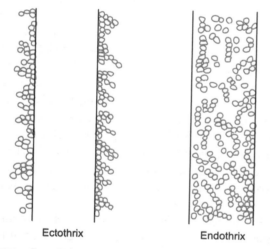

Ectothrix Endothrix

Fig. 63.3 Ectothrix and endothrix types of hair infection

3. Culture: Species identification is possible only by examination of the culture. The specimen is inoculated onto

- Sabouraud dextrose neopeptone agar containing chloramphenicol (the antibiotic suppresses growth of contaminating bacteria)
- Sabouraud agar containing chloramphenicol and cycloheximide (to suppress bacteria and non-dermatophytic filamentous fungi)

The plates are incubated aerobically at 25–30°C for up to 21 days, and are checked daily for the appearance of fungal colonies. **Identification** of dermatophytes in the laboratory is by examining the **macroscopic characteristics** of the fungal colonies (rate of growth, texture, colour on the observe and reverse) (Table 63.3).

Trichophyton: Colonies may be powdery, velvety or waxy, with pigmentation characteristic of different species.

Microsporum: Colonies are cotton-like, velvety or powdery, with white to brown pigmentation.

Epidermophyton: Colonies are powdery and greenish yellow.

Microscopic examination of material teased out from the fungal colony (culture mount) or material taken on cellotape (cellotape mount) or slide culture. Growth is carefully transferred to a slide so that the structural arrangement is preserved, and suspended in a drop of alcohol. A wet preparation is made by staining the growth with lactophenol cotton blue. The hyphae and conidia are observed. Conidia (asexual spores) are of two types: small unicellular microconidia and larger septate macroconidia.

Table 63.3 *Some characteristics of common dermatophytes*

Species	Colony	Morphology
T.rubrum	Velvety, red pigment on reverse	Few, long, pencil-shaped macroconidia
T.mentagrophytes	White to tan, cottony or powdery Pigment variable	Clusters of microconidia. Cigar-shaped macroconidia with terminal rat-tail filaments
T.tonsurans	Cream or yellow, with central furrows	Abundant microconidia. Thick-walled, irregular macroconidia
T.schoenleinii	Smooth, waxy, brownish	Hyphal swellings, chlamydospores, favic chandelier
T.violaceum	Very slow-growing, waxy, violet/purple pigment	Distorted hyphae, conidia rare.
M.audouinii	Velvety, brownish, slow-growing	Thick-walled chlamydospores, conidia rare and irregular
M.canis	Cottony, orange pigment on reverse	Abundant, thick-walled, spindle-shaped macroconidia with up to 15 septa
M.gypseum	Powdery, buff-coloured	Abundant, thin-walled macroconidia with 4–6 septa
E.floccosum	Yellowish green, powdery	Club-shaped macroconidia in clusters

Trichophyton: Microconidia are abundant and arranged in clusters along the hyphae or borne on conidiophores (Fig. 63.4). Macroconidia are relatively scanty, generally thin, elongated, with blunt ends and have distinctive shapes in different species, which aids species identification. Some species possess special hyphal characters, such as spiral hyphae, racquet mycelium and favic chandeliers. Trichophyton species infect skin, hair and nails. *T.rubrum* (*Case* 1), the most common species infecting human beings, often causes chronic, treatment-resistant lesions.

Microsporum: Microconidia are relatively scanty and not distinctive. Macroconidia, the predominant spore form, are large, multicellular, spindle-shaped structures, borne singly on the ends of hyphae (Fig. 63.5). Microsporum species infect the hair and skin but usually not the nails.

Epidermophyton: Colonies are powdery and greenish yellow. Microconidia are absent. Macroconidia are multicellular, pear-shaped and typically arranged in clusters (Fig. 63.5). Epidermophyton attacks the skin and nails but not the hair.

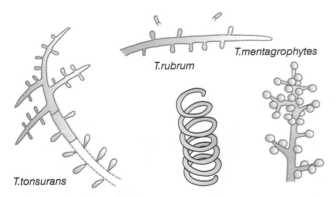

Fig. 63.4 *Trichophyton* species showing typical spiral hyphae and microconidia

Identification of species can be based on certain **physiological tests**, such as testing the ability of the fungus to penetrate the hair under experimental **conditions (in vitro hair perforation test)**, hydrolyse urea, grow on polished rice grains and on certain special media and withstand elevated temperatures (temperature tolerance and enhancement). The requirement of the fungus for certain special amino acids and vitamins can also be tested.

Hypersensitivity can be demonstrated by skin testing with the fungal antigen, trichophytin.

Treatment: This is by topical agents (ointments or gels) containing azoles (miconazole, clotrimazole, econazole) or terbinafine. Oral preparations of griseofulvin (dose 100 mg thrice daily), azoles (ketoconazole, itraconazole) or terbinafine may also be used.

Mild infections are treated by topical imidazole (clotrimazole or miconazole). **Severe infections** are treated by oral griseofulvin for 4–6 weeks. If hair is involved, treatment is given for 3–6 months. If nails are involved, treatment needs to be continued for one year. Alternative treatment consists of administration of an oral imidazole (ketoconazole 200 mg twice daily), triazole (itraconazole 100 mg once daily, fluconazole 150 mg once daily) or terbinafine.

Epidemiology and prevention: Dermatophytoses occur throughout the world but certain types of disease and some species of fungi show geographically restricted distribution. Social and cultural patterns also influence dermatophytoses. Many factors such as age, hormones and intercurrent diseases affect the susceptibility to dermatophytoses.

Habitat: Depending on their natural habitat, dermatophytes may be classified as **anthropophilic, zoophilic** and **geophilic** species. Human beings are the main or only hosts for anthropophilic dermatophytes. *T.rubrum*,

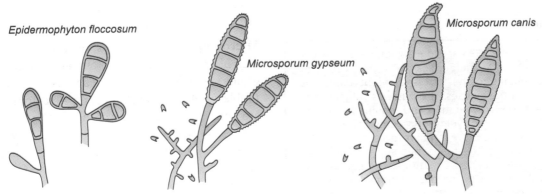

Fig. 63.5 Characteristic macroconidia

E.floccosum and *M.audouinii* are examples. They cause mild but chronic lesions. Zoophilic species are natural parasites of animals. Examples are *T.verrucosum* in cattle and *M.canis* in dogs and cats. Human infections with zoophilic dermatophytes cause severe inflammation but are readily curable. Geophilic species, which occur naturally in soil, are relatively less pathogenic for human beings. Examples are *M.gypseum* and *T.ajelloi*.

Epidemics of *Tinea capitis* may arise due to the use of shared barbershop hair clippers.

Control: This depends on personal cleanliness, avoiding contact with infectious material and effective treatment. *Tinea pedis* occurs only in people who wear socks with closed shoes. Candida infection of the nail is known as Onychomycosis. This is often seen in persons who come into contact with water and whose hands are often soggy. Details of the yeast-like fungus will be dealt with in detail in Chapter 64 (Systemic and Opportunistic Mycoses).

SUBCUTANEOUS MYCOSES

These are principally seen in tropical and subtropical areas. The most frequent predisposing (risk) factor is trauma. The disease may remain localised or may spread by contiguity. Fungi causing such subcutaneous mycoses are either normally present in the soil or are pathogens of plants. The outcome of such infections depends on fungal virulence and host defences. The various types include:
- Mycotic mycetoma
- Chromomycosis (chromoblastomycosis and phaeohyphomycosis)
- Sporotrichosis
- Rhinosporidiosis
- Subcutaneous phycomycosis (now referred to as entomophthoramycosis)

Mycetoma

Clinical Case 2   A 45-year-old man, a farmer by occupation, presented to the Surgical OP with a history of multiple swellings in the foot and seropurulent pus discharge from the sinuses. The pus was subjected to Gram's stain, KOH preparation and modified acid fast stain (to check for a botryomycotic, eumycotic or actinomycotic cause). KOH preparation revealed the presence of dark, pigmented, fungal hyphae, and *Madurella mycetomatis* was isolated on culture. The patient was treated with oral ketoconazole; debridement of the infected tissue with split graft was also performed.

Mycetomas are chronic, slowly progressive, post-traumatic infections of the subcutaneous tissue, usually of the foot and rarely of the other parts of the body. The disease was first reported by Gill (1842) from Madurai, South India. Carter (1860) established its fungal origin. It is commonly known as Maduramycosis or Madura foot. This has been referred to in the Atharva Veda as *padavalmika* (foot anthill).

Distribution: It is seen mainly in the tropics, though occasional cases have been reported from the temperate countries. In India, it is common in Tamil Nadu but rare in Kerala.

Causative agents and types: There are three types:
- **Eumycetoma** (e.g., maduramycosis) caused by fungi namely, *Scedosporium* (*Pseudallescheria*), *Madurella mycetomatis*, *M.grisea*, *Acremonium* spp., *Exophiala* spp., *Aspergillus nidulans* and *Fusarium* spp.
- **Actinomycetoma** caused by actinomycetes namely, *Actinomadura*, *Streptomyces* and *Nocardia*.
- **Botryomycosis** caused by *Staphylococcus aureus* and some other bacteria.

Epidemiology: The disease is endemic in regions with long dry seasons and short rainy spells, such as Central and South America, West and East Africa, India and Sri Lanka. Actinomycetoma occurs more commonly than eumycetoma. Persons engaged in agriculture are especially at risk.

Pathogenesis: The causative agent is believed to enter through minor trauma. The disease usually begins as a small subcutaneous swelling of the foot, which enlarges, burrowing into the deeper tissues and tracking to the surface as multiple sinuses discharging viscid, seropurulent fluid containing granules. The lesions are painless (*Case 2*).

Diagnosis: Diagnosis is based on examination of the granules from the sinus tracts on the swelling, culture of the granules and biopsy of the lesion.

Microscopy: The '**granules**' or '**grains**' are microcolonies of the agents. The colour and consistency of the grains vary with the different agents causing the disease (Table 63.4). In actinomycotic mycetoma, the grains are soft, composed of very thin (<1 μm in diameter) filaments, while in mycotic lesions, they are harder, broader and often show septae and chlamydospores. Growth of organisms in culture on SDA at 37°C or room temperature, gross appearance of colony, rate of growth and typical microscopic appearance of hyphae

Table 63.4   *Characteristics of Eumycotic Mycetoma and Actinomycotic Mycetoma*

	Eumycetoma	Actinomycetoma
Causative agents	**Fungal etiology**	**Actinomycete (Filamentous bacteria)**
Granules	Mostly **hard** in consistency (consist of tangled, tightly packed fungal hyphae and tissue)	**Soft in consistency** (consists of tissue elements and Gram-positive filamentous bacilli)
	Brown to black:	**White to yellow:**
	Madurella mycetomatis, Madurella grisea, Exophiala jeanselmei	*Nocardia asteroids*
		Nocardia brasiliensis
	White	*Actinomadura madurae*
	Scedosporium apiospermum	*Streptomyces somaliensis*
	Acremonium falciforme	**Red:**
		Actinomadura pelletierii
Treatment	Surgical debridement, controlling secondary bacterial infection Antifungals: Topical Nystatinor miconazole. Itraconazole, Fluconazole, Amphotericin B (for Madurella infection)	Streptomycin, Trimethoprim-Sulphamethoxazole and Dapsone

(pigments), conidiogenous cells, conidia and their arrangements help in establishing the diagnosis.

Treatment: Surgery is the mainstay of treatment of eumycetoma and actinomycetoma.

Medical therapy for eumycetoma depends on the infecting fungus. *Scedosporium apiospermum* is treated with miconazole and ketoconazole; *M.mycetomatis*, with ketoconazole and griseofulvin; and *M.grisea* and *Fusarium*, by itraconazole. Resistant lesions may require amputation. Medical therapy for actinomycetoma consists of the use of dapsone (100 mg thrice daily for 6–24 months), sulphonamides, cotrimoxazole or rifampicin. **Therapy should be continued even after absence of clinical or laboratory evidence of infection for 18–24 months.**

Chromomycosis

The term chromomycosis includes a group of clinical manifestations caused by various dematiaceous (pigmented) fungi.

Chromoblastomycosis (verrucous dermatitis): This is the most common form of chromomycosis. The disease is mainly tropical and is more common among barefoot agricultural workers and woodcutters.

Clinical features: The lesions consist of warty, cutaneous nodules which resemble the florets of a cauliflower. The disease is usually confined to the subcutaneous tissue of the feet and lower legs. The infecting fungi enter the skin by traumatic implantation. The lesion develops slowly around the site of implantation.

Causative agents: The most common fungi responsible are species of the genera *Fonsecaea: F.pedrosoi,* and *F.compacta; Exophiala dermatitidis; Phialophora (P.verrucosa)* and *Cladophialophora (C.carrionii).* Infections caused by *F.pedrosoi* and *P.verrucosa* have been reported to disseminate to other areas, especially the brain.

Diagnosis: Histologically, the lesions show the presence of the fungus as round or irregular, dark brown, yeast-like bodies with septae, called **sclerotic bodies** (Fig. 63.6). Diagnosis can be established by demonstration of these sclerotic bodies in KOH mounts or in tissue sections, and by culture on Sabouraud agar.

Treatment: Amphotericin B, thiabendazole, 5-fluorocytosine, itraconazole and (recently) voriconazole have been found to be useful.

Other infections caused by dematiaceous fungi (ph aeohyphomycosis): This group includes localised or

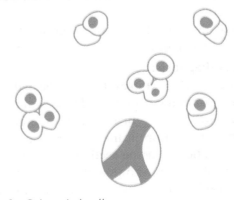

Fig. 63.6   Sclerotic bodies

systemic infections caused by certain species such as *Phialophora, Cladosporium* or other dematiaceous soil fungi, showing brown filaments in the affected tissues. The sites of lesions may be cutaneous, subcutaneous, deeper tissues, or organs like the brain or lung. **Sclerotic bodies are not found.** The fungi appear in lesions as distorted hyphal strands. Phaeohyphomycosis is generally seen in debilitated or immunodeficient hosts. Some of the clinical types are:

- Brain abscess caused by *Cladophialophora bantiana* (formerly *Cladosporium bantianum*)
- Subcutaneous or intramuscular lesions with abscesses or cysts containing masses of brown hyphae (formerly known as *phaeosporotrichose*) caused by *Exophiala* (formerly *Phialophora*) *jeanselmei, E.spinifera, E.dermatitidis* or *P.richardsiae*.

Sporotrichosis

This is a chronic infection involving cutaneous, subcutaneous and lymphatic tissue. It is frequently encountered in gardeners, forest workers and manual labourers. It may develop in otherwise healthy individuals. It occurs worldwide, but especially in Central and South America and South Africa.

Causative agent: Dimorphic fungus *Sporothrix schenckii* is the causative agent.

Pathogenesis and clinical presentation:

- Lesions on the exposed parts of the skin follow minor trauma or horn prick. Nodules are first formed at the site of lesion, followed by ulceration and necrosis of the nodules.
- From the lesions in the skin and subcutaneous tissue, the infection can spread via the lymphatic channels to the lymph nodes. This results in secondary ulcers on the lymph nodes, and the lymphatics are hardened and cord-like. This is 'lymphocutaneous' sporotrichosis.
- Systemic dissemination may occur to the bones, joints and meninges.

Laboratory diagnosis:

1. **Specimens:** The samples to be collected include aspiration from the nodules and biopsy material.
2. **Microscopy:** Direct microscopic examination of KOH mounts of necrotic material or histopathological examination of tissue sections stained by methenamine silver stain shows a characteristic feature, the **asteroid body**: a rounded or oval, basophilic, yeast-like body 3–5 μm in diameter, with rays of an eosinophilic substance radiating from the yeast cell.

3. **Culture:** Culture is done on media incubated at 25°C and 37°C. *S.schenckii* is a dimorphic fungus occurring in the yeast phase in tissues and in cultures at 37°C, and in the mycelia phase in nature and cultures at 25°C. The septate hyphae are very thin (1–2 μm in diameter) and carry flower-like clusters of small conidia borne on delicate sterigmata (Fig. 63.7).

4. **Serology:** Serological tests are especially helpful in the diagnosis of extracutaneous or systemic infection, where distinct clinical features are lacking. A slide latex agglutination test, using peptido-L-rhamno-D-mannan (outer layer of the fungal cell wall) as antigen, is a reliable, sensitive and specific test; results are obtained in minutes. A titre of 1:4 or greater is considered as presumptive evidence of sporotrichosis. In fixed cutaneous, subcutaneous,

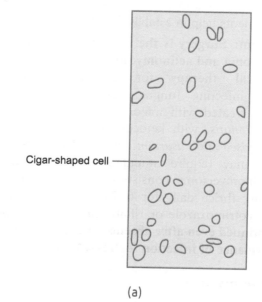

Cigar-shaped cell

(a)

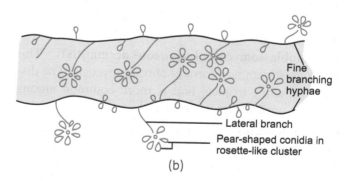

Fine branching hyphae

Lateral branch

Pear-shaped conidia in rosette-like cluster

(b)

Fig. 63.7 *Sporothrix schenkii:* (a) Yeast phase, (b) Mould phase

lymphocutaneous or systemic sporotrichosis, titres of 1:4 to 1:128 occur. A rising titre or sustained high titre is seen in pulmonary sporotrichosis. Serological tests have poor prognostic value).

Treatment: Spontaneous healing is possible.

- Potassium iodide, given topically or orally (250 mg thrice daily) for 2–4 months is effective in cutaneous infection.
- Itraconazole is effective in over 90 per cent of patients with lymphocutaneous infection; fluconazole (400 mg/day) and terbinafine (250 mg/day) can also be administered. Cryotherapy with liquid nitrogen is another treatment modality.
- For disseminated infection, amphotericin B is the drug of choice.

Rhinosporidiosis

This is a chronic granulomatous disease characterised by the development of friable polyps, usually confined to the nose, mouth or eye but rarely seen on the genitalia or other mucous membranes.

Distribution: Although the disease was first identified in Argentina, most cases have been reported from India and Sri Lanka.

Causative agent: The causative fungus is *Rhinosporidium seeberi*. The taxonomic position of this organism is currently uncertain, with doubts being raised about whether it can be considered a fungus.

Pathogenesis and clinical features: The mode of infection is not known, though infection is believed to originate from stagnant water or aquatic life.

Rhinosporidiosis is a localised condition which frequently presents as polypoidal growth in the nasal cavity, lesions can also be seen in the eye, skin, buccal cavity or genitalia.

While the disease is generally confined to mucous membranes, hematogenous dissemination has been recorded very rarely.

Diagnosis: Histologically, the lesion is composed of large numbers of fungal spherules embedded in a stroma of connective tissue and capillaries. The spherules are 10–200 µm in diameter and contain thousands of endospores (Fig. 63.8). *Rhinosporidium seeberi* has not been cultivated in artificial culture media.

Treatment: Excision of the polyp is the treatment of choice.

Subcutaneous zygomycosis (Entomophthoromycoses)

Distribution: It was originally reported from Indonesia and, subsequently, identified in many Asian and African countries.

Causative agent: *Conidiobolus coronatus* and *Basidiobolus ranarum* are saprophytic zygomycetes found in decaying vegetation and in the intestines of many reptiles and amphibians.

Pathogenesis and clinical features: A painless subcutaneous nodule develops which enlarges to involve a whole limb or large areas of the body. The lesions are now known to be acquired by insect bites.

Diagnosis: The causative fungi can be isolated by culture. Histopathological examination shows the presence of short, broad fragmented hyphae with beak-like projections.

Treatment: The treatment of phycomycosis is difficult and surgery may be required. Antifungal drugs like itraconazole and terbinafine hydrochloride are used for two to three months following surgery.

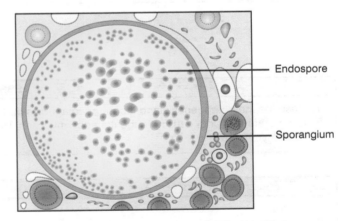

Fig. 63.8 Rhinosporidiosis: sporangium with numerous endospores

RECAP

- Superficial mycoses include Pityriasis versicolor, Tinea nigra and black and white piedra.
- Cutaneous infections include dermatophytosis (caused by three genera of dermatophytes: *Trichophyton*, *Microsporum* and *Epidermophyton*). Dermatophytosis manifests as ringworm (*Tinea*). Dermatophytes grow relatively slowly on laboratory culture media at room temperature.
- Subcutaneous mycoses are fungal infections of subcutaneous tissue. They remain localised or spread by contiguity. The main types are mycotic mycetoma (eumycetoma), chromoblastomycosis, phaeohyphomycosis, sporotrichosis, rhinosporidiosis and entomophthoromycosis.
- Mycetoma (maduramycosis, Madura foot) occurs worldwide. The causative agents are bacteria (cause actinomycetoma and botryomycosis) and fungi (cause eumycetoma) found in soil or plants. The colour and texture of granules ('grains') from lesions is of diagnostic value.
- Sporotrichosis is a subcutaneous granulomatous infection caused by *Sporothrix schenckii* (thermally dimorphic fungus). It remains confined to the skin (fixed cutaneous form) or involves local lymphatics. It commonly follows trivial trauma from thorns or wood splinters. The asteroid body is of diagnostic relevance.
- Chromoblastomycosis (chromomycosis) is a chronic localised mycosis of skin and subcutaneous tissues of the limbs. It is characterised by raised crusted lesions and is caused by several brown-pigmented (dematiaceous) fungi. Sclerotic bodies in the infected tissues are of diagnostic relevance.
- Rhinosporidiosis is a chronic granulomatous disease characterised by friable polyps usually confined to nose, mouth or eye. It is caused by *Rhinosporidium seeberi* (hitherto not cultivated in culture).
- Entomophthoramycosis is characterised by painless subcutaneous nodules which enlarge to involve the entire limb or large areas of the body. It is caused by *Conidiobolus coronatus* and *Basidiobolus ranarum*. The lesions are acquired by insect bites.

ESSAYS

1. Describe the pathogenesis and laboratory diagnosis of dermatophytes.
2. Enumerate the fungi causing subcutaneous mycoses. Describe the pathogenesis and laboratory diagnosis of eumycotic mycetoma.

SHORT NOTES

1. Piedra
2. Superficial mycosis
3. *T.capitis*
4. Trichophyton
5. Laboratory diagnosis of dermatophytes
6. Rhinosporidiosis
7. Subcutaneous phycomycosis
8. *Pityriasis versicolor*
9. Favus
10. Species of dermatophytes (list and draw a diagram for each)

64 Systemic and Opportunistic Mycoses

INTRODUCTION

Systemic mycoses refer to disseminated or deep fungal infection not restricted to the superficial areas. They are caused by fungi that are mostly soil sapro-phytes. Systemic mycoses occur in varying degrees of severity, ranging from asymptomatic infection to fatal disease.

The fungi causing systemic mycoses are **dimorphic** (they are in the yeast form at 37°C and mould at 25°C) and include:

- *Histoplasma capsulatum*
- *Blastomyces dermatitidis*
- *Paracoccidioides brasiliensis*
- *Coccidioides immitis*

Opportunistic mycoses occur in patients who are immunosuppressed, those with haematological malig-nancies or diabetes, those on immunosuppressive drugs, corticosteroids, x-rays or broad-spectrum anti-biotics. Opportunistic mycoses are caused by fungi that are of low virulence and found as contaminants in the environment, such as *Mucor*, *Penicillium*, *Aspergillus* species, etc.

SYSTEMIC MYCOSES (DIMORPHIC FUNGI)

HISTOPLASMOSIS

> **Clinical Case 1** A 35-year-old farm worker, who worked with chicken coops, presented with fever, cough, anorexia and lymphadenopathy. X-ray of the chest showed focal infiltrates and patchy opacities. Aspiration from lymph nodes showed the presence of intracellular yeast. Culture incubated at 25°C and at 37°C yielded yeast forms (at 37°C and mould at 25°C). The mycelial form showed the presence of thick-walled spherical spores with tubercles (tuberculate macro-conidia) and microconidia. The fungus was identified as *H.capsulatum*. The patient was put on liposomal amphotericin B for a period of two weeks following which he responded well to therapy.

Histoplasmosis is an intracellular infection of the reticuloendothelial system caused by the thermally dimorphic fungus *Histoplasma capsulatum*. The dis-ease was originally described by Darling (1905) who believed the causative agent to be a protozoon related to *Leishmania donovani*.

Distribution: The disease occurs worldwide; however, it is most common in the USA where it is endemic in many central and eastern states. In endemic areas, the fungus is present in the soil, decaying trees and is particularly abundant in bird droppings.

Causative agent: *Histoplasma capsulatum* is differ-entiated into two varieties: *Histoplasma capsulatum* var. *capsulatum*, which causes the classical, ubiquitous form of histoplasmosis; and *Histoplasma capsulatum* var. *duboisii*, which causes 'African histoplasmosis'.

Pathogenesis and clinical features: Infection is acquired by inhalation. Most infections of classical histoplasmosis are asymptomatic and heal spontaneously, leaving behind an area of miliary calcification (*Case* 1). Some infected individuals develop pulmonary disease which resembles tuberculosis. Disseminated histoplasmosis develops only in a minority of infected individuals. Infection of the reticuloendothelial system manifests as lymphadenopathy, hepatosplenomegaly, fever and anemia with a high rate of fatality. Granulomatous and ulcerative lesions may develop on the skin and mucous membranes.

African histoplasmosis involves mainly the skin, subcutaneous tissues and bones. The lungs are not commonly affected and disseminated disease is infrequent.

Laboratory diagnosis: Diagnosis of histoplasmosis involves microscopic examination of stained smears of blood, bone marrow, scrapings from lesions or biopsies of lymph nodes. In classical histoplasmosis, small intra- and extracellular yeast cells are seen in Giemsa- or Wright-stained smears of infected tissues. In tissues, the yeast phase occurs within phagocytic cells. The yeast appears as an oval, budding cell measuring 2–4 μ (Fig. 64.1) while in African histoplasmosis, much larger yeast-like cells (7–15 μ) are seen. The yeast phase also grows out in culture on blood agar at 37°C. On Sabouraud or other agar plates at room temperature, white, cottony, mycelial growth appears, with large (8–20 μ) thick-walled, spherical spores with tubercles (finger-like projections). These **'tuberculate' spores** are of diagnostic relevance; the mycelial phases of both varieties are indistinguishable.

Serodiagnosis: Antibodies formed during the course of systemic mycoses increase in titre in progressive disease. Hence, serological tests such as latex agglutination, complement fixation and precipitation tests are useful in the diagnosis of histoplasmosis. Titre is considered positive at reciprocal dilutions greater than 1:8. A titre with dilutions greater than 1:32 suggests active histoplasmosis infection.

Antigens can be detected in urine and serum. These tests are useful in immunocompromised individuals in whom antibody formation is impaired.

Skin tests: Delayed hypersensitivity develops following infection. It can be demonstrated by skin testing with **'histoplasmin'**, which is analogous to the tuberculin test for tuberculosis. In histoplasmosis, skin tests are more specific than serological methods.

BLASTOMYCOSIS

This is a chronic infection, characterised by the formation of suppurative and granulomatous lesions with a marked predilection for lungs and skin. It can also occur in any part of the body.

Distribution: The infection is largely confined to North America; hence, it is known as North American blastomycosis (to be differentiated from paracoccidioidomycosis, which is also known as South American blastomycosis). In recent years, several cases have been reported from Africa and India. The fungus has also been isolated in Delhi from the bronchial aspirates of a patient and from the lungs of insectivorous bats.

Causative agent: Blastomycosis is caused by the thermally dimorphic fungus *Blastomyces dermatitidis* (teleomorph [perfect state] is *Ajellomyces dermatitidis*).

Pathogenesis and clinical features: Infection is acquired by inhalation of contaminated soil which is the habitat.

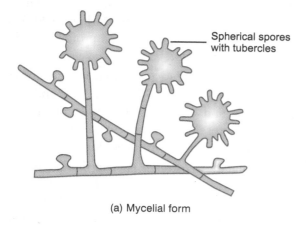

(a) Mycelial form

Spherical spores with tubercles

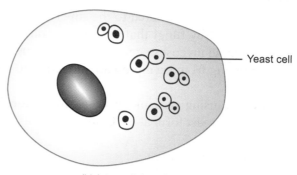

(b) Intracellular yeast forms

Yeast cell

Fig. 64.1 *H.capsulatum*: mycelial and yeast forms

- **Primary infection** of the lungs may resemble tuberculosis or histoplasmosis. The condition may be asymptomatic or may lead to focal or diffuse consolidation, miliary lesions or abscess formation.
- **Disseminated disease** may occur through the bloodstream to form multiple abscesses in various parts of the body. The fatality rate is high in this form of the disease.
- **Cutaneous disease** usually affects the skin of the face or other exposed parts of the body. The initial lesion is a papule, around which secondary nodules develop and coalesce, leading to large, elevated ulcerative lesions.

Laboratory diagnosis:

Culture: In tissues and in culture at 37°C, the fungus appears as a budding yeast cell, which is large (7–20 μ) and spherical, with a thick, double-contoured wall. Each cell carries only a single broad-based bud. At room temperature, the culture is filamentous with septate hyphae and many round or oval conidia, and, in older cultures, chlamydospores also occur (Fig. 64.2).

PARACOCCIDIOIDOMYCOSIS

This is a chronic granulomatous disease of the skin, mucosa, lymph nodes and internal organs.

Distribution: As the disease is confined to South America, it is called South American blastomycosis.

Causative agents: Paracoccidioidomycosis is caused by the thermally dimorphic fungus *Paracoccidioides brasiliensis*.

Pathogenesis and clinical features: The spores are inhaled and result in primary pulmonary infection that spreads by the hematogenous route to the mucosa of the nose, mouth, gastrointestinal tract, skin and lymphatics. This leads to ulcerative granulomas of the buccal and nasal mucosa, which are a prominent feature of this disease.

Laboratory diagnosis: The yeast phase occurs in tissues and in cultures at 37°C as large, globose or oval cells with multiple buds encircling the mother cell; this mariner's wheel or pilot's wheel appearance is characteristic. The mycelial phase is found in nature and can be isolated in culture after incubation at 25–30°C for two to three weeks (Fig. 64.3).

COCCIDIOIDOMYCOSIS

Coccidioidomycosis is a primary pulmonary infection that may be inapparent, benign, severe or even fatal.

Distribution: The disease is endemic in the dry, arid regions of southwestern USA, where the fungus is present in the soil and in rodents.

Causative agents: Coccidioidomycosis is caused by the thermally dimorphic fungus *Coccidioides immitis*.

Pathogenesis and clinical features: Infection is acquired by inhalation of dust containing arthrospores of the fungus. In most cases, the respiratory infection is asymptomatic and leads to lifetime immunity.

A self-limited influenza-like fever (known as 'valley fever' or 'desert rheumatism') may occur in some individuals. Less than one per cent of infected persons develop chronic progressive disseminated disease (coccidioidal granuloma) which is highly fatal.

Laboratory diagnosis: The fungus is thermally dimorphic, occurring as a spherule in tissues and in culture at 37°C and as the mycelial form in soil and in

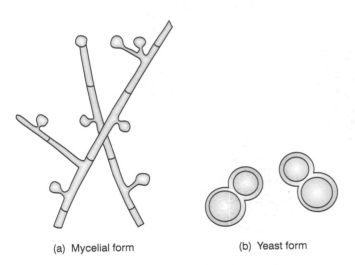

(a) Mycelial form   (b) Yeast form

Fig. 64.2 *B.dermatitidis.* Mycelial and yeast forms

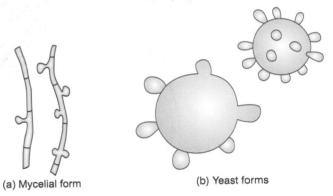

(a) Mycelial form   (b) Yeast forms

Fig. 64.3 *P.brasiliensis.* Mycelial and yeast forms

culture at room temperature. The spherule is 15–75 μm in diameter, with a thick, doubly refractile wall and filled with endospores (Fig. 64.4). The mycelial phase consists of hyphae which fragment into arthrospores that are highly infectious. Culture confirmation can be performed rapidly and with less risk to staff by DNA probe or exoantigen testing in a biological safety cabinet.

Skin test: Delayed hypersensitivity can be demonstrated by a positive skin test with 'coccidioidin' (analogous to the tuberculin test).

TREATMENT OF SYSTEMIC MYCOSES

Liposomal amphotericin B is the drug of choice for severe (invasive) disease. Oral azoles (ketoconazole, itraconazole, fluconazole and, more recently, voriconazole) are used for less severe infections. For paracoccidioidomycosis, oral itraconazole 50–100 mg/day is the drug of choice; ketoconazole and fluconazole are less effective. Fluconazole is useful for coccidioidal meningitis. Corrective surgery may be used for pulmonary and cutaneous lesions.

OPPORTUNISTIC MYCOSES

These are caused by fungi which are part of the normal commensal flora of the human body (for example, *Candida albicans*) or which are found in the environ-ment or nature (*Aspergillus fumigatus*). Such mycoses occur in **immunocompromised** individuals or in individuals with defective immune system and metabolic disorders such as diabetes.

ASPERGILLOSIS

Aspergillus and *Penicillium* constitute the commonest moulds seen on damp bread or almost any other organic matter. Their habitat is also soil and dust. The spores are ubiquitous. Of the 300-odd species of *Aspergillus*, *Aspergillus fumigatus* is the main pathogen. It causes invasive disease in immunocompromised human beings. Other species associated with infection include *A.niger*, *A.flavus* and *A.nidulans*.

Pathogenesis and clinical features: *Aspergillus* species can cause a variety of clinical syndromes:

1. **Allergic bronchopulmonary aspergillosis:** Inhaled spores provoke a hypersensitivity reaction which may be:
- Type I hypersensitivity (asthma), which occurs in atopic individuals following sensitisation to inhaled aspergillus spores
- Type III hypersensitivity (extrinsic alveolitis)
- Combined Type I and Type III hypersensitivity reactions

In bronchopulmonary aspergillosis, the fungus grows within the lumen of the bronchioles, which may be occluded by fungal plugs; the fungus can

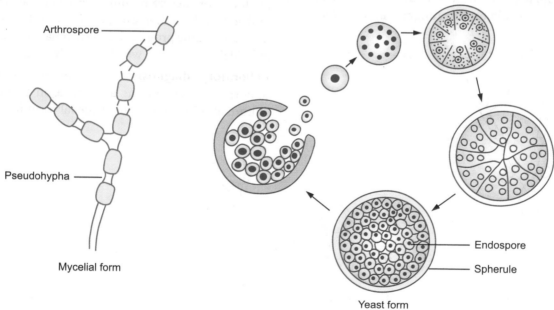

Fig. 64.4 *C.immitis:* arthrospore and spherule stages

be demonstrated in sputum. The condition is made worse by the development of hypersensitivity to the fungus.

2. **Aspergilloma**: Here, a fungal ball grows within and is usually restricted to an existing lung cavity, for example, due to old tuberculosis or bronchiectasis. In this type of 'colonising aspergillosis', surgical removal becomes necessary as the disease commonly causes massive hemoptysis.

3. **Invasive aspergillosis**: Here, the fungus first causes pneumonia and later disseminates to involve other organs, for example, the brain, kidneys or heart. Patients who develop this type of disease, which may be fatal, are usually immunocompromised or debilitated due to prolonged treatment with antibiotics, steroids and cytotoxic drugs.

4. **Superficial infections** of the external ear (otomycosis), the eye (mycotic keratitis) and nasal sinuses.

Diagnosis: Demonstration of septate hyaline hyphae from tissues or specimen by direct microscopy is suggestive of aspergillus infection, but not diagnostic.

1. **Specimen**:

- **Exudates, bronchial washings and bronchoalveloar lavage**. Samples are first examined for the presence of fungal elements by wet mount preparation in 10% potassium hydroxide. Repeat specimens to demonstrate similar findings must be done for confirmation.

- **Tissue sections** of, for example, biopsy or postmortem material stained by the periodic acid Schiff method. The hyphae are poorly stained by hema-toxylin and eosin. Typical dichotomous branching at acute angle is characteristic of aspergillus infection.

- **Detection of galactomannan** (a component of the *Aspergillus* cell wall) in serum or bronchoalveolar lavage fluid is a marker for the diagnosis of invasive aspergillosis in adults and children, in hematopoietic stem cell transplant recipients or patients with hematologic malignancies.

2. **Isolation by culture**: Colonies grow after 48 hours but longer incubation may be required before characteristic morphological features develop.

- After 3–4 days' incubation on **Sabouraud agar** at 25–37°C, the colonies have a velvety to powdery surface and are characteristically coloured: *A.fumigatus*—dark green, *A.niger*—black and *A.flavus*—yellow-green.

- **Microscopic appearance of the colony:** A wet preparation stained with lactophenol cotton blue demonstrates septate hyphae and conidiophores (specialised aerial hyphae that bear spores or conidia). The conidiophores have swollen rounded ends ('vesicles') with chains of conidia borne on elongated cells called sterigmata. The general morphology is characteristic of the genus and there are also inter-species differences that are useful in identification (**Fig. 64.5**).

3. **Serology**: Precipitating antibodies to aspergillus antigens can be demonstrated by counter-current immunoelectrophoresis, immunodiffusion and enzyme-linked immunosorbent assay (ELISA). Antibodies are usually absent in the sera of healthy

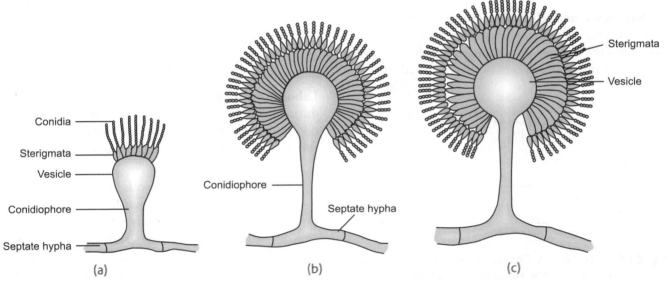

Fig. 64.5 *Aspergillus* spp. (a) *A.fumigatus,* (b) *A.flavus* and (c) *A.niger*

individuals: they can be detected in the majority (70 per cent) of patients with allergic aspergillosis and approximately the same proportion of those with pneumonia or invasive disease.

4. **Polymerase chain reaction and nucleic acid sequence-based amplification** are other advanced methods for establishing the diagnosis of aspergillosis tracheobronchitis.

5. **Skin tests**: **Dual immediate** (after 15 minutes) and **Arthus type** (after 4–6 hours) skin test reactions which develop after the intradermal injection of *Aspergillus* spp. antigens are important criteria to establish a diagnosis of allergic broncho-pulmonary aspergillosis.

Treatment: Invasive aspergillosis is treated with intravenous amphotericin B/liposomal amphotericin B. However, the mortality is high. Intravenous formulations of azoles (voriconazole, itraconazole and posaconazole) are currently used.

PENICILLOSIS

Penicillium are present in the environment and grow on various substrates such as bread, jam, fruit and cheese. They cause opportunistic infections in diabetics. In the laboratory, they are common airborne contaminants of culture media. Colonies are blue-green in colour with a white border and a powdery surface. Microscopy demonstrates septate hyphae with branched conidiophores, with two rows of sterigmata bearing chains of spores; the appearance is like a brush or broom (Fig. 64.6). *Penicillium* may cause opportunistic mycoses.

Pathogenesis and clinical features: *P.marneffei*, a dimorphic fungi, unlike other species of *Penicillium* has been reported to be an important opportunist pathogen in the HIV-infected. It causes disseminated infection

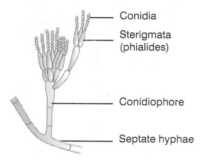

Conidia

Sterigmata (phialides)

Conidiophore

Septate hyphae

Fig. 64.6 *Penicillium.* Chains of conidia are produced by phialides, which are supported by branched conidiophores. Terminal conidium is oldest.

with multiple organ involvement. This fungus is unique among *Penicillium* in that it is a true pathogen.

Laboratory diagnosis: The yeast are small, oval, 2–4 mm in diameter. The mycelia form produces red diffusible pigment and morphologically resembles other members of the *Penicillium* species.

Treatment: Penicillosis can be treated with amphotericin B, followed by oral itraconazole.

ZYGOMYCOSIS (MUCORMYCOSIS, PHYCOMYCOSIS)

Zygomycosis (commonly referred to as '**mucormycosis**') is an invasive disease caused by zygomycetes (phycomycetes), principally of the species of *Rhizopus*, *Mucor* and *Absidia*. These fungi are ubiquitous in soil and their spores are present in air and dust. They are often seen to contaminate stale bread.

Pathogenesis of infection and clinical features: Zygomycosis occurs as a systemic infection following dissemination from a primary focus in the upper respiratory tract or nasal cavity, where the spores germinate and the mycelia invade the adjacent tissues. Angio-invasiveness is one of the characteristics of zygomycosis which makes it fatal in invasive infections —the orbit, sinuses and the brain; the lung may also be the primary site of infection. Almost all patients are immunocompromised. The rhinocerebral (or rhino-orbito-cerebral) form, in which the nose, nasal sinuses and orbit are involved, is well recognised and is usually a fatal complication of diabetes mellitus. When the lung is the primary site of infection, the fungi may invade the arteries to cause thrombosis and infarction.

The incidence of the disease has increased considerably as a result of the widespread use of antibacterial antibiotics, corticosteroids and antimetabolites.

Laboratory diagnosis: Diagnosis is usually made, during histological examination of autopsy material, by noting the presence of broad and bizarre, non-septate (or sparsely septate) hyphae in tissues.

1. **Specimen:**
   - **Exudate:** A wet preparation is made in 10% potassium hydroxide. Broad, ribbon-like hyphae are seen.
   - **Tissue:** Hyphae stain readily with hematoxylin and eosin (unlike aspergillus) showing non-septate, broad hyphae, often invading into blood vessels.
2. **Culture:** Isolation is by culture on Sabouraud agar with antibacterial agent but without cycloheximide,

on which the fungi grow easily (however, growth may sometimes be difficult to achieve from necrotic material even when abundant hyphae are seen). Culture characteristics of the three main genera are similar.

After incubation for 3–4 days on Sabouraud agar at 30–37°C, the colonies are grey-white with a thick cottony, fluffy surface. Under the microscope, non-septate, broad hyphae with aerial sporangiophores which end in a sporangium (a sac containing spores) are seen.

Mucor shows branched sporangiophores arising randomly along aerial mycelium. Rhizoids are absent. Rhizopus has rhizoids, and sporangiophores arise in groups directly above the rhizoids (Fig. 64.7).

Note: These common environmental moulds are frequent contaminants of culture plates.

Treatment: Intravenous amphotericin B combined, where appropriate, with surgical drainage is the recommended treatment. Good medical control of diabetes is required.

CANDIDOSIS (CANDIDIASIS/MONILIASIS)

Candidosis refers to an infection of the skin, mucosa, and rarely of the internal organs, caused by a yeast-like fungus, *Candida albicans*. Other *Candida* species are being increasingly reported from clinical infections. Candidosis is an opportunistic endogenous infection, the commonest predisposing factor being diabetes.

Distribution: *Candida* species are normal inhabitants of the skin and mucosa.

Causative agents: *Candida albicans* is an ovoid or spherical budding cell, which produces pseudomycelia both in tissues and in culture (Figs 64.8a and 64.8b).

> ***Candida* species of growing clinical importance**
> Other *Candida* species involved in human infection include *C.glabrata*, *C.tropicalis*, *C.keyfr* (formerly *C.pseudotropicalis*), *C.krusei*, *C.guilliermondii*, *C.parapsilosis* and *C.stellatoidea*.

Pathogenesis and clinical features:

- **Cutaneous candidosis** may be intertriginous or paronychial. The former is an erythematous, scaling or moist lesion with sharply demarcated borders, where papular lesions are most prominent. The sites affected are those where the skin is macerated by perspiration: the groin, perineum, axillae and inframammary folds. **Paronychia** and **onychomycosis** are seen in occupations that lead to frequent immersion of the hands in water.

- **Mucosal lesions**: Common lesions are **vaginitis**, characterised by an acidic discharge and found frequently in pregnancy, and **oral thrush**, found commonly in bottle-fed infants and the aged and debilitated. In these conditions, creamy white patches appear on the tongue or buccal mucosa; following removal, these leave a red oozing surface. This is also seen in HIV and other immunocompro-

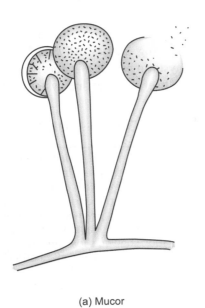

(a) Mucor

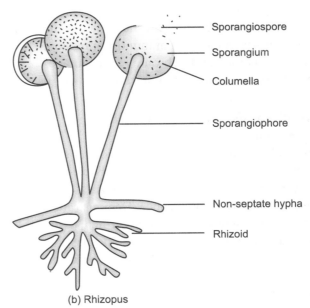

Sporangiospore

Sporangium

Columella

Sporangiophore

Non-septate hypha

Rhizoid

(b) Rhizopus

Fig. 64.7   Zygomycetes: (a) *Mucor* and (b) *Rhizopus*

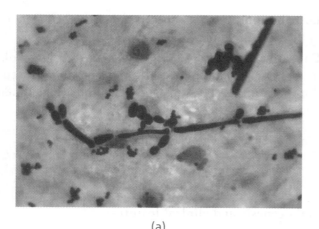

(a)

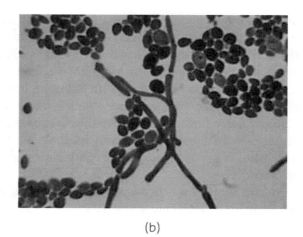

(b)

Fig. 64.8 Gram stain showing Gram-positive (a) *Candida* yeast with pseudohyphae and pus cells in tissue; and (b) *Candida* yeast with pseudohyphae in culture.

mised individuals. Oesophageal candidosis is now considered an AIDS-defining illness.

- **Intestinal candidosis** is a frequent sequel to excessive oral antibiotic therapy and may present as diarrhea not responding to antibacterial treatment.

- **Bronchopulmonary candidosis** is seen as a rare complication of pre-existing pulmonary or systemic disease.

- Candida has now emerged as a hospital-acquired pathogen in catheterised patients. **Catheter-associated UTI or bloodstream infections** are caused due to catheter colonisation.

- **Systemic infections** such as septicemia, endocarditis and meningitis may occur as terminal complications in severe generalised diseases such as leukemia and in persons on prolonged immunosuppression. Candida granuloma and chronic mucocutaneous candidosis are serious manifestations seen in immunodeficiencies.

Laboratory diagnosis: This can be established by microscopy and culture.

- Wet films or Gram-stained smears from lesions or exudates show budding Gram-positive cells (Fig. 64.8). *Candida* can colonise normal skin or mucosa as well. Abundant presence is of significance. Demonstration of mycelial forms indicates colonisation and tissue invasion and is, therefore, of greater significance.

- Cultures can be obtained readily on **Sabouraud agar** and on ordinary bacteriological culture media. Colonies are creamy white, smooth and with a yeasty odour. *Candida albicans* can be differentiated from other *Candida* species by growth characteristics,

sugar assimilation and fermentation tests. *C.albicans* alone forms **chlamydospores** (Fig. 64.9a) on corn meal agar cultures at 20°C. A rapid method of identifying *C.albicans* is based on its ability to form **germ tubes** within two hours when incubated in human serum at 37°C (Reynolds–Braude phenomenon; Fig. 64.9b).

Treatment: Amphotericin B, 5-fluorocytosine, imidazoles (miconazole, ketoconazole), triazoles (itraconazole, fluconazole, voriconazole) and echinocandins (caspofungin, micafungin) may be used for disseminated candidosis. Some clinical isolates of *C. albicans* are resistant to fluconazole and *C. krusei* to amphotericin.

Prevention of infection: This is mainly by eliminating possible predisposing factors. All *Candida* strains are susceptible to nystatin but, as it is poorly absorbed from the gut, it is not useful in treating systemic diseases.

CRYPTOCOCCOSIS (TORULOSIS)

Clinical Case 2 A 27-year-old woman presented to the emergency department with altered sensorium and neck rigidity. The patient was HIV seropositive. A lumbar puncture was carried out under aseptic conditions and sent to the laboratory. Gram stain revealed Gram-positive, round, budding yeast (no pseudohyphae). India ink preparation showed capsulated budding yeast cells. Serum cryptococcal latex agglutination test was positive (1:512). The culture on bird seed agar showed black coloured colonies, urease test was positive and culture confirmed the organism as *Cryptococcus neoformans*. The patient was treated with amphotericin B and flucytosine.

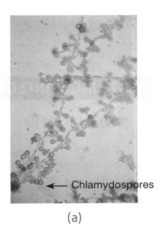

Chlamydospores

(a)

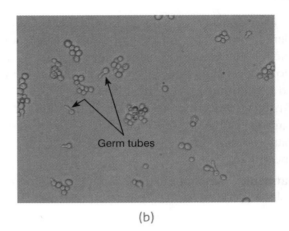

Germ tubes

(b)

Fig. 64.9   (a) Chlamydospores, (b) Germ tubes

Cryptococcosis (torulosis) is a subacute or chronic infection caused by the yeast *Cryptococcus neoformans* and, less frequently, other species.

Distribution: Cryptococcosis occurs worldwide, since the fungus is a soil saprophyte, and is particularly abundant in the feces of pigeons and other birds. Since cryptococcosis was originally reported from Europe, it was formerly referred to as European blastomycosis. Cryptococcosis has been identified as a common opportunistic infection in AIDS patients.

Causative agent:
- *Cryptococcus neoformans* is a round or ovoid budding cell, 4–20 μm in diameter, with a prominent polysaccharide capsule. While *C.neoformans* var. *neoformans* is the principal pathogenic species, other species *C.neoformans* var. *gatti* is also implicated in human infection. Others include *C.albidus* and *C.laurentii*.
- Four serological types of cryptococcal capsular polysaccharide—A, B, C and D—have been identified.
- Teleomorphs of the fungus belong to the class *Basidiomycetes: Filobasidiella neoformans* and *F.basilispora*.

Pathogenesis and clinical features: Infection is usually acquired by inhalation but may sometimes be through the skin or mucosa. Most infections are asymptomatic.

Pulmonary cryptococcosis may lead to mild pneumonitis.
- Dissemination of infection leads to visceral, cutaneous and meningeal disease. Visceral cryptococcosis may simulate tuberculosis and cancer clinically;

bones and joints may be involved. Cutaneous cryptococcosis varies from small ulcers to large granulomata.
- Cryptococcal meningitis and meningoencephalitis, the most serious type of cryptococcal infection, can mimic tuberculous or other chronic types of meningitis. Its onset is insidious and the course slow and progressive. It is often seen in AIDS (*Case* 2).

Laboratory diagnosis: This is established by direct microscopic examination and by culture.
1. **Microscopy:**   Microscopic examination of **India ink-stained** CSF and other material from lesions reveals capsulated, budding yeast cells; the capsules are prominent in the India ink preparations (Fig. 64.10).
2. **Culture:**   The fungus grows readily on **Sabouraud agar**, forming smooth, mucoid, cream-coloured colonies. The ability to grow at 37°C and hydrolyse urea differentiates *C.neoformans* var. *neoformans* from non-pathogenic cryptococci.

Fig. 64.10   *Cryptococcus neoformans* var. *neoformans*: India ink preparation of spinal fluid showing yeast cells surrounded by a large capsule

Pathogenicity of a cryptococcal isolate can be demonstrated by intracerebral or intraperitoneal inoculation into mice, which develop a fatal infection. Capsulated budding yeast cells can be demonstrated in the brain of infected mice.

3. **Antigen detection tests:** Demonstration of the capsular antigen by precipitation and latex agglutination can be of value in diagnosing cryptococcal meningitis.

Treatment: Amphotericin B, 5-fluorocytosine, imidazoles (miconazole, ketoconazole), triazoles (itraconazole, fluconazole, voriconazole) and echinocandins (caspofungin, micafungin) may be used.

PNEUMOCYSTIS JIROVECII

Pneumocystis was until recently thought to be a protozoan, but nucleic acid sequencing has conclusively showed that the organism is a fungus related to Ascomycetes. There are two known species: *P.carinii*, commonly found in rats, and *P.jirovecii*, seen in humans. Pneumocystis pneumonia is one of the common opportunistic infections in AIDS.

P.jirovecii has three morphological forms:
- Trophozoite—thin-walled, irregularly shaped, 1–5 μm in size
- Precyst—an intermediate stage of the sexual phase, 5–8 μm in size
- Cyst—thick-walled, spherical containing up to 8 intracystic bodies and up to 8 μm in size

Pathogenesis and clinical features: Infection is transmitted by respiratory droplets and is asymptomatic in immunocompetent individuals. In immunocompromised patients, life-threatening pneumonia develops.

Laboratory diagnosis:
1. **Specimen:** Induced sputum, bronchoalveolar lavage or lung biopsy
2. **Microscopy:** Trophozoites can be demonstrated by Giemsa, toluidine blue, methenamine silver and calcofluor white stains. The cyst wall stains black with methenamine silver stain.
3. **Culture:** The organism cannot be cultured.
4. **Serology:** Complement fixation test with titres of 1:4 or above indicate active disease. Latex agglutination test can also be used.

Treatment: Trimethoprim-sulfamethoxazole (TMP-SMZ) and pentamidine isothionate are the drugs of choice for the treatment of acute cases. TMP-SMZ is also used as prophylaxis in the management of HIV-infected individuals.

SPECIFIC FUNGAL INFECTIONS

OTOMYCOSIS

Otomycosis is a fungal infection of the external ear. It is a very common disease and is usually caused by species of *Aspergillus* (*A.niger, A.fumigatus*) and *Penicillium*. The symptoms are itching, pain and deafness. Secondary bacterial infection, commonly due to *Pseudomonas* species and *Proteus* species, causes suppuration. Diagnosis can be made by demonstration of the fungi in scrapings and by culture.

OCULOMYCOSIS (KERATOMYCOSIS, FUNGAL KERATITIS, MYCOTIC KERATITIS)

Mycotic keratitis is an invasive infection of the cornea usually following corneal trauma.

Causative agents: Many saprophytic fungi can cause ocular infection. *Aspergillus* species (*A.fumigatus, A.flavus* and *A.niger*), *Fusarium, Curvularia, Alternaria, Acremonium* and *Candida albicans* are most often responsible.

Pathogenesis and clinical features: Corneal injury and bacterial infection are predisposing factors for fungal keratitis. The widespread use of corticosteroids in ophthalmology has resulted in the increased incidence of keratomycosis.

Fungal spores colonise the injured tissue and initiate an inflammatory reaction, leading to hypopyon ulcer and endophthalmitis.

Laboratory diagnosis:

Specimen: Corneal scrapings collected under slit lamp examination are used for microscopy and culture.

Treatment: Local application of amphotericin B, nystatin and pimaricin (natamycin) may be useful.

MYCOTIC POISONING

Many fungi form poisonous substances. Mycotic poisoning is of two types: **mycetism** in which a fungus which is eaten for itself causes toxic effects and **mycotoxicosis** in which fungal toxins contaminate food.

Mycetism has been known from ancient times, several varieties of poisonous mushrooms having been identified as inedible. Mycetism may cause gastrointestinal disease, dermatitis or death. The hallucinogenic agents (d-lysergic acid, psilocybin) produced by the *Psilocybe* species and other fungi have attracted much attention in recent years.

Examples:

- *Claviceps* species—ergot poisoning
- *Coprine* species—coprine poisoning
- *Inocybe* species—muscarine poisoning

Mycotoxicosis: Mycotoxins are natural products produced by fungi and found in some articles of food. Mycotoxicosis results from ingestion of food contaminated with mycotoxins (fungal toxins) (Table 64.1).

Aflatoxin: The best known mycotoxin is that of the aflatoxin group: *Aspergillus flavus* secretes aflatoxin B1 while *Aspergillus parasiticus* secretes aflatoxins B1, B2, G1 and G2, among others. Aflatoxins are frequently present in mouldy foods, particularly in groundnuts, corn and peas. These toxins are highly toxic to animals and birds, as well as to human beings. Aflatoxins are known to cause hepatomas in ducklings and rats, and their possible carcinogenic effect in human beings has caused great concern. There have been several reports of aflatoxicosis from India, involving human beings and animals.

Ergot alkaloids: Ergotoxicosis (ergotism) is due to the toxic alkaloids produced by the fungus *Claviceps purpurea*, while growing on the fruiting heads of rye. Trichothecenes are toxins produced by certain species of *Fusarium*. Zearalenone is a toxin produced by *Fusarium graminearum*; animals which consume grains contaminated with this toxin may develop symptoms and signs mimicking an estrogenic disorder.

Table 64.1 *Important mycotoxins and their source*

Mycotoxin	Fungus	Contaminated food item
Aflatoxin	*Aspergillus* sp.	Groundnuts, corn and peas
Fumonisin	*Fusarium*	Maize
Ochratoxin	*Aspergillus* and *Penicillium*	Cereals and bread
Ergotoxin	*Claviceps purpura*	Rye
Zearalenone	*Fusarium graminearum*	Grains
Trichothecenes		

RECAP

- Histoplasmosis is caused by *Histoplasma capsulatum* var.*capsulatum* (classical form) and *Histoplasma capsulatum* var.*duboisii* (African histoplasmosis). The fungi are found in soil (bird droppings), and enter the body by inhalation.
  - ❖ African histoplasmosis frequently spreads to skin and bones. Classical histoplasmosis manifests as a pulmonary infection (usually self-limiting).
- In tissues, small intra- and extracellular yeast cells (classical form) or large, thick-walled yeast cells and giant cells (African form) are diagnostic; in culture, tuberculate spores are characteristic.
  - ❖ Serological tests and skin test (histoplasmin) may aid diagnosis.
- Blastomycosis is caused by *Blastomyces dermatitidis* (thermally dimorphic fungus). It grows as a yeast at 37°C and as a filamentous fungus at room temperature.
  - ❖ Following inhalation of spores, pulmonary and systemic granulomatous lesions result.
  - ❖ The diagnostic form is the large yeast with a single broad-based bud.
- Paracoccidioidomycosis is a chronic granulomatous disease of the skin, mucosa, lymph nodes and internal organs, caused by *Paracoccidioides brasiliensis*, a thermally dimorphic fungus.
  - ❖ The yeast phase (in tissues and in cultures at 37°C): large, globose or oval cells with multiple buds encircling the mother cell—mariner's wheel or pilot's wheel appearance.

- ❖ The mycelial phase: found in nature; also isolated in culture at 25–30°C after 2–3 weeks incubation.
- Coccidioidomycosis is caused by *Coccidioides immitis*, a thermally dimorphic fungus. The hyphal phase is found in soil of the southwestern USA; conidia (arthrospores) are inhaled with dust.
  - ❖ Most cases are asymptomatic; some progress to self-limiting pneumonitis.
  - ❖ Cultures are dangerous to laboratory workers due to release of arthrospores. The diagnostic tissue form is the spherule.
- Aspergillosis is an opportunistic mycosis caused by hyaline filamentous fungi of the genus *Aspergillus*. The key species, *A.fumigatus*, *A.flavus* and *A.niger;* produce a spectrum of diseases ranging from superficial (otitis externa) to invasive lesions affecting all tissues.
  - ❖ Diagnosis is by demonstration of septate hyaline hyphae in tissue material, and isolation of the species in culture.
- Zygomycosis is an opportunistic mycosis by fungi of the class Zygomycetes (mainly Mucor and Rhizopus). Fungi appear in biopsy material as broad-branched hyphae with no cross-walls; surrounding tissue necrosis, thrombosis and hemorrhage are prominent. They grow as moulds on ordinary culture media.
  - ❖ Rhino-orbito-cerebral zygomycosis runs a rapid course in poorly controlled diabetics.
- Candidosis is an opportunistic mycosis caused by yeast-like fungi of the genus *Candida*; *C.albicans* is the main pathogen. Lesions (thrush) may occur on oral and vaginal mucous membranes of otherwise healthy individuals. In immunocompromised hosts (including diabetics), lesions may be widespread.
  - ❖ *Candida* species grow on ordinary culture media at 37°C or 25°C yielding smooth or butyrous colonies.
  - ❖ *Candida albicans* forms chlamydospores on corn meal agar and germ tubes in human serum; in tissues and exudates, yeasts and pseudohyphae are found.
- Cryptococcosis is an opportunistic mycosis caused by yeast fungi of the genus *Cryptococcus*; *C.neoformans*, the principal pathogen, is heavily encapsulated, reproduces by budding and is widely distributed in nature (particularly soil and pigeon droppings).
- Human pulmonary infection follows inhalation of spores of *Filobasidiella neoformans* (the perfect [sexual] stage found in nature).
- *P.jirovecii* commonly associated with pneumonia in AIDS patients has the following features:
  - ❖ It has three morphological forms: trophozoite, precyst and cyst.
  - ❖ Infection occurs by respiratory droplets and clinically may vary from asymptomatic to life-threatening pneumonia.
  - ❖ The organism cannot be cultured.
  - ❖ The treatment of choice is trimethoprim-sulfamethoxazole (TMP-SMX).
- Otomycosis is fungal infection of the external ear, commonly caused by *Aspergillus* and *Penicillium*.
- Oculomycosis (or) keratomycosis is a fungal infection of the cornea.
  - ❖ The common causative agents include *Aspergillus, Fusarium, Curvularia* and *Alternaria*.
  - ❖ Diagnosis is made by microscopy and culture of corneal scrapings.
- Mycotic poisoning is of two types: mycetism in which a fungus eaten for itself causes toxic effects and mycotoxicosis in which fungal toxins contaminate some article of food.

ESSAYS

1. Name the fungi causing systemic infection. Describe the pathogenesis and laboratory diagnosis of *H.capsulatum*.
2. Name the fungi causing opportunistic fungal infections. Describe the pathogenesis and laboratory diagnosis of any one.

SHORT NOTES

1. Dimorphic fungi
2. Candidosis
3. *Cryptococcus neoformans*
4. *Histoplasma capsulatum*
5. Opportunistic fungi
6. Aspergillosis
7. Mucormycosis
8. Otomycosis
9. Oculomycosis
10. Penicillosis
11. *Penicillium marneffei*
12. *Pneumocystis jirovecii*
13. Mycotoxins
14. Mycetism

65 Normal Microbial Flora of the Human Body

Human beings, like other animals, harbour a wide array of microorganisms both on and in their bodies. The normal microbial flora are more or less constant for each species and are broadly divided into **residents** and **transients**.

Resident flora: Constitute a constant population which cannot be completely removed permanently, while the latter vary from time to time and are temporary. The residents prevent permanent colonisation of the body by other organisms. A knowledge of the normal flora of the body is essential for an understanding of the interaction of human beings and their pathogen laden environment.

Transient flora: May be potentially pathogenic or non-pathogenic organisms that are present at some point of time but not always.

Role of normal microbial flora: Normal flora play an important role in body economy. They can:

- become pathogenic when host defences falter,
- prevent or interfere with colonisation/invasion of the body by pathogens,
- raise the overall immune status of the host against pathogens having related or shared antigens, and
- cause confusion in diagnosis due to their ubiquitous presence in the body and their resemblance to some of the pathogens. Members of the normal flora form part and parcel of the host and include saprophytes, commensals, facultative pathogens and true pathogens.

- The microflora of the intestinal tract synthesise vitamin K and several B vitamins which supply on occasion the body's needs.
- The antibiotic substances produced by some, for example, colicins, have a harmful effect on pathogens.
- The endotoxins liberated by them may help the defence mechanism of the body by triggering the alternative complement pathway, as long as they are not produced in excessive amounts.

On the contrary, the **opportunistic pathogens** among them cause disease when the body's defence mechanisms fail. Their abnormal multiplication can cause diseases such as enteritis and endotoxic shock. Penicillinase producing organisms can aggravate infection by interfering with therapy. Certain streptococci of the mouth cause dental caries.

In environments laden with pathogens, for example, hospitals, a **shift in the normal flora** of the individuals there can cause an increase in carriage of antibiotic resistant staphylococci. It has also been shown that such people can be recolonised with penicillin sensitive staphylococci of strain 502 A which are harmless and thus overcome the damage done. When large numbers of people congregate from different parts of the country as in army camps, the new recruits experience increased colonisation rates of *Neisseria meningitidis* and Group A streptococcus and viruses such as rhino viruses and adenoviruses, sometimes resulting in epidemics.

Normal flora of the skin

The human skin is constantly and continuously bombarded by organisms present in the environment. It is also contaminated by one's own secretions and excretions, the extent depending on the individual's personal hygiene. The flora depend on the area of the body, the clothing one wears, one's occupation and environment. Transient microflora tend to occur more frequently on the skin.

Cultures from the skin have frequently demonstrated diphtheroids (including propionibacteria); staphylococci (aerobic and anaerobic); Gram-positive, aerobic, spore bearing bacilli; *S.viridans; S.faecalis;* Gram-negative bacilli such as *E.coli*, Proteus and other intestinal organisms; mimieae; mycobacteria (non-pathogenic); *Candida albicans;* cryptococci and *Pityrosporum ovale.*

Often the skin of the face, neck, hands and buttocks carries pathogenic hemolytic streptococci and staphylococci. Penicillin resistant staphylococci are seen in individuals working in hospitals.

Hair frequently harbours *S.aureus* and forms a reservoir for cross-infection.

Normal flora of the conjunctiva

The conjunctiva is relatively free from organisms due to the flushing action of tears. The predominant organisms of the eye are diphtheroids (*Corynebacterium xerosis*), Moraxella species, staphylococci and nonhemolytic streptococci.

Normal flora of the nose, nasopharynx and sinuses

The floor of the nose harbours corynebacteria, staphylococci and streptococci. Haemophilus species and *Moraxella lacunata* may also be seen.

The nasopharynx of the infant is sterile at birth but, within 2–3 days after birth, acquires the common commensal flora and the pathogenic flora carried by the mother and the attendants. The nasopharynx can be considered the natural habitat of the common pathogenic bacteria which cause infections of the nose, throat, bronchi and lungs. Certain Gram-negative organisms from the intestinal tract such as *Pseudomonas aeruginosa, E.coli,* paracolons and Proteus are also occasionally found in normal persons. After penicillin therapy, they may be the predominant flora.

Normal flora of the mouth and upper respiratory tract

The mouth contains a plethora of organisms—pimented and nonpigmented micrococci, some of which are aerobic, Gram-positive, aerobic, spore bearing bacilli, coliforms, Proteus and lactobacilli. The gum pockets between the teeth, and the crypts of the tonsils have a wide spectrum of anaerobic flora—anaerobic micrococci, microaerophilic and anaerobic strept cocci, vibrios, fusiform bacilli, corynebacterium species, actinomyces, leptothrix, mycoplasma, neisseria and bacteroides are all found in varying extents. Among fungi, Candida and geotrichum have been reported.

The mouth of the infant is not sterile at birth. It generally contains the same types of organisms in about the same relative numbers as those present in the mother's vagina, that is a mixture of micrococci, streptococci, coliform bacilli and Doderlein's bacilli. These organisms diminish in number during the first 2–5 days after birth and are replaced by the types of bacteria present in the mouth of the mother and nurse.

Within 12 hours after birth alpha hemolytic streptococci are found in the upper respiratory tract and be come the dominant organisms of the oropharynx and remain so for life. In the pharynx and trachea, flora similar to that of the mouth establish themselves. Few bacteria are found in normal bronchi. Smaller bronchi and alveoli are normally sterile.

Normal flora of the gastrointestinal tract

In 80–90 per cent of newborn infants, the meconium is sterile but in 10–20 per cent a few organisms, probably acquired during labour, may be present. In all cases, within 4–24 hours of birth intestinal flora is established partly from below and partly by invasion from above. In breastfed children the intestine contains lactobacilli (*L.bifidus* constituting 99 per cent of total organisms in the feces), enterococci, colon bacilli and staphylococci. In artificially fed (bottlefed) children *L.acidophilus* and colon bacilli and in part enterococci, Gram-positive aerobic and anaerobic bacilli are seen. With the change of food to the adult pattern, the flora change. Diet has a marked influence on the relative composition of the intestinal and fecal flora.

In the normal adult, the microorganisms on the surface of the esophageal wall are those swallowed with saliva and food. Because of the low pH of the stomach, it is virtually sterile except soon after eating. In patients with carcinoma of the stomach or achlorhydria or pyloric obstruction, there is proliferation of Grampositive cocci and bacilli.

The number of bacteria increases progressively beyond the duodenum to the colon, being comparatively low in the small intestine. In the adult duodenum there are $10^3 – 10^6$ bacteria per gram, in the jejunum and proximal ileum $10^5 – 10^8$ bacteria per gram, and in the lower ileum and cecum $10^8 – 10^{10}$ bacteria per gram of con tents. In the duodenum and upper ileum, lactobacilli and enterococci predominate but in the lower ileum and cecum the flora resemble the fecal flora. There are about 10^{11} bacteria per gram of contents in the colon and rectum, constituting 10–20 per cent of the fecal mass. In the adult normal colon, the resident bacterial flora are mostly

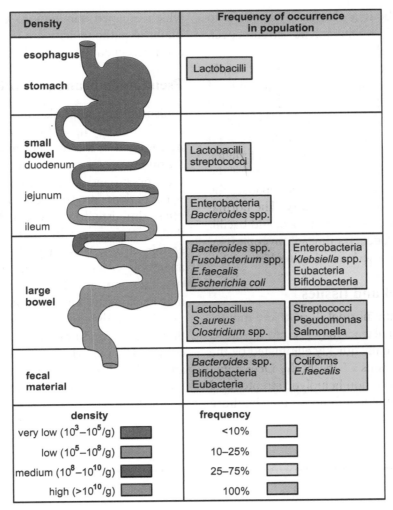

Density	Frequency of occurrence in population
esophagus **stomach**	Lactobacilli
small bowel duodenum	Lactobacilli streptococci
jejunum ileum	Enterobacteria *Bacteroides* spp.
large bowel	*Bacteroides* spp. / Enterobacteria; *Fusobacterium* spp. / *Klebsiella* spp.; *E.faecalis* / Eubacteria; *Escherichia coli* / Bifidobacteria
	Lactobacillus / Streptococci; *S.aureus* / Pseudomonas; *Clostridium* spp. / Salmonella
fecal material	*Bacteroides* spp. / Coliforms; Bifidobacteria / *E.faecalis*; Eubacteria

density	frequency
very low (10^3–10^5/g)	<10%
low (10^5–10^8/g)	10–25%
medium (10^8–10^{10}/g)	25–75%
high (>10^{10}/g)	100%

Fig. 65.1   The longitudinal distribution, frequency of occurrence and densities of the bacteria making up the normal flora of the human gastrointestinal tract

(96–99 per cent) anaerobes—anaerobic streptococci, anaerobic lactobacilli, clostridia and bacteroides and about 1–4 per cent aerobes—enterococci, coliforms and small numbers of Proteus, Pseudomonas, lactobacilli, mycoplasma, Candida and others (Fig. 65.1).

Normal flora of the genitourinary tract

Mycobacterium smegmatis, a harmless commensal, is found in the smegma of the genitalia of both men and women. This may, by its presence in the voided specimens of urine, cause confusion. From apparently normal men, aerobic and anaerobic bacteria can be cultured from a high proportion, including lactobacilli, *G.vaginalis, alpha hemolytic streptococci and Bacteroides species. C.trachomatis* and *Ureaplasma urealyticum* may also be present. The female urethra is either sterile or contains a few Gram-positive cocci.

The vulva of the newborn child is sterile but after 24 hours it acquires a varied flora of nonpathogenic organisms from the skin, vagina and intestines. The nature of the flora in the vagina depends on the pH of its secretions and its enzyme content. In the first 24 hours it is invaded by micrococci, enterococci and diphtheroids. In 2–3 days, the maternal estrin induces glycogen deposition in the vaginal epithelium. This facilitates the growth of a lactobacillus (Doderlein's bacillus) which produces acid from glycogen, and the flora for a few weeks is similar to that of the adult. After the passively transferred estrin has been eliminated in the urine, the glycogen disappears, along with Doderlein's bacillus and the pH of the vagina becomes alkaline. This brings about a change in the flora to micrococci, alpha and nonhemolytic streptococci, coliforms and diphtheroids.

At puberty, the glycogen reappears and the pH changes to acid due to the metabolic activity of Doderlein's bacilli, *E.coli* and yeasts. This change probably helps prevent colonisation by possible harmful microorganisms. During pregnancy there is an increase in *Staphylococcus epidermidis*, Doderlein's bacilli and yeasts. Occasionally other members of the intestinal flora may be present. After menopause, the flora resembles that found before puberty. The normal vaginal flora often includes anaerobic cocci and bacilli, listeria, anaerobic streptococci, mimeae, mycoplasma, *Gardnerella vaginalis*, neisseriae and spirochetes.

Bacteria in the blood and tissues

The commensals from the normal flora of the mouth, nasopharynx and intestinal tract may get into the blood and tissues. They are usually quickly eliminated by the normal defence mechanisms of the body. Occasional isolation of diphtheroids or non hemolytic streptococci from normal and abnormal lymph nodes may be those which escaped elimination. Unless the organisms of doubtful pathogenicity are isolated more than once in serial blood cultures, they have little significance.

Pseudomembranous colitis

Indiscriminate administration of antibacterial agents may completely upset this function of the normal flora by eliminating the resident microorganisms, thus permitting exogenous and endogenous pathogens to gain the upper hand and to cause disease. In particular, when patients are treated with broad-spectrum antibiotics administered orally, diarrhea may be a side effect due to overgrowth by yeast or staphylococci. When certain drugs, especially clindamycin, are given, the anaerobic Gram-positive bacillus, *Clostridium difficile* (itself a minor member of the normal flora of the gut), may be allowed to multiply due to suppression of other members of the flora; this may result in a serious, life-threatening condition known as **pseudomembranous colitis**. Hence, wherever possible, narrow-spectrum antibiotics should be used at the correct dosage and for the correct duration of time, to prevent suppression of gut flora.

RECAP

- The normal microbial flora are more or less constant for each species and are broadly divided into residents and transients
- The flora can become pathogenic when host defences falter, prevent or interfere with colonisation/invasion of the body by pathogens, raise the overall immune status of the host against pathogens having related or shared antigens, and cause confusion in diagnosis due to their ubiquitous presence in the body and their resemblance to some of the pathogens.
- The microflora of me intestine produce substances like colicins, that have a harmful effect on pathogens.
- In environments laden with pathogens, for example, hospitals, a shift in the normal flora of the individuals there can cause an increase in carriage of antibiotic resistant staphylococci.

SHORT NOTES

1. Normal flora of intestine
2. Pseudomembranous colitis

66 Bacteriology of Water, Air, Milk and Food

It should also be safe, that is, free from chemical toxins and pathogenic microorganisms. Many major human diseases, for example, typhoid fever, cholera and other diarrheal diseases, poliomyelitis and viral hepatitis A and E are waterborne. These pathogens reach water sources through fecal or sewage pollution. It is essential to prevent such contamination, treat the water suitably to remove or destroy microorganisms, and also to ensure the safety of such protected water supplies by regular bacteriological surveillance.

Natural water sources, even when unpolluted, frequently contain some saprobic (saprophytic) bacteria, such as species of *Pseudomonas*, *Serratia*, *Flavobacterium*, *Chromobacterium*, *Acinetobacter* and *Alcaligenes*. Soil bacteria, such as aerobic spore forming bacilli, and those found on decaying vegetation, such as the *Enterobacter* species, may also be washed into natural waters during the rains; fortunately, these are harmless. Only pathogens introduced into water polluted by excreta or sewage pose a risk to human health (Table 66.1).

BACTERIOLOGICAL EXAMINATION OF WATER

Bacteriological analysis of water supplies should be performed at regular intervals, and not be a random exercise. Fequency of such analysis may range from daily to monthly sampling, depending on the size of the populations served.

Drinking water should be free of any pathogenic microorganisms. Ideally, therefore, tests should be aimed at detecting such pathogens. However, these are generally present in such small numbers that they escape detection. The practice, therefore, is to test for **fecal pollution**; if fecal pollution is detected in a water sample, it is inferred that the water from which the sample was drawn may be harbouring enteric pathogens. The primary test employed as an indicator of fecal pollution of water is the presence of **coliform bacteria** because they are invariably present in the feces of human beings and other warm-blooded animals in large numbers and can be easily detected even in high dilutions. Although coliform bacteria are

BACTERIOLOGY OF WATER

Drinking water must be visually acceptable, clear and colourless, and without a disagreeable taste or odour.

Table 66.1 *Pathogens spread through water*

In the community		In the hospital (Rangel-Frausto 2002b)		
Organism	Disease caused	Organism	Found in	Disease caused
A. Bacteria 1) *Shigella* spp. 2) *Vibrio cholerae* 3) *Salmonella enterica* serotypes *typhi* and *paratyphi* A, B,C 1) *Leptospira* spp.	**A. Bacteria** 1) Bacillary dysentery 2) Cholera 3) Enteric fever 4) Leptospiremia, leptospiruria	**Bacteria** 1) *Legionella pneumophila* 2) *Serratia marcescens* 3) *Mycobacterium xenopi* 4) *Pseudomonas paucimobilis* 5) *Mycobacterium chelonei* 6) *Acinetobacter* spp. 7) *Pseudomonas aeruginosa* 8) *Clostridium difficile*	1) Hospital water, cooling towers 2) Water of humidifier 3) Hot water taps 4) Water bottles for tracheal suction 5) Contaminated equipment and water tanks 6) Water bath used to thaw fresh plasma 7) Water bath used to thaw cryoprecipitate; tub water 8) Bath water	1) Pneumonia 2) Pneumonia 3) Pneumonia 4) Pneumonia 5) Otitis and nasal septum cellulitis 6) Bacteremia 7) Bacteremia; folliculitis and skin infections 8) Diarrhea
B. Parasites 1) Protozoa a) *Giardia lamblia* b) *Entamoeba histolytica* 2) Helminths a) *Schistosoma haematobium* b) *Dracunculus medinensis*	**B.Parasites** 1) Protozoa a) Diarrhea, malabsorption b) Amebic dysentery 2) Helminths a) Hematuria b) Skin lesions			
C. Due to viruses Enteroviruses	**C. Enteritis Viruses**			

not exclusively of fecal origin, they serve as presumptive evidence of the presence of bacteria of fecal origin, to be confirmed by the detection of thermotolerant *Escherichia coli*, which provides definite proof of fecal pollution.

Other bacteria are also sometimes used as indicators of fecal pollution. These include 'fecal streptococci' (resistant to 45°C, 40% bile, potassium tellurite and sodium azide concentrations inhibitory to coliforms) and *Clostridium perfringens*.

Guidelines have been laid down for the collection of water samples for bacteriological tests. Sodium thiosulphate should be added to samples of chlorinated water to inactivate residual chlorine which may lower bacterial counts by continued activity. Samples should be sent to the laboratory and tested without delay.

The following tests are generally done for routine bacteriological analysis of water:

Plate count

Principle: A count is made of the numbers of colonies formed in pour plate cultures of water samples, on nutrient agar incubated aerobically, in parallel, at 37°C for 1–2 days and at 22°C for 3 days.

- Bacteria growing at 37°C are most likely those associated with organic material of human or animal origin.
- Bacteria growing at 22°C are most likely to be saprobic, which normally inhabit water or are derived from soil and vegetables.

Interpretation: The plate count at 22°C provides an indication of the quantity of decomposing organic matter in the water; the greater the amount of organic matter present, the more likely the water is to be contaminated with parasitic and potentially pathogenic organisms. The plate count at 37°C is an important index of dangerous pollution; an increase in the plate count should serve as an alert to some defect in filter beds, requiring immediate correction.

Detection of coliform bacteria and *Escherichia coli*

Presumptive coliform count—multiple tube technique
Principle: This test is deemed presumptive because the reaction observed may occasionally be due to the presence of organisms other than coliform bacteria (hence the presumption that the reaction is due to coliform organisms has to be confirmed). An estimate of the number of coliform organisms is usually made by adding varying quantities of water (0.1–50 ml) to bile salt lactose peptone water (with an indicator for acidity) and incubation at appropriate temperatures; double strength MacConkey's broth has also been described as a suitable alternative medium. Since acid and gas formation indicate that coliform bacilli have grown, it is possible to estimate the smallest quantity of water containing a coliform bacillus and to express the degree of contamination by this group of organisms.

Methodology: The following range of quantities is usually prepared (Fig. 66.1):

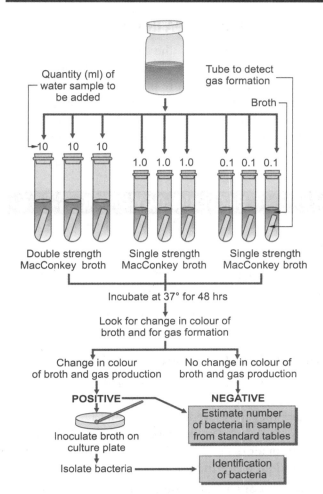

Fig. 66.1 Standard method for bacteriological analysis of water

- One 50 ml quantity of water added to 50 ml double strength medium
- Five 10 ml quantities each to 10 ml double strength medium
- Five 1 ml quantities each to 5 ml single strength medium
- Five 0.1 ml quantities each to 5 ml single strength medium
  MacConkey's fluid medium (modified) is used.

The range of quantities prepared depends on the likely intensity of contamination. For highly contaminated waters, smaller volumes are tested. The bottles are incubated at 37°C and examined after 18–24 hours. The 'presumptive positives' are read and the remaining negative bottles are re-incubated for another 24 hours. Any further positives are added to the previous figures.

Interpretation: The probable number of coliforms per 100 ml is read from the probability tables of McCrady. This is known as the 'presumptive coliform count' or the most probable number (MPN) of coliforms present in the water sample being tested (Table 66.2).

Differential coliform test (Eijkman test)

Principle: This test is usually employed to determine whether the coliform bacilli detected in the presumptive test are, in fact, *E.coli*.

Methodology: Following the presumptive test, subcultures are made from all the bottles showing acid and gas to fresh tubes of **single strength** MacConkey medium pre-warmed to 37°C. These tubes are incubated at 44°C (performed in thermostatically controlled water baths that do not deviate more than 0.5°C from 44°C) and examined after 24 hours.

Interpretation: Tubes exhibiting gas in Durham's tubes are deemed to contain *E.coli*. From the number of positive tubes obtained, the number of *E.coli* bacteria present in the water sample tested can be estimated by referring to McCrady's probability tables. The presence of *E.coli* can be further confirmed by testing for indole production and citrate utilisation.

Membrane filtration method

Principle: A measured volume of water is filtered through a membrane filter with a pore size of 22 µm (bacteria-stopping filters). Bacteria, if present, are retained on the surface of the filter.

Methodology: The membrane filter with the retained bacteria is placed on suitable media face upwards and incubated at the appropriate temperature; colonies that develop on the surface of the membrane are counted. After 18 hours' incubation, the presumptive coliform counts and *E.coli* counts can be made.

Table 66.2 *Classification of the quality of drinking water based on bacteriological tests*

	Presumptive coliform count per 100 ml	E.coli count per 100 ml
Class I Excellent	0	0
Class II Satisfactory	1–3	0
Class III Suspicious	4–10	0
Class IV Unsatisfactory	More than 10	0.1 or more

Detection of fecal streptococci

Principle: Fecal streptococci (such as the *Enterococcus* species) may be present in water samples, but usually only for short durations. Hence, if fecal streptococci are detected in a water sample, it suggests recent fecal contamination of the water.

Methodology: All positive bottles in the presumptive coliform test are subcultured to tubes containing 5 ml of glucose azide broth and incubated at 45°C. The presence of *Enterococcus faecalis* is indicated by the presence of acid in the medium within 18 hours of incubation. The positive tubes are plated onto MacConkey's agar for confirmation. The membrane filter technique can also be adopted for this purpose.

Detection of *Clostridium perfringens*

Principle: *Cl.perfringens* may be present in water samples over a long duration. Hence, if *Cl.perfringens* alone is detected in a water sample (without *E.coli* or fecal streptococci), it suggests fecal contamination that is not recent.

Methodology: Varying quantities of the water samples are incubated in litmus milk medium (anaerobically) at 37°C for five days; '**stormy clot**' formation is looked for, to infer the presence of *Cl.perfringens*.

Tests for pathogenic bacteria

Under special circumstances, specific pathogenic bacteria, such as typhoid bacilli or cholera vibrios, may have to be looked for in water. This was formerly performed by adding the water samples to tenfold concentrated liquid media, incubating and finally subculturing onto appropriate solid media.

A simpler and more sensitive method is to filter the water sample through membrane filters and to then incubate the filters on appropriate solid media.

VIRUSES IN WATER

Enteroviruses and other cytopathogenic viruses can be isolated from water, but this is not routinely performed. Generally, it is assumed that viruses in water are destroyed by chlorination, when the concentration of free residual chlorine is at least 0.5 mg per litre, for a minimum contact period of 30 minutes at pH below 8 and a turbidity of 1 nephelometric turbidity unit or less.

PROTOZOA IN WATER

Entamoeba histolytica, the *Giardia* species and *Balantidium coli* may contaminate drinking water. However, there is currently no sensitive indicator of protozoal contamination of water. Coliform counts do not reliably indicate protozoal contamination of chlorinated water as protozoa are more resistant to chlorine than are coliforms.

BACTERIOLOGY OF AIR

Definitions

Airborne infection: Transmission of infection produced by respiratory droplets less than 5 μm in size

Droplet infection: Transmission of infection produced by respiratory droplets larger than 5 μm in size

Microbial content of air

In the course of a day, a person inhales over 15 cubic metres of air. Hence the microbial content of the air one breathes in is important, particularly when it contains pathogens. The microbial, particularly bacterial, content of air depends on the location, that is, whether it is outdoor air or indoor air.

Microbial content of outdoor air: This depends on many **factors,** including:

- the density of human and animal populations
- the nature of the soil
- the density of vegetation
- atmospheric conditions (humidity, temperature, wind conditions, rainfall, sunlight)

It is important to remember that spores and fragments of moulds are more numerous than bacteria. Most of the bacteria are non-pathogenic and even the rare pathogen that may contaminate the air is seldom able to survive the adverse conditions of outdoor air to cause disease. Bacteria in the upper air consist largely of aerobic spore-bearing bacilli and, to a lesser extent, *Achromobacter, Sarcina* and *Micrococcus*. They are mainly derived from soil and surface dust and may be carried horizontally and vertically for miles. Infective microbes are seldom carried for more than short distances and their capacity to cause infection is impaired, except in rare cases such as the foot and mouth disease virus. **Pathogenic bacteria do not multiply in air.**

Microbial content of indoor air: Here, bacteria may be distributed through gross droplets and droplet nuclei from the nose and mouth and through dust particles.

- **Dust** consists of particles of varying sizes originating from animal, vegetable or mineral sources. The ultimate source of common pathogenic organisms is dust derived from human beings.
  - Nasal secretions via the ala nasi and upper lip are carried by the hands to the skin, clothing and bedding from where they become detached as dust particles.
  - Organisms may also get directly detached from the skin of different parts of the body including the perineum and septic wounds.
  - Intestinal organisms, through dried particles of feces from napkins of infants, are also disseminated.

  Heavy particles fall to the ground, while those 1 mm or less in diameter mostly remain suspended in air. **Hemolytic streptococci** from patients or carriers, **tubercle bacilli** and **diphtheria bacilli** and **staphylococci** are found in ward dust where

such patients are treated. Under favourable conditions, they may remain alive for many weeks. Bed clothes are an abundant source of bacteria laden dust. Desquamated epithelial cells from the body are liberated into the environment through physical activity. The stream of air enveloping the body also serves as a source of organisms in the dust.

- **Droplets and droplet nuclei:** While **coughing, sneezing and talking**, varying numbers of droplets are expelled from the body, ranging in size from less than 1 mm to 15 mm (Table 66.3). Depending on their size, they may be carried or remain suspended in air or fall to the ground and, in the process, evaporate—the smaller the size, the faster the evaporation. On evaporation, these droplets are converted to very minute particles called 'droplet nuclei' and their fate depends on air currents in the atmosphere.

  The viability of bacteria in droplet nuclei depends on numerous factors and is unpredictable. Experiments show that the proportion of dust particles and droplet nuclei reaching the lung depends on their size. All particles over 5 mm are retained in the

Table 66.3 *Pathogenic microorganisms spread through air*

Features	Droplet transmission	Airborne transmission
1. Size of droplet	> 5 µm in size (droplet nuclei)	< 5 µm in size
2. Source of droplets	Produced during coughing, sneezing, talking, invasive procedures (e.g. bronchoscopy)	Produced during coughing, talking, sneezing, invasive procedures (bronchoscopy, suction aspiration)
3. Characteristics of droplets	• Droplet nuclei arise due to evaporation • Present in air for short time and travel only short distances (≤1 m) • Close contact needed for this mode of transmission	• Remain suspended in air for long periods • Travel several metres • Susceptible individual may become infected even if some distance from infected person
Microorganisms involved a) Bacteria	• *Streptococcus pyogenes* • *Neisseria meningitidis* • *Corynebacterium diphtheriae* • *Haemophilus influenzae* type B • *Bordetella pertussis* • *Yersinia pestis* (pneumonic plague) • *Mycoplasma pneumoniae*	*Mycobacterium tuberculosis*
b) Viruses	• Influenza viruses • Rubella virus • Mumps virus • Adenovirus • Parvovirus B19	Varicella-zoster virus Measles virus Influenza viruses

Note:
1) *S. aureus* and *S.pyogenes* are known to be shed and dispersed into air in operating rooms and newborn nurseries.
2) Outbreaks of pneumonia due to *Legionella pneumophila* are associated with the presence of cooling towers close to the ventilation systems of hospitals.
3) *Aspergillus* and other fungal spores dispersed through the air during construction, renovation and maintenance of buildings.
4) Although carpets, linen, potted plants and flowers are known to be reservoirs of opportunistic pathogens, epidemiological evidence linking these to nosocomial infections is lacking.

nose, most of 1 mm reach the lung and are retained in the alveoli but below 1 mm the proportion retained in the lung diminishes. Infective or potentially infective droplets may also be liberated in the form of aerosols by various laboratory procedures, dental manipulations and in the flushing of water closets.

MEASUREMENT OF AIR CONTAMINATION

Sedimentation 'settle plate' method

Definition: A means of estimating the number of bacteria present in the air by permitting bacteria to 'settle' on open petri dishes (containing culture media) over a fixed duration. Droplet nuclei require more time to settle than larger particles.

Method: Open plates of culture media are exposed for specific periods, for example, half to one hour; then the plates are incubated at 37°C for 24 hours and the number of colonies counted. When pathogenic staphylococci and streptococci are looked for, blood agar plates are used; when fungi are sought, Sabouraud agar plates are used in addition.

Interpretation: This method provides an idea of the relative numbers and species of microorganisms present in air and is specially used for testing the quality of air in surgical theatres and hospital wards.

Slit sampler

Definition: A means of estimating the number of bacteria present in the air by passing a known volume of air through a 'slit'.

Since the plate exposure method has many limitations, a more elaborate method, the slit sampler, has been introduced. In this, a known volume of air is directed onto a plate through a slit 0.25 mm wide, the plate being mechanically rotated so that the organisms are evenly distributed over it.

BACTERIOLOGY OF MILK

Types of bacteria in milk

- **Acid-forming bacteria:** The commonest are lactic streptococci including *S.lactis* and *Enterococcus faecalis.* Lactobacilli are also found. These ferment lactose in the milk, producing acids, mainly lactic acids, which lead to the formation of a smooth gelatinous curd.

- **Alkali-forming bacteria:** These consist of the *Alcaligenes* spp, some aerobic spore bearers and the *Achromobacter* species. These render the milk alkaline.

- **Gas-forming bacteria:** Coliform bacilli are the commonest. Others are *Cl.perfringens* and *Cl.butyricum.* Acid and gas are produced. A smooth gelatinous curd riddled with gas bubbles is formed. Coliform bacilli are responsible for the ropiness in milk.

- **Proteolytic bacteria:** Spore-bearing aerobes, such as *Bacillus subtilis* and *Bacillus cereus*, *Proteus vulgaris,* staphylococci and micrococci come under this category.

- **Inert bacteria:** These are bacteria that produce no visible change in milk. These include some cocci of the udder, members of the *Achromobacter* group and most of the pathogenic organisms in milk.

- **Human milk:** Breast milk contains small numbers of *S.epidermidis, S.mitis, Gaffkya tetragena* and *S.aureus.* A few other species may also be found in some samples.

Milkborne diseases

The most important diseases that can be transmitted by milk are tuberculosis, brucellosis, streptococcal and staphylococcal infections, salmonellosis and Q fever. Diseases of less importance include cowpox and milker's nodes which are usually transmitted during milking rather than through ingestion of milk. Foot and mouth disease, anthrax and leptospirosis have been transmitted on rare occasions. Tickborne encephalitis virus may be transmitted through goat milk. Milkborne infectious hepatitis has been reported.

Occasionally, milk may be contaminated with *Streptobacillus moniliformis* from the nasal secretion of rats and with *Campylobacter jejuni* from animal feces. *Yersinia enterocolitica* is not uncommon in milk and may give rise to gastroenteritis if present in large numbers (Table 66.4).

BACTERIOLOGICAL EXAMINATION OF MILK

Routine bacteriological examination of milk consists of the following:

Viable count

Method: This is estimated by performing plate counts with serial dilutions of the milk sample. Raw milk always contains bacteria, varying in number from about 500 to several million per ml.

Table 66.4 Pathogenic microorganisms spread through milk

Organisms derived from infected cow			Organisms from sources external to animal	
Organism	Disease in cow	Disease in humans	Organism	Disease in humans
A. Bacteria	A.	1) Tuberculosis	A. Non-pathogenic organisms	A.
1) *Mycobacterium bovis*	1) Tuberculosis	2) Anthrax	1) Non-chromogenic lactic streptococci, *Lactobacillus* spp. *Bacillus subtilis*	1) Non-pathogenic but may cause unpleasant taste and odor of milk
2) *Bacillus anthracis*	2) Anthrax	3) Undulant (remittent) fever		2) Non-pathogenic but may cause changes resulting in milk of blue, red or yellow color
3) *Brucella abortus*	3) Brucellosis	4) Sore throat, scarlet fever	2) Chromogenic bacteria *Chromobacterium violaceum*	
4) *Streptococcus spp.**	4) Mastitis	5) Diarrhea, vomiting		
5) *S. aureus*	5) Mastitis	6) Enteric fever, food poisoning		
6) *Salmonella spp.**	6) Bacteremia	7) Q fever		
7) *Coxiella burnetii***	7) Q fever			
B. Viruses	B.		B. Pathogenic bacteria **	B.
1) Cowpox virus	1) Vesicles on cow udder	1) Lesions on skin of milker	1) *Shigella* spp.	1) Dysentery
2) Foot and mouth disease virus	2) Foot and mouth disease	2) Mild disease (fever, vesicles on skin and mucous membranes)	2) *Vibrio cholerae*	2) Cholera
			3) *Corynebacterium diphtheriae*	3) Diphtheria
			4) *S.pyogenes*	4) Scarlet fever
			5) Diarrheagenic *Escherichia coli*	5) Diarrhea
			6) *Salmonella*	6) Enteric fever
			7) *S.aureus*	7) Food-poisoning
			C. Pathogenic viruses**	C.
			1) Polioviruses	1) Paralytic poliomyelitis
			2) Hepatitis A virus	2) Infective hepatitis

* May be spread through milk in the form of ice-cream
** Milk may not be the usual vehicle of spread of these pathogens

Significance: The plate count gives a rough and direct assessment of the viable bacteria in the milk. It is easily explainable to the producer and gives a fair idea of the improvement or deterioration in the conditions of production.

Test for coliform bacilli

Method: This is performed by inoculating varying dilutions of milk into MacConkey's fluid medium and noting the production of acid and gas after incubation.

Significance: Contamination with coliforms comes mainly from dust, dirty utensils and dairy workers. The coliform test is a useful indicator of fecal contamination, and also of contamination by dust or unclean utensils.

Methylene blue reduction test

Method: This is a simple substitute for the viable count. It depends on the reduction of methylene blue by bacteria in milk when incubated at 37°C in complete darkness.

Significance: The rate of reduction is related to the degree of bacterial contamination. Raw milk is considered satisfactory if it fails to reduce the dye in 30 minutes under standard conditions. The dye test is a rough and quick test to determine the quality of the milk as it arrives from the producer.

The **Resazurin test** is similar but the dye resazurin, on reduction, passes through a series of colour changes—from blue to pink to colourless—the shade of colour after incubation with milk for a particular period of time, depending on the degree of contamination. Generally, the 10-minute resazurin test is done, in which the shade of colour is noted after incubation with the milk for 10 minutes.

Phosphatase test

Method: This is a check on whether milk has been pasteurised. The enzyme phosphatase, which is normally present in milk, is inactivated if pasteurisation has been performed properly.

Significance: Residual phosphatase activity indicates that pasteurisation has been inadequate. This test, if positive after proper pasteurisation of milk, shows contamination after pasteurisation.

Turbidity test

This is a check on the **sterilisation of milk**. If milk has been boiled or heated to the temperature prescribed for sterilisation, all heat-coagulable proteins are precipitated. If ammonium sulphate is then added to the milk, filtered and boiled for five minutes, no turbidity results. This test can distinguish between pasteurised and sterilised milk.

Examination for specific pathogens

Tubercle bacillus: The milk is centrifuged at 3000 rpm for 30 minutes and the sediment inoculated into two guinea pigs. The animals are observed for a period of three months for tuberculosis. Tubercle bacilli may also be isolated in culture. Microscopic examination for tubercle bacilli is unsatisfactory.

Brucella: Isolation of brucella may be attempted by inoculating cream heavily on serum dextrose agar or by injecting a centrifuged deposit of the milk sample intramuscularly into guinea pigs. The animals are sacrificed after six weeks and the serum tested for agglutinins and the spleen inoculated in culture media. Brucellosis in animals can also be detected by demonstrating the antibodies in milk, by the milk-ring or the whey agglutination tests.

The tests adopted for the routine examination of milk should reveal the degree of bacterial contamination and thereby indicate whether the milk is produced and handled in a hygienic manner.

BACTERIOLOGY OF FOOD

Foodborne infections are a significant public health problem since they may be a major cause of morbidity, although, fortunately, an infrequent cause of mortality. Food is very easily contaminated and, in addition, is an excellent medium for the growth of various kinds of microorganisms.

Etiologic patterns of foodborne infections vary throughout the world. These patterns are influenced by factors such as food preferences, awareness by physicians and the public, and laboratory capabilities. For example, in the USA, *S.aureus* and *Salmonella* are responsible for more than half the foodborne outbreaks of disease, whereas in the United Kingdom, *Clostridium perfringens* is responsible for more than 90 per cent and in Japan, *Vibrio parahaemolyticus* is responsible for more than 50 per cent of such outbreaks.

Definitions

Outbreak of foodborne disease: This is said to have occurred when two or more persons experience a similar illness, usually gastrointestinal, after ingestion of the same food and epidemiologic analysis implicates food as the source of the illness

Food poisoning: A group of diseases caused by consumption of food contaminated with microbes or microbial toxins (usually caused by bacteria)

Source of food contamination

Food should not normally contain microorganisms. If microbes are detected in food, particularly in cooked food, it indicates a breakdown of sanitary procedures and precautions. Food can be contaminated by the following means:

- **Feces**: Feces may contaminate food directly through the hands of the infected person or indirectly through objects which he has handled.
- **Sewage**: Water used for cooking may have been contaminated by sewage at some stage.
- **Flies**: These insects carry pathogenic organisms from feces, or from waste in refuse dumps or dustbins, to food; they also contaminate food by their excreta
- **Hands of infected individuals**: Food may be contaminated by the hands of individuals who are either infected or who are carriers and who handle food
- **Air**: Uncovered food may be contaminated by organisms present in air and dust which settle on it
- **Domestic animals and pets**: Food may inadvertently be contaminated by the excreta of domestic animals and pets, either directly or indirectly (through the hands of persons handling the animals)

Laboratory diagnosis of suspected foodborne infection or food poisoning

1. Clinical history: Since time is of the essence, a careful and detailed history should be taken, to eliminate unlikely causes altogether.

2. Samples for investigation: Samples include the food consumed, and the vomitus and feces from the affected person.

3. Investigations on samples:

- Direct microscopic examination for the presence of parasites
- Culture of the samples for bacteria and other microorganisms
- Tests for detection of bacterial toxins
- Analysis of food products to determine the total microbial count and to detect the presence of coliform bacilli (similar to the principles followed in microbiological analysis of water)

Prevention

- Food may be contaminated prior to cooking. The contamination may be because the food has been taken from an infected animal or because the food may be contaminated during slaughter in the abattoir or when it is canned improperly. To overcome this, while cooking, the heat has to **penetrate all parts** of the food so that all bacteria are killed.
- Refrigeration does not kill microorganisms; it only serves to temporarily inhibit their growth.
- Reheated foods are often sources of food poisoning, particularly if they have been contaminated by enterotoxin-producing *S.aureus*, since the heat does not affect the heat stable enterotoxin secreted by the bacterium. Imperfectly or undercooked food, for example meat that has been broiled, could be a potential source of danger.
- Overall hygiene practices must be maintained and the water used must come from protected or certified water supplies.

RECAP

WATER

- Drinking water must be visually acceptable, clear and colourless, and without a disagreeable taste or odour.
- Water is a potential source of microbial diseases and may contain potential pathogens (species of *Salmonella*, *Shigella* and *Vibrio*, polioviruses and hepatitis A virus), suggesting contamination with human excreta (less commonly, animal or bird droppings).
- It is monitored by bacteriological methods to ensure its safety:
  - Plate count (total microbial count) at 22°C, if increased, suggests large quantity of decomposing organic matter in water sampled and increased risk of parasitic and potential pathogens being present.
  - Plate count at 37°C , if increased, suggests defective water-filtering beds requiring immediate remedy.
  - Increased presumptive coliform count suggests possible fecal contamination of a water supply.
  - A positive differential coliform count (even one *E.coli* present per 100 ml of water) confirms fecal contamination of a water supply, and strengthens the possibility of pathogens being present.
  - The presence of fecal streptococci suggests recent contamination while if *C.perfringens* alone is present (without *E.coli* or fecal streptococci) it suggests fecal contamination that is not recent.
  - Passing a known volume of the test water through a cellulose acetate membrane filter (22 μm pore size) which is then cultured permits simultaneous determination of total counts, counts of coliform bacilli and counts of specific fecal *E.coli*.

AIR

- The bacterial content of the air is important, particularly when pathogens are present. In outdoor air, spores and mould fragments outnumber bacteria, which are mostly non-pathogenic. In indoor air, pathogenic organisms (tubercle and diphtheria bacilli, staphylococci) are distributed through large droplets and droplet nuclei (1–15 mm in size) generated, while coughing, sneezing and talking, from nose and mouth, and through dust particles from nasal secretions (carried by hands to skin, clothing and bedding), skin epithelial cells and dried fecal particles from infant napkins.

- Heavy particles fall to the ground; particles <1 mm in size remain suspended in air

MILK

- Human milk is seldom a vector of pathogens. Cow's milk may contain pathogens derived from cow pathogens excreted in the milk or derived from the animal's udders (*Mycobacterium tuberculosis* and *Brucella abortus*), or in the animal's feces (salmonellae and campylobacters).
- Regular tuberculin testing of cattle and examination of milk for brucella antibodies enables the detection and slaughter of infected animals.
- To eliminate potential pathogens, milk undergoes
  - ❖ Pasteurisation, where milk is heated to 63–66°C, kept at this temperature for 30 minutes (the holder process) or heated to 71°C (at least 15 seconds) to kill all vegetative pathogens, and then rapidly cooled to 10°C or less. The phosphatase test is used to check adequacy of pasteurisation.
  - ❖ Heating at or around boiling point (destroys all but most resistant spores) is adequate for less long-term purposes. The efficacy of such treatment is evaluated by the `turbidity test'.
  - ❖ Ultraheat treatment, where milk is heated to 132°C (1 second under specified conditions).
- Milk is examined for the presence of coliforms and other bacteria by tests as used for water.

FOOD

- Foodborne infections are serious causes of morbidity.
- Food may be contaminated by feces, sewage, flies, infected hands, air, and domestic animals and pets. Food-poisoning may be caused by toxin-producing organisms (*Clostridium botulinum*) and invasive organisms (non-typhoid salmonellae).

ESSAYS

1. Write an essay on the bacteriological examination of water. How is the quality of water classified based on bacteriological tests?
2. Discuss in detail the microbiology of air.
3. Write an essay on the microbiology of milk, with special emphasis on bacteriological examination of milk.

SHORT NOTES

1. Presumptive coliform count—multiple tube technique
2. Plate count
3. Detection of fecal streptococci and *Clostridium perfringens* in water supplies
6. Eijkman test
7. Droplets and droplet nuclei
8. Types of bacteria in milk
9. Methylene blue reduction test
10. Examination of milk for tubercle bacilli and *Brucella abortus*
11. Phosphatase test and turbidity test for milk

67 Laboratory Control of Antimicrobial Therapy

ANTIBIOTIC SENSITIVITY TESTS
   Diffusion test
   Dilution test
   Mechanism of action of antimicrobial agents
   Antimicrobial resistance
ANTIBIOTIC POLICY

ANTIBIOTIC SENSITIVITY TESTS

Optimum therapy of bacterial infection depends on choosing the antibiotic active against the causative agent. Therefore, it is essential to determine the susceptibility of isolates of pathogenic bacteria to antibiotics that are likely to be used in treatment. Laboratory testing to detect susceptibility is carried out by diffusion or dilution methods (Fig. 67.1).
- Diffusion tests
  - Kirby–Bauer disk diffusion method
  - Stokes disk diffusion method
- Dilution tests
  - Broth dilution method
  - Agar dilution method

Diffusion test

Here, the drug is allowed to diffuse through a solid medium so that a gradient is established, the concentration being highest near the site of application of the drug and decreasing with distance. The test bacterium is seeded on the medium and its sensitivity to the antibiotic determined by the zone of inhibition of its growth.

The **disc diffusion** method uses filter paper discs, 6.0 mm in diameter, charged with appropriate concentrations of the antibiotic. The discs are stored dry in the cold. They may be prepared in the laboratory or purchased commercially.

Kirby–Bauer method:
- A suitable standard dilution of a broth culture of the test bacterium is inoculated on the surface of a solid medium **(Cation-adjusted Mueller–Hinton agar (CAMHA))** as a lawn culture.
- After drying the plate (37°C for 30 minutes), antibiotic discs (4–6 per 9 cm plate) are applied with sterile forceps.
- After overnight incubation, the degree of sensitivity is determined by measuring the zones of inhibition of growth around the discs. Growth will be inhibited around discs containing antibiotics to which the bacterium is susceptible but not around those to which it is resistant (Fig. 67.2).

The diameter of the zone of inhibition is influenced by a variety of factors, such as diffusibility of the drug, disc concentration, nature and composition of the medium, its thickness, presence of inhibitory or stimulatory substances, pH and time of incubation. It is also necessary to check the potency of the discs periodically using standard ATCC strains *S.aureus* ATCC

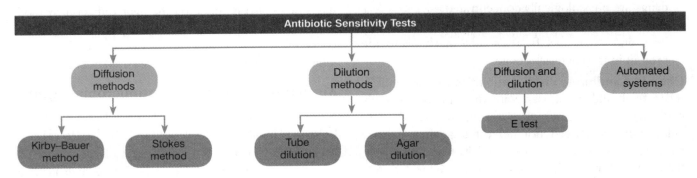

Fig. 67.1 Antibiotic sensitivity tests

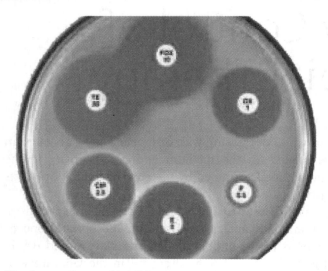

Fig. 67.2 Zone of inhibition around antibiotic discs on the lawn culture of test bacteria

25923, *E.coli* ATCC 25922 or *P.aeruginosa* ATCC 27853 with known zone diameters for antibiotics.

Zones of inhibition around the disc are recorded and interpreted according to the zone diameters available in the tables of the guidelines as recommended by **Clinical and Laboratory Standards Institute (CLSI)** guidelines that are internationally acceptable. The other guidelines used are **European Committee on Antimicrobial Susceptibility Testing (EUCAST)**.

Stokes method: Comparison of the zones of inhibition between the standard and test bacteria indicates the sensitivity/resistance of the latter.

A bacterium can be:

- **Susceptible** when it is inhibited by the concentration of the drug usually achieved in the blood following administration at the recommended dosage.
- **Intermediately** susceptible when it is susceptible to the drug at higher than normal dosages or when the drug has clinical efficacy at the body site where the drugs are physiologically concentrated.
- **Resistant** to the drug when it is not inhibited by the drug and when specific resistance mechanisms are present in the bacterial isolate.

Choice of antibiotic disk: Antibiotics for susceptibility tests should be chosen with discrimination. Only clinically relevant antibiotics should be tested, e.g., chloramphenicol need not be tested against urinary pathogens as the drug is excreted in urine mostly in the inactive form. Nitrofurantoin needs be tested only against urinary pathogens.

E-test: A recent modification of the agar diffusion susceptibility test employing a quantitative diffusion gradient is known as the **Epsilometer** or E-test. The MIC is obtained by noting the lowest concentration of the gradient which inhibits bacterial growth.

Dilution test

Here, serial dilutions of the drug are prepared and inoculated with the test bacterium. Dilution tests are generally employed when the therapeutic dose is to be regulated accurately as in the treatment of bacterial endocarditis, for slow-growing bacteria such as tubercle bacilli, and when small degrees of resistance are to be demonstrated.

Broth dilution: In this method, serial dilutions of the drug in a broth-tested against a standardised suspension of the test bacterium. After overnight incubation, the **'minimum inhibitory concentration' (MIC)** is read by noting the lowest concentration of the drug that inhibits growth.

The **'minimum bactericidal concentration' (MBC)** is the lowest concentration of the drug that kills the bacterium which is estimated by subculturing on solid medium.

Agar dilution: This method is more convenient when several strains are to be tested at the same time. Serial dilutions of the drug are prepared in agar and poured into plates. Many strains are inoculated on each plate containing an antibiotic dilution.

Automated versions of sensitivity tests are available and are in use in large laboratories.

Antibiotic assays in body fluids: These are required to verify whether adequate drug concentrations are achieved in blood and other body fluids, and to guard against excessive blood levels of potentially toxic drugs. The assays are done by serial dilutions of the body fluid and inoculating standard suspensions of bacteria with known MIC. Assays can also be done by the agar diffusion method. This depends on the direct relationship between antibiotic concentration in the fluid and the diameter of the zone of inhibition with a standard sensitive strain of bacterium.

Mechanism of action of antimicrobial agents

Antimicrobial agents are often categorized according to their principal mechanism of action (Fig. 67.3).

Mechanisms include:

- Interference with cell wall synthesis (e.g., beta lactams and glycopeptides)

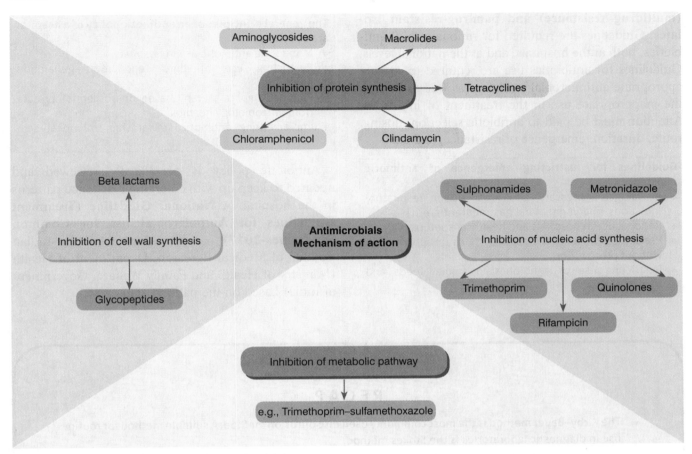

Fig. 67.3   Mechanism of action of antimicrobials

- Inhibition of protein synthesis (e.g., macrolides and tetracyclines)
- Interference with nucleic acid synthesis (e.g., fluoroquinolones and rifampicin)
- Inhibition of a metabolic pathway (e.g., trimethoprim–sulphamethoxazole)

Antimicrobial resistance

Bacteria may be **intrinsically** resistant to one or more class of antimicrobials, e.g., Pseudomonas to Penicillin G.

They may acquire resistance by mutation or acquisition of resistance genes from other organisms, resulting in any of the following actions:

- Produce enzymes that destroy the antibacterial drug
- Express efflux systems that prevent the drug from reaching its intracellular target
- Modify the drug's target site
- Produce an alternative metabolic pathway that evades the action of the drug

Acquisition of new genetic material may be through

1. Vertical gene transfer (VGT): Resistance genes are transferred directly to all bacterial progeny during DNA replication. A spontaneous mutation in the bacterial chromosome imparts resistance to a member of the bacterial population.

2. Horizontal gene transfer (HGT): Genetic material contained in small packets of DNA can be transferred between individual bacteria of the same species or even between different species by

- Conjugation
- Transformation
- Transduction

Transposons or, at times, plasmids facilitate the incorporation of the multiple resistance genes into a host genome (see Chapter 7).

ANTIBIOTIC POLICY

Antimicrobial resistance has become a matter of great concern globally, including in our country. Resistance has emerged even to newer, more potent antimicrobial agents like carbapenems giving rise **to MDR** (multidrug resistance) and pandrug-resistant isolates. Guidelines are required for rational use of antibiotics, both at the hospitals, and at the national levels. Guidelines for antibiotics use are required to ensure appropriate antimicrobial treatment as well as to limit the inappropriate use in the treatment of infections. Attention must be paid to antibiotic selection, dosing, route, duration, emergence of resistance, and cost.

Guidelines for restricting emergence of antibiotic resistance

- Avoiding unnecessary use (viral upper respiratory infections, pharyngitis, viral gastroenteritis, etc.)
- Rational use in hospitals and healthcare setups
- Prevention of over-the-counter sales in pharmacies without prescription
- Restricting use of antibiotics in animal feeds and industrial sectors

The general principles of an antibiotic policy of a hospital are as follows:

- Monitoring antibiotic use in hospitals
- Restricting use of third- and fourth-generation antibiotics
- Rational empiric therapy based on susceptibility data from microbiology hospital
- Implementing antibiotic stewardship in critical care units

Antibiotic policy is periodically reviewed and updated to keep up with emerging resistance patterns in the hospital. A **National Guideline (Treatment Guidelines for Antimicrobial use for Common Syndromes-2017)** has been formulated by Indian Council of Medical Research, Department of Health (Ministry of Health and Family Welfare, Government of India) based on the national data.

RECAP

- The Kirby–Bauer method is the most commonly used disc diffusion method. A suitable method for routine use in diagnostic laboratories is the Stokes method.
- Results are reported as susceptible, intermediately susceptible or resistant to the different drugs. Antibiotics for susceptibility tests should be clinically relevant. Susceptibility tests should be done only with known or presumed pathogens.
- A recent modification of the agar diffusion susceptibility test is the Epsilometer test.
  - The MIC of the drug against the bacterium is determined by noting the lowest concentration at which growth is inhibited.
  - The agar dilution method is more convenient for simultaneously testing several bacterial strains on agar plates containing different concentrations of the drug.
- Antibiotic assays in body fluids are required to verify whether adequate drug concentrations are achieved in blood and other body fluids. Antibiotic policy and national guidelines are required for rational antibiotic use to restrict emergence of MDR and pandrug-resistant isolates.

SHORT NOTES

1. Mechanisms of antibiotic action on bacteria
2. Mechanisms of antibiotic resistance
3. Rational antibiotic use
4. Antibiotic policy

68 Immunoprophylaxis

INTRODUCTION

Immunisation has been an important contribution of microbiology to medicine. This is one of the most effective methods of controlling infectious diseases. By systematic active immunisation programs, many developed countries have virtually eliminated 'vaccine preventable diseases' (VPD) such as diphtheria, pertussis, tetanus, measles, mumps, rubella and poliomyelitis. The global eradication of smallpox has, of course, been the crowning glory of immunisation.

Immunoprophylaxis may be in the form of **active or passive immunisation**, of individuals or selected groups exposed to risk of specific infections.

ACTIVE IMMUNISATION

Active immunisation is carried out using specific vaccines which provide protection against specific diseases. Vaccination evokes both humoral and cell-mediated immunity. Active immunity is associated with specificity and immunological memory (primary and secondary responses). The vaccines used for immunisation may be live, killed or in other forms like toxoids, subunits and recombinant vaccines (Table 68.1).

Live attenuated vaccines

Organisms that have been made to lose their ability to cause disease (pathogenicity) but retain ability to induce immune response (immunogenicity) and generate memory cells are said to be **attenuated**. They are grown in altered culture conditions for prolonged periods to achieve attenuation. Live vaccines are more potent immunising agents than killed vaccines as they multiply, with resulting higher antigenic dose than what is injected, thus evoking an immune response. Live vaccines retain all major and minor antigenic components. Oral polio, measles, mumps and BCG vaccines are common examples. **Live attenuated vaccines are avoided in immunocompromised individuals due to the danger of the vaccine strain causing the disease in the absence of host immune response.**

Killed or inactivated vaccines

Killed vaccines are relatively less efficacious as the pathogens are inactivated by heat or chemicals, and hence do not cause disease. Killed vaccines require primary and booster doses. They are stable and safer and do not require cold facilities for storage; however, they generate a weaker immune response. Examples of killed vaccines are the cholera, influenza, pertussis, plague, rabies and hepatitis A vaccines.

Live Vaccines	❖ Primary course provides relatively long-lasting protection.
	❖ The immune response is broad, providing both humoral (antibody-mediated) and cell-mediated immunity.
	❖ They exhibit wide antigenic diversity,

Table 68.1 *Types of vaccines*

Live attenuated	Measles, mumps, rubella, varicella zoster, BCG, rotavirus, oral polio (Sabin)
Killed vaccine	Rabies, pertussis, cholera, hepatitis A, killed polio (Salk)
Recombinant subunit	Hepatitis B
Toxoid	Tetanus, diphtheria
Protein conjugated	*H.influenzae* type-b (Hib), meningococcal, pneumococcal (13PCV)
Polysaccharide	Meningococcal and pneumococcal vaccines

Killed Vaccines	❖ Live vaccines have demonstrated good cross-reactivity against heterologous strains. ❖ They are safe. ❖ They do not result in infection and, therefore, the immune response produced is not as complete as that which is stimulated by a live vaccine. ❖ Repeat doses have to be given.

Toxoids

Exotoxins produced by certain microorganisms are responsible for causing diseases such as diphtheria and tetanus. Toxoids used as vaccines are purified toxins inactivated by treatment with formaldehyde. Antibodies generated against toxoids neutralise the toxic moiety produced during infection, rather than acting upon the pathogen. Some toxoids are mixed with other vaccines to enhance their antigenicity. In the DPT (diphtheria, pertussis, tetanus) vaccine, diphtheria and tetanus toxoids are combined with the pertussis vaccine (acts as adjuvant). The two toxoid vaccines commonly used for immunisation are diphtheria and tetanus.

Cellular fractions (bacterial polysaccharides)

Certain vaccines are prepared from extracted cellular fractions of microorganisms. Examples are the meningococcal vaccine from the polysaccharide antigen of the cell wall and the pneumococcal vaccine from the polysaccharides contained in the capsule of the organism. Their safety and efficacy is high but they are of limited use.

Conjugate vaccines

Vaccines with carbohydrate polysaccharide antigens require a protein conjugate to increase the immunogenicity, e.g., heptavalent pneumococcal conjugate vaccine (7PCV).

Other vaccines

- **Subunit vaccines:** They are produced from purified macromolecules derived from immunogenic components of pathogenic microorganisms by recombinant DNA technology. Other candidate vaccines for influenza, HbSAg and HIV are now being incorporated in micelles, liposomes, isocoms and virosomes for better delivery.
- **Recombinant vaccines:** Genes encoding antigens are cloned in bacteria, yeast and mammalian systems using recombinant technology. The expressed antigenic proteins are purified and used as vaccines. Examples are the hepatitis B and pertussis vaccines. Surface antigen of the hepatitis virus was the first recombinant vaccine cloned in yeast. Since purified proteins are used, adverse reactions are minimal.

Routine immunisation schedules

Routine immunisation schedules have been developed for different countries and modified from time to time, based on the prevalence of infectious diseases, their public health importance, availability of suitable vaccines, their cost benefit factors, and logistics. In India, the Expanded Programme on Immunisation (EPI) and the Universal Immunisation Programme (UIP) have been able to provide protection against VPDs for much of the target population.

- **National Immunisation Schedule:** The National Immunisation Schedule in force in India is shown in Table 68.2.
- **WHO Universal Immunisation Programme:** A global immunisation programme launched by WHO (1974) to protect all children from six diseases—diphtheria, tetanus, whooping cough, poliomyelitis, tuberculosis and measles—by the year 2000 was later called the Expanded Programme of Immunisation (EPI). Now this programme has been named Universal Immunisation Programme (UIP) in India.

In India, EPI and UIP have led to a significant decline in the recorded incidence of VPDs, as well as of infant and child mortality. Immunisation with three doses of oral polio vaccine (OPV) has not been consistently effective in India and other developing countries, with high rates of seroconversion failure. This is sought to be met through the strategy of 'mop up' rounds by giving OPV to all the children in an area on the same day, expecting natural spread of the vaccine virus among the children to reinforce immunisation. These rounds are held preferably during October to April, as the polio season in India is from May to October, with a peak in July–August.

New vaccines for children Newer vaccines in the schedule are **HiB, Rotavirus vaccine (Rotorix). Pneumococcal vaccine, 7PCV or 13PCV** are available for immunisation of children.

PASSIVE IMMUNISATION

In some diseases, the need for immune intervention is so acute that treatment cannot await the recipient mounting his own immune response. Also, sometimes the recipient may be incapable of generating an immune response. In such cases, preformed antibodies

Table 68.2   *National Immunisation Schedule (India)*

Age	Vaccine	Route of administration	Diseases against which vaccines are given
Birth	BCG	Intradermal	Tuberculosis
	OPV-0* (Dose at birth)	Oral	Poliomyelitis
	Hepatitis B	Intramuscular	Jaundice (Hepatitis B)
6 weeks	DPT-1	Intramuscular	Diphtheria, tetanus, pertussis (whooping cough)
	OPV-1	Oral	Poliomyelitis
	BCG**	Intradermal	Tuberculosis
	Hepatitis B	Intramuscular	Jaundice (Hepatitis B)
10 weeks	DPT-2	Intramuscular	Diphtheria, tetanus, pertussis
	OPV-2	Oral	Poliomyelitis
	Hepatitis B	Intramuscular	Jaundice (Hepatitis B)
14 weeks	DPT-3	Intramuscular	Diphtheria, tetanus, pertussis
	OPV-3	Oral	Poliomyelitis
	Hepatitis B	Intramuscular	Hepatitis B (Jaundice)
9 months	Measles	Subcutaneous	Measles
16–24 months	DPT	Intramuscular	Diphtheria, tetanus, pertussis
	OPV	Oral	Poliomyelitis
5–6 years	DT***	Intramuscular	Diphtheria, tetanus
10 years	TT****	Intramuscular	Tetanus
16 years	TT	Intramuscular	Tetanus
Pregnancy	TT*****	Intramuscular	Tetanus

Note:
1. Numbers 1, 2, 3 are the number of doses (first, second or third)
2. * For institutional births only. OPV-0 is additional, and not to be counted for the primary course of 3 doses starting at 6 weeks.
3. ** Only for infants not given BCG at birth.
4. *** A second dose of DT to be given to children with no documentary evidence or history of primary DPT immunisation.
5. **** A second dose of TT to be given after one month to those with no record or history of prior DPT, DT or TT immunisation.
6. ***** For prevention of tetanus in the neonate primarily, but also in the mother.
7. Hepatitis B vaccine has been added to the immunisation schedule by many of the states in India.

are transferred and human or animal sera used for passive immunisation.

Human sera

Normal immunoglobulins can be injected in two forms: pooled and specific.

- **Pooled immunoglobulins** are used for short-term prophylaxis in case of exposure to hepatitis A or measles.
- **Hyperimmune immunoglobulins** are prepared from patients in the convalescent phase and recovering from that infection. Passive immunisation is deployed using specific human immunoglobulins (IG) for protection against different diseases. Examples are hepatitis B (HBIG), tetanus (HTIG), rabies (HRIG), vaccinia (HVIG), etc.

Administration of human sera: Human sera are injected intramuscularly. For rabies, half the dose is given around the wound bite and the other half intramuscularly.

Animal sera

Equine sera were used earlier but now human hyperimmune sera is preferred to animal sera to avoid hypersensitivity.

COMBINED ACTIVE AND PASSIVE IMMUNISATION

In special cases, combined active and passive immunisation is preferred, where immediate passive immunity has to be provided, till active immunisation generates specific immune responses to the particular disease/infection. Here, a combination of vaccines (diphtheria/tetanus and rabies) is given simultaneously but injected at two different sites.

INDIVIDUAL IMMUNISATION

The vaccines offered under national programmes are limited by economic considerations and so some important vaccines may be omitted because they are costly. These may be supplemented by individual initiative, whenever possible.

Hepatitis B vaccine

Many developing countries, including India, have high endemicity for this virus. Perinatal transmission and acquisition of the viral infection in the first five years of life are common in such areas. Inclusion of the hepatitis B vaccine in routine childhood immunisation will therefore be beneficial. The fact that a quarter to half the adult dose of the vaccine is adequate for children brings down the cost. The recent reduction in the cost of the vaccine as a result of indigenous manufacture has made mass vaccination more feasible by some of the states in India. Several healthcare guidelines advocate HepB vaccine to all healthcare professionals.

Varicella vaccine

Chickenpox is a very mild disease in children, but in adults it can be serious and even fatal. The varicella vaccine had been used for many years in immuno-compromised children. Recently, with the development of a more stable and effective vaccine, its scope has been extended for general use for prevention of varicella and herpes zoster. All children should routinely receive the first dose of varicella vaccine (live-attenuated Oka strain of VZV) at 12 to 15 months of age. The second dose of the vaccine is recommended at 4 to 6 years of age. Vaccination is contraindicated in pregnancy.

Typhoid vaccine

Typhoid fever continues to be a major public health problem in the developing countries. Two recent typhoid vaccines, the live oral Gal-E mutant vaccine and the injectable purified Vi polysaccharide vaccine, may be acceptable because they offer prolonged protection and are free from reactions. They are recommended for immunisation of those five years old or above and so may be employed at school entry.

Immunoprophylaxis of individual diseases has been described in the respective chapters.

VACCINATION DURING OUTBREAKS

Population protection during outbreaks or epidemics of infections is an important measure of infection containment. Some of the vaccines used are flu vaccines (seasonal flu, H1N1 vaccines), cholera vaccines, etc.

IMMUNOMODULATION

In certain instances, the immune system needs to be modulated or suppressed. Immunomodulators are agents that weaken immunocompetent cells which, in turn, decreases the inflammatory response. Immunomodulators are most often used in organ transplantation to prevent rejection of the new organ, and in autoimmune disorders such as rheumatoid arthritis. Other conditions which have been associated are Crohn's disease, irritable bowel syndrome and ulcerative colitis, where the immune system is overactive. The drugs often used are Cycloserine, Azathiaprine and 6-Mercaptopurine. Corticosteroids are more commonly used as mild immunomodulators.

> **Cold Chain**
>
> The purpose of the vaccine 'cold chain' is to maintain product quality from the time of manufacture until the point of administration by ensuring that vaccines are stored and transported within WHO-recommended temperature ranges. Vaccine vial monitors attached to the vaccine container are used for temperature monitoring. These are chemical indicator strips which change colour in a gradient manner if the temperature goes beyond the prescribed limit (Fig. 68.1).

Fig. 68.1 Vaccine vial monitor

RECAP

- Immunoprophylaxis provides specific protection against infectious diseases by stimulating the immune system.
- Active immunisation involves both humoral and cell-mediated immunity and is associated with specificity and immunological memory.
- Vaccines used for immunisation may be live, killed or in other forms like toxoids, subunits and recombinant vaccines.
- The transfer of preformed antibodies, human sera or animal sera is used for passive immunisation.
- Immunoprophylaxis may be in the form of routine immunisation, which forms part of basic healthcare, or immunisation of individuals exposed to the risk of specific infections.
- In the National Immunisation Schedule in India, BCG, oral polio, DPT and measles, are given to infants and children at different intervals according to the schedule.
- Newer vaccines like HiB, rotavirus vaccine and pneumococcal conjugate vaccine are available for use.

SHORT ANSWERS

1. Define the term passive immunisation. Explain how human sera/immunoglobulins are beneficial in this.
2. Describe comprehensively the National Immunisation Schedule in force in India.

SHORT NOTES

1. Live attenuated vaccines
2. Killed vaccines
3. Toxoids
4. Subunit vaccines
5. Passive immunisation
6. National Immunisation Schedule

69 Healthcare-associated Infections

INTRODUCTION

Approximately 5–10 per cent of patients admitted to healthcare setups in developed countries, and more than 25 per cent of such patients in developing countries, have been found to acquire infections which were not present or which were not incubating at the time of admission. Such **healthcare-associated (HCAI)** infections (earlier called **hospital-acquired** or **nosocomial infections**) increase the burden of morbidity, mortality and costs, to the existing illness. It is believed that up to 20 per cent of healthcare-associated infections in developed countries, and 40 per cent in developing countries, can be prevented. Moreover, in developed countries, 5–10 per cent of such infections occur in an epidemic or cluster pattern; this figure is probably higher for developing countries. All this has led to concerted efforts to implement infection control programmes in hospitals and health centres.

Infection control programs have become a part of patient care and management in almost all hospitals in the developed nations and are fast catching up in the developing countries as governments and managements realise its importance.

Iatrogenic infection: This is infection resulting from treatment or investigative procedures; it is not included in the concept of healthcare-associated infection, although both topics may be dealt with simultaneously.

Nosocomial infection (*nosocomion* means hospital): It is a clinical infection that develops after 48–72 hours of admission to a hospital resulting from exposure to organisms endemic within the hospital. These infections were neither overtly present nor within the incubation period in the patients at the time of admission. Infections contracted in the hospital, but not clinically evident until after discharge, also form a part of this spectrum. The term '**healthcare-associated infections**' is now used to denote these infections since it is recognised that such infections may be acquired in any facility that offers healthcare and not only in hospitals.

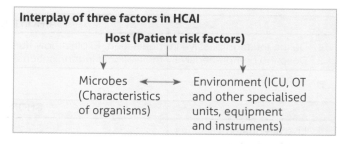

Interplay of three factors in HCAI

Host (Patient risk factors)

Microbes (Characteristics of organisms) ← → Environment (ICU, OT and other specialised units, equipment and instruments)

Common types of healthcare-associated infections

The exact distribution of such infections in India and other developing countries is unclear. In the developed world, they commonly manifest as infections of the urinary tract, surgical and non-surgical wounds, lungs and respiratory tract, blood (bacteremia) and of the gastrointestinal tract; tetanus and hepatitis B infection are also noted. The risk factors for some of these infections, the common infecting organisms and methods of preventing such infections are outlined below and in Table 69.1.

Catheter-associated urinary tract infections (CAUTI): Even with adequate precautions, catheterisation in hospitals leads to urinary infections in about 2 per cent; with indwelling catheters, the rate goes up to 50 per cent or more. *E.coli, Proteus, Ps.aeruginosa* and other Gram-negative bacilli are the causative agents. Mixed infection is common. Infection can be prevented

Table 69.1   *Risk factors, common infecting organisms and measures to prevent common nosocomial infections*

Type of infection	Risk factors	Common infecting organisms	Measures to prevent infection
Urinary tract infection	80% of such infections are associated with the use of indwelling urinary (bladder) catheters because of: • Poor aseptic preparation at the time the catheter is inserted • Disconnection of catheter and drainage tube • Contamination during irrigation • Colonisation of drainage bag and retrograde flow of contaminated urine into bladder*	**From commensal bacterial flora** *Klebsiella pneumoniae* and *K.oxytoca* *Enterococcus faecalis* *Proteus* and *Enterobacter* spp. *Escherichia coli* **From exogenous sources** *Pseudomonas aeruginosa* or *P.cepacia* *Serratia marcescens*	• Use a continuously closed sterile drainage system • Proper catheter care by following the standard practice known as 'bundle' care • Proper cleaning of periurethral area prevents colonisation by bacteria • Avoid an indwelling catheter; if not possible, use only for a short duration and restrict manipulation • Use a catheter having the smallest bore*
Bacteremia/ septicemia	Indwelling intravenous catheter	*Staphylococcus epidermidis* *Enterococcus faecalis* *Staphylococcus aureus* *Candida* species	• Intravenous fluid therapy to be used only when essential • Lower extremity to be cannulated only when essential • Stainless steel needles, not plastic catheters, to be used. • Proper prior skin disinfection and complete asepsis needed during cannulation. Cannula to be firmly anchored at insertion site, which is covered by sterile dressings. Cannulation site to be checked daily for sepsis; cannula to be changed every 48 hours.
Pneumonia/ lower respiratory tract infection	Ineffective gag and cough reflexes in partly conscious patients Impaired pulmonary clearance mechanisms due to underlying pulmonary disease or congestive heart failure Use of respiratory tract instrumentation or ventilatory assistance	*Klebsiella pneumoniae* *Pseudomonas aeruginosa* *Staphylococcus aureus* *Enterobacter* species *Escherichia coli* *Acinetobacter baumannii*	• Patient to be maintained in a swimmer's or Gatch position to prevent aspiration pneumonia • Perform frequent suctioning of secretions using sterile techniques, particularly in tracheostomised or intubated patients • Respiratory assistance apparatus to be maintained in as sterile a state as possible
Surgical wound infection	Prolonged surgical procedure Prolonged immobilisation Some types of surgery (e.g., abdominal)	*Escherichia coli* *Enterococcus faecalis* *Staphylococcus aureus*	• Maintain strict asepsis during surgery, and restrict the duration of surgery • Use chemoprophylaxis if feasible • Try to restore mobility to the patient as soon as possible after surgery

* Schönwald and Baršíc, 2002

by strict asepsis during catheterisation. Indwelling catheters are to be used only when unavoidable, and care must be taken to have proper closed drainage.

Healthcare-associated bacteremia (Bloodstream infections (BSI)): These may be consequences of infections at any site but are commonly caused by infected intravenous cannulae, such as central venous catheter, peripheral lines. The longer the cannulae are kept in situ, the greater the risk of infection.

Healthcare-associated pneumonia and ventilator-associated pneumonia (VAP): Aspiration in unconscious patients and pulmonary ventilation or instrumentation may lead to nosocomial pneumonia, particularly in those with pre-existing cardiopulmonary disease. Multidrug-resistant *S.aureus* and Gram-negative bacilli are the common pathogens. VAP due to multidrug-resistant *Acinetobacter baumannii* has also increased in the recent past.

Healthcare-associated wound infections (Surgical site infections (SSI)): Several factors influence the occurrence of postoperative wound infections, such as the site and duration of surgery, health of the patient and skill of the operator. Most wound infections manifest within a week of surgery. *S.pyogenes* and clostridial infections appear within a day or two, while staphylococcal infections typically take four or five days and Gram-negative bacillary infections six or seven days to appear. Routine preoperative antibiotics do not prevent wound infections, though they may sometimes be delayed.

Healthcare-associated infections due to hepatitis viruses B and C (Transfusion-associated infections): These infections are a serious risk for patients receiving blood transfusions or undergoing renal dialysis. Such infections are also a major risk for hospital personnel working with patients in dialysis and cardiac surgery units, and in those who handle blood specimens. Although screening for hepatitis B surface antigen (HbsAg) and anti-hepatitis C virus antibody has markedly reduced the risk of acquiring such infections, other predisposing factors still exist. Strict attention to aseptic techniques would greatly reduce this risk in hospital personnel.

Healthcare-associated episodes of acute gastroenteritis: Outbreaks of Salmonella food poisoning, enterotoxic manifestations due to staphylococcal contamination of cooked food, and outbreaks of diarrhea due to *Escherichia coli*, *Clostridium difficile* and certain enteroviruses are well-known examples.

Other causes not commonly seen now are:

Healthcare-associated episodes of tetanus: Factors that lead to such episodes include failure to implement strict aseptic precautions during surgical procedures, the use of contaminated or improperly sterilised dressings and suture material, improper (or non-) disinfection of the site of intramuscular injections, particularly those given in the gluteal region, and inadequate care while cutting the umbilical cord of the newborn child.

Sources and reservoirs of healthcare-associated infections

Endogenous source of infection: This is often the most common source. Here, the infecting microorganism is not pathogenic under normal conditions. However, when there is an underlying (usually debilitating) disease, or when invasive diagnostic and therapeutic procedures (including the use of immunosuppressives and antibiotics) have been performed, this microbe can reproduce, spread and localise at a site where it may produce infection.

Cross-infection: In this condition, the microorganism is spread by:

- **Direct contact** between an infected patient and another individual (by droplets of saliva or respiratory secretions, by the patient's hands)
- **Air** (dust from a fabric that carries the patient's normal microbial flora)
- **Hospital personnel**, on whose hands or clothes the microorganisms settle; from these sites, the microbes may be directly transmitted to a patient. Alternatively, the organisms may be harboured in the respiratory or intestinal mucous membranes of the hospital personnel, where multiplication occurs, followed by transmission by direct contact or air to patients.

Infections from environmental sources: In these types of infections, the microorganisms concerned are derived from:

- Hospital **air**, which usually harbours many bacteria that are often pathogenic and resistant to multiple drugs.
- **Surfaces**, which are contaminated by the patient's secretions, excreta, blood or body fluids, or by animals and insects.
- **Inanimate objects**, which are contaminated by patients, hands of healthy or unhealthy hospital personnel, visitors, food or infected water, animals

and insects. Examples of objects contaminated by patients include hospital equipment (sanitary installations, lights, tables, beds) and medical equipment (endoscopes, catheters, vesical probes, needles, lancets, spatulas and instruments used for invasive and non-invasive procedures). Examples of objects contaminated by hospital staff include items in the kitchen, laundry and treatment room.

Modes of transmission of microorganisms

In healthcare settings, especially in hospitals, the four main routes of transmission of microorganisms that cause infections are the:

- Aerial route
- Oral route
- Contact route (especially the 'hand-borne' route)
- Parenteral route

MEASURES TO CONTROL INFECTION IN THE HEALTHCARE SETTING

Every healthcare institution should have a properly constituted and functioning infection control team. The basic principles of personal and institutional hygiene should be strictly observed to ensure patient safety.

Infection control aims to:

1. Reduce the microbial population of the hospital environment
2. Eliminate the danger of transmission of microorganisms from one individual to another:
   - From hospital personnel to patient
   - From patient to personnel to patient
   - From patient to patient
3. Manage linen, equipment and other inanimate objects to prevent them from becoming sources of cross-contamination
4. Practice safe methods of biomedical waste disposal

Observing standard precautions is crucial to the success of infection control measures in a healthcare setting.

Standard precautions

Standard precautions are the minimum infection prevention practices that apply to all patient care, regardless of suspected or confirmed infection status of the patient, in any setting where healthcare is delivered (Fig. 69.1). They include: hand hygiene, use of

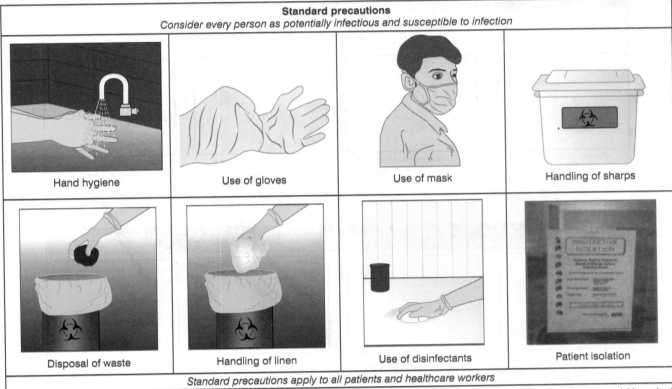

Fig. 69.1　Standard precautions (Source: Department of Clinical Microbiology, Christian Medical College and Hospital, Vellore)

personal protective equipment, safe injection practices, safe handling of potentially contaminated equipment or surfaces in the patient environment, and respiratory hygiene/cough etiquette (details taken from www.cdc.gov/HAI/settings/outpatient/outpatient-care-gl-stand-ared-precautions.html, accessed 8 February 2013).

1. Hand hygiene: Good hand hygiene, including the use of alcohol-based hand rubs and handwashing with soap and water (Fig. 69.2), is critical to reduce the risk of spreading infections in ambulatory care settings.

Key situations where hand hygiene should be performed include (Fig. 69.3) the following:

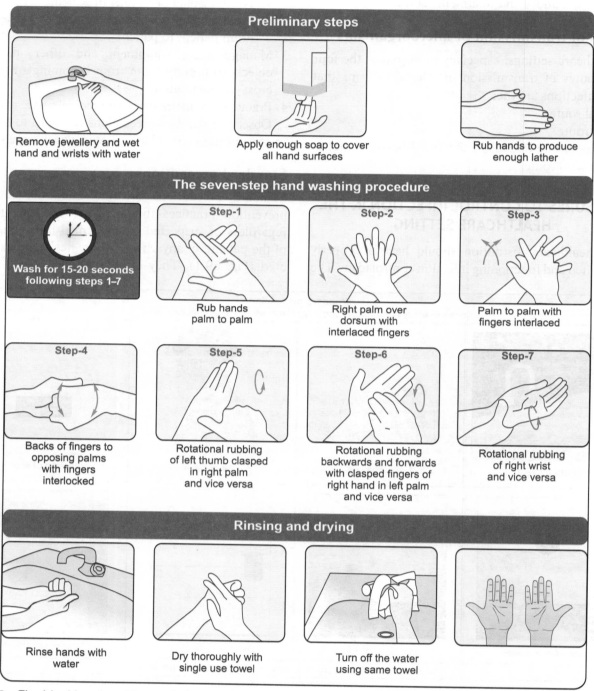

Preliminary steps

Remove jewellery and wet hand and wrists with water

Apply enough soap to cover all hand surfaces

Rub hands to produce enough lather

The seven-step hand washing procedure

Wash for 15-20 seconds following steps 1–7

Step-1
Rub hands palm to palm

Step-2
Right palm over dorsum with interlaced fingers

Step-3
Palm to palm with fingers interlaced

Step-4
Backs of fingers to opposing palms with fingers interlocked

Step-5
Rotational rubbing of left thumb clasped in right palm and vice versa

Step-6
Rotational rubbing backwards and forwards with clasped fingers of right hand in left palm and vice versa

Step-7
Rotational rubbing of right wrist and vice versa

Rinsing and drying

Rinse hands with water

Dry thoroughly with single use towel

Turn off the water using same towel

Fig. 69.2   The ideal handwashing technique

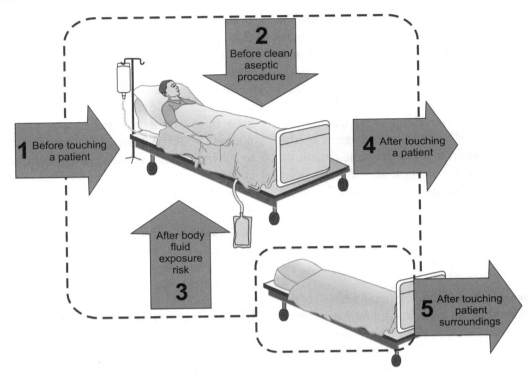

Fig. 69.3 Five moments for hand hygiene

- Before touching a patient, even if gloves are to be worn
- Before coming out of the patient's care area after touching the patient or the patient's immediate environment
- After contact with blood, body fluids or excretions, or wound dressings
- Prior to performing any aseptic task (for example, placing an intravenous line or preparing an injection)
- If hands are likely to move from a contaminated-body site to a clean-body site during patient care; and after removal of gloves.

2. Personal protective equipment (PPE): This refers to wearable equipment intended to protect healthcare workers (HCWs) from exposure to or contact with infectious agents; examples include gloves, gowns, face masks, respirators, goggles and face shields.

With reference to gloves, it is recommended that:

- Gloves should be worn when there is a possibility of contact with blood, body fluids, mucous membranes, non-intact skin or contaminated equipment.
- The same pair of gloves should not be worn for the care of more than one patient.
- Gloves should not be washed for the purpose of reuse.

- Hand hygiene should be performed immediately after removing the gloves.

Other key recommendations are as follows:

- A gown should be worn to protect skin and clothing during procedures or activities where contact with blood or body fluids is anticipated.
- The same gown should not be worn for the care of more than one patient.
- Mouth, nose and eye protection should be in place during procedures likely to generate splashes or sprays of blood or other body fluids.
- A surgical mask should be worn when placing a catheter or injecting material into the spinal canal or subdural space.

3. Injection safety (safe injection practices): This refers to practices intended to prevent transmission of infectious diseases between patients or between a patient and a healthcare worker (HCW) during preparation and administration of parenteral medications.

The following are recommended:

- Aseptic techniques should be used when preparing and administering medications.
- Access diaphragms of medication vials should be cleaned with 70% alcohol before inserting a device into the vial.

- Medications should never be administered from the same syringe to multiple patients, even if the needle is changed or the injection is administered through an intervening length of intravenous tubing.
- A syringe should not be reused to enter a medication vial or solution.
- Medications should not be administered from single-dose or single-use vials, ampoules or bags or bottles of intravenous solution to more than one patient.
- Fluid infusion or administration sets (for example, intravenous tubing) should not be used for more than one patient.
- Multi-dose vials should be dedicated to a single patient whenever possible.
- Used needles should **not** be capped on any account.

4. Environmental cleaning: Cleaning refers to the removal of visible soil and organic contamination from a device or environmental surface using the physical action of scrubbing with a surfactant or detergent and water, or an energy-based process (for example, ultrasonic cleaners) with appropriate chemical agents. This process removes large numbers of microorganisms from surfaces and must always be performed before disinfection.

Disinfection is generally a less lethal process of microbial inactivation (compared to sterilisation) which eliminates virtually all recognised pathogenic microorganisms but not necessarily all microbial forms (for example, bacterial spores).

5. Medical equipment: Medical equipment may be **reusable** or for **single-use**. Reusable medical equipment (for example, endoscopes) should be accompanied by instructions for cleaning and disinfection or sterilisation as appropriate. Single-use devices are labelled by the manufacturer for only a one-time use and do not have reprocessing instructions.

Healthcare facilities should ensure that reusable medical equipment (for example, blood glucose meters and other point-of-care devices, surgical instruments, endoscopes) is cleaned and reprocessed appropriately before being used on another patient.

6. Respiratory hygiene/cough etiquette: This represents an element of standard precautions that highlights the need for prompt implementation of infection prevention measures at the first point of encounter with the facility/ambulatory settings. Any individual with signs of illness including cough, congestion, rhinorrhea or increased production of respiratory secretions needs to be promptly identified when entering the facility and should be monitored throughout the duration of the visit.

To prevent transmission of respiratory secretions in individuals (patients, accompanying individuals) who have signs and symptoms of a respiratory infection, notices should be posted at entrances with instructions to all individuals to cover their mouths/noses when coughing or sneezing; use and dispose of tissues; and perform hand hygiene after hands have been in contact with respiratory secretions (Fig. 69.4).

7. Isolation: All patients admitted with contagious infections must be isolated. Patients with MRSA and pandrug-resistant organisms need to be isolated and treated by barrier nursing.

Biomedical waste management

Definition: According to the guidelines on Biomedical Waste (Management and Handling) Rules (Government of India 2016), biomedical waste refers to 'any waste which is generated during the diagnosis, treatment or immunisation of human beings or animals or in research activities, pertaining thereto or in the production or testing of biologicals'.

The following practices are mandatory for all healthcare setups.
- Colour-coded bags for infectious, non-infectious and general waste
- Puncture-proof containers for sharps and needles
- Pre-treatment, autoclaving of infectious waste (blood and body products) prior to disposal
- Deep burial and incineration of appropriate hospital waste

Precautions in the operating theatre

Conventional or **plenum** type ventilation in operating theatres maintains approximately 20 air changes per hour; however, in laminar flow operating theatres, there may be as many as 300 air changes per hour. Airborne organisms or colony forming units (cfu) typically occur in counts of between 150 and 300 cfu/m^3 in conventional operating theatres, while with laminar flow ventilation, the number of cfu's should be at 10 cfu/m^3 or less.

It is recommended that for conventional operating theatres, the bioload (bacteria-carrying particles per cubic metre) should not exceed 35 in an empty

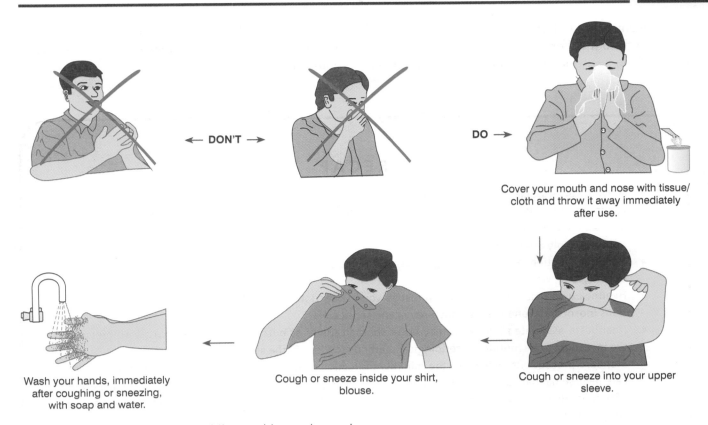

DON'T

DO →

Cover your mouth and nose with tissue/cloth and throw it away immediately after use.

Wash your hands, immediately after coughing or sneezing, with soap and water.

Cough or sneeze inside your shirt, blouse.

Cough or sneeze into your upper sleeve.

Fig. 69.4 Respiratory hygiene while coughing and sneezing

theatre or 180 during an operation. For ultraclean air operating theatres, the bioload should be less than 1.0 in the centre of an empty theatre and less than 10 during an operation, and should not exceed 20 at the periphery.

Investigation and follow-up of outbreaks of disease

Although all preventive measures are in place, outbreaks of healthcare-associated infection may still occur. In the unfortunate event of an outbreak in any area of the hospital, investigations are needed to determine whether:

- Carriers are responsible for the outbreak by providing a continuous reservoir of pathogenic microorganisms.
- There has been a single source of pathogens (food served at a particular meal).
- There have been deficiencies in the technique adopted in the day-to-day operations in the affected area.
- If the outbreak is caused by a notifiable disease, it should be reported to the authorities.

Monitoring and regulation of HCAI: Hospital Infection Control Committee (HICC)

With increasing incidence of HCAI, most hospitals have to monitor, regulate, implement and take preventive measures to control and contain HCAI. A Hospital Infection Control Committee (HICC) is constituted to plan, monitor, evaluate, update, and educate healthcare professionals on standard infection control practices. The scope of the committee is to:

- Meet periodically to evaluate the infection rates in the hospital
- Monitor infection control practices
- Look at infrastructural corrections required to contain spread of infection
- Detect hospital outbreaks of infection

The committee is chaired by the Medical Superintendent, while the head of the microbiology department is the member secretary who coordinates the meetings and HICC activities. The other important member is the infection control nurse (ICN) who visits all areas of patient care, OTs, Central Sterile Supply

Department (CSSD), hospital laundry, and biomedical waste units, to monitor the practices. The other members include heads of surgical and medical specialties, engineering and nursing, heads of housekeeping and hospital kitchen to prevent food-borne infection outbreaks.

RECAP

- A healthcare-associated infection (hospital-acquired infection, nosocomial infection) is one that develops in a hospitalised patient but which was not present or was not in incubation at the time of admission; such an infection usually becomes evident 48–72 hours after admission to the hospital, but sometimes manifests only after discharge.
- Hospital infections are usually exogenous, the source being any part of the hospital ecosystem (people, objects, food, water, air).
- Healthcare-associated infections manifest as wound infections, urinary tract infections, respiratory infections (nosocomial pneumonia), bacteremia and septicemia.
- Healthcare-associated infections may occur sporadically or as outbreaks; possible sources of infection are investigated by routine bacteriological methods to identify the source.
- Standard precautions, which are the minimum infection prevention practices that apply to all patient care include hand hygiene, use of personal protective equipment, safe injection practices, safe handling of potentially contaminated equipment or surfaces in the patient environment and respiratory hygiene/cough etiquette.
- For conventional operating theatres, the bioload (bacteria-carrying particles per cubic metre) should not exceed 35 in an empty theatre or 180 during an operation; for ultraclean air operating theatres, the bioload should be less than 1.0 in the centre of an empty theatre and less than 10 during an operation, and should not exceed 20 at the periphery.

SHORT NOTES

1. Types of healthcare-associated infections
2. Hand hygiene
3. Personal protective equipment
4. Safe injection practices
5. Role of HICC in infection control in the hospital
6. Biomedical waste management in hospitals

70 Biomedical Waste Management

INTRODUCTION

Definition: Biomedical or hospital waste refers to any waste generated while providing healthcare, performing research and undertaking investigations or related procedures on human beings or animals in hospitals, clinics, laboratories or similar establishments.

Potential hazards: Biomedical waste is far more dangerous and offensive than domestic waste because:

- It contains **infectious** or other **hazardous materials** that may injure, infect or otherwise harm patients, their visitors, hospital personnel and the public at large in several ways.
- It may contain **'sharps'**, such as needles or broken glass, that can cause injury and infection, or harmful chemicals and radioactive materials.
- If kept untreated, it **undergoes fermentation** and tends to attract flies and other insects, birds and animals, rendering the site of generation and storage filthy and unhygienic.
- It can **attract rag pickers**, who repack disposables or drugs and sell them.

Since biomedical waste can be serious pollutants of soil, water and air, unless carefully managed, governments across the world have been forced to introduce legal restraints in this area. The Government of India has promulgated the **Medical Waste (Management and Handling) Rules, 1998,** under which the persons who are in charge of medical and other institutions where such wastes are generated (called **'occupiers'**) are held legally responsible for maintaining the conditions prescribed in the rules, which have come into effect from 1 January 2003.

Types of biomedical waste

The amount of waste generated under Indian conditions has been estimated as 1 to 2 kg per bed per day and is composed of different types of waste, of which, on an average about 85 per cent is harmless and only 15 per cent is hazardous, which includes infectious waste (Table 70.1).

General principles of waste management

Effective waste management requires a clean and tidy environment, since waste tends to accumulate in dirty surroundings. The hospital and its premises should be maintained in a clean and hygienic state. This requires frequent soap and water washing, mopping and good housekeeping practices. The objectives of biowaste management are to prevent harm resulting from waste, minimise its volume, retrieve reusable materials, and ensure safe and economical disposal.

Table 70.1   *Types of biomedical waste*

Harmless waste	Paper, cardboard, cartons, flowers and ordinary office or kitchen waste (akin to domestic waste).
Infectious waste	• Human or animal tissues or organs removed during biopsy, surgery or autopsy • Placenta and other products of conception • Any pathological fluid or discharges • Dressings, swabs and other soiled items • Laboratory samples sent for microbiology, pathology and biochemical tests
Non-infectious hazardous waste • Chemical • Radioactive • Pharmacological	Toxic, corrosive, inflammable, reactive and otherwise injurious waste, handling and management of which are under the direction of the Bhabha Atomic Research Centre Surplus or time-expired drugs

Steps in waste management:

- **Reduction** in volume can be achieved by proper planning and using reusable items wherever safely possible.
- **Segregation** refers to the separation of waste at the point of generation into the various types with respect to their category and mode. When potentially harmful waste is mixed with harmless waste, such as paper or packing materials, the entire load becomes contaminated and will have to be autoclaved, instead of only the originally infected items. Segregated waste is to be put into different coloured containers as prescribed in the rules, for appropriate treatment. This has been modified in 2016. The colour coding is shown in Table 70.2.
- **Storage** refers to the measures taken to ensure that biomedical waste is kept safely at the point of generation before being sent to the biomedical waste treatment facility.

- **Transportation** refers to the movement of waste from the point of generation to the treatment facility.
- **Treatment** here means all the procedures and processes intended to reduce the bulk of the waste and make it non-infectious and harmless.

Methods of waste management

Several methods of waste treatment are available and the choice of method depends on the item of waste and the facilities available. The place of final disposal may be in the premises or, if possible, away from crowded areas. Some methods of waste treatment are indicated below.

Waste treatment

Chemical disinfection: This is a very useful method for many items, particularly in small healthcare settings such as clinics. For some materials, it is also an important preliminary process before final treatment. For example, contaminated materials, such as sputum or pus, must be disinfected before being buried or autoclaved.

Table 70.2   Colour-coded bags for biomedical waste segregation as per 2016 rules

Colour of the bag	Type of waste	Waste treatment
Yellow	a) Human anatomical waste	Incineration or plasma pyrolysis or deep burial
	b) Animal anatomical waste	
	c) Soiled waste	Incineration or plasma pyrolysis or deep burial
	d) Expired or discarded medicines	Returned back to the manufacturer or supplier for incineration at temperature >1200°C
	e) Chemical waste	Incineration or plasma pyrolysis or deep burial or encapsulation
	f) Chemical liquid waste	Pre-treatment and then disposal
	g) Discarded linen, mattresses, beddings, contaminated with blood or body fluids	Non-chlorinated chemical disinfection followed by incineration or plasma pyrolysis
	h) Microbiology, biotechnology, and other clinical laboratory waste	Pre-treat to sterilize with non-chlorinated chemicals on-site as per NACO or WHO guidelines thereafter for incineration
Red	i) Contaminated waste (recyclable) like plastic bag, bottles, pipes or containers	Autoclaving or microwaving/hydroclaving followed by shredding or mutilation Treated waste to be sent to registered or autoclaved recyclers or for energy recovery of plastics to diesel or fuel oil or for road-making
White translucent	Waste sharps including metals: Needles, syringes with fixed needles, needles from needle tip cutter or burner, scalpels, blades	Autoclaving or dry-heat sterilization; followed by shredding or mutilation or encapsulation in metal container or cement concrete. Sent for final disposal to iron foundries (having consent to operate from the state pollution control committees) Or sanitary landfill or designated concrete waste sharp pit
Blue cardboard box with blue label	Glassware: Broken or discarded and contaminated glass including medicine vials and ampoules except those contaminated with cytotoxic wastes; metallic body implants	Disinfection (by soaking the washed glass waste after cleaning with detergent and sodium hypochlorite treatment) or through autoclaving or microwaving or hydroclaving; then sent for recycling

Deep burial: Where large areas of uninhabited land are available, this is a convenient method for waste treatment. After chemical disinfection, materials are placed in deep trenches, covered with lime and filled with soil. This is also a safe method for the disposal of sharps.

Incineration: This is a safe method to treat large solid infectious waste, particularly anatomical waste and amputated limbs, animal carcasses and similar materials. The incinerator exposes the waste material to a very high temperature, converting the material into ash, which would be only about a tenth of the original volume. However, it is expensive and is generally used only by very large establishments.

Autoclaving: This is widely used in laboratories and clinics for treating infectious waste before disposal.

Microwaving: This is another useful method of sterilisation of small-volume waste at the point of generation. This cannot be used for animal or human body parts, metal items or toxic or radioactive material.

Inertisation: This process involves mixing waste with cement and other substances before disposal, in order to minimise the risk of toxic substances contained in the wastes migrating into the surface water or ground water.

Liquid waste: Pathological, chemical and toxic liquid waste should be appropriately treated with disinfectants or reagents and neutralised before flushing into the sewer.

Proper disposal of hospital waste constitutes an important measure to prevent healthcare-associated infections, for the first rule in medicine as well as nursing is *Primum non nocere*—First, do no harm.

BMW 2016 Rules

These were published in the Gazette of India, Extraordinary, Part II, Section 3, Sub-section (i), Government of India, Ministry of Environment, Forest and Climate Change as a notification on 28 March 2016 (details available at http://mpcb.gov.in/biomedical/pdf/BMW_Rules_2016).

The major change in segregation is the change in the colour code and the waste categories (see Table 70.2).

RECAP

- Biomedical or hospital waste refers to any waste generated during healthcare, research, testing or related procedures on human beings or animals conducted in hospitals, clinics, laboratories or similar establishments. Biomedical waste can be serious pollutants of soil, water and air. The Government of India has brought in legal restraints in this area by enacting Medical Waste Management and Handling Rules, 2016.

- In Indian conditions, about 1–2 kg of waste per bed per day is generated, 15 per cent of which is hazardous. The different steps in waste management are reduction, reuse, segregation, storage, transportation and treatment. The methods of waste treatment, depending on the item of waste and the facilities available, include chemical disinfection, deep burial, incineration, autoclaving and microwaving.

- The most essential part of hospital waste management is the segregation of biomedical waste, which should be performed within the premises of the institution where the waste is generated.

- BMW 2016 rules have changed the colour codes and categories of waste.

SHORT NOTES

1. Types of biomedical waste
2. Segregation of biomedical waste

71 Emerging and Re-emerging Infections

Transmission from animals to humans
Zika virus disease
Drug resistance
Indian scenario
Bioterrorism

INTRODUCTION

Infectious diseases continue to be among the leading causes of death worldwide due to the emergence of new infectious diseases, re-emergence of old infectious diseases and persistence of intractable infectious diseases.

Emerging infectious diseases can be defined as those that have appeared for the first time in a population or which have existed previously but are rapidly increasing in incidence or geographical range.

The factors that contribute to emerging infections are given in Fig. 71.1.

Infectious agents known for some time but which had fallen to such low levels that they were no longer considered public health problems and which are now showing an upward trend in incidence or prevalence worldwide are called **re-emerging infections**.

Transmission from animals to humans

About two-thirds of emerging infections originate from animals—both wild and domestic—and, therefore, are **zoonotic**.

* Animals displaced from their original habitation due to deforestation or climate change and which move

in search of food have been cited as a possible cause of Lassa fever.

* Human penetration in unpopulated areas brings them closer to animal reservoirs or vectors. This may have contributed to the development of organisms causing diseases like yellow fever and malaria.
* Deforestation forces animals into closer human contact.
* Global warming has helped spread malaria, dengue, leishmaniasis and filariasis.
* Poverty and malnutrition have contributed to a severe infection–disease cycle.
* Changes in agricultural and food production patterns may have led to the development of food-borne infection agents such as *E.coli*.
* Increased international travel and outdoor activity may also have led to closer contact between humans and animals.

Table 71.1 lists the new infectious diseases identified since 1977.

A novel reassortant avian origin influenza A (H7N9) virus was isolated from respiratory secretions of three critically ill patients from Shanghai, China, in March 2013.

Zika virus disease

WHO declared Zika virus disease as a public health emergency of international concern in February 2016.

This is a viral infection transmitted through the bite of the *Aedes* mosquito (*A. aegypti, A. albopictus*) and is related to dengue, yellow fever and the West Nile virus. Though identified in 1947 in the Zika forest of

Factors

Agent	Host	Environment
• Evolution of agent (microbial adaptation and changes) • Development of resistance to drugs • Resistance of vectors to pesticides	• Human demographic change: population growth and migration (movement from rural areas to cities) • Human behaviour (sexual and drug use) • Human susceptibility to infection (immunosuppression) • Poverty and social inequality	• Climate and changing ecosystem • Economic development and land use (urbanisation, deforestation) • Technology and industry (food processing and handling) • International travel and commerce • Breakdown of public health means (war, unrest, overcrowding) • Deterioration in surveillance system

Fig. 71.1 Factors contributing to emerging infections

Table 71.1   *New infectious diseases recognised since 1977*

Year	Agent	Disease
1977	Ebola virus	Ebola hemorrhagic fever
1977	*Legionella pneumophila*	Legionnaires' disease
1977	Hantaan virus	Hemorrhagic fever with renal syndrome (HRFS)
1977	*Campylobacter jejuni*	Enteric pathogen
1980	Human T-lymphotropic virus I	T-cell lymphoma-leukemia
1981	Toxin-producing strains of *S.aureus*	Toxic shock syndrome
1982	*Escherichia coli* O157:H7	Hemorrhagic colitis
1982	*Borrelia burgdorferi*	Lyme disease
1983	Human immunodeficiency virus	Acquired immunodeficiency syndrome
1983	*Helicobacter pylori*	Peptic ulcer disease
1986	BSE agent	Bovine spongiform encephalopathy
1988	Human herpesvirus 6	Exanthem subitum
1989	Hepatitis C virus	Hepatitis
1992	*Vibrio cholerae* O139	Epidemic cholera
1993	Sin Nombre virus	Hantavirus pulmonary syndrome
1995	Human herpesvirus 8	Kaposi's sarcoma
1997	H5N1	Avian flu (Bird flu)
1999	Nipah virus (Paramyxoviridae, genus *Henipavirus*)	Encephalitis and respiratory illness in Malaysia and Singapore
2003	Coronavirus	SARS
2009	H1N1	Pandemic (H1N1) influenza
2011	CCHF	Crimean Congo hemorrhagic fever outbreak reported in Gujarat.
2012	MERS CoV	Middle East respiratory syndrome caused by a coronavirus—first identified in Saudi Arabia
2013	H7N9 Influenza	Avian influenza reported in China
2016	Zika virus	First appeared in Brazil. Spread to other parts of South and North America.

Uganda, its presence was recognized recently in 2015 as a 'mystery disease' when it was reported from Brazil. There was concern in the developed world because of the threat of its spread to the western hemisphere. If the index of suspicion is not high, it is difficult to detect. The symptoms are not specific and resemble that of other viral fevers like fever, headache, joint pains, rash and bloodshot eyes. It is worrisome as it can be passed from a pregnant mother to the fetus and can cause some birth defects, especially microcephaly. At present, pregnant women have been advised not to travel to areas where the Zika virus infection has been reported. No vaccine or antiviral drug is available as yet.

In India, Zika virus was first reported in three cases from the Bapunagar area of Ahmedabad, Gujarat, in the month of January 2017. These cases tested positive for the virus by RT-PCR. This was later confirmed by WHO. All three cases recovered. The low level of transmission of Zika virus may lead to new cases in the future. There is a need to strengthen surveillance.

Drug resistance

The number of drug-resistant bacteria has increased in the last decade. The main cause of the current crisis in antimicrobial resistance is the uncontrolled and inap-

propriate use of antibiotics in both industrialised and developing countries. Of major public health concern are the following:

- Multidrug-resistant tuberculosis (MDR and XDR -TB)
- Methicillin-resistant *S.aureus* (MRSA)
- Penicillinase-producing *N.gonorrhoeae* (PPNG)
- Vancomycin-resistant enterococci (VRE)
- Extended-spectrum beta-lactamase (ESBL)-producing Gram-negative bacteria
- Carbapenemase-producing enterobacteriaceae (CRE)

Surveillance at natural, regional and global levels is a must. This would include:

- Epidemiological surveillance
- Laboratory surveillance
- Ecological surveillance
- Anthropological surveillance
- Investigation and early control measures
- Monitoring and evaluation under the supervision of the global outbreak alert and response network (GOARN) for containment of these infections

Humans, domestic animals and wildlife are inextricably linked by the epidemiology of infectious diseases. Human-induced environmental changes, interspecies contact, altered social conditions, demography and medical technology affect the survival of microbes.

Indian scenario

The bacterial and viral infections pertaining to the Indian scenario are given in the Table 71.2.

In Gujarat, Crimean Congo hemorrhagic fever (CCHF) was reported for the first time in 2011. It was reported as zoonotic in origin with ticks as the vectors. The outbreak was caused due to person-to-person transmission in hospitals.

Bioterrorism

Definition: Bioterrorism, as defined by the Centre for Disease Control and Prevention, is the deliberate release, by attackers, of an agent that causes one or more of a variety of different diseases.

Table 71.2 *Emerging and re-emerging infections in India*

Bacterial infections	Viral infections
Plague	Influenza
Leptospirosis	Chikungunya
Brucellosis	Chandipura
Anthrax	Dengue
Cholera	Japanese encephalitis; SARS coronavirus; Hantavirus; Human enterovirus 71; Crimean Congo hemorrhagic fever

Categories: Based on the risk to national security, the agents have been categorised as A, B and C (Table 71.3). These disease agents exist in nature (with the exception of smallpox, which has been eradicated in the wild), but they could be manipulated to make them more dangerous.

Table 71.3 *Categories of bioterrorism agents*

Category	Property	Examples
Category A	High risk. Pose a threat to national security. Have ability to cause social disruption	Anthrax, botulism (via botulinum toxin, which is not transmitted from person to person), plague, smallpox, tularemia, and a collection of viruses that cause hemorrhagic fevers, such as ebola, marburg, lassa, and machupo.
Category B	Moderately easy to disseminate and result in low mortality	These include brucellosis, glanders, q fever, ricin toxin.
Category C	Agents that can be engineered for mass dissemination	Nipah virus

---

RECAP

- Infectious diseases continue to be among the leading causes of death worldwide due to the emergence of new infectious diseases, re-emergence of old infectious diseases and persistence of intractable infectious diseases.
- Climatic change, deforestation, etc., are important factors and most of these infections are zoonotic.
- In India, emerging viral infections include influenza, chikungunya, Chandipura, dengue, Japanese encephalitis, SARS coronavirus and CCHF. Emerging bacterial infections include plague, leptospirosis, brucellosis and cholera.
- Surveillance and early control measures help in containment of these infections.
- Zika virus infection is transmitted through the bite of the *Aedes* mosquito (*A. aegypti, A. albopictus*) and is related to dengue, yellow fever and West Nile fever and has been declared as a public health emergency of international concern by WHO in February 2016.

SHORT ANSWER

1. Emerging infections
2. Re-emerging infections in India

72 Recent Advances in Diagnostic Microbiology

INTRODUCTION

Conventional laboratory techniques for diagnosis of infectious diseases, such as culture and related methods, are widely used as they are sensitive and inexpensive, but tend to be labour- and resource-intensive, requiring considerable expertise. They often require further characterisation by molecular techniques to confirm identification.

Molecular methods are useful in situations where conventional methods are slow, insensitive or unavailable.

Advances have been made in decreasing the turnaround time (from specimen collection to the final report reaching the patient) in culture, identification and antibiotic susceptibility testing.

Automated and semi-automated systems: They fall into two main groups:
- Blood culture systems
- Identification and susceptibility testing instruments

Whereas some identification and susceptibility testing instruments take as long as traditional methods, others provide results within a single working day. One of the newer methods to enter the chain is the MALDI-TOF MS (matrix-assisted laser desorption/ionisation–time of flight mass spectrometry). It is a technology for identification of any bacteria or fungi based on the unique protein composition of the bacterial cell. Its advantage is rapid (in minutes) and reliable results.

The most advancement in diagnostic microbiology has been made in the application of molecular techniques.

MOLECULAR METHODS

They can be broadly classified into one of three categories:
- Hybridisation
- Amplification
- Sequencing and enzymatic digestion of nucleic acid

Hybridisation

This is based on the ability of two nucleic acid strands that have complementary base sequences to bind specifically with each other and form a double-stranded molecule or hybrid. The assay requires one nucleic acid strand **(probe)** from an organism of known identity and another **(target)** from an unknown organism.

Hybridisation is detected by the use of a **reporter molecule** that forms a complex with the single-stranded probe DNA. Probes may be labelled with a variety of molecules—radioactive, biotin-avidin and chemiluminescent labels. One of the major advancements of this technique has been in the application of line probe assay for diagnosis of tuberculosis and detection of drug resistance.

Amplification

Polymerase chain reaction (PCR): This is the most widely used target nucleic acid amplification method. It combines the principles of complementary nucleic acid hybridisation and replication.

Conventional PCR involves the following steps:

1. **Extraction and denaturation:** The nucleic acid is first extracted from the organism or clinical sample

by heat, chemical or enzymatic method, and the target nucleic acid is then added and placed in a thermal cycler to undergo amplification.

2. **Annealing:** Short strands of DNA sequences (primers) are selected to specifically hybridise (anneal) to a particular nucleic acid target.

3. **Extension of the primer:** Taq polymerase is the enzyme commonly used for primer extension at a temperature of 72°C. Annealing provides a template that allows DNA polymerase to add nucleotides and produce by extension a sequence that is complementary to the target template.

4. **Detection of PCR products**: The amplification product of PCR (amplicon) contains the target nucleic acid of interest. A labelled probe is used for detecting specific amplicons.

Types of PCR used in diagnostic microbiology

Multiplex PCR: Two or more unique target sequences can be amplified simultaneously. One primer pair is directed at sequences present in all clinically relevant bacteria (**control primer**) and the second is directed at a specific sequence (**test primer**). This is used to detect infectious agents where the exact cause is not known.

Nested PCR: This involves the sequential use of two primer sets. The first set is used for amplification of a target sequence. The second set of primers are used to amplify a particular region within the first target sequence. This gives a more specific test result and is used for specific disease detection. Gene Expert for detecting *M.tuberculosis* and resistance to Rifampin is widely used and has become a mandated test by the Revised National Tuberculosis Program (RNTCP) as a diagnostic tool and for monitoring of drug resistance.

Quantitative PCR: In addition to detection of the agent, the actual number of targets in the clinical sample is detected, for example, detecting viral load in HIV.

Reverse transcriptase PCR (RT-PCR): Conventional PCR amplifies dsDNA, but not RNA. The enzyme reverse transcriptase directs the synthesis of DNA from the viral RNA template. The DNA thus obtained is subjected to routine PCR method. This is used to detect H1N1 virus from nasopharyngeal swab.

Real-time PCR: This combines nucleic acid amplification with qualitative or quantitative measurement of the amplified product. Most molecular detection methods used in clinical microbiology use this technique.

Transcription-mediated amplification (TMA)

This is an isothermal RNA amplification and uses three enzymes: RNase, DNA-dependent RNA polymerase and reverse transcriptase enzymes. The RNA target is converted to cDNA using reverse transcriptase and then RNA copies are synthesised with the help of RNA polymerase.

Nucleic acid sequence-based amplification (NASBA)

This is similar to TMA and is also an isothermal RNA amplification method. The RNA target is converted to cDNA using reverse transcriptase and then RNA copies are synthesised with the help of RNA polymerase.

Ligase chain reaction (LCR)

This reaction is based on the ligation of two adjacent synthetic oligonucleotide primers, which uniquely hybridise to one of the strands of the target DNA. A second pair of oligonucleotides is designed to hybridise to the complementary DNA, in the same region. When the nucleotides are present, the DNA polymerase and the ligase create a gap between the adjacent primers, which will then be filled with the appropriate nucleotides, leading to ligation of the primers. LCR allows the discrimination of DNA sequences differing in only a single base pair. Hence, it is used to differentiate products.

SEQUENCING AND ENZYMATIC DIGESTION OF NUCLEIC ACID

Nucleic acid sequencing: This involves methods that determine the exact nucleotide sequence of a gene or gene fragment of an organism.

High-density DNA probes: This uses hybridisation of a fluorescent-labelled nucleic acid target to a set of oligonucleotides synthesised on a miniature glass substrate or 'chip'.

Methods of typing isolates

Ribotyping: This involves the enzymatic digestion of chromosomal DNA followed by hybridisation using probes that encode ribosomal RNA.

Restriction fragment length polymorphism (RFLP): Restriction enzyme analysis is the process by which enzyme digestion patterns are analysed.

Restriction patterns are obtained after gel electrophoresis, the differences in restriction patterns of microorganism is known as restriction fragment length polymorphism.

Pulsed-field gel electrophoresis (PFGE): Specialised electrophoresis devices are used to separate chromosomal fragments obtained by enzymatic digestion of intact bacterial chromosomal DNA. The DNA is then digested using restriction endonuclease enzymes.

Use of a pulsed electrical field across the agrose gel subjects the DNA fragment to different voltages from varying angles at different time intervals.

Applications

There is increasing application of molecular techniques in diagnostic microbiology.

Diagnosis

- Detection of infectious agents from clinical specimens, CSF and body fluids
- Identification of bacteria, antimicrobial resistance (tuberculosis)
- Diagnosis of infections due to non-cultivable organisms

Epidemiology and disease detection

- Typing of isolates for epidemiological purposes and tracing path of transmission

Research

- Research into understanding genetic makeup of infectious agents
- Drug discovery and newer diagnostics

RECAP

- Advances have been made in microbial detection by automated culture and susceptibility systems.
- Molecular methods are useful in situations where conventional methods are slow, insensitive or unavailable.
- The molecular methods used are hybridisation, amplification and sequencing, and enzymatic digestion of nucleic acids.
- In diagnostic microbiology, PCR, TMA, NASBA and LCR are commonly used for detection of bacteria, fungi and toxins.

ESSAYS

1. Explain the principle and steps of PCR.
2. Enumerate the different types of PCR used in clinical microbiology.

SHORT NOTES

1. Principle of TMA
2. Principle of LCR

Part VII | Clinical Microbiology

73 Bloodstream Infections

INTRODUCTION

Bacteremia indicates the presence of a focus of disease or may represent the transient presence of bacteria in the bloodstream without multiplication. **Septicemia** or sepsis occurs when active bacterial multiplication or bacterial products (toxins) causes harm to the host.

Bacteremia may be transient, continuous or intermittent:

Transient bacteremia may occur spontaneously, with minor events such as brushing of teeth or chewing of food or by procedures like manipulation of infected tissues, instrumentation of contaminated mucosal surfaces and surgery involving non-sterile sites.

Continuous bacteremia is associated with bacterial endocarditis, endovascular infections and septic shock wherein organisms are released into the bloodstream at a fairly constant rate.

Intermittent bacteremia, as seen with the causative agents of meningitis, pneumonia, pyogenic arthritis and osteomyelitis, are often recovered from blood early in the course of these diseases. In case of sequestered focus of infection, such as an abscess, bacteria are released into the blood approximately 45 minutes before a febrile episode.

Clinical presentation

The two main categories of bloodstream infections are **intravascular** (from within the cardiovascular system) and **extravascular** (those entering blood circulation through the lymphatic system from the site of infection).

Signs and symptoms of septicemia include fever or hypothermia, chills, hyperventilation and subsequent respiratory alkalosis. Septic shock is characterised by fever, acute respiratory distress, shock, renal failure and intravascular coagulation and can be initiated by exotoxins or endotoxins.

Pathophysiology of shock

Septic shock is mediated by activated mononuclear cells producing cytokines, such as tumour necrosis factor and interleukins. Gram-negative bacteria release endotoxin, which is a lipopolysaccharide (LPS). The core of LPS, lipid A, mediates systemic response including fever activation of complement and certain clotting factors. Gram-positive bacteria produce exotoxins which generate a similar response.

Etiology

Etiological agents of blood stream infection are listed in Table 73.1.

Table 73.1 *Etiological agents of bloodstream infections*

Bacteria	Virus	Fungi	Parasites
Staphylococcus aureus	HIV	Candida	Plasmodium
Coagulase-negative staphylococci	Epstein-Barr	Cryptococcus	Trypanosoma
B.haemolytic streptococci	Cytomegalovirus	Coccidiodes immitis	Babesia
Enterococcus species		Histoplasma capsulatium	Wuchereria
S.pneumoniae			
Viridans streptococci		Blastomyces dermatitidis	
Salmonella species			Loa loa
Escherichia coli		Mucor species	
Klebsiella pneumoniae		Aspergillus species	
Enterobacter cloacae			
Proteus species			
Pseudomonas species			
Brucella species			

Approach to diagnosis of bloodstream infections

Figure 73.1 provides an approach to the diagnosis of bloodstream infections.

Laboratory diagnosis

Diagnosis depends on the isolation of the causative organism from blood.

Preparation of site: The skin should be prepared with 70% isopropyl alcohol before collecting the blood sample.

Specimen: For infants and small children, 1–5 ml of blood is drawn for culture. In adults, 7–10 ml of blood per culture is recommended. In patients with suspected infective endocarditis, three samples within a 24-hour period are collected (due to intermittent bacteremia). Samples should be collected before antimicrobial therapy is initiated.

Culture: Blood obtained by aseptic venipuncture is inoculated in blood culture media, for example, brain heart infusion (BHI) broth, trypticase soy broth or thioglycolate broth. Incubation is at 37°C for two weeks. Subcultures are made on MacConkey agar, blood agar and chocolate agar after 24 hours, 48 hours, 5th day, 7th day and 14th day of incubation.

The HACEK bacteria, certain fungi and *Brucella* are slow growing and may require incubation for up to two weeks. *Coxiella burnetii* and *Chlamydia* species do not grow in cell-free culture media.

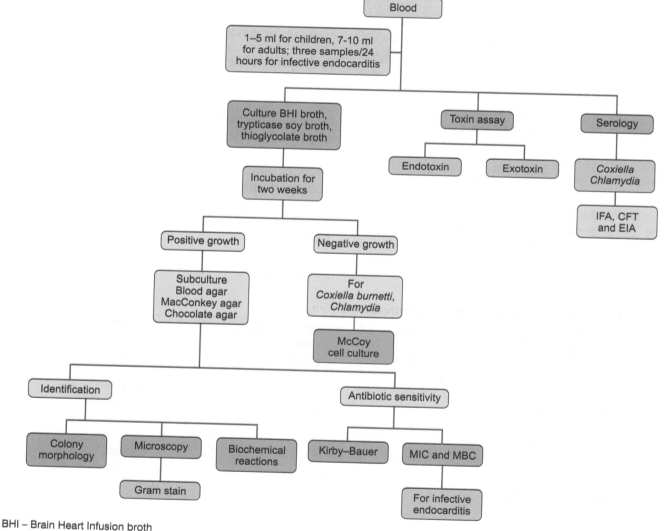

BHI – Brain Heart Infusion broth

Fig. 73.1 Approach to diagnosis of bloodstream infections

Identification: The organism isolated on subculture is further identified by colony morphology, Gram stain and biochemical reactions.

Antibiotic sensitivity test is performed by the Kirby–Bauer disc diffusion method. In addition, it is necessary to determine the minimum inhibitory concentration (MIC) and minimum bactericidal concentration (MBC) as a guide to treatment (adequate dose of antibiotic) in infective endocarditis.

Serology: It is a convenient and commonly used method for identification of *Coxiella burnetii* and *Chlamydia*. The tests available are indirect immunofluorescent antibody (IFA) complement fixation test (CFT) and enzyme immunoassay (EIA)

Other tests:
- Total count – leukocytosis
- Erythrocyte sedimentation rate (ESR) – elevated
- C reactive protein – detectable
- Urine – culture
- Chest X-ray
- Echocardiography for detection of vegetation
- Detection of bacterial endotoxin–limulus lysate test is a sensitive test for the detection of bacterial endotoxin.

74 Respiratory Tract Infections

INTRODUCTION

The respiratory tract is the most common site for infection by pathogenic microorganisms because it is in direct contact with the environment and is continuously exposed to microorganisms suspended in the air. Respiratory tract infections may occur in the nasopharynx, oropharynx, middle ear and paranasal sinuses, epiglottis, larynx, trachea, bronchi, bronchioles and lungs.

UPPER RESPIRATORY TRACT INFECTIONS

Upper respiratory tract infections (URTIs) present commonly as two types: pharyngitis (more common) and tonsillitis.

Clinical presentation

Pharyngitis (sore throat): This is the most common presentation, and usually manifests as high-grade fever. Other features include cervical lymphadenopathy and the presence of exudates on the tonsillar area.

In **diphtheria,** a pseudo-membrane may be present.

In **viral infections,** the main features are runny nose with cough and fever.

Etiology

Etiological agents of respiratory tract infections are listed in Table 74.1.

Approach to diagnosis of upper respiratory tract infections

Figure 74.1 provides an approach to the diagnosis of respiratory tract infections.

Collection and transport of specimens

Collection:

Bacteria: Two throat swabs should be collected: one for direct microscopic examination and another for culture from the tonsillar pillars. If diphtheria is suspected, a part of the membrane must be taken for processing.

Viruses: Nasopharyngeal swabs, aspirates or throat washings are collected. Calcium alginate or Teflon-coated swabs are used.

Serum is collected when streptococcal pharyngitis or infectious mononucleosis is suspected.

Table 74.1   *Etiological agents of respiratory infections*

Bacteria	Virus	Fungi	Parasites
Streptococcus pyogenes	Adenovirus	C.albicans	P.westermani
Corynebacterium diphtheriae	Rhinovirus	Aspergillus species	C.sinensis
Mycoplasma pneumoniae	Influenza virus	C.neoformans	A.lumbricoides
Staphylococcus aureus	Respiratory syncytial virus	H.capsulatum	A.duodenale
Haemophilus influenzae	Parainfluenza virus	B.dermatitidis	
Streptococcus pneumoniae	Epstein Barr virus	C.immitis	
Group B streptococci	Echovirus	P.jirovecii	
Mycobacterium tuberculosis	Measles virus		
Atypical mycobacteria	Varicella zoster virus		
Pseudomonas aeruginosa			
Bordetella pertussis			
Klebsiella species			
Neisseria meningitidis			

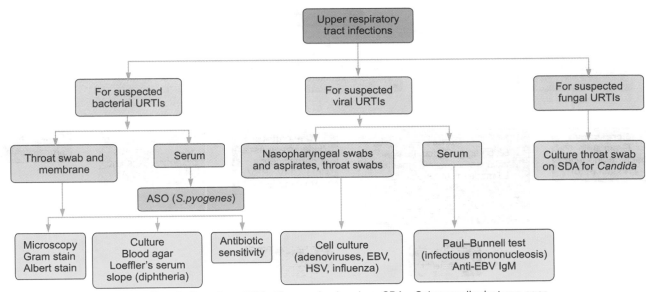

ASO – Antistreptolysin O; EBV – Epstein-Barr virus; HSV – Herpes simplex virus; SDA – Sabouraud's dextrose agar

Fig. 74.1 Approach to diagnosis of upper respiratory tract infections

Laboratory diagnosis

Gram stain: This is used to identify Gram-positive and Gram-negative bacteria.

Albert stain: This is used for metachromatic granules in *C.diphtheriae*.

Culture:

Culture is done on BA (5% sheep BA) and incubated under 5% CO_2 overnight. For diphtheria, culture on Loeffler's serum and potassium tellurite agar is carried out. SDA medium is used for *Candida albicans*. Figure 74.1 provides an approach to the laboratory diagnosis of URTI.

LOWER RESPIRATORY TRACT INFECTIONS

Pneumonia syndromes may present as acute (community-acquired or nosocomial), subacute or chronic (pulmonary tuberculosis, fungal, aspiration pneumonia and lung abscess) diseases and as pneumonia in immunocompromised individuals.

Clinical presentation

In **adult acute community-acquired pneumonia**, the main presenting features are cough, fever and chest pain. **Acute healthcare-associated (nosocomial) pneumonia** tends to occur in comatose patients, and those with left ventricular failure or who have been intubated or anaesthetised, and those who are on the ventilator. In **chronic pneumonia**, the main presenting features are chronic cough, fever, night sweats and weight loss. In **lung abscess**, the main presenting features are chest pain, cough and fever.

Collection and transport of specimens

Sputum is a good sample and easy to collect. If cough is present but not productive, the patient should be asked to first inhale hypertonic saline, which may induce the production of sputum, which is then collected.

If the patient is not able to provide a sputum sample, then an endotracheal aspirate or bronchoalveolar lavage (BAL) sample must be collected from the lower respiratory tract. If the patient is on a ventilator or intubated, a non-bronchoscopic lavage or BAL sample may be collected to diagnose ventilator-associated pneumonia (VAP).

Approach to diagnosis of upper pneumonia

Figure 74.2 provides an approach to the diagnosis of pneumonia.

Laboratory diagnosis

Microscopy

Gram stain: An acceptable specimen is that with <10 squamous epithelial cells per low-power field (100×)

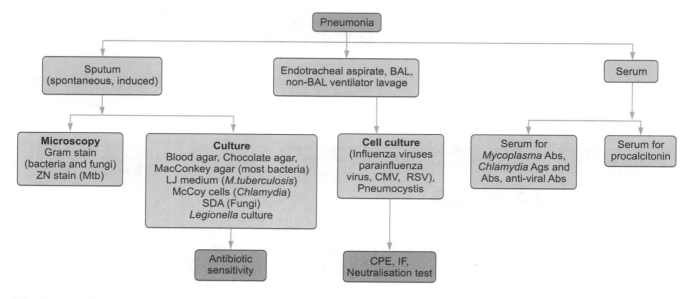

BAL – Bronchoalveolar lavage; CPE – Cytopathic effect; IF – Immunofluorescence

Fig. 74.2 Approach to diagnosis of pneumonia

and the presence of ≥ 25 polymorphonuclear leukocytes per 100× field.

Ziehl–Neelsen stain: Acid fast bacilli (AFB) are suggestive of tuberculosis.

Giemsa stain: This is used for the detection of *P.jirovecii*.

Culture: Culture is done on BA (5% sheep BA) and incubated under 5% CO_2 overnight. For diphtheria, culture on Loeffler's serum and potassium tellurite agar is carried out. SDA medium is used for *Candida albicans*.

Antibiotic sensitivity test: This is done if *S.pneumoniae* is isolated to detect penicillin-resistant *S.pneumoniae*; if *S.aureus* is isolated in healthcare-associated pneumonia (HAP) to detect methicillin-resistant *S.aureus* (MRSA); if *K.pneumoniae* is isolated in HAP to detect extended-spectrum beta-lactamases (ESBLs) which will result in resistance to many antibiotics; and for other organisms isolated in VAP and HAP.

Serology

To make a serological diagnosis of infection by *Mycoplasma pneumoniae*, specific tests using mycoplasmal antigens are very sensitive. If these are not available, the streptococcus MG agglutination test (significant titre ≥ 1:20) or cold agglutination test (significant titre ≥ 1:32) can be performed.

To make a diagnosis of infection due to chlamydiae, tests that detect antigen or antibody can be used:

- **Chlamydial antigens**, particularly lipopolysaccharide antigen, can be detected by microimmunofluorescence (micro-IF) or ELISA tests. Molecular methods are also being increasingly used.
- **Procalcitonin** is another biomarker which is elevated in invasive pneumococcal disease, including pneumonia, and the levels are monitored to determine prognosis and response to treatment.

75 Meningitis

INTRODUCTION

Meningitis is an inflammation of the meninges, the membrane covering the brain and spinal cord. When a microorganism (usually a bacterium or virus) enters the subarachnoid space, there is an inflammatory response in the meninges.

Clinical presentation

Symptoms: Headache, fever and altered sensorium
Signs: Neck rigidity and positive signs for meningism such as Kernig's and Brudinsky's sign; older children and adults develop a stiff neck, usually with fever and headache. Infants and young children may have a high or low body temperature, be irritable or drowsy, or have a poor appetite.

Clinical case presentations of meningitis due to *Streptococcus pneumonia*, *Neisseria meningitidis*, *Bacteroides fragilis* (brain abscess), *Haemophilus influenzae*, *Mycobacterium tuberculosis*, Herpes simplex virus (aseptic meningitis) and poliovirus 1 (aseptic meningitis) have been described earlier.

Etiology

Etiological agents of meningitis are listed in Table 75.1.

Meningitis may be of bacterial origin—pyogenic (caused by pyogenic organisms) and tuberculous (caused by *M.tuberculosis*). Aseptic meningitis is caused by viruses.

Pyogenic meningitis is further classified as that which occurs in neonates, in children, in adults and in the elderly. Aseptic meningitis is categorised according to viral and non-microbial causes.

Approach to diagnosis of meningitis

Figure 75.1 describes the approach to the diagnosis of meningitis.

Table 75.1 *Causes of meningitis*

Bacteria	*Virus (Aseptic meningitis)*	*Fungi*	*Parasites*
Neonates and infants • *E.coli* • Group B Streptococci (*Streptococcus agalactiae*) • *Staphylococcus aureus* • *H.influenzae* • *Streptococcus pneumoniae* • *Klebsiella* species • *Listeria monocytogenes* **Children** • *Haemophilus influenzae* • *Neisseria meningitidis* • *Streptococcus pneumoniae* **Adults** • *Neisseria meningitidis* • *Streptococcus pneumoniae* **Elderly** • *Streptococcus pneumoniae* • *Staphylococcus aureus* • Gram-negative enteric bacilli	• Enteroviruses (ECHO, Coxsackie, Polio) • Paramyxoviruses (Mumps, Measles) • Herpesviruses (Herpes simplex, Varicella zoster) • Adenoviruses • Arboviruses(Flavivirus, Buniyavirus)	• *Cryptococcus neoformans* • *Candida albicans* • *Aspergillus* species • *Histoplasma capsulatum* • *Coccidioides immitis*	• *Entamoeba histolytica* • *Naegleria* • *Acanthamoeba* • *Toxoplasma gondii*

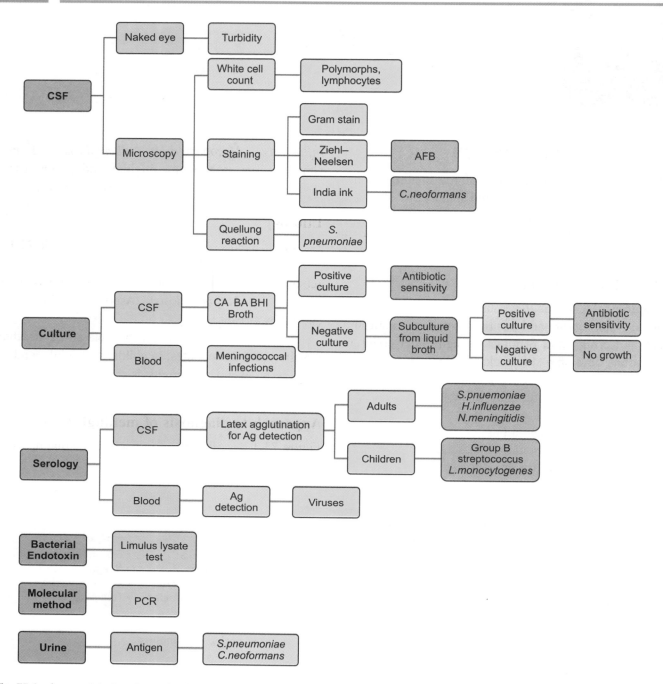

Fig. 75.1   Approach to the diagnosis of meningitis

Collection and transport of specimens

CSF is the most important sample. In addition, it may be necessary to obtain:

- Blood culture (especially in neonates)
- Serum (for viral serology)
- Urine (for antigen detection)

Collection of CSF: CSF is collected in a sterile container by lumbar puncture under aseptic conditions.

It is collected in three sterile containers, one each for cell count, biochemical examination and culture.

Transport of CSF: The CSF must not be refrigerated when bacteriological examination is required; however, for viral isolation, it must be transported on ice. For bacterial culture, it should be transported at room temperature. In case of delay, the CSF sample should be kept in an incubator at 37°C and not in a refrigerator.

Laboratory diagnosis

Tests on CSF:

- **Routine (non-microbiological) tests:** Certain procedures can be performed on the CSF, along with microbiological procedures. These may aid in arriving at an etiological diagnosis. These include the appearance of the CSF, total WBC count and lymphocyte count, and estimation of protein and glucose concentration (Table 75.2).

- **Microscopic examination:**
  - Microscopic examination of a Gram-stained smear of CSF is done to detect the presence of microorganisms. If organisms are not detected, an attempt can be made to demonstrate bacterial antigens by latex agglutination test on the CSF sample or in blood.
  - Microscopic examination of a Ziehl–Neelsen-stained smear is performed to demonstrate tubercle bacilli; if negative, polymerase chain reaction for detection of *M.tuberculosis* DNA can be done.
  - Microscopic examination of an India ink preparation of the CSF is done to demonstrate capsulated budding yeast cells of *Cryptococcus neoformans*.

- **Bacterial culture:** Chocolate and blood agar are used. The specimen is also inoculated into an enriched liquid medium such as BHI broth since the specimen is likely to contain only small numbers of bacteria which may not grow on solid culture media. After overnight incubation of the liquid culture medium, subcultures can be made from the liquid broth in solid culture media. If there is growth of bacteria in culture, an **antibiotic sensitivity** test is performed.

Blood culture: This is important when a meningococcal infection is suspected.

Fungal culture is done on Sabouraud's dextrose agar or brain heart infusion agar. Two sets of media are inoculated and incubated at 25°C and 37°C, growth is identified by its morphology. Bird seed agar is used for culture of Cryptococcus species.

Viral culture is done using tissue culture, egg inoculation or animal inoculation.

Serology:

Latex agglutination tests for antigen detection: This can be done for *S.pneumoniae*, *H.influenzae* and *N.meningitidis*. In neonates, the test for antigens of group B streptococcus (*S.agalactiae*) and *Listeria monocytogenes* may also be performed.

Serological tests for antibodies to different viruses: This will be done for viruses depending on the clinical diagnosis.

Tests to detect microbial antigen in urine: Tests are available to detect *S.pneumoniae* antigen (immunochromatography-based) and *Cryptococcus neoformans* antigen (latex agglutination-based) in urine.

Detection of bacterial endotoxin: The **limulus lysate test** is extremely sensitive for the detection of bacterial endotoxin. The principle of the test is based on coagulation of horse shoe crab (*Limulus polyphemus*) amebocytes (blood cells) with blood containing endotoxin.

Molecular methods:

To detect microbial nucleic acid: For suspected infections due to *M.tuberculosis* and viral infections, PCR-based tests are increasingly being used.

To detect microbial nucleic acid in blood: PCR-based tests can also be done on blood samples if CSF-based tests do not yield results.

Table 75.2 *Interpretation of abnormal results*

	White cell count		Biochemistry	
	Neutrophils (× 10⁶/L)	**Lymphocytes (× 10⁶/L)**	**Protein (g/L)**	**Glucose (CSF:blood ratio)**
Normal	0	≤ 5	< 0.4	≥ 0.6 (or ≥ 2.5 mmol/L) (>1 month of age)
Normal neonate	0*	< 20	< 1.0	≥ 0.6 (or ≥ 2.5 mmol/L)
Bacterial meningitis	100–10,000 (but may be normal)	Usually < 100	> 1.0 (but may be normal)	< 0.4 (but may be normal)
Viral meningitis	Usually <100 (but may be normal)	10–1000 (but may be normal)	0.4–1	Usually normal
TB meningitis	Usually <100 (but may be normal)	50–1000 (but may be normal)	1–5 (but may be normal)	< 0.3

* Some studies have found up to 5% of white cells in neonates without meningitis comprise neutrophils

76 Urinary Tract Infections

INTRODUCTION

The urinary tract, from the calyces of the kidneys to the urethra, is lined with a sheet of epithelium that is continuous with that of the skin. Although the flow of urine and the sloughing of these epithelial cells serve to protect the urinary tract from infection, microorganisms, particularly bacteria, may enter the urinary tract through the potential pathway of the epithelial surface to cause infection. Urinary tract infections (UTIs) are an important cause of illness in humans.

While all portions of the urinary tract may be affected, the most common UTIs are those of the bladder (cystitis) and the renal pelvis or the kidneys (pyelonephritis).

Types of UTI

Infections of the urinary tract can be anatomically classified as:
- **Upper UTI** – involves the kidney or ureter
  Acute pyelitis – infection of the pelvis of the kidney
  Acute pyelonephritis – infection of the parenchyma of the kidney
- **Lower UTI** – involves infection from the urinary bladder downwards
  Urethritis – infection of the urethra
  Cystitis – infection of the urinary bladder
  Prostatitis – infection of the prostate

Predisposing factors

Age: Incidence increases with age.

Sex: Sexually active females are more prone to UTI due to the short urethra, proximity to the anus and urethral trauma during intercourse.

Pregnancy: Dilatation of ureters and renal pelvis, stasis, incompetence of the vesico-urethral valves and hormonal changes.

Structural and functional abnormality of the urinary tract:
- Obstruction due to urethral stricture, calculus, prostatic hypertrophy and tumour
- Neurogenic bladder
- Vesico-urethral reflux
- Genital prolapse

Metabolic: Diabetes mellitus

Intervention: Instrumentation including catheterisation and any surgical procedure.

Bacterial virulence: Pili and adherence to uroepithelium

Clinical presentation

Asymptomatic bacteriuria: About 5–7% of pregnant women have been reported to have urinary infection without any symptoms. Such asymptomatic bacteriuria, undetected and untreated, may lead to symptomatic infection later in pregnancy, pyelonephritis and hypertension in the pregnant women, as well as to prematurity and perinatal death of the fetus.

Symptomatic UTI: The common symptoms include urgency, frequency of micturition, associated with discomfort or pain. Pyelonephritis is characterised by loin pain, tenderness, high fever and rigour.

Common presentation of cystitis or lower UTI is dysuria, fever with chills and frequency. In upper UTI (pyelitis or pyelonephritis), patients present with fever and flank pain.

Etiology

Etiological agents of urinary tract infection are listed in Table 76.1.

Laboratory diagnosis

Quantitative cultures are necessary for the diagnosis of urinary tract infection as it differentiates between infection, colonisation and contamination.

Collection and transport of specimens

Figure 76.1 summarises the different types of urine samples that can be collected.

Collection:

Midstream urine (MSU): A midstream urine sample is appropriate for bacterial culture. The patient should

Table 76.1 *Etiological agents of urinary tract infection*

Bacteria	Virus	Fungi	Parasites
Gram-negative bacilli	Adenovirus	Candida albicans	Trichomonas vaginalis
• E.coli			
• Proteus species			
• Klebsiella			
• Enterobacter			
• Pseudomonas			
Gram-positive cocci			Schistosoma haematobium
• Staphylococcus aureus			
• Staphylococcus epidermidis			
• Staphylococcus saprophyticus			
• Enterococcus species			
Others			Enterobius vermicularis
• Mycobacterium tuberculosis			
• Gardnerella vaginalis			

Note: Some organisms can be recovered in the urine, without causing UTI, during the course of a systemic infection, e.g., *Salmonella typhi* in the second week of enteric fever or *N.gonorrhoeae* in gonococcal urethritis.

be provided with a wide-mouthed, screwcapped, leak-proof, sterile universal container. It is important to give instructions for proper collection. The patient is advised to clean the area and to void the first part of the urine into the toilet, then to collect the 'midstream' urine in the container, and finally to void the last part into the toilet.

Catheter sample urine (CSU): If the patient has been catheterised, the sample is collected as follows: The area over the catheter is first cleaned with alcohol, after donning clean gloves. Then, with the help of a sterile syringe and needle, the urine sample is drawn and put into the universal container. At no time should the urine be collected from the uro-bag or by opening the connecting draining tube.

Suprapubic aspirate: If the sample for culture is from an infant, a suprapubic aspirate is collected with a sterile syringe and needle under aseptic precautions by puncturing the suprapubic area.

Early morning urine (EMU): If renal tuberculosis has to be investigated, three urine samples are collected on consecutive days. The entire first-morning urine sample is collected.

If pyelonephritis or upper urinary tract infection is suspected, a blood culture is also required. If the site and side of the kidneys must be identified then an invasive sample collected with a catheter from each ureter is required.

Transport: The sample must be transported at room temperature within half an hour, or refrigerated at 4°C for up to four hours. Beyond this time, such a sample

should not be processed for bacterial culture. For the interpretation of the results, quantitative cultures need to be done. Since urine is a good culture medium, there may be multiplication of contaminating bacteria if the sample is kept outside for a long period, thus increasing bacterial counts and leading to a false positive result.

If the sample is from a patient who has no immediate access to a healthcare facility, and transport to the facility would exceed four hours, a special container with 1.8% boric acid is provided. Urine is collected as described above and this can be kept for up to 24 hours.

Approach to diagnosis of urinary tract infection

Figure 76.2 describes the approach to the diagnosis of urinary tract infection.

Microscopy: An uncentrifuged sample is examined by direct microscopy for pus cells and bacteria.

Screening: Because urinary tract infection is such a common problem and bacteriological facilities are not always available, several screening techniques have been introduced for the presumptive diagnosis of significant bacteriuria:

- **Griess nitrite test:** Based on the absence of nitrite in normal urine. The presence of nitrite indicates the presence of nitrite reducing bacteria in urine.
- **Catalase test:** The presence of catalase as evidenced by frothing on addition of hydrogen peroxide indicates bacteriuria, though a positive result is obtained in hematuria also.

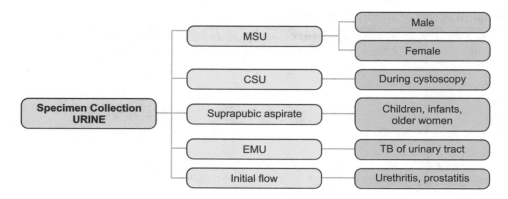

MSU – Midstream urine; CSU – Catheter specimen of urine; EMU – Early morning urine

Fig. 76.1   Types of urine samples to be collected

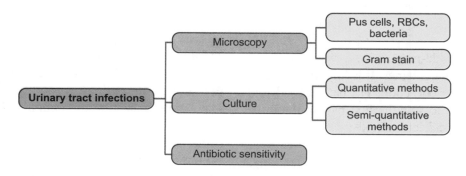

Fig. 76.2   Approach to diagnosis of urinary tract infections

- **Triphenyltetrazoliun chloride (TTC) test:** This is based on the production of a pink red precipitate in the reagent caused by respiratory activity of growing bacteria.
- **Gram stain:** Microscopic demonstration of bacteria in Gram-stained films of urine.
- **Glucose test paper:** This is based on the utilisation of minute amounts of glucose present in normal urine by bacteria causing infection.
- **Dip slide culture:** Agar-coated slides are immersed in urine or even exposed to the stream of urine during voiding, incubated and the growth estimated by colony counting or by colour change of indicator.
  None of the screening methods is as sensitive or reliable as culture.

Culture: Semi-quantitative cultures are done on blood agar and MacConkey agar with a calibrated loop. Colony count of 10^5/ml is considered significant. Counts between 10^4/ml and 10^5/ml are of doubtful significance. Counts less than this are considered significant if:

- The patient is on prior antibiotics
- There is obstruction in the urinary tract
- A fungal infection is present
- If pyelonephritis is present
- If the specimen has been collected by suprapubic aspiration

If ≥ 3 types of organisms are grown, these are considered as contaminants, which may have been introduced into the urine sample from the perineal region or skin or external urethral meatus due to improper collection.

Antibiotic sensitivity testing: If culture is suggestive of infection, an antibiotic sensitivity test is done. If a rapid report is needed and direct microscopy suggests significant pyuria, a primary susceptibility test with the urine specimen itself is done to permit initiation of early specific antibiotic treatment. This must be further confirmed by an antibiotic sensitivity test using the bacterium that is recovered in culture.

Sexually Transmitted Infections

INTRODUCTION

Sexually transmitted infections (STIs) are a group of contagious conditions transmitted predominantly or entirely by sexual or close body contact.

Clinical presentation

Sexually transmitted diseases may present in the following ways:

Vaginal discharge, which may be:

- profuse watery discharge, as in **bacterial vaginosis**;
- thick white discharge, as in **candidosis**; or
- frothy discharge, as in **trichomoniasis**.

Cervical/urethral discharge (sometimes vaginal discharge). This is due to *Neisseria gonorrhoeae* or *Chlamydia trachomatis*.

Genital ulcer: This is caused by Herpes simplex virus types 1 and 2 (lesion is called 'genital herpes'), *Treponema pallidum* ('chancre'), *Haemophilus ducreyi* ('chancroid'), certain serotypes of *Chlamydia trachomatis* ('lymphogranuloma venereum') and *Klebsiella granulomatis*, formerly called *Donovania granulomatis* and *Calymmatobacterium granulomatis* ('granuloma inguinale').

The main presenting features are ulceration, pain and lymphadenopathy.

In **chancre,** a single ulcer is the usual presentation, and is indurated (hard), painless and not tender, with moderate lymph node swelling and no bubo.

In **genital herpes**, multiple, non-indurated, painful and markedly tender ulcers are seen with moderate-to-no lymph node swelling and no bubo.

In **chancroid,** single (or multiple), non-indurated (soft), painful and markedly tender ulcer (or ulcers) occur, with marked lymph node swelling and bubo formation.

Pelvic inflammatory disease: The main presenting features are lower abdominal pain, vaginal discharge and fever. *N.gonorrhoeae* and *C.trachomatis* are the principal pathogens.

Etiology

Etiological agents or sexually transmitted infections are listed in Table 77.1.

Approach to diagnosis of suspected sexually transmitted infections

Figure 77.1 provides an approach to the diagnosis of suspected sexually transmitted disease.

Collection and transport of specimens

Specimen:

Discharge from the infected area: When the vaginal, cervical or urethral discharge is profuse, it can be collected in a sterile container.

Swabs: When the discharge from the infected area is scanty or very thick, it is collected with a sterile swab or endocervical curette from the base and edges of the ulcer.

Fluid from genital vesicles: Sterile capillary tubes are used to collect material from incised genital vesicles.

Blood: This is collected for serological tests and for culture (in suspected gonococcal bacteremia).

Table 77.1 *Etiology of sexually transmitted infections (STIs)*

Bacteria	Virus	Fungi	Parasites
T.pallidum	Herpes simplex virus	Candida albicans	T.vaginalis
N.gonorrhoeae	Cytomegalovirus		
Chlamydia trachomatis	Human papilloma virus		
Gardnerella vaginalis	Human immunodeficiency virus		
Haemophilus ducreyi	Hepatitis B virus		
Klebsiella granulomatis	Molluscum contagiosum		

Transport: The causative organisms are delicate and do not remain viable for long outside the body. Immediate transport to the laboratory and inoculation is necessary. The transport medium used is modified Stuart's medium.

Laboratory diagnosis

Microscopy:

- A wet mount is made of a vaginal discharge:
  - In **trichomoniasis**, pus cells and motile trophozoites of *Trichomonas vaginalis* are seen.
  - In **candidosis**, yeast cells and pseudohyphae of *Candida albicans* are noted.
- A Gram-stained smear is made of the discharge or swabs from a genital ulcer:

- By examining a Gram-stained smear of vaginal discharge, a diagnosis of bacterial vaginosis can be made based on the Nugent score, which takes into consideration the decreased number of lactobacilli (normal flora), increased number of Gram-variable pleomorphic coccobacilli (suggestive of *Gardnerella vaginalis*) and the presence of curved Gram-negative bacilli (suggestive of *Mobiluncus*).

- 'Clue cells' are vaginal epithelial cells with adherent bacteria (*G.vaginalis*), that cause a stippled appearance; the presence of such cells and absence of pus cell suggests a diagnosis of bacterial vaginosis.

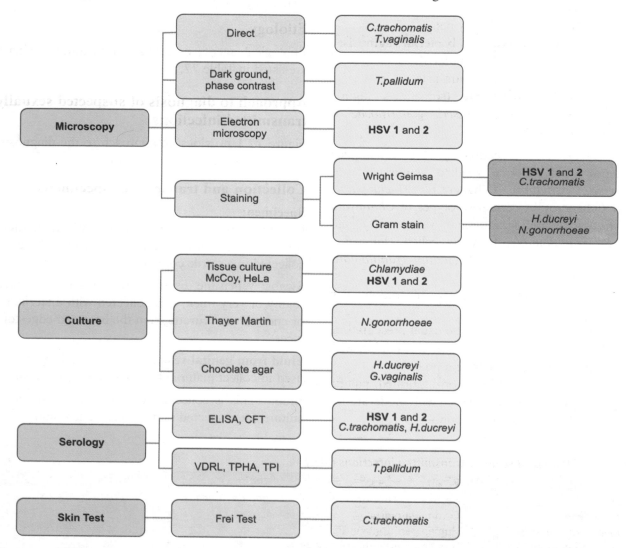

VDRL – Venereal Disease Research Laboratory test; TPHA – T.pallidum Hemagglutination Assay; TPI – T.pallidum Immobilisation test

Fig. 77.1   Approach to diagnosis of sexually transmitted infections

- In gonorrhoea in women, numerous polymorphs and Gram-negative intracellular diplococci are seen in the cervical/urethral discharge, and sometimes in the vaginal discharge.
- In chancroid due to *Haemophilus ducreyi*, Gram-negative coccobacilli are seen in pairs.
- Gram-positive budding yeast cells can be seen in vaginal infection due to *Candida albicans*.

- **Giemsa-stain**: *Klebsiella granulomatis* (the cause of granuloma inguinale) is usually demonstrated in Giemsa-stained direct smears of material from lesions on the genitalia, in the groin and on the perineum; the coccoid rod-shaped organisms are found within histiocytes and giant cells.
- **Dark ground microscopy**: In suspected primary or secondary syphilis, dark ground microscopy is performed on preparations of material from the chancre (primary syphilis) or from mucous membranes (secondary syphilis) to demonstrate spirochetes.

Culture: This is done to isolate some of the organisms listed above:

- Irradiated McCoy cells are used to isolate Chlamydiae.
- Thayer Martin medium, among others, is used to isolate *N.gonorrhoeae*.
- Chocolate agar is used to isolate *H.ducreyi* and *G.vaginalis*.
- Cell culture is done for herpes simplex viruses types 1 and 2.
- Sabouraud dextrose agar is used for *Candida albicans*.
- *K.granulomatis* is difficult to cultivate.

Serology:
Blood and serum samples
- Blood may be taken for culture during suspected gonococcal bacteremia.
- Serum samples are used for serological tests to establish the diagnosis of syphilis (VDRL, TPHA, TPI), chlamydial infection (CFT) and genital herpes infections (ELISA).

Skin test: The Frei test may be used as a diagnostic aid for lymphogranuloma venereum.

78 Diarrhea and Food Poisoning

INTRODUCTION

Acute diarrhea with or without vomiting is the predominant symptom of infective gastroenteritis. The pathogenic mechanisms of gastroenteritis are given in Table 78.1. **Diarrhea** is an increase in fluid frequency or volume of bowel movement relative to the usual habit of the individual.

Dysentery is the presence of blood and mucus in stool, often with tenesmus.

Food poisoning is an acute manifestation of diarrhea or vomiting caused by toxins produced by microorganisms.

Clinical presentation

Small intestinal pathology—manifests as large voluminous watery stools (enteritis), without pus or blood (unaided eye and microscopy).

Large intestinal pathology—usually manifests as frequent, small-volume stools with pus and/or blood (unaided eye and microscopy).

Etiology

Etiological agents responsible of infective diarrheas are listed in Table 78.2.

Approach to diagnosis of infective diarrheas

Figure 78.1 provides an approach to the diagnosis of infective diarrheas.

Laboratory diagnosis

Collection: A sterile screw-capped wide-mouthed container is used to collect feces for culture. If collection of feces is not possible, a rectal swab can be submitted. For an outbreak of food poisoning, the food implicated and the vomitus of the patient is collected along with the feces sample.

Transport: Fresh feces are ideal, but a transport medium such as Cary–Blair or Venkatraman–Ramakrishnan is used if a delay in transport to the laboratory is anticipated. For *Vibrio cholerae*, alternatively, alkaline peptone water, which also serves as an enrichment medium, can be used for transport.

Microscopy:

Wet preparation: Microscopy of feces is done to detect pus cells and RBCs, motility of the organism and ova or cyst of parasites.

Table 78.1 *Pathogenic mechanism of gastroenteritis*

| | Toxins | | |
	Enterotoxins	*Cytotoxins*	*Neurotoxins*
Pathogenesis	Cause outpouring of electrolytes and fluid into the lumen of intestine, resulting in profuse watery diarrhea	Disrupt the intestinal epithelium, leaving raw, unprotected mucosa. The resulting inflammatory response causes neutrophils and blood to be shed in stool.	Result of ingesting toxins produced by microorganisms.
Disease	Diarrhea	Dysentery	Food poisoning or intoxication
Organisms	*V.cholerae* Non-cholera vibrios Enterotoxigenic *E.coli* *Salmonella* species *Campylobacter jejuni* *Clostridium perfringens* *Clostridium difficile* *Bacillus cereus* *Giardia lamblia*	*Shigella dysenteriae* Enterohemorrhagic *E.coli* *Clostridium difficile* *Staphylococcus aureus* *Clostridium perfringens* *Entamoeba histolytica*	*Staphylococcus aureus* *Bacillus cereus* *Clostridium perfringens* *Clostridium botulinum*

Table 78.2 *Etiology of infective diarrhea*

Bacteria	Virus	Fungi	Parasites
Vibrio cholerae	Rotavirus	Candida albicans	*E.hislolytica*
Non-cholera vibrio	Norwalk virus		*G.lamblia*
E.coli (ETEC, EIEC)	Adenovirus		*B.coli*
(EPEC, EHEC)	Calcivirus		*Cryptosporidium* species
	Coronavirus		*Isospora belli*
	Astrovirus		*F.hepatica*
Salmonella species	Enterovirus		*T.saginata*
Shigella species			*T.solium*
C.botulinum			*H.nana*
C.difficile			*T.trichiura*
Staphylococcus aureus			*A.duodenale*
Campylobacter species			
Yersinia enterocolitica			

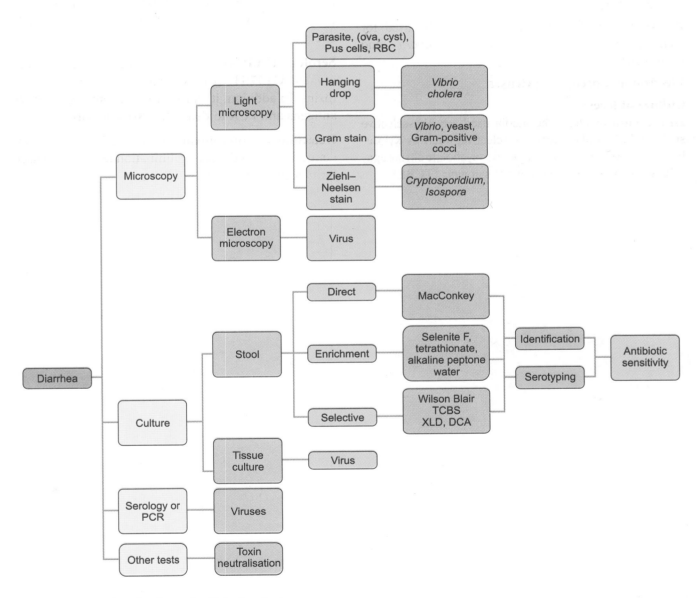

Fig. 78.1   Approach to the diagnosis of infective diarrheas.

Saline and iodine preparation: Microscopy of a wet preparation of feces is also done to detect helminth ova, protozoan cysts and protozoan trophozoites.

Hanging drop preparation: This is used to detect darting motility, which can suggest the presence of *Vibrio cholerae* in a given sample. If specific 01 antiserum is available, inhibition of motility by adding this can lead to a specific diagnosis.

Gram-stained smear: This is only helpful in certain situations as feces contain many bacteria in a healthy person. Such situations include:

- Presence of curved bacilli suggestive of *Vibrio*
- Presence of yeasts in an immunocompromised host or an infant

ZN stain: Modified acid fast stain can be used for identification of *Cryptosporodium*, *Isospora* and *Cyclospora*.

Electron microscopy for viruses

Culture of feces:

Direct culture: Here, the media used are non-selective such as MacConkey agar, or selective, such as xylose-lysine-deoxycholate (XLD) agar, deoxycholate citrate agar (DCA) or thiosulphate citrate bile salt agar (TCBS).

Enrichment culture: Fresh feces are introduced into a liquid culture medium. For example, selenite F broth, tetrathionate broth (incubated for 12–18 hours) or alkaline peptine water (6–8 hours). Following this, a subculture is made on the solid culture medium used for direct plating. By this method, if the sample contains only a small number of pathogens, the enrichment medium allows selective growth of the pathogen, which then becomes easier to isolate.

The organism is identified by **biochemical test** and **serotyping**.

Antibiotic sensitivity test is carried out.

Tissue culture is used for culture of viruses. ETEC penetrate HeLa and HEp-2 cells in culture. EHEC Verotoxin (VT) can be detected by cytotoxic effect on Vero cells.

Serology (ELISA): ELISA is used for the detection of *E.coli* O157:H7 (EHEC), Shiga toxin and *C.difficile* toxins. In addition, it can be used to detect rotaviruses antigens and PCR to detect the Norwalk virus.

Detection of enterotoxin: Immunodiffusion, ELISA, neutralisation and latex agglutination tests can be used for detection of toxins.

79 Skin and Soft Tissue Infections

INTRODUCTION

Skin infections can arise from the invasion of organisms from the external environment through breaks in skin or from organisms that reach the skin through the blood as a part of a systemic disease.

Infections of the subcutaneous tissue may manifest as:

Necrotising fasciitis, that is, infection of the fascia overlying the muscle with involvement of overlying soft tissue caused by group A streptococci, *S.aureus*, and *Bacteroides* and *Clostridium* species.

Progressive bacterial synergistic gangrene, which is usually a postoperative complication to thoracic or abdominal surgery, caused by *S.aureus*, *Proteus* and anaerobic streptococci.

Myositis, which may vary from necrosis of muscle to necrotising cutaneous myositis or anaerobic myonecrosis.

Etiology

Etiological agents of infections of the skin, subcutaneous tissue and wounds are given in Tables 79.1 to 79.4.

Approach to diagnosis of skin and soft tissue infections

Figure 79.1 provides an approach to the diagnosis of skin and soft tissue infections.

Laboratory diagnosis

Specimen:
- Pus from the wound, collected by:
  - Incision and drainage
  - Needle aspiration
  - Sterile swab
- Vesicle fluid, collected by:
  - Needle aspiration
  - Sterile swab
- Dermatophyte infection:
  - Scrapings from the active border of the lesion
- Erysipeloid:
  - Skin biopsy
- Subcutaneous infection:
  - Sample collected from the base of the lesion
  - Surgical biopsy of deep tissues

Microscopy: Gram stain is routinely performed on all samples. KOH mount is done for suspected dermatophyte infection. Tzank smear is carried out for infection from vesicle fluid for detection of herpes simplex virus and varizella zoster virus.

Culture: For aerobic bacteria, culture specimen are inoculated onto MacConkey agar, blood agar and chocolate agar. For atypical mycobacteria, LJ medium and blood agar are inoculated. For anaerobic culture,

Table 79.1   *Etiology of infection of the epidermis and dermis*

Bacteria	Virus	Fungi	Parasites
Streptococcus pyogenes (Erysipelas) (Impetigo) (Cellulitis)	Herpes zoster Varicella zoster Herpes simplex	Dermatophytes Sporothrix schenckii	Cutaneous larva migrans (A.braziliensis)
Staphylococcus aureus (Impetigo) (Cellulitis) (Furuncle)			
Corynebacterium minutissimum (Erythrasma)			

Table 79.2   *Etiology of infections of subcutaneous tissue*

Bacteria	Fungi	Parasites
Clostridium perfringens	M.mycetomatis	Trichivella
Clostridium novyi	M.grisea	Taenia solium
Clostridium septicum	Candida species	W.bancrofti
Bacillus species		D.medinensis
Bacteroides species		
Peptostreptococcus species		
Staphylococcus aureus		
Group A streptococci		

Table 79.3   *Etiology of post-operative wound infections*

Bacteria	Fungi
• S.aureus	Candida species
• Coagulase-negative staphylococci	
• Streptococcus pyogenes	
• Proteus species	
• Pseudomonas species	
• Bacteroides species	
• Prevotella species	

Table 79.4   *Etiology of burn wounds*

Bacteria	Fungi
S.epidermidis	Candida species
Enterobacteriacea	Aspergillus species
Pseudomonas species	
Proteus species	
Bacteroides species	

thioglycollate broth and Robertson's cooked meat medium are inoculated and incubated in Gaspak or anaerobic jar. For fungal culture, Sabouraud's dextrose agar is used with and without cycloheximide.

Identification: This is done by colony morphology, Gram/ZN stain and biochemical reactions. **Antibiotic sensitivity** test is performed by the Kirby–Bauer disc diffusion method.

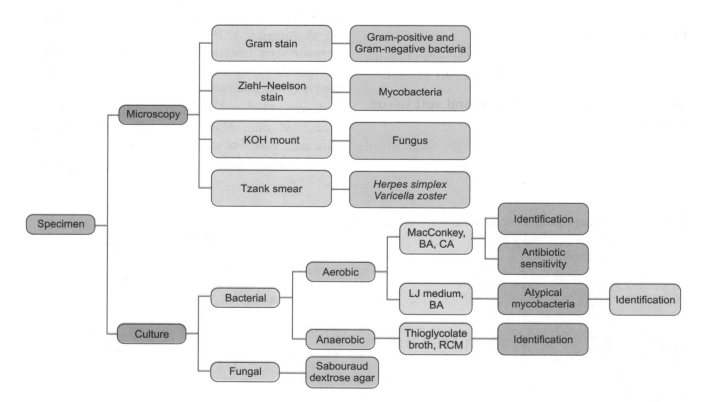

Fig. 79.1   Approach to the diagnosis of skin and soft tissue infections

80 Pyrexia of Unknown Origin

INTRODUCTION

Pyrexia of unknown origin (PUO) is defined as temperature above 38°C for more than three weeks and without diagnosis even after one week of investigations. PUO can be due to infectious or non-infectious causes (Tables 80.1 and 80.2).

Clinical presentation

Classic PUO: The patient exhibits temperature > 38.3°C (101°F) on several occasions, has had the illness for more than three weeks and a diagnosis has not been established despite a week of inpatient investigation.

Nosocomial PUO: In addition to temperature > 38.3°C, the patient has been hospitalised ≥ 24 hours but had no fever or was not incubating a fever on admission, and has undergone evaluation for at least three days.

Immune-deficient PUO: In addition to temperature > 38.3°C and evaluation for at least three days, the patient has a neutrophil count ≤ 500 per mm³.

HIV-associated PUO: In addition to temperature > 38.3°C and evaluation for at least three days, the patient has had the fever for > 4 weeks (outpatient) and > 3 days (inpatient), and HIV infection has been confirmed.

Etiology

Etiological agents of infections of PUO are given in Tables 80.1 and 80.2.

Approach to diagnosis of PUO

Figure 80.1 provides an approach to the diagnosis of PUO due to infectious and non-infectious causes.

Collection of specimens

Prior to specimen collection, a complete clinical history (including details of travel, immunisation, exposure to diseases) should be obtained, followed by a detailed physical examination; information from the history and examination may influence the choice of specimens taken for processing.

Table 80.1 *Etiology of pyrexia of unknown origin (PUO) – infectious causes*

Bacterial	Viral	Fungal	Parasitic
M.tuberculosis	Cytomegalovirus	Candida albicans	
Salmonella spp	Epstein – Barr virus	Cryptococcus neoformans	Plasmodium spp
Brucella spp	Arboviruses	Histoplasma capsulatum	Leishmania spp
Chlamydia psittaci	Enteroviruses	Aspergillus spp	Trypanosoma spp
Leptospira spp	HIV	Coccidiodes immitis	Toxoplasma gondii
Rickettsia spp			Wuchereria bancrofti
Coxiella burnetti			Brugia malayi
Mycoplasma spp			
Atypical mycobacteria			

Table 80.2 *Etiology of pyrexia of unknown origin (PUO) – noninfectious causes*

Neoplasms	Connective tissue disorder	Granulomatous diseases
Lymphoma	Systemic lupus erythematosus (SLE)	Crohn's disease
Leukaemia	Polyarteritis nodosa	Sarcoidosis
Myeloma		Rheumatoid arthritis
Renal cancer		Polymyositis
Colon cancer		
Liver cancer		
Metabolic disorder		
Gout		
Porphyria		

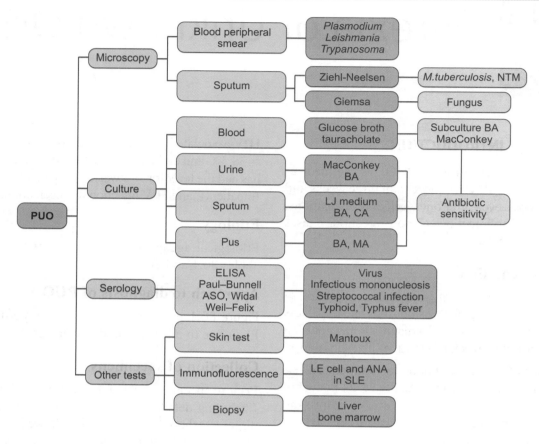

Fig. 80.1 Approach to the diagnosis of PUO due to infectious and non-infectious causes

Blood: For complete blood counts (CBCs), erythrocyte sedimentation rate (ESR), microscopy (wet films and Leishman-stained smears), culture and serological tests.

Urine: For urinalysis and culture

Bone marrow: For biopsy and culture

Material from abnormal tissues, endoscopy, temporal artery, lung and abdominal viscera are used for biopsy.

Diagnostic procedures

Tests that may suggest or confirm that an infection is the cause of PUO

CBCs and erythrocyte sedimentation rate: For example, neutrophilic leucocytosis in CBC may suggest a pyogenic infection; markedly elevated ESR may suggest a tuberculous etiology.

Microscopy of blood: For example, a wet film may demonstrate microfilariae or trypanosomes; a stained smear may demonstrate malarial parasites, trypanosomes and Microfilariae.

Culture of blood: For example, for enteric (salmonella) or other pathogens (organisms causing infective endocarditis).

Serological tests:

- ELISA for diagnosis of **viral diseases** (for example, HIV, cytomegalovirus [CMV] or Epstein Barr virus [EBV] infections)
- CFT for certain **bacterial diseases** (lymphogranuloma venereum [*C.trachomatis* serotypes L1-L3], psittacosis [*C.psittaci*], tularaemia [*Francisella tularensis*], Q fever [*Coxiella burnettii*])
- ASO titre for rheumatic fever
- SAT for brucellosis [*Brucella* species]
- Weil–Felix for rickettsia
- Paul–Bunnell for infectious mononucleosis
- Widal test for typhoid fever
- RA factor for rheumatoid arthritis

Microscopy:

- Wet mount, for Entamoeba (liver abscess)
- Gram stain, for Gram-negative bacilli, Brucella species
- Ziehl–Neelsen stain, for Mycobacterium species
- Giemsa stain, for fungus

Culture:

- Urine for pyogenic bacteria, or tubercle bacilli
- Bone marrow for fungus

Antibiotic sensitivity test is performed for all bacterial isolates.

Chest X-ray may demonstrate the presence of pulmonary tuberculosis.

Echocardiography may demonstrate findings indicative of rheumatic fever or infective endocarditis.

Skin tests: Delayed hypersensitivity reactions may suggest that the PUO is due to tuberculosis (Mantoux skin test) or a fungal infection (for example, the histoplasmin skin test for histoplasmosis).

Tests that may suggest or confirm other (non-infective) causes for the PUO.

Serological tests that detect, for example, antinuclear antibody or anti-DNA antibody (suggestive of SLE), anti-thyroglobulin antibody (suggestive of subacute thryoiditis) or tests to detect other collagen vascular diseases.

Imaging studies such as chest X-rays, echocardiograms, upper and lower gastrointestinal tract barium studies, CT and MRI scans, intravenous urograms, and scans of lung, bone and other tissues to detect neoplastic processes or collagen vascular diseases.

Biopsies of, for example, bone marrow (to detect leukemia), lymphoid tissue (Hodgkin's disease), gastrointestinal tract structures by endoscopy, temporal artery, lung and other tissues to detect neoplastic processes.

81 Zoonoses

INTRODUCTION

Zoonoses are diseases and infections of animals; their causative agents are transmitted between animals and humans.

Etiology

Zoonotic diseases commonly occur in individuals who handle animals/animal products. The most common zoonotic diseases are listed in Table 81.1.

Table 81.1 *Common zoonotic diseases*

Bacteria	Rickettsia	Virus	Parasite	Fungus
Anthrax Plague	Scrub typhus	Rabies	Taeniasis	
Brucellosis	Murine typhus	Yellow fever	Echinococcosis	Zoophilic dermatophytes
Leptospirosis	Tick typhus	Japanese encephalitis	Leishmaniasis	
Salmonellosis	Q fever	KFD	Toxoplasmosis	
		Chikungunya		

Table 81.2 *Laboratory procedures for bacterial zoonoses*

Disease	Sample	Microscopy	Culture	Serology	Others
Cutaneous anthrax	Fluid from eschar	Gram-positive bacilli (bamboo stick appearance)	Nutrient agar (Medusa head)	Ascoli's thermoprecipitin test CFT	Lysis by gammaphage
Pulmonary anthrax	Sputum Stool		Blood agar (string of pearls)	ELISA	Direct fluorescent antibody test
Intestinal anthrax		McFadyean's reaction	Gelatin stab (inverted fir tree)		
Acute brucellosis (undulant fever)	Blood	Gram-negative coccobacilli	Casteneda method	Standard agglutination test ELISA CFT	Skin test
Bubonic plague	Fluid from buboes	Gram-negative bacilli	Nutrient agar	Passive hemagglutination	PCR
Pneumonic plague	Sputum	Bipolar staining	Blood agar		
Septicemic plague	Blood	Safety pin appearance	Ghee broth ('stalactite' growth)		
Salmonellosis	Stool Food	Gram-negative bacilli	MacConkey agar Wilson and Blair medium	Widal test	
Leptospirosis	Blood Urine	Dark ground microscope; spirochete	Korthof's medium	Microscopic agglutination test	
			Stuart's medium Fletcher's medium		
Tuberculosis (*M.bovis*)	Sputum	Acid fast bacilli	L J medium		PCR

Laboratory diagnosis

Is important for the diagnosis of zoonoses. In humans and animals this is based on:

- Isolation of causative agent
- Serology
- Autopsy

Collection of specimens

Specimens are collected according to the site of lesion. Tables 81.2, 81.3, 81.4, 81.5 and 81.6 list the types of specimens to be collected and laboratory diagnosis tests for bacterial, rickettsial, viral, parasitic and fungal zoonoses, respectively.

Table 81.3 Laboratory procedures for rickettsial zoonoses

Disease	Sample	Culture	Serology
Scrub typhus	Blood	Yolk sac of chick embryo	Weil–Felix test
Murine typhus	Blood	Yolk sac of chick embryo	Weil–Felix test
Tick	Blood	Yolk sac of chick embryo	CFT

Table 81.4 Laboratory procedures for viral zoonoses

Disease	Sample	Microscopy	Culture	Serology
Rabies	Antemortem – corneal impression smear Skin biopsy; Saliva	Immunofluorescence	Tissue culture (WI 38, BHK 21)	
	Postmortem–brain	Negri bodies		
Yellow fever	Blood	Yolk sac of chick embryo		Hemagglutination inhibition
Japanese encephalitis	CSF	Intracerebral inoculation into suckling mice		CFT Neutralisation
KFD				Immunofluorescence
Chikungunya		Tissue culture		ELISA

Table 81.5 *Laboratory procedures for parasitic zoonoses*

Disease	Sample	Microscopy	Serology
Taenia	Stool	Egg	ELISA
Echinococcus	Stool		ELISA Hemagglutination Indirect fluorescent antibody
Leishmania	Blood	Peripheral blood, amastigote (LD bodies)	Aldehyde test Antimony test CFT

Table 81.6 *Laboratory procedures for fungal zoonoses*

Disease	Sample	Microscopy	Culture
Zoophilic dermatophytes			
Microsporum canis	Skin scraping	KOH preparation	SDA
Trichophyton verrucosum	Hair clipping		
T.equinum	Nail clipping		

82 Principles of Laboratory Diagnosis of Infectious Diseases

INTRODUCTION

Laboratory investigations use scientific methods for the rapid and accurate diagnosis of infectious diseases. Once the causative agent for a particular infection has been identified, appropriate and rational therapy can be instituted. With rapidly improving diagnostic techniques that give reliable and timely results, laboratory procedures have to be standardised and have to adhere to good practices. The diagnosis of infectious diseases relies upon the isolation and identification of the causative agent or the demonstration of the specific antigen in infected tissue. Recent or past infections can be diagnosed by the demonstration of antibodies in the serum of the patient. Detection of IgM in the serum denotes recent or ongoing infection, whereas demonstration of IgG reflects a past infection. Before requesting laboratory investigations, the clinician should have arrived at a provisional diagnosis or the probable cause of infection, based on an accurate and detailed history related to the illness and careful physical examination.

Appropriate clinical specimens have to be collected from sites most likely to yield the microorganism. Once the sample has been received by the laboratory, tests are performed using standard operating procedures. The outcome of the test results that are generated are then documented and sent to the treating clinician for appropriate treatment. A communication between the clinician and laboratory personnel is very essential to get the best result from the laboratory. It is therefore prudent to consult the laboratory on the tests to be performed, the types of specimens to be collected for the tests, and the mode of transport of these specimens. Hence, it is important to have an understanding of the principles behind the collection of appropriate specimens for microbiological examination.

The details of laboratory diagnosis have been discussed in individual chapters. This chapter gives an overview of the laboratory process and quality control.

Steps in the laboratory diagnostic process

- Pre-test (pre-analytical) specimen collection and transport
- Test procedures and (analytical) processing of the specimen in the laboratory
- Post-test process (post-analytical) reporting to the clinician

Specimen collection and transport (pre-test)

The outcome of a laboratory test depends to a large extent on the appropriateness of the specimen in terms of selection, quality, quantity, time (prior to antibiotics or other treatment) and method of collection.

Precautions for sample collection

- If culture and isolation of the pathogen is required, asepsis during collection of the sample is essential to avoid contamination by skin flora or environmental organisms. The container for collection of the sample must be sterile in most instances and has to be adequate to contain the material. Samples for anaerobic culture require an anaerobic container or transport media.
- The specimen has to be transported to the laboratory without undue delay. If that is not possible, it has to be stored at an appropriate temperature for a specified time until transport.
- For culture of viruses, specimens need to be transported in viral transport media. Viral transport media prevents drying of the specimen, maintains viability of the viruses and prevents overgrowth by contaminating flora. The specimen should be held at 4°C during transport for most viral isolation studies.

Sites of sample collection

The sample should be representative of the infection, for example, sputum and not saliva to diagnose pulmonary tuberculosis. The type of specimen to be examined is determined by the clinical presentation of the infection.

> Some of the samples usually received in the microbiology laboratory include:
> 1. Skin: scrapings, swabs and biopsies
> 2. Pus: aspirates and drained fluid
> 3. Nail and hair: clippings
> 4. Conjunctiva: swabs
> 5. Ear: swabs
> 6. Respiratory tract:
>   ❖ Upper tract: throat swabs, nasopharyngeal/nasal swabs/nasal wash/sinus aspirates
>   ❖ Lower tract: sputum (not saliva), bronchoalveolar lavage
> 7. Gastrointestinal tract: stool samples, vomitus, endoscopic biopsies
> 8. Genito-urinary tract: vaginal and cervical swabs, urethral discharge
> 9. Urinary tract: urine, suprapubic aspirate
> 10. Central nervous system: cerebrospinal fluid (CSF)
> 11. Bloodstream infections: blood, bone marrow
>
> Besides these, intraoperative samples from internal organs may be sent to the laboratory. Clotted blood (serum) or plasma may be required for immunological tests to demonstrate antigens or antibodies.

Processing of the samples in the laboratory (test procedure)

Once the appropriate specimens have been collected, they are processed as speedily as possible to ensure that the organisms do not die before being transferred to the culture media, and that the reports are available as early as possible.

Microscopy

This is the first step in the laboratory procedure and often helps in giving a rapid diagnosis. Generally, a portion of the specimen is placed on slides stained appropriately, and then examined under the microscope. If bacteria and fungi are swiftly detected, specific therapy can be started at once.

Staining

The Gram stain is the most common stain used in diagnostic microbiology. It helps in provisionally identifying the organism as Gram-positive or Gram-negative. Based on this empiric evidence, antibiotics may be started. The Gram stain is found most useful for the rapid diagnosis of pyogenic meningitis. Sterile body fluids and aspirates can also be stained for rapid diagnosis. This can also be used to detect inflammatory

cells in the specimen, thus providing additional information.

Some of the preliminary staining methods are:
- Acid fast staining (Ziehl–Neelsen and Kinyoun stain)
- Fluorochrome staining (calcofluor white or acridine orange)

Fungal elements can be detected by adding 10–20% KOH to the specimen and examining under the microscope or by staining with calcofluor white.

Culture and identification

Based on the outcome of the preliminary microscopy result, the specific media and method of incubation (at 37°C, ambient temperature or in CO_2) can be selected for culture of the specimen. Generally, after overnight incubation, the colonies on culture plates are processed for identification of the organisms.

Some of the common tests used to identify bacteria are hanging drop test for motility; breakdown of carbohydrates, glucose, sucrose and lactose using composite media like triple sugar iron agar (TSI); tests for production of gas and hydrogen sulphide; utilisation of citrate as the sole source of carbon; and tests for production of enzymes like oxidase and urease. These tests identify most of the common Gram-negative pathogenic bacteria. Final identification of some bacteria like *Salmonella* and *Shigella* are based on serotyping with specific antisera. Similarly, tests like coagulase, hippurate hydrolysis and bacitracin susceptibility are performed for Gram-positive cocci. The organisms are simultaneously subjected to antibiotic susceptibility test by Kirby–Bauer disc diffusion method. Some laboratories identify the microorganisms by automated Vitek/Microscan systems. (Details are described in the respective chapters.)

Rapid diagnostic methods

To decrease the **turnaround time** (the time from the collection of sample to reporting of the results to the physician), several automated and rapid diagnostic methods such as automated culture and identification systems are used (discussed in Chapter 6).

Rapid identification of infectious diseases

Some life-threatening infections like acute pyogenic meningitis, peritonitis, sepsis and some viral infections need to be diagnosed rapidly to start treatment immediately.

Immunological tests for antigen detection

- Latex agglutination test for detecting Haemophilus, Pneumococcus, Meningococcus, Group B Streptococcus or *E.coli* antigen from the CSF in acute pyogenic meningitis
- Cryptococcal antigen in meningitis in immunocompromised individuals
- NS1 antigen from the serum of patients with dengue
- Enzyme immunoassay (EIA) including enzyme-linked immunosorbent assays (ELISA) for detection of antigens (for example, scrub typhus)

Molecular methods

- Detection of DNA or RNA by various molecular methods like conventional PCR, real-time PCR, multiplex PCR, etc. (Chapter 72).

Serological tests for detection of IgM and IgG

Etiological agents cannot always be isolated or detected in the laboratory by conventional or automated culture systems. This is overcome by detecting specific antibodies in the patient's serum.

- Detection of IgM by ELISA: This denotes the early phase of the infection. The antibodies disappear in the later phase. It is done to detect dengue virus infection.
- Detection of IgG: Presence of IgG denotes exposure to the infection (*Brucella* agglutination test).
- Western blot: This test is done to detect antibodies against specific antigens of a microorganism, for example, antibodies against an array of antigens in HIV confirm the infection.

Isolation of the virus requires cell culture systems, which are not available in most clinical diagnostic laboratories. Hence, most viral infections are diagnosed by detection of either viral antigens (HIV) or antibodies (IgM or IgG—arbovirus infections).

Reporting of results (post-test)

This is a crucial step in the laboratory process. The results of the tests must be conveyed to the treating physician who has requested the investigation. They must be conveyed in standard reporting formats in such a way that the physician or patient is able to get accurate and reliable results which are clear and easy to understand. A wrong report or an incomplete one might put the patient in danger of wrong treatment or inadequate management, for example, reporting an HIV-reactive sample as non-reactive or vice versa.

QUALITY CONTROL IN CLINICAL MICROBIOLOGY LABORATORY

Clinical microbiology laboratories play an important role in ensuring the quality of care. This is ensured by adhering to quality control in all laboratory procedures. In clinical microbiology laboratories, a large number of procedures are used to generate test results. These tests include direct smears such as the Gram stain and the use of different aerobic and anaerobic media, including fungal and mycobacterial media for culture of the suspected pathogens. Several tests for the identification of these pathogens such as biochemical tests, enzymatic reactions and, most importantly, antibiotic sensitivity tests are routinely performed. Immunological tests are done to detect antigens or antibodies from the blood/serum or specimen of patients. Each individual test and procedure, each type of medium used and even the reporting of results must adhere to prescribed standards. The quality of the procedures must be regularly checked by **quality control (QC) measures**.

All procedures must undergo quality checks, to give reliable results which will ultimately benefit the patient. These procedures are tested against standard controls whose range of activity is known. When tested in laboratory conditions, they must give predetermined results. These checks have to be performed periodically to ensure the quality of the laboratory procedure.

The frequency and type of QC varies according to the test, medium or reagent. For some tests like coagulase or catalase, QC must be performed along with every test. For other tests, QC must be performed only when a new lot number is to be used, for example, when a new lot of antibiotic discs are used. Automated systems in the laboratory, like the ELISA or blood culture systems, require calibration of the instruments to give reliable results.

Clinicians and infectious disease specialists need to be aware of the quality control systems used in microbiology laboratories. Such awareness helps in the understanding of the laboratory process, right from specimen collection to the time required to report test results.

Laboratory accreditation is a process by which an external agency (a regulatory body) assesses the laboratory practices by checking the procedures and certifies specific tests, to see if they meet the standards of the International Organization for Standardization (ISO). In India, the **National Accreditation Board for Testing and Calibration Laboratories (NABL)** provides certification for a specified period of time.

RECAP

- Diagnosis of infectious diseases relies upon the isolation and identification of the causative agent or demonstration of the specific antigen in infected tissue.
- Another evidence of recent or past infection is the demonstration of antibodies. IgM denotes recent or ongoing infection; whereas demonstration of IgG reflects past infection.
- The laboratory report is only as good as the specimen that is sent.
- The precautions to be followed while collecting specimens include the following:
  - The process of laboratory investigation should not cause harm to the patient.
  - Specimen should be collected in an aseptic manner.
  - It should be collected before starting antimicrobial therapy.
  - The swab or container used to collect the specimen should be sterile.
- General procedure followed in the laboratory includes:
  - Microscopic examination of the sample smeared and stained on a slide by Gram, acid fast or other specific stains
  - Culture on battery of solid (basal/differential, enriched or liquid) media
  - Processing of culture isolates for further characterisation and identification
  - Antibiotic susceptibility test
  - Generation of final report for the clinician or patient
  - Detection of antigens or antibodies by immunological/serological tests.
- Quality control in all test procedures must be adhered to for reliable reports.
- Accreditation for tests done by clinical laboratories is based on adherence to ISO standards, which is certified by a regulatory body. In India, it is the NABL which accredits test procedures done by clinical microbiology laboratories.

ESSAYS

1. Outline the procedures adopted in the laboratory to isolate and identify pathogens.

SHORT NOTES

1. Common samples received in the microbiology laboratory
2. Precautions required for sample collection

Further Reading

1. Abbas AK *et al.* 2012. *Cellular and Molecular Immunology, 7ᵗʰ edition*. Elsevier Saunders, Philadelphia.
2. Arvans DL, SR Vavricka, H Ren, MW Musch, L Kang, FG Rocha, A Lucioni , JR Turner, J Alverdy and EB Chang. 2005. Luminal bacterial flora determines physiological expression of intestinal epithelial cytoprotective heat shock proteins 25 and 72. *Am. J. Physiol. Gastrointest. Liver Physiol.* 288: G696–704.
3. *Bailey & Scott's Diagnostic Microbiology, 10ᵗʰ edition*. 1998. BA Forbes, DF Sahm and AS Weissfeld (eds). Mosby.
4. Bell E. 2005. MHC: Driving diversity, *Nat. Immunol.* 5: 518–24.
5. Biological and chemical terrorism: strategic plan for preparedness and response. *MMWR* 2000 (RR4): 1–14.
6. Brostoff DMJ *et al.* 2012. *Immunology, 8ᵗʰ edition*. Saunders, Philadelphia.
7. Cappuccino JG and N Sherman. 1985. *Microbiology: A Laboratory Manual, 1ˢᵗ edition*. Massachussets: Addison-Wesley Publishing Company.
8. Centers for Disease Control and Prevention. *Guide to Infection Prevention for Outpatient Settings: Minimum Expectations for Safe Care*. www.cdc.gov/HAI/settings/outpatient/outpatient-care-gl-standard-precautions.html. Accessed 8ᵗʰ February 2013.
9. Chapel H *et al.* 2006. *Essentials of Clinical Immunology, 5ᵗʰ edition*. Blackwell Science, London.
10. Claeson M *et al.* 2000. Reducing child mortality in India in the New Millenium, *Bull. World Health Organization* 78: 1192–99.
11. *Clinical Microbiology Procedures Handbook, 3ʳᵈ edition*. 2010. LS Garcia (ed.). ASM Press Washington, DC.
12. Colonna *et al.* 2004. Plasmacytoid dendritic cells in immunity. *Nature Immunol.* 5: 1219–26.
13. Delves PJ *et al.* 2011. *Roitt's Essential Immunology (Desktop edition), 12ᵗʰ edition*. Wiley-Blackwell.
14. Duse AG. 2002. Keeping the environment safe with limited resources *In*: A Guide to Infection Control in the Hospital, 2ⁿᵈ edition. R Wenzel, T Brewer and J-P Butzler (eds). Boston: International Society for Infectious Diseases.
15. Fiocchi C. 2005. Inflammatory bowel disease pathogenesis: therapeutic implications. *Chin. J. Dig. Dis.* 6: 6–9.
16. Firestein GS *et al.* (eds). 2008. *Kelley's Textbook of Rheumatology, 8ᵗʰ edition*, Saunders Elsevier, Philadelphia.
17. Franz DR *et al.* 1997. Clinical recognition and management of patient exposed to biological warfare agents. *JAMA* 278: 399.
18. Gangal S and S Sontakke. 2013. *Textbook of Basic and Clinical Immunology*. University Press, India.
19. Guan Y, KF Shortridge, S Krauss and RG Webster. 1999. Molecular characterization of H9N2 influenza viruses: were they the donors of the "internal" genes of H5N1 viruses in Hong Kong? *Proc. Natl. Acad. Sci. USA*. 96: 9363–7.
20. Gupta BK and A.Sharma. 2012. *Immunology Basic Concepts*. Peepee Publishers, India.
21. Hewlett, EL. 2000. Bordetella species, p. 2414–2422. *In*: Principles and Practice of Infectious Diseases, vol. 2, 5ᵗʰ edition. GL Mandell, JE Bennett and R Dolin (eds). Churchill Livingstone, Philadelphia, Pa.
22. Hozumi N and S Tonegawa. 1974. Evidence for somatic rearrangement of immunoglobulin genes coding for variable and constant regions. *Proc. Natl. Acad. Sci.* 73: 203–7.
23. *Jawetz, Melnick & Adelberg's Medical Microbiology, 25ᵗʰ edition*. GF Brooks, KC Carroll, JS Butel, SA Morse and TA Mietzner (eds). 2010. McGraw-Hill.
24. Jensen PE. 2007. Recent advances in antigen processing and presentation, *Nat. Immunol.* 8: 1041–48.
25. Kelly D and S. Conway. 2005. Bacterial modulation of mucosal innate immunity. *Mol. Immunol.* 42: 895–901.
26. Kennedy DM and SJ Challacombe. 1998. *ELISA and Other Solid Phase Immunology*. John Wiley, New York.
27. Khanna M, P Kumar, K Choudhary, B Kumar and VK Vijayan. 2008. Emerging influenza virus: a global threat. *J. Biosci.* 33: 475–82.
28. Khanna M, B Kumar, A Gupta and P Kumar. 2012. Pandemic influenza A H1N1 (2009) virus: Lessons from the past and implications for the future. *Indian J. Virol.* 23: 12–17.
29. Kindt TJ *et al.* 2006. *Kuby Immunology, 6ᵗʰ edition*. WH Freeman and Company, New York.
30. Klein J and A Sato. 2000. HLA System. *New Engl. J. Med.* 343: 702–709.
31. *Koneman's Color Atlas and Textbook of Diagnostic Microbiology, 6ᵗʰ edition*. 2006. CW Washington, Jr., SD Allen, WM Janda, EW Koneman, GW Procop, PC Schreckenberger, GL Woods (eds). Lippincott Williams & Wilkins.
32. Kwiatkowski D. 2000. Susceptibility to infection. *BMJ* 321 (7268): 1061–1065.
33. Lott TJ, RE Fundyga, RJ Kuykendall and J Arnold. 2005. The human commensal yeast, *Candida albicans*, has an ancient origin. *Fungal Genet. Biol.* 42: 444–451.
34. *Mackie & McCartney Practical Medical Microbiology, 14ᵗʰ edition*. 1999. JG Collee, AG Fraser, BP Marmion and A Simmons (eds). Churchill Livingstone.
35. Macpherson AJ and T Uhr. 2004. Compartmentalization of the mucosal immune responses to commensal intestinal bacteria. *Ann. N. Y. Acad. Sci.* 1029:36–43.
36. *Mandell, Douglas and Bennitt's Principles and Practice of Infectious Diseases, 7ᵗʰ edition*. 2010. GL Mandell, JE Bennett and R Dolin (eds). Churchill Livingstone.
37. *Manual of Clinical Microbiology, 10ᵗʰ edition*. 2011. J Versalovic, KC Carroll, G Funke, JH Jorgensen, ML Landry and DW Warnock (eds). ASM Press, Washington, DC.

38. Matusiewicz SP, RJ Ferguson, AP Greening, GK Crompton and SM Burns. 1994. *Pneumocystis carinii* in bronchoalveolar lavage fluid and bronchial washings. *BMJ* 308: 1206–1207.
39. Melchers F and A Rolink. 1999. B lymphocyte development and biology. *In*: Fundamental Immunology, 4th edition, WE Paul (ed.). Lippincott Raven Philadelphia and New York.
40. Merz WG and RJ Hay (eds.). 2005. *Medical Mycology: Topley and Wilson's Microbiology and Microbial Infections, 10th edition*. Hodder Arnold, London.
41. Millard J and M Sandrin. 2006. ABO blood group and related antigens, natural antibodies and transplantation. *Tissue Antigens* 68:459–66.
42. Moscona A. 2009. Global transmission of oseltamivir-resistant influenza. *N. Engl. J. Med.* 360: 953–6.
43. Murphy K *et al.* 2008. *Janeway's Immunology, 7th edition*, Garland Science, New York.
44. Murphy K. 2011. *Janeway's Immunobiology: The Immune System, 8th edition*. Garland Science, New York.
45. Operario DJ, MJ Moser and K St. George. 2010. Highly sensitive and quantitative detection of the H274Y oseltamivir resistance mutation in seasonal A/H1N1 influenza. *J. Clin. Microbiol.* 48: 3517–24.
46. Patrick S and MJ Larkin. 1995. *Immunological and molecular aspects of bacterial virulence*. J Wiley, Chichester.
47. Peakman M and D Vergani. 2009. *Basic and Clinical Immunology*. Elsevier Health Sciences. Churchill Livingstone.
48. Perham P. 2009. *The Immune System, 3rd edition*, Garland Science, New York.
49. Peruski LF and AH Peruski. 2003. Rapid diagnosis assay in the genomic biology era; detection and identification of infectious disease and biological weapon agents. *Bio. Tech.* 35: 840.
50. Pifer LL, HB Niell, BJ Morrison, JD Counce Jr, JM Freeman, DR Woods and CL Neely. 1984. *Pneumocystis carinii* antigenemia in adults with malignancy, infection or pulmonary disease. *J. Clin. Microbiol.* 20: 887–890.
51. Plotkin SA. 2005. Vaccines: Past, present and future, *Nat. Med.* 11:S5–11.
52. Puttaswamy S, BD Lee and S Sengupta. 2011. Novel electrical method for early detection of viable bacteria in blood cultures. *J. Clin. Microbiol.* 49(6):2286–2289.
53. Rangel-Frausto MS. 2002. Water. *In*: A Guide to Infection Control in the Hospital, 2nd edition. R Wenzel, T Brewer and J-P Butzler (eds). Boston: International Society for Infectious Diseases.
54. Remick DG and JF Friedland. 1997. *Cytokines in Health and Disease, 2nd edition*, revised and expanded. Marcel Dekker, Inc. New York.
55. Richardson MD and DW Warnock. 2012. *Fungal Infection: Diagnosis and Management, 4th edition*. Wiley Blackwell, UK.
56. Robbins, JB. 1999. Pertussis in adults: introduction. *Clin. Infect. Dis.* 28 (Suppl. 2): S91–S93.
57. Roitt IM and PJ Delves. 1998. *Encyclopedia of Immunology, 2nd edition*. Academic Press Inc, San Diego and London.
58. Rook GAW and LR Brunet. 2005. Microbes, immunoregulation and the gut. *Gut* 54: 317–320.
59. Rose NR *et al.* 2002. *Manual of Clinical Laboratory Immunology, 6th edition*. American Society for Microbiology, Washington.
60. Schaechter M. 1989. Normal microbial flora. *In:* Mechanisms of Microbial Disease, M Schaechter, G Medoff and D Schlessinger (eds). Baltimore: Williams and Wilkins.
61. Schreiber GB *et al.* 1996. The Risk of Transfusion-Transmitted Viral Infections. *NEJM* 334: 1685–1690.
62. Schwartz RS. 2003. Diversity of immune response. *New Eng. J. Med.* 348: 1017.
63. Senior BW. 1996. Examination of water, milk, food and air. *In*: Mackie and McCartney Practical Medical Microbiology, 14th edition. JG Collee, AG Frasier, BP Marmion and A Simmons (eds). New York: Churchill Livingstone.
64. Sheldon S and K Poulton. 2006. HLA typing and its influence on organ transplantation. *Methods Mol. Biol.* 333: 157–74.
65. Shlomchik WD. 2007. Graft–versus-host disease. *Nat. Rev. Immunol.* 7: 340–52.
66. Shriniwas. 1992. *Hospital-acquired Infections: Guidelines for Control*. New Delhi: Ministry of Health and Family Welfare, Government of India.
67. Snydman DR. 1989. Foodborne diseases. *In*: Mechanisms of Microbial Disease, M Schaechter, G Medoff and D Schlessinger (eds). Baltimore: Williams and Wilkins.
68. Speers DJ. 2006. Clinical applications of molecular biology for infectious diseases. *Clin. Biochem. Rev.* 27(I): 39–51.
69. Stephen J *et al.* 2000. *Mims' Pathogenesis of Infectious Disease, 5th edition*. Academic Press, London.
70. Stites DP *et al.* 1994. *Lange Series - Basic and Clinical Immunology, 8th edition*. Lange Medical Publishers, Los Altos.
71. Stringer JR, CB Beard, RF Miller and AE Wakefield. 2002. *Pneumocystis jirovecii. Emerg. Infect. Dis.* 8: 891–896.
72. Tabbara KF and AL al-Jabarti. 1998. Hospital construction-associated outbreak of ocular aspergillosis after cataract surgery. *Ophthalmology* 105: 522–526.
73. Tomlinson S. 1993. Complement defense mechanisms. *Curr. Opin. Immunol.* 5(1): 83–9.
74. Tonegawa S. 1983. Somatic generation of antibody diversity. *Nature* 302(5909): 575–81.
75. URL: http://www.emedicine.com/derm/byname/candidiasis_cutaneous
76. Weiner *et al.* 2009. Monoclonal antibodies for cancer immunotherapy. *Lancet* 373: 1033–38.
77. Weir DM and J John Stewart. 1997. *Immunology, 8th edition*. Churchill Livingstone, Edinburg.
78. Westwood MR and FC Hay. 2001. *Epitope Mapping: A Practical Approach*, Oxford University Press, Oxfordshire.
79. Xavier R and DK Podolsky. 2005. Commensal flora: Wolf in sheep's clothing. *Gastroenterology* 128: 1122–1126.

Index

GREYSCALE

BIN TRAVELER FORM

Cut By: _Mhnan_ #19 Qty _23_ Date _10 21_

Scanned By: _____ Qty _____ Date _____

Scanned Batch IDs

Notes / Exception